R B

PRINCIPLES OF ANIMAL PHYSIOLOGY

PRINCIPLES OF ANIMAL PHYSIOLOGY

James A. Wilson, Ohio University

Illustrated by **John Richardson**

Southern Illinois University

The Macmillan Company, New York · Collier-Macmillan Limited, London

The Macmillan Company
866 Third Avenue, New York, New York 10022
Collier-Macmillan Canada, Ltd., Toronto, Ontario

Library of Congress catalog card number: 78-126512
PRINTING   3456789   YEAR   3456789

Preface

THIS textbook was begun, as it seems many textbooks are, because of a felt need for a better source of material for the students taking a course. Although several excellent texts are available in the areas of cellular biology, general physiology, and biochemistry, it seemed to me that students at the introductory level needed a text combining discussion of the important aspects of these three areas with a consideration of higher levels of animal structure and function—plus some consideration of the comparative aspects of physiology. To meet this need, this book is entitled *Principles of Animal Physiology*—an indication that important ideas from all areas of physiology are presented and that the approach is a broader one than is usually found in textbooks. I tend to think of physiology as a unit, not as a series of discrete areas, and I have tried here to examine animal functioning at all levels from the molecular to the whole organism.

Any textbook requires a central theme, and in this book I have taken regulation as a major concept. In addition, I have felt it important to incorporate the similarities and differences of structure and function found in various animals —in one sense, an incorporation of data from comparative physiology.

I did not hesitate to think in terms of a lengthy book. Most available texts, in my opinion, suffer from the major defect of shortness. To present adequately the basic terms, definitions, and concepts of physiology is a lengthy undertaking. Writing a short book also necessitates a degree of selectivity that amounts to mind reading on the part of the author as to what is going to be taught in physiology courses in many colleges and universities. Such a treatment can only drastically reduce the usefulness of a text. Nevertheless I too have omitted some topics or given them only sketchy treatment. However, I have tried to include sufficient references to the literature so that the interested student can proceed on his own.

This book is written primarily for the interested student—not one who is necessarily majoring in physiology, but one who finds some fascination in the subject matter of physiology. My philosophy is that if a text is written in such a manner, it will also be good for any student taking a physiology course.

The main purpose of this book is to describe how physiological systems work, and such descriptions are presented primarily in physical-chemical terms. Since physiology is an experimental science, I have tried to include as much as possible on the instrumentation, methods, and approaches used in the study of different levels of animal functioning. As much data as possible are given so that the student may have some opportunity to see the sources of physiological hypotheses and theories. Naturally, space places a limit on such material but, again, references are provided that discuss methods and data not completely covered in the text itself.

The book is divided into four parts, beginning with the most basic levels of structure or function in animals and progressing to the most complex. Part I is concerned with molecules and cell organization and with the chemical and physical principles upon which biochemical reactions and energy exchanges are based. The first chapter contains a brief consideration of systems analysis, feedback regulation, adaptation, and regulation. These are extremely useful concepts to the physiologist, and they are used in all later chapters of the book. I have outlined the nature of biochemical evolution in Chapter 5. Evolution at any level is one of the most important of biological theories and especially deserves recognition in a physiology book that includes elements of comparative physiology. In Chapter 5, I have also included a listing of the names, and a rough indication of the relationships, of living animals. I find that many students taking physiology courses have either forgotten or have never been acquainted with animal names and relations. It is hoped that this listing can be used by the student to identify and relate the organisms discussed in later chapters of the book.

Part II contains the basic cellular mechanisms upon which much regulatory ability, adaptation, and responsiveness to environment are based, including a discussion of specialized cells, especially nerve and muscle cells, which exhibit such mechanisms to a high degree.

Part III on homeostasis carries regulation one step further—to the level of organized systems. The many differences that may be found among animals in the structures and functional abilities used in homeostasis are emphasized, although, as stressed in the first two parts of the book, cellular organization and functioning have many similarities in all animals.

Part IV includes elements of sensory physiology and a brief discussion of animal behavior based on selected examples. It is hoped that these examples will give an indication of how the cellular and organismal activities of the whole animal are coordinated and integrated to produce successful responses to the environment.

Each chapter has its own reference and reading list, usually a lengthy one. Although textbooks are not the place for presenting long lists of shorter research papers, monographs and reviews by workers in various specialized fields are an aid in a bibliography that includes discussions of the research and its results. Therefore, research papers of proven significance or with important methodological details are given in the reference lists. Citations are inserted in the text in a way that creates a minimum of disruption. The citations were chosen to provide both a chronological map of physiological discoveries and also a listing of researchers associated with particular fields of study. Recognizing that some readers will not have all important sources of physiological information available to them, I have tried to provide two or more references to a given subject when possible, hoping that at least one will be available to the interested reader.

The book certainly has shortcomings, but I hope it will be of value to students, the people for whom it is written. I have not designated it as suitable for any particular level of student. Anyone with a background containing some chemistry, a little physics and mathematics, and some biology can easily learn to appreciate the physiological data. Graduate students may find it useful both for the material covered and for the references to the literature; however, it is a textbook and not an advanced treatise.

No author could be an expert in all the areas covered by this book. I have tried to present those ideas which appear most generally accepted by workers in a given area. At the same time I have not hesitated to present less well-accepted hypotheses, to give my own opinions or interpretations where necessary, and to go out on a limb when extrapolating present knowledge (or lack of it) to future work in physiology. It is hoped that the reader of this book will arrive at the conclusion that comparatively little is settled in physiology and that much remains to be done.

I gratefully acknowledge the many people who have read and criticized all or part of the manuscript. These include Professors G. S. Araki, K. S. Guthe, W. N. Holmes, T. C. Jegla, L. E. Moore, L. M. Passano, and J. Thomas. Of course, all errors both of omission and commission are my responsibility.

I also wish to thank John and Mary Richardson for their invaluable help in the preparation of the illustrations and in the preparation of the manuscript. Nearly all of the illustrations are either new or completely redrawn and corrected. Originally I had planned to use many more electron micrographs, but it appeared that in too many cases such micrographs would be of value only to people expert in their interpretation. Therefore, many morphological details are illustrated by line drawings rather than original halftones.

Last, but certainly not least, I wish to express my sincere gratitude to Mr. William D. Eastman, Executive Editor at The Macmillan Company, for his enthusiasm, his help, and especially for his patience when deadlines arrived but manuscript did not.

J. A. W.

Brief Contents

Detailed Contents

Part II

Fundamental Units of Animal Regulatory Systems

Chapter 6

Biological Membranes and Material Transport

Part III

Homeostasis: Regulation of the Internal Environment

Chapter 12

Circulatory Systems—Nature and Functions

Chapter 13

Circulatory Systems—Types, Hearts, and Controls

Chapter 14

Water and Solute Regulation

Chapter 15

Nutrition and Body Temperature Regulation

Chapter 16

Animal Respiration

Part IV

Some Aspects of Sensory Physiology and Information Processing

Chapter 17

Light and the Animal

Chapter 18

Chromatophores and Bioluminescence

REGULATION, control, and adaptation are basic to all living systems, and these activities are defined in the sections of Chapter 1 that follow a brief introduction to the history and nature of physiology and its subdisciplines. Feedback regulation and systems analysis are presented because they provide a conceptual framework upon which physiological regulation may be placed and because the method of systems analysis is one of several important ways in which living systems can be studied. The idea of regulation in animals was conceived long before the development of cybernetics. However, cybernetics provides a language and the mathematics for describing rigorously any regulatory system.

Also basic to all living systems are certain types of molecules and these are described in Chapter 2. Some emphasis is placed on that unique and ubiquitous molecule, water. The nature and general functions of all types of biochemical entities are described, but most stress is given to macromolecules, especially the proteins. Macromolecules are of importance because they can provide the information required by all living systems for synthesis, growth, development, regulation, and adaptation. All the activities and structures discussed in later chapters are based upon the molecules described here.

The organization of molecules into cellular organelles and cell structure generally is described in Chapter 3. Some stress is given to instrumentation and methods, because at the molecular and cellular levels instrumentation becomes of importance for analyzing organizational levels far smaller than can be perceived directly by human senses. The biological membrane—a structure that must be considered as basic to all living systems—is introduced in this chapter.

Cell structure and organization, as well as whole animal structure and function, depend upon specific and controlled reactions and a proper supply of energy. Chapter 4 presents the basic concepts of enzyme catalyzed reactions: the specific and rapid reactions that permit cells to function at their low (chemically speaking) temperatures. The basic ideas of thermodynamics that govern energy exchanges in all systems are discussed as they apply to living systems. The basic metabolic pathways by which energy is provided to the cell are briefly described. These descriptions demonstrate the complexity of metabolic pathways—a complexity perhaps made necessary by the need to control and regulate cellular metabolism and activity. The general nature of cellular regulation, as exemplified by control of these energy pathways, concludes the discussion in this chapter.

Chapters 2, 3, and 4 lay some stress on the fact that molecular classes, reactions, and organiza-

Part I

Some Basic Properties of Living Systems

tion are very similar in all living cells. The topic of biochemical evolution and the origin of life, given in Chapter 5, is of interest today for several reasons. Geology, geochemistry, astronomy and other related sciences can better estimate the age of the earth and solar system and the early physical conditions on the earth. Thus it has become possible to simulate primitive earth conditions and to experimentally determine possible pathways for the evolution and origin of biochemical molecules. Organic evolution was the forerunner of biological evolution, and evolutionary theory underlies explanations for the basic

similarities of all living cells as well as explanations for the diversity of animal life known today. Comparative physiology and biochemistry depend on and also contribute to details of evolutionary theory.

Finally Chapter 5 includes a table of the animal kingdom that will aid in identifying and relating organisms whose physiology is considered in the remaining chapters of the book. This part of the book stresses the similarities of living systems and introduces some physical-chemical concepts upon which molecular reactions and energy exchanges in cells are based.

1-1. Purpose and Scope of Physiology. Physiology may be defined as the area of science devoted to analyzing and gaining an understanding of the events and activities—the functions—occurring in living systems. Because these systems themselves are complex and varied, so also the science that attempts to describe them becomes complex and varied. When one considers the wide array of functional phenomena found in organisms, or the large number of known animal species (approximately one million) each with its own major or minor differences from the others; or the range of organizational levels now open to study—from animal societies and populations to the whole animal through organ, tissue, cellular, and subcellular systems to the molecular and atomic levels—all with their own types and ranges of activities and required methods of study, then an appreciation of the extent and complexity of physiology appears.

I believe that any discussion of physiology should include some indications of the nature and direction of the changes that have occurred and are still occurring in this field. The word "physiology" has meant different things at different times, and physiology has undergone an evolution of outlook and methodology during its history. At present physiology is changing, as are most scientific disciplines, because of the extremely rapid advances in technology and instrumentation made since about 1940. Some of these advances, for example, make possible the isolation, observation, identification, and experimentation on single cells, parts of cells, or macromolecules. Thus the description of some basic physiological mechanisms is placed on a much firmer basis than was possible when only indirect methods of study were available.

Also, advances in the analyses and design of complex engineering and communications systems, together with the development of computers and other mathematical tools, have increased the ability to study the highly organized, interacting, and controlled systems of animals. The introduction of new and miniaturized electronic circuits and devices makes possible studies ranging from investigations of bioelectrical potentials in parts of single cells to monitoring activity in organ systems of

Chapter 1

The Nature of the Subject

intact animals to analyzing telemetrically the behavior and activity of animals under natural conditions.

These changes are important because they yield new knowledge, help to consolidate previously diverse areas of experimental biology, and aid in demonstrating the basic unity of the mechanisms underlying living systems and their activities. But they also add to the amount of information needed to understand animal functioning. Although it is now possible to study molecular events or to begin to analyze the nature of the organizational levels of animals and their interactions, we gain such understanding only by having an arsenal of concepts from mathematics and the physical sciences to back up our zoological knowledge. An understanding of mathematics is especially important so that physiological ideas can be expressed as clearly, concisely, and rigorously as possible.

Because physiology does encompass such a large amount of material, it is necessary to limit the areas covered in a textbook in as rational a way as possible and still include the important generalizations together with the data and experimental methods from which they were derived. It is imperative to find some conceptual scheme(s) about which the subject matter may be organized in order to present a unified and comprehensible picture of physiology. A discussion of some of these concepts and also some of the subdivisions and approaches to physiology make up the remainder of this chapter.

A word of caution seems appropriate here regarding schemes of classification or divisions made in physiology (or any science). Such classifications are made for practical reasons: to split a subject into chunks suitably sized for digestion in a course or textbook; to outline the scope of a particular researcher's area of interest, from an incomplete knowledge of a given area; or for the convenience of administration. Classifications are also made to organize and systematize knowledge; the increase of knowledge usually means a modification of the classification scheme.

The separation of physiology into the areas to be described in the next few sections, for example, is arbitrary and incomplete. Such separations should not cause one to forget that although life is complex, it also has a unity and an evolutionary history that the life sciences should attempt to reflect. In many cases a general view of life is expressed with difficulty in any simple format because of the inherent difficulties of language (and the nature of the human mind).

The serious student of physiology is urged to read other articles and textbooks not only for their physiological presentation but also to obtain other authors' ideas and descriptions of the various areas of physiology, their history, and relationships.

The Fields of Physiology

1-2. Morphology and Physiology. Structure and function are, of course, inseparable entities in the animal, and there has always been a correspondingly close relationship between the areas engaged in their study. A good understanding of function is impossible without a good knowledge of the responsible structure, whether at the organ or the molecular level. Morphology, the analysis of structure, classically included **anatomy**, **histology**, and **cytology**—the study of organs, tissues and cells, respectively. Now it also includes the submicroscopic realms of subcellular and molecular organization.

Frey-Wyssling (1953) suggested that the element of time was a major factor differentiating morphological from physiological studies. Because of the nature of the methods required or the organisms being studied, morphology usually uses dead materials whose spatial and physical attributes are described.

Physiology must use living, or at least functional, materials, recording changes in them with the passage of time under the influence of various stimulating agents. These include not only physical and chemical factors in the environment but also other living structures or their products, as well as time itself. In this sense, most morphological studies are static (not time varying), whereas physiological studies are dynamic (time varying).

In physiological experiments the time factor is usually of short duration—fractions of a second, a few minutes, or days. When time is involved in morphological studies, it is generally of longer duration. Both the comparative anatomist and the embryologist are concerned with the changing structural patterns of organisms either during evolutionary history or during the time of the organisms' growth and development. The experimental embryologist bridges the gap between the strictly morphological and the strictly physiological aspects of development. Biochemistry and cellular physiology, with their emphasis on subcellular and molecular events, add a new dimension to developmental studies.

Although human (or mammalian) physiology is one of the oldest of the biological sciences (reflecting not only the intellectual curiosity of the human being about the human

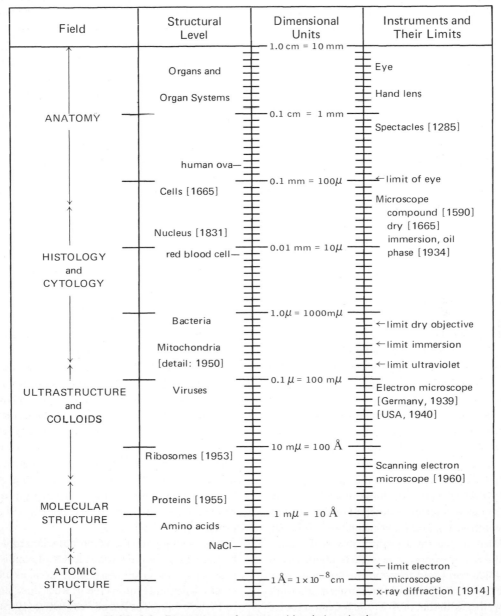

Table 1-1   Dimensions of structural levels in animals.

body, but also having practical application to medicine and animal husbandry), such studies were limited to the organ level until about the nineteenth century—the time of the development and refinement of the light microscope. Until recent times much of what was called physiology was primarily concerned with mammalian anatomy and was strongly oriented toward the human (Franklin, 1949).

The development of experimental techniques and instruments capable of recognizing and manipulating smaller and smaller structures and organisms was a primary factor in the creation of modern physiology. Today both physiological and morphological researches depend heavily upon instrumentation that can extend the human senses.

Table 1-1 lists some of the structural levels found in animals, together with their average dimensions and the instruments needed to see them. The approximate dates given point out that often a lengthy span of time elapses after the invention of an instrument before its refinement permits critical biological observation. The table is concerned only with observational instruments that are prerequisites to adequate morphological information. Structure-function relationships are accurately obtained only after suitable physiological instruments are devised.

Table 1-1 also shows that the cellular level of biological structure has been open to direct analysis for little more than a hundred years. The direct study of subcellular structures and macromolecular complexes has been possible for only about thirty years.

Other factors also limited the scope of early physiology. From the time of Hippocrates (ca. 420 B.C.) and of Aristotle (384–322 B.C.), often called the fathers of medicine and biology, respectively, until the era of Harvey (1578–1657) very little physiological analysis was made in terms of observation followed by hypothesizing and experimentation. Although Galen in the third century dissected animal bodies and reported new facts about mammalian form and function, his methods were not generally followed, and instead, his work together with that of Aristotle became a source

of authority not much implemented by further experimentation for over a thousand years. The philosophical and mental outlook of the times were not suitable for what is called modern scientific method.

Harvey in *Exercitatio Anatomica de Motu Cordis et Sanguinis in Animalibus*, published in 1628, explained how he used experimentation, observation, and deduction to overthrow Galen's ebb and flow concept of blood movement and to introduce the idea of a continuous cycle of circulation through a closed circulatory system. This model received confirmation when Malphighi in 1661 identified capillaries —direct connections between arteries and veins —by use of the light microscope (see Keilin, 1966). Harvey was the first to make use of mathematical analysis for the solution of a physiological problem (see Leake's, 1931, translation of Harvey's book).

Unfortunately Harvey's methods were slow to be accepted, and many historians consider that modern physiology did not begin until the time of Claude Bernard in the middle nineteenth century. During this time the word physiology was used for a wide variety of subject matter including both anatomy and physiology as we know them today and also such tangentially related areas as geology.

Today the popular frontiers of physiology are at the molecular level, and an understanding of many basic physiological mechanisms awaits the elucidation of their molecular basis. The close relationship of the early anatomists and physiologists is now seen between the submicroscopic morphologist and the general or cellular physiologist. Although molecular biology receives much of the publicity at present, there is still a large amount of knowledge to be acquired about the functioning and interactions of organ systems and other higher levels of animal organization. The analysis of whole animal activities and behavior is still a primary goal of physiology.

Representative textbooks on mammalian and human physiology at various levels of sophistication include Grollman (1964); Mountcastle (1968); Ruch and Fulton (1960); Ruch and Patton (1965); and Tuttle and Schottelius (1965).

1-3. Comparative Physiology and Evolution. The object of comparative physiology is to describe the different methods used by animals to meet their physiological needs. The area includes studies at all levels of animal organization, although organ systems are highly stressed (Prosser and Brown, 1961). Comparative studies are also concerned with the relationships of organisms and their places in the evolutionary scheme. Thus it is intimately associated with one of the most important biological theories—evolution. The introduction of biochemical concepts has added to evolutionary information and has also led to experimentation designed to answer questions regarding the origin and evolution of life.

Although comparative studies are not new (Aristotle, Galen, and Harvey, for example, all worked with many species of organisms), invertebrate animals have generally been neglected until a few decades ago (Rogers, 1927). But in many cases an invertebrate organism has cells, organ systems, or behavioral patterns that are more suitable for study than are their counterparts among the vertebrates. Thus, much of our knowledge of the mechanisms underlying nerve action potentials results from studies on the giant axons of squids. These nerve fibers have diameters up to one millimeter, an order or two of magnitude greater than those of the nerve cells usually found in animals. Such large cells are easier to analyze physiologically and biochemically than smaller ones.

Researchers are constantly seeking for organisms that in some way overcome the usual difficulties of small size, rapid activity, small amounts of individual substances, complexity, or supply or maintenance problems that characterize most animals. Part of the role of comparative physiology is to discover such organisms. Once methods have been devised for studying simpler systems, it is often possible to modify them to work with the more complicated ones, especially when some background of physiological information exists to proceed on.

These practical reasons for studying invertebrate or lower vertebrate animals should not overshadow the interest in and importance of these organisms in their own right. Although mammalian and human physiologies often have eclipsed the study of other animals, physiology to be a complete science cannot ignore the functional activities of any animal group. Where possible, in this book function will be approached from the comparative viewpoint.

Increasing knowledge and interest in any scientific area is often reflected in an increasing number of publications in that area. In recent years new information and many books on the physiology of special animal groups have appeared. These include insect physiology (Rockstein, 1965); avian physiology (Marshall, 1960); crustacean physiology (Waterman, 1960); molluscan physiology (Wilbur and Tonge, 1964); amphibian physiology (Moore, 1964); protozoan physiology (Hutner, 1964); earthworm physiology (Laverack, 1963); physiology of the echinoderms (Boolootian, 1966); the biology of Hydra (Lentz, 1967); and the physiology of fishes (Brown, 1957).

1-4. Cellular and General Physiology. The cellular physiologist is interested in the structure and function of cells. The general physiologist attempts to determine the basic principles underlying biological activity of all living systems and bases these principles upon the theories of physics and chemistry.

The two fields are similar in many respects, but general physiology is wider in scope. Although the attempt is often made to explain physiological activity in terms of specific cellular events, there is a supracellular organization and activity outside the immediate scope of cellular physiology but accessible to the ideas of general physiology.

It has been the role of both these disciplines to produce generalities which are applicable to all cells and to point out that all living systems in the cell operate on the basis of very similar mechanisms. Since cellular functioning is so closely allied to cell structure and the area of cytology, the term "cell biology" is often used to designate these combined fields.

The development of the light microscope

made possible the observation of the cellular level of biological structure and led to the formulation of the **cell theory**, the concept that all living organisms are composed of basic units, or cells. Hooke in the seventeenth century saw little boxes making up the structure of cork, but not until the nineteenth century were lenses and microtechniques sufficiently perfected to allow detailed cellular studies.

Mirbel in 1809 seems to have been the first to state that all plant tissues are composed of cells. Following a succession of other observers, Schwann in 1839, after examining a variety of plant and animal tissues, concluded that all living organisms are composed of cells.

The growth of cellular studies can conveniently be divided into three phases. The first, an early morphological-physiological period, found a majority of researchers listing the nature and number of visible cell structures (an early categorization-characterization period is typical of the beginnings of most scientific areas). Much of the physiological emphasis was based on the structural changes and role of the nucleus (first observed by Brown in 1831) in cell division, cell growth and development, and embryological development: the latter culminating in the field of experimental embryology in the twentieth century. From these origins sprang the major advances made in genetics and molecular biology during the past few decades.

The second phase, an analytical period, began with the arising interest in the nature of the material making up cells. This clear, homogeneous appearing (in the light microscope), gelatinous substance was called **protoplasm** by von Mohl in 1846. Schultze in 1861 proposed that all cells were composed of protoplasm which contained a nucleus and was bounded by a membrane. The idea—that life was based upon a physical substance, analyzable for its chemical and physical properties—was called the **protoplasm theory** by Hertwig and represents the second unifying principle to arise from cellular studies.

Although our ideas concerning the nature of protoplasm have changed considerably since the advent of the electron microscope,

this concept and that of cell theory had profound philosophical as well as scientific implications. The interest in the chemical and physical properties of cells initiated at this time could not have been carried far had it not been for the advances in chemistry and physics made in the seventeenth and eighteenth centuries.

The nineteenth century saw all necessary factors present for the beginning of modern experimental physiology, and there was a rapid introduction of instrumentation to study the chemical, physical, and biological properties of life. The experimental method backed by quantitative analysis became a dominating force in physiological research at all levels.

The third phase of cellular studies can be designated the ultrastructural period. The commercial introduction of the electron microscope in 1939–1940 made possible detailed examination of cellular organelles and other subcellular entities. It changed the concept of protoplasm from a homogeneous, clear, colloidal suspension to that of a multiphased complex system, containing numerous membranous elements. It also made possible the observation and characterization of protein fibers and other macromolecules. The physiologist could, for the first time, discuss many cellular activities in terms of mechanisms based on direct observations of the structures involved. Simultaneously a variety of methods including ultracentrifugation, chromatography, electrophoresis, x-ray diffraction, isotopic techniques, histochemistry, cytochemistry, and various micromethods for dissection, observation, or measurement were developed or greatly improved.

Textbooks on cellular or general physiology include: Giese (1968); Davson (1964); DeRobertis et al. (1960, 1965); Brachet (1957). A six volume treatise on the cell has been published (Brachet and Mirsky, 1959–1964). Also a five volume work on bacteria has been published (Gunsalus and Stanier, 1960–1964).

1-5. Biochemistry and Related Areas. Biochemistry is the study of the nature, reactions, and interactions of biological substances. At its inception it was closely allied with organic (living) chemistry. The latter had its beginning when Wohler in 1828 synthesized urea from ammonia and carbon dioxide. This synthesis was a departure from previous ideas because until that time it was thought that organic compounds differed in some special way from the compounds of nonliving objects and that only living organisms could produce them.

From an initial interest in the isolation and classification of these molecules, biochemistry soon turned to the study of their reactions and syntheses by the organism. One of the major achievements of biochemists was the elucidation of the metabolic pathways by which energy transformations occur in cells. Another was the analysis of the role and nature of the protein catalysts (enzymes) that speed up and regulate cellular reactions.

In recent times more attention is being paid to the organization and activity of compounds as they exist in the cell, and there has been a gradual merging of biochemical and physiological goals. Biochemistry has also reached a comparative stage and a variety of organisms are now studied (Baldwin, 1964; Florkin and Mason, 1960). There are many good biochemistry textbooks available including Baldwin (1963); Fruton and Simmonds (1958); Mahler and Cordes (1966); White et al. (1964); West et al. (1966); Karlson (1965); Conn and Stumpf (1963); and Downes (1962).

Molecular biology includes elements of biochemistry, biophysics, general physiology, cellular physiology, and genetics. It uses concepts and instrumentation that disclose the nature and reactions of the macromolecules responsible for much of cellular structure and function. The work has been largely with DNA and RNA, the molecules guiding protein synthesis and the transmission of hereditary traits from one generation to the next. Although some authors treat molecular biology as being concerned with only these two classes of molecules, the field has wider scope than this.

It is unfortunate that some enthusiasts have characterized DNA as the "basic living molecule" and that others, the extremists of Mommaerts (1962), claim that only DNA and RNA need be understood in order to understand life. Life is far too complex a phenomenon for any one molecule to be thought of as living even though that molecule can reproduce under certain conditions (Commoner, 1962, 1964; see also Chapter 5). The activities of DNA and RNA do not exist isolated from the rest of the cellular apparatus.

Such problems rest partially on the question of what is meant by "living". For example, are viruses, which are basically nucleoprotein macromolecules, living entities? Living systems have many interwoven levels of organization, even at the subcellular level, most of which are very imperfectly understood. In fact, one of the main attractions of physiology is its breadth of subject matter and the many problems still to be solved with many possible avenues of research still open (Simpson, 1962, discusses some of these points).

There are other areas, somewhat difficult to delineate precisely, related to biochemistry and physiology. Biophysics stresses the use of physical models and instrumentation in its researches, which range from the analysis of molecular structure to the effects of radiation on organisms. Textbooks include Ackerman (1962); Casey (1962); and Snell et al. (1965). Also see Oncley (1959).

Physical biochemistry applies physical-chemical models to the study of biological systems (Bull, 1964; Martin, 1964).

The increasing application of mathematics to biological problems has seen the inception of mathematical and theoretical biologies. One aim of this type of approach is to provide a framework for organizing the facts and relationships of biology. Another is to provide adequate models of biological phenomena (Bailey, 1967; Bertalanffy, 1952; Rashevsky, 1962; Riggs, 1963; Stibitz, 1966; Thrall et al. 1967; Waterman and Morowitz, 1965).

1-6. Other Areas of Physiology. Although the areas of study already discussed give a general picture of the scope of physiology, there are many other areas of specialization. Some researches stress one particular organ system or activity, for example, endocrinology is concerned with endocrine glands, their secretions and function; neurophysiology is the study of the nervous system and its operations.

Animal behavior is of increasing interest and is the object of many types of investigations ranging from the molecular basis of sensory reception to the analysis of the behavior of societies. One branch, ethology, attempts to quantitatively analyze behavior under natural conditions. An engineering inspired field is bionics, where the activities of living systems are simulated in mechanical or electronic devices.

In the treatment of physiology in this book, I shall have occasion to use information and ideas from all of the areas mentioned. The first two parts of the book are directed mainly toward a general discussion of the general and cellular aspects of function. The last two parts of the book are concerned primarily with organ system and whole animal functions. Whenever possible the comparative approach will be used.

The remaining sections of this chapter will consider some ideas that are fruitful for organizing the subject matter of physiology and that underlie many physiological researches.

Some Concepts Underlying Physiological Research

1-7. Experimentation, Mechanism, and Vitalism. As I have said, the introduction of experimentation, rather than mere theorizing, was one factor that aided the development of physiology. The scientific approach, as a general rule, uses observation, followed by the creation of hypotheses to tentatively explain the observations, followed by experimentation *under controlled conditions* to test the validity of the hypotheses. This process is repeated to refine the explanations and bring them as close to reality as possible. Of all these steps, the creative one of forming hypotheses and experimental procedure—an imaginative ac-

tion of the human mind—is the most important, the most difficult to explain, and the most overlooked.

Waterman (1965) classifies biological explanations into two types. One is based on biological concepts, and the hypothesis or theory is stated in terms of evolution, genetics, adaptation, or development in biological systems. The second type uses chemical or physical models to describe certain biological functions or structures. All explanations are approached from the point of view that life is based on materials and laws which do not differ significantly from those of the nonliving world. Philosophers call this idea **mechanism.** It was first used definitively by Descartes in one of the first physiology books, *De Homine* (On Man), published in 1664. Even here Descartes did not accept mechanistic principles for the mental processes or the soul of man.

Mechanism gradually replaced the theory of **vitalism,** which was accepted by most philosophers from the time of Aristotle until the early twentieth century. Vitalistic theory had many forms, but all were based on the assumption that life was the result of a special substance or principle not part of the mechanistic cause-and-event forces of the nonliving world. Because the life force [variously called the "entelechy" by Driesch, the "sensitive soul" by Stahl, *spiritus animalis* (= animal spirit or vital force) by Galen] lies outside the realm of physical matter, it is not amenable to scientific study and is an unsatisfactory means of answering questions concerning the nature of life. It was part of vitalistic theory to assume that the compounds found in living organisms were of a different nature than those of the nonliving world and it was this concept that organic chemistry and biochemistry overthrew.

Another philosophy of life is **finalism,** which holds that life (as well as the entire universe) is goal oriented—that life is evolving toward some final goal or purpose. Life is approaching this goal not because of the basic nature of the evolutionary process, but rather the evolutionary process is determined by the final goal to be reached. The idea that biological systems evolve, develop, or function in a goal oriented manner is **teleology.** For example, teleologically speaking, birds evolved wings so that they would be able to fly. Such teleological answers are generally considered unsatisfactory. But it is interesting to note that according to the nature of feedback systems used in control and regulation (to be shortly described) goals are a built-in feature of such systems. And the concept of goal orientation becomes a useful idea without the need for invoking vital forces or conscious will or purpose (Beckner, 1959; Quastler, 1965).

Although physiologists hope to arrive eventually at an understanding of the chemical, physical, and biological basis of function, such an explanation is far from reality at this time. The complexity of biological systems far exceeds that of the chemical or physical ones usually studied. And although, for example, chemists have analyzed successfully closed systems and equilibrium reactions in aqueous solutions, we shall see that the nature of living systems is of quite different character. These facts do not discourage (for long) the physiologist but rather lead him to recognize the need for new chemical and physical theories as well as for new biological concepts and techniques to clarify these complexities. It is on this basis that modern physiology must proceed.

The ideas just mentioned underlie present day biological philosophy. References to more detailed information on these concepts include Simpson (1949, 1964); Bonner (1962); Bates (1950); Beveridge (1957); Dampier (1961). Pap (1962) has a rigorous analysis of scientific philosophy. *The Journal of the History of Biology* provides up-to-date discussions of the historical development of biological ideas.

1-8. Systems Analysis. One of the goals of any science is to find some conceptual schemes, quantitative and rigorous, that may be used to organize the experimental data of the science, its theories and hypotheses, and its relationships and laws. Such schemes should also aid in pointing the way to further experimentation and lead to predictive ability. Especially needed in biology is an indication of how to analyze and describe complex systems, where many different structural and functional levels are organized and where many variables affect the system. As Waterman points out, biology for much of its history has not had such generalizations and has been primarily a descriptive, nonmathematically oriented science.

Systems analysis is one approach that is beginning to prove useful in all areas of biology. Only its physiological implications will be considered here. Applications to other areas of biology are discussed in Amen (1966), Bertalanffy (1952), Bertalanffy and Rapoport (1956), Patton (1959, 1966), and Waterman and Morowitz (1965).

Systems analysis is presented here not because it is necessarily the best or only approach to physiological problems but because it permits a logical presentation of many physiological ideas and indicates a method of attack and definition of complex problems.

It enables one to think about organisms as entities built of smaller systems such as organs, cells, or subcellular structures and leads to new experimental ideas. Although systems analysis is primarily a mathematically based science, I shall use verbal descriptions. Milsum (1966) and Milhorn (1966) give a more rigorous treatment of systems analysis.

Systems analysis was originated by engineers interested in the design and analysis of electronic, mechanical, power, and communications systems and networks. In most cases, the engineer wishes to build a complex system from known components in order to accomplish some given function. The physiologist is presented with an already formed (and miniaturized) functioning system that has evolved over the course of hundreds of millions of years and that he must first study by dismantling (dissecting) in order to gain some information about its component parts. For this and other reasons some differences have developed in the language and approaches used by engineers and physiologists in systems analysis, but at least the engineer had established a mathematical approach to systems.

Mathematical formulations are extremely

useful in the description of systems because they are compact and rigorous. The physiologist has long recognized the presence of control and regulation in animal functions; systems analysis presents primarily a new language for such ideas. Early control theory used linear differential equations. During the last decade there has been an introduction of nonlinear differential equations, stochastic processes, study of large scale systems by linear algebra, and applications of group theory. Although the physiologist may not be acquainted with all of these mathematical tools, controls system theory still permits a better analysis of at least some functional systems of animals. Partridge (1969) has an excellent paper on these ideas.

1-9. What Is a System?   In the most general sense a system is any part of the universe that a scientist wishes to study. But in systems analysis a system is defined as any collection of objects or components functioning or coordinated together according to a set of relationships or laws (Hall and Fagin, 1965). Systems possess at least the following parts: (a) one or more inputs; (b) one or more outputs; (c) relationships between the inputs and outputs; and (d) a surrounding, or in biological terms, an environment. Figure 1-1 illustrates how systems are usually represented.

Systems range in size from gigantic to minute. They may contain as components one or more subsystems that can also be treated as systems in further study. The overall behavior of a system is determined by its components and their natures, its input variables, and the modes of connection and communication between the various components.

Organisms and their parts have these characteristics and may be treated as systems. In fact the term "living system" has been used repeatedly because it can cover any or all of the various structural and functional levels of the animal without involving the use of such limited terms as organism or cell. As will be shown, commonly used biological terms such as organ system or enzyme system, all happen to fall into the definition of system presented

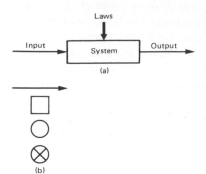

Figure 1-1   (a) Representation of a simple system containing an input, an output, and a set of rules governing the input-output relationship. (b) Conventional symbols used to represent various parts of systems. Square or rectangular boxes indicate the system under analysis. Lines represent information flow pathways, that is, electrical wires, nerve cells, or other mechanisms which convey information, either as energy or matter, from one part of the system to another. Arrows show the direction of information flow. Circles represent sites in the system where several lines of information merge. Open circles are mechanisms where manipulation or control of activity occurs. Quartered circles are sites at which algebraic addition of signals takes place often with reference to some set-point level of information. Such comparators may or may not be included as part of the controlling system. These components are used, for example, in the feedback system of Figure 1-7.

above, as does the whole animal or even a population of animals.

Depending on the nature of the inputs and outputs, systems may be classified into two general types. **Open systems** exchange matter with their environment and they also may exchange energy in any of its forms. A **closed system** does not exchange matter with the environment, although energy may be exchanged. An example of the latter type of system is a chemical (or biochemical) reaction taking place in a test tube. Although heat or light may move into or out of the reacting system, no substances do so. We shall see that open and closed systems have quite different properties.

Organisms and their subsystems must be considered as open types because there is a continual requirement for the inflow of nutrients, oxygen, and water to provide the chemical energy and the structural materials for the maintenance of the organism. Salts, minerals, and vitamins, are also required. Waste materials and secretions move out of the living system.

Figure 1-2 represents in highly simplified form a systems flow diagram for glucose transport into and through a mammal. Glucose is used as an example because it is a major source of cellular energy and its reaction pathways are well known (Chapter 4). The diagram portrays the complexity arising when many subsystems join together in complicated networks within the organism or cell. Note that the output of one subsystem may serve as the input of another subsystem. All the systems shown are of the open type and include, in addition to the whole animal, the circulatory, respiratory, and excretory systems; and cells and subcellular systems, including enzyme systems.

The basic elements of glucose distribution in Figure 1-2 lead to questions about such things as the nature of the chemical transformations of glucose to water, carbon dioxide, and useful cell energy, the site of these reactions, the methods of glucose movement, or the mechanisms for controlling glucose movement and utilization. The unraveling of such functional and structural networks is part of the goal of biochemists and physiologists interested in energy metabolism, transformation, and utilization.

In addition to inputs and outputs of material substances, all living systems have information inputs about changes in the external and internal environments and outputs that are responses to such changes. Most of the emphasis on input-output systems in this book will be on those that aid in communication, control, and regulation in animals.

1-10. The Stimulus and White and Black Boxes. Irritability is recognized as a major characteristic of living systems and is defined as the ability of a system to change in response to changes in the environment. Such a change in

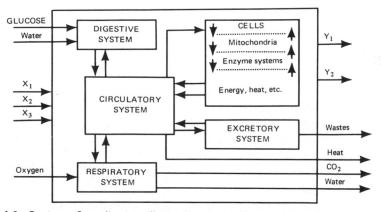

Figure 1-2 Systems flow diagram illustrating, in highly simplified form, the movement (input) of glucose into an animal and its passage, utilization, and transformations in various subsystems (organs and cells). The circulatory plays a central role in the distribution of glucose between various subsystems. Each box represents a subsystem and can be considered as a system in its own right in further studies of the detailed metabolism of glucose. As indicated in the diagram, the metabolism of glucose requires the movement and transformations of other substances so that a variety of inputs and outputs must be considered, including energy and heat exchanges. The diagram suggests many questions about the mechanisms of glucose transport and metabolism that must be answered by the physiologist and biochemist. The diagram does not attempt to indicate the nervous and hormonal controls that play a part in regulating glucose concentrations and transformations in the animal. X's and Y's indicate other inputs and outputs are present.

the environment is the **stimulus** and may have any of the various forms of energy (mechanical, chemical, thermal, electrical, and so forth). The concept of a stimulus implies not only a change in the stimulating agent but also a response on the part of the living system. Florey (1961) defines the term **stimulation** to include not only the environmental change but also any sequence of events which accompany it. Thus the stimulus duration, cessation, and frequency can all alter or affect the response. This use of the term allows a differentiation between the situation where a series of stimuli cause a response rather than a single change in the stimulating agent. Here, the stimulus refers only to the environmental factor that changes; the stimulation includes the whole series of events which cause the response. The response of a living system may result either from **excitation,** the initiation of activity, or from **inhibition,** the active prevention of activity. The environment includes not only the external environment of an organism but also the environment surrounding any organ, tissue, cell, or subcellular system under analysis.

By analyzing the nature of the stimulus and response, information can be obtained about a system whether it be an animal society, a single whole animal, an organ, a cell, or a molecular complex. Such analysis effectively uses the **black box concept** of Wiener (1948). A black box is a system whose components and mechanisms are unknown but which has a stimulus-response relation that can be established. The physiologist by stimulating his black box under controlled conditions hopes to obtain clues about the nature of its contents as well as ideas for further research that will give more facts about the nature of the system.

To illustrate this concept and also to provide some basic definitions, we shall consider an excitable cell—one such as muscle or nerve that responds to stimulation with a wave of electrical activity—the action potential or impulse, and we shall examine the effects of stimulating such a cell with electrical impulses of variable strength and duration. Note that I am not saying that early physiologists con-

cerned with this type of experimentation used the black box concept as such. The example shows only how such experimentation may be conceptually organized. It should also be noted that we are dealing here with only one of many stimulus-response relationships of the excitable cell.

An adequate stimulus, one of sufficient strength and duration, applied to the excitable

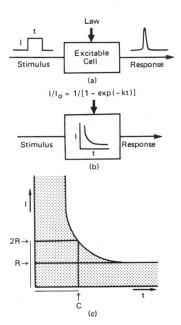

Figure 1-3 (a) Systems representation of one stimulus-response relationship of an excitable cell. The stimulus is a square wave electrical pulse of strength, I, and duration, t. The response is an all-or-none action potential when suitable values of I and t are used. (b) The mathematical law relating stimulus strength and duration to the response of the system. (c) The strength-duration curve of excitable cells, determined by altering input variables of the system. All cases in which either the strength or the duration of the stimulus is too low to produce a response fall in the shaded region under the curve. R is the rheobase strength—the lowest strength of stimulation that fails to produce a response regardless of stimulus duration. C is the chronaxie—defined as the shortest duration of stimulus that will produce a response when the stimulus strength is twice rheobase. Note that the mathematical model given here to define the strength-duration relationship is but one of several and is not necessarily the best. See equation 1.2, page 15.

cell elicits a response in the form of an action potential (Figure 1-3 and Chapter 7). From a number of early investigations it was found that

1. The stimulus has a threshold value, that is, there is a minimal strength of stimulus needed to produce a response at any given duration of stimulus. At currents below threshold, there is no overt response.
2. The response in this case is an all-or-none event. Either a maximal action potential is produced or none at all. The action potential is not graded, at least when the condition of the excitable cell remains the same.
3. If the duration of the stimulus is too short, no response is obtained regardless of how strong the stimulus is.
4. There is a minimal current strength, the **rheobase,** below which no response is obtained regardless of how long the duration of the stimulus.
5. Lapicque (1926) introduced the **chronaxie** as a measure of the excitability of a tissue. The chronaxie is defined as the minimal duration of a current of twice rheobase strength that is needed to produce a response. The **utilization time,** which is defined as the minimum current-duration needed to stimulate an excitable cell, is also used as a measure of the excitability of a tissue. Both chronaxie and utilization time are dependent on many factors and are, therefore, somewhat unreliable as indexes of excitability.

The experimentally determined relationship between the strength and the duration of a constant current stimulus yields a **strength-duration curve** when plotted as shown in Figure 1-3b. Each point on the curve is found by determining the lowest strength of stimulus that will produce a response at each given duration.

In a black box analysis of the strength-duration curve of the excitable cell, the next step is to determine some relationship between the stimulus input and the response, preferably a mathematical expression. An examination of the strength-duration curve shows that at higher stimulus strengths:

$$(I)(t) = \text{a constant} \tag{1.1}$$

where I is the stimulus strength (electrical current) and t is the stimulus duration. But this relationship does not hold for smaller currents and is not an adequate input-output relationship (Johnson et al., 1954). A better solution is given by:

$$I/I_0 = 1/\left[1 - \exp\left(-\frac{k}{t}\right)\right] \tag{1.2}$$

where I_0 is the rheobase current; I is current strength at any duration, t; and k is a constant whose value depends on the particular system studied. Equations (1-1) and (1-2) are mathematical models of the excitable cell input-output system. Other equations, as well as other considerations of strength-duration theory, are found in Blair (1932), Lefevre (1950), and Rushton (1927, 1934).

These models of the black box of the excitable cell are not the only ones possible nor are they the most complete or accurate. The physiologist must refine and repeat his experiments and hypotheses continuously until the most adequate solution is found. As stated, the example is only one of the many input-output relations of an excitable cell, and a complete description of the activities of this type of cell would require other types of experiments. In most cases there are so many inputs and outputs of living systems that no present mathematical treatment can consider the entire activity of the system. The physiologist tries to maintain all but one or two input variables constant in a given experiment and attempts to inhibit or reduce other responses than the one in which he is interested.

These physiological experiments and results lead immediately to other questions concerning the system. What mechanisms produce the response? What structures and mechanisms react directly to the stimulus? What is the meaning of the parameter k? The answers to these questions will be a major topic in Part II of this book. However, I can state here that the **white box concept** aids in answering such questions. A white box is a collection of known components, assembled in a known fashion and has the same stimulus-response relationships as the black box. A white box might be a hardware model of the black box; it might be a computer simulation of the black box; or it might be actual knowledge of the structure of the biological system.

Whatever the nature of the white box, its role is to lead to further information about the system, to further investigational approaches, or to aid predictions about the black box and its behavior under new conditions. There is a continual cycling between white and black boxes in research (Figure 1-4). We may hope that each cycle will improve the accuracy of the models and arrive closer to the true nature of the system. Research need not begin with a black box, it may be initiated with some observation of a known system (Quastler, 1965). I stress again that the concepts of black and white boxes are useful aids only, and are not necessarily in the mind of the experimenter when doing his research.

As indicated previously, the physiologist uses a variety of stimulating agents to elicit responses from systems in which he is interested. Stimuli are physiological when their nature and parameter values are similar to those that excite the living system *in vivo*.

Observation of actual system

Observation of actual system

Figure 1-4 Cycling between white and black boxes in research. On this basis research begins with an observation which provides a system for study with a determinable input-output relationship generated by unknown components (the black box) or in a system of known components producing a given input-output relationship (the white box). There is a continuous replacement of black boxes by white boxes until a model of the system under study is produced which is as close as possible to known facts about the real system. This is but one form of the scientific method which may also operate on human intuition and induction.

Stimuli are nonphysiological when they are qualitatively or quantitatively different from those exciting a living system *in vivo*.

The electrical stimuli used for the strength-duration experiment are nonphysiological because excitable cells are not stimulated normally by electrical pulses of this type, but the electrical stimulus has all the desired properties of an experimental stimulating agent. It is not harmful to the cells; it is repeatable; its frequency and other parameters are readily controllable and quantitized. This example illustrates several important parameters of a stimulus: strength, duration, and shape (in this case a square wave pulse).

Although electrical stimuli are suitable for eliciting action potentials from excitable cells, the analysis of other properties of these cells or of other cell types may require other types of stimulating agents. Thermal, chemical, mechanical, or biological stimuli are all useful, depending on the nature of the system under study.

1-11. Models in Physiology. Models are representations of systems and are used to increase understanding. Models are simplifications of real complex systems and are needed for a variety of reasons Most living systems are too complex to be treated mathematically as they exist *in toto*. By making simplifying assumptions and considering smaller parts of the system or certain of its responses, it is often possible to arrive at a mathematical model of the simplified system.

Mathematical models are desirable because they can be rigorous and also because mathematics is a concise, universal, communications system. It is the multivariate and often nonlinear character of living systems that make mathematical treatment difficult. The number of variables to which organisms or their subsystems respond is immense, and the responses are numerous and complex. Simply in order to control or eliminate unwanted variables affecting his system, the physiologist must dissect, isolate, or inhibit some part of it.

Often the isolation of a system permits the use of variables over ranges not normally encountered in the animal. Often a model is made using components or hardware whose functional relationships are known more accurately than their counterparts in the living system. The laws governing electrical circuits, thermal exchanges, hydraulic systems, levers and pulleys, as well as the behavior of gases and of chemical reactions in solution are well understood. If the physiologist can construct a white box from components showing any of these properties then he can hope to gain some understanding of the necessary structural and functional elements of the living system whose actions are mimicked by the model system.

The use, and the need for, such models is a primary reason why a knowledge of physics, chemistry, and electronics is becoming a prerequisite to adequate physiological understanding. As an example, some major models of the activities of excitable cells are based upon diffusion and conductance of ions through membranes, upon electrical circuit analogs, computer analogs, and mathematical equations. Ignorance of these basic model elements must mean an incomplete understanding of the system they model.

Models can be classified as

1. Conceptual models.
   a. Verbal concepts (laws, theories, hypotheses, etc.).
   b. Mathematical and statistical models.
   c. Mental images.
2. Material Models and Analogs.
   a. Chemical and physical models.
   b. Biological models.
   c. Computer simulations (analog and digital computers).

This listing gives some idea of what is meant by a model. Some scientists feel that only conceptual schemes are models, that all others are analogs. Here the term model will be used to refer to all the types listed. An analog is a form of model in which the activity of the model is based on quite different elements or principals than are found in the actual system. Both a nerve cell and an analog computer can produce electrical potentials of similar charac-

teristics, but obviously the components responsible for this activity in the two cases are different.

Some of the reasons for the importance of models have been given above. *The Symposia for the Society of Experimental Biology*, volume 14 (1960) contains a series of papers on biological models. Stibitz (1966) and Thrall et al. (1967) discuss mathematical models.

Young (1964, *A Model of the Brain*, p. 323) summarizes the situation by saying about models

Why then be concerned with all this talk about models? . . . I confess that I often have doubts, being myself fascinated, indeed obsessed, by the beauty and interest of the structure and function of the nervous system. Yet this beauty is far enhanced when attention to it seems to lead to something that we have called "understanding" of how the nervous system works. This experience in turn has led to exciting problems of what is meant by "understanding" and by "function." Equally exciting is the discovery that one can play a part in the process of model-building itself, producing artefacts that are both interesting and useful. Models themselves have great beauty. It is true that theirs is only a dim representation of the glories of the world around. But without them how else are we to know these beauties. . .?

(By permission Oxford University Press)

1-12. Control, Regulation, and Adaptation. To this point I have ignored an outstanding feature of living systems and one that is readily treated by the ideas of systems analysis. Living systems at all levels not only react to changes in their environment, but more, they control and regulate their reactions. Regulation of both structure and function is basic to the biological world. In 1879 Claude Bernard, a great French physiologist, proposed that the stability of the internal milieu of organisms was a prerequisite for their survival.

The American physiologist, W. B. Cannon (1929) extended this idea and introduced the term **homeostasis** to refer to the constancy of the internal environment of animals and the mechanisms by which such constancy is maintained. Homeostasis includes the regulation of such variables as temperature, salt and water content, pH, and nutrient concentrations. Animals with the best regulatory abilities are those highest on the evolutionary scale. Mammals and birds regulate the largest number of internal factors and with the greatest precision.

Any change or response on the part of an organism that favors survival in the face of changes in the external environment is called **physiological adaptation** (Prosser, 1958; Prosser and Brown, 1961). Because adaptation has several meanings in physiology, Hoar (1966) and others have suggested that the term **compensation** is a better word to use in refer-

ence to those functional properties of animals which favor survival in a changing environment.

Homeostatic regulation is one such compensatory activity. **Regulation** means that an animal maintains some condition relatively constant internally although that factor in the environment is changing (Figure 1-5a). Some organisms are **conformers** whose internal conditions alter as the environment changes (Figure 1-5b). There are many gradations between strict conformation and strict regulation and, for example, an organism may shift from

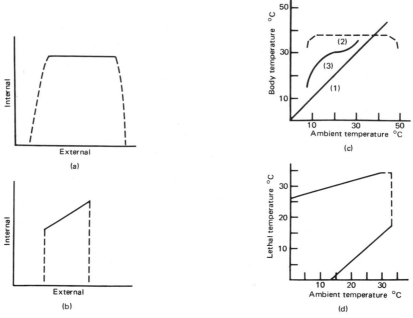

Figure 1-5 Graphical representations of (a) regulation—the maintenance of an internal variable at a constant level as the variable's value changes in the environment; and (b) conformation—the changes in value of an internal variable in proportion to alteration of the variable's value in the environment. Few animals are strict regulators over a wide range of values of a given environmental factor. Outside of the regulating range, they may conform; and at extremes of the range (which varies according to the animal) they die. (c) Different animals show different degrees of regulatory ability according to their condition and past history. Curve 1 is typical for the relationship between body temperature and environmental temperature of cold-blooded animals, including immature rats. Curve 2, for a mature rat, shows that the ability to regulate body temperature has been achieved with aging and maturation. Curve 3, the temperature regulation curve of platypus, a very primitive mammal, illustrates imperfect regulatory ability. (d) The relationship between lethal temperature—a measure of thermal tolerance—and thermal acclimation for the golden shiner, *Notemigonus crysoleucas*. [Data from J. S. Hart (1952) "Geographic variations of some physiological and morphological characters in certain freshwater fish" *University of Toronto Biology Series*, **60**: 1–79.]

conforming to regulating as it matures (Figure 1-5c).

Animals also react to changes in their environment by behavioral mechanisms that may or may not be part of a homeostatic system. Small changes in the environment may stimulate an organism to move away from unfavorable or toward favorable conditions. In many lower animals unfavorable conditions lead to increased locomotor activity and a greater possibility for escaping those conditions; on the other hand, favorable conditions lead to decreased locomotion, and the animal tends to remain in the favorable environment.

Adaptation also includes **acclimation** and **acclimatization.** Acclimation refers to compensatory changes that occur under controlled laboratory conditions where only one parameter is varied. Acclimatization refers to the complex changes that occur under natural conditions where multiple parameters vary.

Any organism has limits to its ability to regulate or conform. Each animal, according to its genetic makeup, can live within a certain range of environmental variations. This range is its **tolerance.** Beyond the tolerance range, the organism may exhibit some capacity for **resistance** to environmental extremes. However, outside the tolerance range the organism is suffering damage and will eventually succumb. At either end of the range of the environmental factor are the **upper** and **lower incipient lethal levels** at which death occurs. A lethal level is usually defined as the level of an environmental factor that kills some stated fraction of a population (usually 50 per cent) within an indefinitely prolonged exposure. Acclimation and acclimatization modify tolerance and resistance to changing conditions.

Temperature effects present familiar examples of these terms, although the processes underlying temperature compensation are not well known. The same is true of compensation generally. Figure 1-5d shows the relation between acclimation temperature and lethal temperature for the golden shiner. It can be seen that when fish are acclimated to a temperature of 30°C for a week or more, both the upper and lower lethal temperatures are raised slightly

as compared with fish adapted to a lower temperature. The previous temperature history of an organism affects the lethal temperatures; and, in fact, there is a family of upper and lower lethal levels; and the range of tolerance is actually a zone of tolerance bounded by a zone of resistance. For temperature effects, Precht (1958) uses the term **capacity adaptation** for the compensation within the range of normal temperatures and **resistance adaptation** for that in the extremes of the range. Although there are major differences between species with regard to their tolerances and resistances, there is also a plasticity within a single species.

Adaptation and regulation are needed because of the narrow range of conditions under which life can exist. Seemingly the complex structural and functional relations of the cell require special conditions, and it is the task of regulatory mechanisms to provide and maintain these conditions. At the same time animals must maintain the ability to compensate for long term changes in their external environment.

Physiological compensation and regulation of any of the various environmental parameters may be found in a given animal. A discussion of these various factors will be found in later appropriate chapters. Physiological compensation and regulation are considered in Adolph (1943, 1961); Cannon (1939); Fry (1947); Prosser (1958, 1964); and Yamamoto and Brobeck (1965). *The Handbook of Physiology*, Sec. 4, Vol. 1, "Adaptation to the Environment" (1964) contains a series of papers on all types of adaptation (Dill, 1964).

1-13. Cybernetics, Feedback, and Control. In 1947 Norbert Wiener coined the word "cybernetics" (from the Greek for "steersman") to designate a science concerned with control and communication in machines and animals. Cybernetics attempts to build precise models based on mathematical theory (Ashby, 1957; George, 1965; Wiener, 1948, 1961). Control problems often require the concepts of information theory (Quastler, 1953, Shannon and Weaver, 1949); of decision theory (Thrall et al.

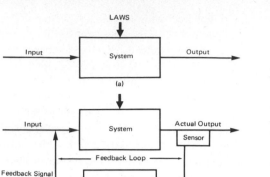

Figure 1-6 General representation of a feedback system. (a) An input-output system as previously diagrammed. (b) The input-output system with a closed loop (negative feedback loop) added. Part of the output is sensed by an element of the feedback system and a signal is sent back to the input. In negative feedback regulating systems, the feedback system is algebraically subtracted from the input, causing an appropriate increase or reduction in the system's output—thereby achieving a relative constancy of output.

1954); or of games theory (von Neumann and Morgenstern, 1947). These various fields of study center upon systems theory and, again, are useful as aids in solving problems and unifying control and regulation concepts in all types of systems including those of animals (Kalmus, 1967).

Feedback is a basic idea in cybernetics and is defined as the influence of the output of a system on its input (Figure 1-6). **Positive feedback** occurs when the output, or some function of the output, is added to the input—resulting in a greater output. Although positive feedback is sometimes spoken of as a vicious circle phenomenon, often such systems are useful because they can provide stability under certain conditions. For example, in mammals, orientation, searching, and cleaning reflexes possess a motor innervation that tends to increase the sensory input; and they are reflexes with a positive feedback (Kozak and Westerman, 1966). Orientation and searching reflexes direct the sense organs toward a source of stimulation; cleaning reflexes direct claws, tongue, or teeth toward a source of irritation and the consequent act of scratching, licking, or biting increases the stimulation of the skin in the irritated region. Excessive increase of the reflex activity is prevented by habituation—a lessening of nervous system responses upon continued stimulation. Positive feedback is also found in metabolic pathways, where the formation of a given product acts as a catalyst to increase the rate of some previous reaction in the system. Autocatalysis—the use of the product of a reaction to increase the rate of that same reaction—is another common example of positive feedback. Positive feedback

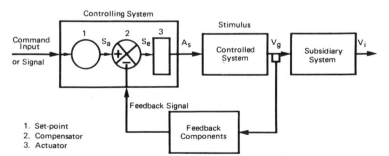

Figure 1-7 Schematic of a negative feedback system and its components. Each of the required components is shown as a separate entity, but in the organism many of the mechanisms required for feedback control in homeostasis may be combined in one cell or tissue. In most cases the actual location and mode of operation of the feedback system components in the organism are not known. Note that there are inputs and outputs for each subsystem and that information flow is an important factor in the system. The input labeled "stimulus" at the level of the controlled system may alter the output, which must then be regulated to overcome the effect of the disturbance. For a description of the components of this system see text.

also operates in some endocrine functions, for example, in the gonadotrophin-estrogen secretion mechanism under some conditions (see Hinde and Steel, 1966).

Negative feedback occurs when the output, or some function of the output, is algebraically subtracted from the input of a system, resulting in an increasing or decreasing output about some set level so that the entire system is controlled. *To exhibit regulation, a system must contain a negative feedback loop.*

Figure 1-7 is a generalized schematic of a feedback system and its components and subsystems. It contains

1. A controlled system: the part of the feedback system which is to have one or more output variables controlled. The directly controlled variable (V_d) often is the input to a subsidiary system whose output is then indirectly controlled (V_i).
2. The feedback loop contains components to sense the magnitude of the controlled output and to relay information via a feedback signal (*FBS*) to a controlling system.
3. The controlling system includes
   a. An actuator responsible for increasing or decreasing the value of the controlled output variable. The actuator signal or forcing signal (S_a) is determined by:
   b. The strength of the error signal (S_e) derived by comparing the feedback signal with a reference signal in the component known as the comparator.
   c. The set-point device selects the required value of the controlled output variable. It can be set by a command signal so that a reference signal (S_r) results.
4. Lines of communication between the different components and subsystems.

This system is similar to a homeostatic system. Any stimulus (disturbance) will affect the output and thus the feedback signal. The latter then changes the actuating signal depending on whether the output is larger or smaller than some predetermined value. The level of the feedback signal alters the value of the output signal, and thus control to the desired level is achieved (Figure 1-8a). In some cases the output level is required to follow the

stimulus strength: such a system is a servomechanism (Figure 1-8b). The principle of a servomechanism is often used in the control of animal movements and in the positioning of moving parts of animals.

In both parts of Figure 1-8, the line marked *e* indicates that feedback systems are not perfect, that is, there is always some slight difference between the desired output and the actual output at any time. It is inherent in feedback systems that such error exists. In a given organism the level of any controlled variable fluctuates about the set-point level. There may also be slight differences from individual to individual of a species insofar as the set-points for homeostatic parameters are concerned. Physiological data must be examined with the consideration that there are average levels not

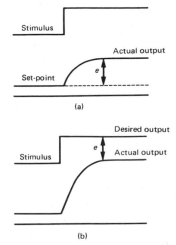

Figure 1-8 Differences between regulating and servomechanism systems. (a) When a "step" stimulus or input is applied to a homeostatic system (feedback system), the output and feedback signals are compared with the desired level as determined by the set-point, and the output variable is maintained at nearly constant level. (b) In a servomechanism there is no set-point. The system serves the function of maintaining the output as close as possible to the stimulus level. In both cases when the steady-state levels are reached there is an error, *e*, that is, the desired level in both cases differs from the actual output level. The use of sudden changes of stimulus levels and the measurement of steady-state values of the system simplify the analyses of such systems as far as mathematical models are concerned (Stibitz, 1966).

absolute ones of homeostatic variables. Further, external conditions, daily cycles of activity, and other factors may alter homeostatic levels.

As previously mentioned, feedback systems are goal oriented, that is, they operate to bring some output variable to a set value (Wiener, 1961; Waterman, 1965). But little is known about the elements of the set-point control that determine the value at which homeostatic functions are to be maintained.

The feedback system as diagrammed in Figure 1-7 is a system of information flows. **Information** is any feature of a system or its environment that gives an organism (or a machine) a chance to make a choice or decision about taking action. Information is a flow of energy around a system and is often quantitated in terms of entropy—a thermodynamic property of a system that measures its degree of organization (see Chapter 4).

Information adds order to biological systems and permits their maintenance and functioning. The stimulus, as already defined, is one form of information input to organisms. Information may be carried in macromolecules such as proteins or the nucleic acids; in the nervous system and its nerve impulses; and in the endocrine system. It is the need for information and regulation and decision making that necessitates the use of the various theories mentioned at the beginning of this section. Information and feedback are not new ideas in physiology, but systems analysis and its various correlates are often used now because they present a mathematical basis for examining the systems of the physiologist.

Wiener and others point out that the nineteenth century was an era concerned with energy and energy transformations—the age of power and power machinery development— the time when the concepts of thermodynamics were developed. At this time it became fashionable to think of organisms in terms of energy exchanges and heat engines. The twentieth century is the age of control and regulation and interests now center on the use of small energy changes to control large power outputs, creating the age of the feedback system, information flow, and the computer. Animals are now thought of in these terms. One character-

istic of the biological stimulus is that a small energy change in the environment can produce large scale responses and energy output by the organism. Each age tends to consider animals in terms of the prevalent technology.

1-14. Components of Biological Control Systems. We can now ask what biological structures and mechanisms play the roles of the various components of feedback systems. The following discussion is based primarily on a consideration of a whole metazoan animal, not with cellular control systems.

The actuators of the engineer can be translated as the **effectors** or **effector organs** of the physiologist. The two primary effectors are muscles, and glands. Effectors also include cilia, flagella, chromatophores, and electric organs. Effectors are the components of the cell or organism that perform some action in response to appropriate stimulation.

Information transfer in animals is accomplished by nerve cells and their action potentials (= nerve impulses) or by chemical means (hormones) secreted by endocrine glands and released into the circulatory system. In recent years many neurons have been found that are specialized for secretory activity. The neuroendocrine relationship is a very close one.

Generally, nerve impulses are used to excite effectors when rapid action is needed; and hormonal stimulation is used for slower processes such as those of metabolism, growth, and color changes. At the organism level it is remarkable how many biological activities are based upon either contractile mechanisms, bioelectric potential generation, or differential permeability of membranes.

Sensory receptors of nerve cells collect information from the internal and external environments. All sensory receptors (as well as the effectors) are examples of biological **transducers**—elements that transform one form of energy into another. For example, the eye converts radiant energy into nerve electrical potentials; muscles convert chemical into mechanical energy. Sensory receptors are selective in that they respond preferentially to one form of energy stimulus, although higher strengths of other energy forms may also cause a response.

The central nervous system acts as a co-ordinating and integrating center. Because most of the information received by receptors including feedback sensors, is relayed to the central nervous system for processing before being acted upon, it is usually assumed that this is the site of the set-point mechanisms and comparators of biological feedback systems. But in biological control systems, the nature, location, or even the existence of such elements is usually hypothetical.

In this chapter some of the ideas and terms used by the physiologist have been discussed. The remainder of the book will elaborate on these in terms of specific animal activities. It is worth stressing again that regulation, sensors, effectors, feedback, and similar ideas have been used by the physiologist for a long time. The concepts of systems analysis that have been used to present them here have not been responsible for the discovery of these biological facts.

In physiology writing out systems diagrams of physiological activities is often helpful if for no other reason than to gain understanding of the structural and functional hierarchies involved. Such diagrams aid in emphasizing which parts of the system are black boxes and which are white and the nature and direction of information flows. As often as possible I shall refer to research approached from the systems point of view, but there is still a wide gap between the potentialities of the method and its actual practice.

1-15. Instrumentation and Techniques. Once observation of a living system has been made and hypotheses formed to explain some observed behavior, the physiologist enters the experimental phase of his research. It is at this point that instrumentation and methodology become important (although the observational phase may also involve the use of instrumentation).

One of the basic concepts underlying modern experimental biology is that of explicit quantification or measurement. The investigator is concerned not only with the observation: a rat feels warmer than a frog at normal room temperatures—but also with the measurement of how much warmer it is. The verifica-

tion of quantitative hypotheses requires exact measurement of the time course of the physiological change as well as the amount of change.

Such measurements are made routinely using electronic equipment. In modern physiology measurement of temperature, pH, gas and fluid flows, bioelectric potentials, volumes, and contractile forces and movements is accomplished by the use of transducers that convert these various forms of energy into electrical signals. Such signals are readily and precisely amplified and recorded on oscilloscopes, multichannel recorders, galvanometers, and so forth. Modern physiology requires the use of high-fidelity instrumentation; older methods, while often still useful for preliminary work, give only approximations of many of the quantities and activities basic to the understanding of physiological mechanisms.

Instruments are used to extend the human senses, and they permit the measurement and recording of events either too small, too fast, or of a nature not directly detectable by human sensory receptors. Very precise measurements or the measurement of minute quantities or times may require complex instrumentation, but many measurements can be made using less complex instruments. It is important in any case that the investigator understand the limitations, accuracy, time response, and so forth, of his instruments.

Physiological research may also require the use of microscopic techniques, cytochemical or histochemical methods, or biochemical or biophysical instruments and methods. The array of techniques available to the physiologist is large, and space cannot be given to their description in this textbook. At best, the general nature of some methods and instruments required to produce suitable data from experimental studies will be mentioned, and some of the limitations and sources of error described.

Many books and monographs are available on instrumentation and methods. These include electronics and electrophysiology: Bûres et al. (1962), Donaldson (1958), Stacy (1960), Whitfield (1959, 1964), Nastuk (1962, 1963); physical and organic methods: Oster and Pollister (1955–), Weissberger (1959–); general experimental techniques: Kay (1964), New-man (1965); cell techniques: Prescott (1966, 1968), Danielli (1958, 1961). Instruments and their modifications are discussed in the *Review of Scientific Instruments*.

Literature

A primary responsibility of the scientific researcher is to publish significant findings in the appropriate journals. The facts and theories of physiology are to be found in these journals.

Because the volume of research literature is immense, it is impossible for a physiologist to read even a small part of the papers published on all matters that interest him. Abstracting journals and services provide brief summaries of all published papers. Abstracts may be indexed by title, author, field of specialization, biological structure or classification, or key words in titles.

Experts in given areas of specialization write brief reviews or longer monographs on their subjects. Such reviews include extensive bibliographies of pertinent literature. Symposia volumes cover physiological meetings at which experts discuss and summarize the knowledge in a narrow (usually) field of physiology.

Students should be familiar with the popular magazine, *Scientific American*, which contains up-to-date articles on all aspects of physiology and other sciences. Reprints of articles including their excellent illustrations are available at nominal cost from W. H. Freeman and Co., 660 Market St., San Francisco, Cal.

Another important source of physiological information is the *Handbook of Physiology*, a series published by the American Physiological Society, Washington, D.C. (the first volume appeared in 1959 and further volumes continue to appear at irregular intervals). Also of value to students are various annual series including *Advances in Protein Chemistry* (New York: Academic Press, Inc.); *Advances in Enzymology* (New York: Interscience Publishers, Inc., a division of John Wiley & Sons, Inc.); and the *Cold Spring Harbor Symposium on Quantitative Biology* (Long Island, New York: Cold Spring Harbor Laboratory of Quantitative Biology).

All sources of information referred to in this book are listed, alphabetically by author, at the end of each chapter. In many cases, in order to limit the number of references used, monographs or reviews are given as sources because they often summarize many papers by a particular researcher or include a broad treatment of a given subject. Research papers are, of course, the best sources of original experimental data and methodology.

The indices of this textbook serves not only as a page reference to topics but also list all authors mentioned. In addition all abbreviations used, together with their meanings, are listed in the Subject Index.

Lists of some of the sources of physiological information are given below. The abbreviations generally used in literature citations are indicated by bold-face type.

Table 1-2. Reviews, Symposia, and Abstracting Journals

Advances in **Enzymol**ogy	**Chem**ical **Abstracts**
Advances in **Insect Physiol**ogy	**Chem**ical **Reviews**
Advances in **Protein Chem**istry	**Cold Spring Harbor Symp**osia on **Quant**itative **Biol**ogy
American **Scient**ist	**Ergeb**nisse der **Physiol**ogie
American **Zool**ogist	**Fortschr**itte der **Zool**ogie
Annals of the New York **Acad**emy of **Sci**ences	**Harvey Lect**ures
Annual **Rev**iew of **Biochem**istry	**Physiol**ogical **Reviews**
Annual **Rev**iew of **Pharmacol**ogy	**Progress** in **Biophys**ics (and Molecular Biology)
Annual **Rev**iew of **Physiol**ogy	**Quart**erly **Rev**iew of **Biology**
Berichte über die **ges**amte **Physiol**ogie	**Symp**osia of the **Soci**ety for **Experi**mental **Biology**
Berichte über die **ges**amte **Biol**ogie	
Biological **Abstracts**	

Table 1-3.   Research Publications

Acta Physiologica Scandinavica
Acta Physiologica Academiae Scientarum
  (Hungary)
American Journal of Physiology
Archives of Biochemistry and Biophysics
Archives internationales de Physiologica
Archiv für die gesamte Physiologie (Germany)
Biochemical Journal (England)
Biochemical and Biophysical Research
  Communications
Biochemische Zeitschrift (Germany)
Biochimica et Biophysica Acta
Biological Bulletin
Biophysical Journal
Bulletin of Mathematical Biophysics
Canadian Journal of Biochemistry and
  Physiology
Comparative Biochemistry and Physiology
Endocrinology
Enzymologia
Experimental Cell Research
Federation Proceedings
General and Comparative Endocrinology
Helvetica Physiologica Acta
Japanese Journal of Physiology
Journal of Animal Morphology and Physiology
Journal of Biological Chemistry
Journal of Biophysical and Biochemical
  Cytology

Journal of Comparative Neurology
Journal of Cell Biology
Journal of Cellular and Comparative
  Physiology
Journal of Endocrinology
Journal of Experimental Biology
Journal of Experimental Zoology
Journal of General Physiology
Journal of Insect Physiology
Journal of the Marine Biological Association
  (U.K.)
Journal of Marine Research
Journal of Molecular Biology
Journal of Neurophysiology
Journal of Nutrition
Journal of Pharmacology and Experimental
  Therapeutics
Journal of Physiology (London)
Journal of Theoretical Biology
Journal of Ultrastructure Research
Nature
Naturwissenschaften (Germany)
Physiological Zoology
Proceedings of the National Academy of
  Sciences (Wash.)
Proceedings of the Royal Society (London)
Science
Zeitschrift für vergleichende Physiologie
  (Germany)

References and Readings

(Note: The style of citation used here does not always follow the procedures recommended by style manuals for scientific journals. For example, all book titles are given in bold-face letters to facilitate recognition of books from journal articles or other sources.)

Ackerman, E. (1962). **Biophysical Science**. Englewood Cliffs, N.J.: Prentice-Hall, Inc. 626 pp.

Adolph, E. F. (1943). **Physiological Regulations.** Lancaster, Pa.: Cattell Press. 502 pp.

Adolph, E. F. (1961). "Early concepts of physiological regulation." *Physiol. Rev.* **41**: 737–770.

Amen, R. D. (1966). "A biological systems concept." *Bioscience* **16**: 396–401.

American Physiological Society. (1959–). **Handbook of Physiology.** Many volumes. Washington, D.C.

Ashby, W. R. (1957). **An Introduction to Cybernetics.** London: Chapman and Hall. 295 pp.

Bailey, N. T. (1967). **Mathematical Approach to Biology and Medicine.** New York: John Wiley & Sons, Inc.

Baldwin, E. (1963). **Dynamic Aspects of Biochemistry**, 4th ed. New York: Cambridge University Press. 554 pp.

Baldwin, E. (1964). **An Introduction to Comparative Biochemistry**, 4th ed. New York: Cambridge University Press. 554 pp.

Bates, M. (1950). **The Nature of Natural Science.** New York: Charles Scribners' Sons. 309 pp.

Beckner, M. (1959). **The Biological Way of Thought.** New York: Columbia University Press. 200 pp.

von Bertalanffy, L. (1952). **Problems of Life.** New York: Harper and Row, Publishers, Inc. 216 pp.

von Bertalanffy, L., and A. Rapoport, eds. (1956). **General Systems, Yearbook of the Society for the Advancement of General Systems Theory,** Vol. 1. Bedford, Mass.: Society for General Research. 240 pp.

Beveridge, W. B. (1957). **The Art of Scientific Investigation.** New York: W. W. Norton & Company. 171 pp.

Blair, H. A. (1932). "On the intensity-time relations for stimulation by electrical currents." *J. Gen. Physiol.* **15:** 709–755.

Bonner, J. T. (1962). **The Ideas of Biology.** New York: Harper and Row, Publishers, Inc. 190 pp.

Boolootian, R. A., ed. (1966). **Physiology of Echinodermata.** New York: Academic Press, Inc. 840 pp.

Brachet, J. (1957). **Biochemical Cytology.** New York: Academic Press, Inc. 516 pp.

Brachet, J., and A. E. Mirsky, eds. (1959–1964). **The Cell: Biochemistry, Physiology, and Morphology.** 6 volumes. New York: Academic Press, Inc.

Brown, M. E., ed. (1957). **The Physiology of Fishes.** 2 volumes. New York: Academic Press, Inc.

Bull, H. B. (1964). **An Introduction to Biophysical Chemistry.** Philadelphia: F. A. Davis Co. 433 pp.

Bûres, J., M. Petrán, and J. Zachar, (1952). **Electrophysiological Methods in Biological Research.** New York: Academic Press, Inc. 515 pp.

Cannon, W. B. (1929). "Organization for physiological homeostasis." *Physiol. Rev.* **9:** 399–431.

Cannon, W. B. (1939). **The Wisdom of the Body,** revised edition. New York: W. W. Norton & Company. 333 pp.

Casey, E. J. (1962). **Biophysics.** New York: Reinhold Publishing Corporation. 335 pp.

Commoner, B. (1962). "Is DNA a self-duplicating molecule?" In **Horizons in Biochemistry.** (M. Kasha, and B. Pullman, eds.) pp. 319–334. New York: Academic Press, Inc.

Commoner, B. (1964). "DNA and the chemistry of inheritance." *Am. Sci.* **52:** 365–388.

Conn, E. E. and P. K. Stumpf, (1963). **Outlines of Biochemistry.** New York: John Wiley & Sons, Inc. 391 pp.

Dampier, W. C. (1961). **A History of Science and Its Relations with Philosophy,** 4th ed. New York: Cambridge University Press. 544 pp.

Danielli, J. F., ed. (1958, 1961). **General Cytological Methods.** 2 volumes. New York: Academic Press, Inc.

Davson, H. (1964). **A Textbook of General Physiology,** 3rd ed. Boston: Little, Brown and Company. 1166 pp.

DeRobertis, E. D. P., W. W. Nowinski, and F. A. Saez (1960). **General Cytology,** 3rd ed. Philadelphia: W. B. Saunders Company.

DeRobertis, E. D. P., W. W. Nowinski, and F. A. Saez (1965). **Cell Biology,** 4th ed. Philadelphia: W. B. Saunders Company. 446 pp.

Dill, D. B., ed. (1964). "Adaptation to the Environment." **Handbook of Physiology,** Sect. 4. Washington, D. C.: American Physiological Society. 1056 pp.

Donaldson, P. E. K. (1958). **Electronic Apparatus for Biological Research.** New York: Academic Press, Inc. 718 pp.

Downes, H. R. (1962). **The Chemistry of Living Cells,** 2nd ed. New York: Harper and Row, Publishers, Inc. 645 pp.

Florey, E. (1961). "Excitation, inhibition, and the concept of the stimulus." In: **Nervous Inhibition.** (E. Florey, ed.), pp. 318–325. New York: Pergamon Press, Inc.

Florkin, M. and H. S. Mason, eds. (1960–1964). **Comparative Biochemistry.** 7 volumes, New York: Academic Press, Inc.

Franklin, K. J. (1949). **A Short History of Physiology,** 2nd ed. New York: Staples Press, Inc. 147 pp.

Frey-Wyssling, A. (1953). **Submicroscopic Morphology of Protoplasm,** 2nd ed. New York: American Elsevier Publishing Company, Inc. 411 pp.

Fruton, J. S. and S. Simmonds (1958). **General Biochemistry,** 2nd ed. New York: John Wiley & Sons, Inc. 1077 pp.

Fry, F. E. J. (1947). "Effects of the environment on animal activity." *Univ. Toronto Biol. Ser.* **55:** 1–62.

Fry, F. E. J. (1964). "Animals in aquatic environments: fishes." In **Handbook of Physiology,** Sect. 4. "Adaptation to the Environment." (D. B. Dill, ed.), pp. 715–728. American Physiological Society.

George, F. H. (1965). **Cybernetics and Biology.** San Francisco: W. H. Freeman & Company, Publishers. 283 pp.

Giese, A. C. (1968). **Cell Physiology,** 3rd ed. Philadelphia: W. B. Saunders Company. 671 pp.

Grollman, S. (1964). **The Human Body.** New York: Macmillan Company. 611 pp.

Gunsalus, I. C. and R. Y. Stanier, eds. (1960–1964). **The Bacteria.** 5 volumes. New York: Academic Press, Inc.

Hall, A. D. and R. E. Fagin (1956). "Definition of a System." In: **General Systems: Yearbook of the Society for the Advancement of General Systems Theory,** Vol. 1. (L. von Bertalanffy and A. Rapoport, eds.), pp. 18–28.

Hill, A. V. (1936). "The strength-duration relation for electric excitation of medullated nerves." *Proc. Roy. Soc.* **B119:** 440–453.

Hinde, R. A. and E. Steel (1966). "Integration of the reproductive behavior of female canaries." *Symp. Soc. Exp. Biol.* **20:** 401–426.

Hoar, W. S. (1966). **General and Comparative Physiology.** Englewood Cliffs, N.J.: Prentice-Hall, Inc. 815 pp.

Hutner, S. H. (1964). **Biochemistry and Physiology of Protozoa.** Vol. 3. New York: Academic Press, Inc. 616 pp.

Johnson, F. H., H. Eyring, and M. J. Polissar (1954). **The Kinetic Basis of Molecular Biology.** New York: John Wiley & Sons, Inc. 874 pp.

Kalmus, H. (1967). **Regulation and Control in Living Systems.** New York: John Wiley & Sons, Inc. 468 pp.

Karlson, P. (1965). **Introduction to Modern Biochemistry.** New York: Academic Press, Inc. 436 pp.

Kay, R. H. (1964). **Experimental Biology.** New York: Reinhold Publishing Corporation. 416 pp.

Keilin, D. (1966). **The History of Cell Respiration and Cytochrome.** London: Cambridge Univ. Press. 416 pp.

Kosower, E. (1962). **Molecular Biology.** New York: McGraw-Hill Book Company, Inc. 304 pp.

Kozak, W. and R. Westerman (1966). "Basic patterns of plastic change in the mammalian nervous system." *Symp. Soc. Exp. Biol.* **20:** 509–544.

Lapicque, L. (1926). **L'excitabilité en fonction du temps; la chronaxie, sa signification et sa mesure.** Paris: Presses Universitairses.

Laverack, M. S. (1963). **The Physiology of Earthworms.** International Series of Monographs on Pure and Applied Biology. Vol. 15. New York: Pergamon Press, Inc. 206 pp.

Leake, C. D. (1930). **Anatomical Studies on the Motion of the Heart and Blood.** (translation of William Harvey's *De Motu Cordis*). Baltimore: Charles C. Thomas, Publisher.

Lefevre, P. G. (1950). "Excitation characteristics in giant squid axon. A test of excitation theory in the case of rapid accommodation." *J. Gen. Physiol.* **34:** 19–36.

Lentz, T. L. (1967). **The Cell Biology of Hydra.** New York: John Wiley & Sons, Inc. and Amsterdam: North Holland Publishing Co. 199 pp.

Mahler, H. R. and E. H. Cordes (1966). **Biological Chemistry.** New York: Harper & Row, Publishers, Inc. 872 pp.

Marshall, A. J., ed. (1960). **Biology and Comparative Physiology of Birds.** 2 volumes. New York: Academic Press, Inc.

Martin, R. B. (1964). **Introduction to Biophysical Chemistry.** New York: McGraw-Hill Book Company. 365 pp.

Milhorn, H. T. (1966). **The Application of Control Theory to Physiological Systems.** Philadelphia: W. B. Saunders Company. 386 pp.

Milsum, J. H. (1966). **Biological Control Systems Analyses.** New York: The McGraw-Hill Book Company. 466 pp.

Mommaerts, W. F. H. M. (1962). "Molecular physiology—analysis and synthesis." *Am. Sci.* **50:** 497–504.

Moore, J. A., ed. (1964). **Physiology of Amphibia.** New York: Academic Press, Inc. 654 pp.

Morowitz, H. J. (1970). **Entropy for Biologists.** New York: Academic Press, Inc. 195 pp.

Mountcastle, V. B., ed. (1968). **Medical Physiology.** 2 volumes. St. Louis, Mo.: The C. V. Mosby Company.

Nastuk, W. L., ed. (1962). **Physical Techniques in Biological Research.** Vol. 5, Electrophysiological Methods, Part I. New York: Academic Press, Inc. 460 pp.

Nastuk, W. L., ed. (1963). **Physical Techniques in Biological Research.** Vol. 6. Electrophysiological Methods. New York: Academic Press, Inc. 425 pp.

von Neumann, J. and O. Morgenstern (1947). **Theory of Games and Economic Behavior.** Princeton, N.J.: The Princeton Univ. Press. 641 pp.

Newman, D., ed. (1965). **Instrumental Methods of Experimental Biology.** New York: The Macmillan Company, Inc. 560 pp.

Oncley, J. L. ed. (1959). **Biophysical Science— A Study Program.** New York: John Wiley & Sons, Inc. 568 pp.

Oster, G. and A. W. Pollister, eds. (1955–1967). **Physical Techniques in Biological Research.** 3 volumes, several revised editions. New York: Academic Press, Inc.

Pap, A. (1962). **An Introduction to the Philosophy of Science.** New York: The Free Press. 444 pp.

Partridge, L. D. (1969). "Signal handling aspects in the control of muscular activity." *Fed. Proc.* **28:** 65–72.

Patton, B. C. (1959). "An introduction to the cybernetics of the ecosystem, the trophic-dynamic aspect. *Ecology* **40:** 221–231.

Patton, B. C. (1966). "Systems ecology." *Bioscience* **16:** 593–598.

Precht, H. (1958). "Concepts of the temperature adaptation of unchanging reaction systems of cold-blooded animals." In: **Physiological Adaptation** (C. L. Prosser, ed.), pp. 50–78. Washington, D.C.: American Physiological Society.

Prescott, D. M. (1966–1968). **Methods in Cell Physiology.** 3 volumes. New York: Academic Press, Inc.

Prosser, C. L., ed. (1958). **Physiological Adaptation.** Washington, D.C.: American Physiological Society. 186 pp.

Prosser, C. L., ed. (1964). "Perspectives of adaptation." In: **Handbook of Physiology.** Sec. 4, "Adaptation to the Environment" (D. B. Dill, ed.), pp. 11–26. Washington, D.C.: American Physiological Society.

Prosser, C. L. and F. A. Brown (1961). **Comparative Animal Physiology,** 2nd ed. Philadelphia: W. B. Saunders Company. 688 pp.

Quastler, H. (1953). **Essays on the Use of Information Theory in Biology,** 2nd ed. Urbana: University of Illinois Press. 272 pp.

Quastler, H. (1965). "General principles of systems analysis." In: **Theoretical and Mathematical Biology.** (T. H. Waterman and H. J. Morowitz, eds.), pp. 313–333. Waltham, Mass.: Blaisdell Publishing Co.

Rashevsky, N., ed. (1962). **Physicomathematical Aspects of Biology.** New York: Academic Press, Inc. 584 pp.

Riggs, D. S. (1963). **The Mathematical Approach to Physiological Problems.** Baltimore: The Williams & Wilkins Company. 445 pp.

Rockstein, M., ed. (1964, 1965). **The Physiology of Insecta.** 3 volumes. New York: Academic Press, Inc.

Rogers, C. G. (1927). **Textbook of Comparative Physiology.** New York: The McGraw-Hill Book Company. 635 pp.

Ruch, T. C. and J. F. Fulton, eds. (1960). **Medical Physiology,** 18th ed. Philadelphia: W. B. Saunders Company. 1242 pp.

Ruch, T. C. and H. D. Patton, eds. (1965). **Medical Physiology and Biophysics,** 19th ed. Philadelphia: W. B. Saunders Company. 1242 pp.

Rushton, W. A. H. (1927). "The effect upon the threshold for nervous excitation of the length of nerve exposed and the angle between current and nerve." *J. Physiol.* London, **63:** 357–377.

Rushton, W. A. H. (1934). "A physical analysis of the relation between threshold and interpolar length in the electric excitation of medullated nerve." *J. Physiol.,* London, **82:** 332–352.

Shannon, C. E. and W. Weaver (1949). **The Mathematical Theory of Communication.** Urbana: University Illinois Press. 117 pp.

Simpson, G. G. (1949). **The Meaning of Evolution.** New Haven, Conn: Yale University Press. 192 pp.

Simpson, G. G. (1962). "The status of the study of organisms." *Am. Sci.* **50:** 36–45.

Simpson, G. G. (1964). **This View of Life: The World of an Evolutionist.** New York: Harcourt Brace, & World, Inc.

Snell, F. M., S. Shulman, R. P. Spencer, and C. Moos (1965). **Biophysical Principles of Structure and Function.** Reading, Mass.: Addison-Wesley Publishing Co., Inc. 390 pp.

Stacy, R. W. (1960). **Biological Electronics.** New York: The McGraw-Hill Book Company. 308 pp.

Stacy, R. W. and J. A. Santolucito (1966). **Modern College Physiology.** St. Louis, Mo.: The C. V. Mosby Company. 428 pp.

Stibitz, G. R. (1966). **Mathematics in Medicine and the Life Sciences.** Chicago: Yearbook Medical Publishers. 391 pp.

Thrall, R. M., C. H. Coombs, and R. L. Davis, eds. (1954). **Decision Processes.** New York: John Wiley & Sons, Inc. 332 pp.

Thrall, R. M., J. A. Mortimer, K. R. Rebman, and R. F. Baum (1967). **Some Mathematical Models in Biology.** Ann Arbor: University of Michigan.

Tuttle, W. W. and B. A. Schottelius (1965). **Textbook of Physiology,** 15th ed. St. Louis: The C. V. Mosby Company. 562 pp.

Waterman, T. H., ed. (1960, 1961). **The Physiology of Crustacea.** 2 volumes. New York: Academic Press, Inc.

Waterman, T. H. (1965). "The Problem." In: **Theoretical and Mathematical Biology.** (T. H. Waterman and H. J. Morowitz, eds.), pp. 3–23. Waltham, Mass.: Blaisdell Publishing Co.

Waterman, T. H. and H. J. Morowitz, eds. (1965). **Theoretical and Mathematical Biology.** Waltham, Mass.: Blaisdell Publishing Co. 426 pp.

Weissberger, A., ed. (1959–). **Technique of Organic Chemistry.** Several volumes. New York: Interscience Publishers, Inc.

West, E. S., W. R. Todd, H. S. Mason, and J. T. van Bruggen (1966). **Textbook of Biochemistry,** 4th ed. New York: The Macmillan Company. 1596 pp.

White, A., P. Handler, and E. Smith (1964). **Principles of Biochemistry,** 3rd ed. New York: The McGraw-Hill Book Company, 1106 pp.

Whitfield, I. C. (1959). **An Introduction to Electronics for Physiological Workers.** London: Collier-Macmillan, Ltd. 263 pp.

Whitfield, I. C. (1964). **Manual of Experimental Physiology.** London: Macmillan & Company, Ltd. 208 pp.

Wiener, N. (1948). **Cybernetics.** Cambridge, Mass.: The M.I.T. Press. 194 pp.

Wiener, N. (1954). **The Human Use of Human Beings.** New York: Doubleday Anchor. 199 pp.

Wiener, N. (1961). **Cybernetics,** 2nd ed. Cambridge, Mass.: M.I.T. Press. 212 pp.

Wilbur, K. M. and C. M. Yonge (1964, 1966). **The Physiology of Mollusca.** 2 volumes. New York: Academic Press, Inc.

Yamamoto, W. S. and J. R. Brobeck (1965). **Physiological Controls and Regulation.** Philadelphia: W. B. Saunders Company. 362 pp.

Young, J. Z. (1964). **A Model of the Brain.** New York: Oxford University Press. 348 pp.

2-1. General Composition of Animals. Before considering the functional systems of animals, we must have some understanding of the important biological compounds responsible for cellular structures and functions. Biological substances do not have different properties or obey different laws than compounds of the nonliving world, but they are distinct because they are highly organized and often macromolecular. In the past the cell has sometimes been modeled as a bag of chemicals, but the properties of a cell cannot be reconstituted merely by mixing together extracts of chemicals from living systems.

Although it is relatively easy to identify the major classes of cellular constituents: water, salts, lipids, carbohydrates, proteins, nucleic acids; it is less easy to obtain a quantitative picture of their cellular distribution. Further, other molecules and atoms present in cells and vital to cellular activities are often difficult to discover because of their small size, minute concentrations, or heterogeneous nature.

Although the distribution of major chemical classes in organisms or cells is often given, the accuracy of such data is debatable. For analysis, the materials of living systems are separated into (1) water content and (2) dry weight substances, including organic (lipids, proteins, etc.) and inorganic (salts and minerals) compounds. Water content is determined from the difference in weight of a sample before and after drying at 105°C (Kleiber, 1961). However, water is not the only volatile substance in cells and some error is present in such measurements. Water content varies from 96 per cent of fresh tissue weight in jellyfish to about 50 per cent in some insects.

Minerals are determined quantitatively by weighing the dry residue (ash) after heating at 800°C. Such determinations include not only free minerals but also elements such as sulfur or phosphorous, which were constituents of proteins or nucleic acids. Protein content is often calculated from the nitrogen content of a tissue by assuming an average nitrogen content of protein of 16 per cent (see Hawk et al., 1954). Error results if many tissue proteins differ from this assumed average.

Chemical distributions vary markedly from one species to another, from one part of an

Chapter 2

Cellular Constituents

organism to another, and also depend on the condition of the organism. Liver and bone of different mammals, for example, contain quite different quantities of water, protein, and minerals (Altman and Dittmer, 1964). The differences in this case are reflected in obvious differences in physical characteristics.

The relative numbers of different molecular classes in a cell varies. Although proteins make up much of the dry weight of a cell (average about 10 per cent, Sponsler and Bath, 1942), their molecular weights are so high that there are few protein molecules present compared with water. The nucleic acids are in a similar situation. Their concentration is about 1.1 per cent of the dry weight of the cells, and because of their high molecular weights, they are present in smaller numbers of molecules than the proteins. But the relatively few DNA molecules in a cell are responsible for guiding protein synthesis, cellular growth, and genetic transmission.

Of more interest to us here is a description of the nature and the types of functions of the major classes of biological substances.

Water

2-2. The Role of Water.   It is believed that life originated in water and, as far as we know, life is impossible without water. Although some animals have achieved a terrestrial existence, they must still carry a self-contained ocean in the form of various body fluids and they have evolved often elaborate controls over their water content. An aqueous environment is essential for embryological development, and terrestrial animals must either return to water or have developed mechanisms such as shelled eggs or internal fluid spaces in order to provide this necessary environment for their young.

Water is essential to life, but its direct role in most cellular activities is unknown. Water is ubiquitous in living systems and often appears forgotten or neglected when functional mechanisms are discussed. At the same time its high concentration in cells and tissues,

and the fact that the true nature of liquid water is still unknown, add to the experimental difficulties of determining its specific roles in animal functioning.

Water is almost a universal solvent for biological compounds and the medium in which most biochemical reactions of the cell occur. The unique biological properties of water are a reflection of its exceptional physico-chemical characteristics (see Fogg, 1965). A comparison of some of the properties of water with those of other, similiar-sized or constituted molecules shows significant differences (Table 2-1). The explanation for these differences lies in the structure of the water molecules.

Water is formed from hydrogen and oxygen through the formation of two covalent bonds:

$$2H\cdot + :\overset{..}{\underset{..}{O}}: \rightarrow H:\overset{..}{\underset{..}{O}}:H$$

If the two p-bonds were completely covalent, the H—O—H angle would be 90° (Pauling, 1960), but infrared and microwave spectroscopy show that the H—O—H angle is 104.5° (Figure 2-1a).

Part of the explanation for this greater than expected bond angle is that the oxygen atom is more electronegative than the hydrogen atom, and as a result the O—H bond has about

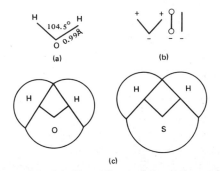

Figure 2-1   (a) Dimensions of the water molecule. (b) Some symbols used to represent the water molecule and its dipole nature. (c) A comparison of the dimensions and shapes of the water and hydrogen sulfide molecules. van der Waals radii (the effective distances of covalent forces) are shown for the atoms and are: H = 1.2 Å; O = 1.4 Å; S = 1.85 Å. The S—H bond length is 1.35 Å and the H—S—H bond angle is 92.2°C. [Data from L. Pauling (1960).]

40 per cent ionic character. The water molecule bonding electrons are more strongly attracted to the oxygen atom, resulting in a negative charge in the vicinity of the oxygen and a positive charge near each hydrogen. The positive charges on the hydrogen atoms cause their mutual repulsion, thus increasing the H—O—H angle to its measured value.

Water is a **dipole,** a particle with two charges of opposite sign (Figure 2-1b). The dipolar nature of the water molecule accounts for its unusual properties. The similar-sized analogous H_2S molecule has quite different properties from water because sulfur and hydrogen have similar electronegativities and because the hydrogen sulfide molecule is less polar (Figure 2-1c).

2-3. Hydrogen Bonding and Water Structure. Covalent and ionic bonds are the primary bonds of molecular structure. In ionic (or polar) bonds the bonding electrons are somewhat more associated with one of the two nuclei that they are bonding. Covalent bonds are nonpolar and the term implies an equal sharing of electron pair bonds by two nuclei. Depending on the electron attracting character of the two nuclei in a bond, various degrees of ionic character may be found.

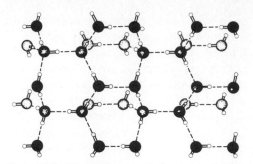

Figure 2-3 The arrangement of water molecules in the ice crystal. The orientation of the water molecules, as represented in the illustration, is arbitrary. There is one proton along each oxygen-oxygen axis, closer to one or the other of the two oxygen atoms. [Redrawn from L. Pauling (1960) *The Nature of the Chemical Bond*, 3rd ed. © 1960 by Cornell University. By permission of Cornell University Press.]

Secondary bondings cause intermolecular attractions and intramolecular organization. The most important of these secondary forces is the hydrogen bond. When a covalent bond is formed between hydrogen and an electronegative atom such as O, N, or F, the hydrogen atom becomes essentially a bare proton with an intense positive charge because the electrons shielding the nucleus are drawn toward the electronegative atom. Such a positively charged hydrogen can form a bond—of primarily ionic character—with another electronegative atom. This is the **hydrogen bond**, and the structures of liquid and crystalline water depend on it.

The structure of ice I (normal ice—there are six varieties of ice known whose existence depends upon temperature and pressure conditions) is an open structure (density 0.9 g/cm³ compared to 1.0 g/cm³ for pure water) consisting of a hexagonal crystal lattice with each oxygen atom surrounded tetrahedrally by four other oxygens (Figure 2-2, Figure 2-3). The two covalently-bonded hydrogen atoms (+) occupy two corners of the tetrahedron. The two pairs of unshared electrons (−) occupy the other two corners. Hydrogen bonds (usually represented by dotted bonding lines) are formed between the hydrogen of one water molecule and the oxygen of two other water molecules. This pattern repeats itself, building up a three-

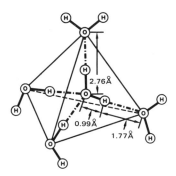

Figure 2-2 Hydrogen bonding in ice. An oxygen is shown at the center of a tetrahedron. Hydrogen bonds are indicated by dot-dash lines. The H—O—H bond angle is close to 109°C; the H . . . O bond length is 1.77 Å; and the H—O . . . H length is 2.77 Å. The ice structure is three dimensional forming an open lattice crystalline structure as shown in Figure 2-3.

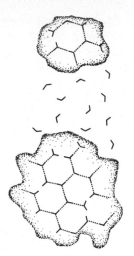

Figure 2-4 Diagrammatic representation of the flickering cluster model of water structure. The water molecules within the clusters (= icebergs) are joined by hydrogen bonds. Molecules of water outside the clusters are not hydrogen bonded. The stability of the array is maintained by van der Waals forces. The life of each cluster is brief—on the order of 10^{-10} seconds.

dimensional lattice of water molecules in the ice structure.

Liquid water retains much of this lattice-structure, and the three-dimensional organization of liquid water makes it unique among liquids since other strongly dipolar molecules such as NH^3 or HF have molecular geometries that permit the formation only of hydrogen bonded rings or chains, not three-dimensional lattices.

Although the structure of ice is understood, it must be emphasized that that of liquid water is not, and many models for liquid water have been proposed (see Kavanau, 1965, for a discussion of some of these models). Water has a partial ice structure in which about 15 per cent of the hydrogen bonds of ice have been broken (published estimates range from 0.1 per cent to 29 per cent). This gives water a more random labile structure than ice. On this basis liquid water would have a higher density than ice because more water molecules could be packed into a given volume if the relatively rigid structure of ice is partially destroyed.

The **Flickering Cluster** or **Iceberg Model** is based on the fact that when one hydrogen bond

is formed in water, there is a tendency for others to form (Frank, 1965). There are produced short-lived (10^{-6} seconds) clusters of hydrogen bonded water molecules—miniature icebergs (Figure 2-4). Between the clusters are non-hydrogen bonded water molecules or at least a looser structured collection of water molecules—the entire system held together by van der Waals forces. The latter are weak attractive forces resulting from the continuous movement of electrons in atoms or molecules that otherwise have a symmetrical charge distribution. This movement produces momentary asymmetric charge distributions and therefore

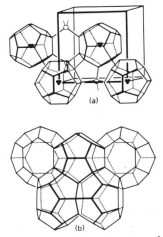

Figure 2-5 (a) The structure of the 12 Å hydrate crystals of small molecules, such as xenon. The unit cube is about 12 Å on an edge. The hydrogen bonded framework of water molecules consists of 46 water molecules per unit cube. Of these there are two sets of 20 at the corners of pentagonal dodecahedra, one about the corner of the cube, and one about the center of the cube. Six more water molecules aid in holding the dodecahedra together by hydrogen bonds. All hydrogen bonds, indicated by lines in the illustration, are about 2.76 Å long, as in ordinary ice. There is room in each dodecahedrom for a small molecule. (b) Another model of the structure of the 12 Å hydrate crystals. One dodecahedron is shown in the upper center. Around it are tetrakaidecahedra which provide room for somewhat larger molecules than can fit into the dodecahedra. [Redrawn from L. Pauling (1961) *Science*, **134**: 15–21 with permission. Copyright 1961 by the American Association for the Advancement of Science.]

transient dipoles, which can induce dipoles in neighboring particles. These secondary attractive forces between particles, although very weak individually, play a role in molecular interactions in solutions because of their large numbers (see Snell et al., 1965).

Pauling suggested a clathrate structure for water (Figure 2-5). A clathrate is formed when small molecules are entrapped in the interstices of a crystalline latticework. Pauling (1961) extended this concept to account for the anesthetic action of xenon and other inert gases on the central nervous system. Although the inert gases do not readily enter into chemical reactions, such a physical reaction with the water of the nervous system is possible. The structured water so formed could alter the structure of the nerve membrane and therefore inhibit nerve activity. Lately evidence has indicated that xenon may also interact with some functional proteins of the nerve cell membrane (see *Federation Proceedings,* 1968, Vol. 27(3), pp. 870–913).

The clathrate structure is compatible with the flickering cluster model that does not specify any particular structure for the iceberg. Several clathrates are known to exist (Figure 2-5). Structure I contains 46 water molecules in a 12 Å unit cell (the smallest crystalline structure from which the entire crystal can be constructed). The water molecules are arranged in eight cavities. Two are pentagonal dodecahedra, each formed of 20 water molecules; six larger cavities are tetrakaidecahedra each formed of 24 water molecules. The former cavities can hold molecules with diameters of 5.1 Å or less. Structure II clathrates contain 136 water molecules in a 17 Å unit cell and possess 24 cavities. Sixteen are pentagonal dodecahedra, while eight are hexakaidecahedra.

The structure of water plays a role in the stabilization of macromolecular conformation and in the organization of lipid-containing structures. Clathrates, for example, can be formed about nonpolar solutes including the

Table 2-1 Some Important Physical Properties of Water Compared with Those of Other Similar Types of Molecules*

PROPERTY	WATER† $\begin{smallmatrix} H \quad H \\ \diagdown \diagup \\ O \end{smallmatrix}$	HYDROGEN SULFIDE† $\begin{smallmatrix} H \quad H \\ \diagdown \diagup \\ S \end{smallmatrix}$	AMMONIA† $\begin{smallmatrix} H \quad H \\ \diagdown \diagup \\ N \\ | \\ H \end{smallmatrix}$	METHANOL† $\begin{smallmatrix} H \\ | \\ H-C-OH \\ | \\ H \end{smallmatrix}$
Molecular weight	18.02	34.08	17.03	32.04
Density (g/ml)	1.00[4]	1.54[0]	0.77[0]	0.79[15]
Melting point (°C)	0.00	−82.9	−77.7	−97.8
Heat of fusion (cal/g)	79.7[0]	—	108.1[−75]	16.0[−97]
Boiling point (°C)	100.0	−61.8	−33.3	64.6
Heat of vaporization (cal/g)	595.9[0]	181.9[−61]	301.6[0]	262.8[65]
Specific heat (cal/g-deg)	1.01	0.24	1.1	0.57
Surface tension (dyne/cm)	72.7[20]	—	23.4[20]	22.6[20]
Dielectric constant (esu)	80.3[20]	9.2[−55]	16.5[25]	33.6[20]
Viscosity (centipoise)	1.0[20]	0.12[17]	0.09[20]	0.82[20]

* Data from: *Handbook of Chemistry and Physics,* 40th ed. (Cleveland, Ohio: Chemical Rubber Company, 1958).
† Superscript numerals indicate temperatures at which measurements were made.

nonpolar side-chains of proteins. These bond-ings will be considered in later sections of this chapter, after the nature of proteins and lipids has been discussed. Bernal (1959), Bjerrum (1952), and Klotz, (1962, 1965) discuss the problems of water and ice structuring.

2-4. Thermal Properties of Water.

Water has one of the highest heat capacities of any liquid (Table 2-1). **Heat capacity**, in terms of specific heat, is the quantity of heat, in calories or joules, required to raise the temperature of one gram of substance one degree Celsius. The standard unit of heat, the calorie, is the amount of heat required to raise the temperature of one gram of water from 14.5 to 15.5°C. One calorie equals 4.185 joules, the unit now recommended by the National Bureau of Standards for expressing heat energies.

The higher the specific heat of a substance the smaller its rise in temperature upon the absorption of a given amount of heat. This is important not only for the body temperature of organisms, but also for the stability of the environmental temperature. The amount of heat reaching the earth's surface during the day is large and is mostly absorbed by oceans and other large bodies of water. Because of the high heat capacity of water, these bodies of water experience relatively little temperature increase. During the night the absorbed heat is released to the now cooler atmosphere, again with little change in water temperature. The released heat serves to maintain the atmo-spheric temperature at relatively high levels during the night hours. Through this and other mechanisms, the temperature of the earth and atmosphere is prevented from fluctuating greatly, as it would otherwise do, during the day-night cycle.

A 65 kg man produces about 2,000 kcal of heat daily (1 kcal = 1,000 calories). This is enough heat to raise his body temperature by about 30°C (ignoring the facts that not all this heat is produced at the same time, nor is all of the body mass affected by this heat). Since the bodies of man and other animals are composed mainly of water, metabolic heat is prevented from greatly increasing the body temperature and the water, which has a high specific heat, acts as a reservoir for the heat until it can be eliminated. 2,500 kcal of heat is enough to raise the temperature of other liquids of similar volumes by from 50 to 100°C.

The heat energy of a substance is present in several forms including the kinetic energy of molecular rotation and translation, the energy of molecular and atomic vibrations, and the energy of inter- and intramolecular forces. Water has a high heat capacity because a large amount of absorbed heat is used to break intermolecular hydrogen bonds and does not go into other forms of internal energy that would raise the temperature of the water molecules.

The high heat of vaporization of water is important to many organisms. The heat of vaporization is the amount of heat absorbed when a liquid is transformed into a gas. Organisms can vaporize relatively small amounts of water from the skin surface or from respiratory organ surfaces and thus eliminate a large amount of heat. This is an important mechanism in temperature regula-tion. The high heat of vaporization of water also results from the large number of hydrogen bonds that must be broken in order to free water molecules as vapor from the body of the liquid.

2-5. The Anomalous Density of Water.

Water is an unusual liquid in that on the transfor-mation of ice to the liquid form there is an increase in its density which reaches a maximum at 4°C. Part of the explanation for the chang-ing density is that ice is a relatively open structure without close packing of water molecules in the crystalline lattice—hydrogen bonds keep water molecules separated in the ice structure. As hydrogen bonds are broken during liquifaction, water molecules can ap-proach each other more closely, thus increas-ing the density.

If it were not for this density change most bodies of water would be frozen since, in the words of L. J. Henderson (*The Fitness of the Environment*, 1913, Macmillan, N.Y., p. 109):

The coldest water would continually sink to the bottom and there freeze. The ice, once formed, could not be melted, because the warmer water would stay at the surface. Year after year the ice would increase in the winter and persist in the summer, until eventually all or much of a body of water, according to the locality, would be turned to ice. As it is, the temperature of the bottom of a body of fresh water cannot be below the point of maximum density, on cooling further the water rises; and ice forms only on the surface. In this way the liquid water below is effectually protected from further cooling, and the body of water persists. In the spring the first warm weather melts the ice and at the earliest possible moment all ice vanishes.

2-6. The Dielectric Constant and Solubility. The dielectric constant D is a measure of the extent to which the force between charges is reduced by a medium that separates the charges. The force between charges is given by Coulomb's law:

$$F = \frac{q_1 q_2}{D r^2} \qquad (2.1)$$

where F is the force between two charges, q_1 and q_2, separated by the distance r. The force is negative and attractive if the two charges are of opposite sign; and positive and repulsive if the charges are of similar sign. D is defined as unity for a vacuum and has a value greater than one for all other media.

When we consider the relation between the dielectric constant and ionic bonding forces, an examination of Equation (2-1) shows that the greater the dielectric constant of a medium, the smaller the forces holding ions together. Water has one of the highest dielectric constants known, exceeded only by that of hydrogen cyanide. Consequently, more than other media, water decreases the attractive forces between charged particles thus bringing about a greater separation between them. As particles in a medium are separated, molecules of the medium fill the spaces between them, that is, the particles go into solution. Water is one of the best known solvents. To possess a high dielectric constant, a liquid must be composed of dipolar molecules that can orient themselves between charged particles in such a way as to decrease the attractive forces between them. Not only is the water molecule itself a strong dipole, but the clusters formed by hydrogen bonding are even stronger dipoles.

The charged character of the water molecule permits it to form oriented layers around macromolecules such as proteins that contain many charged groups. This action not only aids in the separation and solution of proteins but also forms a protective field around them that cuts down the forces of their charged groups. Otherwise these groups might affect adversely other biological molecules or structures, for example by holding them firmly and irreversibly bound to the protein, thus not permitting them to perform their normal functions. Edsall and Wyman (1958) discuss in detail the dielectric constant and other aspects of the behavior of electrolytes in biological solutions.

2-7. Dissociation and Conduction in Water. Although normally each hydrogen of a water molecule is covalently bound to the oxygen of that molecule and is hydrogen bonded to the oxygen of another water molecule, it is possible for the hydrogen to approach closer to the second oxygen and become covalently bonded to it. In this way hydronium (H_3^+O) and hydroxyl (OH^-) ions are formed. The reaction is as follows:

$$H_2O + HO_2 \rightleftharpoons H_3^+O + OH^-$$

although a more accurate representation is given by

Usually the hydronium ion immediately reacts with a hydroxyl to form water, that is, the reaction is readily reversible. At equilibrium and 25°C, one kilogram of pure water (55.5 moles) contains only about 10^{-7} moles of hydronium ions and an equal concentration of hydroxyl ions, thus the dissociation of pure water is a relatively rare event. The concentration of hydrogen ions (this term is used to include either H^+ or H_3^+O) in solution is expressed as the negative logarithm of its molar concentration, the pH. Pure water at 25°C, therefore, has a pH of 7.0. The pH scale ranges from 0 (very acid, high [H^+]) to 14 (very alkaline, low [H $^+$]). Note that the pH scale is logarithmic. Thus a difference of 2 pH units represents a 100-fold difference in [H $^+$]. The hydroxyl ion concentration is found from the relation: [H $^+$] [OH $^-$] = 10^{-14}.

The movement of ions through solutions and across biological membranes is an important event in many physiological activities. Ions in solutions move in response to chemical and electrical potential gradients and to solution flows. Not only do ions move in response to electrical potential gradients, but ionic movements can create such gradients. Potentials of this type are found at liquid junctions and across membranes (Chapter 6).

When considering the movements of ions through solutions or across membranes several terms are used. Ohm's law gives the relation between current flow, I (in amps or milliamperes); electrical potential, E (in volts or millivolts); and the resistance to electrical current flow, R (in ohms). The mathematical expression of this relation is $I = E/R$. The ohm is the resistance that requires the application of one volt to produce a current of one ampere. By definition, the **conductance**, Γ, is the reciprocal of resistance. The relations are as follows:

$$I = \frac{E}{R} = \Gamma E \qquad (2.2)$$

Γ has the units of reciprocal ohms or mhos. Ion movements are usually discussed in terms of conductances rather than resistance.

The resistance of a cube of material with sides of unit length is the **specific resistance**. Its reciprocal is the **specific conductance**, γ, with units of mhos/cm. If a battery were attached to two opposite faces of such a cube of material (or solution), it can be shown experimentally that Γ is directly proportional to the area, A, of the face of the cube and inversely proportional to the distance, r, between the two faces. Thus

$$\Gamma = \frac{A\gamma}{r} \qquad (2.3)$$

γ is used because it uniquely characterizes the ability of a substance to conduct an electrical current, Γ, which depends on the size and proportions as well as on the intrinsic nature of a substance.

Since electrical current flow in ionic solutions depends, among other factors, on the concentration of electrolyte, another useful quantity is the **equivalent conductance**, Λ, defined by

$$\Lambda = \frac{\gamma}{nc} \qquad (2.4)$$

where n is the number of equivalents associated with one mole of electrolyte and c is the molar concentration. Λ has the units of mhos-cm^2/gram equivalent. Another useful relation is as follows:

$$\Lambda = \gamma_+ + \gamma_- \qquad (2.5)$$

where γ_+ and γ_- are the **ionic equivalent conductances** of positive and negative ions, respectively.

Finally, the **mobility**, μ, of an ion is defined as its velocity of movement under the influence of an applied electrical field of 1 volt per centimeter; its units are cm-sec/volt-cm. It can be shown that the equivalent conductance of an electrolyte solution is related to the ionic mobilities by

$$\Lambda = \alpha F(\mu_+ + \mu_-) \qquad (2.6)$$

where α is the fraction of dissociated electrolyte and F is Faraday's constant, 96,500 coulombs. The terminology of Edsall and Wyman (1958) is followed here and these authors may be consulted for the derivation of these relationships. The terms given here are used in discussing the movement of ions through solutions (Chapter 6) and through membranes (Chapter 7) and are introduced here to show that several factors play a role in the movement of ions in water.

The measurement of ionic mobilities shows that although protons move rapidly through both liquid water and ice, other univalent ions such as Li $^+$ move much less rapidly through water than protons and have almost no mobility through ice (Table 2-2).

The explanation for this difference is thought to be that protons do not literally move through the medium. Rather protons transfer along a hydrogen bonded chain of water molecules (Figure 2-6). When a proton

Table 2-2 Ionic Equivalent Conductances
(λ_0) for some Ions*

Ion	λ (0°C)[†]	λ (25°C)[†]
H⁺	225.0	349.8
OH⁻	105.0	198.6
Li⁺	19.4	38.7
Na⁺	26.5	50.1
K⁺	40.7	73.5
Mg²⁺	28.9	53.0
Ca²⁺	31.2	59.5
Cl⁻	41.0	76.4
Br⁻	42.6	78.1
I⁻	41.4	76.8
CH₃COO⁻	20.1	40.9

* Data from: Robinson and Stokes (1959).
† Conductances given as mhos-cm²/gram equivalent (at infinite dilution).

enters the chain, it forms a hydronium ion. In turn this ion can transfer a proton to the oxygen of the next water molecule in the chain, forming another hydronium ion. If this chain-reaction continues, there will appear at the end of the chain a proton that has not literally moved through the water but that is the result of the initial proton entering the chain. Processes of this type may play a role in the proton transfers which characterize many metabolic reactions (Klotz, 1962, but see also Green and Fleischer, 1962). Similar mechanisms have been proposed for the movement of electrons through water especially in the presence of iron atoms. As will be discussed in Chapter 4, iron atoms are a functional constituent of several electron transfer systems of the cell. This mode of conduction is closely related to

conduction in the solid state and attempts have been made to fit some biological reactions into such a framework (Szent-Györgyi, 1960).

2-8. Surface Tension and Viscosity. Molecules beneath the surface of a liquid are bonded on all sides to neighboring molecules by intermolecular forces. Molecules at the surface have one side free of such attractions. To bring molecules to the surface, expanding the surface area, requires the expenditure of energy so that intermolecular bonding forces can be broken. Surface tension is a measure of the energy required to expand a surface and bears some relation to the heat of vaporization because the same attractive forces must be broken to free molecules from the surface of a liquid during evaporation.

Water has a high surface tension, a factor that may play a role in the formation of lipo-protein membranes (Hechter, 1965; Kavanau, 1965). These thin membranes are of vital importance to the structure and function of cells. The high surface tension of water has also been used as a partial explanation for capillary rise of water in topsoils and in plant roots and stems. Presumably it also aids in the movement of materials through tissues. The high surface tension of water is also of value to many insects whose weight is not great enough to break the skin of the surface and which therefore can walk or glide over the water surface.

Viscosity is a measure of the ease or difficulty of flow of a liquid. Although highly structured fluids usually have low flow rates and high viscosities, the viscosity of water is relatively low, and it flows readily. This unusual feature of water has been interpreted as another indication of the lability of the hydrogen bonding of water molecules. Viscosity will be further discussed in the chapters on the circulatory system.

Macromolecules

2-9. Macromolecular Basis of Life. Living systems are unusual in their possession of macromolecules, especially the proteins and nucleic acids. The definition of a macromole-

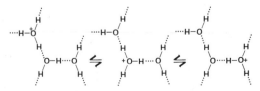

Figure 2-6 One model for the conduction of protons through chains of hydrogen bonded water molecules.

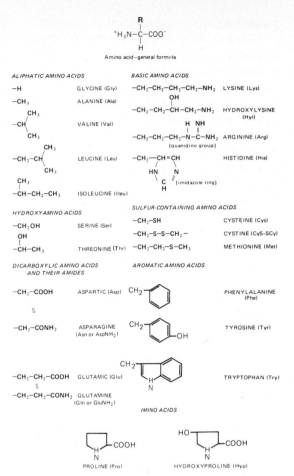

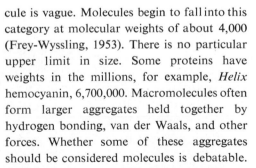

Figure 2-7 The amino acids found in proteins. The general structural formula for amino acids is shown at the top. Only the R groups of the amino acids are given.

cule is vague. Molecules begin to fall into this category at molecular weights of about 4,000 (Frey-Wyssling, 1953). There is no particular upper limit in size. Some proteins have weights in the millions, for example, *Helix* hemocyanin, 6,700,000. Macromolecules often form larger aggregates held together by hydrogen bonding, van der Waals, and other forces. Whether some of these aggregates should be considered molecules is debatable.

Biological macromolecules are polymers built up of small subunits. For example, proteins are composed of about twenty different amino acid subunits. The isomeric possibilities of such combinations is immense.[1] Thus one feature of macromolecules is that from a few simple starting compounds, a large num-

ber of biologically active molecules can be derived.

The large size of macromolecules confers important biological properties on them. They can carry more biological information than smaller molecules. The biological catalysts,

these can be arranged in a straight chain is given by

$$N = \frac{n!}{r_1! \, r_2! \, r_3! \ldots r_m}$$

Thus for a polypeptide containing six residues which are all different, there are $6!$ ($= 720$) ways of arranging these in a straight chain. If a polypeptide contains 2 glycine, 3 alanine, and 1 serine residue, there are $6!/2!3!1!$ ($= 60$) ways of arranging these in a straight chain. When proteins, with their thousands of amino acids, are considered, the number of possible arrangements becomes very large indeed.

[1] If a protein consists of n amino acids of m types, such that there are r_i of type i; the number of ways

protein enzymes, are noted for their specificity of reaction and specificity of substrate. This specificity is a form of information as already defined (Section 1-13), for a choice is made about the nature of the reaction and the reactant molecules. A large protein molecule can possess a particular three-dimensional structure to which only those molecules having the proper shape and size can attach—a necessary prerequisite for reaction. Because the configuration of proteins determines their reactivity, it is possible to use alteration of protein shape as a mechanism for controlling cellular reactions. The factor of isomerization also allows proteins to confer species-specific properties on organisms (see Simpson, 1964).

The nucleic acids also contain a large amount of information—the genetic code and the information controlling protein synthesis—which is part of the mechanism for controlling the growth and development of new individuals and for regulating normal cellular activities (Jukes, 1963, 1965).

Smaller molecules cannot contain as much information as larger molecules and they can neither replicate nor cause the directed replication of other molecules—a necessity for species survival. The possibilities of macromolecular changes, coupled with a retention of biological activity, must lie at the basis of variation and compensation in organisms (Anfinsen, 1959; Cohen, 1963; Vogel et al., 1963).

2-10. Amino Acids and Primary Protein Structure.   Proteins are polymers built up from about twenty amino acids, the monomers of protein structure. All amino acids, except glycine, have an asymmetric α-carbon atom and are optically active (structural formulas of the amino acids found in proteins are given in Figure 2-7). Natural amino acids, excepting proline and hydroxyproline, belong to the family of L-α-amino acids, so designated because their configuration about the α-carbon resembles that about the second carbon of L-glyceraldehyde, a carbohydrate whose absolute configuration is known and which is used as a reference compound for the structures of both amino acids and carbohydrates.

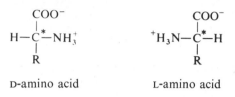

L-glyceraldehyde   D-glyceraldehyde

D-amino acid   L-amino acid

The asymmetric carbon (*) is the α-carbon of the amino acids. R is the amino acid side-chain which distinguishes the different amino acids. D-Amino acids are rarely found in organisms (see Corrigan, 1969) and the specificity of protein enzyme catalysis usually precludes their involvement in metabolism.

The structural formulas indicate that amino acids are charged molecules (zwitterions or dipoles) at neutral pH, approximately the condition found in cells.

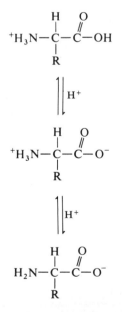

The free α-amino group of one amino acid can react with the free carboxyl group of another amino acid to form a **dipeptide:**

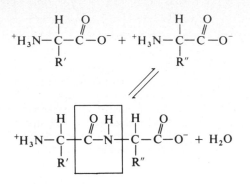

The group outlined is the covalent, planar, peptide bond. Moderate sized chains of amino acids, joined by peptide bonds, are **polypeptides.** Longer chains, of about 4,000 molecular weight or greater, are **proteins.**

The amino acids in a protein and their sequence in a chain make up the **primary structure** of the protein. Also included as part of the primary structure are metal atoms, phosphate groups, or organic compounds bound to the peptide chain. The binding of two polypeptide chains by —S—S— (disulfide) linkages between cystein residues is also usually considered as part of the primary structure. The sequence of amino acids in a protein is part of the information content of the molecule and this sequence is responsible, at least in part, for the biological activity of the protein as well as its three-dimensional geometry.

Following the brilliant work of Sanger and

his colleagues in which the primary structure of the protein hormone, insulin, was determined (Figure 2-8), the primary structure of a variety of smaller proteins and polypeptides has been established (Sanger, 1952, 1956). Major techniques developed by these workers include protein hydrolysis (the breaking of peptide bonds and the release of small peptide fragments or single amino acids) by mineral acids or by specifically-acting enzymes; chromatographic techniques for the separation and identification of the fragments; and end-group analysis (the determination of the amino acids with free α-amino or carboxyl groups, that is, those at the ends of the chain). Discussion of these methods is found in Alexander and Block (1960); Moore and Stein (1965); and Neurath (1963–1966).

The laboratory synthesis of many simpler peptides has been accomplished (see Merrifield, 1965) and the protein insulin has been completely synthesized (Katsoyannis, 1966; see also the review by Wieland and Determann, 1966). Ribonuclease was the first protein enzyme to be synthesized outside the cell.

2-11. Protein Conformation.   A protein has both a specific chemical composition and, in its native state—the biologically active or normal condition—a particular three-dimensional conformation (the term "configuration" is reserved for the structures of optical isomers).

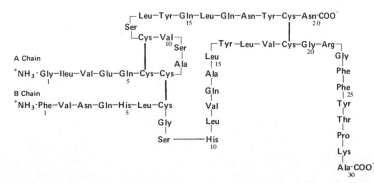

Figure 2-8 *Primary structure of bovine insulin. Both inter- and intrachain disulfide linkages are illustrated (heavy lines). The folding shown for the chains is arbitrary in order to fit cysteine residues properly. The figure shows the usual method for portraying polypeptide chains with the free amino group at the left. The numbers count off amino acid residues in each chain.*

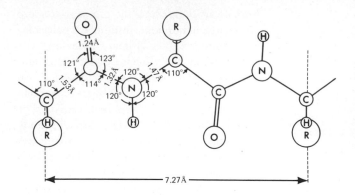

Figure 2-9 Dimensions of the fully extended polypeptide chain. The sequence of amino acids, linked by peptide bonds, is the backbone of protein molecules. The R groups represent the various sidechains of the constituent amino acids.

The conformation of a protein depends on intra- and interchain bondings other than covalent peptide linkages. Secondary, tertiary, and quaternary levels of protein structure are recognized (Linderstrøm-Lang, 1952; Bernal, 1965), although these divisions are somewhat arbitrary (Wetlauffer, 1962) and have been generalized so that they may also apply to nucleic acid structure.

Secondary structure is the result primarily of hydrogen bonding that maintains a regular, repeating, stable conformation of the peptide chain. Such secondary structure is characteristic of fibrous proteins that serve as structural or contractile elements in cells and tissues. Fibrous proteins have been classified in either of two groups. The keratin, or k-m-e-f, group includes keratin (hair, hoofs, wool); myosin, F-actin, tropomyosin, and paramyosin (contractile proteins); elastin (elastic connective

tissues); and fibrin (blood clots) and fibroins (silk). The second group includes collagen, the major protein of fibrous connective tissues. The structural and functional features of these various proteins will be considered later (see Brown and Danielli, 1955).

Members of the keratin group exhibit extensibility and can undergo reversible stretching upon treatment with heat or alkali. The molecule in the contracted or α-form may be only half the length of the extended or β-form. The dimensions of an extended polypeptide chain are shown in Figure 2-9.

In some cases the polypeptide chains of fibrous proteins may be hydrogen-bonded together, forming a **pleated sheet** secondary structure (Figure 2-10.) This is found in keratin, fibroin, and other members of the keratin group when the polypeptide chains are in the β-condition.

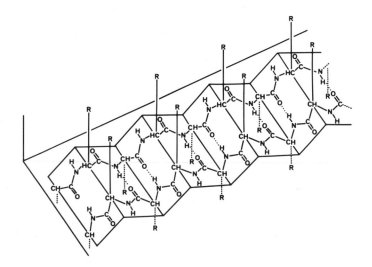

Figure 2-10 The pleated sheet arrangement—one form of protein secondary structure. Adjacent polypeptide chains are held together by hydrogen bonds between —C=O and —NH groups. R groups alternately extend above and below the plane of the backbone structure. [Redrawn from P. Karlson (1965) *Introduction to Modern Biochemistry*, 2nd ed. By permission of Academic Press, New York.]

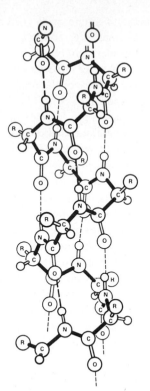

Figure 2-11(a) Representation of the right-handed alpha helix composed of L-amino acids. The side chains, R, and the hydrogen atoms attached to the α-carbons lie in positions corresponding to the known dimensions and configurations of the L-amino acids. Hydrogen bonds are represented by dashed lines. [Redrawn from L. Pauling (1960) *The Nature of the Chemical Bond*, 3rd ed. © 1960 by Cornell University. Used by permission of Cornell University Press.]

Although there is no connection between the α-form and the α-helix in keratin group proteins, these macromolecules as well as many globular proteins often have this secondary structure. The α-helix is a rigid, coiled, rod-like structure produced by hydrogen bonding between —NH and —CO groups of amino acids on adjacent turns of a helix (Figure 2-11; Astbury, 1945; Pauling and Corey, 1951; Pauling et al., 1951).

Globular proteins are ovoid-shaped macromolecules which may or may not have some α-helical structuring but which must have less regular foldings of the polypeptide chain in order to fit their complement of amino acids into their measured dimensions. They are more compact than would be possible for an entirely α-helix structure. (A comparison of the dimensions of some fibrous and globular proteins is shown in Figure 2-12).

The globular proteins include the myoglobins, hemoglobins, most enzymes, the protein hormones, and generally the so-called soluble proteins of cells and body fluids. The distinction between globular and fibrous proteins is not always absolute because some globular proteins reversibly aggregate to form fibrous polymers.

The irregular foldings of globular proteins constitute their **tertiary structure** (Figure 2-13a). The binding forces leading to tertiary structure are the result of interactions between side-chains of amino acids. Why polypeptide chains fold in particular places is not fully understood, but some generalities can be made. In some cases the presence of the amino acids proline and hydroxyproline is responsible because these molecules will not fit into the dimensions of an α-helix and also cause a bend in the polypeptide chain. From work with synthetic polypeptides composed of only one amino acid, for example, polyglycine or polyalanine, it has been found that alanine, glutamate, leucine, lysine, methionine, phenylalanine, and tyrosine readily enter into α-helix

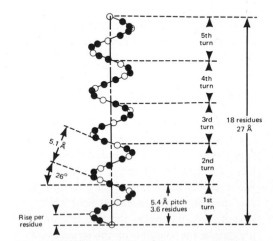

Figure 2-11(b) A schematic representation of the alpha helix showing the pitch and number of amino acid residues per turn. [After C. B. Anfinsen (1959) *The Molecular Basis of Evolution* John Wiley & Sons, New York.]

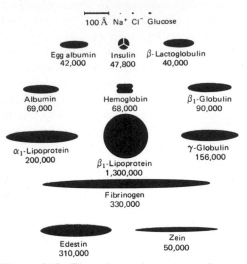

100 Å   Na⁺ Cl⁻ Glucose

Egg albumin   Insulin   β-Lactoglobulin
42,000   47,800   40,000

Albumin   Hemoglobin   β₁-Globulin
69,000   68,000   90,000

α₁-Lipoprotein   γ-Globulin
200,000   156,000
                β₁-Lipoprotein
                1,300,000

Fibrinogen
330,000

Edestin   Zein
310,000   50,000

Figure 2-12 The relative dimensions of some typical proteins. [Redrawn from West et al. (1966) *Textbook of Biochemistry*, 4th ed. By permission of the Macmillan Company, New York.]

formation. Valine isoleucine, threonine, glycine, serine, glutamate, asparate, and lysine + do not form α-helices. There is either steric hindrance (the atoms of the molecules will not fit into the necessary dimensions of the helix) or there are more stable structures than the helix (see Stahman, 1962).

Generally it can be assumed that a polypeptide chain folds in such a way as to reach the most stable of all possible conformations. Part of the stability arises from the distribution of polar and nonpolar amino acids between the surface and the interior of the globular protein. Those amino acids with electrically charged side-chains (glutamate, lysine and so on) strongly attract water molecules about them. Amino acids that are essentially neutral but that possess atoms such as N or O in the side-chains can form dipoles and therefore also attract water about them. The attachment of water, as discussed in Section 2-6, minimizes the strength of the electrical field about the side-chains and lowers the free energy, thus increasing the stability of the structure. Free energy is a measure of the energy available for doing work in a system, and as the free energy is decreased, the stability of a system increases (see Chapter 4).

Side-chains of amino acids such as leucine or phenylalanine are nonpolar and these groups repel water. Not only is water repelled but the crowded water molecules become more orderly in the vicinity of the nonpolar groups —the water becomes more ice-like. The entropy of the water decreases. Entropy is a measure of the orderliness and stability of a system. Highly structured systems are less stable and have a lower entropy than less structured systems. In the structures of myoglobin, hemoglobin, and lysozyme—proteins whose tertiary structure is known—the polar amino acids, because of the foldings of the polypeptide chain, are on the outside of the molecule. The nonpolar side-chains are on the inside of the molecule. Thus the conformation assumed by these proteins is such that the nonpolar side-chains are removed from water and the entropy of side-chains and water is greatest, while the polar side-chains, being exposed to water, reach a free energy minimum. Because both free energy and entropy are in directions leading to greatest stability, the conformation is the most stable.

Some globular proteins, for example, hemoglobin (Figure 2-13b), possess a quaternary structure—the aggregation of subunits to form a functional macromolecule (Bernal, 1959, 1965).

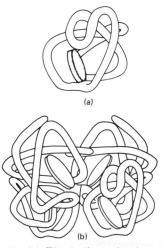

(a)

(b)

Figure 2-13 (a) The tertiary structure of myoglobin. (b) Showing how tertiary units are complexed together to form the quaternary structure of hemoglobin.

A major achievement in the determination of molecular structure was the elucidation of the conformations of myoglobin and hemoglobin by Kendrew, Perutz, and their coworkers. This has led to the exciting hope that in the near future it will be possible to predict and generalize about protein structure-function relationships—relationships that lie at the base of cellular form and function. The method employed by these workers was x-ray diffraction analysis (details of the method may be found in Buerger, 1960; James, 1950; Dickerson, 1964).

x-Ray diffraction analysis has many uses including the measurement of bond lengths and angles in molecules; the determination of molecular weights; the determination of the absolute configuration of optical isomers. It is used to measure the repeat period—regularly spaced indications of submolecular organization—of fibrous proteins (Astbury, 1933, 1945); of contractile proteins and tissues. Membrane structure is analyzed by this method (Engström and Finean, 1968). The presence of the α-helix was determined by x-ray diffraction analysis. It is the only method available for determining the position of atoms in proteins (Kendrew, 1963; Perutz, 1963).

Myoglobin was chosen by Kendrew because

it is a relatively small protein, with a molecular weight of 17,500 and is available in large quantities. As shown in Figure 2-14, the polypeptide chain of myoglobin is highly convoluted and the globular protein is extremely compact with no room for water within the structure. The myoglobin chain has a similar primary sequence and conformation to one of those of the hemoglobin molecule (Figure 2-13). Hemoglobin has a quarternary structure consisting of two pairs of polypeptide chains. The structures of several enzymes, including ribonuclease and lysosyme, are also known at the tertiary level (see Dayhoff and Eck, 1968).

While x-ray diffraction is used to determine the precise three-dimensional structure of proteins and other macromolecules, other methods are used to purify, isolate, or determine the weight and shape of macromolecules. These include optical rotatory dispersion, ultracentrifugation, light scattering, diffusion and osmotic pressure measurements, electrophoresis and chromatography, and electron microscopy. Such methods are described in Bull (1964), Martin (1964), Oster and Pollister (1955–), and in the series *Advances in Protein Chemistry*, (New York: Academic Press, Inc.). (For example, Wetlauffer, 1962). Tanford (1961)

Figure 2-14 The three-dimensional conformation of the myoglobin molecule obtained from 2 Å x-ray diffraction studies. The large dots represents positions of the α-carbons of the L-amino acids. Numbers indicate amino acid sequence. α-Helical portions of molecule are represented by smooth helices; nonhelical regions by zigzag lines between α-carbons. [Redrawn from R. E. Dickerson (1964) in *The Proteins* (H. Neurath, editor) Vol. 2, 2nd ed. By permission Academic Press, New York.]

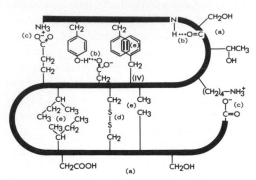

Figure 2-15 A summary of the types of linkages found in proteins. (a) Polar group reactions with water; (b) hydrogen bonds; (c) electrostatic oriionic bonds; (d) inter- or intrachain disulfide (covalent) bonds; (e) van der Waals forces and nonpolar side chain interactions resulting from solvent exclusion (hydrophobic bonds). [Modified from C. B. Anfinsen (1959) *The Molecular Basis of Evolution* John Wiley & Sons, New York.]

has an excellent discussion of the properties of macromolecules.

2-12. Summary of Protein Linkages. The stable, native conformation of a protein is established by the various covalent and non-covalent bonds that result from inter- and intrachain reactions of the amino acid side-chains. These linkages are summarized in Figure 2-15 (see also Anfinsen, 1959; Schachman, 1963).

The side-chains of alanine, valine, leucine, and isoleucine, as well as of proline, are non-polar. They do not react with polar molecules such as water or with other polar side-chains. But they can form weak attractions with each other and with hydrophobic molecules such as lipids. These groups can form **hydrophobic bonds**—weak attractive forces between non-polar groups which can add to the stability of the protein molecule. The nonpolar side-chains are repelled by water—a factor which tends to move them towards the inner space of globular proteins.

The sidegroups of lysine, hydroxylysine, serine, arginine, histidine, asparagine, and glutamine are polar. They can form strong ionic bonds and can hydrogen bond with

other polar groups or molecules. Cysteine and cystine can enter into oxidation-reduction reactions through the —SH group. This is an especially active center for combinations with metal atoms and for conferring stability to the tertiary structure of some proteins.

The overall reactivity and nature of a protein depends on the nature of its amino acid residues. Since proteins possess a variety of chemically reactive groups, they can readily combine with other types of molecules, forming conjugate proteins. Proteins are found complexed with lipids (lipoproteins); with nucleic acids (nucleoproteins); and with carbohydrates (glycoproteins). The lipoproteins are of fundamental importance in membrane structure and function and also many enzymes appear to be lipoprotein complexes, often associated with membranous structures. In many cases proteins serve as carriers for transporting other molecules. Some otherwise inert proteins are converted to active enzymes by the addition of a nonprotein moiety—a coenzyme or cofactor.

Denaturation is a change in the native state of a protein. Such change is reflected in the loss or reduction of enzymatic or other biological activity or by a change in a physical property such as solubility. When the denaturing agent is mild, denaturation is often reversible. But extremes in pH, temperature, pressure, or other environmental factors can cause irreversible destruction of the protein (Joly, 1965). Most denaturing agents act by altering secondary or tertiary structure essential to the normal functioning of proteins. Factors that can affect the electrical charge or the position of side-chains can affect the conformation of proteins. The lability of proteins—their sensitivity to environmental factors—appears to be a major factor limiting life to a relatively narrow range of conditions.

But it should be noted that changes in the conformation of a protein or changes in positioning of some side-chains often are part of the normal activity of a protein. Such changes, for example, often result from combination of substrate with a protein enzyme or from the interaction of a protein and a hormone. These activities as they apply to

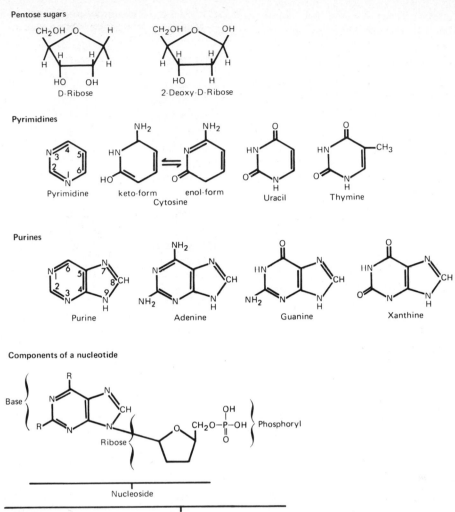

Figure 2-16 Structures of the important building blocks of nucleosides, nucleotides, and nucleic acids. The usual numbering system of ring atoms is shown for each type of compound.

enzyme reactions and to the control of metabolism are discussed in Chapter 4.

2-13. Primary Structure of Nucleic Acids. The nucleic acids are another group of information-bearing macromolecules. Their major functions are concerned with the control of cellular growth, reproduction, and differentiation and with the transmission of genetic information. Much of their activity is expressed through the control of protein synthesis. Here only their basic structural features are considered.

The monomers making up the primary structure of nucleic acids are **nucleotides**—compounds composed of a heterocyclic organic base, a pentose sugar, and phosphoric acid. The pentose sugar is *d*-ribose in most nucleotides and in the ribonucleic acids (RNA). The pentose sugar, 2-*d*-deoxyribose is found in the deoxyribonucleic acids (DNA; Figure 2-16).

The organic bases in most nucleotides are derivatives of either purine or pyrimidine. Adenine, guanine and cytosine are found in both DNA and RNA; in addition RNA contains the pyrimidine base, uracil; DNA has thymine. These are the five common bases found in nucleic acids although others have been discovered.

DNA and RNA are class designations. Each class consists of a family of molecules differing in molecular weight and base composition. It is difficult to isolate individual species of nucleic acids from cellular extracts. Part of the difficulty stems from the instability of the larger nucleic acids and part from the difficulty of separating nucleic acids from the proteins with which they are associated in the cell. Some care, therefore, must be exercised during the extraction and purification of nucleic acids in order to prevent degradation and denaturation.

The nucleic acids are acidic compounds with many negatively charged groups at physiological pH. They form complexes with cations such as Mg^{2+} or with cationic proteins. The nucleic acids differ in size, cellular location, and function. DNA is confined mainly to the nucleus of the animal cell, although a significant amount is found also in the mitochondria (Sager and Ishida, 1963; Gibor and Granick, 1964). DNA is found also in plant cell chloroplasts and mitochondria (Sinclair et al., 1967). The ability of cellular organelles to replicate, especially their membranous components, may result from the presence of this DNA.

The Svedberg sedimentation constant, s, determined by ultracentrifugation, is often used to compare the sizes of macromolecules. The sedimentation constant (with units of

Table 2-3 Sedimentation Constants and Molecular Weights of Some Macromolecules

MACROMOLECULE	$s_{20,w}$	M
Insulin (monomer)	1.6	6,000
Ribonuclease	1.85	12,700
Lysozyme*	2.15	17,200
Ovalbumin	3.6	44,700
Alcohol dehydrogenase	7.6	150,000
Catalase*	11.35	250,000
Actomyosin	12	3,900,000
tRNA (yeast)*	4.56	—
Tobacco mosaic virus	174	59,000,000
DNA (bacteriophage*	33.6	
DNA (bacteriophage)*	32.5	

* Indicates molecules used as standards for the determination of s values.

reciprocal seconds) is a measure of the rate of sedimentation or movement of a molecule in a centrifugal force field. It is a reflection of both the molecular weight and the conformation of a molecule. Values of s are usually expressed in Svedberg units (one unit $= 10^{-13}$ seconds). They are also usually corrected for standard conditions with reference to the viscosity of water at 20°C—symbolized by $s_{20,w}$. A convenient way to obtain the s-value of an unknown substance is to compare the unknown with a standard of similar composition

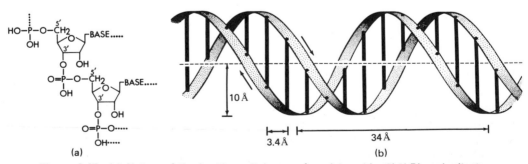

(a)   10 Å   3.4Å   34Å

(b)

Figure 2-17 (a) Nature of the backbone linkages of nucleic acids. 3′-5′-Phosphodiester bonds unite the component nucleotides. Primes are used to designate ribose ring carbons to distinguish them from ring atoms of the purine and pyrimidine bases. (b) Schematic of the helix of DNA. The ribbonlike structures represent the backbones of two chains joined together by hydrogen bonding between base pairs (see also Figure 2-18).

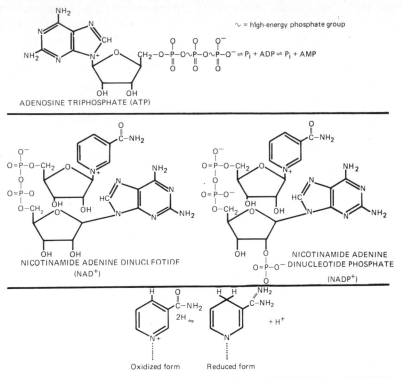

Figure 2-18 Structures of some important nucleotides: ATP, NAD$^+$, and NADP$^+$. ATP contains two high energy phosphate groups that can be successively hydrolyzed to yield first adenosine diphosphate (ATP) and then adenosine monophosphate (AMP). NAD$^+$ and NADP$^+$ are coenzymes associated with oxidation-reduction reactions in the cell (Chapter 4). The functional group in this activity is the nicotinamide, whose reduction is shown at the bottom of the figure.

and known s-value under similar conditions in the ultracentrifuge. Table 2-3 gives the molecular weights and s-values for some proteins and nucleic acids. Molecular weights of DNA range as high as 1×10^9 in some of the viruses where the DNA of the genetic material is considered as one large molecule. On this basis some DNA molecules are the largest known macromolecules.

At least four types of RNA are known: (1) viral RNA—varieties of RNA found in some viruses. (2) Messenger RNA (mRNA)—has molecular weights of up to 5×10^6. mRNA is formed in the cell nucleus and moves into the cytoplasm. Its function is to transmit the protein-synthesizing code of DNA to sites in the cell where protein synthesis can occur. (3) Soluble or transfer RNA (tRNA)—with molecular weights of about 25,000. Functions as a catalyst for activating amino acids, preparing them for incorporation into polypeptide chains as directed by mRNA. (4) Ribosomal RNA (rRNA) is a constituent of ribosomes—particles found associated with segments of the endoplasmic reticulum (Chapter 3). The ribosomes are the major sites of protein synthesis in the cell. Thus rRNA acts in the binding of mRNA and tRNA to the smaller ribosomal unit. Although ribosomes are partially composed of protein, little is known about the proteins except that they contain large quantities of basic amino acids and have molecular weights of about 25,000 (see Peterman, 1964; Watson, 1965).

The combination of an organic base and a pentose sugar is a **nucleoside**. The reaction of a nucleoside with phosphoric acid yields the nucleotide. The primary chain of nucleic acids is built up of nucleotides covalently linked by 3′-5′-phosphodiester bonds (Figure 2-17a). Long chains of nucleotides are **polynucleotides.**

The number and sequence of nucleotides determines the properties of a nucleic acid. Differences in nucleic acids are determined by the number and sequence of only four monomers, as compared with the twenty amino acids of proteins. The first primary sequence for a nucleic acid (tRNA) was determined in 1965 (Holley et al., 1965; see Dayhoff and Eck, 1968). Details of nucleic acid chemistry can be found in Fresco et al. (1960); Spirin (1964); Michelson (1963); Davidson and Cohn (1963–); or Chargaff and Davidson (1955–1960).

During the course of evolution, nucleotides have come to serve other functions than as building blocks for nucleic acids. The nucleotide triphosphate, adenosine triphosphate (ATP), is found in all cells and is considered the direct energy source for most cellular activities. Another ubiquitous compound is nicotinamide adenine dinucleotide (NAD$^+$), a coenzyme essential for many oxidation-reduction reactions in cellular metabolism. One of the bases of NAD is nicotinamide, a vitamin derivative. Another closely related compound is NADP, nicotinamide adenine dinucleotide. NADP is also a coenzyme needed in oxidation-reduction reactions (see Chapter 4). The structures of ATP, NAD, and NADP are given in Figure 2-18.

2-14. Secondary Structure of Nucleic Acids. The secondary structure of DNA is well modeled but less is known about that of the RNA's. Primary sequences of most DNA and RNA molecules have not yet been determined. The introduction of a suitable model of DNA secondary structure was based upon several properties of the primary sequence: (1) The use of x-ray diffraction analysis showed that DNA consisted of a regular array of planar bases, stacked upon one another (Astbury, 1947). (2) Although the base sequence was complex and varied from one species of DNA to another, there was always

a one-to-one ratio of adenine to thymine and of guanine to cytosine (Chargaff, 1950). (3) Gulland and Jordan (1947) found that bases were hydrogen bonded together and Gulland proposed that polynucleotide chains were linked together by this base hydrogen bonding.

Using these observations and the further confirmatory results of x-ray diffraction studies by Wilkins et al. (1953), Watson and Crick (1953) developed the double-stranded helical model of DNA. This model (Figures 2-17b, 2-19) has been confirmed and refined (see, for example, Wilkins, 1963; Langridge et al., 1960a,b). The model also accounts for the ability of DNA to replicate. The major characteristics of the molecule are as follows: (a) DNA contains two long polynucleotide strands forming a double helix around a central axis. (b) The strands are held together by hydrogen bonding between pairs of bases. (c) There is a distance of 10.7 Å separating sugar residues on opposite nucleotide chains. This distance can be filled only by two combinations of bases: adenine with thymine or

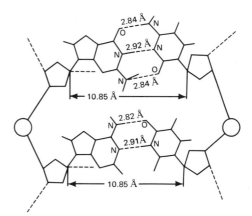

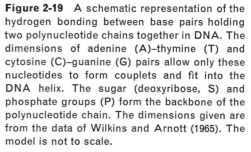

Figure 2-19 A schematic representation of the hydrogen bonding between base pairs holding two polynucleotide chains together in DNA. The dimensions of adenine (A)–thymine (T) and cytosine (C)–guanine (G) pairs allow only these nucleotides to form couplets and fit into the DNA helix. The sugar (deoxyribose, S) and phosphate groups (P) form the backbone of the polynucleotide chain. The dimensions given are from the data of Wilkins and Arnott (1965). The model is not to scale.

FATTY ACIDS

Molecular Formula	Common Name	Systematic Name	Structural Formula
		SATURATED FATTY ACIDS	
$C_2H_4O_2$	Acetic	n-Ethanoic	CH_3COOH
$C_3H_6O_2$	Propionic	n-Propanoic	CH_3CH_2COOH
$C_4H_8O_2$	n-Butyric	n-Butanoic	$CH_3(CH_2)_2COOH$
$C_6H_{12}O_2$	Caproic	n-Hexanoic	$CH_3(CH_2)_4COOH$
$C_8H_{16}O_2$	Caprylic	n-Octanoic	$CH_3(CH_2)_6COOH$
$C_9H_{18}O_2$	Pelargonic	n-Nonanoic	$CH_3(CH_2)_7COOH$
$C_{10}H_{20}O_2$	Capric	n-Decanoic	$CH_3(CH_2)_8COOH$
$C_{12}H_{24}O_2$	Lauric	n-Dodecanoic	$CH_3(CH_2)_{10}COOH$
$C_{14}H_{28}O_2$	Myristic	n-Tetradecanoic	$CH_3(CH_2)_{12}COOH$
$C_{16}H_{32}O_2$	Palmitic	n-Hexadecanoic	$CH_3(CH_2)_{14}COOH$
$C_{18}H_{36}O_2$	Stearic	n-Octadenanoic	$CH_3(CH_2)_{16}COOH$
$C_{20}H_{40}O_2$	Arachidic	n-Eicosanoic	$CH_3(CH_2)_{18}COOH$
$C_{22}H_{44}O_2$	Behenic	n-Docosanoic	$CH_3(CH_2)_{20}COOH$
$C_{24}H_{48}O_2$	Lignoceric	n-Tetracosanoic	$CH_3(CH_2)_{22}COOH$
$C_{26}H_{52}O_2$	Cerotic	n-Hexacosanoic	$CH_3(CH_2)_{24}COOH$
		UNSATURATED FATTY ACIDS	
$C_{16}H_{30}O_2$	Palmitoleic	9-Hexadecenoic	$CH_3(CH_2)_5CH=CH(CH_2)_7COOH$
$C_{18}H_{34}O_2$	Oleic	cis-9-Octadecenoic	$CH_3(CH_2)_7CH=CH(CH_2)_7COOH$
$C_{18}H_{34}O_2$	Elaidic	$trans$-9-Octadecenoic	$CH_3(CH_2)_7CH=CH(CH_2)_7COOH$
$C_{18}H_{34}O_2$	Vaccenic	11-Octadecenoic	$CH_3(CH_2)_5CH=CH(CH_2)_9COOH$
$C_{18}H_{32}O_2$	Linoleic	cis,cis-9,12-Octadecadienoic	$CH_3(CH_2)_3(CH\ CH=CH)_2(CH_2)_7COOH$
$C_{18}H_{30}O_2$	Linolenic	9,12,15-Octadecatrienoic	$CH_3(CH_2CH=CH)_3(CH_2)_7COOH$
$C_{20}H_{32}O_2$	Arachidonic	5,8,11,14-Eicosatetraenoic	$CH_3(CH_2)_3(CH_2\ CH=CH)_4(CH_2)_3COOH$

GLYCERIDES

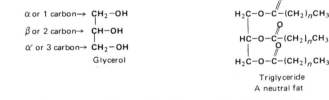

α or 1 carbon→ CH_2-OH
β or 2 carbon→ $CH-OH$
α' or 3 carbon→ CH_2-OH
Glycerol

$$H_2C-O-\overset{O}{\overset{\|}{C}}-(CH_2)_nCH_3$$
$$HC-O-\overset{O}{\overset{\|}{C}}-(CH_2)_nCH_3$$
$$H_2C-O-\overset{O}{\overset{\|}{C}}-(CH_2)_nCH_3$$

Triglyceride
A neutral fat

Figure 2-20 Structures of fatty acids. Even-numbered fatty acids, especially those with 16, 18, and 20 carbons, are most commonly found. Neutral fats and oils consist of a molecule of glycerol combined with two or three fatty acids (di- and triglycerides, respectively). The fatty acids may be the same or different, thus providing a variety of glycerides. Neutral fats and oils are simple lipids in contrast to the more complex glycerophosphatides, sphingolipids, and so on.

guanine with cytosine. Although the sequence of bases along a chain may vary considerably from one nucleic acid to another, in a given DNA molecule, the paired strands must be complementary. (d) Replication of DNA is possible since if the two strands are separated by some mechanism, each may act as a template for the formation of its complementary strand.

The Watson-Crick model holds generally for DNA molecules. One exception has been found in the *E. coli* bacteriophage ΦX174, which possesses a single-stranded DNA molecule. The structures of most RNA molecules are uncertain, although most appear to be single-stranded and some are cyclic (Stent, 1963).

Proteins and nucleic acids are large polymers with capabilities for variation and adaptation, and they are the major carriers of information in the cell—proteins acting as structural and functional units—whereas the nucleic acids are responsible for the genetic transmission of information and the guidance of protein synthesis. Next we shall consider some smaller molecules of importance to the cell.

GLYCEROPHOSPHATIDES
Phosphatidyl Ethanolamines (Cephalins)

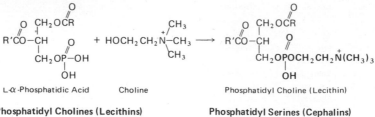

L-α-Phosphatidic Acid   Choline   Phosphatidyl Choline (Lecithin)

Phosphatidyl Cholines (Lecithins)   **Phosphatidyl Serines (Cephalins)**

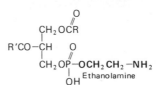

Figure 2-21 Structures of phospholipids. R groups symbolize fatty acids attached to the basic glyceride structure. Variations in the fatty acids produce the various species of phospholipids in each class.

Lipids and Carbohydrates

2-15. Structure and Functions of Lipids. The group of compounds known as lipids is characterized by being sparingly soluble in water but soluble in organic nonpolar solvents such as benzene, ether, or chloroform. Lipids are a chemically heterogeneous collection of organic substances. They do not polymerize to form macromolecules although they are

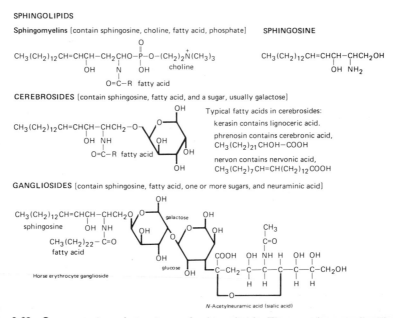

Figure 2-22 Components and structures of sphingolipids. The complex gangliosides have had structures established in only a few cases. The example given, horse erythrocyte ganglioside, is one known one. Sphingolipids are characterized by the presence of the complex alcohol, sphingosine.

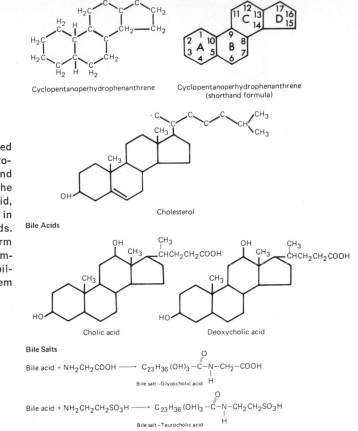

Cyclopentanoperhydrophenanthrene

Cyclopentanoperhydrophenanthrene
(shorthand formula)

Figure 2-23 Steroids are derived from the cyclopentanoperhydrophenanthrene skeleton. In man and other mammals, cholesterol is the quantitatively predominant steroid, and is an important intermediate in the biosynthesis of other steroids. The bile acids, in the esterified form of bile salts, are physiologically important as emulsifiers and solubilizers of neutral fats, preparing them for intestinal hydrolysis.

Cholesterol

Bile Acids

Cholic acid

Deoxycholic acid

Bile Salts

Bile acid + $NH_2CH_2COOH \longrightarrow C_{23}H_{36}(OH)_3 - \overset{\overset{\displaystyle O}{\|}}{C} - \underset{\underset{\displaystyle H}{|}}{N} - CH_2 - COOH$

Bile salt—Glycocholic acid

Bile acid + $NH_2CH_2CH_2SO_3H \longrightarrow C_{23}H_{36}(OH)_3 - \overset{\overset{\displaystyle O}{\|}}{C} - \underset{\underset{\displaystyle H}{|}}{N} - CH_2CH_2SO_3H$

Bile salt—Taurocholic acid

often found complexed with proteins in the cell. Since many lipids possess both polar and nonpolar chemical groups, they can act as links between proteins and other molecules.

Neutral fats and oils are triglyceride esters of glycerol and fatty acids (Figure 2-20). Fats are solids at 20°C, whereas oils are liquid at this temperature. Most of the common fatty acids are straight-chain hydrocarbons, with an even number of carbon atoms. Fatty acids may be either saturated or unsaturated. Neutral fats serve as energy reservoirs in animals and are also constituents of biological membranes. The fatty acids and glycerol are components of many of the more complex lipids described below.

Phospholipids (phosphatides) are derivatives of phosphatidic acid (Figure 2-21). They include the lecithins (phosphatidyl cholines) and the cephalins (phosphatidyl serines and ethanolamines). Members of a class differ

according to their particular complement of fatty acids. The role of these substances in membrane structure and function will be of concern in later chapters.

Sphingolipids are compounds containing the complex alcohol, sphingosine (Figure 2-22). They include the sphingomyelins and glycolipids. The latter, divided into cerebrosides and gangliosides, also contain a carbohydrate moiety. As the names indicate, the sphingolipids are prominent constituents of nervous tissue. They are found as constituents in many cellular membranes.

Steroids are a lipid class distinguished from other lipids because they are not saponifiable—they are not converted into water-soluble substances upon alkaline hydrolysis. The steroids are derived from the cyclopentanoperhydrophenanthrene ring structure (Figure 2-23). Cholesterol is a key intermediate in the biosynthesis of steroids. Among the

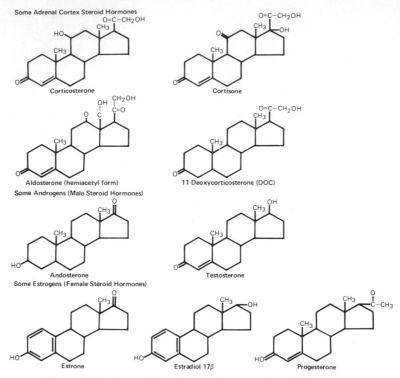

Figure 2-24 A sampling of some important steroid hormones.

important physiological steroids are the adrenocortical hormones (including aldosterone, corticosterone, deoxycorticosterone, and cortisone) which are involved in the control of electrolytes and of carbohydrate and nitrogen metabolism (Figure 2-24). Estrogens and androgens are hormones secreted by the ovary and testis, respectively (Figure 2-24). The bile acids, including cholic and deoxycholic acids, are also steroids (Figure 2-23).

Other lipids act as vitamins, visual pigments, or color pigments in cells. These will be discussed in appropriate sections of later chapters.

2-16. Carbohydrates. The simplest carbohydrates are the monosaccharides and include the hexoses, glucose and fructose, and the pentose sugar, ribose (Figure 2-25). A primary function of monosaccharides is to

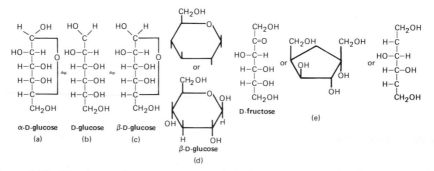

Figure 2-25 Structures of some common carbohydrates and methods of representation.

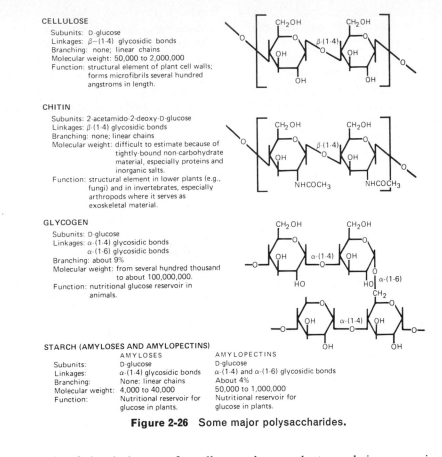

CELLULOSE

Subunits: D-glucose
Linkages: β-(1-4) glycosidic bonds
Branching: none; linear chains
Molecular weight: 50,000 to 2,000,000
Function: structural element of plant cell walls;
forms microfibrils several hundred
angstroms in length.

CHITIN

Subunits: 2-acetamido-2-deoxy-D-glucose
Linkages: β-(1-4) glycosidic bonds
Branching: none; linear chains
Molecular weight: difficult to estimate because of
tightly-bound non-carbohydrate
material, especially proteins and
inorganic salts.
Function: structural element in lower plants (e.g.,
fungi) and in invertebrates, especially
arthropods where it serves as
exoskeletal material.

GLYCOGEN

Subunits: D-glucose
Linkages: α-(1-4) glycosidic bonds
α-(1-6) glycosidic bonds
Branching: about 9%
Molecular weight: from several hundred thousand
to about 100,000,000.
Function: nutritional glucose reservoir in
animals.

STARCH (AMYLOSES AND AMYLOPECTINS)

	AMYLOSES	AMYLOPECTINS
Subunits:	D-glucose	D-glucose
Linkages:	α-(1-4) glycosidic bonds	α-(1-4) and α-(1-6) glycosidic bonds
Branching:	None: linear chains	About 4%
Molecular weight:	4,000 to 40,000	50,000 to 1,000,000
Function:	Nutritional reservoir for glucose in plants.	Nutritional reservoir for glucose in plants.

Figure 2-26 Some major polysaccharides.

serve as sources of chemical energy for cells. Many carbohydrate structures are shown in the metabolic pathways of Chapter 4. Carbohydrate metabolism centers around glucose. Ribose, as we have already seen, is a structural component of the nucleotides and their derivatives.

Monosaccharides can polymerize to form polysaccharides. Glycogen, starch, and cellulose are homopolysaccharides, composed of only one type of simple sugar (glucose) as the monomeric unit. Figure 2-26 illustrates the bonding arrangements in these polymers. The names are class designations only, since each group consists of a variety of different-sized molecules. Glycogen and starch are glucose storage molecules in animals and plants, respectively. Cellulose is a structural component in plants.

Another important homopolysaccharide is **chitin**—a structural carbohydrate found in lower plants and in many invertebrates, especially in the exoskeleton of arthropods. Chitin is composed of a linear array of β-linked 2-acetamido-2-deoxy-D-glucose (Figure 2-26). Polysaccharides such as chitin, that contain amino sugars or their derivatives are known as **mucopolysaccharides**. Chitin also contains tightly bound noncarbohydrate material including proteins and inorganic salts.

Carbohydrates are important elements in membrane structure and in the extracellular matrix upon which cells live, but their roles here are not known. The glycoproteins and mucoproteins are carbohydrates complexed with protein. They include the hyaluronic acids, mucoitin sulfuric acids, and chondroitin sulfuric acids (the structures of these materials are considered in Section 3-15 of the next chapter). These substances are found in the cement substances and connective tissues that bind cells together. They are also found in special body fluids such as the saliva, vitreous and aqueous humors of the eye, and the lubricating fluids at bone joints.

The main purpose of this chapter has been to outline the general nature and potentialities of the more important biological compounds upon which cellular structure and function is based. Continuous reference will be made to their roles in physiological activities considered in the remaining chapters. The references listed in this chapter and those of Section 1-5 may be consulted for more detailed treatment of these materials.

References and Readings

Ackerman, E. (1962). **Biophysical Science.** Englewood Cliffs, N.J.: Prentice-Hall, Inc. 626 pp.

Alexander, P. and R. J. Block, eds. (1960). **A Laboratory Manual of Analytical Methods of Protein Chemistry.** Vol. 2. New York: Pergamon Press, Inc. 518 pp.

Altman, P. L. and D. S. Dittmer, eds. (1964). **Biology Data Book.** Washington, D.C.: Federation of American Societies for Experimental Biology. 633 pp.

Anfinsen, C. B. (1959). **The Molecular Basis of Evolution.** New York: John Wiley & Sons, Inc. 228 pp.

Astbury, W. T. (1933). **The Fundamentals of Fiber Structure.** New York: Oxford University Press. 187 pp.

Astbury, W. T. (1945). "The forms of biological molecules." In: **Essays on Growth and Form.** (Le Gros Clark and Medawar, eds.), 408 pp. Oxford: Clarendon Press.

Astbury, W. T. (1947). "X-ray studies of nucleic acids." *Symp. Soc. Exp. Biol.* **1:** 66–76.

Astbury, W. T. and H. J. Woods (1933). "X-ray studies of the structure of hair, wool, and related fibers." *Phil. Trans. Roy. Soc., London.* **A232:** 333–394.

Bernal, J. D. (1959). "The function of hydrogen bonds in solids and liquids." In: **Hydrogen Bonding.** (D. Hadzi, ed.), pp. 7–22. New York: Pergamon Press, Inc.

Bernal, J. D. (1965). "Molecular structure, biochemical function, and evolution." In: **Theoretical and Mathematical Biology.** (T. H. Waterman and H. J. Morowitz, eds.), pp. 96–135. Waltham, Mass.: Blaisdell Publishing Co.

Bjerrum, N. (1952). "Structure and properties of ice." *Science* **115:** 385–390.

Brown, R. and J. F. Danielli, eds. (1955). **Fibrous Proteins and Their Biological Significance.** *Symp. Soc. Exp. Biol.* **9.** New York: Academic Press, Inc. 371 pp.

Buerger, M. J. (1942). **X-ray Crystallography.** New York: John Wiley & Sons, Inc. 531 pp.

Buerger, M. J. (1960). **Crystal Structure Analysis.** New York: John Wiley & Sons, Inc. 668 pp.

Bull, H. B. (1964). **An Introduction to Physical Biochemistry.** Philadelphia: F. A. Davis Co. 433 pp.

Chargaff, E. (1950). "Chemical specificity of nucleic acids and mechanism of their enzymatic degradation." *Experentia* **6:** 201–209.

Chargaff, E. and J. N. Davidson (1955–1960). **The Nucleic Acids.** 3 volumes. New York: Academic Press, Inc.

Cohen, S. S. (1963). "On biochemical variability and innovation." *Science* **139:** 1017–1026.

Corrigan, J. J. (1969). "D-amino acids in animals." *Science* **164:** 142–149.

Crick, F. H. C. and J. C. Kendrew (1957). "X-ray analysis and protein structure." *Adv. Protein Chem.* **12:** 133–214.

Davidson, J. N. and W. E. Cohn, eds. (1963–). **Progress in Nucleic Acid Research.** Continuing series. New York: Academic Press, Inc.

Dayhoff, M. O. and R. V. Eck (1968). **Atlas of Protein Sequence and Structure: 1967–1968.** Silver Springs, Md.: National Biomedical Research Foundation. 356 pp.

Dickerson, R. E. (1964). "X-ray analysis and protein structure." In: **The Proteins.** (H. Neurath, ed.), Vol. 2, 2nd ed., pp. 603–778. New York: Academic Press, Inc.

Durchon, M. and M. Lafon (1951). "Quelques donnees biochimiques sur les annelides." *Ann. Sci. Nato., Zool.* **11:** 427–452.

Edsall, J. T. and J. Wyman (1958). **Biophysical Chemistry.** Vol. 1. New York: Academic Press, Inc. 699 pp.

Engström, A. and J. B. Finean (1967). **Biological Ultrastructure,** 2nd ed. New York: Academic Press, Inc. 326 pp.

Fogg, G. E., ed. (1965). **The State and Movement of Water in Organisms.** *Symp. Soc. Exp. Biol.* **19.** New York: Academic Press, Inc. 432 pp.

Frank, H. S. (1965). "The structure of water." *Fed. Proc.* **24,** suppl. 15: S1–S11.

Fresco, J. R., B. M. Alberts, and P. Doty (1960). "Some molecular details of the secondary structure of ribonucleic acid." *Nature* **188:** 98–101.

Frey-Wyssling, A. (1953). **Submicroscopic Morphology of Protoplasm,** 2nd ed. New York: American Elsevier Publishing Co. 411 pp.

Frey-Wyssling, A. (1957). **Macromolecules in Cell Structure.** Cambridge, Mass.: Harvard University Press. 112 pp.

Gibor, A. and S. Granick (1964). "Plastids and mitochondria: inheritable systems." *Science* **145:** 890–897.

Green, D. E. and S. Fleischer (1962). "On the molecular organization of biological transducing systems." In: **Horizons in Biochemistry.** (M. Kasha and B. Pullman, eds.), pp. 381–420. New York: Academic Press, Inc.

Gulland, J. M. (1947). "The structure of nucleic acids." *Cold Spring Harbor Symp. Quant. Biol.* **12:** 95–103.

Gulland, J. M. and D. O. Jordan (1947). "The macromolecular behavior of nucleic acids." *Symp. Soc. Exp. Biol.* **1:** 56–65.

Hawk, P. B., B. L. Oser, and W. H. Summerson (1954). **Practical Physiological Chemistry,** 13th ed. New York: The McGraw Hill Book Company, Inc. 1439 pp.

Hechter, O. (1965). "Role of water structure in the molecular organization of cell membranes." *Fed. Proc.* **24,** suppl. 15: S91–S102.

Henderson, L. J. (1913). **The Fitness of the Environment: An inquiry into the biological significance of the properties of matter.** New York: The Macmillan Company. 317 pp.

Hodgkin, D. C., et al. (1957). "The structure of vitamin B_{12}. I. An outline of the crystallographic investigation of vitamin B_{12}." *Proc. Roy. Soc.* (*London*) **A242:** 228–263.

Holley, R. W., et al. (1965). "Structure of a ribonucleic acid." *Science* **147:** 1462–1465.

James, R. W. (1950). **X-ray Crystallography.** London: Methuen & Co., Ltd. 101 pp.

Joly, M. (1965). **Denaturation of Proteins.** New York: Academic Press, Inc. 350 pp.

Jukes, T. H. (1963). "The genetic code." *Am. Sci.* **51:** 227–247.

Jukes, T. H. (1965). "The genetic code II." *Am. Sci.* **53:** 477–487.

Katsoyannis, P. G. (1966). "Synthesis of insulin." *Science* **154:** 1509–1514.

Kavanau, J. L. (1965). **Structure and Function in Biological Membranes.** 2 volumes. San Francisco, Calif.: Holden-Day, Inc.

Kendrew, J. C. (1963). "Myoglobin and the structure of proteins." *Science* **139:** 1259–1266.

Kendrew, J. C. and M. F. Perutz (1957). "X-ray studies of compounds of biological interest." *Ann. Rev. Biochem.* **26:** 327–372.

Kleiber, M. (1961). **The Fire of Life.** New York: John Wiley & Sons, Inc. 454 pp.

Klotz, I. M. (1962). "Water." In: **Horizons in Biochemistry.** (M. Kasha and B. Pullman, eds.), pp. 523–550. New York: Academic Press, Inc.

Klotz, I. M. (1965). "Role of water structure in macromolecules." *Fed. Proc.* **24:** suppl. **15:** S24–S33.

Langridge, R., H. R. Wilson, C. W. Hooper, M. H. F. Wilkins, and L. D. Hamilton (1960a). "The molecular configuration of deoxyribonucleic acid. I. X-ray diffraction study of a crystalline form of the lithium salt." *J. Mol. Biol.* **2:** 19–36.

Langridge, R., D. A. Marvin, W. E. Seeds, H. R. Wilson, M. H. F. Wilkins, and L. D. Hamilton (1960b). "The molecular configuration of deoxyribonucleic acid. II. Molecular models and their Fourier transforms." *J. Mol. Biol.* **2:** 38–64.

Linderstrøm-Lang, K. (1952). **Proteins and Enzymes.** Lane Medical Lectures. Palo Alto, Calif.: Stanford University Press.

Low, B. W. (1961). "The use of X-ray diffraction in the determination of protein structure." *J. Polymer Sci.* **49:** 153–175.

Martin, R. B. (1964). **Introduction to Biophysical Chemistry.** New York: The McGraw-Hill Book Company, Inc. 365 pp.

Merrifield, R. B. (1965). "Automated synthesis of peptides." *Science* **150:** 178–185.

Michelson, A. M. (1963). **The Chemistry of Nucleosides and Nucleotides.** New York: Academic Press, Inc. 622 pp.

Moore, S. and W. H. Stein (1956). "Column chromatography of peptides and proteins." *Adv. Protein Chem.* **11:** 191–237.

Nemethy, G., I. Z. Steinberg, and H. A. Scheraga (1963). "Influence of water structure and of hydrophobic interactions on the strength of side-chain hydrogen bonds in proteins." *Biopolymers* **1:** 43–69.

Neurath, H. (1963–1966). **The Proteins,** 2nd ed. 4 volumes. New York: Academic Press, Inc.

Oster, G. and A. W. Pollister, eds. (1955–1967). **Physical Techniques in Biological Research,** several volumes. New York: Academic Press, Inc.

Pauling, L. (1960). **Nature of the Chemical Bond,** 3rd ed. Ithaca, N.Y.: Cornell University Press. 644 pp.

Pauling, L. (1961). "A molecular theory of general anesthesia." *Science* **134:** 15–21.

Pauling, L. and R. B. Corey (1951). "Configurations of polypeptide chain with favored orientations around single bonds." *Proc. Natl. Acad. Sci.* (*U.S.*) **37:** 729–740.

Pauling, L. and R. B. Corey (1954). "The configuration of polypeptide chains in proteins." *Fortschr. Chem. Organ. Naturstoffe* **11:** 180–239.

Pauling, L., R. B. Corey, and H. R. Branson (1951). "Two hydrogen bonded helical configuration of the polypeptide chain." *Proc. Natl. Acad. Sci.* (*U.S.*) **37:** 205–211.

Perutz, M. F. (1962). "Relation between structure and sequence of haemoglobin." *Nature* **194:** 914–918.

Perutz, M. F. (1963). "X-ray analysis of hemoglobin." *Science* **140:** 863–869.

Peterman, M. L. (1964). **The Physical and Chemical Properties of Ribosomes.** New York: American Elsevier Publishing Co. 872 pp.

Rich, A. and D. W. Green (1961). "X-ray studies of compounds of biological interest." *Ann. Rev. Biochem.* **30:** 93–132.

Robinson, R. A. and R. H. Stokes (1959). **Electrolyte Solutions,** 2nd ed. London: Thornton Butterworth, Ltd.

Sager, R. and M. R. Ishida (1963). "Chloroplast DNA in *Chlamydomonas.*" *Proc. Natl. Acad. Sci.* (*U.S.*) **50:** 725–730.

Sanger, F. (1952). "The arrangement of amino acids in proteins." *Adv. Protein Chem.* **7:** 1–67.

Sanger, F. (1956). "The structure of insulin." In: **Currents in Biochemical Research.** (D. Green, ed.), New York: Interscience Publishing, Inc. 697 pp.

Schachman, H. K. (1963). "Considerations on the tertiary structure of proteins." *Cold Spring Harbor Symp. Quant. Biol.* **28:** 409–430.

Simpson, G. G. (1964). "Organisms and molecules in evolution." *Science* **146:** 1535–1538.

Sinclair, J. H., B. Stevens, P. Sanghavi, and M. Rabinowitz (1967). "Mitochondrial-satellite and circular DNA filaments in yeast." *Science* **156:** 1234–1237.

Snell, F. M., S. Shulman, R. P. Spencer, and C. Moos (1965). **Biophysical Principles of Structure and Function.** Reading, Mass.: Addison-Wesley Publishing Co., Inc. 390 pp.

Spirin, A. S. (1964). **Macromolecular Structure of Ribonucleic Acids.** New York: Reinhold Publishing Corp. 192 pp.

Sponsler, O. L. and J. D. Bath (1942). "Molecular structure of protoplasm." In: **The Structure of Protoplasm.** (W. Weifriz, ed.), pp. 41–73. Ames: Iowa State College Press.

Stahman, M. A., ed. (1962). **Polyamino Acids,**

Polypeptides, and Proteins. Madison: University of Wisconsin Press.

Stent, G. (1963). **Molecular Biology of Bacterial Viruses.** San Francisco: W. H. Freeman & Company, Publishers. 474 pp.

Szent-Györgyi, A. (1960). **Introduction to a Submolecular Biology.** New York: Academic Press, Inc. 135 pp.

Tanford, C. (1961). **Physical Chemistry of Macromolecules.** New York: John Wiley & Sons, Inc. 710 pp.

Vogel, H., V. Bryson, and J. Lampen, eds. (1963). **Informational Macromolecules.** New York: Academic Press, Inc. 542 pp.

Watson, J. D. (1965). **Molecular Biology of the Gene.** New York: W. A. Benjamin, Inc. 494 pp.

Watson, J. D. and F. H. C. Crick (1953). "Molecular structure of nucleic acids—a structure for deoxyribose nucleic acid." *Nature* **171:** 737–738.

West, E. S., W. R. Todd, H. S. Mason, and J. T. van Bruggen (1966). **Textbook of Biochemistry,** 4th ed. New York: The Macmillan Company. 1595 pp.

Wetlaufer, D. B. (1962). "Ultraviolet spectra of proteins and amino acids. "*Adv. Protein Chem.* **17:** 303–390.

Wieland, T. and H. Determann (1966). "The chemistry of peptides and proteins." *Ann. Rev. Biochem.* **35:** 651–690.

Wilkins, M. H. F. (1963). "Molecular configuration of nucleic acids." *Science* **140:** 941–950.

Wilkins, M. H. F., A. R. Stokes, and H. R. Wilson (1953). "Molecular structure of deoxypentose nucleic acids." *Nature* **171:** 738–740.

Methods of Cell Study

3-1. Observational Methods and Resolution. The chemical constituents of cells are not distributed randomly; rather the cell and its parts, as well as the extracellular matrix, have a highly organized and complex state of existence—a state that is dynamic and changeable (Goodwin, 1963; Mazia, 1956; Weiss, 1963). As stated in Chapter 1, good physiological understanding must be accompanied by good morphological data. The description of many physiological mechanisms depends on an accurate knowledge of cellular and subcellular organization and structure—dimensional realms outside normal human experience and beyond unaided human sensory perception. For such study instruments to extend sensory perception are required. Although space does not permit a detailed discussion of the methods used to observe cells or to isolate and analyze their components, the capabilities and limitations of these techniques deserve some mention. For example, cellular membranes are basic to many physiological activities, and yet their dimensions are such, ca. 100 Å thick, that they lie on the borderline of present-day observational techniques, and there is no clear relationship between membrane structure and membrane function (Section 3-8, also Chapter 6).

The capabilities of observational systems are often expressed as the resolving power or, more generally, its reciprocal, the **limit of resolution**, l—defined as the smallest distance that may separate two points on an object and still permit their observation as distinct separate points. The unaided human eye, under optimal conditions in green light (the eye is most sensitive to green light) cannot distinguish between points less than 0.1 mm apart. Structural detail smaller than this is unresolvable unless some instrument capable of increasing resolution is used. The light microscope was the first such useful instrument in biology, and only with its development could the cellular level of animal organization be seen (see Table 1-1).

Resolution depends, among other factors, on the wavelength of the radiation used and on the nature of the lens system. Abbé gave an

Chapter 3

Cellular Organization

Table 3-1   Optimal Resolution of Several Optical Systems

Optical system	Optimal NA	Optimal limit of resolution* (μ)
Visible light, dry objective lens	0.95	0.35
Visible light, water objective lens	1.25	0.26
Ultraviolet light, oil immersion lens	1.60	0.10
Electron microscope	—	5–10Å†

* With no condenser lens in the system, these values double. The limits of resolution for visible light systems are given for green light (5,500 Å).

† Resolutions of 3 to 5 Å are obtained only under most optimal conditions.

approximation to the resolving power of the microscope which indicates that three factors may be varied in order to improve resolution:

$$l = \frac{\lambda}{2n \sin i} \qquad (3.1)$$

λ is the wavelength of radiation used for illumination; n is the refractive index of the medium between the objective lens and the object; i is the half-angle of the cone of light entering the objective lens. $n \sin i$ is the numerical aperture (NA) of the lens system.

Using immersion oil, not air, in the space between objective lens and specimen increases the resolution (Table 3-1), but immersion oils have maximum values of n of about 1.6. The angle of the cone of light entering the lens may be increased, in order to increase resolution (make l smaller) but $\sin i$ has a maximum limiting value of 1 (for angles of 90°) and this value is approached by most lenses made today. The wavelength of illumination remains the only factor which might be changed to improve l.

At best, the light microscope allows gross visualization of some subcellular entities but not their detailed structure. The use of shorter wavelength ultraviolet radiation improves resolution only by a factor of 2. In addition, the ultraviolet microscope must use expensive quartz lenses since glass does not transmit UV-radiation. Further, the human eye cannot perceive ultraviolet, and photographic or other recording methods must be used. It is the use of electron or x-ray beams with their very short

wavelengths that have brought about significant improvements in resolution. Details of optical theory are found in Hardy and Perrin (1932); Jenkins and White (1957); and Martin (1955). The electron microscope is discussed in Section 3-3 after first considering specimen contrast.

3-2. Improving Contrast. The human eye perceives only differences in light intensities or colors (wavelength differences dependent on light absorption properties of materials). Even with good resolving power in an optical system, little details will be seen if there is a lack of contrast between different parts of a specimen. The cell is optically homogeneous —most materials in it have only minute differences in refractive index, which would result in light intensity differences. However, the large percentage of water in the cell precludes any great differences in light absorbing powers of different regions to be observed.

To overcome this lack of contrast, stains are used to color selected parts of cells differentially. But many dyes are toxic to cells, and the accessory techniques of fixation, embedding, sectioning, and dehydration of tissues required to stain a preparation successfully and make it thin enough for light to pass through readily can produce artifacts—alterations due to experimental manipulations. This necessary treatment means that care must be exercised in examining specimens and using them as criteria for normal living cellular structure and organization.

Increased contrast without staining or killing cells is achieved by the phase contrast microscope developed in 1934 by Zernike (1955). This optical system converts small differences in phase (which occur as light waves pass through regions differing minutely in refractive index) into amplitude (=intensity) changes to which the eye is sensitive. The resolution of the phase microscope is not better than that of any visible light microscope; it is the contrast that is improved without the need for staining or killing the preparation (Barer, 1966). Figure 3-1 illustrates how light wave amplitude and phase are affected by a specimen.

Other microscopes are used in biological studies. The interference microscope measures phase differences between two bundles of plane polarized light passed through a specimen. These differences are converted into intensity differences as in the phase micro-scope. Because such phase alterations depend on the dry mass of the object (and are related to the refractive index or thickness of the object), the interference microscope can be used to measure the densities of small regions of a specimen (Engström and Finean, 1958, 1968). Interference and phase optics are described by Osterberg, 1965).

The polarizing microscope converts alterations in the plane of vibration of polarized light into intensity or into color differences. Such alterations can be the result of either atomic structuring of molecules or of molecular organization. The method is extensively used to obtain information about the organization of tissues that contain fibrous elements.

All of these instruments, although they play important roles in biological studies, are limited to resolving structural details of dimensions greater than 0.2 μ.

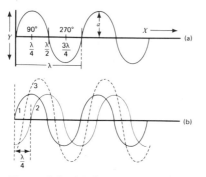

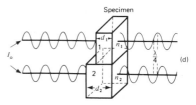

Figure 3-1 (a) Characteristic parameters of a wave. The amplitude, *a*, is proportional to the intensity. λ is the wavelength. The number of wavelengths per unit time is the frequency of the wave. Such waveforms are typical of electromagnetic radiations, including light. Two points at similar positions of two different waves are in phase; points at different positions on different waves are out of phase. Phase is measured in units of angular rotation or in units of fractions of wavelengths. (b) Two waves (1 and 2) which are 90° (= 1/4 wavelength) out of phase. Wave 3 is the resultant of the algebraic summation of the amplitudes of waves 1 and 2 at each point. (c) When a light wave passes through a material, some absorption may occur, indicated here by the decreased amplitude of the transmitted (*I*) as compared with the incident (*I*$_0$) light waves. In the microscopy of biological specimens such absorption in different regions of the protoplasm is too slight to be distinguishable by the human eye. Such absorption effects also lie at the basis of colorimetry and spectrophotometry. (d) A biological specimen may have regions of varying thickness or refractive index. In those areas where either thickness or refractive index is greater than that of the surrounding medium or other parts of the specimen, the optical pathlength (*d* × *n*; *d* is specimen thickness, *n* its refractive index) is greater, and transmitted waves from this region (2) are out of phase with waves transmitted through adjacent regions (1) of the specimen. The phase microscope converts such phase differences, normally unperceptible to the human eye, into intensity differences that the eye can perceive.

3-3. The Electron Microscope. By using the much shorter wavelengths of electrons (ca. 0.05 Å), the electron microscope achieves resolutions better by a factor of about 200 than those of the light microscope. The nature of the magnetic lenses and the limitations of building extremely small apertures limits the overall numerical aperture of the instrument; and under the best of conditions the limit of resolution is about 3 to 5 Å, whereas the usual working limit is about 8 to 15 Å (Crewe, 1966).

In the electron microscope (Figure 3-2) magnetic coils are used to control and focus a beam of electrons accelerated from a cathode. Electrons are scattered by a specimen placed in the path of the beam. Electrons that pass through the specimen are focused by an objective lens, and a final magnified image is produced by a projector lens. The final image is viewed on a fluorescent screen or recorded on a photographic emulsion. Recently television monitors have been incorporated into the system for image viewing. Details of electron optics and the electron microscope are found in Burton and Kohl (1946); Hall (1966); Siegel (1964). Freundlich (1963) has a short history of the instrument.

A major limitation of the electron microscope is that only completely dehydrated specimens can be used because the electron beam must operate in a vacuum to avoid collisions with air molecules that would disrupt the beam. With complete dehydration, and at the very high magnifications possible, care must be used when extrapolating observations back to normal cellular dimensions and organization (Agar, 1961). Luckily, in its lower range the electron microscope overlaps the higher magnifications of the light microscope, and some comparison of images is possible. More is known about light microscopy artifacts than about those resulting from electron microscopy.

The penetrating power of electrons is low and therefore biological specimens of thicknesses ordinarily used in the light microscope (ca. 1 to 40 μ) are far too thick for the electron microscope. Not only is the resolution poor, but thick sections are destroyed by the heat generated by absorbed electrons. The development of thin-sectioning microtomes, the use

Figure 3-2 Schematic outline of the optical pathways in the light microscope and the electron microscope. In the latter instrument electromagnetic lens are used to focus a beam of electrons, and the final image of the thin specimen is either viewed on a fluorescent screen or is permanently recorded on a photographic emulsion.

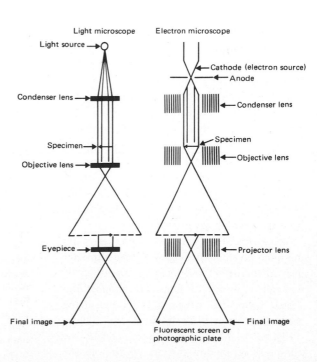

of glass or diamond knives, and the use of plastic embedding resins to support the specimen now allow sections as thin as 50 Å to be cut from tissues. Thin sections are required for the best contrast and resolution but the processes that produce them also can produce serious artifacts in delicate biological materials (Wachtel et al., 1966, review these methods and their history).

Staining to improve contrast is also used in electron microscopy. Electron stains contain heavy atoms whose large numbers of electrons enhance electron densities in those regions of the specimen to which they attach and therefore limit the number of electrons passing through the object. Osmium tetroxide, permanganate, and glutaraldehyde are commonly used fixatives and stains. Negative staining methods employ phosphotungstic acid or uranyl acetate to improve contrast especially of protein molecules or fibers. To avoid fixing and staining, freeze-etching is often used. The specimen is placed in 20 per cent glycerol and frozen at $-100°C$. After being mounted on a holder, the specimen is fractured along its natural cleavage planes. The broken fragments are freeze-dried and then covered with a platinum and carbon coating in a vacuum. After drying, the material is placed in water, and a film replica of the material is obtained that can be studied in the electron microscope. In addition to the stains mentioned above, the use of electron dense proteins, such as the iron-containing ferritin, either alone or in conjunction with antibody techniques, is becoming common (Sriram et al., 1963). Examples of these various methods will be found throughout the book. Because each stain and procedure has its own specific effects and possible artifacts, it is important to note which has been used with a given specimen.

Specimens for electron microscopy are mounted on small metal grids (about a quarter inch in diameter) and must be supported by thin plastic or carbon films. The support film should have little structure of its own if the best resolution is to be obtained.

Figure 3-3 illustrates diagrammatically the technique of shadow-casting, which was one of the first processes used to increase specimen contrast. By adding a thin layer of heavy metal to parts of a specimen, the electron densities of various regions are enhanced. Shadow-casting also has been used to determine the heights of objects (Williams and Wyckoff, 1944, 1945).

Only a relatively short time has been available for developing electron stains and other

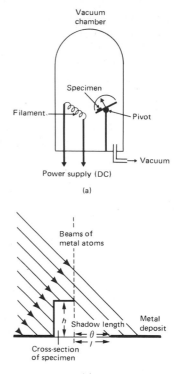

Figure 3-3 The technique of shadow-casting. (a) A specimen is mounted at a known angle to a source of heated, vaporized heavy metal atoms in an evacuated chamber. When the metal is vaporized, it moves in straight lines, depositing a layer of electron-dense metal around the specimen as shown in (b). The height of the particle can be determined from the relation: length of shadow (l) = particle height (h) cot θ, where the angle θ is that made by the specimen grid to the metal source. This method, which is one of the first developed for improving electron microscope contrast, is still used for protein studies. The technique is also used to spread thin specimen-supporting carbon films on a specimen grid.

techniques in electron microscopy. Since uncertainty exists concerning the chemical groups to which particular electron stains attach, it follows that there is some doubt as to the chemical nature of the structures revealed. This is a problem, for example, in the study of thin lipoprotein membranes (Korn, 1966, Robertson, 1960; see also Figure 3-9). In addition to the various types of artifacts that may be produced when preparing specimens for electron microscopy, the electron microscope gives a static and highly magnified image of systems that are dynamic and of dimensions far below those normally encountered.

3-4. Histochemistry and Cytochemistry. A variety of chemical, physical, and biological methods used for the identification, localization, or quantitative analysis of the chemical constituents of cells and tissues are part of the disciplines of histochemistry and cytochemistry.

Some reagents react specifically with certain cellular compounds, producing colored complexes that can be observed in the microscope. One of the earliest and best known examples of this type of chemical analysis is the localization and identification of DNA by the Feulgen reaction. DeRobertis et al. (1965)

describe this and other histochemical techniques. Enzymes and enzyme reaction products are commonly identified today in the electron, as well as the light, microscope (Sahr and Zeitler, 1965; Pease, 1964; Shugar, 1962).

The x-ray microscope can be used to examine larger and thicker specimens than the electron microscope, for example, small whole organisms such as insects, but its resolution is presently limited to about 500 Å. x-Ray microautoradiography is used to measure small quantities of mineral and trace elements as small as 10^{-15} g/μ^2 (Engström, 1966). Other recent developments in cellular analysis include the use of ultrasonic microscopes (Fry and Dunn, 1962) and scanning electron microscopes (Crewe, 1966).

Optical methods such as colorimetry and absorption spectrophotometry have been adapted for microwork with single cells. Like most optical methods, these have the advantage of not requiring cellular disturbance or disruption. Biological compounds can be localized, and sometimes quantified, if they possess specific absorption maxima. Classic examples of this type of analysis include the detection of nucleic acids by microspectrophotometry (Casperson, 1941; 1956), and the detection of cytochromes in cells as well as the

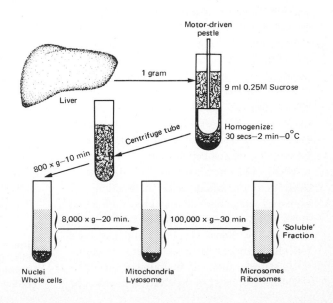

Figure 3-4 Diagram of the steps used in cell fractionation by the process of differential centrifugation.

measurement of changes in them during oxidative metabolism (Chance and Williams, 1956). The latter is one of the few cases where it has been possible to study enzyme activity *in vivo*. Fluorescence microscopy and spectrophotometry are used to locate naturally fluorescing materials or materials that will react specifically with a fluorescent dye.

Autoradiography is used to locate radioactive elements in organs, tissues, or cells. When a specimen has been previously exposed to a tagged compound and is then placed on a photographic emulsion, the radiation emitted by the incorporated isotope will cause dark spots to appear on the film (Ficq, 1959; Stevens, 1966). This is but one of many uses of isotopes in biology (Wolf, 1964).

3-5. Cellular Fractionation. Cell membranes may be disrupted by sonic treatment, homogenization, blending, freeze-thawing, or enzymatic activity. Such disruption releases the cellular contents into the medium (Anderson, 1956; Umbreit et al., 1964). By centrifuging such suspensions at varying centrifugal forces for different times, various cellular fractions can be isolated (Claude, 1946; Hogeboom, 1955; deDuve, 1965; deDuve et al., 1962).

Differential centrifugation was the first technique used to obtain isolated fractions of cellular components (Figure 3-4). The fractions obtained do not represent pure preparations of individual cellular organelles or molecules. A fraction may also consist of damaged cellular components. For example, the microsomal fraction is comprised of the broken fragments of the endoplasmic reticulum membranes. The technique, based on differences in the mass and density of various cellular components, has been invaluable in assigning functions to particular cell structures. It is easier to perform biochemical tests on isolated fractions than on whole cells. A fraction, for example, will contain all the mitochondria of a given volume of tissue, not just the few hundred to a few thousand, to be found in a single cell. Biochemical analyses generally require more material than can be found in one cell.

The development of the electron microscope

made possible the identification of the major components of cellular fractions. It also allowed comparison of the isolated structures with normal cellular constituents, therefore, any alterations produced by the methodology can be detected.

Gradient density centrifugation is now commonly used in place of differential centrifugation because it permits separation of components that are close in density. In this method (Figure 3-5) a homogenate or cell fraction is placed on the top of a series of stratified layers of sucrose or cesium chloride solutions that increase in density from the top to the bottom of the tube. A continuous density gradient may also be used. Upon centrifugation, components are retained within that layer whose density most closely approaches their own (deDuve, 1965; deDuve et al., 1959; Oster and Yamamoto, 1963).

High-speed centrifugation and ultracentrifugation (with forces up to $260,000 \times g$) are used to separate out components of mixtures of macromolecules and viruses. These methods of centrifugation may also be used to obtain molecular weights or molecular shapes and sizes (Kegeles, 1968). During the characterization of macromolecules especially, the use of more than one method is required to help eliminate the possibility that artifact or impurity is obscuring the true nature or activity of the component of interest.

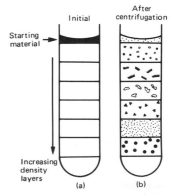

Figure 3-5 Schematic representation of the initial (a) and final (b) distribution of fractions following centrifugation in the technique of gradient density centrifugation.

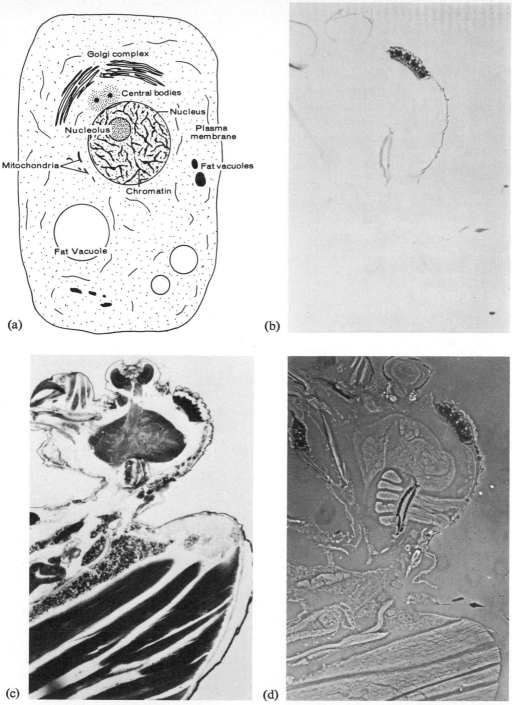

(a)

(b)

(c)

(d)

Figure 3-6 (a) The generalized cell model that resulted from observations made with the light microscope (compare with Figure 3-7). (b) Light microscope views of a mosquito head (100×) unstained. (c) after staining, (d) phase. The pigments of the compound eye stand out in all three photomicrographs. Note the better resolution of structures in the stained and phase micrographs as compared with the untreated section. [Photomicrographs supplied through the courtesy of Dr. William Romoser].

This brief survey of some of the methods used to isolate, purify, observe, and analyze cells and their components has been included here because knowledge of cellular structure and organization is basic to the understanding of many physiological mechanisms. It is through these techniques that such knowledge is obtained, and the correctness of physiological hypotheses will depend upon the accuracy of the methods. Examples of the need and use of these methods will be given in many places throughout this textbook.

Cellular Structures and Organization

3-6. The Generalized Cell. Classical concepts of cellular organization, exemplified by the work of E. B. Wilson (1925), are diagrammed in Figure 3-6. A generalized cell is a model only; real cells, for example, have a dynamic existence that cannot be portrayed in diagrams. Real cells also differ from the model in size, shape, and structural detail. But such a model

points out the known major structural features of cells. The classical model, resulting from light microscope observations (Figure 3-6b,c,d), shows the presence of an outer limiting membrane—the **plasma membrane** or **plasmalemma**; a mass of cytoplasm containing a membrane-bounded nucleus; and a variety of organelles, vacuoles, and granules.

The introduction of the electron microscope into cellular studies altered the model of the generalized cell (Figure 3-7). Especially in highly metabolizing cells such as secretory cells, an array of membranous channels and vesicles occur that often appear interconnected and that can sometimes be seen to link with the outer limiting membrane or with the nuclear membrane. Organelles such as the mitochondria, which in the light microscope appear as rod-shaped bodies, in the electron microscope are seen to be membranous elements with a highly organized structure. Figure 3-8 shows a comparison between a cell seen in the light and in the electron microscopes.

The matrix of the cell, originally called the

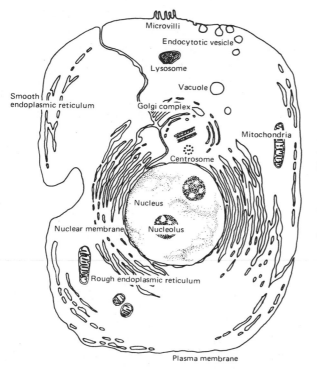

Figure 3-7 A model of the generalized cell resulting from observations made with the electron microscope. Note the increase in structural detail over that of the classical model of Figure 3-6. The model shown here is most representative of secretory cells of the mammalian liver or pancreas. The structural elements shown differ considerably in detail and arrangement from cell type to cell type.

protoplasm, in the electron microscope is shown to contain a high degree of structured components. There has been some question about retaining the name protoplasm, but the term has a use in referring to the common type of material found in all cells as long as no attempt is made to define it chemically.

The cell is best considered as a three-phase system (Robertson, 1964). The nucleocytoplasmic matrix, connected through pores in the nuclear membrane, is one phase. The membranes themselves constitute a second phase. And the contents of membranous elements are a third phase. The membranes collectively can be thought of as a single phase because there is a seeming continuity between them, at least during certain stages in the life history of most cells. Also, as we shall see in later sections, there is evidence that one type of membranous organelle often is derived from another.

The presence of membranes prevents free mixing of the phases, and cellular organization is such that foreign substances from outside the cell do not normally come into contact with cellular cytoplasm. Materials, when they do enter the cell (excluding water, ions, and other small molecules), are first surrounded by a segment of the plasma membrane that forms a vesicle containing the foreign substances. The type of organization just described has many important effects on the functioning of cells and also means that there can exist many microenvironments within the cell. Biological organization is a topic of interest at all structural levels (Allen, 1967; Ehret, 1960; Goodwin, 1963; Harris, 1963; Kuyper, 1962; Schmitt, 1945; and Weiss, 1962).

3-7. Compartmentation. Membranes play a vital role in the cell and organism. They act as barriers to free diffusion and they govern a differential exchange of materials across biological surfaces. Their presence is responsible for differences in chemical composition between the inside and outside of cells. The nature of cells is such that they can be thought of as collections of compartments separated from one another by membranes. But all levels of biological organization show compartmentation, not all necessarily due to the presence of physical barriers such as membranes. The idea of compartmentation is important for the analysis of either material exchanges or chemical transformations in living systems.

Riggs (1963) defined a compartment as follows:

If a substance is present in a biological system in several distinguishable forms or locations: and if it passes from one form or location to another form or location at a measurable rate, then each form or location constitutes a separate compartment of that substance.

Chemical transformations and material movements can be lumped together in this way because they are studied in terms of mathematical models which are almost identical (see Chapters 4 and 7). A few examples may clarify the concept of compartmentation.

Water makes up about 75 per cent of the weight of an average animal; but water is not homogeneously distributed throughout the animal's body. Body water can be classified into two major compartments: (1) intracellular water and (2) extracellular water. These compartments differ physically from each other and also differ chemically. Neither of these compartments is homogeneous, and each can be divided into further compartments. There are as many intracellular water compartments as there are cells—in fact, there are more because each cell contains further compartments. The major compartments of extracellular water are considered in Chapter 11.

Intracellular water is either free or bound. The highly charged proteins in the cell can attract to them a firmly bound water layer that is distinct from the unbound water in the cell. The latter is mobile compared with the protein-bound water. Bound water is generally not available for acting as a solvent for other cellular molecules. In this case no physical barrier is needed to compartmentalize the water.

Other water compartments exist within the cell. The water contained within mitochondria for example, may not exchange freely with

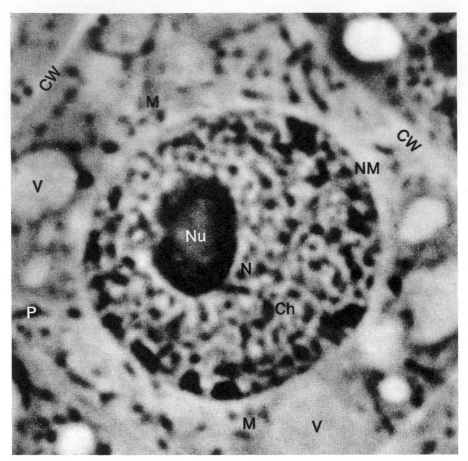

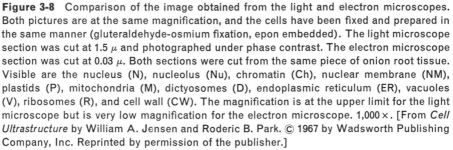

Figure 3-8 Comparison of the image obtained from the light and electron microscopes. Both pictures are at the same magnification, and the cells have been fixed and prepared in the same manner (gluteraldehyde-osmium fixation, epon embedded). The light microscope section was cut at 1.5 μ and photographed under phase contrast. The electron microscope section was cut at 0.03 μ. Both sections were cut from the same piece of onion root tissue. Visible are the nucleus (N), nucleolus (Nu), chromatin (Ch), nuclear membrane (NM), plastids (P), mitochondria (M), dictyosomes (D), endoplasmic reticulum (ER), vacuoles (V), ribosomes (R), and cell wall (CW). The magnification is at the upper limit for the light microscope but is very low magnification for the electron microscope. 1,000×. [From *Cell Ultrastructure* by William A. Jensen and Roderic B. Park. © 1967 by Wadsworth Publishing Company, Inc. Reprinted by permission of the publisher.]

other cellular water and has a different physical and chemical environment. Uncertainty about water and other compartments often leads to experimental difficulties. A fluid compartment may exist as a 100 Å thick layer about cells and can contain concentrations of materials quite different from the rest of the extracellular water. Such a compartment is difficult to detect or study and yet may be of importance in cellular activity. For example, the distribution of ions across the plasma membrane is a critical factor in the production and maintenance of bioelectric potentials, but it is difficult to determine the external ion concentration in many cases because the thin layer of boundary water may be the important ion site.

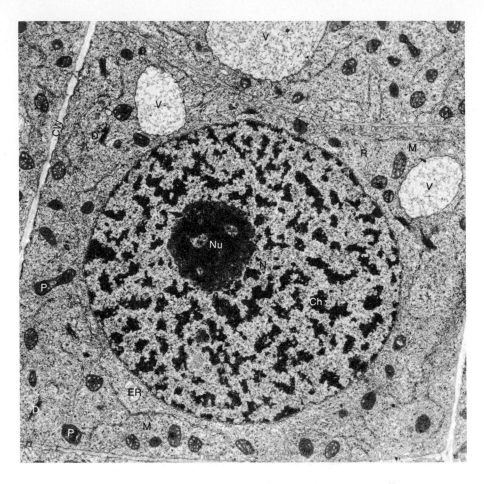

Because compartments exist at all levels of biological structure, the concept has many uses when studying material exchanges in animals. We shall see that the idea is valuable when analyzing the distribution and functions of ions; the flows and concentrations of respiratory gases; the control and distribution of heat; the kinetics of chemical systems (Berman et al., 1962a,b); and fluid movements in circulatory systems. Since ions, enzyme substrates, and other substances often attach to specific sites on macromolecules, these chemical sites have been considered as individual compartments. But such extensions of the compartment concept may not be justified (Goodwin, 1963).

3-8. Gross Membrane Structure. The diagrams of Figure 3-9 give a good example of how electron microscopy has changed the concept of membrane structure. In the light microscope the plasma membrane appears as a 0.2 μ thick line surrounding the cell (Figure 3-9a). Low resolution electron microscopy resolved this single line into a series of light and dark bands (Figure 3-9b). The arrows labeled "1" show the size of a 0.2 μ band at this magnification; obviously no structure of this thickness is present. Some electron microscopists thought that "3" was the actual membrane, but others felt that only a single line next to the cytoplasm should be considered the plasmalemma. The outer dense line measuring ~ 150 Å they called the **basement membrane**.

At high resolution (Figure 3-9c) the original single inner line now appears to consist of two dense lines separated by a middle light zone "4". The basement membrane is not a

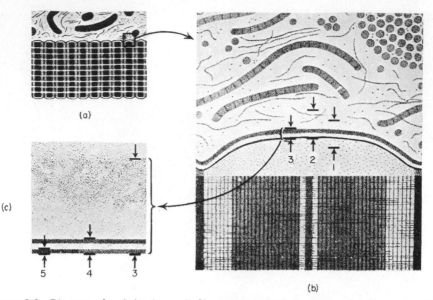

Figure 3-9 Diagram of a skeletal muscle fiber as seen (a) in the light microscope. (b) The rectangular area in (a) is enlarged in (b) to illustrate the structures shown by electron microscopy. A further enlargement is shown in (c). For description see text. [Redrawn from J. D. Robertson (1960). "The molecular structure and contract relationships of cell membranes." *Prog. Biophys.* **10**: pp. 343–418. By permission of Pergamon Press, New York.]

membrane in the usual sense. It represents a denser zone of the matrix or ground substance in which cells lie.

The combination of two outer dense lines and a less dense central zone is the **unit membrane** (Robertson, 1960). The unit membrane hypothesis states that all biological membranes have a similar, three-layered appearance in the electron microscope. The two outer dense lines may represent monomolecular layers of protein; the less dense inner zone may be the location of a bilayer of lipid molecules. This model agrees with that of the older Davson-Danielli membrane model (see Chapter 6).

The thickness of the unit membrane varies according to the method of membrane preparation for electron microscopy and also to the source of the membrane material (Yamamoto, 1965). The thickness is usually considered to be 75 Å. Each dense line is about 20 Å thick, and the inner less dense layer is about 35 Å. The latter dimensions are those resulting from permanganate fixation. When

osmic acid is used, the dimensions increase to a total thickness of about 100 Å.

The concept of the unit membrane has been criticized (Korn, 1966, 1969). There is some question as to the chemical substances to which various electron stains are attaching. Unfortunately, membrane organization at the molecular level is not known, and this hinders understanding of microscopic observations and the building of good models of membrane structure and function. It is also questionable whether differences in thickness of different membrane preparations represent actual membrane differences or differences in preparative methods. Remember that membranes as seen in the electron microscope have lost their water content. Figure 3-10 is a high resolution electronmicrograph of the unit membrane of a red blood cell.

Density gradient centrifugation and analytical ultracentrifugation, together with other methods, are now being used to isolate and study membrane constituents. For example, Barclay et al. (1967) isolated three large

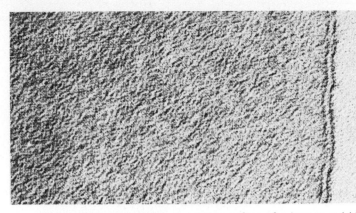

Figure 3-10 Unit membrane at the surface of a human red blood cell (280,000 ×). [From J. D. Robertson (1966) "The Unit Membrane and the Danielli-Davson Model" in *Intracellular Transport* (K. B. Warren, editor), *Symp. Int. Soc. Cell. Biol.* **5**, 1–31. © 1966 Academic Press, New York. By permission.]

lipoprotein complexes from rat liver cell plasma membranes. Enzyme markers and electron microscopy were used to determine how free of cytoplasmic contaminants the membranes were.

Green and Perdue (1966) proposed that biological membranes are built up of lipoprotein macromolecular repeating units. Such a model would account for many of the chemical and physical properties of membranes. Frey-Wyssling (1957); Sjöstrand (1963) and others have reported seeing globular particles as repeating units in a variety of animal and plant cell membranes. Many complex reaction systems are known to be associated with large macromolecular complexes in membranes. These include the mitochondrial electron transport system, the mitochondrial enzyme system catalyzing tricarboxylic acid cycle reactions, the endoplasmic reticular system for protein synthesis, and the mitochondrial enzyme complex for fatty acid synthesis (see the review by Green and Perdue, 1966).

The model, then, of large lipoprotein complexes acting as structural and functional elements within the membrane helps to explain in part the dynamic nature of membranes and complements the morphological model of the unit membrane.

In addition to the thin plasma membrane, extraneous coats surround many cells. They are especially prominent about the eggs of marine invertebrates and of amphibians. A major constituent of these coats is **mucin**—a glycoprotein. Mucins are also found forming protective coatings of cell surfaces lining gastrointestinal tracts. A mixture of glycoproteins and polysaccharides called **glycocalyx** is found about the base of most epithelial and endothelial cells (Bennett, 1963). The nature and role of these coatings, as well as of the extracellular matrix generally will be considered in later sections. Further information can be found in Brandt, 1962; Pierce et al., 1963.

3-9. Mitochondria. In the following sections we shall consider briefly the nature and general functions of some of the major cell organelles. Excellent sources of detailed information and electron micrographs of cellular structures include Bloom and Fawcett (1962); Fawcett (1966); Jensen and Parks (1967); Brachet and Mirsky (1959–1964).

Mitochondria are usually rod-shaped organelles, although in some cells they are spherical or ovoid. They have a limiting double unit membrane (Figure 3-11). Their size is variable depending on cell type, but in many cells they are about $0.5\,\mu$ wide and $3\,\mu$ long. The number of mitochondria in a cell depend on its type and stage of development. A normal mouse

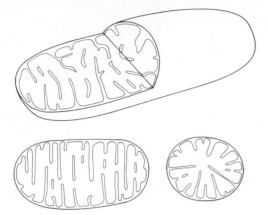

Figure 3-11 Schematic drawings of mitochondria. The double outer membrane is shown together with the invaginations of the inner membrane that form the mitochondrial cristae. As indicated, mitochondria occur in different shapes.

liver cell—a metabolically active cell type—contains about 2,500 mitochondria.

The inner unit membrane of the mitochondrial limiting double membrane invaginates into the body of the mitochondrion, forming **cristae** that occur either as sheets or tubules. Cristae are most common in the mitochondria of cells with a high metabolic activity. The membranes of the cristae contain the enzymes and other molecules associated with oxidation-reduction reactions and phosphorylation reactions associated with energy metabolism. Fatty acid synthesis also occurs in mitochondria.

Negative staining and freeze-etching methods have given evidence in the electron microscope that the mitochondrial membrane consists of subunits about 100 Å in diameter (Parson, 1967; Fernández-Moran et al., 1964). The subunits associated with inner membranes of mouse liver mitochondria, and the outer membrane of rat liver mitochondria are shown in Figure 3-12. The cristal subunits have been named elementary particles (EP). The subunits are too small to contain a complete complement of oxidation-reduction enzymes and coenzymes and they may be artifacts. But they do seem to represent some small repeating unit along the cristal membrane.

There have been suggestions that mitochondria arise from other membranous structures. Suggested origins include the endoplasmic reticulum (Robertson, 1961) and the nuclear membrane (Pappas and Brandt, 1959). However, with the discovery that mitochondria contain DNA (see Section 2-13) there was a revival of older ideas that mitochondria could replicate and that one of their functions was to assure the genetic continuity of the mitochondria. It has been shown experimentally that mitochondria synthesize proteins, and fission and replication have been seen in electron microscope studies of *Neurospora* (see the review by Wagner, 1969). It has also been shown that when a pulse of radioactive choline is fed to a choline requiring strain of *Neurospora* during the log phase of rapid growth, the mitochondria take up the choline. Observation of the mitochondria after the period of choline pulse injection showed that all mitochondria contained the same amount of radioactivity. This makes it appear that new mitochondria are derived from older mitochondria—probably by fission following a period of growth. Mitochondrial protein appears to be derived both from mitochondrial protein synthesis, presumably directed by mitochondrial DNA and also from protein synthesis in the cytoplasm, directed by nuclear DNA. The antibiotic chloramphenicol, at low concentrations, inhibits protein synthesis in the mitochondria but has no effect on protein synthesis in the endoplasmic reticulum—another indication that the two processes are different.

Mitochondria are dynamic organelles. For example, Palade (1952) found that in fasted guinea pigs mitochondria could surround and absorb lipid droplets mobilized as energy sources in the cells. Although mitochondria are usually considered as cytoplasmic entities, Brandes et al. (1965) found mitochondrion-like particles in the nucleus. The structure and function of mitochondria have been thoroughly reviewed by Lehninger (1964). Their metabolic activities will be considered in Chapter 4.

3-10. The Endoplasmic Reticulum. The cytoplasm of many cells contains a membranous system of vesicles, flattened sacs, cisternae, and

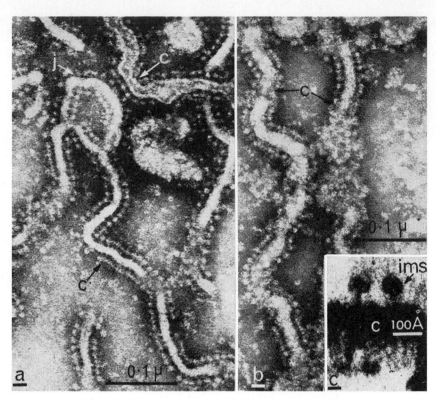

Figure 3-12 The subunit associated with the inner membranes or cristae of mitochondria. (a) Part of a mitochondrion from a negatively stained preparation of mouse liver. A few of the cristae (C) are shown. They consist of long filaments that branch at some points (J). The surfaces of the cristae are covered with projecting subunits (192,000 ×). (b) Negatively stained cristae (C) prepared by spreading isolated lysed rat liver mitochondria. The subunits on the cristae appear similar to those of Figure 3-12(a) (192,000 ×). (c) Higher magnification—a few subunits from the same preparation as (b). The spherical heads are 75 to 80 Å in diameter and the stems 30 to 35 Å wide and 45 to 50 Å long. Reversed print (770,000 ×). [From D. F. Parsons (1963) *Science* **140** : 985–987. Copyright 1963 by the American Association for the Advancement of Science. Reprinted by permission.]

canals, originally called the "ergastoplasm" by Garnier in 1897, and now known as the **endoplasmic reticulum**. Part of the endoplasmic reticulum bears small granules (∼150 Å in diameter). These are the RNA-containing **ribosomes**, and this portion of the endoplasmic reticulum is the rough endoplasmic reticulum (RER). The RER is the site of protein synthesis in the cytoplasm.

The part of the endoplasmic reticulum that lacks granules is the smooth endoplasmic reticulum (SER), which has connections with the outer unit membrane of the nucleus and in some cases with the plasma membrane (Figure 3-7). In some cells it also appears to connect

with the Golgi complex and is also sometimes intimately associated with the mitochondria. The appearance and therefore the probable functions of the endoplasmic reticulum depend on the cell type.

The endoplasmic reticulum in addition to being the site of cytoplasmic protein synthesis is also thought to function as a transport and storage system. However, the nature of the contents of the endoplasmic reticulum are not known. In many striated muscle cells the endoplasmic reticulum (here called the sarcoplasmic reticulum) takes on a specialized appearance and functions in triggering contractile events after stimulation by muscle cell

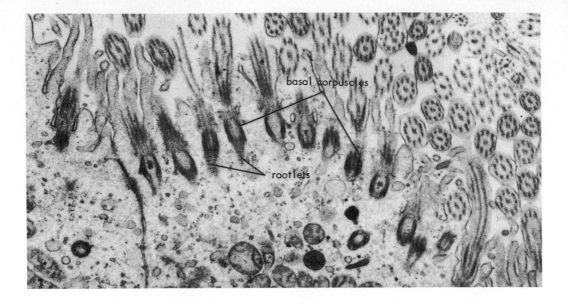

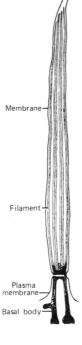

Membrane—

Filament—

Plasma
membrane—

Basal body—

Figure 3-13 (a) Electron micrograph of surface of dog tracheal epithelium showing basal corpuscles of cilia and rootlets with axial periodicity. Those cilia seen in cross section exhibit the typical 9+2 filament arrangement (14,000X). [By permission from J. A. Freeman (1964) *Cellular Fine Structure.* © 1964 The Blakiston Division, McGraw-Hill Book Company.] (b) Diagram of ciliary structure.

action potentials (Chapter 10). The endoplasmic reticulum also is the source of the nuclear membrane formed during cell mitosis. As already mentioned, the microsomal fraction resulting from homogenization and differential centrifugation is a preparative derivative of the endoplasmic reticulum.

Much of cellular compartmentation is due to the presence of the endoplasmic reticulum. This system possesses chemically different membranes in different parts of the cell and can therefore produce different environments within the cell with regard to chemical composition and reactivity.

3-11. Other Cellular Elements. The **golgi complex** is a mass of smooth-surfaced membranous canals and vesicles (Figure 3-7), sometimes considered to be a specialized portion of the SER. It usually has a characteristic position and polarity in the cell, close to the nucleus (Grassé, 1957). It is thought to function in secretory and intracellular digestive processes (Caro and Palade, 1964) and is considered the source of primary lysosomes—membrane-bounded particles containing hydrolytic enzymes. The functions and interrelationships of these various membrane systems are discussed in the next section.

Centrioles are membranous and fibrous bodies found in the cytoplasm. They are cylindrical elements composed of nine bundles of three **microtubules**. Centrioles are centers for spindle fiber formation during cell division. The spindle fibers are also formed of microtubules 230 to 270 Å in diameter. Microtubules are also found in the cytoplasm of mature cells.

Centrioles form the bases of cilia and flagella whose structure is an almost universal $9+2$ arrangement of fibers (Figure 3-13). The nine peripheral fibers are extensions of the centriolar groupings of microtubules. Many visual receptor cells, for example, retinal rod cells, are derived from centrioles and cilialike bodies. It appears that centrioles in some way can initiate and control the formation of fibrous protein structures. The ultrastructure of microtubules was first described by Ledbetter and Porter (1964) working with plant cells.

The **nucleus** contains the genetic material and also functions in the control of cellular activities such as protein synthesis, cellular growth, and cellular reproduction. The nucleus contains most of the DNA of a cell. The DNA is associated with chromatin or chromosomal structures and special proteins such as histones. A major structural feature of the nucleus is the **nucleolus**—a body composed of compact RNA-protein granules similar to ribosomes. The nucleolus also contains long fibers, presumably composed of protein and perhaps serving as structural elements.

The double nuclear membrane (composed of two unit membranes) is one of the few that have been shown to contain large (~ 150 Å in diameter) pores. Because of the presence of these openings, which may be closed with some type of diaphragm, the nuclear membrane is not considered as a complete barrier between the cytoplasm and nucleoplasm. Discussions of nuclear functioning can be found in Watson (1965), Grell (1964).

The membranes of all of these structures, as well as those surrounding the many other vesicles and vacuoles of the cell, all have the appearance of unit membranes in the electron microscope. Because membranes of different organelles have different functions and because membrane structure and function can vary markedly within the same organelle, it appears that membrane differences lie almost entirely at the molecular level, not at the grosser level of unit membrane structure seen in the microscope.

3-12. The Lysosome Concept. In order to present some idea of the complexity and dynamic interactions of cellular organization, the lysosome concept and its relation to cellular digestion and secretion will be considered. The lysosome concept originated with the work of deDuve (1959) who in 1955 isolated a cellular fraction, intermediate in density between the mitochondrial and microsomal fractions. Upon treatment of this fraction with techniques that destroy cell membranes, a high degree of hydrolytic activity was released. Hydrolytic enzymes are the catalysts that break down larger molecules to smaller ones and are thus degradative or digestive enzymes. deDuve suggested that these enzymes were confined within a membranous vesicle in order to protect normal cellular materials from their catalytic action.

Following the biochemical description of lysosomes by deDuve, Novikoff et al. (1956) observed in the electron microscope a membrane-bounded vesicle that was smaller than mitochondria and that proved identical with the **dense bodies** earlier seen in sections from rat liver cells. The biochemical entity of deDuve was finally shown to be the same as the

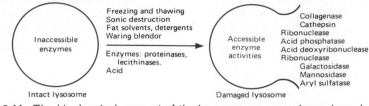

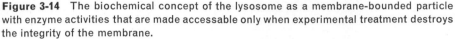

Figure 3-14 The biochemical concept of the lysosome as a membrane-bounded particle with enzyme activities that are made accessible only when experimental treatment destroys the integrity of the membrane.

morphological entity of Novikoff. The **lysosome** is now defined as a unit-membrane bounded vesicle containing a large complement of various hydrolytic enzymes—especially acid phosphatase, an enzyme used as a marker because its presence and location in cells is easily determined by histochemical methods. Although different lysosomes may differ in their particular enzyme content, they are considered to be part of the apparatus for the intracellular digestion of macromolecules. Figure 3-14 illustrates the concept of the lysosome and the types of enzyme activities associated with this organelle. The discovery of lysosomes and the subsequent need to determine the sites of intracellular enzyme activities was responsible in part for stimulating the development of new histochemical procedures for enzyme identification and localization in both the light and electron microscopes (Caro, 1961; Holt and Hicks, 1962; Sheldon et al., 1955).

Once it had been determined that lysosomes were heterogeneous in size, distribution, and enzyme content and once it had been shown that lysosomes were implicated in intracellular digestion (deDuve and Wattiaux, 1966; de-Reuch and Cameron, 1963), the lysosome concept was extended to include lysosomal relationships to other cellular organelles and to the processes of ingestion, digestion, and secretion by cells.

Many cells can engulf particles (**phagocytosis**) or liquid droplets of the extracellular medium (**pinocytosis**). Collectively these activities by which materials are brought into cells are termed **endocytosis**. Endocytosis is begun by an invagination of the plasma membrane, which traps a portion of the extracellular

medium (Figure 3-15). Further invagination and finally a pinching-off of the membranous invagination produces an intracellular vesicle —the **phagosome**—whose membrane, derived from the plasma membrane, prevents the extracellular material from coming in contact with the cytoplasm. The phagosome is thought to combine with a primary lysosome to form a **digestive vacuole**. After enzymatic breakdown of the phagosome's contents—presumably accompanied by the diffusion of small molecules such as amino acids or glucose across the membrane and into the cytoplasm—the digestive vacuole, now termed a **residual body**, may be eliminated from the cell together with its undigestible materials. The residual body is excreted by the cell through a process that is the reverse of endocytosis—called **exocytosis**.

The **primary lysosome**—the lysosome that has not combined with any other type of vesicle—may arise either from the endoplasmic

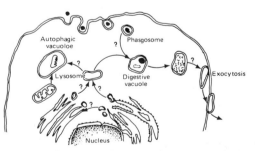

Figure 3-15 Diagramatic representation of the formation of a phagocytic vesicle by endocytosis. The invagination of the membrane and pinching off of an intracellular vesicle results in part of the external medium being brought into the cytoplasm and yet remaining separated from it by the membranous covering. Phagosomes can combine with lysosomes to form digestive vacuoles.

reticulum, the Golgi complex, or both (Dalton, 1961; Novikoff et al., 1964). The endoplasmic reticulum is the site of protein synthesis, and the hydrolytic enzymes of the lysosomes must originate in the RER. The Golgi complex is thought to form by the coalescence of small vesicles that break off from the endoplasmic reticulum. Primary lysosomes are formed when membranous vesicles break off from the Golgi complex. The latter also is involved in the storage of cellular secretory products. These materials leave the cell as needed by the movement of vesicles to the plasma membrane, followed by their secretion by exocytosis. These ideas are hypothetical and are derived from electron microscopic observations that do not allow the sequence of events to be followed in the living cell.

Lysosomes provide a mechanism for digesting and destroying cellular organelles when the latter are aged, no longer needed as in metamorphosis, or when the cell is under starvation conditions and needs a source of energy. A body, similar in appearance to a phagosome, is sometimes seen in cells. This **autophagic vesicle** appears to digest damaged or unneeded organelles. For example, partially decomposed mitochondria are seen within these vesicles. Lysosomes might also be the agents responsible for cell death, either accidentally or in response to some type of control mechanism.

Studies on lysosomal structure, function, and origins, emphasizes the interrelationships of cellular membranes and organelles. It raises questions concerning the mechanisms by which membranes invaginate upon proper stimulation, fuse together or pinch off vesicles, or show other dynamic activities.

Criticisms of these ideas have been raised (for example, Conchie and Levvy, 1963; Levvy and Conchie, 1964), and it is true that more work is required to clarify the nature of these complex systems. Although an early criticism was that only rat liver cells had been studied, lysosomes have now been found in the cells of all animals studied including the protozoans (Elliot, 1965).

Lysosomes are not the only type of membranous vesicles containing enzymes in cells.

Improved differential and density gradient centrifugation techniques have shown that a second group of vesicles, the **microbodies**, also contain enzymes: including catalase, D-amino acid oxidase, and urate oxidase.

3-13. Stimulation of Endocytosis. The engulfment of particles by endocytosis is a widespread property of cells throughout the animal kingdom. Amoeboid phagocytic cells are found in the tissues of all metazoans (Wagge, 1955). Phagocytic cells function in excretion, digestion, repair and regeneration of tissues. In higher organisms phagocytes remove debris and protect animals from invading microorganisms. Often phagocytes are organized into organ systems. **Lymphogenous organs** in annelids, cephalopods, and some arthropods are masses of cells in blood sinuses. They are bound together by networks of connective tissue (Huff, 1940). **Nephrophagocytes**, found in annelids, molluscs, and echinoderms, are clumps of cells scattered throughout the body tissues. They function in both excretion and phagocytosis. **Phagocytic organs** consist of reticular networks filled with phagocytes and are usually located in the pericardial spaces, where they are bathed by the blood. These organs are found in insects, crustaceans, molluscs, and some annelids and nematodes. In the vertebrates the phagocytic system is the **reticulo-endothelial** or **macrophage system**. It consists of both fixed and wandering cells including leucocytes and amoeboid cells and also contains extensive reticular networks. In mammals phagocytic activity is displayed by a variety of cells including blood monocytes and neutrophils; microglial cells of the central nervous system; Kupffer cells of the liver, bone marrow, spleen, and lymph nodes; and by tissue macrophages.

Epithelial cells lining the digestive tracts of most animals also act as phagocytes. In Lamellibranchiata phagocytic amoebocytes take up food particles from the digestive tract or mantle cavity and transport them to other tissues (Yonge, 1937; Owen, 1966). Similar activities are found in Echinodermata, Coelenterata, Platyhelminthes, and so forth.

Excretory cells, known as **athrocytes**, pick

up and store solid particles or dissolved substances from the body fluids of many animals. In this way toxic or unneeded materials are removed. In birds and mammals part of the phagocytic system is found in the form of compact cellular clumps in the lymph channels. The lymphatic fluids are filtered through this system (Young, 1957). Clark and Clark (1930) found macrophages in the tail region of developing amphibian larvae before any development of the circulatory system. Phagocytosis by wandering cells may serve to transport materials to and away from regions of development.

Obviously a wide array of endocytic activity occurs in organisms. An important question concerns the nature of the stimuli required to initiate endocytosis. Knisely et al. (1948) found that all cells lining mammalian liver sinusoids were potential phagocytes (Kupffer cells) and that to be phagocytized a particle needed to be coated with a protein present in the blood. Lison (1948) and Lison and Smulders (1949) found that there were two types of Kupffer cells. Type G cells phagocytized particles with a diameter of 80 Å or greater and bearing a negative charge. Type F cells phagocytized small particles only.

Thus it appears that in this case phagocytosis occurs only when the membrane of the phagocytic cell can recognize a particle by its protein coating. Selectivity presumably depends on the nature of the molecules constituting the cellular membrane, particularly on the nature of the membrane proteins. Certain macrophages ingest old red blood cells, and they must be able to distinguish between the surfaces of old and young erythrocytes. Related activities are the molecular and cellular mechanisms associated with antigen-antibody reactions. Macrophages are known to fix antigens and possibly may produce antibodies (see Raffel, 1961).

The initiation of pinocytosis in amoebae has been well studied. Pinocytosis is stimulated by the presence of proteins in the medium if the pH is such that they are positively charged. Carbohydrates have no effect. Some amino acids and salts induce pinocytosis; cations

being more effective than anions (Chapman-Andresen, 1962). Nucleic acids are also taken up by some cells (Ledoux, 1955).

In amoebae pinocytosis occurs in two steps. First, there is deposited on the surface of the cell a heavy coat of protein. This coat is placed on the mucopolysaccharide layer that covers the plasma membrane. Protein is selectively adsorbed until its concentration may be 50 times greater than that of the medium. Second, the cell invaginates the area of protein-coated membrane. Pinocytosis is a form of active transport—a movement into or out of a cell of a material against an electrochemical gradient. The movement requires the expenditure of metabolic energy (see Chapter 6).

The electron microscope has shown that most cells undergo **micropinocytosis**—a form of pinocytosis in which the vesicles are small (~650 Å). Micropinocytotic vesicles have been seen in endothelial cells lining capillaries, Schwann cell and other neuroglia associated with neurons, macrophages, muscle cells, and many others. The pinocytotic process has been reviewed by Holter (1960) and Rustad (1964).

Although it seems evident that proteins are the primary stimulating agents for inducing endocytosis, further understanding of the process requires more knowledge about the molecular architecture of plasma membranes. In the next section other similar selective activities of this membrane will be described.

The Extracellular Environment

3-14. Intercellular Contacts. To this point I have treated the cell as a discrete entity; but most cells of metazoan animals do not live in an isolated or free state, rather they live in, act on, and are acted upon by an extracellular matrix, which in many cases forms a loosely structured connective tissue.

The plasma membrane is more than a barrier to the free movements of materials into and out of cells. It must also function as a protective device: undergoing and in certain conditions resisting mechanical changes. It must also serve as a selective mechanism for interactions with other cells and the materials of the extracellular environment. In most cases, the cells of a tissue do not come into direct contact. There is a small gap between the adjacent plasma membranes. The width of this gap ranges from 75 to 500 Å depending on cell type and animal. Within this gap is an amorphous appearing material usually containing small fibrils. This material is often thought of as a cement substance, and adjacent epithelial cells, for example, are bound to-

gether so strongly by the material that extremely strong forces are required to separate them.

There are often found specialized regions of contact between the plasma membranes of adjacent cells. In epithelial tissues is found the **desmosome**—a region where the innermost layer of each plasma membrane is considerably thickened and an intercellular space of about 240 Å is maintained. A mass of dense material is seen in the cytoplasm adjacent to each membrane and a mass of amorphous material is seen in the intercellular space. Fine fibrils— the **tonofibrils**—run from the membranes into the cytoplasm. The nature of desmosomes, as well as that of other types of membrane junctions, is diagrammed in Figure 3-16. The desmosome is a discontinuous area of cell contact. It does not run along the membrane for large distances. Whenever desmosomes are found in the membranes of adjacent cells, they occur in pairs, but single desmosomes were seen when the cell membrane bordered on a basement membrane (Kelly, (1966).

In the **tight junction** the outer layers of the unit membranes of two adjacent cells fuse so that there is no intercellular space. This type of junction, which lacks tonofibrils and other characteristics of desmosomal structure, has been variously called the **nexus** (especially in smooth muscle and cardiac muscle), the **synaptic disc** (for junctions between neurons), and the **zona occludens**.

The **intermediary junction (zonula adhaerens)** has an intercellular space about 200 Å wide containing an amorphous material of relatively low density. In epithelial tissues the intermediary junction is usually continuous. The cytoplasm adjacent to the membranes is dense but lacking in tonofibrils.

Tight junctions and desmosomes may represent regions where the passage of materials between cells is restricted. The tight junction is thought to be a pathway of low electrical resistance between cells. This permits the ready passage of electrical currents through masses of cardiac and smooth muscle tissues and allows them to act in a coordinated fashion. There are many structural and functional

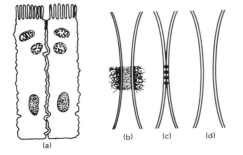

Figure 3-16 Schematic representations of some types of cellular junctions. (a) Epithelial cells such as those lining the intestinal tract often possess microvilli—infoldings of the surface plasma membrane—which give the appearance of the brush border in the light microscope. Often the membranes between adjacent cells interdigitate. The typical gap between the membranes of adjacent cells serves as a pathway for the movement of water and some solutes. Toward the luminal surface the membranes may fuse forming a darkened region—the terminal bar. Typically unit membranes of adjacent cells do not touch. (b) A desmosome type of contact between adjacent cells, often found in endothelial, epithelial, and some nerve-nerve contacts. Although there is a gap between adjacent unit membranes, the gap is filled with an amorphous material, and the outer layer of each unit membrane presents a thickened appearance. Tonofibrils run into the cytoplasm of each cell from these thickened regions. (c) A tight junction where the outer layers of two adjacent unit membranes fuse, obliterating the gap between them. Often a beaded appearance of this middle layer is seen in the electron microscope. (d) The typical type of junction between cells in which a gap exists between the unit membranes. The gap ranges in width from about 75 to 750 Å depending on the cell types.

varieties of both desmosomes and tight junctions, and specific roles will be described for these intercellular contacts in the appropriate chapters to follow.

As illustrated in Figure 3-16, cellular membranes are also distinguished by infoldings, invaginations, and interdigitations. In the light microscope many epithelial cell layers showed the presence of a brush border; in the electron microscope this has been shown to be the result of many small folds in the membrane— the **microvilli**. Microvilli are 0.6 to 0.8 μ long and about 1,000 Å in diameter. Generally their presence greatly increases the surface available for absorption of materials. They are especially prominent in intestinal epithelium, mesothial cells, and hepatic cells. The kidney tubule also possesses a brush border on certain of its epithelial cells, but the dimensions of

the microvilli are larger than those of the intestinal epithelial microvilli.

Aggregation, adhesion, and selectivity of interaction are important intercellular activities. It has long been known that cells can adhere together and aggregate in a selective fashion. Wilson (1907) devised a technique for separating the cells of sponges by squeezing the animal through cheesecloth (see also Galtsoff, 1925). If cells from a single animal are allowed to reaggregate, they do so forming a new sponge. If the dispersed cells of two different species are mixed, the cells separate according to species and form two new sponges. There is a species specific selective force operating in the aggregation of the cells. This is one example of the ability of plasma membranes to recognize and react with one another.

Aggregation and adhesion reactions of cells

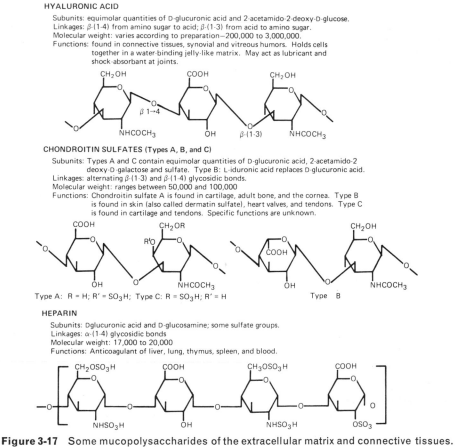

HYALURONIC ACID

Subunits: equimolar quantities of D-glucuronic acid and 2-acetamido-2-deoxy-D-glucose.
Linkages: β-(1-4) from amino sugar to acid; β-(1-3) from acid to amino sugar.
Molecular weight: varies according to preparation—200,000 to 3,000,000.
Functions: found in connective tissues, synovial and vitreous humors. Holds cells
together in a water-binding jelly-like matrix. May act as lubricant and
shock-absorbant at joints.

CHONDROITIN SULFATES (Types A, B, and C)

Subunits: Types A and C contain equimolar quantities of D-glucuronic acid, 2-acetamido-2
deoxy-D-galactose and sulfate. Type B: L-iduronic acid replaces D-glucuronic acid.
Linkages: alternating β-(1-3) and β-(1-4) glycosidic bonds.
Molecular weight: ranges between 50,000 and 100,000
Functions: Chondroitin sulfate A is found in cartilage, adult bone, and the cornea. Type B
is found in skin (also called dermatin sulfate), heart valves, and tendons. Type C
is found in cartilage and tendons. Specific functions are unknown.

Type A: R = H; R′ = SO_3H; Type C: R = SO_3H; R′ = H   Type B

HEPARIN

Subunits: Dglucuronic acid and D-glucosamine; some sulfate groups.
Linkages: α-(1-4) glycosidic bonds
Molecular weight: 17,000 to 20,000
Functions: Anticoagulant of liver, lung, thymus, spleen, and blood.

Figure 3-17 Some mucopolysaccharides of the extracellular matrix and connective tissues. These polysaccharides are almost always associated with proteins.

are important during embryological development (Moscona, 1957, 1963; Steinberg, 1963; Curtis, 1962). Tissue culture methods are often useful in studying these properties of cells because individual cell types can be maintained and analyzed while isolated from other cells. For example, Moscona found that when a mixture of dispersed mammalian kidney and fibroblast cells were grown in tissue culture, there was an aggregation of each cell type into a different mass. When a mixture of chicken and mammalian cells were kept under similar conditions, all kidney cells collected in one mass, all fibroblast cells in another. In this case there was no species specificity, only a cell type specificity. Again, an understanding of the mechanisms underlying these processes awaits further information on the structure of membranes.

3-15. The Intercellular Matrix. Most cells live in a loose connective tissue framework in which four phases are distinguishable: the ground substance (also called cement substance or intercellular matrix); fibrillar elements including fibers of the proteins collagen, elastin, or reticulin; a scattering of cells; and a mixture of ions, other small molecules, and water.

The major constituents of the ground substance include polysaccharides composed of hexosamine or glucuronic acid and often esterified with sulfuric acid (Figure 3-17). Unfortunately, relatively little is known about the origins, organization, or specific activities of the ground substance. The basement membrane is found in many epithelial layers. This membrane is considered by some to be a special secretion of the epithelial cells and by others to be a denser zone of the ground substance.

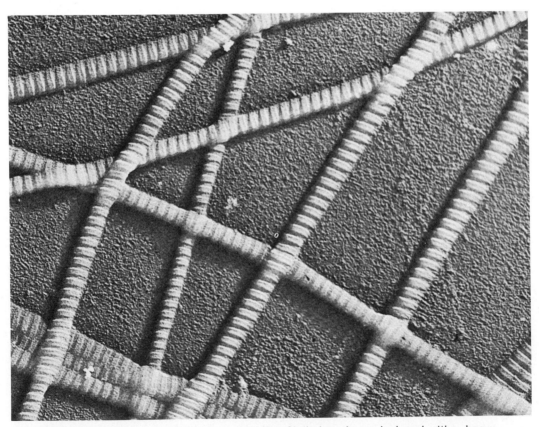

Figure 3-18 Fibrils of collagen from skin. The fibrils have been shadowed with a heavy metal to bring out their banded structure. [Courtesy of J. Gross].

3-16. Collagen. The major fibrous constituent of connective tissues—those that support and strengthen—is the protein collagen. It is an unusual protein on several counts. It is ubiquitous—and is found in all metazoan animals. Further it is present in large amounts: it has been estimated that collagen accounts for about 30 per cent of the total protein of mammals (Neuberger, 1955). The comparative biochemistry of collagen has been reviewed by Gross (1963); Jackson (1964) discusses its role in cellular activity.

Collagen has an unusual structure also. Some 30 per cent of its amino acids are in the

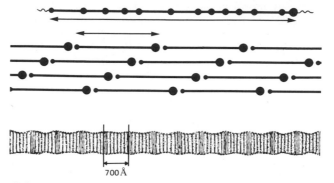

Figure 3-19a Schematic representation of the organization of collagen fibers. Top, tropocollagen molecule with head and tail regions and also regions of interactions with other tropocollagen molecules. Middle, collagen fibril with the 700 Å repeat period due to the staggered arrangement of tropocollagen molecules in the fibril. Bottom, sketch of a collagen fibril with its bands seen in the electron microscope. The alignment of head and tail regions in staggered array leads to the appearance of the dense main bands. The alignment of other reactive regions leads to the inter-period spacing.

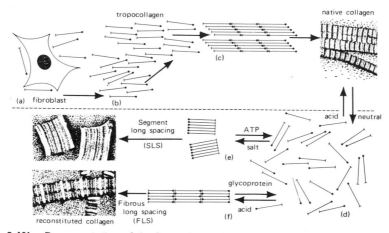

Figure 3-19b Representation of the formation and reconstitution of collagen. Fibroblasts (a) synthesize and secrete tropocollagen molecules (b) into the extracellular medium. The tropocollagen forms native collagen (c) with the 700 Å repeat period. Solubilization of collagen fibrils in acid leads to the formation of tropocollagens (d) which in the presence of ATP aggregate head to head (e), forming long segment spacing fibers (SLS). In the presence of glycoprotein, tropocollagen molecules unite (f) to form fibrous long spacing fibrils (FLS) in which adjacent molecules point in opposite directions. The long spacing of 2,800 Å results from a lateral aggregation of tropocollagen molecules without overlap. [Figure 3-19a and Figure 3-19b from "Collagen" by Jerome Gross, *Scientific American*, Oct. 1961. © 1961 by Scientific American, Inc. All rights reserved.]

group: glycine, hydroxylysine, and hydroxy-proline (Harding, 1965; Harkness, 1961; Harrington and von Hippel, 1961). Collagen exists as large fibers in most tissues and has a banded appearance with a repeat period of about 640Å (Figure 3-18). Various experimental treatments of collagen lead to the formation of a variety of abnormal fibers (Figure 3-19). The interpretation of such results is that the fibroblast cells of the intercellular matrix synthesize and secrete tropocollagen—a small precursor molecule of collagen—into the extracellular space where association of tropocollagen fibrils produces the larger collagen. The collagen fibril is a three-chain coiled helix (Rich and Crick, 1961); the aggregation of collagen fibrils produces the collagen fiber.

The formation of collagen fibers from simpler protein fibrils constitutes an information content increase of the system; for as stated in Chapter 1, the increase in complexity and orderliness of a system constitutes an increase in information (somewhat in the fashion that a random series of simple words may be meaningless, but putting them together in a sentence can increase the information content). Seemingly, tropocollagen is incapable of producing the matrix organization needed for cellular interactions and the development of cellular structures during growth and development of the organism. Only the larger, more complex collagen fiber can provide the environment needed to perform these functions. The information content in this case is probably the number and arrangement of chemical side-groupings available for intereaction with other materials.

Collagen is an extremely strong material. In addition to being part of the loose connective tissues, it is also found in tissues such as tendon, where its strength is required to withstand the forces of muscular contraction. Collagen is one of the few fibrous proteins about whose macromolecular organization something is known (Schmitt, 1959), but the mechanisms that regulate tropocollagen synthesis and secretion are not understood. Also unanswered are questions concerning the

effects of aging on collagen and connective tissues in general or the mechanisms that regulate the production of three-dimensional organization of the extracellular matrix during the development of organisms. Such problems are also of concern in tissue regeneration. Specific roles of fibrous proteins such as collagen and elastin will be considered in the appropriate following chapters.

3-17. Discussion. In this chapter we have briefly reviewed some of the more important structural features of cells and have indicated their general functions. Although many structural features have been seen in the electron microscope, it has not been possible in many cases to study their physiological activities directly. In the following chapters we shall examine how cellular structures are often modified to serve specialized purposes in different cell types.

Although the general chemical composition of many cell organelles is known and although their structure and functions are based on the classes of molecules described in Chapter 2, as yet their detailed molecular architecture is not known. This is especially true of membranes, and we shall see in Chapters 6 and 7 that many paradoxes remain concerning the structure and functions of membranes.

Another area requiring much more study concerns the role and nature of the extracellular materials. It has been difficult up to this time even to separate single substances from the heterogeneous collection of carbohydrates, proteins, and salts that make up the cellular ground substance. The latter itself is difficult to isolate in any suitable quantities.

In the next chapter, the specific activities and organization of certain parts of the cell in supplying energy will be considered. The intra- and intercellular organization discussed in this chapter is maintained only by the expenditure of energy. In Chapter 4 the interacting roles of protein enzymes, lipid and carbohydrate energy sources, coenzymes and energy-storage and transfer molecules will be described. These active components are often organized into the structure of membranes.

References and Readings

Agar, A. (1961). "Interpretation of electron micrographs." In: **Techniques for Electron Microscopy.** (D. Kay, ed.), pp. 26–29. Oxford: Blackwell Scientific Publications.

Allen, J. M., ed. (1967). **Molecular Organization and Biological Functions.** New York: Harper and Row, Publishers, Inc. 243 pp.

Anderson, N. G. (1956). "Techniques for the mass isolation of cellular components." In: **Physical Techniques in Biological Research,** Vol. 3. (G. Oster and A. W. Pollister, eds.), pp. 299–352. New York: Academic Press, Inc.

Bahr, G. F., and E. H. Zeitler, eds. (1965). **Quantitative Electron Microscopy.** Baltimore: The Williams & Wilkins Company. 615 pp.

Barclay, M., R. K. Barclay, E. S. Essner, V. P. Skipski, and O. Terebus-Kekish (1967). "Plasma membranes of rat liver: isolation of lipoprotein macromolecules." *Science* **156:** 665–667.

Barer, R. (1966). "Phase contrast and interference microscopy in cytology." In: **Physical Techniques in Biological Research,** Vol. 3, part A, 2nd ed. (A. W. Pollister, ed.), pp. 1–56. New York: Academic Press, Inc.

Bennett, H. S. (1963). "Morphological aspects of extracellular polysaccharides." *J. Histochem. Cytochem.* **11:** 2–13.

Berman, M., E. Shahn, and M. F. Weiss (1962a). "The routine fitting of kinetic data to models: a mathematical formalism for digital computers." *Biophys. J.* **2:** 275–288.

Berman, M., M. F. Weiss, and E. Shahn (1962b). "Some formal approaches to the analysis of kinetic data in terms of linear compartmental systems." *Biophys. J.* **2:** 289–302.

Birbeck, M. S. C. (1961). "Techniques for the electron microscopy of proteins." In: **Analytical Methods of Protein Chemistry.** (P. Alexander and R. J. Block, eds.), pp. 3–22. New York: Pergamon Press, Inc.

Bloom, W. and D. W. Fawcett (1962). **A Textbook of Histology,** 8th ed. Philadelphia: W. B. Saunders Company. 720 pp.

Brachet, J. and A. E. Mirsky, eds. (1959–1964). **The Cell: Biochemistry, Physiology, and Morphology.** 6 volumes. New York: Academic Press, Inc.

Brandes, D., B. H. Schofield, and E. Anton (1965). "Nuclear mitochondria." *Science* **149:** 1373–1374.

Brandt, P. W. (1962). "A consideration of the extraneous coats on the plasma membrane." *Circulation* **26** (Suppl.): 1075–1091.

Burton, E. F. and W. H. Kohl (1946). **The Electron Microscope.** New York: Reinhold Publishing Corporation. 325 pp.

Caro, L. G. (1961). "Electron microscopic radioautography of thin sections: the Golgi zone as a site of protein concentrations in pancreatic acinar cells." *J. Biophys. Biochem. Cytol.* **10:** 37–45.

Caro, L. G. and G. E. Palade (1964). "Protein synthesis, storage, and discharge in the pancreatic exocrine cell." *J. Cell. Biol.* **20:** 473–495.

Caspersson, T. O. (1941). "Studien uber den Eiweissumsatz der Zelle." *Naturwissenschaften* **28:** 33–43.

Caspersson, T. O. (1956). "Quantitative cytochemical determinations on endonuclear structures." *Cold Spring Harbor Symp. Quant. Biol.* **21:** 1–18.

Chance, B. and G. R. Williams (1956). "The respiratory chain and oxidative phosphorylation." *Adv. Enzymol.* **17:** 65–134.

Chapman-Andresen, C. (1962). "Studies on pinocytosis in amoebae." *Comp. Rend. Lab. Carlsberg* **33:** 73–264.

Clark, E. R. and E. L. Clark (1930). "Observations on the macrophages of living amphibian larvae." *Am. J. Anat.* **46:** 91–148.

Claude, A. (1946). "Fractionation of mammalian liver cells by differential centrifugation. II. Experimental procedures and results." *J. Exp. Med.* **84:** 61–89.

Conchie, J. and G. A. Levvy (1963). "The significance of subcellular fractionation as applied to certain hydrolytic enzymes." *Biochem. Soc. Symp.* **23:** 103–107.

Crewe, A. V. (1966). "Scanning electron microscopes: is high resolution possible?" *Science* **154:** 729–738.

Curtis, A. S. G. (1962). "Cell contact and adhesion." *Biol. Rev. Cambridge Phil. Soc.* **37**: 82–129.

Dalton, A. (1961). "Golgi apparatus and secretion granules." In: **The Cell,** Vol. 2 (J. Brachet and A. Mirsky, eds.), pp. 603–619. New York: Academic Press, Inc.

deDuve, C. (1959). "Lysosomes, a new group of cytoplasmic particles." In: **Subcellular Particles.** (T. Hayashi, ed.), *Am. Physiol. Soc. Symp.*, pp. 128–159. New York: The Ronald Press Company.

deDuve, C. (1964). "Principles of tissue fractionation." *J. Theoret. Biol.* **6**: 33–59.

deDuve, C. (1965). "The separation and characterization of subcellular particles." *Harvey Lect.* **59**: 49–87.

deDuve, C. and J. Berthet (1954). "Differential centrifugation and enzymes." *Int. Rev. Cytol.* **3**: 225–275.

deDuve, C., J. Berthet, and H. Beaufay (1959). "Gradient centrifugation of cell particles: theory and applications." *Prog. Biophys.* **9**: 325–369.

deDuve, C. and R. Wattiaux (1966). "Functions of lysosomes." *Ann. Rev. Physiol.* **28**: 435–492.

deDuve, C., R. Wattiaux, and P. Baudhuin (1962). "Distribution of enzymes between subcellular fractions of animal tissues." *Adv. Enzymol.* **24**: 291–358.

deReuck, A. V. S. and M. P. Cameron, eds. (1963). **Lysosomes.** Little, Brown and Co., Boston. 446 pp.

DeRobertis, E. D. P., W. W. Nowinski, and F. A. Saez (1965). **Cell Biology,** 4th ed. Philadelphia: W. B. Saunders Company. 446 pp.

Ehret, C. F. (1960). "Organelle systems and biological organization." *Science* **132**: 115–123.

Elliot, A. M. (1965). "Primary lysosomes in *Tetrahymena pyriformis*." *Science* **149**: 640–641.

Engström, A. (1966). "X-ray microscopy and x-ray absorption analysis." In: **Physical Techniques in Biological Research,** Vol. 3, part A. (A. W. Pollister, ed.), pp. 87–171. New York: Academic Press, Inc.

Engström, A. and J. B. Finean (1968). **Biological Ultrastructure,** 2nd ed. New York: Academic Press, Inc. 326 pp.

Fawcett, D. W. (1966). **The Cell: Its Organelle and Inclusions.** Philadelphia: W. B. Saunders Company. 348 pp.

Fernández-Moran, H. (1964). "A macromolecular repeating unit of mitochondrial structure and function." *J. Cell Biol.* **22**: 63–100.

Ficq, A. (1959). "Autoradiography." In: **The Cell,** Vol. 1. (J. Brachet and A. E. Mirsky, eds.), pp. 67–90. New York: Academic Press, Inc.

Freundlich, M. M. (1963). "Origin of the electron microscope." *Science* **142**: 185–188.

Frey-Wyssling, A. (1957). **Macromolecules in Cell Structure.** Cambridge, Mass.: Harvard University Press. 112 pp.

Fry, W. J. and F. Dunn (1962). "Ultrasound: analysis and experimental methods in biological research." In: **Physical Techniques in Biological Research.** Vol. 4 (W. L. Nastuk, ed.), pp. 261–394. New York: Academic Press, Inc.

Galtsoff, P. (1925). "Regeneration after dissociation. I. Behavior of dissociated cells of *Microciona prolifera* under normal and altered conditions." *J. Exp. Zool.* **42**: 183–222.

Goodwin, B. C. (1963). **Temporal Organization in Cells.** New York: Academic Press, Inc. 164 pp.

Grassé, P. P. (1957). "Ultrastructure, polarite et reproduction de l'appareil de Golgi." *C.R. Acad. Sci.* **245**: 1278–1281.

Green, D. E. and J. F. Perdue (1966). "Membranes as expressions of repeating units." *Proc. Nat. Acad. Sci. (U.S.)* **55**: 1295–1302.

Grell, K. G. (1964). "The protozoan nucleus." In: **The Cell,** Vol. 6. (J. Brachet and A. E. Mirsky, eds.), pp. 1–79. New York: Academic Press, Inc.

Gross, J. (1963). "Comparative biochemistry of collagen." In: **Comparative Biochemistry,** Vol. 5 (M. Florkin and H. S. Mason, eds.), pp. 307–346. New York: Academic Press, Inc.

Hall, C. E. (1955). "Electron densitometry of stained virus particles." *J. Biophys. Biochem. Cytol.* **1**: 1–12.

Hall, C. E. (1966). **Introduction to Electron Microscopy,** 2nd ed. New York: The McGraw-Hill Book Company, Inc. 397 pp.

Harding, J. J. (1965). "The unusual links and cross-links of collagen." *Adv. Protein Chem.* **20**: 109–190.

Hardy, A. C. and F. H. Perrin (1932). **The Principles of Optics.** New York: The McGraw-Hill Book Company, Inc. 632 pp.

Harkness, R. D. (1961). "Biological functions of collagen." *Biol. Rev.* **36**: 399–463.

Harrington, W. F. and P. H. von Hippel (1961). "The structure of collagen and gelatin." *Adv. Protein Chem.* **16**: 1–138.

Harris, R. J. C., ed. (1963). **Biological Organization at the Cellular and Supracellular Level.** New York: Academic Press, Inc. 264 pp.

Hogeboom, G. H. (1955). "Fractionation of cell components of animal tissues." In: **Methods in Enzymology.** Vol. 1. (S. P. Colowick and N. O. Kaplan, eds.), pp. 16–19. New York: Academic Press, Inc.

Hogeboom, G. H., W. C. Schneider, and G. E. Palade (1948). "Cytochemical studies of mammalian tissues. I. Isolation of intact mitochondria from rat liver: some biochemical properties of mitochondria and submicroscopic particles." *J. Biol. Chem.* **172**: 619–636.

Holt, S. and R. Hicks (1962). "Specific staining methods for enzyme localization at the subcellular level." *Brit. Med. Bull.* **18**: 214–219.

Holter, H. (1960). "Pinocytosis." *Int. Rev. Cytol.* **8**: 481–504.

Huff, C. G. (1940). "Immunity in invertebrates." *Physiol. Rev.* **20**: 68–88.

Jackson, S. F. (1964). "Connective tissue cells." In: **The Cell,** Vol. 6. (J. Brachet and A. E. Mirsky, eds.), pp. 387–520. New York: Academic Press, Inc.

Jenkins, F. A. and H. E. White (1957). **Fundamentals of Optics,** 3rd ed. New York: The McGraw-Hill Book Company, Inc. 637 pp.

Jensen, W. A. and R. B. Park (1967). **Cell Ultrastructure.** Belmont, Cal.: Wadsworth Publishing Co. 60 pp.

Kegeles, G. (1968). "Ultracentrifugation." In: **Physical Techniques in Biological Research,** Vol. 2, 2nd ed. (D. H. Moore, ed.), pp. 67–84. New York: Academic Press, Inc.

Kelley, D. E. (1966). "Fine structure of desmosomes, hemidesmosomes and an adepidermal globular layer in developing newt epidermis." *J. Cell Biol.* **28**: 51–72.

Knisely, M. H., E. H. Bloch, and L. Warner (1948). "Selective phagocytosis. I. Microscopic observations concerning the regulation of blood flow through the liver and other organs and the mechanisms and rate of phagocytic removal of particles from the blood." *Kgl. Danske Videnskab. Selskab. Biol. Skrifter.* **4**: 1–93.

Korn, E. D. (1966). "Structure of biological membranes." *Science* **153**: 1491–1498.

Kuyper, C. M. A. (1962). **The Organization of Cellular Activity.** New York: American Elsevier Publishing Co. 272 pp.

Ledbetter, M. C. and K. R. Porter (1964). "Morphology of microtubules of plant cells." *Science* **144**: 872–874.

Ledoux, L. (1965). "Uptake of DNA by living cells." *Prog. Nucleic Acid Res. Molec. Biol.* **4**: 231–267.

Lehninger, A. L. (1965). **The Mitochondrion.** New York: W. A. Benjamin, Inc. 263 pp.

Levvy, G. A. and J. Conchie (1964). "The subcellular localization of the 'lysosomal' enzymes and its biological significance." *Prog. Biophys.* **14**: 105–129.

Lison, L. (1948). "Phénomenes d'athrocytose discriminante dans les cellules de Kupffer des amphibiens." *Compt. Rend. Assoc. Anat.* **52**: 329–334.

Lison, L. and J. Smulders (1949). "Les éléments discriminants du systéme reticulo-endothélial chez la grenouille." *Compt. Rend. Soc. Biol.* **143**: 573–575.

Martin, L. C. (1955). "The light microscope." In: **Physical Techniques in Biological Research,** Vol. 1. (G. Oster and A. W. Pollister, eds.), pp. 326–438. New York: Academic Press, Inc.

Mazia, D. (1956). "The life history of the cell." *Am. Sci.* **44**: 1–32.

Moscona, A. (1957). "The development *in vitro* of chimaeric aggregates of dissociated embryonic chick and mouse cells." *Proc. Nat. Acad. Sci. (U.S.)* **43**: 184–194.

Moscona, A. (1963). "Studies on cell aggregation: demonstration of materials with selective cell-bonding activity." *Proc. Nat. Acad. Sci. (U.S.)* **49**: 742–747.

Neuberger, A. (1955). "Metabolism of collagen under normal conditions." *Symp. Soc. Exp. Biol.* **9**: 72–84.

Novikoff, A. B., E. Essner, and N. Quintana (1964). "Golgi apparatus and lysosomes." *Fed. Proc.* **23**: 1010–1022.

Oster, G. and M. Yamamoto (1963). "Density gradient techniques." *Chem. Rev.* **63**: 257–268.

Osterberg, H. (1955). "Phase and interference microscopy." In: **Physical Techniques in Biological Research,** Vol. 1. (G. Oster and A. W. Pollister, eds.), pp. 326–438. New York: Academic Press, Inc.

Owen, G. (1966). "Digestion." In: **Physiology of Mollusca,** Vol. 1. (K. M. Wilbur and C. M. Yonge, eds.), pp. 53–96. New York: Academic Press, Inc.

Palade, G. E. (1952). "Functional changes in structure of cell components." In: **Subcellular Particles.** (T. Hayashi, ed.), pp. 64–83. New York: The Ronald Press Company.

Pappas, G. D. and B. W. Brandt (1959). "Mitochondria. I. Fine structure of the complex patterns in the mitochondria of *Pelomyxa carolinensis* Wilson (*Chaos chaos* L)." *J. Biophys. Biochem. Cytol.* **6**: 85–90.

Parsons, D. F. (1967). "Mitochondrial structure: two types of subunits on negatively stained mitochondrial membranes." *Science* **140**: 985–987.

Pease, D. C. (1964). **Histological Techniques for Electron Microscopy,** 2nd ed. New York: Academic Press, Inc. 381 pp.

Pierce, G. B., A. R. Midgley, and J. Sri Ram (1963). "The histogenesis of basement membrane." *J. Exp. Med.* **117**: 339–348.

Porter, K. R. and J. Blum (1953). "A study of microtomy for electron microscopy." *Anat. Rec.* **117**: 685–712.

Raffel, S. (1961). **Immunity,** 2nd ed. New York: Appleton-Century-Crofts, 646 pp.

Rich, A. and F. H. C. Crick (1961). "The molecular structure of collagen." *J. Mol. Biol.* **3**: 483–507.

Riggs, D. S. (1963). **The Mathematical Approach to Physiological Problems.** Baltimore: The Williams & Wilkinson Company. 445 pp.

Robertson, J. D. (1960). "The molecular structure and contact relationships of cell membranes." *Prog. Biophys.* **10**: 343–418.

Robertson, J. D. (1961). "Cell membranes and the origin of mitochondria." In: **Regional Neurochemistry. Proc. 4th Intern. Neurochem. Symp.** (S. S. Key, ed.), pp. 497–530. New York: Pergamon Press, Inc.

Robertson, J. D. (1964). "Unit membranes: a review with recent new studies of experimental alterations and a new subunit structure in synaptic membranes." In: **Cellular Membranes in Development.** (M. Locke, ed.), pp. 1–79. New York: Academic Press, Inc.

Rustad, R. C. (1964). "The physiology of pinocytosis." In: **Recent Progress in Surface Science.** (J. F. Danielli, K. G. A. Pankhurst, and A. C. Riddiford, eds.), Vol. 2, pp. 353–376. New York: Academic Press, Inc.

Schmitt, F. O. (1945). "Ultrastructure and the problem of cellular organization." *Harvey Lect.* **40**: 249.

Schmitt, F. O. (1959). "Interaction properties of elongate protein macromolecules with particular reference to collagen (tropocollagen)." In: **Biophysical Science.** (J. L. Oncley, ed.), pp. 349–358. New York: John Wiley & Sons, Inc.

Sheldon, H., H. Zetterquist, and D. Brandes (1955). "Histochemical reactions for electron microscopy: acid phosphatase." *Exp. Cell Res.* **9**: 592–596.

Shugar, D. (1962). "Quantitative staining in histo- and cytochemistry." *Prog. Biophys.* **12**: 153–211.

Siegel, B. M., ed. (1964). **Modern Developments in Electron Microscopy.** New York: Academic Press, Inc. 432 pp.

Sjöstrand, F. S. (1963). "A new ultrastructural element of the membranes in mitochondria and of some cytoplasmic membranes." *J. Ultrastruct. Res.* **9**: 340–361.

Sriram, J., S. Tawde, G. Pierce, and A. Midgely (1963). "Preparation for antibody-ferritin conjugates for immuno-electron microscopy." *J. Cell Biol.* **17**: 673–674.

Steinberg, M. S. (1963). "ECM: its nature, origin and function in cell aggregates." *Exp. Cell Res.* **30**: 257–279.

Stevens, A. R. (1966). "High resolution auto-radiography." In: **Methods in Cell Physiology,** Vol. 2 (D. M. Prescott, ed.), pp. 255–310. New York: Academic Press, Inc.

Umbreit, W. W., R. H. Burris, and J. F. Stauffer (1964). **Manometric techniques,** 4th ed. Minneapolis: Burgess Publishing Company. 305 pp.

Wachtel, A. W., M. E. Gettner, and L. Ornstein (1966). "Microtomy." In: **Physical Techniques in Biological Research,** Vol. 3, Part A, 2nd ed. (A. W. Pollister, ed.), pp. 173–250. New York: Academic Press, Inc.

Wagge, L. E. (1955). "Amoebocytes." *Int. Rev. Cytol.* **4**: 31–78.

Wagner, R. P. (1969). "Genetics and pheno-genetics of mitochondria." *Science* **163**: 1026–1031.

Watson, J. D. (1965). **Molecular Biology of the Gene.** New York: W. A. Benjamin, Inc. 494 pp.

Watson, M. (1956). "Carbon films and speci-men stability." *J. Biophys. Biochem. Cytol.* **2** (Suppl.): 31–36.

Weiss, P. (1962). "From cell to molecule." In: **The Molecular Control of Cellular Activity.** (J. M. Allen, ed.), pp. 1–72. New York: The McGraw-Hill Book Company, Inc.

Weiss, P. (1963). "The cell as a unit." *J. Theoret. Biol.* **5**: 389–397.

Williams, R. C. and R. W. G. Wyckoff (1944). "The thickness of electron microscopic specimens." *J. Applied Phys.* **15**: 712–715.

Williams, R. C. and R. W. G. Wyckoff (1945). "Electron shade micrography of the tobacco mosaic virus protein." *Science* **101**: 594–596.

Wilson, E. B. (1925). **The Cell in Development and Heredity,** 3rd ed. New York: The Macmillan Company. 1232 pp.

Wilson, H. V. (1907). "Some phenomena of coalescence and regeneration in sponges." *J. Exp. Zool.* **5**: 245–253.

Wolf, G. (1964). **Isotopes in Biology.** New York: Academic Press, Inc. 173 pp.

Yamomoto, T. (1963). "On the thickness of the unit membrane." *J. Cell Biol.* **17**: 413–422.

Yonge, C. M. (1937). "Evolution and adaptation in the digestive system of the metazoa." *Biol. Rev. Cambridge Phil. Soc.* **12**: 87–115.

Young, J. Z. (1957). **The Life of Mammals.** Oxford: The Clarendon Press. 820 pp.

Zernike, F. (1955). "How I discovered phase contrast." *Science* **121**: 345–349.

Some Principles of Thermodynamics

4-1. Energy and Work. The maintenance of biological organization, the synthesis of macromolecules, cellular movements, in fact almost all biological activities require the expenditure of energy. Before considering the mechanisms by which cells and organisms convert the chemical energy of nutrients into other useful forms of energy, it will be helpful to examine the laws governing the exchanges and transformations of energy in systems generally. Such laws are part of **thermodynamics**—the mathematically based physical science founded upon two major principles and centered upon the concept of energy. The ideas of thermodynamics, originally derived for physical and chemical systems, apply equally well to biological ones.

Energy is an intangible and conserved property of a system. Energy is a concept only, devised originally by physicists to describe certain phenomena of the external world. Absolute energies cannot be measured, only changes in a system can be measured. Energy is defined as the ability to do mechanical work. In turn, work (W) is defined as the product of a force (F) exerted times the distance (s) moved in the direction of the force. In the integral calculus this is expressed by

$$W = \int_1^2 F\, ds \qquad (4.1)$$

where W is the work done by F in moving from position 1 to position 2. The symbol of differentiation is d—used to indicate infinitesimal changes in some variable.

There are two main types of energy. Kinetic energy is the energy associated with movement—the motion of large bodies, or molecules, or atoms. Potential energy is the energy of position or of bound energy that can be released to produce kinetic energy. Part of the energy changes of a system may include conversions between kinetic and potential energies.

Historically, mechanical energy was the first to be considered, and it was considered that in an ideal, frictionless system, mechanical energy was conserved. All real systems

Chapter 4

Energetics, Enzyme Kinetics, and Metabolism

possess friction, which must be overcome by the expenditure of mechanical energy. In order to preserve the idea of energy conservation in real systems, the energy concept was first expanded to include heat as a form of energy. Joule showed experimentally that when water in a container was stirred mechanically with a paddle, the temperature of the water increased by a number of heat units equivalent to the units of mechanical energy expended in the stirring. Later the concept of energy was further enlarged to include electrical, magnetic, chemical, mass, and other energies.

Accordingly thermodynamic work may appear in any of several forms, all of which have the dimensions of energy: ML^2T^{-2}, where M is the mass, L the length or distance, and T is the time. Physical entities are qualitatively described by their dimensions. The four basic dimensions are mass, length, time, and temperature (θ). Since force is defined as mass times acceleration (MLT^{-2}), the final expression for force or energy is ML^2T^{-2}. Table 4-1 lists some of the more common types of energies found in biological systems and also gives the units in which they are usually expressed. Each work term is the product of a capacity factor and a potential factor. The properties of a system that depend on its size are **extensive properties** or **capacity factors** and include mass, volume, electric charge, and internal energy. The properties that do not depend on the size of the system are **intensive**

properties or **potential factors** and include pressure, temperature, and concentration of chemical components.

Energy changes in a system are associated with changes in the state of the system as reflected by changes in the properties of the system (such as those listed in Table 4-1). In turn, systems are characterized thermodynamically by their properties. Systems whose properties have identical values are said to be in the same state. Although the state of a given system is characterized by an infinite number of variables, it is found that only a few of these need be specified in order to adequately describe a system from an energetic standpoint.

In thermodynamics a system is considered to be some arbitrary and convenient portion of matter selected for study and includes the surroundings or environment—except for the isolated system defined in the next paragraphs, this description of a system is for all practical purposes identical with that described in Chapter 1. There is, however, one restriction in that thermodynamics is concerned only with energy changes in macroscopic systems. Molecular mechanisms or systems too small to possess macroscopic properties are outside its scope, although Tribus (1966) has attempted to develop thermodynamic concepts to cover the microscopic level of organization.

Three types of thermodynamic systems are recognized (Prigogine, 1962):

Table 4-1   Some Energy Terms and Their Units

Type of work	Potential factor	Capacity factor	Units
Mechanical			
physical (Ms, or Fs)	Distance, s	Mass, M	ergs
		Force, F	
expansional (PV)	Pressure, P	Volume, V	liter-atm.
Thermal (TS)	Temperature, $T^\circ\,C$	Entropy, S	calories
Electrical (EZ)	Potential, E	Charge, Z	joules
Chemical ($M\mu$ or $n\mu$)	Potential, μ	Mass, M or n	calories

Conversion of units: 1 erg $= 2.389 \times 10^{-8}$ calories $= 1 \times 10^{-7}$ joules $= 9.87 \times 10^{-11}$ liter-atm.

1. Isolated systems, which exchange neither matter nor energy with their surroundings.
2. Closed systems, which may exchange or transform energy with their surroundings but which do not exchange matter.
3. Open systems, in which both energy and matter may be exchanged with their environments.

The isolated system is a conceptual one only—no real systems are isolated. Reactions taking place in isolated systems are adiabatic processes. Open systems resemble living systems that are constantly exchanging both matter and energy with their environments. Open systems are characterized by an ability to reach a steady state—a condition in which there is a balanced inflow and outflow of some material or energy.

Classical thermodynamics deals with closed or isolated systems undergoing reversible changes (=thermodynamic equilibria). A reversible reaction conceptually involves a continuous succession of thermodynamic equilibrium states between the initial and final states of a system undergoing change. Such processes are only mathematical concepts because in any real system there must be a displacement from equilibrium if any change is to occur.

Classical thermodynamics also is not concerned with the rates of processes. It does not consider the time required to pass from an initial to final state. Nor is classical thermodynamics concerned with the pathway or mechanism of change. In order to deal with irreversible reactions, steady-state systems, or rates of processes, the discipline of nonequilibrium thermodynamics is being developed (Katchalsky and Curran, 1965; Prigogine, 1962).

4-2. First Law: Conservation of Energy. One statement of the first law of thermodynamics is as follows: the amount of energy in a system and its surroundings neither increases nor decreases, although there may be transformations of energy from one form to another. This expression is the result of many experiences and observations, no exception to it ever having been found. It is designated a law because it is assumed that the principle is of universal applicability.

In any system that can exchange heat energy with its environment, the first law may be expressed by

$$U = Q - W \qquad (4.2a)$$
$$\Delta U = \Delta Q - \Delta W \qquad (4.2b)$$
$$dU = \delta Q - \delta W \qquad (4.2c)$$

Equation 4.2a is the general relationship between the internal energy, U, of a system; the heat exchanged, Q, and the work done, W. The internal energy represents all of the various forms of energy in the system except that due its position in space (which is assumed not to change).

Because the absolute value of the internal energy of a system is indeterminate and only changes in energy as a system goes from one state to another are measurable, Equation 4.2b is a better form for expressing the energy relationships of a system. The symbol Δ (delta) is used to indicate finite changes in a variable. Although Q and W are sometimes written without the preceding delta, they always represent changes in heat quantity or work, not absolute amounts.

By convention, when heat is lost by a system, Q is negative ($Q < 0$); when heat is absorbed by a system, Q is positive ($Q > 0$). For work the conventions are as follows: when the system does work on the surroundings, W is positive; when work is done on the system, W is negative.

The internal energy is a **state function** of a system—one whose value does not depend on the pathway or mechanism by which the system changes but only on the initial and final states of the system. Q and W are not state functions—their values do depend on the pathway of change. For example, the complete oxidation of glucose to CO_2 and H_2O may produce only heat, but if correctly coupled, as in the cell, may produce work. Assuming similar initial conditions, the change in internal energy is the same in both cases, but the heat and work are quite different.

Mathematically, these statements are reflected in Equation 4.2c. d symbolizes an exact differential—an infinitesimal change in a variable that depends only on the initial and final states. The symbol δ (small delta) is used to represent infinitesimal changes that do depend on the nature of the path between initial and final states. Such changes are not exact differentials.

Although thermodynamics can evaluate energy changes under a variety of conditions, in the following discussions we shall consider only those conditions pertinent to biological and chemical reactions. At constant temperature and pressure—the conditions often encountered in biological studies—the work done by a system (considering now that only work of expansion is done, that is, the pressure in the system remains constant although volume changes can occur) is given by

$$W = P \int_{V_1}^{V_2} dV = P(V_2 - V_1) = P\Delta V \quad (4.3)$$

Substituting $P\Delta V$ for W in Equation 4.2b and rearranging, gives

$$Q_p = \Delta H = \Delta U + P\Delta V \quad (4.4)$$

The heat exchanged at constant pressure (Q_ρ) is symbolized by ΔH and is called the **enthalpy**. Enthalpy is one of the state functions of a system and is also an extensive property. Since most chemical and biological reactions occur at constant pressure, it is usual to record heat changes of a system undergoing reaction in terms of the enthalpy. If ΔH is negative, the reaction is **exothermic** and heat is given off to the surroundings. If ΔH is positive, the reaction is **endothermic** and heat is absorbed by the system.

These various statements of the first law point out that when one form of energy in a system increases or decreases, there must be an equal and opposite change in some other form of energy. It is impossible to create or destroy energy in a system, that is, it is impossible to create a perpetual motion machine of the first kind—one that operates in a cycle and returns to its initial state with no change or effect other than the performance of mechanical work.

4-3. The Second Law. The second law of thermodynamics, unlike the first, is concerned with the direction of energy changes and with thermodynamically irreversible (spontaneous) processes. Although the experiments of Joule and others showed that mechanical and other forms of energy could be completely converted into an equivalent amount of heat energy; it was also found that heat cannot be completely converted back to an equivalent amount of work. The **entropy** (S) is a thermodynamic function used to measure the degree of randomness or disorder in a system. The more random or disordered a system, the greater is its stability and the greater the probability of its existence as compared with a more highly structured system. In spontaneous processes, the entropy increases and at equilibrium, entropy for that system is at a maximum. At the molecular and atomic levels, entropy increases as potential energy is converted to kinetic energy—the energy of the random movement of particles. Although mechanical energy can be wholly converted to heat, the reverse is not true because some of the energy has been transformed to the unrecoverable form of kinetic energy of the molecules—the process is not reversible (unless energy is supplied to the system from another source). It can be noted that what is measured as temperature is the thermal or random movements of molecules and atoms.

Mathematically the second law can be expressed by

$$dS \geqslant \frac{\delta Q}{T} \quad (4.5)$$

Equation 4.5 indicates that dividing an inexact differential by the proper function results in an exact different and entropy is another state function of a system as well as being an extensive property. Entropy may also be thought of as the capacity factor for thermal work. The inequality applies to all spontaneous processes and all changes in a closed system result in an increase in entropy; a certain amount of energy is not recoverable as useful work energy (Edsall and Wyman, 1958; Katchalsky and Curran, 1965; Kirkwood and

Oppenheim, 1961). The equality sign of Equation 4.5 applies only to reversible processes.

For the condition of constant temperature the first and second laws may be combined into the definition

$$dU = TdS - \delta W \qquad (4.6)$$

The total energy change in a system is the difference between the entropy change and any work performed by the system.

Clausius regarded the universe as a closed system and thought that its entropy was continually increasing so that finally the universe would reach a heat death, where all energy would be in the form of nonuseful heat energy distributed evenly throughout the universe. The correctness of this idea has been a matter of some debate (Bondi, 1952; Hoyle, 1950).

Eddington noted that since entropy increased with time, it could serve as the basis for a biological time scale—a concept expanded on by Blum (1955). Schrödinger (1955) proposed that organisms live on negative entropy. He based this on the fact that the entropy of simple substances, for example, amino acids or glucose, is greater than that of the more structured molecules, for example, proteins or polysaccharides, which organisms synthesize. He spoke of the organisms existing on this entropy loss.

Entropy has also been used as a measure of the probability of existence of a system. The most probable systems are those which are in the most stable state—those that have the least ordered structure. The more random a system is in its structure, the greater the probability of its existence and the greater the entropy content. Entropy has also been used as a measure of the information content of a system—a large amount of information representing a lower entropy. For example, a solution of nucleotides has a greater entropy content than does a solution of nucleic acids formed from the nucleotides. The nucleic acids with their more ordered structure have lower entropy and can carry the information of the genetic code, which the nucleotides alone cannot.

Of concern to us at this point, however, is a consideration of what the various energy and entropy functions can indicate about the nature and possibility of energy metabolism and reactions in living systems.

4-4. Free Energy and Useful Work. To this point we have considered expansional (PV) work, but cells also use chemical, electrical, physical, and other forms of work energy. Gibbs introduced a state function—the Gibb's **free energy**, G, as a measure of the useful work available from a system undergoing change. Free energy is defined by

$$dG = dU - TdS + PdV \qquad (4.7)$$

Substitution from Equation 4.6 into Equation 4.7 gives

$$[-dG]_{T,P} = dW - PdV \qquad (4.8)$$

where the subscripts of the bracketed term indicate that constant temperature and pressure conditions prevail. Equation 4.8 indicates that the free energy change in a system is equal to the total work done minus any work of expansion. This difference Gibbs called useful work, and it represents work contributed by chemical, electrical, or other energy functions. The general form of the equation for any set of conditions is

$$dG = dU - TdS - SdT + PdV + VdP \qquad (4.9)$$

Free energy is sometimes symbolized by F. However, F or sometimes A is used also for another free energy function, the Helmholtz free energy ($dF = dU - TdS$). Since the Helmholtz free energy includes PV work, it is not as useful as the Gibbs free energy in discussing many of the changes in chemical or biological reactions.

It can also be shown that the free energy change is equal to the enthalpy minus TdS work, that is,

$$\Delta G = \Delta H - T\Delta S \qquad (4.10)$$

This equation provides a means for calculating entropy changes because ΔH and ΔG can be measured relatively easily for many reactions. An example is given in Section 4-6.

The sign and value of the ΔG of a reaction is an indication of whether or not the reaction is spontaneous, although as we shall see there are several qualifications to this statement. When $\Delta G < 0$, the reaction releases free energy and is **exergonic**; when $\Delta G > 0$, the reaction is **endergonic** and does not proceed spontaneously. There is no direct relationship between ΔH and ΔG. Because a reaction is exothermic does not necessarily mean that free energy is available.

The change in internal energy of a system may be represented as the algebraic sum of the various energy forms present in the system (see Table 4-1):

$$dU = TdS - PdV + Fds + EdZ + \sum_{i=0}^{c} \mu_i dn_i \quad (4.11)$$

This general equation can be made to fit any situation since terms drop out for those variables not included in a given system. For example, if there is no electrical work done by a system, the change in Z is zero, that is, $dZ = 0$, and the term EdZ drops out.

Ignoring electrical and physical work, we can express the free energy change of a chemical reaction by

$$dG = -TdS + PdV + \sum_{i=0}^{c} \mu_i dn_i \quad (4.12)$$

The summed term is the chemical work done due to the addition of i components to the system. The chemical potential, μ, of the ith component is defined by

$$\mu_i = \left[\frac{\partial G}{\partial n_i}\right]_{P,T,n_j} \quad (4.13)$$

The partial derivative means that the chemical potential is the change in free energy divided by the change in the number of moles of the ith component, when P, T, and n_j (the j denoting all molecular species except the ith) are constant. The chemical potential is a measure of the ability of a component of a system to do useful work by undergoing chemical change or other transformation.

It is important that free energy changes can be related to concentration changes because such changes are basic to many cellular activities. Concentration changes may be brought about by chemical transformations, diffusion, solubilization, active transport, and so forth. It is also important to note that Equation 4.13 applies to both open and closed systems and to either equilibrium or steady-state systems. Therefore, chemical reactions in organisms can be characterized by the principles of thermodynamics.

4-5. Equilibria and Free Energy. Consider the simplest example of a reversible reaction (using "reversible" now in its chemical sense, not its thermodynamic one):

$$a\text{A} \underset{k_2}{\overset{k_1}{\rightleftharpoons}} b\text{B}$$

where the prescripts, a and b, represent stoichiometric proportions of the reactants and products (not their concentrations) and k_1 and k_2 are the rate constants of the forward and reverse reactions, respectively. By definition, at equilibrium the rate of the forward reaction (v_1) equals the rate of the reverse reaction (v_2):

$$v_1 = k_1[\text{A}]^a = v_2 = k_2[\text{B}]^b \quad (4.14)$$

and the equilibrium constant, K, is defined by

$$K = \frac{k_2}{k_1} = \frac{[\text{A}]^a}{[\text{B}]^b} \quad (4.15)$$

where the brackets indicate concentrations.

It can be shown that the free energy change of such a reaction is related to the equilibrium constant by

$$\Delta G = -RT \ln K + RT \ln \frac{[\text{products}]}{[\text{reactants}]} \quad (4.16)$$

R is the gas constant (1.987 cal/degree/mole when free energy is expressed in calories per mole) and T is the absolute temperature.

If the concentrations of products and reactants are taken as 1 molar, we have:

$$\Delta G° = -RT \ln K \quad (4.17)$$

The superscript $°$ means that a thermodynamic function has been measured in the standard state. Standard conditions have been defined as 1 molar activity for solutes; unit activity of pure water; a pH of 0 (=unit activity of hydrogen ions); and a temperature of 25°C

$(T = 298°)$. These activities are far removed from those of normal biological systems. Therefore, biological measurements of thermodynamic functions are made at pH 7.0 and with concentrations in the 0.01 M range—conditions more closely approximating those of biological systems. Free energies measured under these conditions are symbolized as $\Delta G'$.

Biological concentrations are usually expressed on a molar basis, although theory requires the use of activities in thermodynamic measurements. The error introduced is not great especially in biological studies where often the normal conditions of reactants and products are not known in any case. Activity, a, is related to the chemical potential by:

$$\mu = \mu° + RT \ln a \qquad (4.18)$$

Useful equations for free energy can be derived because there is a relation between activity and concentration:

$$a = \gamma \text{ (molar concentration)} \qquad (4.19)$$

where γ is the activity coefficient—a measure of the interaction between molecules at concentrations where molecular behavior departs from the ideal behavior of dilute solutions. At higher concentrations there is an increasing interaction between solute and solvent molecules and between the solute molecules themselves. The activity, therefore, is the concentration of a substance as it appears to be from some measurable characteristic of the system.

The standard chemical potential, $\mu°$, is an intensive property of a system. It represents the free energy change per mole of product formed or transferred from one phase to another at standard conditions. It is numerically equal to the molar free energy change and is sometimes called the molar free energy.

The standard free energy change of a reaction may be calculated from Equation 4.16 or Equation 4.17 if the equilibrium constant is known. Conversion to common logarithms and the insertion of the numerical value of the gas constant gives

$$\Delta G° = -(2.302)(1.987)T \ln K \qquad (4.20)$$

Unless the reaction system is at standard conditions, the value and sign of $\Delta G°$ will not show whether or not a system is exergonic. Only ΔG depends on the actual concentration. If the system is not at standard conditions, substitution of the real concentrations must be made in Equation 4.16.

Although the equilibrium constant is found in Equations 4.16, 4.17, and 4.20, this does not mean that $\Delta G°$ refers to a system at equilibrium. In fact, at equilibrium $\Delta G = 0$. A system at equilibrium can perform no useful work, and its entropy is at a maximum.

As an arbitrary reference point, the standard free energies of the elements are taken as zero. This means that the standard free energy of any reaction in which a compound is formed from its elements is equal to the free energy of formation of that compound. Further the free energy of any reaction is the difference between the sums of the free energies of formation of the products and the sums of the free energies of formation of the reactants:

$$\Delta G° = \Sigma \Delta G°_{products} - \Sigma \Delta G°_{reactants} \qquad (4.21)$$

4-6. Some Comments on Cellular Reactions.
A reaction basic to cellular energy metabolism is the oxidation of glucose to CO_2 and H_2O:

$$C_6H_{12}O_6(s) + 6CO_2(g) \longrightarrow$$
$$6CO_2(g) + 6H_2O(l)$$
$$\Delta G = -686.5 \text{ kcal/mole}$$
$$\Delta H = -673.0 \text{ kcal/mole}$$

The letters in parentheses indicate the physical state (gas, liquid, or solid) of reactants and products. The heat produced in this reaction can be measured in a bomb calorimeter, a device in which a substance is ignited and burned in a thermally insulated container. Part of the insulation is a layer of water that absorbs any heat produced and whose temperature change can be determined. Because no work can be done in the system (which is at constant volume) the change in energy of the reaction is equal to the ΔH. The free energy change of this reaction is calculated from Equation 4.21 because the free energies of both reactants and products are known.

Note that in this reaction there is more free energy produced than there is heat produced. Using Equation 4.10, one can calculate the entropy change at 25°C as 45.3 cal/mole/degree [or 45.3 E.U. (entropy units)]. The source of this thermal work is heat flowing into the reaction system from the surroundings. Because the reaction can utilize this heat, more free energy for useful work is available compared to the situation where a reaction must proceed using only energy liberated by the reaction.

As we shall see later in the chapter, the cell obtains the free energy of glucose oxidation through a different pathway than the simple oxidation shown above. But since free energy is a state function of a system and because the initial and final states are the same in each case, the same amount of free energy is available.

Many cellular reactions occur even though they are endergonic. Any factor that tends to shift the equilibrium of a reaction can cause an endergonic reaction to proceed. Such factors include the formation of an insoluble or gaseous product; the removal of a substance by a circulatory or excretory system; mechanisms that compartmentalize molecular species; or the use of the product of a reaction as the reactant in another reaction. The latter is common because many cellular metabolic schemes are arranged as chains of reactions. An example is shown here:

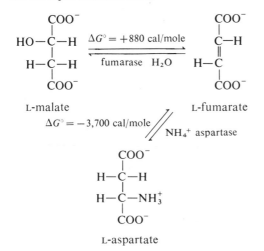

L-malate

L-fumarate

L-aspartate

Malate and fumarate are important intermediates of the tricarboxylic acid cycle—a major metabolic pathway for the production of useful cell energy. Aspartate is an important amino acid serving not only as a structural element in proteins but also acting as one intermediate between amino acid and carbohydrate metabolism. Although the formation of fumarate from malate is an endergonic reaction, it still proceeds in this cellular sequence because any fumarate formed is immediately used to produce aspartate in a highly exergonic reaction. The equilibrium of the first reaction is shifted and its ΔG is exergonic, although $\Delta G°$ is not. The names fumarase and aspartase below the reaction arrows indicate the enzymes needed to catalyze these reactions in the cell.

The free energy of glucose oxidation is trapped and made useful in the cell by the phosphorylation of ADP to ATP. ATP has an unusually high free energy of hydrolysis compared with most other phosphate compounds and is considered the direct source of energy for many cellular activities. Compounds with high free energy changes on hydrolysis were originally called high-energy phosphate bond compounds (Lipmann, 1941), but this term is unsatisfactory because the energy of hydrolysis does not come only from the breaking of a bond. Rather the energy results from resonance changes in the whole molecule, ionization and dissociation of groups, as well as bond energy (George and Rutman, 1960; Edsall and Wyman, 1958). It is better to call substances such as ATP "high energy phosphate compounds."

The hydrolysis of ATP may be written

$$ATP^{4-} + H_2O \underset{\substack{pH\ 7 \\ Mg^{2+} \\ enzyme}}{\rightleftharpoons} ADP^{3-} + HPO_4^{2-} + H^+$$

The reaction is written to indicate that pH, Mg^{2+}, and an enzyme are all factors in the cellular hydrolysis of ATP. The pH, for example, is important because it determines the state of dissociation and charge of ATP and the other charged substances—this charge and its changes will determine the amount of free energy released.

Because the equilibrium of the ATP hydrolysis reaction lies so far to the right that no detectable amounts of ATP can be measured in a reaction system, $\Delta G°$ is determined not from the simple hydrolytic reaction but from the equilibrium constants of reactions of ATP with other substances such as glucose or glutamate. This is possible from Equation 4.21 and the relations between equilibrium constants. Most recent values of $\Delta G°$ for the hydrolysis of ATP are about 7.4 kcal/mole. Since in the cell chemical concentrations are not 1 molar and since uncertainties exist concerning ionization and other effects, it is probable that the value of ΔG is from 10 to 12 kcal/mole. The latter value will be used in our further discussions of ATP. Details of the methods used in these measurements can be found in Robbins and Boyer (1957); Phillips et al. (1963); George et al. (1963).

ATP hydrolysis in solution yields the cell no useful energy because cells cannot use free energy released as heat for most activities. Rather the energy of ATP hydrolysis is trapped in other molecules. Often ATP energy is used to drive an endergonic reaction. The use of an exergonic reaction to cause an endergonic reaction to proceed is called **coupling** or **coupled reactions**. For example, the phosphorylation of glucose is needed to introduce glucose into metabolic pathways, but this reaction is endergonic:

sents a phosphate group attached to an organic molecule such as glucose.

In later chapters we shall consider how free energy changes can be calculated for systems performing mechanical, electrical, or osmotic work. For more detailed discussions of thermodynamics see Bray and White (1966); Glasstone (1946, 1947); Patton (1965). Krebs and Kornberg (1957) review energy transformations in biological systems.

Enzymes and Enzyme Kinetics

4-7. The Enzyme Substrate Complex. The free energy or other thermodynamic characteristics of a reaction do not show how fast it will go; such information comes from chemical kinetics. Enzymes are cellular catalysts whose function is to speed up reactions that otherwise would proceed too slowly to be of use to cells. The phosphorylation of glucose, described in the preceding section, would proceed at an immeasurably slow rate were it not for the enzyme hexokinase. Many reactions in the cell involve the making or breaking of covalent bonds—reactions which are especially slow. Enzymes also have the function of causing reactions to occur along specific lines. Enzymes cannot make thermodynamically impossible reactions go. Nor can enzymes, generally, alter the equilibrium of a reaction;

$$\text{glucose} + H_3PO_4 \underset{\substack{\Delta G° = +4\ \text{kcal/mole}}}{\overset{\text{hexokinase}}{\rightleftharpoons}} \text{glucose 6-phosphate}$$

By combining this hexokinase reaction (named after the enzyme used to catalyze the reaction in the cell) with the exergonic hydrolysis of ATP:

they can only cause the reaction to approach equilibrium more rapidly.

All enzymes are protein molecules. Therefore, like all proteins, enzymes are affected by

glucose + P_i ⟶ glucose 6-P	$\Delta G° = +4$ kcal/mole
ATP + H_2O ⟶ ADP + P_i	$\Delta G° = -12$ kcal/mole
glucose + ATP ⟶ glucose 6-P + ADP	$\Delta G° = -8$ kcal/mole

there results an overall exergonic reaction catalyzed by the enzyme hexokinase and in which the high negative free energy of ATP hydrolysis "drives" the endergonic glucose phosphorylation. The symbol "P_i" is used to represent inorganic phosphate; "P" repre-

pH and temperature changes that can alter either their state of dissociation or their conformation. Only a small portion of the amino acid constituents of an enzyme are actually involved in the catalytic reaction. That region of the protein that participates directly in the reaction is the **active site**. The active site is affected by any factors that alter the spatial relationships of the macromolecule. The active site may be associated with or contain nonamino acid constituents necessary for enzyme activity. These include cofactors such as metal ions and more tightly bound organic moieties—coenzymes.

In order for any chemical reaction to occur, there must be collisions and combinations between reactant molecules. Similarly an enzyme must collide with and combine with the reactant molecule—the substrate of the enzyme. The structural fit between the active site region and the substrate molecule determines the degree of specificity of the enzyme reaction.

A general scheme for enzyme reactions is

$$E + S \rightleftharpoons ES \rightleftharpoons ES^* \rightleftharpoons EP^* \rightleftharpoons E + P$$

where E represents the enzyme, S the substrate, and P the product. ES is the molecular complex formed between enzyme and substrate. Starred (*) compounds are **activated complexes**—molecules that have achieved a state of energy sufficient to allow them to react and form products and free enzyme. Michaelis and Menten in 1913 postulated the existence of enzyme activated complexes. Stern and also Chance (1943) using spectroscopic analysis demonstrated the existence of such complexes in the peroxidase reaction.

The general reaction just presented shows each step as an equilibrium reaction, but in a given reaction this may not be the case. There may also be more than one activated enzyme-substrate complex formed. The details of the model must be altered to fit each particular enzyme reaction.

4-8. Activation Energy and Temperature. In 1889 Arrhenius derived an empirical relationship between the rate of a chemical reaction and the temperature:

$$k = PZ \exp (E_a/RT) \tag{4.22}$$

where k is a rate constant; E_a is the activation energy; P and Z are constants. P was later defined as the steric or probability factor—a

measure of the ability of molecules to combine for reaction. Z is the collision factor.

Arrhenius suggested that only those molecules possessing a certain amount of energy, greater than some critical value, could react. Molecules obtain this energy by colliding with other molecules. P is an expression of the idea that molecules may also require a certain orientation for effective collision with other molecules. It may be noted that a collision between molecules will impart energy to one of them, and the other will lose this energy and fall below the activation energy level. In a population of molecules, the energy distribution falls into a bell-shaped curve.

Differentiation of Equation 4.22 gives

$$\frac{d \ln k}{dT} = \frac{E_a}{RT^2} \tag{4.23}$$

Integrating between two temperatures, T_1 and T_2; converting to common logarithms; and substituting numerically for the gas constant, R, gives

$$E_a = (2.303)(1.987) \frac{T_1 T_2}{T_2 - T_1} \log \left(\frac{k_2}{k_1}\right) \tag{4.24}$$

or rearranging:

$$\log \left(\frac{k_2}{k_1}\right) = \frac{E_a}{4.575} \frac{T_2 - T_1}{T_1 T_2} \tag{4.25}$$

where k_1 and k_2 are the rates of reaction at absolute temperatures, T_1 and T_2, respectively. E_a has units of calories per mole, when R is 1.987 cal/degree/mole. According to Equation 4.25 a plot of log rate against $1/T$ should give a straight line whose slope is equal to $E_a/4.575$. Thus the activation energy of a reaction may be calculated after measuring the reaction rates at two different temperatures. However, this relationship is empirical only and is not based on thermodynamic or reaction mechanism theory.

Values of E_a (sometimes symbolized by A or μ) are used to compare biological rate processes. Another quantity, the **temperature coefficient** or Q_{10}, is also used for this purpose. The Q_{10} is the ratio of the rates of reaction measured at two temperatures 10°C apart

$$Q_{10} = \frac{k_{t+10}}{k_t} \tag{4.26}$$

Note that the temperatures are in degrees Celsius, not absolute.

The temperature coefficient can be calculated from the rates of a process measured at any two temperatures by using

$$\log Q_{10} = \frac{10 \log\left(\frac{k_2}{k_1}\right)}{t_2 - t_1} \qquad (4.27)$$

where t_2 and k_2 are the higher temperature and corresponding rate, respectively. Q_{10} values for most biological rate processes fall in the range of 1.1 to 4. Generally, values of 2 or above are thought to indicate chemical reactions; values close to 1 indicate physical processes such as diffusion. Both Q_{10} and E_a vary depending on the temperature range over which they are measured.

The Arrhenius collision model does not explain why activation energy should vary with the temperature range. Nor does it explain why biological rate processes have optimal temperatures above which the reaction rate decreases. It is a common finding that at temperatures close to 0°C and also close to the optimum temperature, the relation between log rate and $1/T$ is not a straight line as Equation 4.25 predicts.

Absolute reaction rate theory correlates observed reaction rates with thermodynamic functions, equilibrium conditions, and molecular characteristics. It assumes that during a reaction a definite compound, the activated complex, is formed and that there is an equilibrium between reactant molecules and the activated complex (Johnson et al., 1954). For the model enzyme system:

$$E + S \rightleftharpoons ES^* \rightarrow E + P$$

a dissociation constant, K^*, can be written for the equilibrium dissociation reaction of the activated complex:

$$K^* = \frac{[ES^*]}{[E][S]}$$

Thermodynamic functions or equilibrium constants written with a star (*) are for the equilibrium reaction of the activated complex. Using statistical and quantum mechanical analysis Eyring (see, for example, Eyring and

Urry, 1965) found that the specific rate constant, k', for the formation of products and free enzyme from the activated complex is given by

$$k' = \frac{\kappa k T K^*}{h} \qquad (4.28)$$

where κ is the transmission coefficient which indicates the probability that the formation of the activated complex will lead to reaction (κ is unity for most reactions); k is the Boltzman constant, that is, R/N, the gas constant per molecule, numerically 1.38×10^{-16}; and h is Planck's constant, 6.62×10^{27} ergs per second. The term kT/h is the frequency of decomposition of the activated complex to products, assumed to be the same for all reactions. The lifetime of the activated complex is on the order of 10^{-13} seconds.

A set of thermodynamic constants, sometimes called pseudothermodynamic because they are derived from kinetic not thermal data, can be derived for the quasi-equilibrium reactions involving the activated complex. They are similar in appearance to those already given:

$$\Delta G^* = -RT \ln K^* \qquad (4.29)$$
$$\Delta G^* = \Delta H^* - T\Delta S^* \qquad (4.30)$$

By appropriate substitution into Equation 4.28 and using the relations of Equation 4.4, the specific rate constant can be defined by

$$k' = \frac{\kappa k T}{h} \exp\left(\frac{-\Delta G^*}{RT}\right) \qquad (4.31)$$

$$k' = \frac{\kappa k T}{h} \exp\left(\frac{-\Delta H^*}{RT}\right) \exp\left(\frac{\Delta S^*}{R}\right) \quad (4.32)$$

$$k' = \frac{\kappa k T}{h} \exp\left(\frac{\Delta E^*}{RT}\right) \exp\left(\frac{-P\Delta V^*}{RT}\right) \exp\left(\frac{\Delta S^*}{R}\right)$$
$$(4.33)$$

One of the values of absolute reaction rate theory is that, unlike the Arrhenius theory, it provides a means of expressing the variation of reaction rate with pressure (Equation 4-33). The effect of pressure on the rate of reaction is determined by ΔV^*, the change in volume of the reactant molecules on activation. ΔV^* is calculated from the slope of the line obtained when log rate is plotted against P at constant temperature. Such measurements are very useful in determining changes in molecular volumes during enzyme reactions and other biological processes.

Absolute reaction rate theory provides a means of calculating the properties of the activated complex from measured reaction rates and is useful for describing reactions in terms of free energy functions and other thermodynamic properties (Eyring, 1935; Eyring and Urry, 1965).

The activation energy of Arrhenius is related to the enthalpy of reaction of the activated complex:

$$E_a = \Delta H^* + RT \qquad (4.34)$$

By making an Arrhenius plot of log rate against $1/T$, after measuring the rates of reaction at several different temperatures, the ΔH^* of the reaction is easily determined from the straight line portion of the curve. For all practical purposes, $E_a = \Delta H^*$, because the term RT is small (about 600 cal/mole at room temperature) compared with usual values of ΔH^*. The latter ranges from about 5,000 to 30,000 cal/mole.

The relationships just given indicate that any factor tending to lower the value of ΔH^* will increase the rate of reaction. This is exactly what enzymes do. An enzyme-substrate complex is formed that has a lower energy of activation than the activated state in the un-catalyzed reaction. It is easier for the enzyme-substrate complex to attain that energy level necessary for the reaction to proceed. Figure 4-1 compares the free energy of activation for an

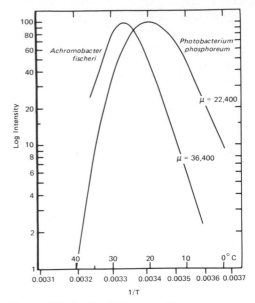

Figure 4-2(a) The influence of temperature on the intensity of light production by two species of luminescent bacteria. The different optimal temperatures are correlated with different habitats. *P. phosphoreum* lives in colder waters than does *A. fischeri*. Bacterial luminescence is one enzyme-catalyzed reaction that can be studied in the intact cell. [Data from Brown et al. (1942)].

enzyme catalyzed and a noncatalyzed reaction. Note that the overall free energy change of the reaction has not been changed by the presence of the enzyme. It is only the activation energy required to produce the activated complex that has been reduced, thus leading to a faster reaction rate because more molecules can reach this level.

Values of ΔH^* are useful for comparing all types of rate processes in living systems. Figure 4-2 gives some Arrhenius plots for a few typical biological reactions. Although the normal range of ΔH^* is 5,000 to 30,000 cal/mole, certain reactions such as the denaturation of proteins have values up to about 90,000 cal/mole.

All of the reactions plotted in Figure 4-2 show temperature optimums. Absolute reaction rate theory explains the fall-off in reaction rate with increasing temperature as being due to the intrusion of another reaction—the denaturation of protein enzymes. To what extent this is true for rate processes in whole organ-

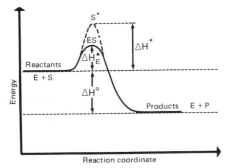

Figure 4-1 Schematic representation of the difference in activation energies of an enzyme- and a non-enzyme-catalyzed reaction.

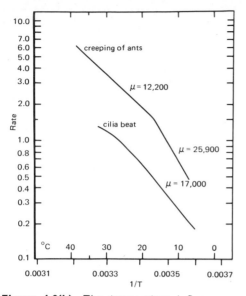

Figure 4-2(b) The temperature influence on more complex processes than single enzyme reactions can also be measured, and such experiments yield useful information. Often the temperature curve shows discontinuities as shown here for the temperature vs. activity curve for the creeping of ants (in cm/sec). [Data of Shapley (1920)]. The temperature dependence of ciliary activity in the clam follows exactly the same curve as does oxygen consumption by the animal. The flow of water past the gills is brought about by the ciliary movement. Ciliary rate is in units of mm $\times 10^{-2}$/sec. [Data of Gray (1923)].

isms or organs is not known, but it holds for isolated enzyme systems. All proteins tend to denature. At higher temperatures the conversion of native enzyme (E_n) to denatured inactive molecules decreases the overall rate of enzyme activity. An enzyme reaction (1) proceeds at a rate determined by the amount of native enzyme present. At temperatures up to about 40°C, most enzymes are reversibly denatured (2) and lowering the temperature again restores them to full activity. A ΔH_d^*, the heat of reversible denaturation, may be determined for this reaction.

$$\begin{array}{c} E_{ir} \\ \uparrow^{(3)} \\ E_n + S \xrightleftharpoons[(1)]{\Delta H^*} ES^* \longrightarrow E_n + P \\ {}^{\Delta H_d^*\uparrow\downarrow(2)} \\ E_r \end{array}$$

At higher temperatures most proteins undergo irreversible denaturation (3), and enzyme

activity is not regained when the temperature is lowered. For such irreversible, nonequilibrium processes, no ΔH^* can be determined that has any theoretical meaning.

The optimal temperature of an enzyme reaction represents the temperature at which the increase in reaction rate due to increasing temperature (increased temperature increases molecular kinetic energy and thus molecular motion. This increases the chance of collision between molecules and thus increases reaction rate) is counterbalanced by the decrease in rate due to loss of the native form of the enzyme. Optimal temperatures are usually poor criteria for characterizing rate processes in biological systems because they depend strongly on the past history of the preparation and on the conditions of measurement. The past temperature history may have caused protein adaptation to higher or lower temperatures than normal, for example.

4-9. Open Steady State Systems. I have already defined open systems as those in which both matter and energy may be exchanged with the environment. A simple open system may be modeled as

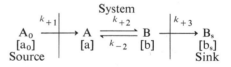

where the vertical lines bounding the system represent actual barriers such as membranes or may be some other type of separating or compartmentalizing mechanism. The system above is general in that it can represent a single enzyme reaction, a whole cell, an organ, an organism, or an ecosystem.

Material enters from a source, is converted to some other material which is then removed from the system into a sink. The transformation of A_0 to A or of B to B_s may represent diffusion, active transport, or chemical reaction. The mathematical treatment of the kinetics of any of these processes is similar. The small letters in brackets symbolize the concentrations of the various substances inside and outside the system.

The rate of change of a substance is equal to

a rate constant multiplied by the concentration of that substance. Therefore, rate equations for changes in concentration of A and B may be written

$$\frac{da}{dt} = k_{+1}(a_0 - a) + k_{-2}b - k_{+2}a \quad (4.35)$$

$$\frac{db}{dt} = k_{+2}a - k_{-2}b - k_{+3}(b - b_s) \quad (4.36)$$

Equation 4.35, for example, indicates that the rate of change of A is equal to the amount of A_0 transformed to A, plus the amount of B converted to A in the equilibrium reaction, minus the amount of A converted to B. The method of designating the rate constants is that suggested by the Enzyme Commission of the International Union of Biochemistry (1965) and will be followed throughout this book.

By definition a steady state system is one in which the concentrations of substances are not changing within the system, although there is a constant inflow and outflow of materials. In the example above, the steady state conditions are given by

$$\frac{da}{dt} = 0 \quad (4.37)$$

$$\frac{db}{dt} = 0 \quad (4.38)$$

Equations 4.35 and 4.36 can be solved for the steady state concentrations of A and B (a' and b', respectively) by equating the net change to zero and solving for a' and b'.

$$a' = \frac{k_{+1}k_{-2}a_0 + k_{+1}k_{+3}a_0 + k_{-2}k_{+3}b_s}{k_{+1}k_{-2} + k_{+1}k_{+3} + k_{+2}k_{+3}} \quad (4.39)$$

$$b' = \frac{k_{+1}k_{-2}a_0 + k_{+1}k_{+3}b_0 + k_{+2}k_{+3}b_s}{k_{+1}k_{-2} + k_{+1}k_{+3} + k_{+2}k_{+3}} \quad (4.40)$$

These equations are given because they point out that the concentration of the substances involved in a steady state system do not depend on the initial concentrations inside the system. The steady state depends only on the values of the rate constants and the concentrations of materials in the source and sink. Once the steady state is established, the concentrations in the system will remain constant (as long as the rate constants and external concentrations

do not change) even though material is passing continuously through the system.

The system shown here is one of the simplest. Real systems become more complex and are more difficult to analyze mathematically. This is especially true of systems incorporating diffusion inflow and outflow, as is found in most cells, since these depend on the geometric configurations and properties of boundaries as well as on rate constants and concentrations. However, the general principles are the same. Open steady state treatment realistically portrays most living systems.

Steady state systems are of interest because they have the capabilities of self-regulation. If mechanisms are present that alter any of the rate constants, the whole system may temporarily shift to a new steady state. After a time it may return to the same levels as were originally present. That such actions do occur is exemplified by the action of some hormones that can alter not only the rate constants of an enzyme-catalyzed reaction but also in some cases the permeability of membranes thus altering rates of inflow and outflow of particular compounds. In this manner control over the concentration levels of materials in cells can be adjusted to meet the needs of the organism. The dynamic aspects of steady state systems, that is, their changes under transient and long-term stimuli, presents a further complication in the analysis of their activities.

Cellular reaction schemes often include long chains of enzyme-catalyzed reactions (catenary systems). This presents a situation where one or two reactions may be rate-controlling or rate-limiting. If mechanisms exist for regulating these reactions, the whole system can be regulated. These various possibilities of control and regulation will be considered in a later section of this chapter after further discussion of the nature of enzymes and of the systems used to provide cellular energy. The nature of open systems and the nature of the enzymes that catalyze most biological reactions present many opportunities for control and regulation.

4-10. Michaelis-Menten Kinetics. Michaelis and Menten in 1913 were the first to derive a quantitative treatment of enzyme kinetics based on the assumption that an enzyme-substrate complex was formed in an enzyme-catalyzed reaction. At that time interest was being shown in the effects of substrate concentration on the reaction rate. Figure 4-3 shows a typical plot of the effects of varying substrate concentration on reaction rate.

It can be seen that as substrate concentration increases, the rate approaches asymptotically a limiting or maximal velocity, V_m. The first part of the curve is typical of a **first-order reaction**—one whose rate depends on the product of a rate constant and the concentration of one molecular species. The enzyme's concentration is usually included as part of the rate constant since it is small and constant. This type of reaction is **pseudomonomolecular** because only the concentration of the substrate appears to determine the reaction rate although the enzyme is also part of the reaction.

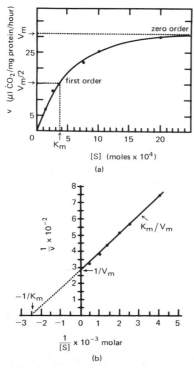

(a)

(b)

Figure 4-3 (a) Michaelis plot of the velocity of an enzyme reaction at different substrate concentrations. (b) The same data plotted according to the method of Lineweaver and Burke. Symbols are explained in text. [Data is for the enzyme DOPA decarboxylase as given in West et al. (1966) from the work of Fellman (1959)].

The horizontal portion of the curve is typical of a **zero-order reaction**—one whose rate depends on a rate constant and not on any concentration term. This is interpreted to mean that the enzyme combines with the substrate for reaction to take place but at high substrate concentrations all available enzyme is saturated with substrate. At this point the rate of reaction is maximal and additional substrate can have no further effect on rate.

Michaelis and Menten, and later Briggs and Haldane, assumed that in a typical enzyme reaction:

$$E + S \underset{k_{+1}}{\overset{k_{+1}}{\rightleftharpoons}} ES \xrightarrow{k_{+2}} E + P \quad (4.41)$$

the formation of products from the enzyme-substrate complex is the rate limiting step, slower than the formation of ES. They further assumed that a dissociation constant can be formulated for the equilibrium reaction:

$$K_m = \frac{[E][S]}{[ES]} \quad (4.42)$$

and the overall rate of reaction, which is usually measurable experimentally, is proportional to the concentration of ES.

Because [ES] is not directly measurable in most enzyme reactions, other relationships are substituted in Equation 4.42 in order to obtain an equation containing only measurable variables. The following notation is used:

[E] = total amount of enzyme present
[S] = total amount of substrate present
[ES] = concentration of enzyme-substrate complex
[E] − [ES] = concentration of free enzyme

Now the dissociation equation can be written

$$K_m = \frac{([E] - [ES])[S]}{[ES]} \quad (4.43)$$

If the measured rate of reaction, v, is considered, then because the reaction on the right (Equation 4.41) is the rate limiting step:

$$v = k_{+2}[ES] \quad (4.44)$$

and substitution into Equation 4.43 and solving for v gives

$$v = \frac{k_{+2}[E][S]}{K_m + [S]} \quad (4.45)$$

When the concentration of ES is maximal, the reaction rate reaches its maximum, V_m, and

$$V_m = K_{+2}[ES] = k_{+2}[E] \qquad (4.46)$$

The equality on the right can be substituted because at maximal velocity, all enzyme present is now complexed with substrate, thus total enzyme [E] equals [ES].

Substituting V_m into Equation 4.45 gives the Michaelis equation:

$$v = \frac{V_m[S]}{K_m + [S]} \quad \text{or} \quad K_m = [S]\left(\frac{V_m}{v} - 1\right) \qquad (4.47)$$

This is the equation of the hyperbolic curve of Figure 4.3. When the measured velocity, v, equals $V_m/2$, then the substrate concentration for that velocity is equal to K_m. That is, the substrate concentration required to reach half

maximal velocity is a constant characteristic of an enzyme reaction with a given substrate and is independent of enzyme concentration. These algebraic manipulations resulted in an equation containing only experimentally determinable variables, but it is still difficult to estimate V_m precisely on a hyperbolic curve.

The assumption that the formation of products from ES is rate-limiting is not always correct. The symbol K_m is used to designate the substrate concentration at which the measured velocity equals half the maximal velocity. The symbol K_s is reserved for the equilibrium dissociation constant of the reaction: $E + S \rightleftharpoons ES$. Only when the formation of products is the rate limiting step, will there be an equilibrium and will $K_m = K_s$. The Michaelis-Menten model also does not apply

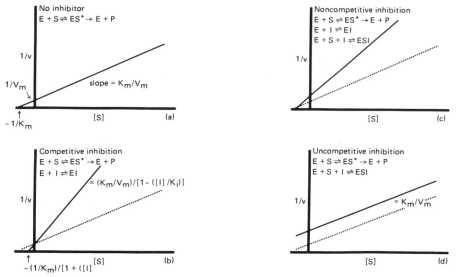

Figure 4-4 Lineweaver-Burke plots that permit various types of enzyme inhibition to be distinguished. (a) Enzyme reaction with no inhibitor. (b) Competitive inhibition: the inhibitor combines with free enzyme but cannot combine with the enzymes-substrate complex. There is a competition between inhibitor and substrate molecules for sites on the enzyme. (c) Noncompetitive inhibition: the reaction between inhibitor and enzyme is unaffected by the presence of substrate. Enzyme, substrate, and inhibitor can complex together but the resultant complex cannot break down to product. (d) Uncompetitive inhibition: the inhibitor combines with the enzyme-substrate complex but not with the free enzyme. These various cases can be distinguished from one another by the indicated shifts in slope or intercepts. The models of inhibition presented here are highly simplified. [I] is inhibitor concentration; K_i is the dissociation constant of the E1 complex; other symbols are as defined in text. The Lineweaver-Burke equation for an enzyme system with inhibitor is

$$\frac{1}{v_o} = \left[\frac{K_m}{V_m}\left(1 + \frac{[I]}{K_i}\right)\right]\frac{1}{[S]}\frac{1}{V_m}$$

fully to those situations where more than one substrate is involved or where activators or inhibitors of enzyme activity play a role in the catalyzed reaction. Under these conditions an S-shaped curve rather than a hyperbolic curve is often found. In other cases the product of the enzyme reaction may inhibit the reaction and reaction rate falls off. Also the substrate may inhibit at higher concentrations, and here also the rate of reaction decreases with increasing substrate concentration. Figure 4-4 illustrates the kinetics of various types of enzyme inhibition. These are discussed in Section 4-20.

A large value of K_m indicates that a high substrate concentration is required to obtain half-saturation of the enzyme, that is, the enzyme has a low affinity for the substrate. Values of K_m generally fall between 10^{-2} and 10^{-5} moles per liter.

4-11. The Lineweaver-Burke Plot.

Lineweaver and Burke (1934) saw that if the Michaelis equation were rectified (change to a straight-line equation) by inversion, a simpler plot was obtained (Figure 4-3b). The Lineweaver-Burke equation is

$$\frac{1}{v} = \frac{1}{[S]} K_m + \frac{1}{V_m} \qquad (4.48)$$

The ease of obtaining values of V_m and K_m from a plot of $1/v$ versus $1/[S]$, which yields a straight line, is seen from Figure 4-3b.

4-12. Units of Enzyme Activity.

The Enzyme Commission has also tried to standardize expressions of enzyme activity and concentration. The **unit** is that amount of enzyme that will catalyze the transformation of one micromole of substrate per minute at standard conditions for the enzyme, that is, at optimal pH and preferably at a temperature of 30°C.

The **specific activity** is defined as the units of enzyme per mg of protein. The **molecular activity** is the number of molecules of substrate (or equivalents of the group concerned) transformed per minute by one molecule of enzyme when substrate is not limiting. The turnover number was previously used for this expression. When the active site is well characterized, enzyme activity can be expressed as **catalytic center activity**—the number of molecules acted upon per minute per catalytic site. Enzyme concentrations should be expressed as units per milliliter.

4-13. Enzyme Nomenclature.

Enzymes are usually designated by the suffix "ase," except for a few of the first discovered ones such as pepsin or trypsin. The Enzyme Commission's nomenclature and systematics will be followed here. An enzyme is identified precisely by the systematic name, which includes the name of the substrate as well as the nature of the reaction. Because substrates or products are often complex molecules with long chemical names, an accepted trivial name is used in general discussions. In addition, a four-part serial number identifies and catalogs each enzyme. The serial number is given in brackets, preceded by the initials E.C. (Enzyme Commission).

There are six main classes of enzymes:

1. Oxidoreductases catalyze oxidation-reduction reactions.
2. Transferases transfer a chemical group from one molecule to another.
3. Hydrolases catalyze hydrolytic reactions.
4. Lyases add (or remove) chemical groups to (or from) double bonds, with no hydrolysis.
5. Isomerases catalyze isomerization reactions.
6. Ligases catalyze condensations of two molecules coupled with the splitting of a pyrophosphate bond of ATP or other high-energy phosphate compound.

Each class is further subdivided into subclasses and subsubclasses according to the nature of the substrate and the reaction. The systematics of the enzyme hexokinase, whose reaction with ATP and glucose was mentioned in Section 4-6, will exemplify the system of nomenclature.

1. Systematic name: ATP:D-hexose-6-phosphotransferase.
2. Trivial name: Hexokinase.
3. Reaction: ATP + D-hexose ⇌ ADP + D-hexose 6-phosphate.
4. Serial Number: [E.C. 2.7.1.1].
   a. Class 2: Transferase.
   b. Subclass 7: Transfers phosphorous-containing groups.

c. Subsubclass 1: Phosphotransferase with an alcohol (OH) group as acceptor.

d. Enzyme number 1: Number of enzyme (in sequence of discovery).

The system is valuable because it gives all the necessary information about the enzyme and provides a cataloging system for enzymes. It also permits the addition of new enzymes, as they are found or the removal of older misclassified enzymes. Enzymes are added only upon their purification or identification as single proteins. Further information is found in Florkin and Stotz (1964). Other sources of information on enzymes and enzyme mechanisms include Bernhard (1968); Boyer et al. (1959–); Dixon and Webb (1964); and the annual series *Advances in Enzymology* (New York: Interscience Publishers). The role of enzymes in cellular regulatory mechanisms will be discussed after a description of the basic energy metabolic pathways.

Energy Metabolism

4-14. Metabolism and Glycolysis. The totality of chemical reactions in a cell is its metabolism. Sometimes metabolism is divided into catabolism, the breakdown of substances into smaller molecules, and anabolism, the synthesis of new compounds. We shall be concerned only with those metabolic reactions by which cells obtain useful energy from food materials.

The primary energy for the operation and maintenance of all life is derived from the energy of sunlight. Green plants use this energy to synthesize carbohydrates from simpler environmental constituents such as CO_2 and H_2O in the photosynthetic process (Calvin, 1962; Duysens, 1964; Park, 1966; Packer and Siegenthaler, 1966).

Animals depend upon carbohydrates and amino acids synthesized by green plants.

Animals obtain substances needed for synthesis of their own molecules or for energy by either eating plants directly or by eating other animals that, in turn, have eaten plants. Since carbohydrate, especially glucose, is the major material photosynthesized by plants, it is not surprising that all cells have evolved enzyme systems that can obtain useful energy from the chemical energy of glucose. In fact, one of the striking early discoveries of biochemists and cellular physiologists was the basic similarity in all cells of the reaction sequences of glycolysis and the tricarboxylic acid cycle—pathways for glucose oxidation and energy release. Although some specialized cells do occur and although the details of metabolism may differ in different cells, the overall energy-obtaining pathways are similar (Racker, 1965).

Krebs and Kornberg (1957) divided the chemical processing of foodstuffs into three phases. In phase 1 the larger molecules of the food are broken down into smaller fragments suitable for absorption by cells. This is part of the digestive process. In phase 2 small molecules are incompletely oxidized to acetate (sometimes oxalacetate or α-ketoglutarate). Some CO_2 and H_2O are produced and a small amount of chemical energy is made available to the cell. In phase 3 the complete oxidation of phase 2 products is accomplished. Most of the cellular waste products of metabolism (CO_2, NH_3, and H_2O) are produced, and much of the chemical energy of the starting materials is converted to useful cell energy. Phases 2 and 3 are intracellular metabolic reactions—the ones with which we shall be concerned here.

Energy metabolism can be considered to begin with the conversion of the 6-carbon glucose to two 3-carbon fragments (pyruvate or lactate) in a series of anaerobic (non-oxygen requiring) reactions known as **glycolysis** (Figure 4-5, and Table 4-2). The overall reaction is

$$(C_6H_{12}O_6)_n + 1ATP + 3ADP + 3H_3PO_4 \rightleftharpoons (C_6H_{12}O_6)_{n-1} + 2(C_3H_5O_3) + 4ATP$$
glycogen (muscle)   lactate

or

$$C_6H_{12}O_6 + 2ATP + 2ADP + 2H_3PO_4 \rightleftharpoons 2(C_3H_5O_3) + 4ATP$$
glucose (most cells)

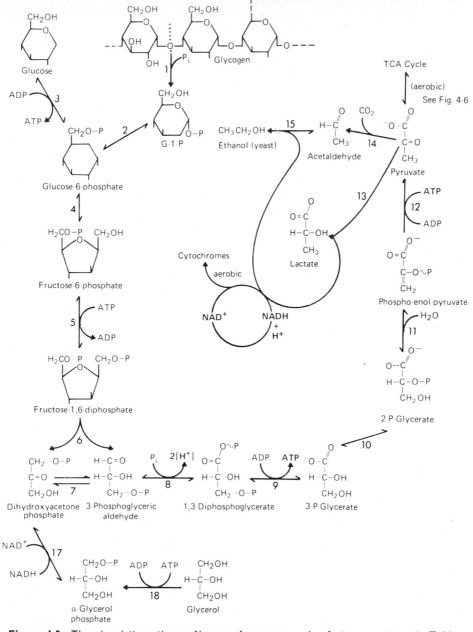

Figure 4-5 The glycolytic pathway. Names of enzymes and cofactors are given in Table 4-2. Note that some organisms or tissues start with glycogen, while others start with glucose. In the latter case an extra unit of ATP is required to phosphorylate the glucose before it can enter the reaction sequence. The fate of pyruvate will depend upon the organism and the oxygen supply. Under aerobic conditions reduced NAD will lead to the formation of more useful cell energy through oxidation in the cytochrome system.

Table 4-2 The Reaction Steps of Glycolysis

STEP*	ENZYME [E.C. NUMBER]	COENZYMES AND COFACTORS	$\Delta G°$ (kcal/mole)
1	Glycogen phosphorylase [E.C. 2.4.1.1]	H_3PO_4	-0.7
2	Phosphoglucomutase [E.C. 2.7.5.1]	Mg^{2+}	-1.7
3	Hexokinase [E.C. 2.7.1.1]	ATP, Mg^{2+}	-3.4
4	Glucosephosphate isomerase [E.C. 5.3.1.9.]		$+0.5$
5	Phosphofructokinase [E.C. 2.7.1.11]	ATP, K^+, Mg^{2+}	-3.4
6	Fructose diphosphate aldolase [E.C. 4.1.2.13]		$+5.7$
7	Triose phosphate isomerase		$+1.8$
8	Glyceraldehyde phosphate dehydrogenase [E.C. 1.2.1.12]	NAD^+, H_3PO_4	$+1.5$
9	Phosphoglycerate kinase [E.C. 2.7.2.3]	ADP, Mg^{2+}	-6.8
10	Phosphoglyceromutase [E.C. 2.7.5.3]		$+1.1$
11	Phosphopyruvate hydratase (*enolase*)† [E.C. 4.2.1.11]	Mg^{2+} or Mn^{2+}	$+0.4$
12	Pyruvate kinase [E.C. 2.7.1.40]	ADP Mg^{2+}- K^+	-5.7
13	Lactate dehydrogenase [E.C. 1.1.1.27]	$NADH+H^+$	-6.0
14	Pyruvate decarboxylase [E.C. 4.1.1.1]		-4.7
15	Alcohol dehydrogenase [E.C. 1.1.1.1]	$NADH+H^+$	-5.2
16	Note: NAD^+, NADH, or NADP always require the presence of a specific dehydrogenase enzyme.		
17	Glycerophosphate dehydrogenase	NAD^+	$+10$
18	Glycerol-3-phosphatase		

* Step numbers refer to Fig. 4-5.
† Former trivial names not recommended by the Enzyme Commission.

Most animal cells start with glucose which requires a molecule of ATP for the endergonic phosphorylation of glucose to glucose 6-phosphate. The latter is an important intermediate in glycolysis because all monosaccharides are interconvertible with it. Glycolysis in higher plant cells begins with starch and in some animal cells with glycogen. Both of these storage molecules for glucose can be broken down and a phosphorylated sugar formed without needing the energy of ATP. The use of glycogen gives a net ATP production of 3 in glycolysis; starting with glucose nets only 2 ATP molecules.

Cells break down glucose in a series of reaction steps; each step has a small energy change, allowing almost all the reactions to be reversible. The energy of glucose is thus not liberated all at once as in combustion. Because certain of the reactions are coupled with the phosphorylation of ADP, the energy of glucose is not liberated as heat. About one-half of the energy of glucose is trapped in ATP, and the remainder is liberated as heat. Thus the cell is not 100 per cent efficient in converting chemical energy to useful cell energy.

Glycolysis, at best, by producing 3 ATP molecules with a high-energy content of about 36,000 calories yields only a small fraction of the total available free energy of glucose (688,000 calories per mole). Glycolysis, although some lower organisms obtain all their energy from it, is basically a preparatory series of reactions that permit other substances to enter into carbohydrate energy metabolism and also permit other materials to be synthesized from the abundant glucose. Glycolysis prepares intermediates to enter into the com-

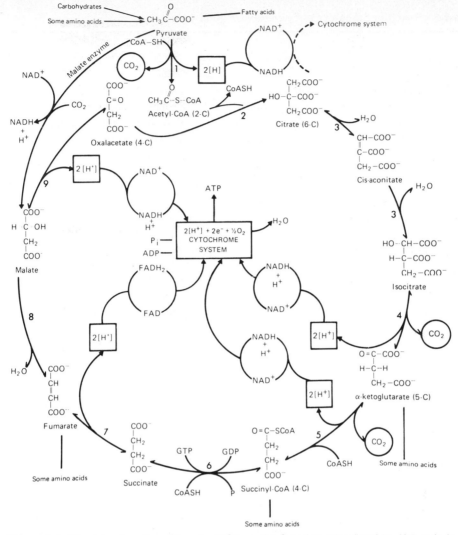

Figure 4-6 The tricarboxylic acid cycle (TCA cycle) found in mitochondria. Not only is useful cell energy finally produced by the further oxidation in the cytochrome system of hydrogens removed from TCA cycle substrates, but the cycle serves as a source of intermediates for the synthesis of amino acids and fatty acids. The names of enzymes and cofactors used in the TCA cycle are given in Table 4-3.

plete oxidation scheme of the tricarboxylic acid cycle (TCA cycle) and oxidative phosphorylation.

Certain materials are present in only very small amounts in cells. These include coenzymes needed in metabolism. At step 8 of glycolysis (Figure 4-5), NAD^+ is used in a dehydrogenation-oxidation reaction. Under anaerobic conditions NADH must be recycled in some fashion, otherwise glycolysis comes to a halt. In microorganisms various pathways

have evolved for restoring NADH to the oxidized form, NAD^+. In the example shown yeast cells form acetaldehyde from pyruvate. The acetaldehyde is then reduced to ethyl alcohol by reacting with $NADH + H^+$ formed at step 8. Another recycling scheme is shown for lactate formation, when muscle cells lack sufficient oxygen

When cells operate under aerobic conditions, any NADH formed is oxidized by the oxidative-phosphorylation system in the

Table 4-3 Reaction Steps of the Tricarboxylic Acid Cycle

Step*	Enzyme [E.C. number], coenzyme, and cofactors	$\Delta G°$ (kcal/mole)
1	A multienzyme pyruvate dehydrogenase system, associated with the mitochondrial membrane. Requires: thiamine pyrophosphate (TPP); Coenzyme A (CoA-SH); lipoic acid; flavin adenine dinucleotide (FAD); see Koike et al. (1963) for a description of the system as found in bacteria. This reaction is not usually considered as part of the TCA cycle proper.	
2	Citrate synthase (citrate condensing enzyme)† [E.C. 4.1.3.7]	−9.1
3	Aconitate hydratase (Aconitase)† [E.C. 4.2.1.3]. Requires Fe^{2+} and glutathione (GSH)	+1.6
4	Isocitrate dehydrogenase [E.C. 1.1.1.41]. Requires ADP, NAD^+, and Mg^{2+}	−1.7
5	α-Ketoglutarate dehydrogenase system. Requires CoA-SH, TPP, NAD^+, and lipoic acid.	−8.8
6	Succinyl-CoA synthetase (succinic thiokinase)† [E.C. 6.2.1.4]. Requires GDP or IDP (inosine diphosphate).	−2.2
7	Succinate dehydrogenase [E.C. 1.3.99.1] Requires FAD, Fe^{2+}	0
8	Fumarate hydratase (Fumarase)† [E.C. 4.2.1.1]	−0.9
9	Malate dehydrogenase [E.C. 1.1.1.37] Requires NAD^+	+6.7

* Step numbers refer to Fig. 4-6.

† Former trivial names not recommended by the Enzyme Commission.

mitochondria with the formation of NAD^+ and energy in the form of ATP. An important generalization is that biological oxidation-reduction reactions result in the removal of a pair of hydrogens from the substrate. These hydrogens (or a pair of electrons removed from them) pass through mitochondrial oxidative-phosphorylation reactions, where a maximum of three high energy phosphate molecules are produced.

The preparation of compounds to form high-energy phosphate molecules is exemplified by the enolization reaction of glycolysis (step 11). The formation of a carbon-carbon double bond by the removal of a pair of hydrogens transforms the phosphate group into a high energy one that can then be transferred to ADP (see Kosower, 1962 or Racker, 1965 for details of these reaction mechanisms).

The enzymes of glycolysis exist as soluble components in the cytoplasm, although the requirement that products of one enzyme reaction must complex with the enzyme system of the next step indicates that some type of organization is present. The term "soluble" is more an indication of a lack of major organelle structure than of a random solution. In contrast, enzymes of the TCA cycle and the oxidative-phosphorylation chain are found associated with the inner mitochondrial membrane in a highly organized pattern.

4-15. The TCA Cycle. In most cells the pyruvate formed at the end of glycolysis enters the tricarboxylic acid cycle (TCA cycle) and is further oxidized. The reaction sequence is diagrammed in Figure 4-6 and the enzymes and cofactors for each step are listed in Table 4-3.

At only one step (6) is useful cell energy produced directly in the TCA cycle. The formation of succinate is accompanied by the production of guanosine triphosphate (GTP) a compound very similar to ATP. The high energy phosphate group of GTP can be transferred to ADP. At other steps in the TCA cycle pairs of hydrogens are removed from the substrates. Through oxidation-reduction reactions in the cytochrome system these hydrogens yield cell energy, primarily in the form of ATP.

During the complete breakdown of pyruvate to CO_2 and H_2O in the cycle, certain intermediates are formed that offer the opportunity for other substances to enter the cycle or be synthesized. The TCA cycle allows fatty acids and amino acids, as well as carbohydrates, to be oxidized for cellular energy. Also amino and fatty acids can be formed from the more abundant carbohydrates. Some of the initial steps of these reaction sequences are shown in Figure 4-6.

Table 4-4 shows the overall energy production of the TCA cycle, glycolysis, and cytochrome chain oxidative-phosphorylation. About 39 units of ATP may be formed. This represents a useful energy of about 470 kcal. This can be compared with the 686 kcal/mole of free energy of glucose oxidation, and the cell is about 65 per cent efficient in recovering this energy for its activities.

Other energy-producing reaction sequences exist in cells. The pentose phosphate pathway of carbohydrate metabolism is used not only to generate ATP (via NADPH) but is also a source of needed carbohydrates such as ribose, xylose, and sedoheptulose from the ubiquitous glucose (Figure 4-7).

Fatty acids are an important source of cellular energy. The complete degradation of a 16-carbon fatty acid yields about 2,500 kcal/mole of free energy. Fatty acids are oxidized to CO_2 and H_2O in the reaction scheme of β-oxidation (Figure 4-8) with the sequential removal of two-carbon fragments in the form of acetyl-CoA and the reduction of NAD^+. This sequence can also be used as a synthetic pathway for fatty acids from acetyl-CoA units formed from glucose. Mahler and Cordes (1966) describe all of these various metabolic pathways. Lioret and Moyse (1963) reviewed cellular acid metabolism including TCA cycle substrates.

4-16. Oxidation-Reduction and Cytochromes. Keilin (1966) wrote an excellent history and discussion of respiration and cytochromes. The major source of cellular energy is the oxidation of NADH or of flavoproteins produced in the TCA cycle, β-oxidation, or other metabolic pathways. Oxidation is generally defined as the loss of electrons, e^-, by a reducing agent (donor) and must always be coupled with the gain of electrons by an oxidizing agent (acceptor).

Table 4-4 Formation of High Energy Compounds in Glycolysis, the TCA Cycle, and the Cytochrome System

REACTION	NO. OF ATP
Pyruvate $\rightarrow$ acetyl-CoA $(2H^+ \rightarrow NAD^+)$	3
Isocitrate $\rightarrow$ α-ketoglutarate $(2H^+ \rightarrow NAD^+)$	3
α-Ketoglutarate $\rightarrow$ succinyl-CoA $(2H^+ \rightarrow NAD^+)$	3
Succinyl CoA $\rightarrow$ succinate $(GDP \rightarrow GTP \rightarrow ATP)$	1
Succinate $\rightarrow$ fumarate $(2H^+ \rightarrow FP)$	2
Malate $\rightarrow$ oxaloacetate $(2H^+ \rightarrow NAD^+)$	3
Considering two pyruvate units from glucose:	$2 \times \overline{15} = 30$
Glucose $\rightarrow$ 2 pyruvate	3
2(3-Phosphoglyceric aldehyde) $\rightarrow$ 2(1,3-diphosphoglycerate) $(4H^+ \rightarrow 2NAD^+)$	6
	$30 + 9 = \overline{39}$ ATP
(39)(12,000 kcal/mole) = 468 kcal free energy stored in ATP	

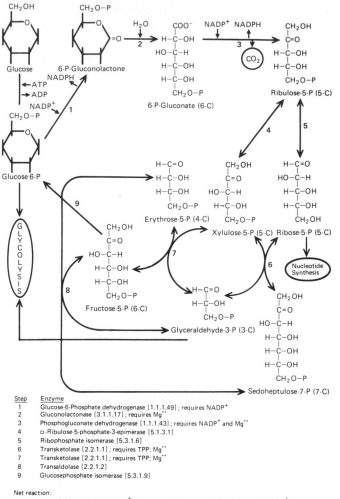

Figure 4-7 The pentose phosphate pathway (also phosphogluconate oxidative or hexose-P–pentose-P pathway). After the formation of ribose or xylulose, another glucose must enter the cycle to provide the necessary carbons for the other reactions to occur. NADPH formed can be oxidized to yield useful free energy in the cytochrome system. The reactions shown are all extramitochondrial.

Step	Enzyme
1	Glucose-6-Phosphate dehydrogenase [1.1.1.49]; requires NADP$^+$
2	Gluconolactonase [3.1.1.17]; requires Mg^{++}
3	Phosphogluconate dehydrogenase [1.1.1.43]; requires NADP$^+$ and Mg^{++}
4	D-Ribulose-5-phosphate-3-epimerase [5.1.3.1]
5	Ribophosphate isomerase [5.3.1.6]
6	Transketolase [2.2.1.1]; requires TPP; Mg^{++}
7	Transketolase [2.2.1.1]; requires TPP; Mg^{++}
8	Transaldolase [2.2.1.2]
9	Glucosephosphate isomerase [5.3.1.9]

Net reaction:

3 Glucose-6-P + 6NADP$^+$ → 2 Glucose-6-P + triose-P + 3CO$_2$ + 6NADPH + 6H$^+$

or   6 Glucose-6-P + 12NADP$^+$ → 5 Glucose-6-P + 6CO$_2$ + 12NADPH + 12H$^+$ + P$_i$

Oxidation-reduction schemes in cellular energy metabolism basically involve the interaction of hydrogen and oxygen to form water:

$$\frac{\begin{array}{r} 2H - 2e^- \rightarrow 2H^+ \\ \tfrac{1}{2}O_2 + 2e^- \rightarrow \tfrac{1}{2}O_2^{2-} \end{array}}{2H^+ + \tfrac{1}{2}O_2 \rightarrow H_2O}$$

Oxidation-reduction equilibrium reactions can be expressed in terms of oxidation-reduction potentials. At 30°C:

$$E = E_0' + \frac{0.06}{n} \log \frac{[\text{oxidized}]}{[\text{reduced}]} \quad (4.50)$$

where E is the measured potential of the system (in volts); E_0' is the oxidation-reduction potential at pH 7 when the concentration of the reduced form equals that of the oxidized form;

and n is the number of electrons participating in the reaction. The convention is used that more negative potentials belong to those systems which have an increasing tendency to donate electrons (become oxidized). The standard for potentials is the hydrogen electrode (Figure 4-9) based on the $H^+ \rightleftharpoons H_2$ oxidation-reduction reaction.

Reduction potentials can also be related to the free energy of a system as well as to other thermodynamic functions and the equilibrium constant:

$$\Delta G^\circ = -nFE_0' \quad (4.51)$$

where F is Faradays constant. Some typical values of E_0' are given in Table 4-5.

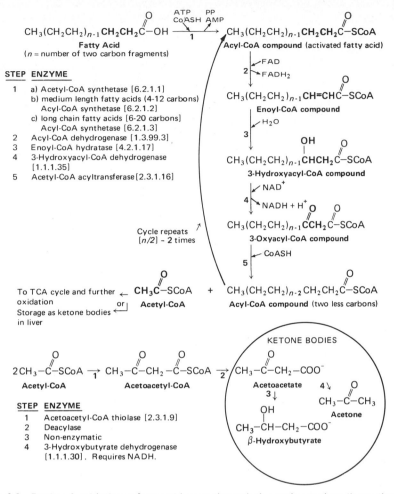

Figure 4-8 During β-oxidation a fatty acid goes through the cycle one less times than the number of pairs of carbons it contains. For example, the 16-carbon palmitic acid enters the cycle 7 times, producing 8 acetyl-CoA's. Complete oxidation to CO_2 and H_2O yields about 130 ATP, equivalent to a free energy of 1560 kcal/mole. Excess acetyl-CoA is transformed into storage ketone bodies in the liver. These are released as needed back into the circulation and oxidized by other cells. All reactions shown occur in the mitochondria.

The free energy change when one pair of electron equivalents passes from NADH to oxygen can be calculated from Equation 4.51 using appropriate values from Table 4-5. Substituting $n = 2$, and $F = 23.06$ kcal: $\Delta G = -52.6$ kcal per electron pair. This is the maximal amount of energy which the cell can obtain for useful work from the oxidation of substrates.

Cellular oxidation-reduction occurs via the cytochrome chain (Figure 4-10) in a series of steps. The components of the cytochrome chain (also called the oxidative-phosphorylation pathway, the electron transport chain, or the respiratory chain) are arranged in ordered fashion along the walls of the mitochondrial cristae (Figure 4-10d). Estabrook and Garfinkel (1962) estimated that each mitochondrion contained 17,000 cytochrome systems. Associated with the cytochromes are the enzymes and coenzymes of the TCA cycle and the β-oxidation pathway of fatty acid metabolism.

Lehninger (1964) discusses the history of mitochondrial research.

As shown in Figure 4-10b, hydrogens are thought to pass from NADH to flavoproteins (FP, FMN, FAD, etc.)—compounds that contain riboflavin derivatives as functional groups.

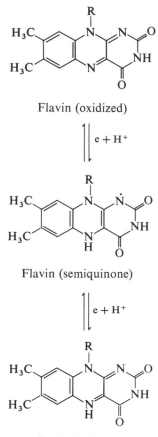

Flavin (oxidized)

$e + H^+$

Flavin (semiquinone)

$e + H^+$

Flavin (reduced)

As indicated in this reaction, the reduction of flavins occurs in two one-electron transfers with the production of an intermediate semiquinone—a free radical (a substance, often unstable, which contains a single unpaired valence electron). Whether this type of two-step reaction is typical of the entire cytochrome chain is still debated. Free radical formation and concepts of proteins as solid state electron conductors are interesting topics in energy systems studies (Commoner et al., 1957; Eley, 1962; Szent-Györgyi, 1960).

Coenzyme Q (ubiquinone) is found in high concentrations in mitochondria as well as in other parts of the cell (Green and Hatefi, 1961). The role of this substance is not entirely clear although it is proposed as an intermediate electron carrier between flavoproteins and cytochromes. Coenzyme Q is related to vitamins K and E. Its structure is as follows:

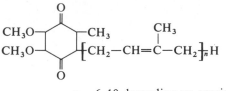

$n = 6\text{–}10$ depending on species

Coenzyme Q (ubiquinone)

The cytochromes are electron carriers and are large proteins complexed with a heme group that contains an atom of iron acting as an electron acceptor/donor. Cytochrome c primary structure has been studied in a wide variety of cells and the evolution of this protein has been examined (Chapter 5). At some early point in evolution the cytochromes (and other heme containing proteins) appear to have been selected for roles in oxidation-reduction reactions in all cells. The major classes of cytochromes include cytochrome a, b, c, and a_3. Others have been found in various cells (Chance, 1963). The cytochrome a + a_3 complex is associated with one or two atoms of copper whose role is not known.

Figure 4-10a indicates that there is a compartmentation of certain components of the cytochrome system. Distinct differences are found for example in the NAD coenzymes. Figure 4-10 also points out that hydrogens removed from succinate enter later in the chain than do hydrogens from other substrates. Those from succinate reduce a flavoprotein, rather than NAD. As a consequence only two ATP units are derived from the oxidation of succinate. Before we consider the phosphorylation reactions of the respiratory chain, it should be pointed out that NAD, flavoproteins, coenzyme Q, and other mitochondrial components of the respiratory chain are also found in the cytoplasm. Although NAD is needed in glycolysis, the roles of the other compounds in the cytoplasm are uncertain.

Table 4-5 Standard Oxidation-Reduction Potentials for Systems of Biological Interest: Values given for pH 7 and 30°C.

OXIDATION-REDUCTION SYSTEM	E_0' (volts)
Succinate/α-ketoglutarate	-0.67
H^+/H_2	-0.42
Pyruvate/malate	-0.33
$NAD^+/NADH + H^+$	-0.32
Riboflavin (oxydized form/reduced form)	-0.21
Oxaloacetate/malate	-0.17
$FMN/FMNH_2$	-0.12
Fumate/succinate	$+0.03$
Ubiquinone (oxidized form/reduced form)	$+0.10$
Cytochrome b (ferric/ferrous)	$+0.12$
Cytochrome c (ferric/ferrous)	$+0.22$
Cytochrome a (ferric/ferrous)	$+0.29$
Oxygen/water	$+0.82$

The phosphorylation reactions that convert the energy of oxidation-reduction into the energy of ATP are separate from the oxidation reactions, although closely linked to them. Uncoupling agents such as dinitrophenol (DNP) can prevent the formation of ATP although oxygen consumption and respiration continue (Loomis and Lipman, 1948). The study of mitochondrial functioning has been greatly aided by the use of specific inhibitors of biological activity. In addition to uncoupling agents, respiration has been studied by using inhibitors that interact with the electron carriers. These include cyanide and Amytal. In addition to DNP, certain polypeptide antibiotics, arsenate, and long-chain fatty acids can act as uncouplers (Lardy, et al., 1958).

The mechanisms by which the energy of electron transfers is transduced into the energy of ATP are not known. Respiration studies and biochemical assays for ATP have shown that mitochondria produce three units of ATP for every oxygen consumed (a P/O ratio of 3) when a pair of hydrogens (or electrons) passes from NADH to oxygen/water (Burton and Krebs, 1953; Lehninger et al., 1959; Lehninger and Wadkins, 1962). A hypothetical scheme by which ADP might be phosphorylated is

shown in Figure 4-10c. The high energy intermediates between elements of the respiratory chain and ATP are not known, although a phosphorylated form of NAD has been suggested as one possibility (Griffiths, 1963).

Recently other proposals have been presented for the mechanism by which the energy of electron transfer is transduced to useful cellular energy. Mitchell (1961), Davies and Ogston (1950) hypothesized that electron transfer energy is used directly as a driving force for active transport—the movement of ions or other substances across cellular membranes against their concentration gradients. Another idea is that electron transfer energy is transduced into mechanochemical energy or conformational changes in proteins and in electrostatic repulsion of chemical groups (see the review by Green and MacLennan, 1969). Other workers have felt that the contractile events, water movements, and structural changes often seen in functioning mitochondria were the result of energy transduction to ATP, rather than the energy transducing process itself (Chance, 1963; Lehninger, 1962; Neubert and Lehninger, 1962; Ohnishi and Ohnishi, 1962).

Considering that 3 units of high-energy phosphate are produced by every electron pair

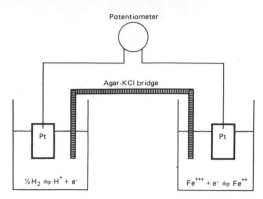

Potentiometer

Agar-KCl bridge

Pt

Pt

$\frac{1}{2}H_2 \leftrightarrows H^+ + e^-$

$Fe^{+++} + e^- \leftrightarrows Fe^{++}$

Figure 4-9 Schematic diagram of an electro-chemical cell suitable for measuring oxidation-reduction potentials. The system is composed of two half cells: one of which donates electrons, the other accepts electrons. Thus electrons can flow through the external circuit and the electro-motive force measured by a potentiometer. The Agar-KCl bridge serves to complete the electrical circuit without permitting the mixing of the solutions in the two half-cells and also provides a path through which ions can move. Since it is not possible to determine the absolute electrode potential of any half cell, the standard hydrogen electrode is assigned a potential of 0.000 volts at any temperature. All oxidation-reduction potentials are measured by comparing another half cell with the hydrogen electrode. Since the latter is an unwieldy device in actual practice, a half cell is used that has been calibrated against a hydrogen electrode for example, the calomel half cell. The hydrogen half cell consists of a platinum electrode plated with platinum black (needed to catalyze the reaction in which molecular hydrogen is oxidized. The standard hydrogen electrode contains hydrogen gas at a partial pressure of one atmosphere, and the hydrogen ions have an activity of unity. On the left, hydrogen supplies electrons to the metal electrode, and hydrogen ions tend to withdraw electrons from the electrode. On the right, ferrous ions supply electrons to the electrode, and ferric ions withdraw electrons from the electrode. When the external circuit is completed, electrons flow from the hydrogen half cell to the electrode in the other half cell. On the left hydrogen is oxidized to H^+; on the right Fe^{3+} is reduced to Fe^{2+}. The migration of ions across the agar-KCl bridge compensates for these changes in ionic concentration.

carried through the cytochrome system from NADH, the use of equation 4.51 and the data of Table 4-5 shows that the efficiency of the cellular energy trapping system is about 27/52.6

or 51 per cent (using a free energy change of 9 kcal/mole for ATP). If some energy is directly used in active transport, conformational changes, and so forth, the cell does better than this.

Control of Cellular Metabolism

4-17. Control of Cellular Respiration. The importance of various types of regulatory activities to organisms has already been stressed. Here we shall consider a few of the principles that guide cellular control and regulation at the molecular level. Enzymes, by their nature, can act as control elements in metabolism, especially when they form chains of reaction sequences. Through various control mechanisms, the cell maintains a marvelous balance between synthetic and degradative metabolism, and there is a selection of which particular pathway out of several a given metabolite will take depending on the needs of the cell.

When cells change their activity state, they should also be capable of changing their respiratory rate and thus to adjust their energy production to their energy needs. Although the concentrations of TCA cycle substrates, individual cytochromes, or amount of available oxygen certainly affect respiratory activity, other factors play a dominant role in regulating respiration. Lardy and Wellman (1952) found that ADP and inorganic phosphate concentrations affected mitochondrial respiratory activity. Chance and Williams (1956) using spectrophotometric analysis and later microfluorometry (Chance et al., 1962) concluded that the level of ADP was a major control mechanism. Low levels of ADP decrease respiration by mitochondria; high levels increase the rate. Fortyfold changes in respiratory rate could be produced by altering ADP concentrations in liver cell mitochondria; and this represents the normal range of respiration changes needed by these cells under varying conditions of activity. Similar findings hold for muscle tissue although here 100- to 1,000-fold changes in respiration occur from the resting

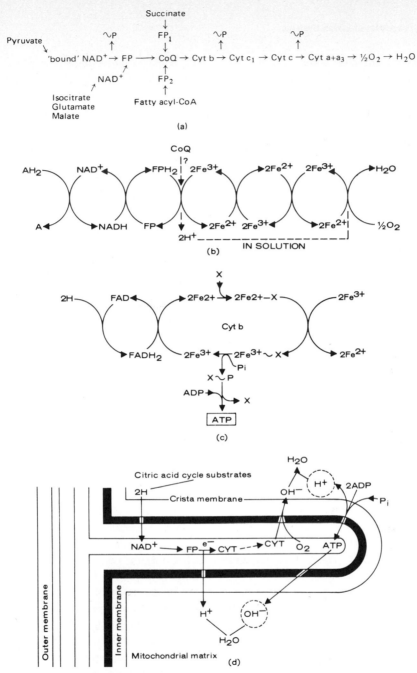

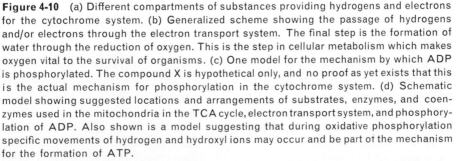

Figure 4-10 (a) Different compartments of substances providing hydrogens and electrons for the cytochrome system. (b) Generalized scheme showing the passage of hydrogens and/or electrons through the electron transport system. The final step is the formation of water through the reduction of oxygen. This is the step in cellular metabolism which makes oxygen vital to the survival of organisms. (c) One model for the mechanism by which ADP is phosphorylated. The compound X is hypothetical only, and no proof as yet exists that this is the actual mechanism for phosphorylation in the cytochrome system. (d) Schematic model showing suggested locations and arrangements of substrates, enzymes, and coenzymes used in the mitochondria in the TCA cycle, electron transport system, and phosphorylation of ADP. Also shown is a model suggesting that during oxidative phosphorylation specific movements of hydrogen and hydroxyl ions may occur and be part of the mechanism for the formation of ATP.

to the actively contracting state depending on the type of muscle.

AMP is the controlling element in some cellular respiration (Atkinson, 1965). The inorganic phosphate concentration is a major control factor in ascites tumor cells (Racker and Wu, 1959). Generally however, mitochondrial respiration depends on the phosphate potential—the ratio ATP/ADP [P_i]. This respiratory control acts in tightly coupled mitochondria, that is, those in which neither substrate nor oxygen is limiting and in which phosphorylation accompanies oxidation. Under these conditions when ATP accumulates (low cellular activity and energy requirements), oxidation is inhibited. In fact, the addition of ATP to purified mitochondrial preparations can inhibit respiration by bringing about a reverse electron flow (for example, from the cytochromes to NAD; see Ernster and Lee, 1964). Although classically it was thought that energy production drove cellular activities, it now appears that cellular activities can pull the energy producing processes (Mitchell, 1961).

4-18. Mitochondrial Compartmentation. The mitochondrial membrane is impermeable to many common metabolites, coenzymes, and high energy compounds. NAD, NADH, ATP, P_i, acetyl-CoA, and TCA cycle intermediates (with the exceptions of citrate, succinate, and malonate) cannot penetrate. The compartmentation of such compounds has an important bearing on metabolic regulation. We shall consider its effect in integrating glycolysis and oxidative-phosphorylation.

The Pasteur effect is the inhibition of glycolysis that occurs when oxidative phosphorylation proceeds at a rapid rate. The reverse is also found. When glycolysis proceeds rapidly and acetyl-CoA builds up, aerobiosis is inhibited (the Crabtree effect). These represent a form of control and integration of glycolytic and respiratory metabolism.

It was originally proposed that glycolysis was controlled by the concentrations of inorganic phosphate because maximal glycolytic rates are found at high concentrations of P_i, while oxidative phosphorylation proceeds maximally at lower levels of P_i. High respiratory rates mean an increased production of ATP and a lower concentration of P_i (Racker, 1965, reviews this work).

Chance and others suggested that ADP concentrations were the determining factor for the relative rates of glycolysis and respiration. Since ADP and ATP are compartmentalized into mitochondrial and extra-mitochondrial pools, there is a competition for ADP. Chance and Hess (1959) proposed that glycolysis is normally maintained in a state corresponding to a low ADP level. Low ADP means a high ATP concentration and energy for the phosphorylation of glucose by hexokinase.

If ATP is compartmented there must exist mechanisms by which its energy is transmitted to the cytoplasm for use in cellular functioning. The nature of this system is not known. Compartmentation also means that NADH formed in the cytoplasm during glycolysis cannot be reoxidized directly in the mitochondria. Such reduced NAD may be oxidized either through the formation of lactate or other side-product or via a shuttle system connecting the cytoplasmic NADH to the cytochrome chain in the mitochondria. One proposed shuttle is based on the presence of the enzyme, α-glycerophosphate dehydrogenase, in large amounts in both cytoplasm and mitochondria. This enzyme reversibly converts dihydroxyacetone phosphate to α-glycerophosphate with the oxidation of NADH to NAD. α-Glycerophosphate readily penetrates the mitochondrial membrane and after entering the mitochondria is converted by the mitochondrial enzyme to dihydroxyacetone phosphate with the reduction of NAD. Dihydroxyacetone phosphate then diffuses back into the cytoplasm, where it can again react with more NADH. The mitochondrial NADH is, of course, reoxidized through the cytochrome system. In this way levels of NAD necessary for glycolysis to proceed are maintained.

Boxer and Devlin (1961) point out that by this shuttle system the relative amounts of NAD in mitochondria and cytoplasm could control glycolysis and respiration and perhaps be responsible for the Pasteur effect. In malignant tumor cells with which much work has been done on the study of metabolic control, the shuttle enzyme is lacking or low in concentration. Boxer & Devlin use this fact to explain the original finding of Warburg (1956) that cancer cells often operate on a glycolytic source of energy only. If α-glycerophosphate dehydrogenase is missing in a cell, only lactate production is available to restore NADH to the oxidized form needed for glycolysis. The significance of these and other metabolic deficiencies in cancer cells is reviewed by Reid (1965).

Lehninger (1965) points out that all theories for explaining the integration of glycolysis and respiration are based on the compartmentation of components common to both systems: ATP, ADP, P_i, or NADH. This discussion of the control of energy metabolism has centered upon the end products of metabolism such as ADP or ATP and the important coenzyme NAD. Other factors are important in the intact cell. The production of ATP must be linked to the hydrolysis of ATP by the nature and state of the ATPase enzymes present in the cell. Much still remains to be discovered about these regulatory mechanisms.

4-19. Enzyme Reversibility, Duplication, and Activation.   In many cellular reaction schemes, a simple reversibility of reaction and the Mass Law or the availability of enzymes or coenzymes are sufficient to control the rate of reaction. The integration of glycolysis and respiration is most likely based ultimately on the reversibility of both of these systems. Reversibility as a control mechanism is excellently demonstrated by the buffering system which maintains blood pH at a constant level (see Chapter 17).

It is clear, however, that while most or all reactions of a given metabolic pathway may be reversible, catabolic and anabolic reactions usually follow different routes using different enzymes. Glycogen breaks down to pyruvate through the series of reversible reactions of the glycolytic pathway. Although glycogen can be formed again from pyruvate, the final step is not the reverse of the initial glycolytic reaction step. Although it is possible for glycogen to be formed from glucose 1-phosphate through the enzyme glycogen phosphorylase (Cori et al., 1939), it is now known that in the cell glycogen is synthesized from glucose 1-phosphate through another series of reactions which require uridine di- and triphosphates and ATP (LeLoir and Goldemberg, 1960) and a series of enzymes found in many tissues. The use of separate enzyme systems for forward and reverse reactions allows greater control over the decision as to which reaction shall proceed under a given set of conditions.

In long reaction sequences one or two critical steps usually exert control over the entire reaction sequence. Davis (1961) classified enzymes as follows: amphibolic—having both catabolic and anabolic functions (they would include all enzymes used from the reaction of glucose 6-phosphate to acetyl-CoA in glycolysis and all enzymes of the TCA cycle); anabolic—those enzymes in pathways that branch from amphibolic reactions to yield essential cellular compounds; and catabolic—those enzymes that convert various carbon sources into intermediates or move them into amphibolic pathways.

In the glycolytic scheme two controlling steps are important. The hexokinase reaction determines how much glucose is utilized, although this step will not determine the fate of glucose. The reaction involving glyceraldehydephosphate dehydrogenase is considered as the determiner of the rate of energy production from glucose activated by the hexokinase reaction.

In the TCA cycle, citrate and oxaloacetate are branch points where reactions can lead either to energy production through oxidation-reduction metabolism or to synthesis of cellular compounds. Similarly, acetyl-CoA is a branch point leading either to the TCA cycle and energy production, or to glycogen synthesis, or to fatty acid synthesis. In yeast there are two enzymes: pyruvate oxidase and pyruvic decarboxylase, which can take pyruvate either into the oxidative phosphorylation

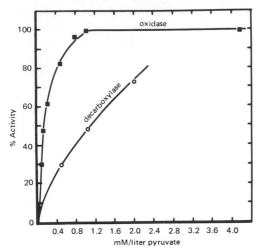

Figure 4-11 A comparison of the reaction rates of pyruvate oxidase and pyruvate decarboxylase. The latter has a low rate at substrate concentrations at which the oxidase has maximal rate. The different rates permit a control of metabolism by determining which pathway will be taken by pyruvate.

or chymotrypsinogen to chymotrypsin. The synthesis of zymogens is a protective device for the cells which must produce these destructive proteins. Digestive enzymes are not produced in functional form until they are released into the lumen of the digestive system whose walls are coated with protective mucins.

Activation in a more general sense involves preparing or altering the active site of an enzyme either by conformational change, by addition of a coenzyme or cofactor, or by other processes that make the enzyme-substrate combination possible or cause this combination to proceed at a faster rate.

Figure 4-12 illustrates the activation of trypsinogen to trypsin. In this case activation occurs with the splitting off of a hexapeptide unit from the zymogen. Once some trypsin is formed, it autocatalyzes the formation of more trypsin from the zymogen. This is a positive feedback system which greatly increases the rate at which active enzyme is

pathway or into the fermentation pathway (Holzer and Goedde, 1957). Figure 4-11 shows the kinetic characteristics of the two enzymes. Pyruvic oxidase has a higher affinity for pyruvate than does the decarboxylase enzyme. A decrease in the steady state concentration of pyruvate below 10 mM first lowers the rate of decarboxylation. No effect on oxidation is seen until pyruvate falls to very low levels. Increases in pyruvate concentration above 1 mM cause increased rates of fermentation without affecting respiration. A relation between the steady state concentrations of pyruvate and the rate of fermentation and respiration is seen in living yeast cells. Here then is a point where control may be exercised over cellular metabolism depending on the immediate needs of the cell—a control which is based upon the affinity of a substrate for two different enzymes.

Another mechanism for controlling enzyme reactions is activation. Activation can be of several types. A familiar example is the transformation of inactive zymogens (enzyme precursors) into active digestive enzymes: pepsinogen to pepsin, trypsinogen to trypsin,

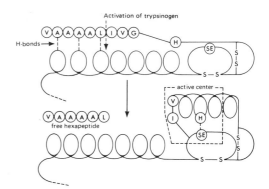

Figure 4-12 A model for the activation of bovine trypsinogen. The amino acids making up the active site are exposed by the removal of a hexapeptide fragment, and there is an accompanying change in the conformation of the protein, which produces the active enzyme trypsin. The activation is initiated by enterokinase in the digestive tract, but once some trypsin is formed, it can act as a catalyst for the reaction. Such autocatalysis is a form of positive feedback: the more trypsin formed, the faster trypsinogen is converted to trypsin. V = valine; A = aspartic; H = histidine; L = leucine; I = isoleucine; G = glutamic; SE = serine; X = specificity site of the enzyme. [After H. Neurath and G. H. Dixon (1957). *Federation Proceedings* **16**: 791].

formed. Initially trypsin is formed in a reaction catalyzed by enterokinase released from the intestinal mucosa as food reaches this point in the digestive tract. Further information on trypsinogen activation can be found in a series of papers in Boyer et al (1960, Vol. 4). Wilson and Pardee (1964) discuss the comparative aspects of enzyme activation and control. Activation of the type described above for trypsinogen is found in many animal activities including the highly regulated and complex formation of blood clots (Kline, 1965; Laki and Gladner, 1964).

One of the better examples of activation as a control mechanism in cellular metabolism involves the enzyme glycogen phosphorylase found in many tissues including liver, skeletal muscle, and cardiac muscle. Glycogen phosphorylase occurs in two forms, the a and b forms. The b form displays little enzyme activity, but the interconversion of the two forms is rapid and involves separate enzymes in each direction. In muscle the activation of phosphorylase b to phosphorylase a—the active form of the enzyme—requires four molecules of ATP and the enzyme, phosphorylase kinase. This enzyme also exists in two forms and the conversion of the inactive to the active form requires adenyl cyclase and adenosine-3′,5′-phosphate (cyclic adenylic acid or cyclic AMP):

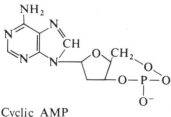

Cyclic AMP

The formation of cyclic AMP is stimulated by the hormone epinephrine. In order to stimulate glycogenolysis—the breakdown of glycogen—epinephrine is often used in experimental studies, and it is now evident that it acts indirectly on the glycogenolytic activity. To initiate glycolysis or a higher rate of glycolysis then involves a series of steps: the release of epinephrine (=adrenalin) by the adrenal glands to activate phosphorylase kinase. This enzyme in turn will activate phosphorylase b to phosphorylase a which can begin the breakdown of glycogen to phosphorylated glucose. What acts as a stimulus for the hormonal control system to begin operation is unclear. The system is similar, but not identical, in other tissues (Krebs and Fischer, 1962; Rall and Sutherland, 1961). Other roles have been proposed for the compound cyclic AMP including a function in water movement through toad bladder (Orloff and Handler, 1961); control of muscle contraction (Mayer and Moran, 1960); and changes in membrane potentials Bülbring, 1960).

From what has been said in this section, it can be seen that activation, duplicate enzymes, and hormonal controls can all be used to achieve regulation of metabolism.

4-20. Feedback Inhibition and Allosteric Effects. In many cases analogs of metabolic intermediates (antimetabolites) can inhibit enzyme activity. Inhibitions have been classed as competitive, noncompetitive, and uncompetitive, according to the nature of the complexes formed. The general types of inhibitory reactions and the ways for determining the type of inhibition from the reaction kinetics are shown in Figure 4-4.

Competitive inhibition is reversible, that is, enzyme activity is recovered when the inhibitor molecule is removed from the enzyme. This type of inhibition results from molecules whose structure resembles that of the normal substrate of the enzyme. There is a loose combination between the inhibitor and the active site of the enzyme. The velocity of the reaction depends on inhibitor concentration, substrate concentration, and the relative affinities of inhibitor and substrate for the enzyme. Noncompetitive inhibition results from the combination of inhibitor molecule with a site on the enzyme other than the active site. The velocity of the reaction depends only on inhibitor concentration and its affinity for the enzyme. In uncompetitive inhibition a complex is formed between ES and the inhibitor molecule; no enzyme-inhibitor complex is formed.

In many instances the product of the last of a chain of enzyme reactions is an inhibitor of an earlier step, and a feedback system is established that controls the rate of the whole sequence. Such feedback is sometimes called "end product inhibition" (Atkinson, 1965; Burland et al., 1965; Umbarger, 1964).

Although it was at first thought that inhibition was due to competition or disruption of the active site of an enzyme by the inhibitor molecule, it is now known that many enzymes have two sites: one for substrate complexing, and a second to which inhibitors (or activators) can attach. The complexing at this second site presumably alters the conformation of the enzyme, decreasing or increasing its activity. One enzyme has had its three-dimensional structure completely analyzed both in the pure state and also when complexed with a substrate and with an inhibitor. This is the enzyme lysozyme. Any factor which can alter the conformation of an enzyme can affect the activity of that enzyme by increasing or decreasing, for example, the ability of substrate to combine with the protein (Koshland, 1962; Goodwin et al., 1964; van Rossum, 1963). The term "allosteric effect" is used to refer to alterations in enzyme activity caused by conformational changes brought about by activators or inhibitors. Such activity through the products of metabolic reactions or by the use of hormones provides an excellent method for controlling enzyme reactions in the cell, although few such systems are known in detail.

4-21. Enzyme Induction and Repression. These mechanisms for controlling enzyme activity operate, not directly on the rate of an enzyme reaction, but on the mechanisms that determine the concentration of an enzyme within the cell. Induction is an increase in the concentration (or synthesis) of an enzyme; repression is the decrease in the concentration (or synthesis) of an enzyme.

Because induction and repression involve changes in the amounts of a protein in the cell, the protein synthesizing sites and their controllers must be the loci affected by induction or repression agents. In genetic terms, regulator genes present in the DNA of the nucleus control the synthesis of proteins. A regulator gene can interact with operators, defined as small regions of the gene structure whose function is to control the activity of the structural genes responsible for protein synthesis. The interaction between the operator and the product of the regulator gene is inhibited or activated by the regulator agent, thus causing the synthesis or nonsynthesis of protein. In bacteria, where this phenomenon has been extensively studied, it is often a new nutrient in the medium that causes the genetic material to begin production of protein enzymes capable of utilizing the nutrient. When the bacteria are removed from the presence of that particular nutrient, the enzyme disapears from the bacterial cell (see Fincham, 1960; Jacob and Monod, 1961; and the *Cold Spring Harbor Symposium on Quantitative Biology*, Vol. 20).

Hormones play a major role in controlling cellular metabolism (Karlson, 1963; Karlson and Sekeris, 1966). A given hormone is but part of a larger feedback system. The secretion of hormones is governed by both the endocrine and nervous systems interacting in a complex manner. The latter system carries information in response to stimuli from cells or the environment, and this information causes hormone synthesis and release. The hormones in turn activate or inhibit various phases of cellular activity according to the demands of the cells or the organism.

Hormones may act in any of several ways. Some induce enzymes by interacting with the genetic material of the cell. Others affect membrane structure and function and may alter membrane permeability and thus also alter the compartmentation of some substance. Hormones may also have allosteric effects and directly attach to an enzyme.

Insulin is an interesting hormone because it seems to do all of these things for different enzymes. It induces the formation of pyruvate kinase (Weber et al., 1965), thus affecting the rate of glycolysis. It also controls the transport of glucose across biological membranes. Its overall activity is to aid in the regulation of carbohydrate metabolism and in the regulation of blood glucose concentrations (see Krahl, 1965).

4-22. Summary of Metabolic Controls. From what has been said in this part of the chapter, it should be evident that the regulation of metabolism involves complex systems and a variety of control agents. Since enzymes are so important in cellular rate processes and are large, structurally complex, macromolecules, it is not surprising that cellular metabolism is primarily regulated by regulating enzyme activity. In the normal cell there is seldom an accumulation of any metabolic product. This will occur only in cells in which a mutation has produced a blocked reaction step (a protein enzyme cannot be formed) or in cells which have been treated with a metabolic inhibitor. The reaction sequences described in this chapter have, in many cases, been determined by the study of such mutant or inhibited cells in which an accumulated product can be measured.

The basic types of enzyme regulation include the following:

1. The Mass Action Law states that an equilibrium amount of product will be formed in an equilibrium reaction unless some mechanism that removes or changes the product is present.
2. Allosteric inhibition and activation operate through conformational changes of the enzyme that alter the active site. Allosteric mechanisms may occur because of the genetically controlled production of specific activators or inhibitors, because of endocrine mechanisms or, because of feedback effects when the end product of one enzyme reaction inhibits an earlier reaction in a reaction sequence. Some of the control mechanisms listed below are actually subheadings under allosteric effects.
3. Enzyme induction and repression: the genetic control of enzyme synthesis or nonsynthesis.
4. Multiple enzyme forms (also known as isozymes). The presence of an inactive form of an enzyme which, under appropriate conditions, can be changed to an active form.
5. Compartmentation: enzyme systems involved with oxidative-phosphorylation, with protein synthesis in the rough endoplasmic reticulum, lipid synthesis in the endoplasmic reticulum, and many other cellular reaction systems are found in membrane-bounded compartments of the cell. Such compartmentation allows control of a given reaction sequence by limiting substrate availability, by producing certain ratios of needed coenzymes, or by limiting the concentration of substances such as ADP, ATP, or inorganic phosphate.
6. Hormonal action: the intercellular regulation system that depends upon the appropriate stimulation of endocrine glands to release hormones into the blood, which will carry these chemicals to the target cells of the organism.
7. Competitive inhibition: the activity of an enzyme is affected by a substance that combines with the active site, preventing the normal substrate from forming an enzyme-substrate complex.
8. Ion availability. Many enzymes require a particular ion for full activity and are inhibited by other ions. Ion availability, as affected for example by membrane permeability, is a further mechanism for enzyme control.

The discussion of energy and the rules governing its transformation and uses was included because energy is of such importance to the cell and the organism. Cellular organization is maintained and cellular activities are carried out by means of energy. That cellular metabolism must be closely regulated so that energy is not wastefully dissipated is a basic requirement of animals that operate in a world of competition for energy. From the evolutionary point of view, it is interesting that many of the basic molecules involved in energy metabolism are so closely alike in all cells. This would indicate that at some time, early in the evolution of living cells, there was a selective process at work to choose those particular pathways and molecules that had a superiority over others. From this basic stem evolved present biochemical systems— a topic to be considered in the next chapter.

References and Readings

Atkinson, D. E. (1965). "Biological feedback control at the molecular level." *Science* **150**: 851–857.

Bernhard, S. A. (1968). **The Structure and Function of Enzymes.** New York: W. A. Benjamin, Inc. 324 pp.

Blum, H. F. (1955). **Times Arrow and Evolution,** 2nd ed. Princeton, N.J.: Princeton University Press. 220 pp.

Bondi, H. (1952). **Cosmology.** New York: Cambridge University Press. 179 pp.

Boxer, G. E. and T. M. Devlin (1961). "Pathways of intracellular hydrogen transport." *Science* **134**: 1495–1501.

Boyer, P. D., H. Lardy, and K. Myrback (1959–1961). **The Enzymes,** 3 volumes. New York: Academic Press, Inc.

Bray, H. G. and K. White (1966). **Kinetics and Thermodynamics in Biochemistry,** 2nd ed. New York: Academic Press, Inc. 343 pp.

Brodie, A. F. and J. Adelson (1965). "Respiratory chains and sites of coupled phosphorylation." *Science* **149**: 265–268.

Bülbring, E. (1960). "Biophysical changes produced by adrenaline and noradrenaline." **Ciba Foundation Symposium on Adrenergic Mechanisms.** Boston: Little, Brown and Company. pp. 275–287.

Burland, L., P. Datta, and H. Gest (1965). "Control of enzyme activity in growing bacterial cells by concerted feedback inhibition." *Science* **148**: 1361–1363.

Burton, K. and H. A. Krebs (1953). "The free energy changes associated with the individual steps of the tricarboxylic acid cycle, glycolysis and alcoholic fermentation and with the hydrolysis of the pyrophosphate groups of adenosine triphosphate." *Biochem. J.* **54**: 94–107.

Calvin, M. (1962). "Evolutionary possibilities for photosynthesis and quantum conversion." In: **Horizons in Biochemistry.** (M. Kasha and B. Pullman, eds.), pp. 23–57. New York: Academic Press, Inc.

Chance, B. (1943). "The kinetics of the enzyme-substrate compound of peroxidase." *J. Biol. Chem.* **151**: 553–577.

Chance, B. (1961). "Control characteristics of enzyme systems." *Cold Spring Harbor Symp. Quant. Biol.* **26**: 289–299.

Chance, B., ed. (1963). **Energy-Linked Functioning in Mitochondria.** New York: Academic Press, Inc. 282 pp.

Chance, B., P. Cohen, F. Jöbsis, and B. Schoener (1962). "Intracellular oxidation-reduction states *in vivo*." *Science* **137**: 499–508.

Chance, B., R. W. Estabrook, and J. R. Williamson, eds. (1965). **Control of Energy, Metabolism.** New York: Academic Press, Inc. 441 pp.

Chance, B. and B. Hess (1959). "Spectroscopic evidence of metabolic control." *Science* **129**: 700–708.

Chance, B. and G. R. Williams (1956). "The respiratory chain and oxidative-phosphorylation." *Adv. Enzymol.* **17**: 65–134.

Commoner, B., P. Lippincott, R. E. Norberg, J. J. Heise, J. V. Passaneua, and J. Townsend (1957). "Biological action of free radicals." *Science* **126**: 57–63.

Cori, G. T., C. F. Cori, and G. Schmidt (1939). "The role of glucose-1-phosphate in the formation of blood sugar and synthesis of glycogen in the liver." *J. Biol. Chem.* **129**: 629–639.

Davies, R. E. and A. G. Ogsten (1950). "On the mechanism of secretion of ions by gastric mucosa and by other tissues." *Biochem. J.* **46**: 324–333.

Davis, B. D. (1961). "The teleonomic significance of biosynthetic control mechanisms." *Cold Spring Harbor Symp. Quant. Biol.* **26**: 1–10.

Decker, J. P. (1965). "Work and energy are misleading concepts." *Bioscience* **15**: 589–591.

Dixon, M. and E. C. Webb (1964). **Enzymes,** 2nd ed. New York: Academic Press, Inc. 950 pp.

Duysens, L. N. M. (1964). "Photosynthesis." *Prog. Biophys.* **14:** 1–104.

Edsall, J. T. and J. Wyman (1958). **Biophysical Chemistry.** Vol. 1. New York: Academic Press, Inc. 699 pp.

Eley, D. D. (1962). "Semiconductivity in biological molecules." In: **Horizons in Biochemistry.** (M. Kasha and B. Pullman, eds.), pp. 341–380. New York: Academic Press, Inc.

Ernster, L. and C. P. Lee (1964). "Biological oxidoreductions." *Ann. Rev. Biochem.* **33:** 729–790.

Estabrook, R. W. and D. Garfinkel (1962). "Studies on the content and organization of the respiratory enzymes of mitochondria." *J. Biophys. Biochem. Cytol.* **9:** 19–28.

Eyring, H. (1935). "The activated complex and the absolute rate of chemical reactions." *Chem. Rev.* **17:** 65–77.

Eyring, H. and D. W. Urry (1965). "Thermodynamics and chemical kinetics." In: **Theoretical and Mathematical Biology.** (T. H. Waterman and H. J. Morowitz, eds.), pp. 57–96. Waltham, Mass.: Blaisdell Publishing Company.

Fincham, J. R. S. (1960). "Genetically controlled differences in enzyme activity." *Adv. Enzymol.* **22:** 1–44.

Florkin, M. and E. H. Stotz, eds. (1965). **Comprehensive Biochemistry,** Vol. 13. Enzyme Nomenclature, 2nd ed. New York: American Elsevier Publishing Co. 219 pp.

George, P. and R. J. Rutman (1960). "The 'high energy phosphate bond' concept." *Prog. Biophys.* **10:** 1–54.

George, P. R. C. Phillips, and R. J. Rutman (1963). "Estimates of thermodynamic data for the formation of the Mg^{++} complex of ATP and ADP at zero ionic strength." *Biochem.* **2:** 508–511.

Glasstone, S. (1946). **The Elements of Physical Chemistry.** New York; D. Van Nostrand Company, Inc. 695 pp.

Glasstone, S. (1947). **Thermodynamics for Chemists.** New York: D. Van Nostrand Company, Inc. 522 pp.

Goodwin, T. W., J. I. Harris, and B. S. Hartley, eds. (1964). **Structure and Activity of Enzymes.** Symp. No. 1, London. New York: Academic Press, Inc. 190 pp.

Green, D. E. (1959). "Mitochondrial structure and function." In: **Subcellular Particles.** (T. Hayashi, ed.), pp. 84–103. Washington, D.C.: American Physiological Soc.

Green, D. E. and Y. Hatefi, (1961). "The mitochondrion and biochemical machines." *Science* **133:** 13–19.

Green, D. E. and D. H. MacLennan (1969). "Structure and function of the mitochondrial cristael membrane." *Bioscience* **19:** 213–222.

Green, D. E., R. E. Beyer, M. Hansen, A. L. Smith, and G. Webster (1963). "Coupling factors and the mechanism of oxidative phosphorylation." *Fed. Proc.* **22:** 1460–1468.

Griffiths, D. E. (1963). "A new phosphorylated derivative of NAD, an intermediate in oxidative phosphorylation." *Fed. Proc.* **22:** 1064–1070.

Holzer, H. and H. W. Goedde (1957). "Zwei Wege von Pyruvat zu Acetyl-Coenzym A in Hefe." *Biochem. Z.* **329:** 175–191.

Hoyle, F. (1950, 1960). **The Nature of the Universe.** New York: Harper and Row, Publishers, Inc. 142 pp.

International Union of Biochemistry. (1965). **Enzyme Nomenclature.** New York: American Elsevier Publishing Co. 287 pp.

Jacob, F. and J. Monod (1961). "Genetic regulatory mechanisms in the synthesis of proteins." *J. Mol. Biol.* **3:** 318–356.

Johnson, F. H., H. Eyring, and M. J. Polissar (1954). **The Kinetic Basis of Molecular Biology.** New York: John Wiley & Sons, Inc. 874 pp.

Karlson, P. (1963). "New concepts on the mode of action of hormones." *Perspectives Biol. Med.* **6:** 203.

Karlson, P. and C. E. Sekeris (1966). "Biochemical mechanism of hormone action." *Acta Endocrinol.* **53:** 505–518.

Katchalsky, A. and P. F. Curran (1965). **Nonequilibrium Thermodynamics in Biophysics.** Cambridge, Mass.: Harvard University Press. 248 pp.

Keilin, D. (1966). **The History of Cell Respiration and Cytochromes.** New York: Cambridge University Press. 416 pp.

Kirkwood, J. G. and I. Oppenheim (1961). **Chemical Thermodynamics.** New York: The McGraw-Hill Book Company, Inc. 391 pp.

Kline, D. L. (1965). "Blood coagulation: reactions leading to prothrombin activation." *Ann. Rev. Physiol.* **27**: 285–306.

Koshland, D. E. (1963). "Correlation of structure and function in enzyme action." *Science* **142**: 1533–1540.

Kosower, E. M. (1962). **Molecular Biochemistry.** New York: McGraw-Hill Book Company, Inc. 304 pp.

Krahl, M. E. (1965). **The Action of Insulin on Cells.** New York: Academic Press, Inc. 202 pp.

Krebs, H. A. and E. H. Fischer (1962). "Molecular properties and transformations of glycogen phosphorylase in animal tissues." *Adv. Enzymol.* **24**: 263–290.

Krebs, H. A. and H. L. Kornberg (1957). **Energy Transformations in Living Matter.** Berlin: Springer-Verlag. 298 pp.

Laki, K. and J. A. Gladner (1964). "Chemistry and physiology of the fibrinogen-fibrin transition." *Physiol. Rev.* **44**: 127–146.

Lardy, H. A., D. Johnson, and W. C. McMurray (1958). "Antibodies as tools for metabolic studies. I. A survey of toxic antibodies in respiratory, phosphorylative and glycolytic systems." *Arch. Biochem. Biophys.* **78**: 587–597.

Lardy, H. S. and H. Wellman (1952). "Oxidative phosphorylation: role of inorganic phosphate and acceptor systems in control of metabolic rate." *J. Biol. Chem.* **195**: 215–224.

Lehninger, A. L. (1962). "Respiration-linked mechanochemical changes in mitochondria." In: **Horizons in Biochemistry.** (M. Kasha and B. Pullman, eds.), pp. 121–135. New York: Academic Press, Inc.

Lehninger, A. L. (1964). **The Mitochondrion.** New York: W. A. Benjamin, Inc. 263 pp.

Lehninger, A. L. (1965). **Bioenergetics.** New York: W. A. Benjamin, Inc.

Lehninger, A. L. and C. L. Wadkins (1962).

"Oxidative phosphorylation." *Ann. Rev. Biochem.* **31**: 47–78.

Lehninger, A. L., C. L. Wadkins, and L. F. Remmert (1959). "Control points in phosphorylating respiration and the action of a mitochondrial respiration-releasing factor. Ciba Symposium on Regulation of Cell Metabolism." Boston: Little, Brown and Company 130 pp.

Leloir, L. F. and S. H. Goldemberg (1960). "Synthesis of glycogen from uridine diphosphate glucose in liver." *J. Biol. Chem.* **235**: 919–923.

Lineweaver, H. and D. Burke (1934). "The determination of enzyme dissociation constants." *J. Am. Chem. Soc.* **56**: 658–666.

Lioret, C. and A. Moyse (1963). "Acid metabolism: the citric acid cycle and other cycles." In: **Comparative Biochemistry,** Vol. 5. (M. Florkin and H. S. Mason, eds.), pp. 203–306. New York: Academic Press, Inc.

Lipmann, F. (1941). "Metabolic generation and utilization of phosphate bond energy." *Adv. Enzymol.* **1**: 99–162.

Loomis, W. F. and F. Lipmann (1948). "Reversible inhibition of the coupling between phosphorylation and oxidation." *J. Biol. Chem.* **173**: 807–808.

Mahler, H. R. and E. H. Cordes (1966). **Biological Chemistry.** New York: Harper and Row, Publishers, Inc. 872 pp.

Mayer, S. E. and N. C. Moran (1960). "Relation between pharmacologic augmentation of cardiac contractile force and the activation of myocardial glycogen phosphorylase." *J. Pharmacol.* **129**: 271–281.

Mitchell, P. (1961). "A chemiosmotic hypothesis for the mechanism of oxidative and photosynthetic phosphorylation." *Nature* **191**: 144–148.

Mitchell, P. and J. Moyle (1967). "Proton-transport phosphorylation: some experimental tests." In: **Chemistry of Mitochondria.** (E. C. Slater, Z. Kaniuga, and L. Wojtczak, eds.), pp. 53–74. New York: Academic Press, Inc.

Neubert, D. and A. L. Lehninger (1962). "The effect of oligomycin, gramicidin and other antibiotics on reversal of swelling of mitochondria by ATP." *Biochim. Biophys. Acta* **62**: 556–565.

Ohnishi, T. and T. Ohnishi (1962). "A contractile protein of mitochondria." *J. Biochem., Tokyo*, **51**: 380.

Orloff, J. and J. S. Handler (1961). "Vasopressin-like effects of adenosine-3',5'-phosphate (cyclic 3,5-AMP) and theophylline in the toad bladder." *Biochem. Biophys. Res. Comm.* **5**: 63–66.

Packer, L. and P. Siegenthaler (1966). "Control of chloroplast structure by light." *Int. Rev. Cytol.* **20**: 97–124.

Park, R. B. (1966). "Subunits of chloroplast structure and quantum conversion in photosynthesis." *Int. Rev. Cytol.* **20**: 67–95.

Patton, A. R. (1965). **Biochemical Energetics and Kinetics.** Philadelphia: W. B. Saunders Company. 116 pp.

Phillips, R., P. George, and R. H. Rutman (1963). "Potentiometric studies of the secondary phosphate ionizations of AMP, ADP, and ATP, and calculations of thermodynamic data for the hydrolysis reactions." *Biochem.* **2**: 501–507.

Prigogine, I. (1962). **Introduction to the Thermodynamics of Irreversible Processes,** 2nd ed. New York: Interscience Publishers, Inc. 132 pp.

Racker, E. (1965). **Mechanisms in Bioenergetics.** New York: Academic Press, Inc. 259 pp.

Racker, E. and R. Wu (1959). "Limiting factors in glycolysis of Ascites tumor cells and the Pasteur effect." In: **Ciba Foundation Symposium on Regulation of Cell Metabolism.** (G. E. W. Wolstenholme and C. M. O'Connor, eds.), pp. 205–209. Boston: Little, Brown and Company.

Rall, T. W. and E. W. Sutherland (1961). "The regulatory role of adenosine-3',5'-phosphate." *Cold Spring Harbor Symp. Quant. Biol.* **26**: 347–354.

Reid, E. (1965). **Biochemical Approaches to Cancer.** New York: Pergamon Press, Inc. 198 pp.

Robbins, E. A. and P. D. Boyer (1957). "Glycogen synthesis from glucose, glucose-1-phosphate and uridine diphosphate glucose in muscle preparations." *Proc. Nat. Acad. Sci., U.S.,* **45**: 6–12.

Schrödinger, E. (1951). **What is Life?** New York: Cambridge University Press. 91 pp.

Slater, E., Z. Kaniuga, and L. Wojtczak, eds. (1967). **Biochemistry of Mitochondria.** New York: Academic Press, Inc. 122 pp.

Stadtman, E. R. (1966). "Allosteric regulation of enzyme activity." *Adv. Enzymol.* **28**: 41–154.

Szent-Györgyi, A. (1960). **Introduction to a Submolecular Biology.** New York: Academic Press, Inc. 135 pp.

Tribus, M. (1966). "Micro- and macro-thermodynamics." *Am. Sci.* **54**: 201–210.

Umbarger, H. E. (1961). "Feedback control by endproduct inhibition." *Cold Spring Harbor Symp. Quant. Biol.* **26**: 301–312.

Umbarger, H. E. (1964). "Intracellular regulatory mechanisms." *Science* **145**: 674–679.

van Rossum, J. M. (1963). "The relation between chemical structure and biological activity." *J. Pharm. Pharmacol.* **15**: 285–316.

Warburg, O. (1956). "On the origin of cancer cells." *Science* **123**: 309–314.

Wassink, E. C. (1963). "Photosynthesis." In: **Comparative Biochemistry,** Vol. 5. (M. Florkin and H. S. Mason, eds.), pp. 347–492. New York: Academic Press, Inc.

Webb, J. L. (1963–1965). **Enzymes and Metabolic Inhibitors.** 3 volumes. New York: Academic Press, Inc.

Weber, G., R. L. Singhal, N. B. Stamm, and S. K. Srivastava (1965). "Hormonal induction and suppression of liver enzyme biosynthesis." *Fed. Proc.* **24**: 745–754.

Wilson, A. C. and A. B. Pardee (1964). "Comparative aspects of metabolic control." In: **Comparative Biochemistry,** Vol. 6. (M. Florkin and H. S. Mason, eds.), pp. 73–118. New York: Academic Press, Inc.

5-1. The Problem. Considerations of the origin, nature, and evolution of life are basic to biological studies; and a brief discussion of these problems is included here for several reasons. Because this book deals in part with comparative physiology, which uses the ideas of evolution, some indications of the relationships of animals are of value. Further, the description of life must include its basic functional characteristics. Also the problem of the origin of life has been attacked by biochemical experiments, and some ideas of evolution are being aided by studies of the evolution of cellular molecules.

At the beginning of this century, to ask about the origin of life was considered taboo by most biologists. Little hope was seen of answering this question except by theories of divine creation, which removed the problem from the sphere of science; or by the Arrhenius spore theory, which postulated that life had floated onto the earth from outer space in the form of spores (only removing the problem of the beginning of life back one step to some unknown point and time in space); or in terms of extraterrestrial visitors bringing life to earth (with the same objections as the previous theory).

One cause of this feeling lay in the acceptance of two major biological theories of the nineteenth century. The Darwin-Wallace (1859) theory of evolution gave a mechanism for and presented the fact that species continually diverge forming new species and subspecies. But if this idea is extrapolated back in time it seems that in the beginning there had to have been one form of life which, by natural selection and evolution, led to all present forms (see Calvin, 1962). During this same period of time Pasteur in 1862, following the work of Spallanzani and others, overthrew the concept of the spontaneous generation of life and experimentally confirmed the idea that life could arise only from other life, not from nonliving matter (Kormandy, 1966, contains reprints of these older papers, as well as studies of recent work). There seemed to be no answer to the origin of life because according to the work of Pasteur life—the first life—could not have arisen from nonliving matter. The entire problem was generally dropped until

Chapter 5

Origin and Evolution of Life

the second quarter of the twentieth century.

Biochemical studies pointed to an underlying unity of living systems at the molecular level, for example, the general similarities of energy metabolism in all cells, discussed in Chapter 4; and this strongly implied that a biochemical evolution and selection must have preceded the development and evolution of plants and animals. Haldane (1954) and Oparin (1964) in the 1930's reopened the question of the origin of life. Since that time, the use of biochemical knowledge and methods, combined with new models of the origin and evolution of the earth itself, have given new insights into these questions.

Studies of **abiogenesis**—the development of living from nonliving material—are now based on the simple premise that while conditions on earth today preclude such a process, on the primitive earth different conditions prevailed and were suitable for abiogenesis. Before discussing recent concepts on the origin of life, we can first consider the nature of life.

5-2. What is Life? Although this question has no good answer at present, a discussion of it brings to light concepts that are of importance to biologists and philosophers. It is interesting to note that organisms are usually thought of in terms of the prevailing technology. In the eighteenth century—the era of clockworks—animals were considered to operate on the principles of clockwork mechanisms, wound up by some unknown agency and living until the works ran down or disintegrated. Many philosophical theories pictured animals as automata and at this time, especially in fiction, the ideas of building robots became popular. In the nineteenth century— the period of the development of steam engines and similar machinery—organisms were thought of as heat engines, and the application of thermodynamic principles to organismal activity was started. In the twentieth century —the age of control and computers—there is a tendency to think of animals as complex feedback systems, regulating and controlling their activities; of small energy sources acting to control large energy outputs. To the cyberneticist and philosopher the question arises: At what stage, if any, does a computer become a living system? What the next stage in this evolution of thought will be is fascinating to consider.

Rather than attempting to rigorously define life, the best approach seems to be to discuss organisms in terms of what they can do. Many introductory biology textbooks give a list of characteristics that distinguish the living from the nonliving system. These are nearly all physiological features of organisms or cells. One such characteristic is that of contractility or movement. All cells that have been examined in the living state show some form of movement. This may range from the contraction of the highly specialized muscle cell to the cytoplasmic movements known as protoplasmic streaming or cyclosis. Even cellular organelles and membranes are considered capable of contraction (Ussing, 1964). And it is interesting that all of these cellular movements seem based on a similar mechanism—the contraction of an actomyosin-like protein reacting with ATP (see Chapter 10).

Irritability is another common feature of living systems. This is the ability to sense and respond to changes in the environment. At the cellular level irritability has its basis in the nature and functioning of cellular membranes, and even subcellular organelles show this feature. Nerve cells are specialized to respond to change and transmit information of such change to sites where action can be taken.

Metabolism, already discussed, is basic to living systems. In its broadest sense metabolism includes the processes of food-gathering, digestion, intermediary metabolism, and excretion. It is through these processes that cells and organisms obtain the necessary energy and materials for maintenance and reproduction and growth and that toxic or useless materials are removed.

The combination of irritability, movement, and metabolism leads to the regulatory systems we know as organisms, which possess an overall capability for responding and reacting to the environment.

Reproduction is another feature of living

systems. Inherent in the Darwinian concept of evolution is the ability of living organisms to change and vary according to long-term changes in the environment and the necessity to meet and survive in new situations. The parent organisms will pass along to their off-spring not only the information needed to continue the species but also the ability to attempt to change with changing conditions. The reproduction, as well as mutations, of organisms is based on the properties of the nucleic acids—macromolecules that can repli-cate and mutate. To some biologists molecules such as DNA are living because they possess four fundamental characteristics of life. They can (1) undergo replication, (2) store infor-mation, (3) mutate and replicate in a new form, and (4) ensure a supply of the raw materials needed for the perpetuation of the system (Horowitz, 1959; Stanley, 1959). Such a definition permits the inclusion of viruses as living organisms.

This viewpoint is opposed by other scientists. For example, Davis (1961) states that DNA by itself can only store information and mutate. Other materials are needed for repli-cation, recombination, or transferal of infor-mation.

Organisms or cells that have all of the characteristics just mentioned are easily classified as living. It is those systems which lack some of these features that introduce difficulties. There is also the problem of whether such a set of characteristics is suffi-cient to define life. In an interesting chapter of his textbook, Barnes (1937) described many chemical and physical models that imitated some or all of the above activities. Pirie (1959) pointed out that there is no sharp demarcation between what is living and what is not. And that life is not a definable quantity but a state-ment of our attitude of mind toward a system. What has been discussed above basically states what living organisms can do, it has not defined life.

Perrett (1952) defined life as any potentially self-perpetuating open system of linked organic reactions, catalyzed stepwise and almost isothermally by complex and specific organic catalysts that are themselves produced by the system. This description fits the attri-butes of organisms as we know them today and does not require the presence of specific molecules or functions. It would, perhaps, be suitable for defining the earliest living sys-tems also. Importantly it includes the thermo-dynamic considerations that must be applied to living systems and also recognizes the com-plexity and organization that distinguishes the living from the nonliving system (Needham, 1959).

5-3. Steps in the Development of Life. When theorizing on the origin of life, we make two simplifying assumptions: (1) life did arise on earth and (2) the laws governing chemical, physical, and biological reactions are the same today as they were when the earth was formed.

It is believed that life developed in several stages. Three major ones are hypothesized as follows: (1) Organic compounds and energy sources required by living systems initially formed and accumulated. This period was one of molecular abiogenesis—the formation of organic compounds from inorganic sources and a period of biochemical evolution. (2) Molecules aggregated to form primitive living systems. Since such systems are thought to have been quite different and much simpler than any presently recognized they are called **eobionts** (Pirie, 1953). (3) Eobionts supposedly evolved into the more complex cells known today. The earliest cells may have been much simpler than present day bacteria, for initially there had been insufficient time for the evolu-tion of the elaborate metabolic and genetic machinery found in these forms.

It is suggested that the first living systems after the eobionts probably had some of the characteristics of plants. They would need to use sunlight, in a form of photosynthesis, to obtain energy and substances for synthesis of their constituents. They were probably auto-trophs—organisms that assimilate simple materials of the environment in order to build more complex ones and that use solar energy (Calvin, 1962, 1964). Later, as conditions changed, heterotrophs could evolve—organisms dependent on materials already synthesized by autotrophs and using only chemical energy in coupled reactions based on phosphate groups.

Most of these suggestions are speculative. Nothing is known about the nature of eobionts or their evolution into cells. Two opposing lines of thought prevail about their origin and nature. The first might be called the genetic theory of the origin of life. It supposes that before a living system can arise, there must be present a genelike element capable of information storage and transferal and of guidance of protein synthesis. In some forms of this hypothesis it is considered that DNA appeared as a type of free-living gene, which made biological organization and evolution possible. Biosynthetic and energetic capabilities arose in a stepwise fashion (see Horowitz, 1945, and the alternate view of Kavanau, 1960). Other treatments of these ideas are found in Muller (1966); Rich (1962); and Sagan (1957).

The alternate hypothesis might be called the metabolic theory (Davis, 1961). It suggests that chemical evolution and aggregation led to the formation of systems capable of metabolism and synthesis, as well as reproduction and variation, before the genetic mechanisms of present day organisms developed. These early systems were based on polypeptides and later proteins, although simple nucleotides or polynucleotides might also have been present.

Reflexive catalysis was proposed as one possible basis for the development of such systems (Allen, 1967; Calvin, 1956). The example below shows that the end product of a final step in a series of reactions might act as a catalyst for an earlier reaction in the sequence:

The nature of one of the final products, E, leads to the rapid production of more of itself. Side reactions could occur with the chance that products other than E become available and may prove more efficient as reflexive catalysts. It has been shown experimentally that such reflexive catalytic systems have a higher rate of accumulation of end product than nonreflexively catalytic ones. Primitive living systems would require some mechanism of this type for ensuring the accumulation of needed substances. By aggregation of reflexive catalytic systems, an eobiont might be formed. Further discussion of various forms of this hypothesis can be found in Steinman (1966); Needham (1959).

The time scales involved in the evolution of biological molecules and life are of importance. Figure 5-1 shows the estimated age of the earth (five billion to six billion years); the durations of the major geological eras; and the estimated times and extents of chemical and organic (Darwinian) evolution. Chemical evolution began sometime between four and five billion years ago. Organic evolution is estimated to have been initiated about three billion years ago. The earliest known fossils of recognizable animals date back about 400 million years although fossil algae have been found in sediments dated 2.7 billion years old (Holmes, 1954). Recorded human history is such an insignificant fraction of the geological time scale that it cannot be represented adequately on the scale of the figure. As the estimated time of the formation of the earth has been pushed further and further back with the introduction of more accurate methods for measuring ancient rocks and sediments, it has become clear that sufficient time has been available for the origin and evolution of life on this planet.

5-4. Abiogenesis of Molecules. The study of the origin of life is now as much a part of biology (and biochemistry) as the study of structure or function (Bernal, 1965). Any questions concerning the origin and development of life become associated with the history and evolution of the earth itself, and the sciences of geology, geochemistry, and paleochemistry must be drawn upon to furnish an adequate background for biological theories of evolution.

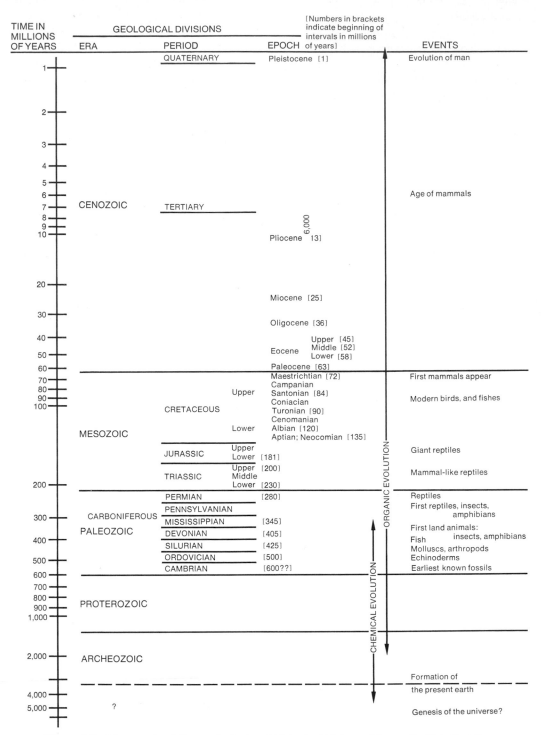

Figure 5-1 Time scale of the geological and biological history of the earth. Note that time scale is logarithmic. Data through Cambrian period after Kulp (1961) from isotopic age determination of rocks.

It is generally agreed that the primitive atmosphere was a reducing one; that the earth was nearly covered with water; and that temperatures averaged below 100°C at the time abiogenesis occurred (for example, see Urey, 1952). However, there have been changes in ideas concerning the composition of the primitive atmosphere. Early hypotheses assumed that the atmosphere consisted largely of nitrogen in the form of ammonia and methane, oxygen in the form of water, carbon monoxide, and gaseous hydrogen. But recent geochemical ideas point to an atmosphere consisting of free nitrogen and hydrogen, hydrogen cyanide, carbon monoxide, and carbon dioxide. The seas were alkaline because volatile substances, from the outgassing of rocks, reacted with the alkaline crust of the earth.

Most significant in formulation of the nature of the origin of life were the early experiments of Miller (1953) and Miller and Urey (1959). In these laboratory studies an electric spark was passed through a reaction vessel containing a mixture of ammonia, water, and methane—a mixture thought to resemble the primitive atmosphere. Any chemical reaction products formed in the electric arc were collected and analyzed by chromatographic and spectrophotometric procedures. Under these conditions several amino acids were formed (glycine, alanine, aspartic and glutamic acids); a variety of organic acids were produced (formic, acetic, proprionic, lactic, and succinic); urea and methyl urea were also formed. Thus, under conditions simulating those thought to exist on the primitive earth, it was possible to synthesize molecules that are basic building blocks of biological systems. The energy source mimicked natural lightning. This type of experimentation first showed that abiogenesis of organic molecules could have occurred on the earth under conditions different from those of today.

In later experiments, atmospheres more closely resembling those now thought to have existed were used. When a mixture of hydrogen, nitrogen, carbon monoxide, and carbon dioxide was irradiated with electric discharges or with ultraviolet light, hydrogen cyanide was produced (Ponnamperuma and Mack, 1965; Ponnamperuma, 1968). HCN is a constituent of comets and very likely of the primitive atmosphere (Oro, 1961). Further irradiation of the HCN yields amino acids, monocarboxylic acids, lipids, and other basic biological compounds (Allen and Ponnamperuma, 1967). Ultraviolet radiation is used because in a primitive atmosphere lacking free oxygen, ultraviolet light would reach the surface of the earth. Today, little ultraviolet radiation gets through the atmosphere because of the blanket of absorbing oxygen and ozone that surrounds the surface. Although it is commonly believed that this oxygen came from the action of photosynthesizing green plants, there may have been other sources (Dole, 1949). In addition to the use of ultraviolet radiation, gamma radiation has also been successfully used to produce organic molecules from inorganic constituents (Calvin, 1962; Paschke et al., 1957).

Thus, according to present beliefs, the materials, energy sources, and conditions necessary for the abiogenesis of organic compounds were present on the primitive earth (Oparin et al., 1959; Fox, 1963; Calvin, 1967).

The next steps toward the evolution of living systems following the formation of biological molecules would include the accumulation of these molecules and their organization into a more complex system. Originally it was suggested that since no bacteria or other microorganisms were present to break down these molecules, they would simply build up into a soupy sea (Ycas, 1955). However on thermodynamic and other grounds this idea has been discarded (Dayhoff et al., 1964; Hull, 1960). For example, the same radiations that provided energy for synthesizing these molecules would also destroy them. It is from this point to the formation of recognizable living systems that good hypotheses are lacking.

In order to account for the preservation and accumulation of organic substances Bernal (1959, 1965) proposed that organic compounds were adsorbed on clays or mud in estuarine regions. Here they could concentrate and be protected from radiation, and the surface might even provide a catalytic bed for the selection of particular chemical reactions.

Another unanswered problem concerns the formation of proteins. In artificial atmosphere experiments amino acids, not proteins, are formed. One group of workers has shown that proteins can be formed from amino acids at higher temperatures (Fox, 1960; Fox et al., 1959; Harada and Fox, 1965). Protein spherules are produced and condensation reactions between amino acids take place in the presence of polyphosphates. Such reactions can occur at 70°C, not an extremely high temperature. This might, on the primitive earth, have led to the beginnings of proteins and ATP systems. With ultraviolet radiation of HCN in the presence of inorganic phosphate, nucleotides are formed (Allen and Ponnamperuma, 1967). It can be envisaged that any polypeptides, proteins, or phosphate compounds could cooperate with polynucleotides or later DNA to stabilize coacervates (large colloidal particles surrounded by a surface phase), catalyze needed reactions, or form selective groupings for replication. Oparin (1964) considers that at some stage organic molecules aggregated to form coacervate droplets whose outer surface acted as a protection for the inner materials and also acted as a differentially permeable surface membrane. The hydrocarbons formed under primitive earth conditions in the laboratory are suitable for forming such a surface layer.

Kavanau (1947, 1960) suggested that the wave surfaces of the oceans could have supplied an environment where materials collected in droplets. Needed materials could accumulate in these droplets, while unwanted materials could be eliminated by reflexive catalysis. Some workers have shown that wave action in salt solutions can cause the aggregation of matter and the formation of organic particles incorporating polypeptides (Baylor and Sutcliffe, 1963; Sutcliffe et al., 1963; Riley, 1963).

These are some of the ideas developed to explain the evolution of the first living systems—none of them is satisfactory. Although reflexive catalysis enters into nearly all of these models, there are still no satisfactory models of this type of system although quantitative work has been done on the probabilities involved in the forming of living systems (Quastler, 1953). Simpson (1964) discusses the need of selection in the evolutionary sense even in the period of chemical evolution.

5-5. Biochemical Evolution. At present biochemistry and physiology are providing clues to add to the information of the morphologist and systematist about the relationships of living and fossil animals and plants. The discoveries of biochemistry and physiology have pointed out that the basic metabolic processes of all cells are similar. The cytochromes, glycolytic enzymes, and TCA cycle enzymes are ubiquitous compounds. So is chlorophyll among plants and the general photosynthetic pathway. All living systems that we know of are composed of proteins, lipids, carbohydrates, and nucleotides and derivatives. This basic similarity of metabolic reactions and cellular reactants leads one to the conclusion that living organisms as we know them today all sprang from one archetypal system. The independent origination of these basic compounds in a large number of different systems seems improbable, unless unknown conditions were in operation during this phase of the evolution of living systems.

This general similarity, of course, vanishes when one considers the specific activities and structures of cells and organisms. But these differences depend upon relatively minor differences in molecular structuring and organization, as well as on deletions and insertions of particular substances. Inherent in all living systems is the ability to change to meet new needs and environments, although severe changes may eliminate some.

In the same way that phylogenetic trees are constructed by biologists using morphological and other data, so also can such trees be constructed from biochemical data. A phylogenetic tree is often used as a model of the relationships between organisms because it can be scaled so that all organisms living at the same time can appear on the same geological time level. The approach has its difficulties. Fossil relationships are often not known. Fossil links may be missing especially in the case of soft-bodied animals since only hard parts of organisms are fossilized. Just the task of classifying species and working out lines of descent is a formidable task. A biochemical phylogenetic tree faces another problem. Biochemical data generally can be obtained only from living species, and the biochemist cannot go back in time as far as the biologist using fossils. There are a few exceptions to this statement. There has been some study of the blood groups of the ancient dead (Smith, 1960). Some compounds, especially hydrocarbons, are stable enough to withstand the pressures of time. Organic compounds that may have been deposited from primitive organisms are found in older sediments and rocks.

Many of the phylogenetic trees drawn from biochemical data are based on the relationships of proteins, especially the globins and cytochromes. These are the proteins which have been most widely studied as far as primary structure is concerned. Changes in these proteins with time represent changes in the nucleotide sequences of the nucleic acids responsible for their synthesis. Amino acid differences in the proteins of a given class may arise either by mutation—a change in the nucleotide sequence of DNA—or by the acceptance by natural selection of a small number of the mutations that do occur. Accidental duplication of a DNA sequence may result in the formation of two units of nucleic acid that may then go their separate ways because of different mutations occurring to each.

Measurement of evolutionary change can be made in PAM's, the unit of accepted point mutations. One PAM is one accepted amino acid mutation per 100 residues of the protein. When only a small change has occurred in a protein, the number of PAM units will equal the number of amino acid changes per 100 residues (Dayhoff and Eck, 1968). As more

changes occur in a protein, there is a greater probability that superimposition of amino acid alterations will happen. Although the maximum number of observable amino acid changes per 100 residues cannot exceed 100, the number of PAM units has no such limits. Thus, if there are 50 differences per 100 residues in two proteins of the same type, the number of PAM units difference has been calculated by probability theory to be about 83 actual changes—23 of which are hidden because they are superimposed on previous changes.

In the construction of biochemical phylogenetic trees, the length of the branches represents the amount of change between sequences, that is, the number of amino acids changes which have occurred. When PAM units are used to express the lengths of branches, these lengths are corrected for the estimation of the number of superimposed changes. The relative geologic times are estimated from the number of mutations per branch. The rate of change, that is, the mutation rate of DNA responsible for protein synthesis, appears to be constant for any given class of proteins but varies considerably between classes. It is assumed that the mutation rate for a given protein has been constant over geological time spans.

5-6. Protein Evolution. Species are usually considered to differ from one another because of their specific proteins whose synthesis is directed by specific nucleic acids. With the rapid development of techniques for determining primary protein structure, a large amount of information is becoming available on the comparative aspects of amino acid sequences in proteins and peptides. It had been supposed that any given protein in an organism showed microheterogeneity—that among a population of protein molecules of a given type, slight differences in amino acid composition would be found (Colvin et al., 1954). The results of Sanger, Kendrew, and others indicate that protein populations are homogeneous in amino acid sequence, at least within the resolution of the methods used to analyze

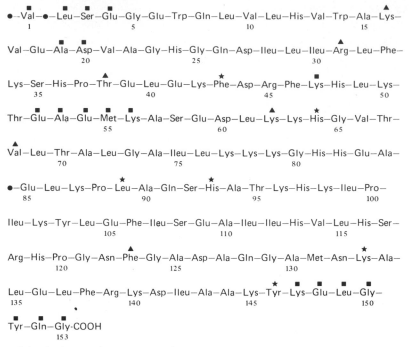

●--Val--●--Leu--Ser--Glu--Gly--Glu--Trp--Gln--Leu--Val--Leu--His--Val--Trp--Ala--Lys--
    1   5   10   15

Val--Glu--Ala--Asp--Val--Ala--Gly--His--Gly--Gln--Asp--Ileu--Leu--Ileu--Arg--Leu--Phe--
        20   25   30

Lys--Ser--His--Pro--Thr--Glu--Leu--Glu--Lys--Phe--Asp--Arg--Phe--Lys--His--Leu--Lys--
   35   40   45   50

Thr--Glu--Ala--Glu--Met--Lys--Ala--Ser--Glu--Asp--Leu--Lys--Lys--His--Gly--Val--Thr--
        55   60   65

Val--Leu--Thr--Ala--Leu--Gly--Ala--Ileu--Leu--Lys--Lys--Lys--Gly--His--His--Glu--Ala--
      70   75   80

●--Glu--Leu--Lys--Pro--Leu--Ala--Gln--Ser--His--Ala--Thr--Lys--His--Lys--Ileu--Pro--
     85   90   95   100

Ileu--Lys--Tyr--Leu--Glu--Phe--Ileu--Ser--Glu--Ala--Ileu--Ileu--His--Val--Leu--His--Ser--
        105   110   115

Arg--His--Pro--Gly--Asn--Phe--Gly--Ala--Asp--Ala--Gln--Gly--Ala--Met--Asn--Lys--Ala--
       120   125   130

Leu--Glu--Leu--Phe--Arg--Lys--Asp--Ileu--Ala--Ala--Lys--Tyr--Lys--Glu--Leu--Gly--
   135   140   145   150

Tyr--Gln--Gly-COOH
   153

Figure 5-2 Amino acid sequences of sperm whale myoglobin. Residue sequence is indicated by numbers. This sequence may be compared with the three-dimensional structure
of myoglobin diagrammed in Figure 2-14. Relatively invariant positions, insertions, and
deletions in other known globin molecules are indicated by the following symbols: (–●–)
amino acids are inserted here in some globins; (★) invariant position in all known globins;
(▲) invariant positions in all globins except lamprey hemoglobin; (■) deleted in some
globins. [Date from Dayhoff and Eck (1968).]

primary structure. Species differences in a given type of protein are often the result of one or two amino acid changes. Subclasses of a given protein class, however, are found. Human hemoglobins, for example, exist in fetal, adult, and about fifteen other forms, many of which are abnormal or pathological. Each subtype is homogeneous in primary structure.

Globins are found in nearly all animal phyla and in many plants as well. All globins contain a functional group, heme—with a porphyrin ring structure. They function primarily in oxygen transport or storage. Hemoglobin consists of two pairs of polypeptide chains, tightly organized into a compact quaternary structure (Figure 2-13). One of the chains is similar to the smaller myoglobin found in vertebrate muscle, where it acts as a storage molecule for oxygen.

The polypeptide chains of globins are relatively small. Their small size, together with their ubiquitous and abundant nature, have made them the object of many comparative studies. Myoglobin has 153 amino acids in its single chain and is a compact molecule (45 Å × 35 Å × 45 Å). The α-chain of human hemoglobin contains 141 amino acid residues. The β-chain contains 146 residues. In all globin chains so far studied, 8 positions are invariant, that is, 8 loci always contain the same amino acid. There are always two histidines, 29 amino acids apart, to which the heme group is attached. All β-chains have 70 common loci, and all α-chains have 58 common loci. There are about 86 differences between the α- and β-chains. This corresponds to a PAM of about 170 actual amino acid alterations.

Figure 5-2 shows the myoglobin chain and indicates points at which amino acids are invariant, deleted, or inserted into various other globin chains. The globins are the only proteins for which both PAM and geological times can be adequately established at present. Figure 5-3 illustrates phylogenetic trees derived from data on globin primary sequences. They point out, for example, that lamprey hemoglobin, which consists only of a single chain, branched off early in the evolution of vertebrates. Note that Figure 5-3 shows divergence points of both the proteins and the species. Myoglobin and hemoglobin diverged early in vertebrate evolution and probably more than 300 amino acid changes have occurred since then. Early hemoglobin consisted of a single chain as found in the lampreys. At some later time the hemoglobin gene duplicated and each resulting chain went on its own mutation pathway resulting in the establishment of the α- and β-chains. Later, in mammals, the β-unit again duplicated, resulting in the β- and γ-chains, the latter is found in human fetuses. Recently, on the geological time scale, the β-gene mutated again, resulting in the δ-chain, which is found in small amounts in the adult human. The β-, γ-, and δ-chains all can form tetramers with the α-chain.

The length of the globin chains makes it impossible to write them out here, so that the data from which these trees were derived could be seen (Dayhoff and Eck, 1968), but from what has been said it should be seen that analyses of protein primary structure from a variety of animals makes possible estimation of the times at which mutations and duplications of genes occurred and also confirms old theories or presents new evidence for animal relationships (Buettner-Janusch and Hill, 1965).

Although slight differences in amino acid sequence may not affect the functional ability of proteins, in some cases differences of one amino acid in a critical locus greatly alters the nature of the macromolecule. Pauling et al. (1949) showed that sickle cell anemia is a molecular disease caused by a single mutation of DNA, which caused, in turn, a change of a valine residue to a glutamic acid residue in one chain of hemoglobin. This substitution of one amino acid for another, at a site far removed from the active site, is responsible for hemoglobin crystallizing out of solution upon deoxygenation. The crystallization distorts the shape of the red blood cells carrying hemoglobin and results in an impaired ability to transport oxygen (Zuckerhandl and Pauling, 1962).

Another protein group that has been studied extensively are the cytochrome c's. Primary

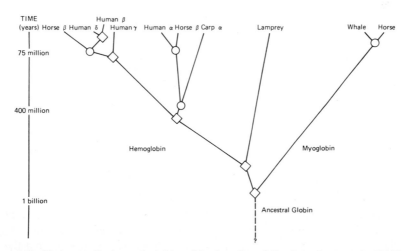

Figure 5-3 Phylogenetic tree of globins. The lengths of the branches are in PAM units (see page 137). The scale at left shows two geological time markers. The time of the ancestral globin is estimated by extrapolation. Circles indicate species divergence; squares, protein divergence. [From: Dayhoff, M. O. and Eck, R. V., *Atlas of Protein Sequence and Structure 1967–1968*, National Biomedical Research Foundation, Silver Spring, Maryland, 1968.]

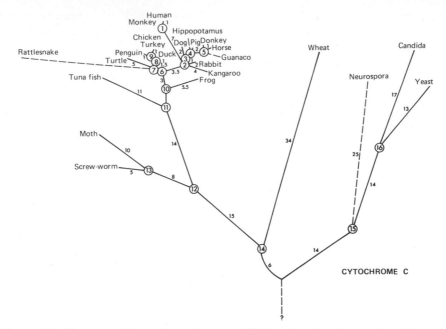

Figure 5-4 Phylogenetic tree of cytochrome c. The topology has been inferred from the sequences. The number of inferred amino acid changes per 100 links are shown on the tree. The point of earliest time cannot be determined directly from the sequences but is estimated by assuming that species change at the same rate. [From: Dayhoff, M. O. and Eck, R. V., *Atlas of Protein Sequence and Structure 1967–1968*, National Biomedical Research Foundation, Silver Spring, Maryland.]

sequences have been established for species as different as yeast, wheat, and man. Figure 5-4 shows a phylogenetic tree derived from primary structure data of cytochrome c. Figure 5-5 shows the amino acid sequences of cytochrome c from man, horse, pig, rabbit, chicken, tuna, and yeast (Margoliash et al., 1961; Margoliash, 1963; Fitch and Margoliash, 1967). Certain amino acid loci have remained invariant during the evolution of cytochrome c. The phylogenetic trees for hemoglobin and cytochrome c may be compared with each other and with those trees derived from other types of biological data (see Figure 5-7).

This type of work helps to clarify biological relationships and the biochemical origins of important molecules. At present work is being done on establishing the evolutionary history of carbohydrate metabolic pathways (Horecker, 1962); on mechanisms which led to particular evolutionary pathways of peptides and proteins (Geschwind, 1967); on mechanisms by which biochemical innovations emerge and become established (Allen, 1966); on biochemical variability and innovation (Cohen, 1963); and on hormone evolution in vertebrates (Acher et al., 1965).

5-7. Phosphagens. The phosphagens are a group of high-energy phosphate compounds (Figure 5-6) found in the muscles of animals where they serve as storage sites for high-energy phosphate groups. During muscular contraction, phosphate is transferred to ADP, forming ATP needed for muscular contraction (Chapter 10).

Early research indicated that creatine phosphate was found in all vertebrates and arginine phosphate was found in all invertebrates (Baldwin, 1964). But both phosphagens were present in various echinoderms and protochordates. This suggested that the vertebrates and echinoderms had common ancestry in agreement with other lines of biological evidence.

Although this general relationship of echino-

Acetyl-**GLY**-*Asp*-Val-Glu-**LYS**-**GLY**-*Lys*-*Lys*-Ileu-**PHE**-Val-Gln-*Lys*-**CYSH**-Ala-*Gln*-**CYSH**-**HIS**-
  1   5   10 | 15 heme |

THR-**VAL**-**GLU**-Lys-**GLY**-**GLY**-*Lys*-**HIS**-**LYS**-Thr-**GLY**-**PRO**-**ASN**-**LEU**-His-**GLY**-Leu-**PHE**-**GLY**-
           20   25   30   35

ARG-*Lys*-*Thr*-**GLY**-**GLN**-**ALA**-Pro-**GLY**-Phe-Thr-**TYR**-**THR**-Asp-**ALA**-**ASN**-*Lys*-Asn-**LYS**-*Gly*-
       40   45   50   55

Ileu-Thr-**TYR**-Lys-Glu-Glu-*Thr*-*Leu*-*Met*-Glu-Tyr-**LEU**-*Glu*-**ASN**-**PRO**-**LYS**-**LYS**-**TYR**-**ILEU**-**PRO**-
        60   65   70   75

GLY-**THR**-**LYS**-**MET**-*Ileu*-**PHE**-Ala-**GLY**-*Ileu*-**LYS**-**LYS**-*Lys*-Thr-*Glu*-**ARG**-Glu-**ASP**-**LEU**-Ileu-
        80   85   90   95

Ala-**TYR**-**LEU**-**LYS**-**LYS**-Ala-Thr-Asn-GluCOOH
        100   104

Figure 5-5 Amino acid sequences of cytochrome c. The residues in boldface are identical in the cytochromes from man, horse, pig, rabbit, chicken, tuna, and baker's yeast. Residues in italics are identical in vertebrate cytochromes only. Residues in regular type are from horse heart cytochrome c. [Data from Fitch and Margoliash (1957); Margoliash (1963).]

derms and vertebrates is true, the phosphagen story is not as simple as was first believed. Here we see the danger of making biological generalizations from the results of work with too few species. Further analysis of invertebrate animals showed that creatine phosphate is a much older compound because it has been found in at least one sponge (*Thetia luncurium*), a coelenterate (*Anemonia sulcata*), several annelids, and a sipunculid worm (*Sipunculus nudis*) (Roche and Thoai, 1957; Huennekens and Whiteley, 1960). This means that creatine phosphate, the enzymes needed for its synthesis, and the nucleotide sequence that carries the information for its synthesis are old in evolutionary history; and, therefore, creatine phosphate is not simply a vertebrate or echinoderm development.

Several other phosphagens have been found in the annelids: guanidyl-seryl-phosphate (*Lumbricus terrestris*), glycocyamine (*Nereis diversicolor*), and taurocyamine (*Arenicola*). The starting point in the evolution of phosphagens was probably the amino acid arginine. The guanidino group of arginine couples with phosphoric acid to produce the high-energy phosphate group of arginine phosphate, and this grouping is found in all phosphagens. Creatine is synthesized from arginine, glycine, and methionine. During its synthesis, glycocyamine is a product of one reaction. The latter is phosphorylated directly and used by some annelids. Although various phosphagens have been tried by animal groups and creatine phosphate has appeared in nearly all stages of animal phylogeny, only the vertebrates use creatine

phosphate exclusively. Many problems of the evolution of phosphagens remain to be solved.

5-8. Exobiology. Another question that has arisen as the result of recent research into biochemical evolution and the origins of biological molecules (and also as a result of the space program) concerns life on other planets. At present most indications are that Mars and Venus, our closest planetary neighbors, are not suitable for life as we know it (although hypotheses concerning the nature of these planets change quite often). At present it is thought that Venus has a surface temperature of about 600°C and has hydrocarbon oceans and atmosphere. Mars has little or no free water and its atmosphere contains large

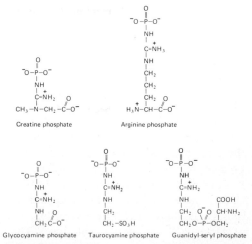

Figure 5-6 The structure of some phosphagens.

amounts of carbon dioxide and dust. Its average temperature is about $-55°C$. The photographs of Mars taken by Mariner IV, although covering only a small percentage of its planetary surface, indicate that Mars is a dead planet (Anders and Arnold, 1965; Horrowitz, 1966; Sagan and Murray, 1965; Siegel et al., 1963).

Shapley (1962) estimated that there were 10^{20} stars in the universe. If 20 per cent were similar to our sun, and if only 1 per cent of these had planets, and if of these only 1 per cent had the proper attributes for life—there would still be 2×10^{15} planets in the universe on which life could exist. Estimates of this nature, although sheer speculation, give rise to the belief that life does exist elsewhere in the universe. Such hope is fostered by the belief that the origin and evolution of life was guided by universal and constant chemical, physical, and biological laws—as evidenced by the laboratory experiments in which abiogenesis of biological molecules results when the proper conditions are used.

Studies of the universe and our solar system indicate a high possibility that the origin and relative abundances of the elements from which terrestrial molecules are formed is similar throughout the universe (Alpher and Herman, 1950; Greenstein, 1961). Sullivan (1964) discusses these possibilities as they relate to the possible presence of life in other systems (see also Huang, 1959, 1965). The nature of the universe and its evolution, together with the possibilities for intelligent life in other systems, are considered in Shklovskii and Sagan (1966). Ross (1962) reviews terrestrial and biological evolution.

In recent years interest has arisen in the question of living matter reaching the earth in meteorites. If this were true it would indicate that life does exist outside the earth. Unfortunately, the carboniferous meteorites of the type most likely to contain carbon compounds are rare, and there is not much material to work with. The Orgueil (Paris) and Murray (USA) meteorites have been analyzed and found to contain about 2 per cent carbon, most of which is in an unextractable form. These bodies also contain salts such as magnesium

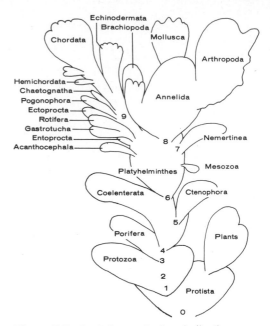

Figure 5-7 A phylogenetic tree indicating one suggested set of relationships between animals. The numbers indicate possible points of origin of the following characteristics: 0, DNA-RNA; 1, Golgi complex, contractile vacuoles, amoeboid movement; 2, cilia; 3, collagen, cellular differentiation of multicellular organisms; 4, nerve and muscle cells; 5, biradial symmetry; 6, bilateral symmetry, flame cells; 7, blood vascular system; 8, coelom, metamerism; 9, radial cleavage. [Modified from R. W. Hegner and J. G. Engemann (1968) *Invertebrate Zoology*, 2nd ed. The Macmillan Company, New York.]

and calcium sulfates. Both meteorites contain ultraviolet and infrared absorbing materials as would be expected for organic compounds (Anders, 1963; Briggs, 1961; Nagy et al., 1961). Claims have been made that fossils of bacteria-like organisms are present in these meteorites and that nucleotides and amino acids have been found. But there are still many debatable points about such findings (Urey, 1966). In any case, the presence of organic compounds may not indicate a living source because, if the conditions were correct, these organic compounds could have been formed by abiogenetic means. Conditions for further evolution of these materials into living systems could have been absent.

The discovery of life on other worlds would

be an exciting one, not only for its own sake, but because of the answers that might be provided to questions concerning life and its development here on earth. At present, there is no evidence for any extraterrestrial life although laboratories of exobiology are already established (Mamikunian and Briggs, 1965). Some of the possibilities for traveling far enough in space to meet with other intelligent life forms are given by von Hoerner (1962).

5-9. Life Today.   As previously mentioned, nothing is known about the events that oc-

curred between the abiogenesis of organic compounds and the appearance of the first living systems. This is not the place for a discussion of Darwinian evolution of present day animals, but because physiology is treated here at times from the comparative point of view and because adaptations of animals to their environments are discussed in later chapters, some indication of the relationships of animals will be helpful. Figure 5-7 presents a phylogenetic tree of the animal kingdom. This tree is highly diagrammatic and is meant to show only the general relationships of the animals whose physiology is of concern in the remainder of the book.

Animals are often grouped according to the type of germ layers, body cavities and spaces, and method of development of these body spaces. Body spaces are of importance, for example, when discussing compartmentation of body fluids or nature of excretory systems. The general nature of animal body plans is given in Figure 5-8 together with some terms used to describe them.

For convenience a listing of the animal phyla, their major living classes, subclasses, and orders is given in Table 5-1. This is meant to be primarily a memory refresher and to allow the reader to place some of the organisms discussed in this textbook. Often it is of help to be able to place an organism upon which physiological studies have been made in proper relation to other organisms. Genera that have been used in physiological studies are indicated in italics. Although not all have been included certainly, the list does give some indication of the large number of animal groups that have received insignificant physiological attention. Table 5-1 is adapted from the work of Hyman (1940–1959), Blackwelder (1963), and Hickman (1967). The rankings and names used here are not agreed upon by all workers. The references above give further information about animals, especially the invertebrates. Young (1962) provides information on vertebrates.

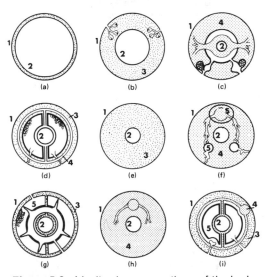

Figure 5-8   Idealized cross sections of the body plans of several animal phyla. 1, ectoderm; 2, entoderm; 3, mesoderm; 4, coelom; 5, interstitial fluid; 5, blood. Beginning with coelenterates all animals form two germ layers during embryological development. The ectoderm, outer body wall, and the entoderm, wall of the digestive tube. Other specialized cells form a cellular mass between the entoderm and ectoderm—the mesenchyme. Any space between ectoderm and entoderm is the primary body cavity or pseudocoel. Outpouchings of the entoderm pinch off to form a third germinal layer—the mesoderm. The mesodermal wall forms the cavity of the coelom which may not persist in the adult in all animal phyla. See also Chapters 12, 13, and 14.

Table 5-1 Phyla of the Animal Kingdom and Their Classes, Subclasses, and Important Orders [Common names, genera (in italics) on which physiological studies have been made, and descriptions are given in parentheses. Numbers are estimates of known living species.]

PHYLUM	CLASS	SUBCLASS	ORDER

PROTOZOA (Unicellular organisms, sometimes colonial. Fresh water, marine, and parasitic. 25,000).

    Flagellata (using one or more flagella as locomotor organelles)

		Phytomastigina	Dinoflagellida
			Euglenida (*Euglena*)
			Phytomonadida (*Volvox, Chlamydomonas*)
			Cryptomonadida (*Chilomonas*)
		Zoomastigina	Rhizomastigida
			Protomonadida (*Trypanosoma*)
			Opalinida (*Opalina*)

    Sarcodina (locomotion by pseudopods)

		Actinopoda	Helioflagellida (sun-animalcules)
			Radiolaria (radiolarians)
		Rhizopoda	Amoebida (*Amoeba, Chaos, Difflugia*)
			Foraminiferida
			Mycetozoida (slime molds, *Dictyostelium*)

    Sporozoa (no locomotor organelles; parasitic)

		Telosporidia	Gregarinida
			Coccidia
			Haemosporidia
		Cnidosporidia	Myxosporidia
			Actinomyxidia
			Microsporidia

    Ciliata (with cilia as locomotor organelles)

		Holotricha	Gymnostomatida (*Didinium*)
			Hymenostomatida (*Paramecium, Tetrahymena*)
			Peritrichida (stalked protozoans, *Vorticella*)
		Spirotricha	Heterotrichida (*Stentor, Bursaria*)
			Hypotrichida (*Euplotes, Stylonychia*)

MESOZOA (With a single layer of cells enclosing one or more reproductive cells; no body spaces. Marine parasites of uncertain phylogenetic origin.   50).

PORIFERA (The sponges. Multicellular (Metazoans), but no organs or mouth. Nearly all sessile. Mostly marine, with one fresh water order.   5,000).

    Calcarea (*Ascon, Leuconia, Sycon*)

    Hexactinelida (glass sponges)

    Desmospongea (*Oscarella, Haliclona*. Includes Family Spongillidae, fresh water)

COELENTERATA (=**Cnidaria**) (Radial or biradial symmetry; sessile polyps or free-swimming medusae; possess nematocysts. One body cavity—the enteron. Freshwater or marine. 10,000).

	Hydrozoa		Hydroida (*Hydra, Tubularia, Obelia, Gonionemus, Craspedocusta* [fresh water])

(continued)

Table 5-1   (continued)

PHYLUM	CLASS	SUBCLASS	ORDER
			Siphonophora (Portuguese man-of-war, *Physalia*)
	Scyphozoa (large jellyfish)		Stauromedusae (*Haliclystus*)
			Semaeostomae (*Aurelia*)
			Rhizostomae
			Subomedusae
	Anthozoa (sea anemones, corals, etc.)		
		Alcyonaria	Stononifera
			Gorgonaceae
			Pennatulacea (sea pansy: *Rennilla;* sea pens, sea feathers).
		Zoantharia	Actiniaria (sea anemones: *Metridium*)
			Scleractinia (reef forming corals)
			Antipatharia (black corals)

CTENOPHORA (comb jellies, sea walnuts. Marine jellyfish with 8 rows of ciliary combs. Radial symmetry. Only body cavity a gastrovascular one.   100).

> **Tentaculata** (with tentacles: *Ctenoplana, Mnemiopsis, Pleurobrachia*)
> **Nuda** (without tentacles: *Beröe*)

PLATYHELMINTHES (Acoelomate flatworms. Bilateral symmetry, three germ layers with a well-developed mesoderm; stinging nematocyts.   15,000).

	CLASS	SUBCLASS	ORDER
	Turbellaria (planarians)		Acoela
			Rhabdocoela (*Stenostomum*)
			Tricladida (*Planaria, Dugesia, Dendrocoelium*)
			Polycladida
	Trematoda (flukes)		Monogenea
			Digenea
	Cestoda (tape worms)		

RHYNCHOCOELA (=**NEMERTINEA**) (Acoelomate ribbon worms. Marine. Complete digestive system and a circulatory system.   570).

	CLASS	SUBCLASS	ORDER
	Anopla		Heteronemertini (*Cerebratulus*)
			Palaeonemertini
	Enopla		Hoplonemertini
			Bdellonemertini

ACANTHOCEPHALA (Pseudocoelomate spiny-headed worms. Endoparasites of vertebrates, with insects as intermediate hosts.   500).

ROTIFERA (Rotifera, Gastrotricha, Kinorhyncha, Nematoda, and **Gordiacea** are grouped by many workers into a single phylum **ASCHELMINTHES**) (Rotifers or wheel animalcules are pseudocoelomate organisms; with protonephridia with flame bulbs.   1,500).

> **Seisonacea**
> **Bdelloidea** (*Rotaria*)
> **Monogonta** (*Asplanchna, Collotheca*)

GASTROTRICHA (Pseudocoelomate. Marine and fresh water.   500).

> **Macrodasyoidea**
> **Chaetonotoidea**

(continued)

Table 5-1   (continued)

PHYLUM	CLASS	SUBCLASS	ORDER

KINORHYNCHA (worm-like pseudocoelomates. Marine.   100).

NEMATODA (Pseudocoelomate round worms. Excretory system with renette cells or intracellular canals.   5,000).

	Nematoidea		Rhabditoidea
			Ascaroidea (*Ascaris*)
			Oxyuroidea (*Enterobius*)
			Strongyloidea (*Ancylostoma, Necator*)
			Filarioidea (*Filaria, Wuchereria*)
			Dracunculoidea (*Micropleura*)

GORDIACEA (Marine and fresh water pseudocoelomate parasites.   300).

ENDOPROCTA (Sessile, stalked pseudocoelomates. Mostly marine.   90).

PHORONIDA (wormlike pseudocoelomates with a lophophore.   18).

PRIAPULIDA (Eucoelomates, wormlike animals. Marine.   8).

BRYOZOA (=ECTOPROCTA) (Moss animals. Protostomial marine and fresh water unsegmented worms.   4,000).

	Gymnolaemata		Ctenostomata
			Cheilostomata
			Cyclostomata (*Crisia*)
	Phylactolaemata (fresh water: *Cristatella, Pophopus, Tectinatella*)		

BRACHIOPODA (Lamp shells. Coelomate, bilaterate, marine organisms.   250).

	Inarticulata		Atremata (*Lingula*)
			Neotremata (*Crania*)
	Articulata		Protremata
			Telotremata (*Terebratula*)

ECHIURIDA (Vermiform, protostomes. All marine.   70). (*Urechis, Thalessema, Echiurus*).

SIPUNCULOIDEA (Protostomate, coelomate unsegmented worms. Marine, fresh water and terrestrial. 250).

	Sipunculoidea (*Sipunculus, Golfingia* (=*Phascolosoma*), *Dendrostomum*)		

ANNELIDA (segmented, protostomate, schizocoelic worms. Marine, fresh water, and terrestrial.   7,000).

	Polychaeta (with parapodia, chaetae)		Errantia (sandworms: *Nereis, Aphrodite*)
			Sedentaria (tube worms: *Arenicola, Amphitrite, Chaetopterus*)
	Clitellata		Oligochaeta (*Aeolosoma, Bracnchiobdella, Eisenia, Lumbricus, Nais*)
			Hirudinea (leeches)

ONYCHOPHORA (Segmented, veriform body with pairs of segmentally arranged legs.   70).

	Peripatidea		(*Peripatus, Opisthopatus*)

PENTASTOMIDA (Veriform body, eucoelomate, unsegmented.   60).

TARDIGRADA (Bear animalcules.   300).

ARTHROPODA (Segmented, eucoelomate animals.   850,000).

Subphyllum **Chelicerata**

	Xiphosura (Horseshoe crab: *Limulus*)		
	Pycogonida (sea spiders)		

(*continued*)

Table 5-1   (continued)

PHYLUM	CLASS	SUBCLASS	ORDER
	Arachnida		Scorpionida (scorpions)
			Amblypygi
			Araneae (spiders)
			Solpugida (false or whip scorpions)
			Phalangida (harvest spiders)
			Acarina (ticks, mites)
Subphyllum **Mandibulata**			
	Crustacea	Cephalocarida	
		Branchiopoda	Anostraca (brine shrimps: *Artemia*)
			Notostraca (tadpole shrimps: *Apus*)
			Conchostraca (clam shrimps)
			Cladocera (water fleas: *Daphnia*)
		Ostracoda	Myodocopa
			Cladocopa
			Podocopa
			Platycopa
		Mystacocarida	
		Copepoda	Calanoida
			Harpacticoida
			Cyclopoida (*Cyclops*)
			Notodelphyoidea
			Monstrilloida
			Caligoida
			Lernaeopodoida
		Branchiura (fishlice)	
		Cirripedia	Acrothoracica (barnacles: *Balanus, Lepus*)
		Malacostraca	Mysidacea (opossum shrimp: *Mysis*)
			Isopoda (sowbugs: *Porcellio*)
			Decapoda (shrimps: *Crangon, Palaemon-etes, Squilla;* lobsters: *Hom-arus, Palinurus;* crayfish: *Astacus, Cambarus;* crabs: *Callinectes, Cancer, Carcinus, Grapsus, Maia;* fiddler crabs: *Uca;* hermit crabs: *Eupagurus*)
	Chilopoda (centipedes)		
	Diplopoda (millipedes)		
	Pauropoda		
	Symphia		
	Insecta (insects, hexapods)		
		Apterygota	Protura
			Collembola (springtails)
			Diplura
			Thysanura (bristletails)

(*continued*)

Table 5-1   (continued)

PHYLUM	CLASS	SUBCLASS	ORDER
		Pterygota	Orthoptera (grasshoppers; crickets; cockroaches: *Blatta, Periplaneta, Gryllus;* praying mantids: *Stagmomantis*)
			Dermaptera (earwigs)
			Plecoptera (stoneflies)
			Isoptera (termites)
			Embioptera
			Odonata (dragonflies, damselflies)
			Ephemeroptera (mayflies)
			Mallophaga (biting lice)
			Anoplura (sucking lice)
			Psocoptera (booklice)
			Thysanoptera (thrips)
			Zoraptera
			Hemiptera (true bugs)
			Homoptera (aphids, cicadas)
			Mecoptera (scorpionflies)
			Trichoptera (caddisflies)
			Neuroptera (lacewings, ant lions)
			Lepidoptera (moths, butterflies)
			Diptera (true flies and mosquitos)
			Siphonaptera (fleas)
			Coleoptera (beetles, weevils)
			Strepsiptera (twistedwing parasites)
			Hymenoptera (ants, bees, wasps)

MOLLUSCA (Molluscs. Ventral foot and dorsal shell. Greatly reduced coelom.   115,000).

PHYLUM	CLASS	SUBCLASS	ORDER
	Amphineura	Aplacophora	
		Polyplacophora (chitons: *Chiton*)	
	Scaphopoda (tusk shells)		
	Gastropoda	Prosobranchia	Aspinobranchia (limpets: *Patella;* abolone: *Haliotis*)
			Pectinibranchia (boat shells: *Crepidula;* periwinkles: *Littorina;* conchs)
			Neogastropoda (oyster drills; rock shells; augers; whelks: *Busycon*)
		Opisthobranchia	Tectibranchia (sea hares: *Aplysia;* bubble shells: *Acteion, Bulla*)
			Pteropoda
			Nudibranchia (sea slugs: *Aeolis*)
		Pulmonata	Basommatophora (pond snails: *Lymnaea, Physa, Planorbis*)

(continued)

Table 5-1   (continued)

PHYLUM	CLASS	SUBCLASS	ORDER
			Stylommatophora (land snails: *Helix, Limax;* slugs).
	Pelecypoda (bivalves or lamellibranchs)		
		Protobranchia (*Solemya*)	
		Lamellibranchia	Filibranchia (mussels: *Mytillus;* scallops: *Pecten;* oysters: *Ostrea*)
			Eulamellibranchia (clams: *Venus, Anodonta, Pinna, Ensis;* shipworms: *Teredo*)
	Cephalopoda	Nautiloidea (*Nautilus*)	
		Coleoidea	Decapoda (cuttlefish: *Sepia;* squids: *Loligo, Architeuthis*)
			Octopoda (octopus; paper nautilus; cuttlefish: *Eledone*)
			Vampyromorpha

ECHINODERMATA (Deuterostomes with radial symmetry. Marine.   6,000).
  Subphyllum **Eleutherozoa** (stemless, unattached echinoderms)

	Asterozoa	Asteroidea (starfish: *Asterias, Astropection, Leptasterias*)	
		Ophiuroidea (brittle stars: *Ophiocoma, Ophioderma*)	
	Echinoidea (sea urchins and sand dollars: *Echinus, Stronglylocentrotus, Arbacia, Echinocardium*)		
	Holothuroidea (sea cucumbers: *Holothuria, Thyone*)		

  Subphyllum **Pelmatozoa**
    Crinoidea (sea lillies and sea feathers)

CHAETOGNATHA (Arrow worms. Marine deuterostomes.   50) (*Sagitta, Spadella*)

POGONOPHORA (Beard worms. Sessile, marine.   50).

PTEROBRANCHIA (Coelomate, enterocoelous, aggregated in secreted tubes.   10).

ENTEROPNEUSTA (Coelomate, enterocoelous, vermiform.   70) (*Balanoglossus, Saccoglossus*).

TUNICATA (Notochord restricted to tail region in young and disappears in adult. Marine. 2,000).

	Larvacea		Larvacea (small sea squirts)
	Ascidiacea (sea squirts, ascidians: *Ciona, Botryllus, Styela*)		
	Thaliacea (pelagic sea squirts: *Doliolum, Salpa*)		

CEPHALOCHORDATA (lancets or amphioxus. Notochord, dorsal hollow nerve cord, pharyngeal gill slits.   29). (*Branchiostoma* [formerly *Amphioxus*])

VERTEBRATA (Chordates with notochord replaced in adult by vertebrae.   38,000).

	Agnatha (jawless fishes)		Cyclostomata (lampreys: *Petromyzon;* hagfish: *Myxine*).
	Chondrichthyes (cartilagenous fishes)		
		Elasmobranchii	Selachii (sharks: *Squalus*)
			Batoidea (skates; rays: *Manta, Raja*)
		Holocephali	Chimaerae (ratfish: *Chimaera*)
	Osteichthyes (fishes with at least partially ossified skeletons; swim bladder or lungs)		

(*continued*)

Table 5-1   (continued)

PHYLUM	CLASS	SUBCLASS	ORDER
		Actinopterygii	Chondrostei (sturgeons)
			Holstei (gars, bowfins)
			Teleostei (tarpons; herrings: *Clupea;* salmon: *Salmo;* carps; catfish; eels; killifish: *Fundulus;* sticklebacks: *Gasterosteus;* cod: *Gadus;* perch, sea horse, etc.)
		Sarcopterygii	Dipnoi (lungfish: *Protopterus*)
	Amphibians		Anura (frogs: *Rana, Xenopus;* toads: *Bufo*)
			Urodela (salamanders: *Necturus*)
	Reptilia	Anapsida	Chelona (turtles: *Pseudemys, Chelonia*)
		Diapsida	Rhynchocephalia (*Sphenodon*)
			Squamata (lizards and snakes)
			Crocodilia (alligators and crocodiles)
	Aves (birds)		
	Mammalia	Prototheria (egg laying mammals)	
			Monotremata (platypus: *Ornithorhynchus;* spiny anteater: *Tachyglossus*)
		Metatheria	Marsupialia
		Eutheria	Insectivora (moles, shrews, hedgehogs)
			Dermoptera (flying lemurs)
			Chiroptera (bats)
			Edentata (sloths, anteaters, armadillos)
			Pholidota (pangolins)
			Primates (lemurs, tree-shrews, tarsiers, monkeys, marmosets, baboons, apes, gibbons, gorillas, orangutans, chimpanzees, men)
			Lagomorpha (hares, rabbits, pikes)
			Rodentia (squirrels, chipmunks, marmots, beavers, rats, mice, muskrats, voles, lemmings, porcupines, guinea pigs)
			Cetacea (porpoises, dolphins, whales)
			Carnivora (dogs, wolves, foxes, bears, pandas, raccoons, weasels, minks, otters, badgers, wolverines, skunks, cats, civets, seals, sea-lions, walruses)
			Tubulidentata (aardvarks)
			Proboscidea (elephants)

(continued)

Table 5-1   (continued)

PHYLUM	CLASS	SUBCLASS	ORDER
			Hydrocoidea (hyraxes)
			Sirenia (sea cows)
			Perissodactyla (horses, tapirs, zebras)
			Artiodactyla (pigs, hippopotamus, camels, llamas, alpacas, deer, giraffes, cattle, sheep, goats)

References and Readings

Acher, R., J. Chauvet, M. T. Chauvet, and D. Crepy (1965). "Phylogeny of vertebrate neurohypophyseal hormones." *Gen. Comp. Endocrinol.* **5**: 662–671.

Allen, G. E. (1966). "A model for the emergence of biochemical novelties." *Bioscience* **16**: 325–331.

Allen, J. M., ed. (1967). **Molecular Organization and Biological Function.** New York: Harper and Row, Publishers, Inc. 243 pp.

Allen, W. V. and C. Ponnamperuma (1967). "A possible prebiotic synthesis of monocarboxylic acids." *Currents Modern Biol.* **1**: 24–28.

Alpher, R. A. and R. C. Herman (1950). "Theory of the origin and relative abundance and distribution of the elements." *Rev. Mod. Phys.* **22**: 153–212.

Anders, E. (1963). "The moon as a collector of biological materials." *Science* **133**: 1115–1116.

Anders, E. and J. R. Arnold (1965). "Age of craters on Mars." *Science* **149**: 1494–1496.

Anfinsen, C. B. (1959). **The Molecular Basis of Evolution.** New York: John Wiley & Sons, Inc. 228 pp.

Baldwin, E. (1964). **An Introduction to Comparative Biochemistry,** 4th ed. New York: Cambridge University Press. 179 pp.

Barnes, T. C. (1937). **Textbook of General Physiology.** New York: McGraw-Hill Book Company, Inc. 554 pp.

Baylor, E. R. and W. H. Sutcliff (1963). "Dissolved organic matter in seawater as a source of particulate food." *Limnol. Oceanog.* **8**: 369–371.

Bernal, J. D. (1959). (a) "Problems of stages in biopoesis" (pp. 38–53); (b) "The scale of structural units in biopoesis" (pp. 385–399). In: **Origin of Life on Earth.** Proc. 1st International Symp., Moscow, 1957. (A. I. Oparin, A. G. Pasynskii, A. E. Braunshtein, and T. E. Pavlovskaya, eds.). Long Island City, N.Y.: Pergamon Press, Inc.

Bernal, J. D. (1965). "Molecular structure, biochemical function, and evolution. In: **Theoretical and Mathematical Biology.** (T. H. Waterman and H. J. Morowitz, eds.), pp. 96–135. Waltham, Mass.: Blaisdell Publishing Company.

Blackwelder, R. E. (1963). **Classification of the Animal Kingdom.** Carbondale, Ill.: Southern Illinois University Press. 94 pp.

Bolker, H. I. (1967), "Phylogenetic relationships of echinoderms." *Nature* **213**: 904–905.

Briggs, M. H. (1961). "Organic constituents of meteorites." *Nature* **191**: 1137–1140.

Buettner-Janusch, J. and R. L. Hill (1965). "Molecules and monkeys." *Science* **147**: 836–842.

Calvin, M. (1956). "Chemical evolution and the origin of life." *Am. Sci.* **44**: 248–263.

Calvin, M. (1962). "The origin of life on earth and elsewhere." *Adv. Biol. Med. Phys.* **8**: 315–342.

Calvin, M. (1962). "Evolutionary possibilities for photosynthesis and quantum conversion." In: **Horizons in Biochemistry.** (M. Kasha and B. Pullman, eds.), pp. 23–57. New York: Academic Press, Inc.

Calvin, M. (1967). "Chemical evolution." *Prog. Theoret. Biol.* **1**: 1–34.

Calvin, M. and G. J. Calvin (1964). "From Atom to Adam." *Am. Sci.* **52**: 163–186.

Cohen, S. S. (1963). "On biochemical variability and innovation." *Science* **139**: 1017–1026.

Colvin, J. R., D. B. Smith, and W. H. Cook (1954). "Microheterogeneity of proteins." *Chem. Rev.* **54**: 687–711.

Darwin, C. and A. R. Wallace (1859). "On the variation of organic beings in a state of nature; on the natural means of selection; on the comparison of domestic races and true species." *J. Proc. Linnaean Soc., London* **3**: 45–62.

Davis, B. D. (1961). "The teleonomic significance of biosynthetic control mechanisms." *Cold Spring Harbor Symp. Quant. Biol.* **26**: 1–10.

Dayhoff, M. O. and R. V. Eck (1968). **Atlas of Protein Sequence and Structure 1967–1968.** Silver Springs, Md.: National Biomedical Research Foundation. 356 pp.

Dayhoff, M. O., E. R. Lippincott, and R. V. Eck (1964). "Thermodynamic equilibria in prebiological atmospheres." *Science* **146**: 1461–1464.

Dole, M. (1949). "The history of oxygen." *Science* **109**: 77–81.

Fitch, W. M. and E. Margoliash (1967). "Construction of phylogenetic trees." *Science* **155**: 279–284.

Fox, S. W. (1960). "How did life begin?" *Science* **132**: 200–208.

Fox, S. W., ed. (1965). **The Origins of Prebiological Systems.** New York: Academic Press, Inc. 482 pp.

Fox, S. W., K. Harada, and J. Kendrick (1959). "Production of spherules from synthetic proteinoid and hot water." *Science* **129**: 1221–1223.

Geschwind, I. I. (1967). "Molecular variation and possible lines of evolution of peptide and protein hormones." *Am. Zool.* **7**: 89–108.

Greenstein, J. L. (1961). "Stellar evolution and the origin of chemical elements." *Am. Sci.* **49**: 449–472.

Haldane, J. B. S. (1954). **The Origin of Life.** New Biology Series, No. 16. London: Penguin Books Ltd.

Harada, K. and S. W. Fox (1965). "Thermal polycondensation of free amino acids with phosphoric acid." In: **The Origins of Prebiological Systems.** (S. W. Fox, ed.), pp. 289–297. New York: Academic Press, Inc.

Hickman, C. P. (1967). **Biology of the Invertebrates.** St. Louis: The C. V. Mosby Company, 673 pp.

von Hoerner, S. (1962). "The general limits of space travel." *Science* **137**: 18–23.

Holmes, A. (1954). "The oldest dated materials of the Rhodesian shield." *Nature* **173**: 612–614.

Horecker, B. L. (1962). "Alternative pathways of carbohydrate metabolism in relation to evolutionary development." *Comp. Biochem. Physiol.* **4**: 363–369.

Horowitz, N. H. (1945). "On the evolution of biochemical synthesis." *Proc. Nat. Acad. Sci.* (US) **31**: 153–157.

Horowitz, N. H. (1959). "On defining 'life'." In: **The Origin of Life on Earth.** (A. I. Oparin et al., eds.), pp. 106–107. Long Island City, N.Y.: Pergamon Press, Inc.

Horowitz, N. H. (1966). "The search for extraterrestrial life." *Science* **151**: 789–792.

Huang, S. (1959). "Occurrence of life in the universe." *Am. Sci.* **47**: 397–402.

Huang, S. (1965). "Life in space and humanity on the earth." *Am. Sci.* **53**: 288–298.

Huennekens, F. M. and H. R. Whiteley (1960). "Phosphoric acid anhydrides and other energy-rich compounds." In: **Comparative Biochemistry.** (M. Florkin and H. S. Mason, eds.), Vol. 1, pp. 107–180. New York: Academic Press, Inc.

Hull, D. E. (1960). "Thermodynamics and kinetics of spontaneous generation." *Nature* **186**: 693–694.

Hyman, L. H. (1940–1959). **The Invertebrates,** 5 volumes. New York: McGraw-Hill Book Company, Inc.

Kavanau, J. L. (1947). "Some physico-chemical aspects of life and evolution in relation to the living state." *Am. Nat.* **81**: 161–184.

Kavanau, J. L. (1960). "On the origin of life." *Science* **131**: 1682.

Kormandy, E. J. (1966). **General Biology: A book of readings,** Vol. 2. Dubuque, Iowa: Wm. C. Brown Company. 241 pp.

Kulp, J. L. (1961). "Geologic time scale." *Science* **133**: 1105–1112.

Mamikunian, G. and M. H. Briggs, eds. (1965). **Current Aspects of Exobiology.** Long Island City, N.Y.: Pergamon Press, Inc. 432 pp.

Margoliash, E. (1963). "Primary structure and evolution of cytochrome c." *Proc. Nat. Acad. Sci.* (Washington, D.C.) **50**: 672–679.

Margoliash, E. and E. L. Smith (1965). "Evolution of cytochrome *c*." In: **Evolving Genes and Proteins.** (V. Bryson and H. J. Vogel, eds.), pp. 221–242. New York: Academic Press, Inc.

Margoliash, E., E. L. Smith, G. Kriel, and H. Typpy (1961). "Amino-acid sequences of horse heart cytochrome *c*. The complete amino acid sequence." *Nature* **192**: 1125–1127.

Miller, S. L. (1953). "Formation of organic compounds on the primitive earth." *Science* **117**: 528–529.

Miller, S. L. and H. C. Urey (1959). "Organic compounds synthesis on the primitive earth." *Science* **130**: 245–251.

Muller, H. J. (1966). "The gene material as the initiator and the organizing basis of life." *Am. Nat.* **100**: 493–517.

Nagy, B., W. G. Meinschein, and D. J. Hennessy (1961). "International control of investigations of rare meteorites." *Nature* **189**: 967–968.

Needham, A. E. (1959). "The origination of life." *Quart. Rev. Biol.* **34**: 189–209.

Oparin, A. I. (1964). **Life, Its Nature, and Development.** New York: Academic Press, Inc. 207 pp.

Oparin, A. I., A. G. Pasynskii, A. E. Braunshtein, and T. E. Pavlovskaya, eds. (1959). **The Origin of Life on Earth.** Long Island City, N.Y.: Pergamon Press, Inc.

Oro, J. F. (1961). "Mechanism of synthesis of adenine from hydrogen cyanide under possible primitive earth conditions." *Nature* **191**: 1193–1194.

Paschke, R., R. W. H. Chang, and D. Young (1957). "Probable role of gamma radiation in origin of life." *Science* **125**: 881.

Pauling, L., H. A. Itano, S. J. Singer, and I. C. Wells (1949). "Sickle cell anemia, a molecular disease." *Science* **110**: 543–548.

Perrett, J. (1952). "Biochemistry and bacteria." *New Biol.* **12**: 68–96.

Pirie, N. W. (1953). "Ideas and assumptions about the origin of life." *Discovery* **14**: 238–242.

Pirie, N. W. (1959). "Chemical diversity and the origins of life." In: **The Origin of Life on Earth.** (A. I. Oparin et al., eds.), pp. 76–83. Long Island City, N.Y.: Pergamon Press, Inc.

Ponnamperuma, C. (1968). "Ultraviolet radiation and the origin of life." In: **Photophysiology.** (A. C. Giese, ed.), Vol. 3, pp. 253–267. New York: Academic Press, Inc.

Ponnamperuma, C. and R. Mack (1965). "Nucleotide synthesis under possible primitive earth conditions." *Science* **148**: 1221–1223.

Quastler, H., ed. (1953). **Essays on the Use of Information Theory in Biology.** Urbana: University of Illinois Press. 273 pp.

Quastler, H. (1964). **The Emergence of Biological Organization.** New Haven, Conn.: Yale University Press. 83 pp.

Rich, A. (1962). "On the problems of evolution and biochemical information transfer." In: **Horizons in Biochemistry.** (M. Kasha and B. Pullman, eds.), pp. 103–126. New York: Academic Press, Inc.

Riley, G. A. (1963). "Organic aggregates in seawater and the dynamics of their formation and utilization." *Limnol. Oceanogr.* **8**: 372–381.

Roche, J. and N. V. Thoai (1957). "Creatine chez les invertebres." *Biochim. Biophys. Acta* **24**: 514–519.

Ross, H. H. (1962). **A Synthesis of Evolutionary Theory.** Englewood Cliffs, N.J.: Prentice-Hall, Inc. 409 pp.

Sagan, C. (1957). "Radiation and the origin of the gene." *Evolution* **11**: 40–55.

Sagan, C. and B. C. Murray (1965). "The biological significance of the Mariner IV television experiments." In: **Biology and the Exploration of Mars.** Washington, D.C.: National Academy of Sciences.

Shapley, H. (1962). "Crusted stars and self-warming planets." *Am. Scholar.* **31:** 512–515.

Shklovskii, I. S. and C. Sagan (1966). **Intelligent Life in the Universe.** San Francisco: Holden-Day, Inc. 488 pp.

Siegel, S. M., L. A. Halpern, C. Giumarro, and G. Renwick (1963). "Martian biology: the experimentalists approach." *Nature* **197:** 329–331.

Simpson, G. G. (1964). "Organisms and molecules in evolution." *Science* **146:** 1535–1538.

Smith, L. F. (1966). "Species variation in the amino acid sequences of insulin," *Am. J. Med.* **40:** 662–666.

Smith, M. (1960). "Blood groups of the ancient dead." *Science* **131:** 699–702.

Stanley, W. M. (1959). "On the nature of viruses, genes, and life." In: **The Origin of Life on Earth.** (A. I. Oparin et al., eds.), pp. 313–321. Long Island City, N.Y.: Pergamon Press, Inc.

Steinman, G. (1966). "Synthesis of amino acid residues with reactive side chains under simple conditions." *Science* **154:** 1344–1346.

Sullivan, W. (1964). **We Are Not Alone: The Search for Intelligent Life on Other Worlds.** New York: McGraw-Hill Book Company, Inc.

Sutcliff, W. H., E. R. Baylor, and D. W. Menzel (1963). "Sea surface chemistry and Langmuir circulation." *Deep-sea Research* **10:** 223–243.

Urey, H. C. (1952). **The Planets. Their Origin and Development.** New Haven, Conn.: Yale University Press.

Urey, H. C. (1966). "Biological material in meteorites: a review." *Science* **151:** 157–166.

Ussing, H. H. (1964). "Transport of electrolytes and water across epithelia" *Harvey Lect.* **59:** 1–30.

Ycas, M. (1955). "A note on the origin of life." *Proc. Nat. Acad. Sci.*, Washington, D.C. **41:** 714–716.

Young, J. Z. (1962). **The Life of Vertebrates,** 2nd ed. New York: Oxford University Press.

Zuckerhandl, E. and L. Pauling (1962). "Molecular disease, evolution, and genetic heterogeneity." In: **Horizons in Biochemistry.** (M. Kasha and B. Pullman, eds.), pp. 189–225. New York: Academic Press, Inc.

IN this part of the book it will be shown that the components of animal regulatory systems depend upon a few basic properties of cells—especially properties of cell membranes. Any living system, being an open system, depends for its existence on a continuous inflow of energy, material, and information and on a continuous outflow of materials (waste products, useful secretions, etc.), energy, and information.

Material transport as well as information flow depend heavily on properties of biological membranes, and in Chapter 6 the physical-chemical laws governing transport both in solutions and through membranes are described. As a result of the permeability properties of membranes, aided by active transport, all biological membranes are characterized by the presence of bioelectric potentials that, among other uses, aid in maintaining an unequal distribution of ions between the inside and outside media.

In Chapter 7 these potentials—called resting potentials in excitable cells such as nerve or muscle—are described, and the ability of the plasma membrane to respond to changes in the environment by specific alterations of membrane permeability to specific ions is shown to be the basis upon which active potential changes are produced. Chapter 7 is concerned primarily with the all-or-none action potential used to convey information from one part of an organism to another over nervous pathways. In Chapter 8 the physiological and morphological basis of potential generation at receptor organs and at synapses—nerve-nerve or nerve-effector junctions—are described.

Chapter 9 considers some of the transport activities found in cell masses exemplified by epithelial layers or by cardiac muscle. In both types of tissues it is shown that spontaneous potentials—potentials elicited by endogenous activity not by stimulation—play an important role. Such spontaneous activity is also vital to nervous system operation.

The phenomena mentioned above are usually studied in either nerve or muscle cells because such cells are highly specialized for this type of activity; however, such activity in one form or another is common to all known animal cells and is also a part of mitochondrial membrane activity.

In Chapter 10 we examine contractility—an activity upon which the operation of many effector responses is based. A variety of examples of contractile activity are discussed, and it becomes evident that cellular contraction depends on specific interactions between contractile proteins —all appearing similar to the actomysin system of muscle—and high energy phosphate compounds such as ATP. The reactions are modified and controlled by divalent ions such as magnesium and calcium ions.

Finally in Chapter 11 the overall organization

Part II

Fundamental Units of Animal Regulatory Systems

Chapter 6

Biological Membranes and Material Transport

Chapter 7

Resting and Action Potentials of Excitable Cells

Chapter 8

Synaptic and Generator Potentials

Chapter 9

Mass Cellular Contacts: Spontaneous and Other Potentials

Chapter 10

Contractility of Muscle and Cells

Chapter 11

Neuromuscular and Neuroendocrine Control Systems

of nervous systems is described, and the nature of neuromuscular control systems is discussed for various animal groups. These systems operate on the basis of principles described in Chapters 6 to 9. However, the organization of complex networks of nerve cells adds a further dimension to nervous system operation, and at present much of the ability of nervous systems to integrate and coordinate animal activities is based on unknown mechanisms. Although the basis of control in the nervous system may rest on the all-or-none action potential, in operation the nervous system does not exhibit such all-or-none behavior. In this chapter the other major control system—the chemical or neuroendocrine system—is also discussed. Stress is given to the fact that these two systems are not independent of one another.

The mechanisms and systems described in this part of the book make up the basis upon which the homeostatic and behavioral regulations of the whole animal are founded. Much of the discussion here is at the cellular level of activity, but it is these cellular operations which aggregate to form the organ system and whole animal operations to be described in Parts III and IV.

6-1. General Role and Nature of Membranes. The chemical composition of animals differs markedly from that of their environment. Further, the composition of the intracellular medium differs from that of the extracellular fluids. Such a difference between two fluid compartments, together with the observed lack of mixing of intra- and extracellular substances, indicates that some type of barrier exists between them. This barrier is the plasma membrane, a differentially permeable membrane, through which some materials cannot pass, while the rate of passage of permeating substances may differ considerably.

Biological membranes are sometimes called semipermeable, which, strictly used, refers to an ideal membrane permeable only to solvent and not to solutes. This definition cannot be applied rigorously to biological membranes which, for example, are associated with open systems. The term is used with the recognition that many solutes are impermeable and those that do pass through do so at much slower rates than water—the chief biological solvent. Biological membranes are better described as selectively permeable or differentially permeable, the latter term being preferred because it does not connotate a selection or choice on the part of the membrane. Either term means that different materials pass through the membrane at different rates and some cannot pass through at all.

The plasma membrane is often called a barrier to diffusion, but this does not mean that the membrane is a passive structural wall. Biological membranes differ in their permeabilities to given substances, and their permeabilities can change with changing conditions. In many cases the passage of materials across a membrane is the result of active alterations in membrane structure. In other cases substances move across biological membranes against electrochemical gradients—a process that is energy-requiring and thus called "active transport."

Membranes play a role in the distribution of water, ions, and other solutes in various compartments. Control of the movement of hydrogen and other ions can aid in the regulation of the pH of a fluid compartment. Secretory and absorptive phenomena,

Chapter 6

Biological Membranes and Material Transport

including endo- and exocytosis, are associated with membrane activities. Changes in membrane permeability and resultant ion movements are essential to cellular irritability and excitability. Movement or nonmovement of substances through a membrane often serves as the basis for a regulatory mechanism. For example, the amount of substrate passing into a cell may determine the rate of cellular metabolism of that compound. A function of some hormones is to alter membrane permeability to metabolites thus assisting in the control of their intracellular metabolism.

Gross animal surfaces such as the epithelial layers of skin or respiratory organs, or the linings of tubular systems such as digestive or excretory organs, or the surfaces of circulatory system vessels such as capillaries—all these determine which substances can enter or leave organisms or their component parts and at what rates. Such surfaces are composed of cells whose individual plasma membranes collectively contribute to the overall passage of materials. Some authors use the term cellular membranes for these surfaces to distinguish them from individual plasma membranes.

Before discussing specific biological membranes and their functional roles and before considering the mechanisms underlying biological transport, we must describe the basic mechanisms by which molecules move through solutions or across membranes.

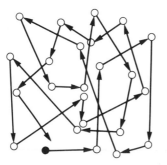

Figure 6-1 The random walk (Brownian movement) of a solute particle. A solute particle moves randomly in jumps whose energy is provided by collisions with other particles. The length of each jump will depend upon the kinetic energy imparted to the particle.

Diffusion, Osmosis, and Related Properties of Solutions

6-2. Simple Diffusion in Solutions. All particles in solution are in continual motion—thermal or Brownian movement—because of their kinetic energy. In dilute[1] solutions solute molecules are constantly colliding with solvent molecules, and the kinetic energy imported to the solute particles causes them to undergo a random walk through the solution (Figure 6-1). In the absence of any external force on the solution the movement of solute molecules is random, and the distance traveled in a given time by any given particle may be in any direction. If, however, there should be a difference of concentration between two parts of a solution, then there will be a net movement of solute from the region of higher to the region of lower concentration. Statistically there are more particles to move randomly from high to low concentration than from low to high.

[1] Dilute solutions are considered to be 0.1 molar or less in concentration. Most laws of physical chemistry are limiting laws—laws which describe the behavior of a system simply and precisely under conditions that diminish the influence of interfering factors. The behavior of real systems is complex and cannot be described in any simple or precise terms. In real solutions, for example, molecules interact with one another in many ways, all of which affect any one property of the system. The analysis of diffusion becomes complex at very high solute concentrations, in the presence of charged particles, when components are impure, and so forth. The more dilute a solution, the less the interactions between solute molecules and the simpler (and more possible) the description of diffusion becomes. This description approaches (but never reaches) ideal behavior at lower concentrations. It is usual to express, if possible, properties of solutions in terms of infinite dilution, obtained by extrapolating experimental data to zero concentration. This brings values of diffusion and other constants closer to the ideal (imaginary) conditions of the limiting law.

Rigorous treatment of real solutions demands the use of activities, not molar or molal units of concentration; but in most biological systems the activity values are not known for the biological conditions. Using dilute solutions and molar or molal concentration terms is the best recourse in most cases and one which is not too far in error.

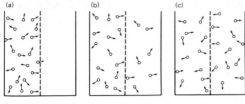

o⁻ Solute Particles

Figure 6-2 Diffusion of a solute across a boundary or membrane freely permeable to the solute. The arrows indicate the random movements of solute particles. (a) Initially a solution is layered against a volume of pure solvent. Some solute molecules will pass across the boundary into the solvent. (b) At some later time, the initially pure solvent layer will contain solute particles. Although some of these in their random motion may cross from right to left, the net movement is still from left to right because more particles of solute are on the left side. (c) At equilibrium there are equal numbers of solute particles on either side of the initial boundary, and there is no net movement in either direction although random movements of solute particles still occur.

This net movement of solute due to the presence of a concentration gradient is **diffusion**. The situation is diagrammed in Figure 6-2. At equilibrium the concentrations of solute become equal throughout the solution, and although solute molecules are still in random motion, no net flow occurs in any direction. Diffusion may be thought of as a process that brings about an equilibrium of the chemical potentials of a solute that initially was unequally distributed so that its chemical potentials were unequal in different parts of the solution. Other considerations come into play when charged particles and their associated electrical fields are involved in diffusion or when a membrane separates two fluid compartments. For now we shall consider only systems of nonelectrolytes in solution in the absence of membranes.

In 1855 the German anatomist, Adolph Fick, set forth an empirical relationship for diffusion now known as Fick's first law:

$$J = \frac{ds}{dt} = -DA\frac{dc}{dx} \qquad (6.1)$$

where the flux, J, of diffusing solute is the amount of material, s, in grams or moles

passing across area, A, per second. The flux is proportional to the concentration gradient, dc/dx, where c is the concentration (in grams or moles per cm^3) and x is distance. The flux is also proportional to the diffusion coefficient, D, a proportionality constant whose value depends on temperature and the particular solute molecule which is diffusing. D has the units of $cm^2 sec^{-1}$. The negative sign of Equation 6.1 indicates that net movement of solute occurs in the direction of decreasing concentration. When the concentration gradient becomes zero, diffusion ceases.

Equation 6.1 contains differential coefficients and this means that the integration of the equation will have different solutions depending on the nature of the system in which diffusion is occurring. The nature of the boundary between the two fluid compartments, whether or not diffusion is occurring across a plane in a one-dimensional direction, the relationship of sizes of solute and solvent—all of these factors will yield different equations from which the diffusion constant may be calculated (Jacobs, 1935).

Several methods are used to determine diffusion coefficients. One important type depends on the fact that the refractive index

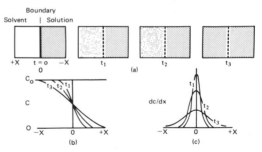

Figure 6-3 (a) Schematic diagram of diffusion cell showing an initial sharp boundary between solvent and solution (shaded) at time zero and the gradual movement of solute into solvent layer with time. (b) A plot of concentration, c, of solute at varying distances, x, from the boundary at different times, t. (c) Typical curves of the change in the concentration gradient, dc/dx, as diffusion progresses. At equilibrium no concentration gradient would exist, and solute is distributed equally throughout the diffusion cell.

159

of a solution is proportional to its concentration. The refractive index in the neighborhood of a boundary between pure solvent and a solution may be observed and measured using Schlieren optics or Rayleigh interference optics (Longsworth, 1968; Martin, 1964). Figure 6-3 illustrates a typical experimental system used to determine the diffusion coefficient. A long rectangular tube (long enough so that diffusing molecules do not reach the end of the tube during the time course of the measurement, thus simulating a case of diffusion over an infinite distance—a situation for which solutions to Equation 6.1 are easily found) is set up with a sharp initial boundary between a layer of solution and a layer of pure solvent. Concentration changes at the boundary region because of diffusion of the solute can be measured. The solution to Equation 6.1 is also simplified because diffusion is occurring in one dimension across a planar area.

The diffusion coefficient is useful for characterizing macromolecules and also for establishing the rate of movement of biologically important substances through solutions, thus giving an indication of their movements through biological materials. Table 6-1 lists the diffusion coefficients of some biological substances. Such values of D are given for diffusion at 20°C, measured against distilled water, and extrapolated to infinite dilution. These factors are symbolized by appropriate super- and subscripts. Thus, in this case the diffusion coefficient is symbolized by $D^{\circ}_{20,w}$.

D is related to both the size and the shape of the diffusing molecules because frictional interactions between solute molecules affect their rate of movement. In dilute solution:

$$D = \frac{RT}{Nf} \tag{6.2}$$

where R is the gas constant; T, the absolute temperature; N, Avogadro's number; and f, the frictional coefficient. Long, fibrous-type molecules develop higher frictional interactions than do spherical ones. The frictional coefficient is related to the viscosity, η, of the liquid solvent—a measure of the ease or difficulty of flow—by the Stoke's expression:

$$f = 6\pi\eta r^2 \tag{6.3}$$

Table 6-1 Some Diffusion Coefficients and Molecular Weights

SUBSTANCE	MOLECULAR WEIGHT	$D^{\circ}_{20,w}$ (cm^2/sec)	f/f_0
H_2	2	5.1×10^{-5}	—
O_2	32	1.9×10^{-5}	—
CO_2	44	1.8×10^{-5}	—
Urea	60	1.2×10^{-5}	—
NaCl	58	1.6×10^{-5}	—
KCl	75	1.9×10^{-5}	—
$CaCl_2$	111	1.3×10^{-5}	—
Glycine	74	9.5×10^{-6}	—
Glucose	180	6.7×10^{-6}	—
Ribonuclease	13,683	1.2×10^{-6}	1.14
Ovalbumin	45,000	7.7×10^{-7}	1.17
Hemoglobin	68,000	6.9×10^{-7}	1.14
Urease	480,000	3.5×10^{-7}	1.20
Collagen	-345,000	6.9×10^{-8}	6.80
DNA	6,000,000	1.3×10^{-8}	15

* Data from Harned and Owen (1953); Tanford (1961).

where r is the radius of a spherical diffusing particle.

Einstein showed that the diffusion coefficient was related to the frictional coefficient which in turn is related to the viscosity, so that:

$$D = \frac{RT}{6N\pi\eta r^2} \qquad (6.4)$$

These relationships are for rigid, spherical particles whose radii are much larger than those of the solvent particles. They require modification when molecules of other shapes are considered.

Asymmetric molecules align themselves in a flowing fluid thus causing η to decrease as the flow gradient increases. Macromolecules increase the viscosity of a liquid even at low concentrations because the viscosity is dependent on the fraction volume of solute, and macromolecules have large volumes. Only indirectly does the size or number of solute molecules affect the viscosity of a solution.

The frictional ratio, f/f_0, is used to measure the departure from sphericalness of solute molecules. The denominator, f_0 is the frictional coefficient of the anhydrous form of the molecule and also takes into account any molecular asymmetry. The numerator, f, is calculated from the measured diffusion coefficient Equation 6.2, whereas f_0 is determined from the Einstein-Smoluchowski relationship:

$$f_0 = \eta(162\pi^2 M\bar{v})N^{1/3} \qquad (6.5)$$

where M is the molecular weight of the solute molecule and $\bar{v}$ is the partial molar volume. Values for the frictional ratios of some macromolecules are given in Table 6-1. As the table shows, larger molecules, with smaller diffusion coefficients, usually move more slowly than do smaller molecules; but the shape of the molecule is also important. Urease, a globular protein, diffuses faster than collagen, a fibrous protein, although both are of approximately the same molecular weight. The asymmetry of the collagen molecule is indicated by its much higher frictional ratio.

Thus, viscosity and frictional forces arising from the nature of the macromolecules in solution can greatly influence fluid flows and rates of diffusion. These factors, for example, are of importance when fluid movement in vascular systems are considered.

6-3. The Rate of Diffusion. Diffusion is the simplest mechanism by which materials may be transported from one part of a solution to another or from one part of an organism to another. Generally, however, diffusion is an extremely slow process at the macroscopic level. A lump of sugar placed in a cup of coffee will require days to diffuse through and sweeten the liquid uniformly; therefore, mechanical stirring is needed. The times of diffusion represented in the graphs of Figure 6-3 are measured in hours, days, or even weeks. In fact, one difficulty in measuring protein diffusion coefficients is that the long time period required to obtain sufficient movement to yield accurate results often gives the proteins time to denature. Diffusion at the macroscopic level is not greatly affected by temperature, and Q_{10} values lie between about 1.0 and 1.3 for the diffusion of solutes in water.

At the cellular level diffusion may be relatively rapid because the distances traveled by solutes are measured in Ångstrom units, not centimeters. The jumps of molecules during diffusion are large enough to make diffusion a rapid process at the molecular level.

All organisms depend on diffusion as a mechanism for transporting solutes into or out of certain compartments. But when cells or organisms become large or possess high activity (requiring a rapid supply of nutrients) the slowness of diffusion becomes a rate-limiting step. To overcome this limitation, animals are built on a subdivisional plan. They are composed of cells arranged in small groups either supplied by minute vessels of a circulatory system or bathed in a circulating fluid. Such systems use the contractile force of muscles or of other contractile organelles to provide a relatively rapid flow of materials to and away from the cells. Once these forces have brought materials close to cells, diffusion may then be used to move them the short distance from extracellular fluid to cell interior.

A. V. Hill (1928) pointed out that if nerves were solid cylinders, 1 cm in diameter, and composed of the same substances found in real nerves; it would require 185 minutes to produce a 90 per cent saturation of such a cylinder with needed oxygen using diffusion from an oxygen-rich atmosphere as the supply mechanism. Nerves that were solid cylinders 700 μ in diameter (the size of many actual nerves) would require 54 seconds for this amount of oxygen to be supplied. Nerve cells, which average about 7 μ in diameter, obtain this amount of oxygen in about 5 milliseconds. Actual nerves are composed of bundles of small nerve cells, and an efficient distribution of a circulating blood overcomes the difficulties of supply attendant upon the slowness of diffusion through solid structures.

6-4. Diffusion through Membranes. The presence of a membrane adds complications to the analysis of diffusion, especially in biological systems whose membranes have a complex structure, not fully understood, and where active changes in both structure and function can occur.

We can consider a membranous diffusion system to consist of three phases—a phase being any part of a system that is macroscopically homogeneous and bounded by an interface. In the case of cells there are the following: (1) the interstitial fluid, the outer or external phase; (2) the intracellular medium, or inner phase; and (3) the membrane. It is also possible to have an interface without the presence of a discrete structural entity—a familiar example being the interface or boundary present in an oil-water system.

In all discussion to follow, the subscript "o" will refer to the external medium; the subscript "i" to the internal phase; and the subscript "m" for the characteristics and properties of the membrane.

The kinetic treatment of **permeability**—defined as the rate of movement of a substance through a permeable layer under some driving force—can be simplified by making certain assumptions based upon seemingly general properties of biological membranes that are

very thin, on the order of 100 Å in thickness.

Experimental evidence (see Tables 6-1 and 6-2) indicates that the rate of diffusion of a given substance through a membrane is often slower than through an aqueous solution. Since movement through the membrane is slow, it will require only small concentration gradients in the external solution (assuming that net diffusion is into the internal phase) to bring solute molecules up to the membrane as fast as they can diffuse through. That is, concentration gradients in the external phase can be neglected in the analysis. The rate of penetration of a substance will depend only on the properties of the membrane and the concentration gradient across the membrane.

If it is assumed that the concentration gradient across a very thin membrane is uniform and that the concentrations of solute at the inner and outer surfaces of the membrane remain constant, then the concentration gradient across the membrane can be considered simply as the difference between the internal and external concentrations of the diffusing solute divided by the membrane thickness: $(c_o - c_i)/x_m$ (Figure 6-4). This quantity is substituted for the differential, dc/dx, of Equation 6.1 giving:

$$J = \frac{ds}{dt} = \frac{D}{x_m}(c_0 - c_i) \qquad (6.6)$$

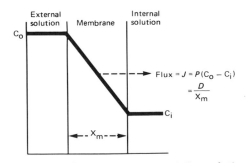

Figure 6-4 Schematic representation of the assumed solute concentrations across a cell membrane and the definition of solute flux. X_m is the membrane thickness; C_o and C_i are solute concentrations outside and inside the membrane, respectively; D is the diffusion coefficient; P is the permeability coefficient; and J is the solute flux.

Table 6-2 Some Permeability Coefficients (cm/sec) of Various Cells*

CELL TYPE	UREA	GLYCEROL	NA$^+$	K$^+$
Ox erythrocyte	7.8×10^{-5}	1.7×10^{-8}	—	—
Capillary	2.6×10^{-7}	—	3.3×10^{-7}	—
Arbacia egg	—	5.0×10^{-8}	—	—
Frog muscle	—	—	2.0×10^{-8}	1.0×10^{-6}
extracellular fluid†	—	—	2.4×10^{-4}	7.0×10^{-4}

* Data from: Davson and Danielli (1952); McLennan (1957); Woodbury (1965).
† Values given are for the diffusion coefficients (cm/sec).

where J is the net flux across the membrane (moles/cm²/sec). Equation 6.6 has been simplified by assuming that the flux takes place across unit area of membrane surface.

Since neither the actual thickness of the functional biological membrane nor the diffusion coefficient inside the membrane is known, D and x_m are combined into a single constant, the **permeability coefficient**, P, whose units are cm/sec:

$$J = P(c_o - c_i) \qquad (6.7)$$

Some representative values of P are given in Table 6-2. The data of this table provide some indication of the fact that the permeability of different cells to the same substance may vary markedly. Comparison of these permeability coefficients with the diffusion coefficients in water indicates that movement through the membrane of a cell is a slower process than through an aqueous solution.

The rate of movement of water through biological membranes is usually higher than that of solutes (Table 6-3). The movement of liquids through a membrane is sometimes expressed as the permeability with units of cm/sec, which, however, is derived from the term: cm³/cm²/sec, that is, the volume of liquid transferred across a given surface area of membrane per second. The permeability of water is also expressed in units of μ^3/μ^2/sec, since these dimensions are closer to those actually encountered in biological systems at the cellular level.

Measured rates of water penetration into cells depend on the method of analysis

(Koefoed-Johnson and Ussing, 1953; Prescott and Zeuthen, 1953). Values obtained by measuring the rate of osmotic inflow of water into cells are about six times greater than those obtained by measuring the inward diffusion of heavy water, D_2O. This difference has been explained on the basis that diffusion is across the material of the membrane, whereas osmotic flow is through pores and the latter pathway presents less frictional resistance to flow. However, the situation is certainly more complex than this.

There are several possible explanations for the slower diffusion of solutes across a membrane than through a solution. Diffusion was defined as the net movement of solute under the influence of a concentration gradient, and it results from the random movement due to the kinetic energies of solute molecules. In gases, where molecules are relatively far apart and can move about freely, diffusion is relatively rapid. In liquids some restraint is placed on molecular movements because attractive

Table 6-3 Permeability Coefficients (cm/sec) for Water*

CELL	P
Arbacia egg	2.1×10^{-4}
Ox erythrocyte	5.2×10^{-3}
Rabbit leucocyte	6.3×10^{-4}
Amoeba	5.6×10^{-3}

* Data from: Dick (1959b); Davson and Danielli (1952).

forces exist between molecules, and also the mean free path—the clear possible distance a molecule can move—is less because molecules are closer together than in a gas. A solute molecule can move only when it achieves sufficient energy by collision to break away from surrounding molecules. In a membranous system a solute molecule must also obtain sufficient energy to enter the substance of the membrane, that is, to enter the interphase.

The same type of kinetic and thermodynamic analyses that are applied to rate constants of chemical reactions (Chapter 4) can be used for the diffusion process. A solute molecule must be "activated" before it can jump. The activated state here is a molecule poised in some intermediate position between the direction of net movement and the reverse direction. Diffusion coefficients are related to free energies of activation as were rate constants (see Equation 4.31 on page 101):

$$D = \lambda^2 \frac{T}{h} \exp\left(\frac{-\Delta G}{RT}\right) \qquad (6.8)$$

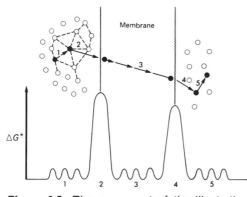

Figure 6-5 The upper part of the illustration portrays the necessary jumps a solute molecule must make to move from the outer solution, through the membrane, and into the inner solution. The dotted lines indicate the intermolecular forces that must be broken in order for the diffusing particle to escape from the solution. The lower part of the illustration indicates the hypothetical activation energies, ΔG^*, required for each type of jump. The numbers correspond to the types of jumps labeled in the upper part of the figure. The energy required to enter the membrane is probably less for a lipid soluble particle.

The jump distance, λ, is the distance through which a solute molecule moves at each step of its diffusion, and it depends on the viscosity of the medium, the frictional resistance to movement, the solute concentration, and the nature of solute, solvent, and membrane materials.

Diffusion through a membrane can be thought of as occurring in three steps (Danielli and Davson, 1935; Davson and Danielli, 1952): (1) a movement from the medium into the membrane; (2) movement across the membrane; and (3) movement from the membrane into the intracellular medium (Figure 6-5).

The first step requires the largest energy of activation. Since fewer molecules are likely to attain this energy than for a similar situation in a simple solution, the slowness of diffusion through biological membranes might be partially explained. It might also explain why some molecules cannot penetrate biological membranes.

It has been assumed that the membrane is homogeneous and that penetration of solute into the membrane occurs over the entire surface area, but the possibility exists that a membrane is porous and that diffusion occurs only through the pores. If a porous plate (whose pores are large compared with the diameters of solute molecules) is placed between two solutions of differing concentration, then the rate of diffusion is reduced because the effective area for diffusion is reduced. Under these conditions molecules pass through the membrane at rates proportional to their concentration gradients and diffusion coefficients.

If the pores are small, however, free movement in the pores is blocked, especially when solute concentrations are high. Several molecules may enter a porous channel, effectively blocking either efflux or influx. Under these conditions, Equation 6.6 no longer applies. Hodgkin and Keynes (1955a, b) discuss this situation for the movement of ions through a membrane.

The presence or absence of pores in biological membranes is an unsatisfactorily answered question. Pores, if they exist, must have diameters on the order of 7 Å or less—small even for the movement of ions through them. Pores have not been seen in plasma membranes examined with the electron microscope. Before discussing evidence for or against pores in membranes, several other aspects of membrane permeability require attention.

6-5. Partition Coefficients. At the end of the nineteenth century, Overton, working with plant cells and following the movements of different dyes into the cells, came to the conclusion that cell membranes contained lipids because lipid-soluble dyes penetrated the membrane faster than water-soluble dyes. Some criticism of this work was made on the basis that some of the dyes used were charged and others were not. Nonelectrolytes generally pass through membranes faster than electrolytes.

Collander and Bärlund (1933) in an extensive study of the unicellular alga, *Chara ceratophyla*, found that lipid-soluble materials generally did move more rapidly through the membrane than did water-soluble substances (Figure 6-6). Ethers and ketones, for example, pass through so rapidly that diffusion rates cannot be measured. Substances such as glycerol, which are more water-soluble, pass through at slower rates.

The **partition coefficient**, B, is used to compare the rates of movement of substances and is defined by

$$B = \frac{\text{solubility in oil}}{\text{solubility in water}} \qquad (6.9)$$

Generally, the greater the value of the partition coefficient of a substance, that is, the greater its lipid solubility, the faster a substance moves through a membrane. A plot of partition coefficient against rate of passage is not linear in most cases because the size of the molecule is also important. Smaller molecules usually pass through more rapidly than larger ones, but this generalization applies principally to homologous series of compounds. All factors—size, partition coefficient, charge, as well as the properties of the mem-

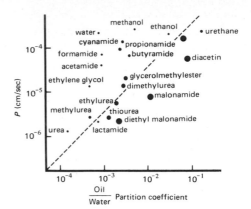

Figure 6-6 Permeability of *Chara ceratophylla* cells plotted against the oil/water partition coefficient of the solutes. The size of the points is roughly proportional to the size of the molecules. Generally, smaller molecules lie above the dashed line, and larger molecules fall below the line. This is an indication that the membrane behaves like a solvent for nonpolar molecules and like a molecular sieve for polar molecules. The general trend of the points substantiates the lipid-solubility rule. [Data from Collander and Bärlund (1933).]

brane itself—determine the permeability of a given substance.

Höber (1945) developed the **mosaic membrane theory**, stating that a membrane is a mosaic structure consisting of patches of porous regions interspersed with patches of lipid regions. The relative proportions of the two types of regions in a given membrane would determine the permeability properties.

After considering the phenomenon of osmosis and other related properties of solutions, we shall return to a discussion of the nature of biological membranes, and the types of membrane models that are used today.

6-6. Osmosis. To this point the movement of solvent molecules through a membrane has been neglected. Normally both solvent and some solutes pass through the membrane, but for simplicity of analysis they are treated separately. Only water movements are considered here because water is the principle liquid solvent in biological systems.

Osmosis is the movement of water from a less concentrated to a more concentrated solution when a semipermeable (or differentially permeable) membrane separates the solutions and when the membrane is impermeable to a solute, s. Note that this definition does not imply any mechanism for water movement. Since some evidence points to the presence of a lipid layer in biological membranes and since water is not soluble in lipids, it is assumed that water must move through pores or water-filled channels in the membrane. But it should be noted that the term pores as used in this connection is a conceptual model only, it does not necessarily imply open channels at right angles to the membrane surface. This type of conceptual scheme is used to account for the extremely rapid movement of water through membranes.

The force which tends to move water in an osmotic system is the osmotic pressure, π, defined by the Van't Hoff expression (see Dick, 1959a, for its derivation):

$$\pi = RT(c_o - c_i) \qquad (6.10)$$

where the gas constant, R, is numerically equal to 0.08 atm/degree/mole when π is expressed in atmospheres of pressure and the internal and external concentrations of solute, c_i and c_o, respectively, are in moles. Osmotic pressure is sometimes given in terms of cm of water or in mm of Hg pressure.

Equation 6.10 shows that the osmotic pressure depends on the difference in concentration of two solutions (separated by a semipermeable membrane). When one concentration is zero, for example, when a solution is separated by the membrane from pure solvent, the osmotic pressure is defined by: RTc. The osmotic pressure is a useful parameter for characterizing solutions. When a value for the osmotic pressure of a single solution is given, this refers to the osmotic pressure the solution would exert if it were separated by a membrane from pure solvent.

Osmotic pressure may be measured in any of several ways (see Bull, 1964; also Chapter 14). One type of system is shown in Figure 6-7. As water moves into the solution compartment and into the vertical capillary tube, a hydraulic pressure is developed. At equili-

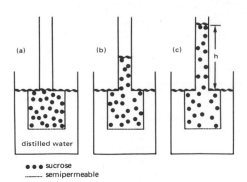

distilled water

• • • sucrose
.... semipermeable

Figure 6-7 A schematic representation of one method for measuring the osmotic pressure of a solution. (a) A semipermeable membrane, impermeable to sucrose, separates an aqueous solution of sucrose from a volume of distilled water. Water moves into the sucrose in an attempt to achieve equal chemical potentials on each side of the membrane. The inflow of water causes a rise of water in the capillary tube and the development of a head of hydrostatic pressure. A capillary tube is used because little water is required to fill the volume of the tube, and there will be only a slight change in the volume of the external compartment. (b) An intermediate position, water is still moving into the inner compartment and rising in the tube. (c) At equilibrium the pressure developed by the head of water, h, in the capillary tube exactly equals the tendency for water to move into the sucrose solution. The pressure, h, is numerically equal to the osmotic pressure, but it is not itself the osmotic pressure. Only at equilibrium, when there is no net water movement, can the osmotic pressure be determined.

brium, this hydraulic pressure exactly counterbalances the force tending to move water into the solution compartment, and the water movement stops. The hydraulic pressure in such a system is equal to the head of water, h, multiplied by the specific gravity of the fluid. This hydraulic pressure at equilibrium is numerically equal to, but opposite in sign from, the osmotic pressure of the solution. The osmotic pressure can be determined only at equilibrium. At intermediate times, such as that shown in Figure 6-7b, the pressure developed is not equal to the osmotic pressure.

The osmosis of water is a mechanism for equalizing the chemical potentials of solvent and solute in each compartment. The statement that water moves from a region of lower to one of higher concentration refers to solute concentrations. As in all energy-containing systems, energy in an osmotic system moves down a potential gradient until equilibrium is reached. A relatively dilute solution contains more water molecules than an equal volume of a more concentrated solution. The latter has solute molecules making up a larger fraction of the solution volume. The chemical potential of water is higher in the less concentrated solution. Therefore water moves down its chemical potential gradient until the activities are the same in both compartments. Osmotic pressures are generally measured in experimental systems in which some force is developed to just counterbalance the water movement.

6-7. Some Terms and Units Used in Osmotic Studies. Osmotic pressure is one of the colligative properties of a solution—properties that depend only on the number of particles present, not on their size or nature. Other colligative properties include the boiling point, freezing point, and vapor pressure.

Electrolytes and nonelectrolytes differ in their osmotic effects in relation to concentration because electrolytes in solution dissociate into two or more particles, each contributing to the osmotic effect. A 0.1 M glucose solution is nearly osmotically equivalent to a 0.05 M NaCl solution because the latter dissociates into two osmotically active ions, each at 0.05 M.

The osmotic activity of a solute is not defined exactly by molar or molal concentrations because solute-solute or solute-solvent interactions occur in solutions, especially at higher concentrations. The result is a decrease of chemical activity. To partially correct for this effect, as well as for the differences between electrolytes and nonelectrolytes, the osmotic coefficient, Q, has been introduced:

$$\pi = QRTc \qquad (6.11)$$

The osmotic coefficient is less than unity. Thus, a 0.05 M NaCl solution behaves

osmotically as though it were slightly less concentrated.

The osmotic activity of any solution may be equated with that of a solution containing a known concentration of an ideal nonelectrolyte. This concentration, representing the osmotic activity, is the **osmolarity** (Osm) of the solution. One can speak of osmoles or milliosmoles per liter (mOsm) in the same way that the terms moles and millimoles per liter are used. One osmole is that amount of solute that, if dissolved in one liter of water, would exert the same osmotic pressure as one mole of the ideal nonelectrolyte. Neglecting the osmotic activity coefficient, a 0.1 molar glucose solution is also 0.1 osmolar and is osmotically equivalent to a 0.05 M NaCl solution. The latter is also 0.1 osmolar (2×0.05). Osmolar units allow comparison of the osmotic effects of electrolyte and nonelectrolyte solutions.

Cells are often designated as osmometers because changes in the concentration of the external medium may produce shrinking or swelling of the cells. **Tonicity** is defined in terms of such cellular responses to the environment. An **isotonic solution** is one which causes neither shrinking nor swelling of a cell placed in it. **Hypertonic** and **hypotonic solutions** of nonpermeating solute are greater or lesser, respectively, than an isotonic solution with regard to their osmotic concentrations. Note that tonicity is based on cellular responses to a given concentration of solute.

Osmoticity is used to compare the osmotic concentrations of solutions. An **isosmotic solution** has an identical osmotic concentration to some other compared solution. **Hyperosmotic** and **hypoosmotic** solutions exert greater or lesser osmotic pressures, respectively, than the solution under comparison.

An isotonic solution is not necessarily identical with an isosmotic solution because the latter may fail to maintain a cell in its normal state. If, for example, an isosmotic solution contains a solute that can interact with the membrane, then changes in the membrane may lead to water loss or uptake—changing the cell volume. On this basis, the solution is not isotonic. Any isosmotic solution containing permeable solutes cannot be isotonic because the solute will penetrate the cell, altering its concentration, and causing osmotic water inflow or outflow.

Solutes that penetrate a cell membrane as rapidly as water exert no osmotic effects. Most membranes are leaky to some substances, that is, the membrane is not completely impermeable to them. In these circumstances an osmotic pressure is observed that is smaller than would be expected from the solute concentration. The ratio of observed osmotic pressure to that calculated for a given concentration of solute is called the reflexion coefficient, σ, and is a measure of the permeability of a membrane to a given solute. An impermeable membrane has a σ equal to 1; a coarse porous membrane has a σ equal to zero (Staverman, 1948; Kedem, 1965).

An important difference between diffusion of solute and osmosis of water is that the latter can produce large volume changes in the system. In diffusion relatively small volumes of material are transferred; but when solvent moves in osmosis, a large volume may be transported, especially when the relatively small sizes of cells is considered.

6-8. Other Colligative Properties. Direct measurement of osmotic pressure or osmotic concentrations is often difficult in biological systems where only small volumes of sample are usually obtainable. To attain osmotic equilibrium may take a long period of time during which proteins can denature. Direct chemical assays are generally impossible with cellular systems. However, other colligative properties of solutions are more easily and accurately determined and since all colligative properties are directly related to one another, the determination of freezing-point depression or vapor pressure lowering is often used as an indirect measure of the osmotic pressure (Newman, 1964).

The **vapor pressure** is the partial pressure of the vapor of a solvent over a solution (or above pure solvent) when equilibrium has been established between the liquid and gaseous phases at constant temperature and constant total pressure. Addition of a solute to a solvent lowers the vapor pressure according to Raoult's law:

$$\frac{p_0 - p}{p_0} = \frac{n_2}{n_1 + n_2} \qquad (6.12)$$

where p_0 and p are the vapor pressures of the pure solvent and of the solution, respectively. The ratio on the right side of Equation 6.12 is the **mole fraction of solute** in the solution, where n_1 and n_2 are the number of moles of solvent and solute, respectively. The ratio on the right is the **relative vapor pressure lowering**. The vapor pressure difference, $p_0 - p$, is also used to characterize a given solution and is symbolized by Δ_p.

Addition of solute to solvent also lowers the freezing point of the solution. The freezing point depression, Δ_f, is related to solute concentration by

$$\Delta_f = K_f(c_2) \qquad (6.13)$$

where K_f is the cryoscopic constant and c_2 the osmolal concentration of solute.

K_f for pure water is 1.86. One mole of a nonelectrolyte lowers the freezing point of water by 1.86°C. The osmotic pressure of a solution may be approximately calculated from a determination of the freezing point depression by the relation

$$\pi = \frac{22.3\Delta_f}{1.86} \qquad (6.14)$$

Freezing point depressions can be measured rather easily with an accuracy of 0.001°C or better, corresponding to osmotic pressures of about 0.01 atm (= 9 mm Hg). In many instances in the biological literature osmotic concentrations are expressed in terms of Δ_f. The techniques for freezing point depression measurements will be discussed in Chapter 14.

A one osmolal solution contained within rigid semipermeable walls will produce an internal pressure of 22.4 atmospheres (760 mm Hg) and will lower the freezing point of water by 1.86°C.

6-9. Ultrafiltration and Dialysis. Two forces are at work in moving water and solutes through certain membranes. One is the osmotic

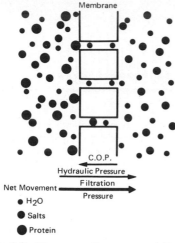

Figure 6-8 Diagrammatic representation of a type of biological membrane across which ultra-filtration occurs. This type of membrane is found for example in capillaries of the circulatory system and in some membranes of excretory organs. The membrane is permeable to smaller solutes (small circles) and is impermeable to colloidal-sized particles (large circles). The arrows at the bottom indicate the relative values of the colloidal osmotic pressure (COP) and a hydraulic pressure in the system. Net movement of water and small solutes will be in the direction of the filtration pressure, the difference between the colloidal osmotic pressure, and the hydraulic pressure. The latter may be established by the action of a heart in a circulatory system, the contraction of body musculature, and so forth.

pressure established by the presence of non-permeating solutes; the other is the hydraulic or fluid pressure. The latter may exist in various parts of organisms because of the pumping action of the heart in a circulatory system or because of muscular contractions squeezing fluid compartments, and so on. The direction of the material movement will depend on the relative values of the osmotic and hydraulic forces.

Figure 6-8 schematically presents a type of membrane system often found in biological systems. It is permeable to water and small molecules such as amino acids, salts, or sugars; and it is impermeable to larger molecules such as proteins. The smaller solutes contribute nothing to the osmotic pressure because they are freely diffusible. The nondiffusible macro-

molecules (colloids) set up an osmotic pressure known as the **colloid osmotic pressure** (COP) or the **oncotic pressure**.

If there is a hydraulic pressure on the colloid-containing solution that tends to

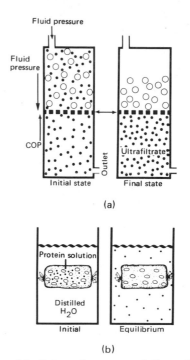

(a)

(b)

Figure 6-9 Schematic representation of the procedures used for (a) ultrafiltration and (b) dialysis of protein solutions. In ultrafiltration a fluid pressure is applied to the chamber that contains the protein (nonpermeating) material. The protein molecules (larger circles) are retained by the membrane while smaller solutes and water move through the membrane. The fluid pressure must be made greater than the colloidal osmotic pressure, which tends to draw water into the protein solution. In the final stages, the protein has been purified with respect to small solutes. The outlet permits a continuous removal of the ultrafiltrate. In dialysis a membranous bag containing the protein solution is placed in a large volume of distilled water. Small solutes diffuse out of the bag until at equilibrium equal amounts of penetrating solutes are found inside and outside the membrane bag. For complete removal of solutes, either a flowing stream of distilled water must bathe the bag or several changes of the external medium must be made. By placing the protein containing bag in a salt or buffer solution, the protein may be equilibrated with any desired salt concentration.

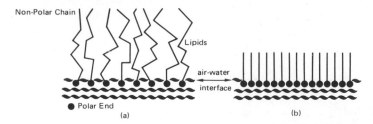

Figure 6-10 (a) Schematic diagram of the formation of a monolayer lipid film upon a water surface. The circles represent the polar ends of the lipid molecules; the zig-zag lines portray the hydrocarbon chains—the nonpolar regions of the lipid. Only the polar ends of the lipid molecules are attracted to the polar solvent, water. (b) The shorthand way of symbolizing a monolayer lipid film on a water surface.

force water out of that compartment—the net movement of water and solutes will be determined by the difference between hydraulic and oncotic pressures—this difference is the **filtration pressure**. In this case, any flow of solvent causes solute to be carried along with it through the freely permeable membrane.

Systems of this type are important in the functioning of capillaries in closed circulatory systems (Chapter 12). The formation of urine in the excretory organs of crustaceans, molluscs, some annelids, and in the glomerulus of the vertebrate nephron is initiated by this type of process. The mechanism is called **ultrafiltration**, and produces a so-called ultrafiltrate that is free of larger molecules but that contains all the smaller permeating substances.

Ultrafiltration is also used as a research tool for purifying macromolecular solutions or for preparing blood fractions and the like (Figure 6-9a). In most instances solvent and small solutes move in the direction of the hydraulic pressure because this is generally higher than the oncotic pressure. A 1 per cent solution of NaCl may lead to several atmospheres of pressure, but a 1 per cent protein solution contains relatively few molecules and can exert an osmotic pressure of only a few cm of water. In most natural systems, the hydraulic pressure is higher than this. Although in cells or in blood capillaries high protein concentrations are encountered and large hydraulic pressures are required to move fluid in the necessary direction, this is not always true of experimental systems.

Another experimental procedure used to purify proteins and other macromolecules or to isolate smaller particles from biological fluids is **dialysis** (Figure 6-9b). Artificial membranes of collodion or cellophane (Visking tubing) are used. If such a membrane, in the form of a sack containing a protein in solution, is placed in a large volume of water or buffer, there will be an outward diffusion of permeable solutes (determined by the pore size of the membrane), and the protein solution will be gradually freed of salts and other smaller materials. In some cases the dialysis bag is placed in a flowing stream of solvent that ensures a continuous outward diffusion of solute. Dialysis is also used to equilibrate salt or buffer solutions with macromolecular solutions in order to achieve desired salt concentrations or pH's. Dialysis is based on solute diffusion only, unlike filtration.

Membrane Structure and Models

6-10. Early Membrane Work. The work of Overton and others led to the idea that cell membranes contained lipids because they were more permeable to lipid soluble compounds than to water soluble compounds. The pore theory was invoked to explain how smaller molecules could pass through a membrane faster than larger ones, whereas some were too large to pass through at all. Before further consideration of transport across biological membranes, the present models of membrane structure are worth discussing. I must stress, however, that the exact nature of biological membranes is still largely unknown.

Langmuir (1917) laid the foundation for experiments with thin films and membranes by pioneering research on monomolecular layers of lipids. He showed that lipid molecules could be made to spread out on a water surface in a monomolecular film in a container of pure and dust-free water (now known as a Langmuir trough). He also showed that at the air-water interface, the polar ends of the lipid molecules pointed into the water, while the nonpolar hydrocarbon chains stood on end (Figure 6-10).

Such films could be compressed, and by measuring the force required to reduce the film to a known surface area, a force-area curve could be drawn (Figure 6-11). The area occupied by each polar group can be calculated from a knowledge of the chemical structure of the lipid, the breaking point of the film, and of the number of molecules on the surface. Much use has been made of such films and the interpretation of the physical properties of these models yields important clues about the nature of biological membranes (Sobotka, 1944; Mueller et al. 1963; van Deenen et al., 1962).

Gorter and Grendel (1925) used ether to extract the total lipids from a known number of human erythrocytes. After determining the

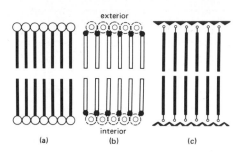

Figure 6-12 The evolution of membrane models. (a) The membrane according to Gorter and Grendel. A bimolecular layer of lipids arranged with polar groups outward. (b) Model of Danielli-Davson—the pauci-molecular model. In addition to a bilayer of lipids, the interior and exterior surfaces are monomolecularly layered with globular proteins. (c) Model of Robertson indicating that outer and inner protein layers are different and that the proteins are probably not globular. All of these models are highly schematic and do not portray actual relationships of the lipid molecules nor of the protein-lipid interrelationships.

total area occupied by the lipid when spread in a monomolecular layer, plotting a force-area curve, and determining the surface area of all the erythrocytes, they concluded that there was enough lipid present to form a bimolecular layer of lipid about each blood cell. They postulated a membrane structured as shown in Figure 6-12a.

Danielli and Davson (1935) formulated the **pauci-molecular membrane model** (Figure 6-12b). By this time chemical analysis had shown the likelihood of both lipids and proteins as constituents of biological membranes, and their model included a monomolecular layer of globular protein spread on either side of a bimolecular lipid leaflet. Another reason for placing proteins in the membrane came from surface tension measurements on erythrocytes and marine invertebrate eggs (Cole, 1932; Danielli and Harvey, 1935). These workers found that values of surface tension of a number of natural membranes ranged between 0.03 and 1.0 dynes per centimeter. Oil droplets from *Arbacia* eggs, as well as other lipid droplets, have surface tensions in the range of 1 to 10 dynes per centimeter. The low values for cell membranes seemed best accounted for by

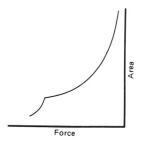

Figure 6-11 The nature of the force area curve for surface membranes. As force is imposed on a film, the area decreases until the film finally breaks. The discontinuity on the curve represents the minimal area of the film. From a knowledge of this point and the chemical structure of the lipids composing the film, the area occupied by the polar end of each molecule can be calculated.

assuming that the membrane was not pure lipid but contained other constituents, especially proteins. The presence of proteins lowers the surface tension due to lipids (Ackerman, 1962).

Danielli and Davson in their original model were careful not to proceed beyond known facts. They gave no value for the thickness of the membrane, the number of lipid layers, or their arrangements. The pauci-molecular hypothesis has developed as new findings are brought to light (Danielli, 1962; Davson, 1962; Davson and Danielli, 1952).

In 1940, Waugh and Schmitt made direct measurements of the thickness of red blood cell ghost membranes, using the analytical leptoscope. This instrument compares the light reflectivity of a red cell ghost dried upon a glass surface with that of barium stearate films of known thickness. By dipping a glass slide into a solution of a purified lipid such as barium stearate, a monolayer of lipid is deposited on the slide (actually one layer is formed as the slide is dipped into the solution and another as the slide is pulled out of the solution. A step film can be formed by repeated dippings and dryings, and varying thicknesses of lipid film obtained.) The results showed that the membranes compared in reflectivity with lipid films 200 Å thick. A major difficulty with this method was the removal of all non-membranous material from the preparation—a problem common to the purification of all cell membranes. Because of this impurity it was thought that the values obtained for the erythrocyte membrane thickness was too high.

Electron microscopy has shown that erythrocyte membranes are about 75 Å thick. The latest membrane model (Figure 6-12c) following that of the pauci-molecular model is based on electron microscope, x-ray diffraction, and polarized light studies, and also on some biochemical analysis (Robertson, 1964, 1965). It agrees in most facets with the Danielli-Davson model. Its major additions include the asymmetric nature of the inner and outer membrane (protein) layers, and the hypothesis that the layers of protein are not formed exclusively of globular proteins because they are so thin, ca. 20 Å.

This model does not attempt to describe the nature of the carbohydrate material known to be associated with membrane structure. Nor is any attempt made to portray the actual arrangement of lipids and proteins in the membrane.

Table 6-4 Lipid Content of Human Brain Myelin*

Substance	6 Years old		55 Years old	
Protein (% dry weight)	19.1		22.0	
Total lipid (% dry weight)	80.9		78.0	
Cholesterol (% total lipid)	42.4		40.4	
Glycerophosphatides (% total lipid)	24.6		24.8	
ethanolamine-containing		11.4		11.8
serine-containing		4.1		5.3
choline-containing		9.1		8.4
Total sphingolids (% total lipid)	28.6		24.5	
sphingomyelin		4.3		4.4
cerebrosides		18.1		15.7
cerebroside sulfates		3.3		3.5
ceramides		1.3		1.5
Unidentified lipids	5.9		9.0	

* Data from: O'Brien (1965).

Table 6-5 Lipid Content of Some Erythrocytes*

SPECIES	TOTAL LIPID (mg $\times 10^{-10}$/cell)	PHOSPHOLIPID DISTRIBUTION (%):			NEUTRAL LIPIDS (%)	CHOLESTEROL (%)
		LECITHINS	CEPHALINS	SPHINGO-MYELINS		
Rat	3.8	56	18	26	28	100
Rabbit	3.5	44	27	29	33	64
Pig	2.2	29	35	36	27	80
Sheep	2.4	19	24	49	28	96
Cat	2.4	—	—	—	—	—
Chicken	7.3	—	—	—	—	—
Human	4.8	35	28	23	29	80
Bovine	2.2	7	32	61	33	94

* Data from: van Deenen and de Gier (1964).

All of the models so far discussed generally follow the unit membrane hypothesis (Section 3-8) that membranes are triple-layered structures: two layers of protein sandwiching a bimolecular lipid layer. Although this is their appearance in the electron microscope, the resolution of the instrument does not yet permit any visualization of the actual molecular arrangements.

This type of membrane model is coming under heavy attack (Korn, 1968; Green and MacLennan, 1969) because of uncertainties of where supposedly specific electron stains such as osmic acid are actually attaching, the difficulties of explaining membrane formation with solid layers of lipids and proteins, and the difficulties of reconciling the triple-layered structure with experimental results on membrane transport. As indicated in Section 3-8, substructural membrane units have been observed in the electron microscope (see the report by Quastel, 1967). Many membranes appear to have a granular substructural unit consisting of a hexagonal pattern of facets, each about 90 Å in diameter and containing a dense spot that might be mucopolysaccharide. Another substructural unit seen in some membranes is globular and appears as dense lines crossing the light central core of the membrane at a repeat interval of 90 Å.

We shall see that other questions concerning

membrane structure exist when the various types of transport activities are described in the following sections. The various models discussed above are convenient generalizations, based on present knowledge. Obviously much more remains to be discovered about membranes and their molecular architecture.

6-11. Myelin. Much of our knowledge of membrane structure comes from studies on the thick lipoprotein sheath—the myelin sheath—that surrounds many nerve cells (Chapter 7). The myelin coating is often very thick and therefore sufficient material is available for chemical analysis as well as for x-ray diffraction and electron microscope studies. It is assumed that myelin is similar in basic structure to all cell membranes, but this assumption is not based on good comparisons with other membranes.

Table 6-4 presents some data on the lipid composition of myelin from human brain tissue. Cholesterol, glycerophosphatides, and sphingolipids are abundant in this myelin (which makes up the greater part of the tissue), whereas free fatty acids and other lipids are absent. Studies on myelin from other sources indicate that large variations may occur in the specific chemical composition. Myelins differ from other membranes in possessing a higher lipid content—another cause for believing that the structure of myelin cannot be assumed similar to other membranes. Myelin does not have the active metabolism that is exhibited by normal membranes.

Table 6-5 shows the lipid distribution found in some erythrocytes. It is difficult to make comparisons since workers have expressed their results in several different units and with varying degrees of accuracy. But the table does give an indication that lipid content may be variable according to species, and there is a variation especially in the distribution of phospholipids (Burt and Rossiter, 1950; Maddy, 1966).

Schmitt and his associates (Schmitt, 1936; Schmitt and Bear, 1939; Schmitt et al., 1941) as well as Schmidt (1936, 1938) initiated the use of x-ray diffraction and polarized light to study the ultrastructure of myelin. Polarized light studies showed that myelin (and also erythrocyte membranes) possesses radial birefringence, which means that there is an orderly

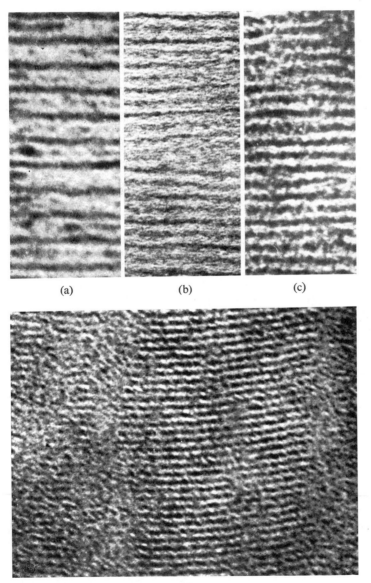

(a)   (b)   (c)

(d)

Figure 6-13 (a) The appearance of myelin after fixation with OsO_4. (b) Appearance of myelin after fixation in potassium permanganate for about 3 hours. (c) Appearance of myelin after fixation in potassium permanganate for about 6 hours ($700,000 \times$). (d) The appearance of egg cephalin fixed with OsO_4, embedded in araldite and sectioned. The dense layers are about 20 Å thick and repeat with a period of about 40 Å ($550,000 \times$). These electron-micrographs demonstrate that the appearance of a structure is determined by the nature of the fixative used as well as by the time of fixation. They also demonstrate the similarity in appearance between myelin and a purified lipid material. [By permission from J. D. Robertson. (1960). "The molecular structure and contact relationships of cell membranes." *Progress in Biophysics* **10**: 343–418 Pergamon Press, Inc. New York.]

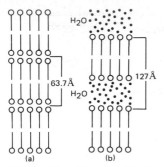

Figure 6-14(a) The diagram illustrates how lipid molecules are arranged in bilayers in the smectic state. (a) When water is excluded, bilayers approach closely. (b) When water enters along the polar ends of the molecules, separate bilayers are split off and the repeat period detected by x-ray diffraction analysis increases. [From data of Schmitt et al. (1941).]

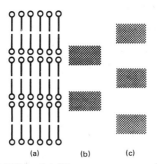

Figure 6-14(b) (a) Bilayer arrangement of lipid molecules when observed in the electron microscope may show dense bands due to presence of opposing polar ends (b) or to the hydrophobic carbon chains (c). Current hypothesis state that it is the polar ends which appear as dense bands in the electron microscope.

repeating structure oriented radially to the long axis of the membrane. This birefringence reversed sign when the myelin was extracted with lipid solvents. This was taken to mean that there was also an orderly layering of protein in the membrane.

X-ray diffraction studies revealed a radial repeating period of 171 Å in frog myelin and 186 Å in mammalian (mouse) myelin. These repeat distances could be correlated with a myelin structure composed of alternating layers of bimolecular lipid leaflets and mono-layers of protein. X-ray diffraction data did not give the information needed to determine the orientation of the lipids or to decide which of several possible structural arrangements were present.

Electron microscopic studies of myelin (Robertson, 1964, 1965; Fernández-Moran and Finean, 1957) revealed a pattern of alternating light and dense bands (Figure 6-13). It was known that proteins, free of lipids, gave dense bands in the electron microscope, and it was assumed that the light bands seen in myelin were lipids and the dense bands were protein. Electron microscopy of pure lipids, treated and stained in the same manner as tissue sections, also gave a pattern of banding (Figure 6-13b). The question arose as to which of the bands represented the polar ends of the lipids and which the nonpolar ends.

Schmitt et al. (1941) showed from x-ray diffraction data that phospholipids in the smectic state (a state of matter intermediate between a crystalline solid and an amorphous liquid—composed of rod-shaped molecules in close array that can rotate only about their longitudinal axis, while their ends remain in definite planes) separated into bilayers upon the addition of water (Figure 6-14). This may be compared with the electron micrograph of similarly treated cephalin (Figure 6-13d). Since the separation into bilayers occurs at the polar groups, it was decided that the dense strata seen in the electron micrographs of myelin represented regions containing the polar groups of the lipids and the protein monolayer. The light central region was thought to represent the site of the nonpolar hydrocarbon chains of the lipid bilayer (see also Stockenius, 1962b).

The myelin sheath may be modeled as shown in Figure 6-15. Here it is seen that the myelin, which is formed from a Schwann cell membrane wrapping itself about a nerve axon (Chapter 7), consists of alternate dark and light bands representing the apposition of layers of the Schwann cell's unit membrane. The alternation in density of the darker bands supposedly results from differences between the inner and outer protein monolayers of the unit membrane. This is taken as further evidence of the asymmetry of the membrane.

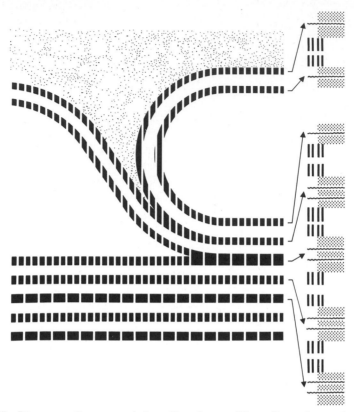

Figure 6-15 Diagrammatic representation of how layers of the unit membrane of a Schwann cell come together to form the different periods of myelin seen in the electron microscope and by x-ray diffraction analysis. The molecular structure of myelin is diagrammed on the right. Stippled areas represent intercellular ground substance. [Modified from Robertson (1960).] See also Figure 7-7, Chapter 7.

6-12. Molecular Arrangements in Myelin. Electron microscopy and x-ray diffraction have been used in attempts to determine the molecular arrangements within the myelin layers (Finean, 1956, 1957, 1961; Finean and Robertson, 1958; Robertson, 1965). Several models have been devised to account for the nature of the lipid packing in myelin. Figure 6-16 illustrates a model proposed by Finean. It shows that polar groups of the lipids are in a position to combine with polar groups of the proteins, whereas the hydrocarbon chains of the lipids are placed compactly together. This model is too specific since it assigns positions to lipid molecules for which evidence is slight. More recent models of a similar nature have been given by Vandenheuvel (1963). O'Brien (1965) reviews work on the molecular structure of myelin.

One of the major gaps in physiological information arises from a lack of knowledge concerning the specific lipids and proteins present in a membrane and their particular arrangements in each membrane. It is not easy to analyze structure at the molecular level, but we may hope that advances in x-ray diffraction analysis and electron microscope techniques will enable scientists to determine the structure of membranes at the molecular level.

Myelin is a very stable structure. Compared with other membranes or tissues, it is metabolically inert. It also has been found that cholesterol is not synthesized in the adult brain. Once cholesterol is incorporated into the white matter—principally composed of the myelinated axons of nerve cells—of the immature brain, there is no turnover of the cholesterol in the adult on the basis of tracer studies. Gray

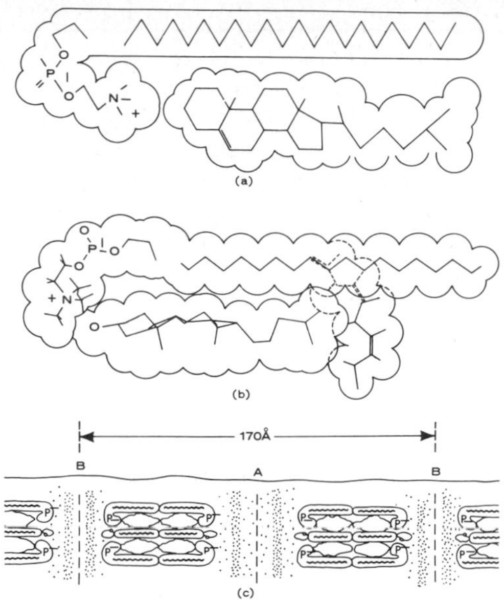

Figure 6-16 (a) and (b) are models of suggested geometries and nature of aggregation of sphingolipids and cholesterol. Lipids containing polyunsaturated acids are thought to be hooklike, whereas lipids containing saturated fatty acids are considered to be rodlike. (c) A model for the arrangement of lipid molecules in myelin that attempts to account for the observed dimensions of myelin periodicity [After Finean (1953)].

matter—consisting of nerve cell bodies, their organelles, and unmyelinated fibers—has a high rate of cholesterol metabolism; indicating, perhaps, that the more usual cellular membranes differ from myelin in their higher metabolic activity.

To explain the relative stability of myelin and the lack of lipid metabolism, it may be supposed that there is a difference in the structural arrangements of lipids, as well as in the actual lipid composition, between myelin and other membranes.

Myelin is a compactly structured membrane with a compressed arrangement of lipids. The major forces holding lipids together, thus giving strength to the structure, are noncovalent and include van der Waals forces between CH_2 groups of hydrocarbon chains. These account for the greater part of the bonding strength. Also present are electrostatic attractions between polar groups of lipids and oppositely charged groups on adjacent proteins.

Hydrogen bonds can form between oxygen and nitrogen atoms of the lipids and proteins. Finally, hydrophobic—or water exclusion forces—can act to hold lipids together.

The introduction of unsaturated fatty acids into the lipid components of the lipid bilayer would result in a less stable structure on two accounts. First, the greater the degree of unsaturation, the fewer the number of CH_2 groups in the lipid. Thus, the van der Waals forces would be lessened. Second, an increase in the double bonding in the fatty acids decreases the number of possible contact points between adjacent lipids. Lecithin molecules containing highly unsaturated fatty acids take on a hook shape, whereas lecithin molecules with saturated fatty acids are in the form of straight rods. Table 6-6 shows that myelin and myelin-rich white matter contain a much lower percentage of unsaturated fatty acids than does gray matter. This could, partially, account for the greater stability of myelin.

The data of Table 6-6 indicate that with aging there is a significant increase in the percentages of fatty acids of the long-chain variety in the gray matter, whereas myelin and white matter remain relatively constant. The significance of this is not known. Erythrocytes with the highest stability and the least permeability have more long chain fatty acids and fewer unsaturated fatty acids in their membrane lipids compared with the less stable and more highly permeable erythrocytes. The ease of membrane rupture, the maximal amount of swelling and membrane stretching, and the like also depend on the particular fatty acids possessed by membrane lipids.

6-13. Artificial Membranes. Much information about properties of thin lipid-containing membranes has come from work with artificial films. Space does not permit any lengthy discussion of these models, but I should indicate that it is possible to form bimolecular lipid films and to study their properties (Eisenman and Conti, 1965; Huang and Thompson, 1965, 1966; Langmuir and Waugh, 1938; Overbeek, 1960; Thompson, 1964; Tobias et al., 1962).

Several interesting features have been found in these model systems. Although such

Table 6-6   Nature of Fatty Acids in Human Brain Tissues*

TISSUE	PERCENTAGE OF POLYUNSATURATED FATTY ACIDS IN:†			PERCENTAGE OF FATTY ACID WITH CHAINS LONGER THAN 18 CARBONS IN:		
	EGP	SGP	CGP	SPHINGO-MYELIN	CEREBRO-SIDES	CEREBROSIDE SULFATES
			6 YEARS OLD			
Gray matter	41.2	36.0	9.5	5.8	15.0	34.0
White matter	24.9	9.0	2.6	50.4	65.7	88.3
Myelin	5.7	2.4	—	54.2	86.5	90.0
			55 YEARS OLD			
Gray matter	41.0	48.5	7.6	25.5	90.2	90.0
White matter	15.5	14.9	2.1	63.2	86.4	82.1
Myelin	4.1	4.4	0.4	50.8	87.5	86.0

* Data from: O'Brien (1965).

† EGP = ethanolamine glycerophosphate; SGP = serine glycerophosphate; CGP = choline glycerophosphate.

membranes are continuous and lack pores, they are very permeable to water (Cass and Finkelstein, 1967; Hanai et al., 1966). Values for the permeability constants of water are on the order of 1.7 cm/sec. This is within the range found in natural membranes. The addition of proteins to the lipid film does not affect the water permeation although glucose and sucrose interact with the film in such a way as to alter the membrane permeability when ox brain lipids were used to form the membrane.

Electrical characteristics are important parameters of membranes. The electrical resistance of natural membranes ranges from 10^3 to 10^5 ohm/cm² (Cole, 1940; Schwan, 1957). The resistance of thin lipid films ranges from 0.2 × 10^7 to 1 × 10^6 ohm/cm². The high electrical resistance of artificial films, combined with a high water permeability, is a paradoxical situation.

In recent years the extraction of lipids from tissues and their use in forming membranes has been increasing (Andreoli et al., 1967; Mueller et al., 1962, 1963). In addition, substances such as collodion, cellulose, and ion-exchange resins and gels have been used to model particular properties of membranes.

Cellular Permeability

6-14. Fluxes and Methodology.   The net flux, J, defined by Equation 6.6 can be broken down into two undirectional solute movements:

$$\text{Influx} = J_{in} = P(c_o) \qquad (6.15a)$$
$$\text{Efflux} = J_{out} = P(c_i) \qquad (6.15b)$$

The subscripts "in" and "out" will be used to indicate the direction of movement of a solute into or out of a cell. The net flux is the difference between the inward and outward flows of solute when the outside concentration is higher than the inside. The area across which flux is occurring has been eliminated from these expressions by assuming that transport is occurring across unit membrane area. The passive movements of solute due to concentration gradients are the only movements considered.

It is of value to be able to measure the individual fluxes of a substance. Either influx or efflux could be measured by setting the external or internal concentrations of a solute equal to zero, but experimentally this is seldom feasible since the properties of the membrane are changed or the biological system is damaged.

But the same type of result can be obtained by adding small amounts of radioactive isotopes of the compound under study to the external medium bathing the cell or tissue. The concentration of isotope inside the cell is initially zero, and the total concentration of the substance is normal. The uptake of isotope can be measured, thus providing a value of its influx. Alternatively, the preparation can be bathed with an isotope-containing solution until the internal medium is loaded with isotope. Replacement of the external solution with fresh physiological fluid containing no isotope allows the rate of efflux to be determined.

Counters are available that will measure accurately extremely small amounts of radiation. In this type of biological measurement it is important to determine the specific activity of the isotope: the radioactivity, disintegrations, or counts, divided by the concentration of the isotope. In many cases, the final concentrations at equilibrium of a given substance are not equal on the two sides of a membrane, and measurement of only changes in activity of isotope may be quite erroneous in determining fluxes.

Some commonly used radioisotopes in biological studies include ^{14}C, ^{32}P, ^{24}Na, and ^{42}K. Isotopes present the only method for accurately following the movements of ions through membranes and at the same time maintaining a close approximation of the normal intracellular and extracellular environments. Tagged compounds, that is, molecules in which one or more radioactive atoms have been incorporated are used to study the movements of compounds in whole animal or organ systems or through cellular metabolic pathways.

Heavy water, D_2O, containing deuterium $(D = {}^2H)$ is used to follow the movements of water through membranes. Unlike the isotopes mentioned above, deuterium is not radioactive. Its higher atomic weight gives heavy water a greater density than that of normal water and methods are available for accurately measuring small changes in density. Tritium $(T = {}^3H)$ is another hydrogen isotope used in biological studies. Tritiated water, HTO, is used to study water flows through membranes as well as hydrogen transfers in metabolic oxidation-reduction and other reactions. This hydrogen isotope is radioactive.

These materials and methods are essential to the determination of membrane functioning as well as to the elucidation of metabolic pathways and other biological activities (Wolf, 1964; Wang and Willis, 1965).

6-15. Mechanisms of Material Movement. To this point I have paid scant attention to actual transport mechanisms in animals, having been more concerned with some definitions and relationships of diffusion, osmosis, and membranes from a physical-chemical point of view. An examination of experimental findings about cellular transport reveals that a variety of mechanisms are used by cells to move substances in or out.

Some of the basic types of transport mechanisms used by biological systems are listed briefly in this section. The biological evidence for, and the use of, these mechanisms will be of concern in the following sections.

1. *Endocytosis.* The process of endocytosis has already been discussed in connection with lysosomes (Chapter 3). Some authors have felt that membrane invaginations and alterations might account for most transport activities of cells (for example, Bennett, 1956), but endocytosis is a phenomenon not found in erythrocytes or bacterial membranes—two active membranes as far as material transport is concerned. Endocytosis is an important mechanism for transport in many cell types, but it cannot account for all the observed phenomena associated with material movements.

2. *Simple Diffusion.* This basic mechanism for the movement of solutes has already been discussed. It is a fundamental process in which movement is in the direction of a concentration gradient.

3. *Restricted Diffusion Through Pores.* It has already been stated that biological membranes may contain pores. The effects of these pores would be to restrict the area available for diffusion, if diffusion must take place along water-filled channels.

4. *Solvent Drag and Bulk Flow.* When a membrane is freely permeable to water and solutes, hydraulic or osmotic forces may move water through the membrane in a bulk flow. Those solutes to which the membrane is permeable will be carried along with the water.

5. *Carrier-mediated Transport.* In order to explain the rapid permeation of many lipid-soluble substances through membranes believed to have a lipid core, it has been hypothesized that within the membrane are carriers —molecules with chemical groups to which specific solutes can attach. The complex so formed is lipid-soluble, and the solute is carried across the membrane by this carrier complex. The translocation process—the means by which a molecule is moved across the membrane—is completely unknown in its details. Several proteins have been isolated that appear to have the necessary characteristics of carrier molecules (Pardee, 1968).

The evidence upon which the carrier hypothesis is based will be presented in later sections. Several subdivisions including facilitated diffusion (carrier-mediated diffusion), exchange diffusion (trans- or counterflow diffusion), and active transport carrier-mediated transport may be included under the carrier model.

6. *Active transport.* Active transport was defined by Rosenberg (1954) in thermodynamic terms as the movement of a substance against its electrochemical gradient. Such a movement requires the expenditure of energy. Wilbrandt (1961) prefers the terms uphill or downhill transport as more descriptive of the process. Here we shall use the term active transport for those material movements that require the expenditure of metabolic energy to move the substance against an electrochemical gradient. It may be carrier-mediated transport, but this is not a necessity. Under some conditions endo- or exocytosis may be considered forms of active transport.

7. *Osmosis and Ultrafiltration.* The general principles underlying these mechanisms have already been discussed.

8. *Adsorption Theory.* Some researchers (Ling, 1962; Ernst, 1958; see also Kleinzeller and Kotyk, 1960) have attempted to explain cellular accumulation or excretion of substances on the basis of their adsorption to specific sites on macromolecules within the cell. In this theory the membrane is considered only as a container for cytoplasmic structures, allowing free movement of all materials into and out of the cell. The function of the macromolecules is to retain or release specific compounds or ions as required.

Although adsorption may play some role in the movement of certain substances, it does not appear to be a universal mechanism for such activity. It is not at all certain how strongly, if at all, substances are adsorbed onto macromolecules within the cytoplasm.

The adsorption hypothesis has been refuted on the basis of experiments performed with squid giant fibers (Baker et al., 1962). These giant nerve axons have been of great value in the study of the nerve action potential and its underlying mechanisms (Chapter 7) and in the chemical analysis of nerve axoplasm. It has been found that the giant axon may be gently extruded by rolling a glass rod over it, thus removing the axoplasm. The remaining membrane, even after perfusion with wash solutions and removal of at least 99 per cent of the axoplasm, retains all its normal transport activities. This implies that the macromolecular content of the axon is not needed for ion transport as predicted by the adsorption theory.

6-16. Erythrocytes and *Arbacia* **Eggs.** Much of our knowledge of cell permeability originated with osmotic studies on two types of animal cells: the enucleated mammalian red blood cell and the eggs of marine invertebrates, especially those of the sea urchin, *Arbacia punctulata.*

The mammalian erythrocyte was chosen as an object of study because it is readily available in large numbers, free of other cell types. It lacks a nucleus and many other structures and reaction systems that in other cells complicate permeability studies. The mature human erythrocyte is a biconcave disc, about 8.5 μ in

Figure 6-17 (a) Dimensions of the human erythrocyte. On the right is illustrated the rouleaux formation. (b) In hypotonic solution the normally biconcave erythrocyte first becomes convex. As swelling continues because of the osmotic inflow of water, the erythrocyte becomes a sphere and finally lyses as hemoglobin leaves the cell. (c) In hypertonic solution the erythrocyte shrinks, and the membrane becomes wrinkled. [Data on erythrocyte dimensions from Ponder (1948).]

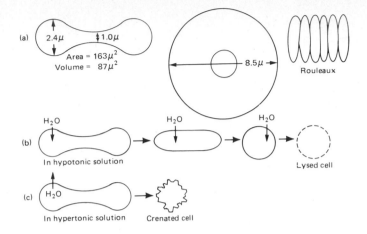

diameter and 2.4 μ thick at the edges (Figure 6-17). Normally it is opaque because it is densely packed with hemoglobin.

Alterations of cell shape due to volume changes are readily apparent. Rupture of erythrocytes—hemolysis (lysis is the general term for the swelling and destruction of cells due to osmotic inflow of water)—changes a suspension of red blood cells from an opaque red to a clear, pink solution as hemoglobin escapes and disperses in solution. After hemolysis red cell membranes can be collected and purified by washing and these ghosts are used as a source of reasonably pure membrane material. Bishop and Surgenor (1964) have edited a comprehensive treatise on erythrocyte structure and function.

Simple, and yet important, experiments can be performed by placing a drop of red cell suspension into a few milliliters of a test solution and noting what happens to the cells. If such an experiment is carried out by placing a drop of erythrocytes into each of a series of tubes containing different concentrations of a nonpermeable solute, it is found that the erythrocyte is isotonic with 0.9 per cent NaCl ($=0.15\ M = 0.3$ Osm NaCl), that is, there is neither shrinking nor swelling of the cells at this concentration. In hypertonic solutions, crenation (shrinking) of the cells occurs; in hypotonic solutions, hemolysis results. There is a range of concentrations in which only slight swelling or shrinking takes place.

Such experiments not only permit deter-

mination of the osmotic concentrations of the cells but also show whether or not a solute can permeate the membrane. For now it can be considered that NaCl is impermeable to the erythrocyte membrane. Later we shall see that this is only an approximation to the real situation because active transport removes Na^+ as quickly as it enters the cell. In any case NaCl passes through the red cell membrane at an extremely slow rate compared with water and many other solutes.

The results of such studies on any particular species of cell may outline general principles

Table 6-7 Glycerol Permeability of some Mammalian Erythrocytes*

SPECIES	TIME FOR 75% HEMOLYSIS IN 0.3 M GLYCERCOL (seconds)
Rat	3.5
Man	5.1
Mouse	12.9
Rabbit	21.8
Guinea-pig	38.2
Dog	253
Pig	340
Cat	459
Ox	612
Sheep	850

* Data of Jacobs as reported by Höber (1945).

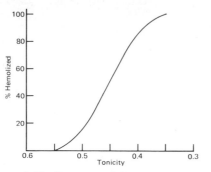

Figure 6-18 Per cent of human erythrocytes hemolyzed at different tonicities. Tonicity is given as fractions of normal human plasma concentration. [Data from Ponder (1948).]

underlying membrane permeability, but the details are not necessarily applicable to other cells. Even cells of a given type, from different species, may show different permeabilities to the same substance. An example is presented in Table 6-7, where the time required for erythrocyte hemolysis is shown for the solute glycerol. On the basis of these results mammals may be divided into two groups: those whose erythrocytes have a relatively rapid permeability to glycerol (man, mouse, rat, rabbit, and guinea pig) and those whose erythrocytes have a lower rate of glycerol penetration (cat, dog, pig, ox, and sheep). Differences of this nature illustrate that while all erythrocyte membranes may appear to be similar when observed in the electron microscope, their molecular architecture must be dissimilar.

Even a population of erythrocytes from a single sample of blood exhibits a range of permeability characteristics. It has been shown that the heterogeneity of a cell population in terms of cell size and cation content results in a necessity for including these factors in any rigorous treatment of osmotic properties. In studies comparing the osmotic concentrations at which cells lyse with the number of cells disrupted at each concentration, it has been found that a range of tonicities exist in which erythrocytes will lyse (Figure 6-18).

It is instructive to examine the effects of various types of solutes at various osmotic concentrations on erythrocytes. Figure 6-19 diagrams some of these situations. The cell in

each case is imagined to be in a large volume of solution such that movement of water or solutes into or out of the cell will produce only insignificant changes in the concentration of the external medium. For the purposes of illustration the events leading to hemolysis, crenation, or other changes are shown in a few steps; in the real situation diffusion and osmosis are continuous and simultaneous events. The relative rates of penetration of water and solutes will determine the speed with which the end result is attained.

Figure 6-19a shows that a hypotonic solution of a nonpermeating electrolyte causes lysis as water flows into the erythrocyte, swelling it, and finally causing it to burst. In this, and the following, examples the cell contents are expressed in terms of their equivalent NaCl osmolarity. Note that the erythrocyte upon swelling changes from a discoidal to a spherical shape. Measurements of rabbit erythrocytes reveal that there is no surface area increase as the change from disc to sphere occurs. But the change does increase the cellular volume. In isotonic media the rabbit erythrocyte has a surface area of about 100 μ^2 and a volume of about 60 μ^3. In hypotonic media the volume of the spherical cell having the same surface area as the disc-shaped cell is about 100 μ^3. On reaching this volume the cell lyses. The volume increase at which the cell membrane ruptures is the **critical hemolytic volume.** Since on swelling from the normal disc to the sphere shape, the rabbit erythrocyte increases in volume to about 167 per cent of normal before rupturing, the critical hemolytic volume is 1.67. The erythrocyte membrane must be relatively rigid in the sense that little swelling or stretching of the membrane can occur without rupturing it.

Another cell type that has been studied in some detail is the *Arbacia* egg. These were chosen for study because they are available in large numbers from the ovaries of females maintained in the laboratory in sea water, and they are large cells, about 75 μ in diameter, so that shape and volume changes in them are readily measured.

The critical volume of the *Arbacia* egg is

about 2 and this means that the membrane is more readily stretchable without damage than that of the erythrocyte. The *Arbacia* egg is spherical in its normal form, and the doubling of volume that occurs before membrane rupture must mean that the membrane is stretched to twice its normal area before being destroyed. The eggs of marine invertebrates must be able to withstand an environment quite different from that faced by the eggs and cells of other animal groups, and it is not surprising that differences are found between these membranes.

Figure 6-19b illustrates that erythrocyte

lysis occurs in a solution of a nonpermeating nonelectrolyte even though the molarity of the medium is the same as the molarity of the cell contents. This is because the nonelectrolyte does not dissociate and thus has only one-half the osmotic effect of the cellular material that is equivalent to an 0.3 M NaCl solution. In the example, water flows into the cell in an attempt to attain osmotic equilibrium, but the critical volume of the cell is exceeded first, and it hemolyses.

Figure 6-19c shows the events occurring when an erythrocyte is placed in an isoosmotic solution of a permeable solute. To analyze

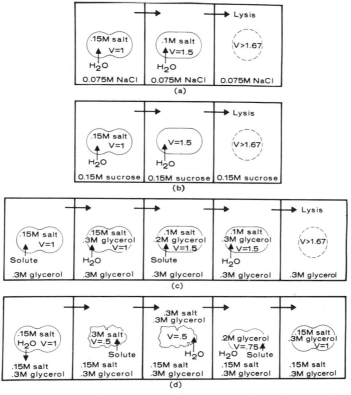

Figure 6-19 Schematic representation of the events that occur when normal erythrocytes are placed in solutions of different tonicities and with solutes differing in their abilities to penetrate the membrane. Cell contents are expressed in terms of their equivalent NaCl concentrations. The cell membrane is assumed impermeable to salt. The external volume is so large compared with that of the cell that any loss of solute does not change its concentration. Osmosis and diffusion occur simultaneously although the actions must here be separated for the purposes of representation. (a) Hypotonic solution of a nonpermeating solute. (b) Nonpermeating nonelectrolyte of same molarity as cell contents. (c) Isoosmotic solution of a permeating solute. (d) A solution containing both a permeating and a nonpermeating solute. See text for discussion of each of these situations.

what must happen in order to achieve a stable equilibrium state, three factors must be considered (Teorell, 1952):

1. There is an attempt to establish osmotic equilibrium by the movement of water. The chemical potentials of water in two different solution compartments must be equal at equilibrium and this is what osmosis tries to achieve. This process can result in large volume changes in the compartments. In biological systems this is often not possible and influx of water destroys cells. As we shall see, osmotic equilibria in cells are often aided by active transport mechanisms moving solutes against electrochemical gradients.

2. There must also be a diffusion equilibrium of permeable solutes in the two compartments. Movement of solute is the mechanism for bringing its chemical potentials to equality at equilibrium.

3. There must also be electrical neutrality. There must be equal numbers of anions and cations in a given compartment. In addition if electrochemical gradients are established across the membrane due to ion movements, other balancing forces must be present. These electrical forces are considered later in this chapter.

In the example of Figure 6-19c, although initially there is an osmotic equilibrium between the 0.3 M glycerol and the 0.15 M salt of the cell, there is a diffusion inequilibrium. A permeable solute is in high concentration on one side of the membrane. Glycerol diffuses into the cell in an attempt to establish an equilibrium of diffusible solutes. At this point, however, an osmotic inequilibrium is established, and water moves into the cell in an attempt to reestablish the osmotic equilibrium. The influx of water dilutes the cellular contents, and glycerol inside becomes less concentrated than outside—and more glycerol diffuses into the cell. The end result is that hemolysis occurs because it is impossible to achieve both an osmotic and a diffusion equilibrium. The cell hemolyzes first because of water inflow. Therefore, a permeable solute, although isoosmotic with the cellular contents, is not isotonic.

Cell volumes can be maintained in an isoosmotic solution of a permeable solute if some impermeable material is also present. This is shown in Figure 6-19d, where the presence of both impermeable salt and permeable glycerol in the external medium causes first a shrinking and then a return to normal volume or greater of the cell. Both osmotic and diffusion equilibria can be achieved.

Arbacia eggs and other cells react in similar fashion to the erythrocyte. Differences arise because of the degree of volume increase possible with different cells or from differences in permeability to given solutes. Isoosmotic concentrations also vary according to species. As indicated, mammalian cells are isotonic with about 0.9 per cent NaCl; the cells of cold-blooded vertebrates are isotonic with 0.7 per cent NaCl; and marine eggs are isotonic with 2.9 per cent NaCl. Although I have stated here that NaCl is impermeable to cells, we shall see that this is not strictly correct; it appears impermeable due to active transport processes.

6-17. Cells as Osmometers. If cells acted as true osmometers, the product of their osmotic pressure, π, and the cell volume, V_c, would equal a constant as defined by

$$\pi V_c = nRT \qquad (6.16)$$

where n is the number of moles of solute. This relation is derived from Boyle's gas law, $PV = RT$, the basis of relations governing the vapor pressure and osmotic pressure of gases and solutions.

To determine whether this relation is valid for cells, measurements of cell volumes may be made in only slightly hypo- and hypertonic media so that distortions of normal cellular shape do not occur and the cell can reach an osmotic equilibrium. Analysis of the spherical eggs of the sea urchin (Table 6-8) demonstrates that πV_c is not a constant (the cell volumes are calculated from measurements of the cell diameters). Several factors may play a part in this deviation from ideal behavior. Part of the cellular material is osmotically inert. Included in this category are the insoluble materials such as some lipids and proteins. Since these

Table 6-8 *Arbacia* Eggs as Osmometers*

PRESSURE†	OBSERVED VOLUME	πV_c	$\pi(V_c - b)$‡
1.0	2.121	2.121	1.881
0.9	2.316	2.084	1.868
0.8	2.570	2.056	1.864
0.7	2.922	2.045	1.878
0.6	3.420	2.053	1.909
0.5	4.002	2.002	1.881

* Data from Lucke and McCutcheion (1932).
† Pressures and volumes are in arbitrary units.
‡ *b* estimated as 11 % of normal volume.

are not solutes, they do not contribute to the osmotic pressure although they take up some cellular volume. It has been suggested also that part of the water of the cell is unavailable for solvation because it is firmly bound to macromolecules. The degree to which this is true is not known.

In any case, a certain fraction of the normal cell volume is osmotically inert and is designated as the nonsolvent volume, *b*, of the cell. When Equation 6.16 is modified to take this inert volume into account, we have:

$$\pi(V_c - b) = nRT \qquad (6.17)$$

Table 6-8 shows that the product $\pi(V_c - b)$ is closer to being constant than is πV_c.

Cells generally contain more impermeable proteins than the medium in which they exist, and there is a slight intracellular excess of colloid osmotic pressure. It is thought that most cells develop a slightly higher internal pressure (turgor), which is balanced by the resistive mechanical forces of the cell membrane. Measurements by Rand and Burton (1963) showed that human erythrocytes have only a slight excess of pressure over that of the medium, amounting to 2 to 3 mm of water pressure.

The proteins and other nonpermeable solutes of the cell are usually charged. For example, most cellular proteins are anions at physiological pH. These impermeable anions give rise to the Donnan effect, which is discussed in the following sections. These and

the other factors mentioned, in addition to the fact that biological membranes are not perfectly semipermeable, cause cells to deviate from ideal osmotic behavior.

6-18. Distribution of Ions. Most of the discussion to this point has been centered upon nonelectrolytes, but ions and their movements and distributions are very important in cellular functioning. Table 6-9 lists the distribution of some important ions between human blood plasma and erythrocytes. Certain differences stand out. The intracellular concentration of potassium is high, and that of sodium is low. The plasma sodium concentration is high, and that of potassium is low. It is generally true that animal cells accumulate potassium ions and exclude sodium ions; the reverse distribution is found in body fluids.

The unequal distribution of sodium and potassium, found in a majority of cells, is an important characteristic, and, for example, lies at the basis of the excitability of many cells. The mechanisms by which ions distribute themselves and the effects they produce are basic to the understanding of many cellular activities. Membranes and their property of differential permeability are highlighted by the data of Table 6-9. Only glucose appears to be in equilibrium, and even this is not true of most cells.

Table 6-9 Chemical Distributions between Human Blood Plasma and Erythrocytes*

SUBSTANCE	PLASMA	ERYTHROCYTE
K^+	5.35	150
Na^+	144	12-20
Cl^-	111	74
Ca^{2+}	3.2	0.6
Mg^{2+}	1.1	2.8
HCO_3^-	28	27
Glucose	4.3	4.3
Hemoglobin	0	33.5 (g/100 ml cells)

* Concentrations in meq/kg water (except hemoglobin).

ANIMAL	K^+†	Na^+†
Man	105	10
Rabbit	99	16
Guinea-pig	105	15
Pig	100	11
Duck (nucleated cells)	110	8
Sheep		
(a) high K^+ cells	121	37
(b) low K^+ cells	17	137
(c) plasma	5	139
Dog	8	97
Cat	6	104

* Data on duck and sheep erythrocytes from Tosteson and Hoffman (1960). Other data from Höber (1945).

† Concentrations in millimoles per kilogram of cells.

There are exceptions to this general distribution. Table 6-10 gives the K^+ and Na^+ concentrations in a variety of vertebrate erythrocytes. Dogs and cats do not follow the general rule because their red blood cells contain high Na^+ and low K^+. An interesting situation is found in sheep. Two genetic strains of sheep have been found, differing by a single gene. One type, HK sheep, have high K^+ and low Na^+ in their erythrocytes. The other strain, LK sheep, have low K^+ and high Na^+ in their erythrocytes. The plasma concentrations of these ions are the same for both strains.

Other variations in ionic concentrations and distributions are found in animals. Marine molluscs maintain high blood levels of Mg^{2+}, an ion that is not concentrated in the body fluids of most marine organisms (Robertson, 1953). Some insects also concentrate Mg^{2+}, for example *Dixippus* (the stick insect) contains 145 mM Mg^{2+} in its blood in contrast to most insects which have 1 to 20 mM Mg^{2+} (Ramsey, 1956).

6-19. The Gibbs-Donnan Equilibrium. One explanation for an unequal distribution of ions across a membrane is the Gibbs-Donnan model. Consider a system containing:

1. Two aqueous compartments separated by a differentially permeable membrane.
2. One compartment having a nonpermeating ion, X^-.
3. A permeating salt initially present in one compartment.
4. Rigid walls so that no volume changes can occur in either compartment, thus limiting the osmotic flow of water.

If such a system is set up initially with all the KCl in the inner compartment, and the one that contains X^-, we have the situation diagrammed in Figure 6-20a. There is obviously a diffusion inequilibrium. Experimentally it can be shown that an equilibrium is established in such a system (Figure 6-20b). But at equilibrium there is not an equal distribution of diffusible ions across the membrane.

At equilibrium the sum of the electrochemical potentials of all diffusible ions in one compartment must equal the sum of the electrochemical potentials of ions in the other compartment, that is:

$$RT \ln [K^+]_i + RT \ln [Cl^-]_i = RT \ln [K^+]_o + RT \ln [Cl^-]_o \qquad (6.18)$$

Dividing by RT and eliminating logarithms yields

$$[K^+]_i \times [Cl^-]_i = [K^+]_o + [Cl^-]_o \qquad (6.19)$$

which is called the "Donnan rule." In general terms, the ratios of all diffusible cations on the inside to those on the outside are inversely proportional to the ratio of anions inside to outside. These ratios are equal to the Donnan constant, r:

$$r = \frac{[K^+]_o}{[K^+]_i} = \frac{[Cl^-]_i}{[Cl^+]_o} \qquad (6.20)$$

This rule must apply to all diffusible ions if a Donnan equilibrium is established.

The distribution of ions in the equilibrium state can be determined as follows. It is obvious that $[K^+]_i > [Cl^-]_i$ because there must be a K^+ associated with each Cl^-, and also a K^+ associated with every X^-. This is required in

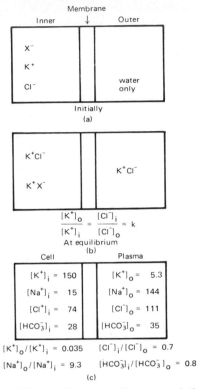

Membrane

Inner ↓ Outer

X⁻

K⁺

Cl⁻

water only

Initially
(a)

K⁺Cl⁻

K⁺X⁻

K⁺Cl⁻

$$\frac{[K^+]_o}{[K^+]_i} = \frac{[Cl^-]_i}{[Cl^-]_o} = k$$

At equilibrium
(b)

Cell		Plasma	
$[K^+]_i$ =	150	$[K^+]_o$ =	5.3
$[Na^+]_i$ =	15	$[Na^+]_o$ =	144
$[Cl^+]_i$ =	74	$[Cl^-]_o$ =	111
$[HCO_3^-]_i$ =	28	$[HCO_3^-]_o$ =	35

$[K^+]_o/[K^+]_i$ = 0.035 $[Cl^-]_i/[Cl^-]_o$ = 0.7

$[Na^+]_o/[Na^+]_i$ = 9.3 $[HCO_3^-]_i/[HCO_3^-]_o$ = 0.8

(c)

Figure 6-20 (a) Diagrammatic representation of the initial stage in a Donnan system (exaggerated because there are no ions represented in the outer compartment). A⁻ is an impermeable anion. (b) When equilibrium is reached, diffusable ions have moved so that the equilibrium ratios and relations shown are reached. (c) Actual ion distribution found for red blood cells and blood plasma. It is apparent that cation and anion distributions are not all following a Donnan distribution. The Na⁺ distribution is out of line with a Donnan equilibrium. Either this ion is not permeable or some other factor is influencing Na⁺ distribution. See text for further description.

order to preserve electrical neutrality. On the outside $[K^+]_o = [Cl^-]_o$, again to preserve electrical neutrality. With the latter information, Equation 6.18 may be written

$$[K^+]_i \times [Cl^-]_i = [K^+]_o^2 \qquad (6.21a)$$

which rearranged gives

$$[K^+]_i = \frac{[K^+]_o^2}{[Cl^-]_i} \qquad (6.21b)$$

Remembering that $[Cl^+]_i < [K^+]_i$, examination of Equation 6.19 reveals that $[Cl^-]_i < [K^+]_o$. In Equation 6.21b the ratio, $[K^+]_o/$

$[Cl^-]_i$, must be greater than one, and therefore $[K^+]_i$ must be greater than $[K^+]_o$. Since $[K^+]_i = [X^-] + [Cl^+]_i$, the total solute concentration inside can be expressed as $[K^+]_i + [K^+]_i = 2[K^+]_i$. Therefore, since $[K^+]_o < [K^+]_i$, the inner compartment must be more concentrated than the outer one. This is one necessary condition for a system to be in a Donnan equilibrium. Although here I have been considering a system that contains KCl as the diffusible salt, similar reasoning would apply to any combination of salts present, as long as they could diffuse through the membrane.

I have noted that electrical neutrality is maintained in each compartment. But there is obviously a diffusion inequilibrium in the system at equilibrium since K⁺ and Cl⁻ are at different concentrations on each side of the membrane. Some force must be present in this equilibrium system to counterbalance the tendency for the ions to move down their concentration gradients. This force is an electrical potential established across the membrane, the so-called "Donnan potential." The magnitude and sign of this transmembrane potential is just great enough to counterbalance the tendency for ions to diffuse.

All measurements made on plant and animal cells have shown that a potential exists across their membranes. As we shall see, this potential plays an important role in the activities of most cells, especially in excitable cells such as nerve or muscle. Before discussing the mechanism that generates the Donnan potential, it is worth asking how closely a Donnan system models the cellular systems that concern us.

6-20. Impermeable Anions. The Donnan equilibrium model is a starting point for analyzing the mechanisms underlying ion distributions between cells and their environment. Although the cell may be referred to as a Donnan-like system, the cell cannot be considered to be in a Donnan equilibrium because

1. In cells, active transport plays a role in determining the distribution of ions. The cell is a dynamic, energy-requiring, open,

steady state system not an equilibrium system.

2. The plasma membrane is a complex and dynamic structure. It is not a perfect semipermeable membrane and even so-called nondiffusible materials may slowly leak through it.

3. The intracellular medium is not a homogeneous aqueous solution.

4. In the Donnan model it is assumed that the diffusible ions of the model system are completely dissociated and free in solution. Although salts such as KCl or NaCl completely dissociate in aqueous solution, they have cryoscopic coefficients that are less than 2, an indication that there is a restriction of free ionic movements because of electrostatic attractions.

Donnan (1911, 1927) formulated his useful equilibrium model on thermodynamic grounds. The model and its biological implications have been discussed in detail by Overbeek (1956).

The nature and effects of the impermeable anions in biological systems deserve some comment (anions are discussed here because most proteins and other charged molecules are anionic at cellular pH's). In a Donnan equilibrium there is a slight excess osmotic pressure in the compartment containing the impermeable anion, and this excess pressure must be counterbalanced by some other force if a stable state is to be achieved. Such forces include the presence of rigid walled compartments, hydraulic forces established by contractile or other mechanisms, or by membrane impermeability to other ions. It was first assumed that the excess osmotic pressure in erythrocytes was counterbalanced by a general impermeability to cations, but this was shown not to be the case. Although cations generally move through the membrane more slowly than anions, radioactive isotope studies proved that both Na^+ and K^+ can move through the membrane. However, active transport acts to bring about a seeming impermeability to Na^+. But the situation in erythrocytes is not fully understood.

Part of the difficulty lies in the complex interactions of proteins. A simplifying assumption can be made that hemoglobin is the major nondiffusible anion of red blood cells, although ATP^{4-}, ADP^{3-}, diphosphoglycerate^{2-}, and other molecules actually play a role (Farmer and Maizels, 1939). A protein such as hemoglobin is not present in high molal concentration within an erythrocyte, and its osmotic effect is relatively low—about the equivalent of a 5 mM/liter solute. But hemoglobin with its many ionizable side groups may contain at cellular pH as many as 12 negative charges per molecule. Thus, although hemoglobin acts osmotically as the equivalent of a 5 mM solute, ionically it acts as a 60 mM solute. In addition, proteins such as hemoglobin can bind ions.

The net charge, z, of a protein is defined as the algebraic sum of all the charged groups plus any charges resulting from the binding of ions. For example, mammalian serum albumin, which makes up about 50 per cent of the protein of blood serum, has a net charge of about -17 (the net result of about 100 negative and 83 positive charges) at a pH of 7.4 in 0.15 M NaCl at 25°C. About 10 Cl^- can be bound to the protein. The state of ionization of a protein's side groups depends on pH, temperature, and salt concentration.

The blood plasma-interstitial fluid system is of interest to physiologists, and there is a requirement that the volumes of these two fluid compartments remain fairly constant. A Donnan equilibrium can be established between the two solutions across the capillary membranes that are freely permeable to all solutes except proteins above about 60,000 molecular weight. This is an ultrafiltration system in which the higher concentration of plasma proteins in the blood creates an oncotic pressure tending to pull water from the interstitial fluid into the capillaries. This pressure is counterbalanced, and a Donnan equilibrium established by the blood (or hydraulic) pressure tending to push water and solutes out of the capillaries.

The osmotic forces tending to draw water from the blood are relatively small and insensitive to relatively large changes in interstitial

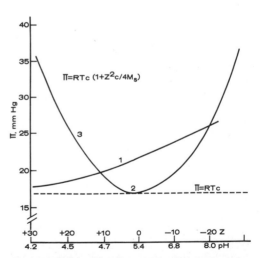

Figure 6-21(a) First derivative of protein osmotic pressure vs. concentration curve to show deviation from van't Hoff law. At infinite dilution the mean number average molecular weight of plasma proteins is almost 100,000, but in normal plasma their osmotic behavior corresponds to an ideal solute of molecular weight 37,000. [After Landis and Pappenheimer (1963).]

Scatchard et al. (1946) derived an equation relating the Donnan and van't Hoff effects

$$\pi = RTc\left(1 + \frac{z^2 c}{m_s}\right) \qquad (6.22)$$

where c is the protein concentration in moles per liter; z is the net charge on the protein; and m_s is the concentration of the salt solution in which the protein is equilibrated. This qualitative relationship indicates that the osmotic pressure of a protein solution increases if the salt concentration is reduced or if the charge is increased. Any binding of salt to protein decreases the amount of salt free to take part in a Donnan distribution.

Quantitatively, however, Equation 6.22 does not account for the Donnan effect or the observed results of plasma protein osmotic pressures or charge relationships. As shown in Figure 6-21b the observed osmotic pressures and those theoretically predicted by the Donnan and van't Hoff models match at only two points, one of which, by chance, happens to be at physiological pH and salt concentra-

fluid protein concentration. The proteins contributing to this osmotic pressure are primarily those smaller than about 60,000 molecular weight. The blood plasma proteins that are not able to pass through the capillary wall have a large osmotic coefficient, and these plasma proteins behave as the osmotic equivalent of an ideal solute of about 37,000 molecular weight. If they were actually this size, they could pass through the capillary wall and no osmotic pressure would be developed in the capillaries. This is a situation where the nonlinear behavior of the plasma proteins with respect to the osmotic pressure-concentration relationship results in the required physiological properties that allow the capillary-interstitial fluid exchange system to function properly (see Chapter 12).

Measurement of the osmotic pressure of human serum proteins demonstrates that the pressure deviates from the van't Hoff relationship as the protein concentration increases (Figure 6-21a). This deviation can be partially explained by the net charges on the molecules, since the net charge determines the particular distribution of ions across a membrane, according to the Donnan hypothesis.

Figure 6-21(b) The discrepancy between osmotic pressure calculated on the basis of Donnan theory and protein osmotic pressure measured experimentally. Agreement with theory occurs fortuitously at pH 4.7 and pH 7.6 [By permission from E. M. Landis and J. R. Pappenheimer (1963) *Handbook of Physiology*, Sect. 2, "Circulation," Vol. 2, pp. 961–1034. American Physiological Society, Washington, D.C.]

tion—the conditions usually chosen for protein studies. Therefore, at present, neither the Donnan nor van't Hoff hypotheses can account fully for the observed osmotic pressures of blood plasma proteins. This discrepancy is partially explained by the complex behavior of proteins with regard to charge, binding of ions, and electrostatic attractions between proteins and between proteins and salts. Such considerations also apply to cellular systems.

6-21. Active and Passive Transport in Erythrocytes.

The first evidence that the distribution of ions between erythrocytes and the external medium was not a true Donnan equilibrium came from the use of metabolic inhibitors such as iodoacetate or fluoride (Wilbrandt, 1940). These glycolytic inhibitors prevent the production of ATP. As soon as the erythrocyte's energy supply is diminished, an influx of Na^+ begins, and the cell hemolyses. Similar results are obtained in those erythrocytes possessing oxidative-phosphorylation pathways, for example, chicken erythrocytes, by using inhibitors such as HCN or DNP (Gourley, 1957). This type of experimental evidence also showed that the erythrocyte membrane is permeable to sodium, the process of active transport only makes it appear impermeable.

Any factors influencing energy metabolism will also influence transport and therefore ionic distributions. Erythrocytes stored at low temperatures (2 to 5°C), as in blood bank storage of whole blood, were found to slowly lose K^+ (DeGowin et al., 1940). On rewarming, the cells again accumulate K^+ against a concentration gradient (Harris, 1957). The glycolytic inhibitor, fluoride, at 2 mM concentration causes the efflux of K^+ from the erythrocyte.

Erythrocytes exposed to ultraviolet radiation begin to accumulate Na^+. This is caused not by membrane destruction but by radiation-induced changes in membrane structure which allow increased Na^+ conductance (Cook, 1956).

The rate of Na^+ efflux from erythrocytes depends on the external concentration of K^+,

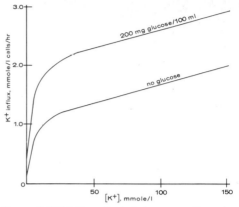

Figure 6-22(a) The effect of glucose on the potassium influx in the human erythrocyte. [From data of Glynn (1956).]

when external K^+ is absent, the active outward transport of Na^+ stops (Harris and Maizels, 1951, 1952).

Ion movements can be related to glucose concentration (Figure 6-22) as might be expected if an active transport mechanism were involved. But the graphs show that two components of flux are present and the K^+ influx occurs even in the absence of glucose. The linear portion of the curve is what would be expected for a passive inward diffusion of K^+ as $[K^+]_o$ increases. The steep portion of the curve indicates a transport process using carrier molecules. As the external $[K^+]$ increases, the carrier sites become saturated, and the rate of transport levels off. In the absence of glucose one expects this initial phase of the curve to disappear. That it does not is attributed to the fact that metabolic inhibitors were not used in the experiments and therefore the metabolism of intracellular substrates was not prevented.

Ion movements in erythrocytes also occurs by **exchange diffusion**—the process in which the influx of a substance is coupled to the efflux of the same substance. For example, tracer studies have demonstrated that part of the potassium movement in erythrocytes is a one-for-one exchange between external and internal K^+. This mechanism accounts for only a small fraction of the K^+ movement in erythrocytes.

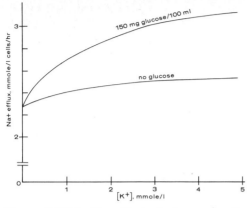

Figure 6-22(b) The effect of glucose on the sodium efflux from human erythrocytes at different external concentrations of potassium. [Data from Glynn (1956).]

There are, therefore, several pathways by which ions move through the erythrocyte membrane. Pathways and mechanisms of ion movement are not similar in all cells. In later sections of this and the following chapter, we will consider ion movements in nerve, muscle, and epithelial cells.

6-22. Energy for Active Transport. Several mechanisms have been suggested for coupling metabolic energy to the active process. These include

1. The use of the high energy of ATP through specific ATPases located in the membrane.
2. The utilization of the energy of electrons flowing down the cytochrome chain to directly promote the movement of ions. This appears to play some role in ion movements across the mitochondrial membrane.
3. The use of mechanical energy produced through ATP-mediated contraction of membrane-localized contractile proteins to move ions, perhaps through conformational changes in proteins.
4. The use of electrical fields associated with free radicals to provide a driving force for ion movements.

Only the first of these mechanisms will be considered here. The human erythrocyte, which has been studied in some detail, does not possess the mechanisms for oxidative-

phosphorylation and other activities associated with cytochrome systems. The evidence used to support the last three hypotheses has come from the study of other cells and will be discussed in the next chapter.

The reconstituted erythrocyte is a valuable experimental tool, used for many types of studies on erythrocyte membrane permeability. When an erythrocyte is hemolyzed, the ghost can be restored with many of its original permeability characteristics by incubation at low temperature in appropriate physiological solutions (Hoffman, 1958; Glynn, 1962). The procedure is useful because during the incubation, a substance not normally permeating the membrane, if placed in the incubation medium, is trapped and contained within the recovering ghost. In this manner substances to which the membrane is not normally permeable can be incorporated into the cell, and the investigator can determine the effects of these substances on the inner surface of the membrane. Important nondiffusible substances include ATP, other high energy phosphate compounds, many ions, and drugs.

The use of this type of model system showed that the addition of ATP to the inside of the cell greatly increased the rate of Na^+ efflux. ADP had the same effect, whereas closely related nucleotides such as ITP, GTP, or UTP had no effect on sodium transport, indicating that ATP is associated with the active transport process through some specific mechanism. Since ATP applied to the outside of the cell has little effect on active transport, it appears that the mechanism is associated only with the inner surface of the membrane, that is, the membrane is an asymmetric structure.

Skou (1957) found in peripheral nerve cells a membrane-located ATPase activated by Na^+ and K^+. A similar type of enzyme has been found in muscle, erythrocytes, sensory organ cells, kidney tubules, and many other types of epithelial cells. These are all cellular types possessing the ability for active transport in high degree (Kuijpers et al., 1967; Post et al., 1967; Skou, 1960, 1964; Whittam, 1958).

Ca^{2+} in appropriate concentrations inhibits the ATPase activity, although when placed in the external medium of a normal erythrocyte, it has no effect on transport. But when placed inside the reconstituted cell, this normally impermeable cation, inhibits the active transport of Na^+. Calcium inhibits both the activity of the isolated enzyme and the active transport process, and it is assumed on this and other grounds that the enzyme is necessary to the transport process.

It is usually assumed that the ATPase enzyme is coupled in some manner with the hypothesized carrier mechanism. The carrier also must have asymmetric properties because it combines with one type of ion on the outside of the membrane and transports this ion to the inside of the membrane, where it must now combine with another type of ion. The asymmetric nature of the active transport system is also emphasized by the fact that the ATPase activity, as well as flux rates, are stimulated by external sodium ions and internal potassium ions (Dunham and Glynn, 1961; Glynn, 1962).

Another type of experimental evidence pointing to the involvement of ATPases in active transport comes from the use of the drug ouabain (strophanthin) and other cardiac glycosides. These drugs inhibit active transport of ions across most cellular membranes and are also potent inhibitors of the activity of isolated enzymes with ATPase activity (Dunham and Glynn, 1961; Whittam, 1958; Schatzman, 1953).

The experimental evidence shows that whatever influences ATPase activity also influences active transport (Bonting et al., 1961). Therefore, it is generally thought that ATP is the direct energy source for the active movement of materials against electrochemical gradients. Figure 6-23 shows a model of how the various components of a carrier-mediated active transport system might operate. The carrier hypothesis has been given a mathematical analysis which leads to the conclusion that such a model fits the experimental observations of ion transport (Silverman and Goresky, 1965). But, at present, there is no good explanation of the molecular mechanisms upon which such a system is based. The carrier

model does not exclude the idea that porous channels are present in the membrane through which water and ions move. Both concepts are hypothetical.

Another important consideration is whether cells can supply the energy needed to maintain active transport and the cellular concentrations of ions. Solomon (1962) calculated that the human erythrocyte required 9 cal/liter of cells/hour to maintain a Na^+ efflux of 3 meq/liter of cells/hour and a K^+ influx of 1.7 meq/liter of cells/hour. Considering that 2.3 mmoles of glucose can be metabolized by a liter of cells in an hour, with the liberation of 120 cal/liter of cells/hour—then only about 10 per cent of the total energy available to the cell is required for active transport. Similar calculations for other types of cells also show that they need not expend large percentages of their energy for these processes.

Not only is active transport a necessary mechanism for maintaining ionic distributions across the erythrocyte membrane, but active transport is also necessary for volume regulation in cells (Tosteson, 1964). Although perfectly impermeable membranes would solve problems of volume regulation, such membranes are of little use to cells that are open systems. Some organisms have developed impermeable cuticles, but there must always be some region of permeable membrane exposed so that oxygen and other materials may be exchanged with the environment. Through

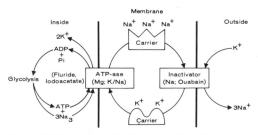

Figure 6-23 A hypothetical model for the role of a carrier and active transport in cation transport by the erythrocyte membrane. The model is based partially on some known locations of enzyme systems within the cell or on the membrane. Various inhibitors or activators and their sites of action are shown.

the evolution of a leaky membrane and an active transport mechanism, cells are enabled to maintain the necessary internal ionic environment as well as to regulate their volumes as demanded by osmotic requirements (Chapter 14). Coupled systems allow changes in one ionic species to affect flux rates of other species as well as uncharged metabolites with the result that the concentrations of these materials can be controlled. The leaky nonrigid membrane endows cells with mechanical properties that are needed to withstand stresses such as volume changes under adverse osmotic conditions, shape changes during contractile activity, and so on. The cell membrane and its dynamic permeability to ions also provides the basis for the ionic current flows essential to the functioning of excitable cells.

6-23. Donnan and Related Potentials. The simplest way to determine whether or not a potential exists across a membrane is to place one electrode inside the cell, another electrode in the external medium, and to measure the potential difference between the electrodes by means of a voltmeter, potentiometer, or cathode ray oscilloscope. Because of the small size of most cells, however, such measurements are not simple. Small microelectrodes are required to penetrate cells without damaging them, and because of the high electrical resistance of microelectrodes, these devices present their own problems (see Chapter 7).

Usually simple wire electrodes cannot be used because they are polarizable. Electric current flow in a wire is carried by the motion of electrons, whereas in aqueous solutions the current is carried primarily by ions or other particles that bear a net charge. In a system consisting of two platinum electrodes immersed in a dilute HCl solution, when a battery between the electrodes is switched into the circuit, current through the solution is carried by the movement of H^+ attracted to the negative electrode (cathode) and by Cl^- attracted to the positive electrode (anode). The Cl^- ions attracted to the metal surface discharge an electron to the metal, leaving a free

atom of chlorine at the surface. The chloride atoms combine to form chloride gas thus surrounding the electrode with gas bubbles. In a similar fashion bubbles of hydrogen gas collect at the cathode. These polarizing actions of direct currents at the metal-electrolyte junctions—arising from two different modes of carrying current—cause the buildup of a charge at each electrode and an opposing electrical potential that blocks any continued current flow. Such electrodes are, therefore, unsuitable for the measurement of direct currents.

The problem is solved by the use of nonpolarizable electrodes—the most common type used in biological work being the silver-silver chloride (Ag-AgCl) electrode (Delgado, 1964). The reactions taking place at these electrodes are shown in Figure 6-24. A coating of silver chloride, whose solubility is low, provides a

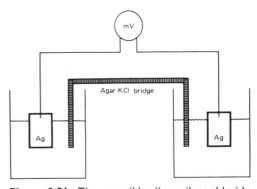

Figure 6-24 The reversible silver-silver chloride electrode. Reversible electrodes operate on the principle of being able to pass an electric current without changing the chemical environment in their vicinity. The electrode consists of a silver wire coated with silver chloride. At the anode chloride ions are attracted to the electrode and form more silver chloride. At the cathode the silver chloride coat is electrolyzed and silver is deposited on the electrode while chloride ions pass into solution. In neither case is the chemical environment changed. Silver chloride is only slightly soluble, and the rate of reduction is slow. To maintain unchanging chemical conditions, currents passed by such electrodes must be kept low. When these electrodes are placed into living tissues, the principal anion present is Cl^- and the anodic reaction will produce the required AgCl.

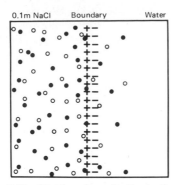

0.1m NaCl   Boundary   Water

Figure 6-25 Highly schematic illustration of the origin of a diffusion or liquid junction potential. When a layer of solution is bounded by a layer of pure solvent, the solute diffuses in the direction of the solvent layer. In the case of an electrolyte, when one ion is faster in its diffusion than the other, a potential can be established across the boundary. Cl^- ions diffuse faster than Na^+ ions and *tend* to move across the boundary faster. This produces a potential across the boundary. The sign of the potential is such that Cl^- is repulsed and Na^+ is attracted to the right side of the boundary. Thus both Na^+ and Cl^- actually move across the boundary at equal amounts. A diffusion potential is not present if both ions diffuse at the same rate, for example, KCl. As diffusion equalizes concentrations of both sides of the boundary, the potential falls to zero at equilibrium. Solid circles represent faster ion, open circles slower ion.

source of Ag^+ and Cl^- ions, and there is a continuous exchange of Cl^- ions between the metal electrodes and the solutions. Chloride is a normal constituent of biological solutions and is not toxic. Nor does enough silver chloride get into solution to harm biological tissues.

This type of reversible electrode system must be used when it is necessary to measure potentials in two parts of a solution or in most biological preparations (several conditions when the use of simple platinum or silver wire electrodes is feasible are described in the next chapters).

Two electrodes placed in a salt solution will detect no potential differences between different parts of the solution. The solution is electrically neutral and the positive and negative charges are distributed evenly throughout.

In order to develop an electrical potential some force must be applied to the system to cause a separation of charges. Consider a simple salt solution bounded by a layer of pure solvent or by another salt solution of different concentration (Figure 6-25). Both the positive and negative ions, acting separately, will move down their concentration gradients until, at equilibrium, diffusion has brought about an equal concentration of solute on both sides of the original boundary.

In some cases the positive and negative ions will have different mobilities (Section 2-7). For example, in a NaCl solution, the Cl^- ions move faster than the Na^+ ions (Table 2-2 gives some ionic conductances; ionic mobilities are given in Table 6-11). Thus, sodium ions tend to become separated from chloride ions. This separation of positive and negative charges during the diffusion process leads to the formation of a **diffusion potential** (or **liquid junction potential**) across the boundary.

Table 6-11   Mobilities of Some Ions*

ION	ATOMIC WEIGHT	ATOMIC CRYSTAL RADIUS (Å)	HYDRATED ION RADIUS (Å)	MOBILITY IN WATER (μ-sec/volt-cm)
Li^+	6.94	0.60	2.37	4.01
Na^+	23.00	0.95	1.83	5.20
K^+	39.09	1.33	1.25	7.64
Cl^-	35.36	1.81	—	7.91

* Data from: Conway (1957); Snell et al. (1965).

The tendency for Cl^- to enter the less concentrated solution faster than the Na^+ acts to make the less concentrated solution more negative than the concentrated one. Or it can be said that the more concentrated solution becomes more positive. The potential exists only across the boundary where net movement of ions is occurring and will decrease and finally vanish when diffusion reaches the equilibrium state. The direction of the potential is such that Na^+ tends to move faster across the boundary, whereas Cl^- movement is retarded. The net result is that Na^+ and Cl^- have equal fluxes in the system. The potential difference results from the tendency of a small number of the total ions in the system to move across the boundary at different rates. The diffusion potential depends both on the relative mobilities of the ions and the concentration gradient across the boundary. If the mobilities of positive and negative ions are similar, the diffusion potential is small or absent. For example, K^+ and Cl^- have similar mobilities and two solutions of KCl, differing in concentration, exhibit no diffusion potential when placed in contact. For this reason, saturated solutions of KCl are often used to form liquid junctions between electrode systems and biological preparations because there will be no junction potential to obscure the true potentials of the system under study. The saturated KCl electrode is often used as a reference electrode in the measurement of pH.

The tendency of two solutions separated by a boundary or membrane to come to equilibrium either by diffusion or osmosis is an expression of the general tendency for chemical systems to arrive at an equilibrium of their chemical potentials and for energies to flow from regions of higher to regions of lower potential. The movement of solute by diffusion, the transfer of materials by active transport and the movement of solvent during osmosis are commonly considered as forms of osmotic work.

As stated in Chapter 4, the free energy of a chemical system is equal to the difference of the chemical potentials of its components and

this difference can be equated to $-RT \ln [a_1]/[a_2]$. Using concentrations, instead of activities, osmotic work, W_{osm}, which equals the free energy change, can be expressed as

$$W_{osm} = -RT \ln \left(\frac{c_1}{c_2} \right) \qquad (6.23)$$

c_1 and c_2 are the initial and final concentrations, respectively. The equation as given is for the case where the initial concentration is 1 molar. Otherwise a factor, n, must be included to give the number of moles.

Although this relationship is suitable for expressing the osmotic work done by a solute, in the case of charged solutes the effects of electrical potentials and charges become of importance. Not only is the concentration gradient of moving solutes to be considered, but also the electrical potential gradient down which they move. Because the two gradients are not independently variable for ions, it is convenient to consider the **electrochemical potential**, $\bar{\mu}$, defined by

$$\bar{\mu}_i = \mu_i + zF\psi \qquad (6.24)$$

where z is the valency of the ionic species, i; F is the Faraday—96,500 coulombs per gram-equivalent transported, and ψ is the electrical potential of that ion. In transferring ions electrical work must be performed. The quantity of electrical work needed to transfer 1 mole of an ion against a potential difference, E ($= \psi_1 - \psi_0$; where the subscripts represent the two compartments between which ions are moving) is given by zFE. The electrochemical potential for a given ionic species is given by the sum of the osmotic and electrical work terms:

$$\bar{\mu} = RT \ln c + zF\psi \qquad (6.25)$$

If a small quantity, dm, of a nonelectrolyte is transferred, the osmotic work, $dmRT \ln (c_i - c_0)$, is zero when equilibrium is reached, that is, the ratio of the concentrations of solute in the two compartments is equal to unity. But when ions are involved, at equilibrium the ratio of ionic concentrations does not necessarily have to be unity. This is the case in the Donnan equilibrium. In addition to osmotic work, electrical work, $dmzF\psi$, is also performed. When the ratio of the concentrations of an ion on two sides of a boundary or membrane is not unity, there is an electrical potential difference across the membrane or boundary:

$$E_a = \psi_1 - \psi_0 = \frac{RT}{zF} \ln (c_i - c_o) \quad (6.26)$$

At equilibrium there is an equality between electrical and osmotic work as shown in Equation 6.26. In the case of active transport, the osmotic and electrical work terms are of opposite sign because osmotic work is performed on the system in moving ions against their concentration gradient, whereas the system does work in accelerating the ion down the electrical potential gradient.

Different types of electrical potentials may, therefore, be found in various systems. No potentials will be present in a system containing an ideally semipermeable membrane because potentials depend on the movements of ions. In systems containing membranes with large pores or in systems with liquid junctions, diffusion potentials may be present. The magnitude of such potentials is given by

$$E_{ij} = \frac{(u - v)}{(u + v)} \frac{RT}{zF} \ln (c_o - c_i) \quad (6.27)$$

where u and v are the mobilities of the cation and anion, respectively. In the liquid junction potential, mobilities are included because such a potential will develop only if they are different for the cation and anion.

A comparison of the mobilities of the alkali metal ions, Li^+, Na^+, and K^+ (Table 6-11) shows that the smaller the atomic weight of the ion, the lower the ionic mobility. It would be expected that the smaller the ion, the faster it would move through the solution, but ionic mobility is determined by the size of the hydrated form of an ion. The smaller an ion, the denser its charge (considering only univalent ions) and the greater the diameter of the layer of water that is attracted about it. Thus a smaller ion with its larger bound water layer will present more resistance to movement through the solution.

In a system containing a differentially permeable membrane such as might be found

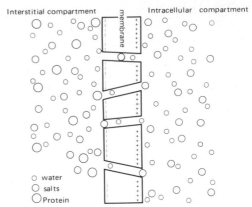

Interstitial compartment   Intracellular compartment

○ water
○ salts
○ Protein

Figure 6-26 At equilibrium in a Donnan system there is a potential established across the membrane. The presence of the impermeable anion causes an imbalance of ions on the two sides of the membrane (see Figure 6-20). In the example shown, K^+ is more concentrated on the inside and tends to move down its concentration gradient to the outer compartment. Cl^- tends to move in the opposite direction. K^+ cannot move without an accompanying Cl^- unless work for separating charges is provided. Electrical neutrality must be preserved in each compartment (in this equilibrium system no energy is provided for the work of separating charges). The tendency of the ions to diffuse down their concentration gradient tends to separate charges and results in the production of a transmembrane potential. Transmembrane potential exists only at membrane surfaces, fluids inside or outside are electrically neutral. The potential is such that it exactly balances diffusion forces of anions and cations.

in a Donnan model or in a cellular system, the potential difference across the membrane may be calculated from relationships developed by W. Nernst, a Swedish physicist (1888, 1889). From a consideration of the equilibrium requirements between osmotic and electrical work, he stated that for any *diffusible ion, a:*

$$E_a = \frac{RT}{zF} \ln \frac{[a]_i}{[a]_o} \quad (6.28)$$

E_a is the potential which would exist across a membrane due to the distribution and movement of a given ion, *if that ion were under equilibrium conditions and the only ion contributing to the membrane potential.* The symbol E_m will be used to refer to the actual transmembrane potential—that potential which is experimentally determined to exist across the membrane. Whereas the transmembrane potential, E_m, depends on the relative permeabilities of the important ionic constituents of biological systems, the equilibrium potential, E_a, is that which would exist if a given ion were at electrochemical equilibrium. At 18°C, and converting to logarithms to the base 10, Equation 6.28 becomes

$$E_a = -58 \log \frac{[a]_o}{[a]_i} \qquad (6.29)$$

In the Donnan equilibrium system (Figure 6-26) there is established a difference in concentration of one or more of the diffusible ions across the membrane. The tendency for these ions to diffuse across the membrane at equilibrium, as already described, leads to the establishment of a potential just great enough, and of proper sign, to oppose the actual movement of ions because of their concentration gradient. In the case of the system of Figure 6-26, the inner compartment becomes positively charged and the outer is negatively charged. This tends to speed up the passage of Na^+ across the membrane while retarding Cl^-. Equal amounts of each ion diffuse across the membrane in a given time.

In the case of the human erythrocyte, any potential developed across the membrane must be caused primarily by anions, since cations have a low permeability and are also actively transported. The tendency for Cl^- to move into the cell establishes a negative charge on the inner surface of the membrane. The cations that tend to get left behind in the external medium establish a positive charge on the outside of the membrane. Again it should be noted that we are talking about tendencies and statistical probabilities of ionic movements. These are reflected in localized and minute accumulations of positive and negative ions at the membrane itself.

The actual membrane potential of the human erythrocyte has recently been measured and has a value of 8 mV with the inside negative (Jay and Burton, 1969). If the internal and external concentrations of K^+, Na^+, and Cl^- are substituted into the Nernst equation,

the equilibrium potentials at 18°C would be

$$E_K = -28mV \qquad E_{Na} = +56mV$$
$$E_{Cl} = -10mV$$

Ionic concentrations used here are those given in Table 6-8 for the erythrocyte and human blood plasma. The actual transmembrane potential is obviously close to the calculated equilibrium potential for Cl^-.

In expressing bioelectrical potential values, it is ordinary to use as the reference point the inside of the cell. Thus, if a membrane is considered to have a potential of $-10mV$ across it, this means that the inside of the membrane is negative with respect to the outside. The potentials of many types of nerve and muscle cells have been measured, and in the next chapter we shall see how their values agree with the theoretical ones calculated from the Nernst equation.

The nature of the membrane itself will greatly determine the magnitude of the electrical potential across it. For example, although K^+ and Cl^- ions have similar mobilities in aqueous solutions and can have no diffusion potential, their rates of movement through a membrane may be quite different and a diffusion potential can exist.

Before returning to the subject of transmembrane potentials and their role in cellular excitability, the transport of some important metabolites and of water deserves some comment.

Transport of Water, Carbohydrates and Amino Acids

6-24. Water Transport. The substances listed in the heading of this part of the chapter deserve discussion because their movement into or out of cells is important to cellular metabolism and maintenance. The transport of carbohydrates and amino acids is especially important as part of the digestive process, where the absorption of these compounds takes place, and in excretory processes, where these substances must be recovered by the organism. Both intestinal tracts and excretory tubules are lined with epithelial surfaces, and the discussion here will center upon transport in epithelial cells.

Water penetrates plasma membranes at rates quite high in comparison with those of other substances, although water moves more slowly through membranes than through water itself. In Section 6-4 it was stated that the permeability coefficients for water differ according to the method of measurement, and it is not always certain whether water moves by osmosis through pores or by diffusion through the membrane substance itself. Dainty and House (1966) attribute the differences in water permeability coefficients to another artifact in the diffusion measurements. According to these authors, a very thin layer of solution adjacent to the membrane is quickly depleted of solute molecules, including THO, which are not rapidly replaced by diffusion. Because of the presence of this unstirred layer the overall rate of water movement is considerably slower than its movement under conditions of a constant hydrostatic or osmotic pressure differential across the membrane. Dainty (1965) has reviewed the theoretical bases of osmotic flow. Generally it appears that water is not actively transported; rather some solute may be actively transported creating an osmotic gradient down which water will flow.

In only a very few cases, so far, has the active transport of water been demonstrated.

Beament (1965) feels that active transport of water does occur across the cuticle of some insects. Cockroach cuticle is covered by a thin layer of a lipid material that is liquid at room temperature. A minute drop of distilled water placed on the cuticle of a cockroach disappears in a few minutes. The use of tritiated water shows that the water does not simply evaporate but enters the body of the animal. The osmotic gradient in this case favors the inward movement of water, the gradient being about 10 atmospheres of pressure.

But solutions of NaCl, $NaHCO_3$, or sucrose at equal or greater osmolarities than the internal body fluids of the organism do not prevent the inward water flux, although no solutes move inward. From experiments of this type, it is concluded that water must be actively transported and that the metabolic energy used for water movement is not coupled to the inward transport of any solute. Similar water fluxes are found in the tracheal and hindgut regions of many insects and may also be active transport processes.

Diamond (1965) used preparations of the gall bladder of fish and mammals to determine the nature of water movement in this

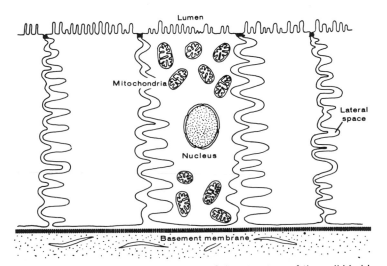

Figure 6-27 Schematic representation of the structure of the gall bladder.

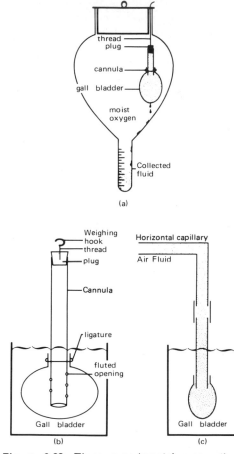

(a)

(b)   (c)

Figure 6-28 Three experimental preparations used to study water and solute movements across gall bladder epithelium. (a) A preparation that requires no external bathing solution. The gall bladder is attached to a cannula filled with the required test solution and plugged. Any fluid transported across the epithelium from the lumen drips into the graduated stem of the glass collecting vessel and can be measured and then chemically analyzed. (b) A preparation that uses an external bathing solution. The cannula and gall bladder can be attached to a balance and weight changes measured. (c) A preparation used to test the influences of hydrostatic pressure on transport by fish gall bladder. [After Diamond (1965).]

epithelial structure. The gall bladder is used because it is a relatively simple organ (Figure 6-27) possessing a single layer of columnar epithelial cells lining the luminal surface. The flow of water and solutes through this sack of cells can be easily followed. One type of experimental preparation is shown in Figure 6-28a. By filling the gall bladder with solutions of different osmolarities or chemical composition, and then measuring the amounts and composition of the fluid secreted, it is possible to obtain information about cellular transport. The results of such experiments show that the secreted fluid is isotonic with the contents of the gall bladder lumen. This appears to be the case also *in vivo* when the gall bladder concentrates and secretes the bile produced by the liver.

Diamond listed seven possible mechanisms for water transport: classical osmosis, ultra-filtration, electro-osmosis, pinocytosis, the double-membrane effect, codiffusion, and local osmosis. Classical osmosis is eliminated as a mechanism for water movement in the gall bladder because the experimental application of various hydrostatic pressures through a tube cannulated to the gall bladder has little effect on water flow. Such flow occurs even in the absence of any pressure differential across the epithelial surface.

Electro-osmosis—the movement of water across a membrane across which an electrical potential is present—cannot account for water movement in the gall bladder. A potential difference of about 70 mV would be required to move the amount of water that flows across the gall bladder surface—the actual measured potential across the membrane is only about 0.1 mV and of the wrong sign to aid water flow. Similarly, objections can be raised to all the mechanisms listed above except to those of local osmosis and the double-membrane hypothesis.

The double-membrane hypothesis is based upon the presence of two membranes, in series, with different pore sizes so that the reflexion coefficients (see page 168) are different for the two membranes. When solute is actively transported across the fine-pored membrane and moves into the space between the membranes, the solute exerts an osmotic pressure across the fine-pored membrane greater than that across the coarse-pored membrane. Water flows across the fine-pored membrane, builds in volume in the inter-membranous space, and causes the build-up of a hydrostatic pressure. This pressure forces water through the coarse-pored membrane. As long as solute is transported into the space, water movement continues, even when equal osmotic pressures exist in the internal and external bathing solutions. Such a system can move isotonic fluid across the cells.

The local osmosis (or endogenous osmosis) hypothesis states that the active transport of a solute such as NaCl sets up local osmotic gradients in the tissue which, in turn, cause a flow of water by osmosis. In such a case, the transported fluid can be isotonic with the tissue fluids or bathing solutions.

Both of these mechanisms depend upon the active transport of a solute that creates favorable conditions for water flow. But the behavior of systems using these different mechanisms would be quite different when varying osmotic pressures were applied to them. The pattern of activity displayed by the gall bladder when solutions of different osmolarities bathe the tissue leads to the conclusion that local osmosis can account for the water movements observed.

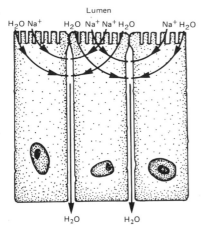

Figure 6-29 Showing the lateral intercellular spaces between cells of the gall bladder. These are thought to serve as routes for water and solute movements across the epithelial layer. Note that the cell membranes form tight junctions (terminal bars) at the luminal ends and that materials must first pass into the cells and then out into the lateral spaces (see also Figure 3-16).

Ultrastructure studies show the existence of intercellular spaces between the epithelial cells of the gall bladder (Tormey and Diamond, 1967). Similar lateral spaces have been also demonstrated in the epithelial linings of the large and small intestines (Kaye and Lane, 1965). According to Tormey and Diamond these lateral spaces serve as the routes for water flow across the epithelial membrane of the gall bladder (Figure 6-29). Active transport of NaCl by the epithelial cells creates an internally higher osmotic pressure, and water flows into the cell and then into the lateral space.

The mechanisms and theory of such solute-linked water transport have been reviewed by Diamond and Bossert (1967) and called standing-gradient osmotic flows. Such transport can occur in those epithelial surfaces which possess long, narrow channels between the cells, open at one end and closed at the other, and which also possess active transport mechanisms for some solute. In tissues such as make up the gastrointestinal tract or kidney tubules are found lateral intercellular spaces, brush borders and microvilli, intracellular canaliculi, and basal infoldings of the membranes—all of which may serve as routes for water or solute movement across the cellular membranes. Lateral intercellular spaces have been found in a variety of gall bladders from different mammals (Hayward, 1962a, b).

Water transport is found and has been studied in the small intestine using preparations as shown in Figure 6-28b, c. By measuring the fluid transport under varying conditions of applied hydrostatic pressure, osmolarity of the bathing solutions, and with different solutes, it appears that there are two mechanisms for water movement in this epithelium (Smyth, 1965). One is a glucose-dependent transport system, the other a glucose-independent system. Both mechanisms require the presence and active transport of Na^+ and both are hypothesized to be carrier-mediated transport systems. Whether the systems function on the basis of local osmosis is not as yet clear.

The mechanisms underlying water movements through most biological membranes are still largely not understood. Active transport of water has been conclusively demonstrated only in a few insects. The lack of understanding of water transport is partially based on ignorance of the true nature of membrane structure. Ussing (1964) has reviewed the transport of water and electrolytes across epithelial surfaces.

6-25. Active Transport of Glucose. Because glucose is a major intermediate in energy metabolism, the efficient transport of this carbohydrate into organisms and cells is needed. Active transport of glucose from the intestinal lumen into the cells is a feature of the intestinal epithelial lining. Kidney tubule epithelia are also noted for their ability to actively transport, over a relatively wide range of concentrations, 100 per cent of glucose from the tubular ultra-filtrate back into the circulation. The regulation of glucose concentrations and

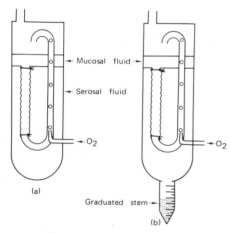

(a)

Graduated stem →

(b)

Figure 6-30 Two preparations used to study transport across intestinal epithelium. (a) The Wiseman preparation in which loops of the intestine transfer solute and fluids from the mucosal to the serosal solutions. Mucosal fluid is circulated by an oxygen lift. (b) The Smyth and Taylor preparation uses no serosal fluid. Transported fluid emerges on the serosal side of the preparation and is collected in a graduated container. Usually three loops of intestine are used, although only one is shown in each of these diagrams. [After Smyth (1965).]

transport is a major function of the vertebrate endocrine system.

The first indication that intestinal absorption of glucose might be an active transport process came from the studies of Cori (1926) and Wilbrandt and Laszt (1933), who found the hexoses, although larger than pentoses, were more rapidly absorbed. In addition, metabolic poisons reduced the rate of glucose and galactose absorption, although the transport of other sugars seemed unaffected. It was concluded that glucose and galactose were actively transported. Verzar and Wirz (1937) calculated that about 65 per cent of the glucose absorption in the small intestine of mammals was due to active transport; the remaining glucose movement was due to passive diffusion and depended on the glucose concentration gradient across the epithelial lining of the intestine.

Wilson and Crane (1958) and Wilson and Landau (1960) pointed out that the active transport of sugars was a selective process dependent on the chemical structure of the transported molecule. One problem associated with measuring the fluxes of a metabolically active molecule such as glucose is that of determining its intracellular concentration. A labeled glucose molecule is rapidly used up in the cell so that its labeled atom quickly becomes incorporated into other molecules. By using sugars with substitutions at various carbon atoms, it was possible to obtain glucose analogs that were transported but not metabolized. Thus, 6-deoxyglucose passes through the membrane as readily as glucose, but cannot be altered in glycolytic or other metabolic pathways, and it becomes possible to measure the intracellular concentration of this molecule (Crane and Krane, 1956). The net transport of glucose across the epithelial lining, as well as accumulation of glucose in cells, was measured using analogs in the bathing medium of intestinal preparations such as those shown in Figure 6-30 (Wilson and Wiseman, 1954).

Generally only D-sugars are transported. The basic requirements in the structure of a molecule for its active transport are indicated by the structural formula:

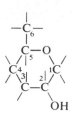

The sugar must have a hexose pyranose ring structure. The need of this specificity of structure of the transported sugar is assumed to reside in the specificity of the conformation of the binding-site of the carrier-molecule to which the transported substance attaches. Although no carrier molecules have been isolated from animal preparations, a protein from the membrane of the bacterium, *Escherischia coli*, has been shown to be the carrier molecule for lactose. The protein has two binding sites, one for lactose and one for galactose (Fox and Kennedy, 1965; Fox et al., 1967).

Na^+ is required for the transport of glucose, galactose, xylose, and 3-methylglucose. There is also present in intestinal cells a sodium-independent transport system for fructose, mannose, sorbitol, and 2-deoxyglucose. This latter system does not require energy. Only the Na^+-dependent carrier system can accumulate sugars against their concentration gradients (Crane, 1966).

A common carrier is used to transport sugars, amino acids, and Na^+ in the small intestine (Alvarado, 1966; Crane, 1968). D-Glucose, D-galactose, L-arginine, and their transported analogs are competitive inhibitors of the transport of neutral amino acids. Kinetically, such inhibition must result from competition for the same site on a carrier molecule. It should be noted that many facts about transport systems are determined by kinetic studies and by determining the type of inhibition produced by various compounds. The effects of various compounds substituted for Na^+, including choline, mannitol, K^+, and Li^+, revealed that only Li^+ could substitute for Na^+ in stimulating transport. It was concluded that Li^+ acts on the carrier-molecule itself, not on the energy providing system. This activation probably represents a change in protein conformation when Li^+ attaches to a specific site on the carrier.

Phlorizin is an inhibitor of glucose transport that has been used in many experimental studies and that can produce an artificial diabetic condition in mammals because it prevents the reabsorption of glucose by the kidney tubules (see Chapter 14). Kinetic studies of glucose transport in the presence and absence of phlorizin reveals that the drug competes with glucose for a common carrier binding site. A close analog, phloretin, decreases glucose transport, but not by competitive inhibition.

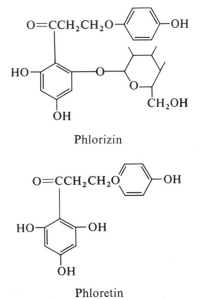

Phlorizin

Phloretin

Phloretin is thought to bind to a phenol-binding site on the carrier, while phlorizin, because it contains a unit of D-glucose, combines to both the phenol-binding site and a sugar-binding site. Different animals respond differently to phlorizin and phloretin suggesting that varying spatial distances exist between the two sites in different carrier proteins (Alvarado, 1967).

Generally then a polyfunctional carrier with different binding sites for various types of molecules is thought to be used in the transport of materials across the epithelial cells of the small intestine.

The continued transport of glucose requires K^+ on the inside of the cell. This requirement is not due to the action of K^+ directly on either sugar permeability or specific carrier molecules, but is based on the need for K^+ during the intracellular metabolism of glucose. As glucose is rapidly and continually metabolized by cells, its concentration gradient across the membrane is enhanced.

Erythrocytes also possess transport systems for glucose. Although some glucose movement is by active transport, the kinetics of glucose transport show that most glucose enters the erythrocyte via a carrier-mechanism that is not dependent on energy—a process sometimes referred to as facilitated diffusion. Glucose exhibits widely varying permeability coefficients in the erythrocytes of different species, reflecting perhaps, differences in the carrier molecule (Bowyer and Widdas, 1956; Lefever, 1961; Miller, 1965a, b). Phloretin and phlorizin also inhibit the carrier-mediated transport of glucose in erythrocytes. The theories of phlorizin and phloretin activity in various cells has been reviewed by Lotspeich (1961).

6-26. Role of the Brush Border.   The epithelial surface lining of the mammalian small intestine

and of the proximal convoluted tubule of the vertebrate nephron possesses a highly infolded membrane. These involuted membranes serve to increase the surface area available for absorption and also to present a chemically specialized area to the luminal space from which materials are transported. Electron microscopy combined with new histochemical methods for enzyme location, together with the ability to prepare pure preparations of brush border membrane by gradient density centrifugation (Eichholz and Crane, 1965; Miller and Crane, 1961a, b) have greatly advanced the study of enzyme and carrier systems of these structures.

Figure 6-31 shows a model with suggested locations of various carriers and enzymes involved in sugar absorption and transport in the hamster small intestine. The model cannot be taken too literally but serves as a map of suggested sites of activity.

The final stages of carbohydrate digestion in which disaccharides are hydrolyzed to

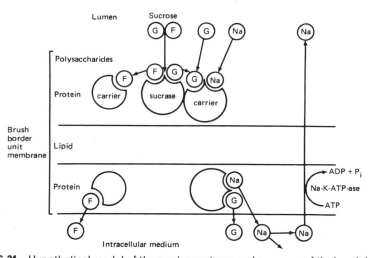

Figure 6-31   Hypothetical model of the carrier systems and enzymes of the brush border of the mammalian intestine for the transport of sugars into the cell and the hydrolysis of disaccharides. F = fructose; G = glucose; Na = sodium ion. Carriers and enzymes are represented by circles with missing segments to represent the needed sites for substrate attachment. On the left is shown the fructose carrier system, which is Na independent. On the right is shown the enzyme sucrose and the glucose carrier, which also requires Na. The positively charged sodium ion may produce a change in protein conformation so that glucose can attach to it. The carrier-glucose-sodium complex diffuses to the inner surface of the membrane, where glucose is released into the cell for use in metabolism. Excess Na is actively transported out of the cell via the membrane-ATPase system. [Based on the work of Crane (1956) (1966).]

monosaccharides by the enzyme disaccharidase (sucrase) are now thought to occur not in the intestinal lumen but in the outer protein layer of the brush border membrane. Disaccharidase and the Na^+-dependent carrier for glucose may be present as a single macromolecular complex in the membrane. The Na^+-independent carrier for fructose is shown in this model as a separate entity. The sodium pump for the active extrusion of Na^+ from the cells is also shown as a separate system (Crane, 1966).

6-27. Amino Acid Transport. Carrier-mediated active transport of amino acids is found in most cells. Although such systems are usually specific for the transport of L-amino acids (Wiseman, 1954, 1956); D-methionine and D-histidine competitively inhibit the transport of their L-forms in the rat intestine. D-Methionine can be transported against a concentration gradient—an activity inhibited by L-methionine (Jervis and Smyth, 1960). Generally, amino acid transport requires amino acids with an α-carboxyl group and an α-amino group (Christensen, 1962).

The transport of neutral amino acids such as glycine, valine, or isoleucine; of acidic amino acids such as glutamic or aspartic; and of basic amino acids such as lysine or arginine requires a separate carrier system for each of these three types of amino acids (Lin et al., 1962; Wilson, 1962; Hagihira et al., 1961). As previously stated, there is some evidence that the transport of some amino acids by the hamster small intestine is linked to a carrier system also used for glucose and Na^+. Heinz (1967) has reviewed the literature dealing with the linkages between Na^+ and amino acid transport.

6-28. The Control of Transport. As already noted, there are several drugs used experimentally to inhibit various transport mechanisms. Na^+ active transport mechanisms are inhibited by ouabain, g-strophanthin, and other glycosides. Active transport systems generally are inhibited by substances that prevent energy metabolism from supplying ATP. Dinitrophenol or cyanide interact with the cytochrome chain; fluoride and iodoacetate stop glycolysis. Phorizin and phloretin prevent sugar transport by interfering with the carrier molecules. Thus, experimentally transport can be inhibited by inhibiting ATPase systems, ATP generating systems, or the carriers. Presumably such activities could also be accomplished by natural substances forming part of a transport control system.

Although there has been an accumulation of information about biological transport systems and the actions of drugs on such systems, much less is known about *in vivo* controls. The pancreatic hormone, insulin, influences membrane permeability to sugars and also affects ion movements. Active transport of amino acids in the rat diaphragm is stimulated by insulin (Eichorn and Hechter, 1961). But insulin, like most hormones, can also effect metabolism or protein synthesis, and it is often difficult to decide at what point insulin is working to cause the inhibition or activation of a given transport system.

Adrenal steroid hormones, including aldosterone and deoxycorticosterone, increase absorption of Na^+ by kidney tubule epithelium (see Chapter 14). Adrenalectomy reduces the active transport of glucose and glycine and also reduces fluid transfer in the rat small intestine. Pituitary hormones such as oxytocin and vasopressin enhance the permeability of the amphibian bladder and other epithelial surfaces to water and salts.

But in general the role of hormones on transport processes cannot be placed into proper perspective because often the stimuli for endocrine secretion, the direct action of many hormones, or the feedback pathways for control and regulation in the whole animal are still open questions. We shall return to the question of transport control in specific tissues in later chapters, after considering transport processes in some specific cell types.

References and Readings

Ackerman, E. (1962). **Biophysical Science.** Englewood Cliffs, N.J.: Prentice-Hall, Inc. 626 pp.

Alvarado, F. (1966). "Transport of sugars and amino acids in the intestine: evidence for a common carrier." *Science* **151**: 1010–1013.

Alvarado, F. (1967). "Hypothesis for the interaction of phlorizin and phloretin with membrane carriers for sugars." *Biochim. Biophys. Acta.* **135**: 483–495.

Andreoli, T. E., J. A. Bangham, and D. C. Tosteson (1967). "The formation and properties of thin lipid membranes from HK and LK sheep red cell lipids." *J. Gen. Physiol.* **50**: 1729–1749.

Baker, P. F., A. L. Hodgkin, and T. I. Shaw (1962). "Replacement of the axoplasm of giant nerve fibres with artificial solutions." *J. Physiol.* (London) **164**: 330–354.

Beament, J. W. L. (1965). "The active transport of water: evidence, models, and mechanisms." *Symp. Soc. Exp. Biol.* **19**: 273–298.

Bennett, H. S. (1956). "The concept of membrane flow and membrane vesiculation as mechanisms for active transport and ion pumping." *J. Biophys. Biochem. Cytol.* **2** (Suppl.): 99–103.

Bihler, I. and S. Adamic (1967). "The effect of lithium on intestinal transport of sugars." *Biochim. Biophys. Acta* **135**: 466–474.

Bishop, C. and D. M. Surgenor, eds. (1964). **The Red Blood Cell.** New York: Academic Press, Inc. 566 pp.

Bonting, S. L., L. L. Caravaggio, and N. M. Hawkins (1962). "Studies on sodium-potassium-activated adenosine triphosphatases. IV. Correlation with cation transport sensitive to cardiac glycosides." *Arch. Biochem. Biophys.* **98**: 413.

Bonting, S. L., K. A. Simon, and N. M. Hawkins (1961). "Studies on sodium-potassium-activated adenosine triphosphatases." *Arch. Biochem. Biophys.* **95**: 416–423.

Booij, H. J. (1966). "Thoughts about the mechanism of membrane movements." In: **Intracellular Transport.** (K. B. Warren, ed.). *Symp. Int. Soc. Cell Biol.* **5**: 301–317.

Bowyer, F. and W. F. Widdas (1956). "The facilitated transfer of glucose and related compounds across the erythrocyte membrane." *Disc. Faraday Soc.* **21**: 251–258.

Bull, H. B. (1964). **"An Introduction to Physical Biochemistry,"** 2nd ed. Philadelphia: F. A Davis Co. 433 pp.

Burt, N. S. and R. J. Rossiter (1950). "Lipids of rabbit blood cells. Data for red cells and polymorphonuclear leucocytes." *Biochem. J.* **46**: 569.

Cass, A. and A. Finkelstein (1967). "Water permeability of thin lipid membranes." *J. Gen. Physiol.* **50**: 1765–1783.

Christensen, H. N. (1962). **Biological Transport.** New York: W. A. Benjamin, Inc. 133 pp.

Clarkson, T. W. (1967). "The transport of salt and water across isolated rat ilium." *J. Gen. Physiol.* **50**: 695–728.

Cole, K. S. (1932). "Surface forces of the *Arbacia* egg." *J. Cell. Comp. Physiol.* **1**: 1–9.

Cole, K. S. (1940). "Permeability and impermeability of cell membranes for ions." *Cold Spring Harbor Symp. Quant. Biol.* **8**: 110–122.

Collander, R. and H. Bärlund (1933). "Permeabilitätstudien und *Chara ceratophylla.*" *Acta Botan. Fennica* **11**: 1–114.

Conway, E. J. (1957). "Nature and significance of concentration relations of potassium and sodium ions in skeletal muscle." *Physiol. Rev.* **37**: 84–132.

Cook, J. S. (1956). "Some characteristics of hemolysis by ultraviolet light." *J. Cell. Comp. Physiol.* **47**: 55–84.

Cori, C. F. (1926). "The rates of absorption of pentoses and hexoses from the intestinal tract." *J. Biol. Chem.* **66**: 691–715.

Crane, R. K. (1966). "Structural and functional organization of an epithelial brush border." *Symp. Soc. Exp. Biol.* **5**: 301–317.

Crane, R. K. (1968). "Absorption of sugars." In: **Handbook of Physiology.** Sect. 6, Vol. 3, pp. 1323–1351. Washington, D.C.: American Physiology Society.

Crane, R. K. and S. M. Krane (1956). "On the mechanism of the intestinal absorption of sugars." *Biochim. Biophys. Acta* **20**: 568–569.

Csaky, T. Z. (1961). "Significance of sodium ions in active intestinal transport of nonelectrolytes." *Am. J. Physiol.* **201**: 999–1023.

Csaky, T. Z. and P. M. Ho (1967). "The effect

of potassium on the intestinal transport of glucose." *J. Gen. Physiol.* **50**: 113–128.

Dainty, J. (1965). "Osmotic flow." *Symp. Soc. Exp. Biol.* **19**: 75–85.

Dainty, J. and C. R. House (1966). "Unstirred layers in frog skin." *J. Physiol.* (London) **182**: 66.

Danielli, J. F. (1935). "The thickness of the wall of the red blood corpuscle." *J. Gen. Physiol.* **19**: 19–22.

Danielli, J. F. (1962). "Structure of the cell surface." *Circulation* **26**: 1163–1166.

Danielli, J. F. and H. A. Davson (1935). "A contribution to the theory of permeability of thin films." *J. Cell. Comp. Physiol.* **5**: 495–508.

Danielli, J. F. and E. N. Harvey (1935). "The tension at the surface of mackeral egg oil with remarks on the nature of the cell surface." *J. Cell. Comp. Physiol.* **5**: 483–494.

Davson, H. (1962). "Growth of the concept of the paucimolecular membrane." *Circulation* **26**: 1022–1037.

Davson, H. and J. F. Danielli (1952). **The Permeability of Natural Membranes**, 2nd ed. New York: Cambridge University Press.

Dedem, O. and A. Katchalsky (1961). "A physical interpretation of the phenomological coefficient of membrane permeability." *J. Gen. Physiol.* **45**: 143–179.

DeGowin, E. L., J. E. Harris, and E. D. Plass (1940). "Studies on preserved human blood. II. Diffusion of potassium from the erythrocyte during storage." *J. Am. Med. Ass.* **114**: 855.

Delgado, J. M. R. (1964). "Electrodes for extracellular recording and stimulation." In: **Physical Techniques in Biological Research.** (W. L. Nastuk, ed.), Vol. 5, part A, pp. 23–88. New York: Academic Press, Inc.

Dervichian, D. G. (1964). "The physical chemistry of phospholipids." *Prog. Biophys.* **14**: 263–342.

Diamond, J. M. (1965). "The mechanism of isotonic water absorption and secretion." *Symp. Soc. Exp. Biol.* **19**: 329–347.

Diamond, J. M. and W. H. Bossert (1967). "Standing-gradient osmotic flow: a mechanism for coupling of water and solute trans-port in epithelia." *J. Gen. Physiol.* **50**: 2061–2083.

Dick, D. A. T. (1959a). "Osmotic properties of living cells." *Int. Rev. Cytol.* **8**: 387–448.

Dick, D. A. T. (1959b). "The rate of diffusion of water in the protoplasm of living cells." *Exp. Cell Res.* **17**: 5–12.

Donnan, F. G. (1911). "Theorie der Membrangleichgewichte und Membranpotentiale bei Vorhandsein von nicht dialysierenden Elektrolyten. Ein Betrag zur Physikallsche-Chemischen Physiologie." *Z. Elektrochem.* **17**: 573–581.

Donnan, F. G. (1927). "Concerning the applicability of thermodynamics to the phenomena of life." *J. Gen. Physiol.* **8**: 685–688.

Dunham, E. T. and I. M. Glynn (1961). "Adenosine triphosphatase activity and the active movements of alkali metal ions." *J. Physiol.* (London) **156**: 274–293.

Eichholz, A. and R. K. Crane (1966). "Fractionation of membrane enzymes present in brush borders of hamster intestinal epithelial cells." *Fed. Proc.* **25**: 656.

Eichorn, J. and O. Hechter (1961). "Insulin induced accumulation of D-xylose against an apparent concentration gradient in diaphragm muscle *in vivo*." *J. Gen. Physiol.* **45**: 15–22.

Eisenman, G. and F. Conti (1965). "Some implications for biology of recent theoretical and experimental studies of ion permeation of membranes." *J. Gen. Physiol.* **48**: 65.

Eisenman, G., J. P. Sandblom, and J. L. Walker (1967). "Membrane structure and ion permeation." *Science* **155**: 965–974.

Emmelot, P., C. J. Bos, E. L. Benedetti, and P. Rumke (1964). "Studies on plasma membranes. I. Chemical composition and enzyme content of plasma membranes, isolated from rat liver." *Biochim. Biophys. Acta* **90**: 126–145.

Ernst, E. (1958). **Die Muskeltätigkeit.** Budapest: Hungarian Academy of Science. New York: Academic Press, Inc. 355 pp.

Evans, J. V. and A. T. Phillipson (1957). "Electrolyte concentrations in the erythrocytes of the goat and ox." *J. Physiol.* (London) **139**: 87–96.

Farmer, S. N. and M. Maizels (1939). "Organic anions of human erythrocytes." *Biochem. J.* **32**: 280.

Fernández-Moran, H. and J. B. Finean (1957). "Electron microscope and low-angle diffraction studies of the nerve myelin sheath." *J. Biophys. Biochem. Cytol.* **3**: 725–748.

Finean, J. B. (1953a). "Further observations on the structure of myelin." *Exp. Cell Res.* **5**: 202–215.

Finean, J. B. (1953b). "X-ray diffraction studies on the polymorphism of phospholipids." *Biochim. Biophys. Acta* **12**: 371–384.

Finean, J. B. (1956). "Recent ideas on the structure of myelin." In: **Biochemical Problems of Lipids.** pp. 127–131. London: Thornton Butterworth, Ltd.

Finean, J. B. (1957). "The role of water in the structure of peripheral nerve myelin." *J. Biophys. Biochem. Cytol.* **3**: 95–102.

Finean, J. B. (1958). "X-ray diffraction studies on the myelin sheath in peripheral and central nerve fibers." *Exp. Cell Res.* **5** (Suppl.), pp. 18–32.

Finean, J. B. (1961). "The nature and stability of nerve myelin." *Int. Rev. Cytol.* **12**: 303–336.

Finean, J. B. (1966). "The molecular organization of cell membranes." *Prog. Biophys.* **16**: 143–170.

Finean, J. B. and J. D. Robertson (1958). "Lipids and the structure of myelin." *Brit. Med. Bull.* **14**: 267–273.

Fox, C. F. and E. P. Kennedy (1965). "Specific labeling and partial purification of the M protein, a component of the β-galactoside transport system of *Escherichia coli.*" *Proc. Nat. Acad. Sci.* (U.S.) **54**: 891–899.

Fox, C. F., J. R. Carter, and E. P. Kennedy (1967). "Genetic control of the membrane protein component of the lactose transport system of *Escherichia coli.*" *Proc. Nat. Acad. Sci.* (U.S.) **57**: 698–705.

Glynn, I. M. (1956). "Sodium and potassium movements in human red cells." *J. Physiol.* (London) **134**: 278–310.

Glynn, I. M. (1962). "Activation of adenosine-triphosphatase activity in a cell membrane by external potassium and internal sodium." *J. Physiol.* (London) **160**: 18–19.

Goldstein, D. A., and A. K. Solomon (1960). "Determination of equivalent pore radius for human red cells by osmotic pressure measurement." *J. Gen. Physiol.* **44**: 1–17.

Gorter, E. and F. Grendel (1925). "On bimolecular layers of lipids on the chromocytes of the blood." *J. Exp. Med.* **41**: 439–443.

Gourley, D. R. H. (1957). "Phosphate transfer in chicken erythrocytes." *Am. J. Physiol.* **190**: 536–542.

Green, D. E. and D. H. MacLennan (1969). "Structure and function of the mitochondrial cristael membrane." *Bioscience* **19**: 213–222.

Hagihira, H., E. C. Lin, A. H. Samly, and T. H. Wilson (1961). "Active transport of lysine, ornithine, arginine, and cystine by the intestine." *Biochem. Biophys. Res. Comm.* **4**: 478–480.

Hanai, T., D. A. Haydon, and J. Taylor (1966). "The permeability to water of bimolecular lipid membranes." *J. Theoret. Biol.* **11**: 370–382.

Harned, H. S. and B. B. Owen (1958). **The Physical Chemistry of Electrolytic Solutions,** 3rd ed. New York: Reinhold Publishing Corporation. 803 pp.

Harris, E. J. (1957). **Transport and Accumulation in Biological Systems.** London: Thornton Butterworth, Ltd.

Harris, E. J. and M. Maizels (1951). "Permeability of human erythrocytes to Na." *J. Physiol.* (London) **113**: 506–524.

Harris, E. J. and M. Maizels (1952). "Distributions of ions in suspensions of human erythrocytes." *J. Physiol.* (London) **118**: 40–53.

Hayward, A. F. (1962a). "Aspects of the fine structure of the gall bladder epithelium of the mouse." *J. Anat.* **96**: 227.

Hayward, A. F. (1962b). "Electron microscopic observations on absorption in the epithelium of the guinea pig gall bladder." *Z. Zellforsch. Mikroskop. Anat.* **56**: 197.

Heinz, E. (1967). "Transport through biological membranes." *Ann. Rev. Physiol.* **29**: 21-58.

Hill, A. V. (1928). "The diffusion of oxygen

and lactic acid through tissues." *Proc. Roy. Soc.* (London) **B104**: 40.

Höber, R. (1945). **Physical Chemistry of Cells and Tissues.** New York: McGraw-Hill Book Company, Inc.

Höber, R. (1946). "The membrane theory." *Ann. N.Y. Acad. Sci.* **47**: 381–394.

Hodgkin, A. L. and R. D. Keynes (1955a). "Active transport of cations in giant axons from *Sepia* and *Loligo.*" *J. Physiol.* (London) **128**: 28–60.

Hodgkin, A. L. and R. D. Keynes (1955b). "The potassium permeability of a giant nerve fibre." *J. Physiol.* (London) **128**: 61–88.

Hoffman, J. F. (1958). "Physiological characteristics of human redblood cell ghosts." *J. Gen. Physiol.* **42**: 9–28.

Huang, C. and T. E. Thompson (1965). "Properties of lipid bilayer membranes separating two aqueous phases: determination of membrane thickness." *J. Mol. Biol.* **13**: 183–193.

Huang, C. and T. E. Thompson (1966). "Properties of lipid bilayer membranes separating two aqueous phases: water permeability." *J. Mol. Biol.* **15**: 539–554.

Jacobs, M. H. (1935). "Diffusion processes." *Ergebn. Biol.* **12**: 1–160.

Jay, A. W. L. and A. C. Burton (1969). "Direct measurement of potential difference across the human red blood cell membrane." *Biochem. J.* **9**: 115–121.

Jervis, E. L. and D. H. Smyth (1960). "The active transfer of D-methionine by the rat intestine *in vivo.*" *J. Physiol.* (London) **151**: 51–58.

Kaye, G. I., and J. D. Cole (1965). "Electron microscopy: sodium localization in normal and ouabain-treated transporting cells." *Science* **150**: 1167–1168.

Kaye, G. I. and N. Lane (1965). "The epithelial basal complex: a morpho-physiological unit in transport and absorption." *J. Cell Biol.* **27**: 50A.

Kedem, O. (1965). "Water flow in the presence of active transport." *Symp. Soc. Exp. Biol.* **19**: 61–73.

Kedem, O. and A. Katchalsky (1958). "Ther-
modynamic analysis of the permeability of biological membranes to non-electrolytes." *Biochim. Biophys. Acta* **27**: 229–246.

Kleinzeller, A. and A. Kotyk, eds. (1960). **Membrane Transport and Metabolism.** New York: Academic Press, Inc. 608 pp.

Koefoed-Johnsen, V. and H. H. Ussing (1953). "The contributions of diffusion and flow to the passage of D_2O through living membranes." *Acta Physiol. Scand.* **28**: 60–76.

Korn, E. D. (1968). "Structure and function of the plasma membrane: a biochemical perspective." *J. Gen. Physiol.* **50**: No. 1, part 2, 257s–274s.

Kuijpers, W., A. C. Van der Vleuten, and S. L. Bonting (1967). "Cochlear function and sodium and potassium activated adenosine triphosphatases." *Science* **157**: 949–951.

Landis, E. M. and J. R. Pappenheimer (1963). "Exchange of substances through the capillary walls." In: **Handbook of Physiology,** Sect. 2: Circulation (W. F. Hamilton, ed.), Vol. 2, pp. 961–1034. Washington, D.C.: American Physiological Society.

Langmuir, I. (1917). "The constitution and fundamental properties of solids and liquids. II. Liquids." *J. Am. Chem. Soc.* **39**: 1848–1906.

Langmuir, I. and E. E. Waugh (1938). "The adsorption of proteins at oil-water interfaces and artificial protein-lipid membranes." *J. Gen. Physiol.* **21**: 745.

Lefevre, P. G. (1961). "Sugar transport in the red blood cell: structure-activity relationships in substrates and antagonists." *Pharmol. Rev.* **13**: 39–70.

Lin, E. C. and T. H. Wilson (1960). "Transport of L-tyrosine by the small intestine *in vitro.*" *Am. J. Physiol.* **199**: 127–130.

Lin, E. C., H. Hagihira, and T. H. Wilson (1962). "Specificity of the transport system for neutral amino acids in the hamster intestine." *Am. J. Physiol.* **202**: 919–925.

Ling, G. N. (1962). **A Physical Theory of the Living State.** Waltham, Mass.: Blaisdell Publishing Co. 680 pp.

Ling, G. N., M. M. Ochsenfeld, and G. Karreman (1967). "Is the cell membrane a universal rate-limiting barrier to the movement of water between the living cell and its surrounding medium?" *J. Gen. Physiol.* **50:** 1807–1820.

Longsworth, L. G. (1968). "Diffusion in liquids." In: **Physical Techniques in Biological Research.** 2nd ed. (D. H. Moore, ed.), Vol. 2, part A, pp. 85–120. New York: Academic Press, Inc.

Lotspeich, W. D. (1961). "Phlorizin and the cellular transport of glucose." *Harv. Lect.* **59:** 63–92.

Lucké, B. and M. McCutcheion (1932). "The living cell as an osmotic system and its permeability to water." *Physiol. Rev.* **12:** 68–139.

McLennan, H. (1957). "The diffusion of potassium, sodium, sucrose, and inulin in the extracellular spaces of mammalian tissues." *Biochim. Biophys. Acta* **24:** 1–8.

Maddy, A. H. (1966). "The chemical organization of the plasma membrane of animal cells." *Int. Rev. Cytol.* **20:** 1–66.

Martin, R. B. (1964). **Introduction to Biophysical Chemistry.** New York: McGraw-Hill Book Company, Inc. 365 pp.

Miller, D. (1965a). "The kinetics of selective biological transport. I. Determination of transport constants for sugar movements in human erythrocytes." *Biophys. J.* **5:** 407–416.

Miller, D. (1965b). "The kinetics of selective biological transport. II. Equations for induced uphill transport of sugars in human erythrocytes." *Biophys. J.* **5:** 417–424.

Miller, D. and R. K. Crane (1961a). "Digestive function of the epithelium of the small intestine. I. An intracellular locus of disaccharide and sugar phosphate ester hydrolysis." *Biochim. Biophys. Acta* **52:** 281–292.

Miller, D. and R. K. Crane (1961b). "The digestive function of the epithelium of the small intestine. II. Localization of disaccharide hydrolysis in the isolated brush border." *Biochim. Biophys. Acta* **52:** 293–298.

Mitchison, J. M. and M. M. Swann (1954). "The mechanical properties of the cell surface. I. The cell elastimeter." *J. Exp. Biol.* **31:** 443–460.

Mueller, P., D. O. Rudin, H. Tien, and W. C. Wescott (1962). "Reconstitution of cell membrane structure *in vivo* and its transformation into an excitable system." *Nature* **194:** 979–980.

Mueller, P., D. O. Rudin, H. Tien, and W. C. Wescott (1963). "Methods for the formation of single bimolecular lipid membranes in aqueous solution." *J. Phys. Chem.* **67:** 534–535.

Nernst, W. (1888). "Zur Kinetik der in Lösung befindlichen Körper." *Z. Physik. Chem.* **2:** 613–637.

Nernst, W. (1889). "Die elektromotorische Wirksamkeit der Ionen." *Z. Physik. Chem.* **3:** 129–181.

Newman, D. W. (1964). **Instrumental Methods of Experimental Biology.** New York: The Macmillan Company. 560 pp.

O'Brien, J. S. (1965). "Stability of the myelin membrane." *Science* **147:** 1099–1107.

Overbeek, J. T. G. (1956). "The Donnan equilibrium." *Prog. Biophys.* **6:** 57–84.

Overbeek, J. T. G. (1960). "Black soap films." *J. Phys. Chem.* **64:** 1178–1183.

Pardee, A. B. (1968). "Membrane transport proteins." *Science* **162:** 632–637.

Ponder, E. (1948). **Hemolysis and Related Phenomena.** New York: Grune & Stratton, Inc., 398 pp.

Post, R. L., C. D. Albright, and K. Dayani (1967). "Resolution of pump and leak components of sodium and potassium ion transport in human erythrocytes." *J. Gen. Physiol.* **50:** 1201–1220.

Prescott, D. M. and E. Zeuthen (1953). "Comparison of water diffusion and water filtration across cell surfaces." *Acta Physiol. Scand.* **28:** 77–94.

Quastel, J. H. (1967). "Membrane structure and function (report on a symposium)." *Science* **158:** 146–161.

Ramsay, J. A. (1956). "Excretion by the malpighian tubules of the stick insect *Dixippus morosus* (Orthoptera, Phasmidae): calcium, magnesium, chloride, phosphate, and hydrogen ions." *J. Exp. Biol.* **33:** 697–708.

Rand, R. P. and A. C. Burton (1963). "Area and volume changes in hemolysis of single erythrocytes." *J. Cell. Comp. Physiol.* **61:** 245.

Rand, R. P. and A. C. Burton (1964). "Mechanical properties of the red cell membrane. I. Membrane stiffness and intracellular pressure." *Biophys. J.* **4:** 115–136.

Riklis, E. and J. H. Quastel (1958). "Effect of cations on sugar absorption by isolated surviving guinea pig intestine." *Canad. J. Biochem. Physiol.* **36:** 347–362.

Robertson, J. D. (1953). "Further studies on ionic regulation in marine invertebrates." *J. Exp. Biol.* **30:** 277–296.

Robertson, J. D. (1955). "The ultrastructure of adult vertebrate peripheral myelinated nerve fibers in relation to myelinogenesis." *J. Biophys. Biochem. Cytol.* **1:** 272–278.

Robertson, J. D. (1960). "The molecular structure and contact relationships of cell membranes." *Prog. Biophys.* **10:** 343–418.

Robertson, J. D. (1964). "Unit membranes: a review with recent new studies of experimental alterations and a new subunit structure in synaptic membranes." In: **Cellular Membranes in Development.** (M. Locke, ed.), pp. 1–81. New York: Academic Press, Inc.

Robertson, J. D. (1965). "The unit membrane and the Danielli-Davson model." In: **Intracellular Transport.** (K. B. Warren, ed.), pp. 1–31. New York: Academic Press, Inc.

Robinson, J. R. (1960). "Metabolism of intracellular water." *Physiol. Rev.* **40:** 112–149.

Rodwell, A. (1968). "Fatty acid composition of Mycoplasma lipids: biomembrane with only one fatty acid." *Science* **160:** 1350–1351.

Rosenberg, T. (1954). "The concept and definition of active transport." *Symp. Soc. Exp. Biol.* **8:** 27–41.

Scatchard, G., A. C. Batchelder, and A. Brown (1946). *J. Am. Chem. Soc.* **68:** 2315.

Schatzmann, A. J. (1953). "Herzglykoside als Hemmstoffe für den aktiven Kalium und Natrium transport durch die Erythrocyten-membran." *Helv. Physiol. Acta* **11:** 346–354.

Schmidt, W. J. (1936). "Doppelbrechung und Feinbau der Markscheide der Nerven-

fasern." *Zell. Forsch. Mikr. Anat.* **23:** 657–676.

Schmidt, W. J. (1938). "Polarizationsoptische Analyse eines Eiweiss-Lipoid-Systems erläutert am Aussenglied der Schzellen." *Kolloidzeltschriften* **84:** 137–148.

Schmitt, F. O. (1936). "Nerve ultrastructure as revealed by X-ray diffraction and polarized light studies." *Cold Spring Harbor Symp. Quant. Biol.* **4:** 7–12.

Schmitt, F. O. (1950). "The ultrastructure of the nerve myelin sheath." *Multiple Sclerosis and the Demyelinating Diseases* **28:** 247–254.

Schmitt, G. O. and R. S. Bear (1939). "The ultrastructure of the nerve axon sheath." *Biol. Rev.* **14:** 27–51.

Schmitt, F. O., R. S. Bear, and K. J. Palmer (1941). "X-ray diffraction studies on the structure of nerve myelin sheath." *J. Cell. Comp. Physiol.* **18:** 31–41.

Schmitt, F. O., R. S. Bear, and E. Ponder (1936). "Optical properties of the red cell membrane." *J. Cell. Comp. Physiol.* **9:** 89–92.

Schwan, H. P. (1957). "Electrical properties of tissues and cell suspensions." In: **Advances in Biological and Medical Physics.** (J. H. Lawrence and C. A. Tobias, eds.), Vol. 1, pp. 147–207. New York: Academic Press, Inc.

Silverman, M. and C. A. Goresky (1965). "A unified kinetic hypothesis of carried mediated transport: its applications." *Biophys. J.* **5:** 487–509.

Skou, J. C. (1957). "The influence of some cations on an adenosine triphosphatase from peripheral nerves." *Biochim. Biophys. Acta* **23:** 394–401.

Skou, J. C. (1960). "Further investigations of Mg^{++}-Na^{+}-activated adenosinetriphosphatase, possibly related to the active, linked transport of Na^{+} and K^{+} across the nerve membrane." *Biochim. Biophys. Acta* **42:** 6–23.

Skou, J. C. (1964). "Enzymatic aspects of active linked transport of Na^{+} and K^{+} through the cell membrane." *Prog. Biophys.* **14:** 131–166.

Smyth, D. H. (1965). "Water movement across the mammalian gut." *Symp. Soc. Exp. Biol.* **19:** 307–328.

Smyth, D. H. and C. B. Taylor (1956). "Transfer of water and solutes by an *in vitro* intestinal preparation." *J. Physiol. (London)* **136**: 632–648.

Snell, F., S. Shulman, R. P. Spencer, and C. Moos (1965). **Biophysical Principles of Structure and Function.** Reading, Mass.: Addison-Wesley Publishing Co. 390 pp.

Sobotka, H. (1944). "Monomolecular layers: their application in physiology and medicine." In: **Medical Physics.** (O. Glasser, ed.), Vol. 1, pp. 763–784. Chicago: Yearbook Medical Pubs., Inc.

Solomon, A. K. (1962). "Pumps in the living cell." *Sci. Am.* **207**: 100–108.

Staverman, A. J. (1948). "Nonequilibrium thermodynamics of membrane processes." *Trans. Faraday Soc.* **48**: 176–185.

Staverman, A. J. (1951). "The theoryof measurement of osmotic pressures." *Rec. Trav. Chim. des Pays-Bas* **70**: 344–352.

Stoeckenius, W. (1962a). "Structure of the plasma membrane. An electron microscope study." *Circulation* **26**: 1066–1069.

Stoeckenius, W. (1962b). "Some electron microscopical observations on liquid-crystalline phases in lipid-water systems." *J. Cell Biol.* **12**: 221–229.

Tanford, C. (1961). **Physical Chemistry of Macromolecules.** New York: John Wiley & Sons, Inc. 710 pp.

Teorell, T. (1952). "Permeability properties of erythrocyte ghosts." *J. Gen. Physiol.* **35**: 669–701.

Teorell, T. (1953). "Transport processes and electrical phenomena in ionic membranes." *Prog. Biophys.* **3**: 305–369.

Thompson, T. E. (1964). "The properties of bimolecular phospholipid membranes." In: **Cellular Membranes in Development.** (M. Locke, ed.), pp. 81–96. New York: Academic Press, Inc.

Tobias, J. M., D. P. Agin, and R. Pawlowski (1962). "Phospholipid-cholesterol membrane model." *J. Gen. Physiol.* **45**: 989–1001.

Tormey, J. M. and J. M. Diamond (1967). "The ultrastructural route of fluid transport in rabbit gall bladder." *J. Gen. Physiol.* **50**: 2031–2060.

Tosteson, D. C. (1964). "Regulation of cell volume by sodium and potassium transport." In: **Cellular Functions of Membrane Transport.** (J. F. Hoffman, ed.), pp. 3–22. Englewood Cliffs, N.J.: Prentice-Hall, Inc.

Tosteson, D. C. and J. F. Hoffman, (1960). "Regulation of cell volume by active cation transport in high and low potassium sheep cells." *J. Gen. Physiol.* **44**: 169–194.

Troschin, A. S. (1958). **Das Problem der Zellpermeabilität.** Jena: Fischer Verlag. 396 pp.

Troschin, A. S. (1960). "Concerning an article by L. M. Chailakhian—Modern concepts of the nature of the resting potential." *Biofizika* (U.S.S.R.) **5**: 104–111.

Ussing, H. H. (1964). "Transport of electrolytes and water across epithelia." *Harvey Lect.* **59**: 1–30.

van Deenen, L. L. M. and J. de Gier (1964). "Chemical composition and metabolism of lipids in red cells of various animal species." In: **The Red Blood Cell.** (C. Bishop and D. M. Surgenor, eds.), pp. 243–307. New York: Academic Press, Inc.

van Deenen, L. L. M., U. M. T. Houtsmuller, G. H. de Haas, and E. Mulder (1962). "Monomolecular layers of synthetic phosphatides." *J. Pharmacol.* **14**: 429–444.

Vandenheuvel, F. A. (1963). "Study of biological structure at the molecular level with stereomodel projections. I. The lipids of the myelin sheath of nerve." *J. Am. Oil Chemists' Soc.* **40**: 455.

Verzar, F. and H. Wirz (1937). "Weitere Untersuchungen und die Bedingungen der selektiven Glucoseresorption." *Biochem. Z.* **292**: 174.

Wang, C. H. and D. L. Willis (1965). **Radiotracer Methodology in Biological Science.** Englewood Cliffs, N.J.: Prentice-Hall, Inc. 382 pp.

Waugh, D. F. and F. O. Schmitt (1940). "Investigations of the thickness and ultrastructure of cellular membranes by the analytical leptoscope." *Cold Spring Harbor Symp. Quant. Biol.* **8**: 233.

Whittam, R. (1958). "Potassium movements

and ATP in human red cells." *J. Physiol.* (London) **140**: 479–497.

Wilbrandt, W. (1940). "Die lonenpermeabilität der Erythrocyten in Michtleiterlösungen." *Pflüg Arch. ges. Physiol.* **243**: 537.

Wilbrandt, W. (1961). "Permeabilität und Stofftransporte." *Fortschr. Zool.* **12**: 28–127.

Wilbrandt, W. and L. Laszt (1933). "Untersuchungen und die Ursachen der selektiven Resorption der Zucker aus dem Darm." *Biochem. Z.* **259**: 398.

Wilson, T. H. and R. K. Crane (1958). "The specificity of sugar transport by hamster intestine." *Biochim. Biophys. Acta* **29**: 30–32.

Wilson, T. H. and B. R. Landau (1960). "Specificity of sugar transport by the intestine of the hamster." *Am. J. Physiol.* **198**: 99–102.

Wilson, T. H. and G. Wiseman (1954). "The use of sacs of everted small intestine for the study of the transference of substances from the mucosal to the serosal surface." *J. Physiol.* (London) **123**: 116–125.

Wiseman, G. (1953). "Absorption of amino-acids using an *in vitro* technique." *J. Physiol.* (London) **120**: 63–72.

Wiseman, G. (1954). "Preferential transference of amino acids from amino acid mixtures by sacs of everted small intestine of the golden hamster (*Mesocricetus auratus*)." *J. Physiol.* (London) **124**: 414–422.

Wiseman, G. (1956). "Active transport of amino acids by sacs of everted small intestine of the golden hamster (*Mesocricetus auratus*)." *J. Physiol.* (London) **133**: 626–630.

Wolf, G. (1964). **Isotopes in Biology.** New York: Academic Press, Inc. 173 pp.

Woodbury, J. W. (1965). "The cell membrane: ionic and potential gradients and active transport." In: **Medical Physiology and Biophysics,** 19th ed. (T. C. Ruch and J. F. Fulton, eds.), pp. 1–24. Philadelphia: W. B. Saunders Company.

Nerve Cell Structure and General Functions

7-1. Transmission of Signals. There are two major pathways by which information can be transmitted in organisms. One is chemical in nature, using specific substances—hormones—secreted by endocrine cells. Hormones are usually carried throughout the organism's body in its circulatory system and cause responses in those cells possessing appropriate receptor sites. Hormonal control is usually used to regulate slower processes such as metabolism, activity of smooth muscles, and the transport of materials across membranes. In single-celled organisms, chemical transmission must play an important regulatory role, and in microorganisms rapid responses could be obtained with this type of mechanism.

The other method of information transmittance in organisms uses electrical signals generated in a nervous system. These nerve impulses are usually associated with fast responses to environmental stimuli. The activity of nerve and other excitable cells is the major topic of this chapter.

Although in the past nervous and endocrine systems were treated as separate entities, it is now apparent that the two are closely integrated in the whole animal. Not only are endocrine systems themselves often under the control of the nervous system, but also many nerve cells are specialized to secrete or store neurohormones (or neurohumors) that activate certain effector cells. Further, the transmission of signals from nerve cell to nerve cell, or from nerve cell to effector cell, is often accomplished by chemical, not electrical, means.

Specialization of cells for the functions of information reception, transmission, coordination and integration evolved early in the development of animal phyla (Bass, 1959; Kappers, 1929; Kappers et al., 1936). Even in the coelenterates, the lowest metazoans with tissue differentiation, is found an organized neuromuscular system providing for relatively rapid responses and a complex behavioral pattern for capturing food and for locomotion. Because nerve and muscle cells, the major excitable cells, are usually specialized to carry

Chapter 7

Resting and Action Potentials of Excitable Cells

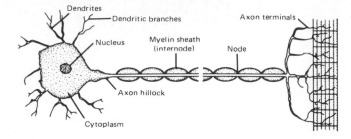

Figure 7-1 Generalized diagram of vertebrate motor neuron.

electrical signals, the discussion of bioelectrical activity in this chapter will include both cell types. Here we shall be concerned only with those potentials used by cells to conduct information; in later chapters the potentials involved in the reception of information by sensory cells, the passage of signals from one cell to another, and potentials associated with transport activities or mass cellular actions will be considered.

7-2. The Neuron Theory. The fundamental unit of nervous systems is the nerve cell or **neuron** (the term "nerve" is reserved for bundles of fibrous processes arising from many nerve cells). Some early histologists thought that the nervous system was a syncytial reticulum of branching fibrous processes with nerve cell bodies lying at nodal points—the reticular theory (for example, Golgi, 1898). As late as 1929, Held argued for a syncytial network of neurons and felt that nerve axons invaded the cytoplasm of the cells they contacted. These ideas were, to a great extent, the result of attempting to extent observations beyond the resolving power of the light microscope—junctions between neuronal processes are far too small to examine in detail with this instrument.

The neuron doctrine—the concept that nervous systems are composed of individual cells which are discrete, separate entities—was championed by the work and arguments of Ramón y Cajal (1909–1911, 1934). Observations of properly stained material with the light microscope often did show nerve fiber endings with swollen tips. Harrison (1907) developed the first reliable method for studying cultures of cells outside the body. His simple hanging drop method is still used today in tissue culture studies. By this method Harrison observed growing neurons and noted that the processes extending from them had enlarged ends, from which fine filaments often extended. These processes grew out of the nerve cell body into the medium, and it appeared that all cells were separate. It might be noted that the mechanisms by which neurons grow and extend fibrous processes during embryological development are still not known. Nor are the mechanisms known by which neurons make the proper connections to other neurons or to effector cells (see, for example, Levi-Montalcini, 1965). The problems of tracing out connections in the nervous system are discussed by Le Gros Clark (1963).

The neuron doctrine was finally substantiated by the electron microscope, which showed that neurons, like most other cells, were bounded by a unit membrane whose presence prevents cytoplasmic continuity between adjoining cells of the nervous system. The gap separating neurons is small (≈ 75 to 400 Å wide), and in some cases there is a fusion of the outer layers of two unit membranes at neuronal junctions.

7-3. The Generalized Neuron. Figure 7-1 shows the structural features of a vertebrate motor neuron, the cell type often used to exemplify neuronal structure. Although this cell clearly shows some of the major features found in nerve cell structure, it is not really typical in the animal kingdom or even in vertebrates. A few of the many nerve cell types known are diagrammed in Figure 7-2.

The nerve cell body—the **perikaryon** or **soma** —contains the nucleus and other typical cell organelles. These include the Nissl bodies (or chromophil substance)—densely staining elements as seen in the light microscope. The electron microscope has shown them to be parallel arrays of the endoplasmic reticulum, with cisternae and ribosomes (see Bloom and Fawcett, 1962). The soma is the site of normal cellular metabolism and contains mitochondria and a Golgi complex. There is also present a reticular network of **neurofibrils** of unknown function. The cytoplasm of the soma is not involved directly in the bioelectrical phenomena to be considered in this chapter. The membrane surrounding the soma is a part of the bioelectrical potential generating mechanism in some neurons. This membrane may also be the site of connections with other neurons.

Since the neuron is especially differentiated to transmit impulses through the nervous system or through the organism's body or to make connections with other neurons or with effector cells, it is noted for its many (usually) processes and branches. These include dendrites, axons, and collaterals. The latter are side-branches of axons.

Dendrites on the basis of the vertebrate motor neuron, were defined as fibrous processes that carry impulses toward the cell body. Axons were defined as processes that carry impulses away from the cell body. But this definition fits only a few neuron types (see Section 7-4).

Anatomically, dendrites are usually shorter, highly branched, and possess numerous finer processes—the sites of connections with axons of other neurons. Many dendrites possess minute spines for such connections. The functional junction between the dendritic region of one nerve and the axon ending of another neuron is the **synapse** (see Chapter 8).

The axon is usually a single, long, slender process, sometimes branched. Axonal endings (**telodendria**) make connections with other neurons or with effector cells. They exist in a variety of types. Some endings are knoblike structures (synaptic knobs or **boutons terminaux**); others are filamentous, ribbonlike endings; still others have a single specialized ending such as the end plate found at junctions with skeletal muscle. Many axons have simple, morphologically undifferentiated endings.

The protoplasm of the axon is called **axoplasm** and at axonal endings, may contain concentrations of mitochondria, numerous small membrane-bounded vesicles, and a collection of enzymes associated with the production of chemical transmitters (Chapter 8). In addition to the plasma membrane, axons

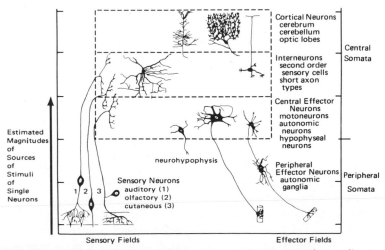

Figure 7-2 Neuron types in the mammalian nervous system, arranged according to general functions and according to estimated magnitude of sources of synaptic connections. [Redrawn by permission from D. Bodian, (1952) "Introductory survey of neurons." *Cold Spring Harbor Symposium on Quantitative Biology* **17**: 1–13.]

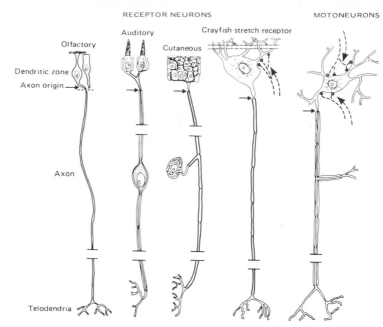

Figure 7-3 Diagrams of some neuronal types. The neurons illustrated point out that the position of the soma is not sufficient to define dendrite and axon on the basis of direction of impulse conduction. [From D. Bodian, (1962) "The generalized vertebrate neuron" *Science* **137** (3527): 323–326. Copyright 1962 by the American Association for the Advancement of Science. Redrawn by permission from the author and publisher.]

may be invested with a myelin sheath or with other types of membranous coverings (Section 7-5). The myelin of axons is interrupted at regular intervals by the nodes of Ranvier— regions possessing no myelin sheath. Often the axon is simply termed the **fiber**.

7-4. Axonal and Dendritic Regions. Even from the brief description given in the preceding section, it should be evident that neurons exist in a wide variety of forms. Figure 7-3 diagrams five types of neurons. It can be seen that definitions of dendrites as processes: (a) arising from the soma, (b) conveying signals toward the soma, or (c) being synaptic regions—do not fit most of these cell types. Such combined morphological-physiological definitions apply primarily to the well-studied, and somewhat atypical, vertebrate motor neuron.

Dendritic and axonal regions are better defined in terms of functional activities after surveying a variety of neurons. The bioelectric potentials developed in these two regions are different in their modes of ionic generation, size, shape and duration (see Figure 7-16). The nature of these potentials can serve to better define these zones. Figure 7-4 presents the relationships between the various types of potentials found in excitable cells. All cells possess a transmembrane potential. In the excitable cell at rest, that is, when not stimulated this potential is called the resting potential. Upon stimulation, this potential changes and other types of potentials arise.

Dendritic zone potentials include generator, synaptic, and spontaneous potentials. These are characterized as graded, nonpropagated potentials. That is, the magnitude of the potential is variable depending on the intensity or frequency of stimulation. This type of potential is not propagated over long distances.

The characteristic potential of the axonal region when stimulated is the **spike of the action potential** (or **nerve impulse**). This is an all-or-none potential and is nondecrementally conducted along the axon. **Conduction** or **propagation** is the passage of an action potential along a neuron or muscle cell membrane. **Transmission** describes the transfer of information from one cell to another.

We shall consider the dendritic zone as the receptive portion of a neuron—either the site of synaptic connections with other neurons, and thus the site of transmitting activity, or the site of transducing activity in sensory receptors in which the energy form of stimuli arising outside the cell is converted by the cell into bioelectrical activity. The axonal region is characterized as the nerve impulse conducting region of the neuron. When the somal membrane is involved in bioelectrical activity, it is usually the site of synaptic functioning and is thus a part of the dendritic zone. In some cases the somal membrane serves as a region of action potential development and is thus a part of the axonal region. The dendritic zone may include part of the axon, especially the portion that arises from the soma or from a receptor zone. Bishop (1956) and Bodian (1962) have reviewed these ideas.

Note that the position of the soma in relation to direction of impulse travel is irrelevant to the definition of axonal or dendritic functioning. In vertebrate sensory neurons (Figure 7-3) it happens that axons conduct impulses both toward and away from the cell body. In some sensory neurons, the soma lies in the middle region of the axon, in others it may lie at the end of an axon collateral.

In this chapter we shall consider the activities of the axonal region and the production and propagation of action potentials. The direction of impulse conduction is an important feature of nervous system activity. In the laboratory isolated axons are often used for experimental purposes. Such a preparation, when electrically stimulated, conducts an impulse in both directions away from the point of stimulation. But in the intact animal, activity that arises in a dendritic zone causes an impulse to arise in the axon that is conducted in one direction—away from the dendritic region. With relatively few exceptions,

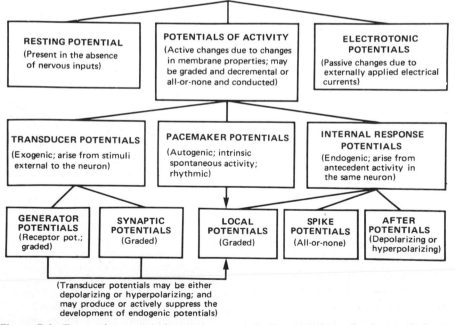

POTENTIALS OF NERVE CELL MEMBRANES

RESTING POTENTIAL
(Present in the absence of nervous inputs)

POTENTIALS OF ACTIVITY
(Active changes due to changes in membrane properties; may be graded and decremental or all-or-none and conducted)

ELECTROTONIC POTENTIALS
(Passive changes due to externally applied electrical currents)

TRANSDUCER POTENTIALS
(Exogenic; arise from stimuli external to the neuron)

PACEMAKER POTENTIALS
(Autogenic; intrinsic spontaneous activity; rhythmic)

INTERNAL RESPONSE POTENTIALS
(Endogenic; arise from antecedent activity in the same neuron)

GENERATOR POTENTIALS
(Receptor pot.; graded)

SYNAPTIC POTENTIALS
(Graded)

LOCAL POTENTIALS
(Graded)

SPIKE POTENTIALS
(All-or-none)

AFTER POTENTIALS
(Depolarizing or hyperpolarizing)

(Transducer potentials may be either depolarizing or hyperpolarizing; and may produce or actively suppress the development of endogenic potentials)

Figure 7-4 Types of potentials found in nerve and other excitable cells. Arrows indicate that a sufficient level of potential change may initiate another change in the membrane. Not shown are several known types of spontaneous potentials including miniature endplate potentials, sinusoidal, and sawtooth potentials.

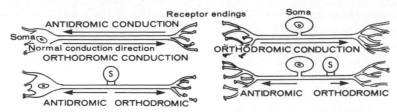

Figure 7-5 Diagrams illustrating orthodromic and antidromic conduction. Normally conduction is from sensory ending or synaptic membrane toward the axon terminals (= orthodromic conduction). In experimental situations and in a few physiological situations, conduction is antidromic—the impulse travels toward the dendritic zone or receptor ending.

impulse propagation is in one direction. The normal direction of conduction in a given neuron is orthodromic conduction (Figure 7-5). In the organism, synapses act as polarizing valves, allowing impulses in most cases to travel in only one direction. Action potentials that travel away from axon endings toward the dendritic zone of the same neuron are antidromically conducted. As we shall see, antidromic conduction is sometimes found normally in the nervous system. Hydén (1960) discusses the general structures and functions of nerve cells. Lowry (1963) describes the microtechniques used to isolate and chemically analyze neurons.

7-5. Sheaths of Peripheral Axons. Excepting sensory and motor nerve endings and the neurons of the nerve nets of simpler organisms such as the coelenterates, nerve cells are closely invested with nonnervous cells, known collectively as **neuroglia** (or simply glia). The term covers several types of cells found in the interstitial tissues of the brain, nerve cords, and ganglia of animals and is also used to refer to interstitial cells of peripheral neurons—the sensory and motor fibers that run out into the body from the central nervous system. Axons, except in the coelenterates and in some giant fibers of annelids, never occur naked. On the basis of the thickness of the investing layer of cells, neuron processes are known as myelinated or unmyelinated, although intermediate categories exist (Figure 7-6). Although glial cells may be intimately wrapped about an axon, there is always a small gap between axon and glial cell membranes.

Vertebrate axons of peripheral neurons are accompanied by Schwann cells, which are similar to lemnoblast cells in arthropods. Geren (1954) and Robertson (1955) showed that myelinated neurons possess a thick sheath that is produced by a Schwann cell wrapping itself around an axon during embryological development (Figure 7-7). The myelin sheath is thus formed of many tightly packed layers of Schwann cell plasma membrane from which the Schwann cell cytoplasm has been squeezed out. The mechanism by which this occurs is not known. So-called unmyelinated fibers, which appear greyish instead of whitish-yellow

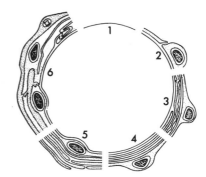

Figure 7-6 Types of nerve sheaths, some of which are commonly found in many phyla and all of which occur in arthropods. 1. Naked without any sheath (found in most axons less than 0.5 μ in diameter; in many central axons, and in coelenterate axons). 2. Single-sheathed (common in peripheral and central axons). 3. Loosely wound myelin with nucleous external (optic nerves and ganglia of crabs; large motor axons of polychaetes). 4. Compact, densely wound myelin (vertebrate axons; optic nerve of *Cancer*). 5. Several participating sheath cells with shingled processes (some crustacean central fibers). 6. Tunicated possessing a thick outer amorphous coat (some arthropod and molluscan giant axons). [Modified after J. H. McAlear in Bullock and Horridge (1965).]

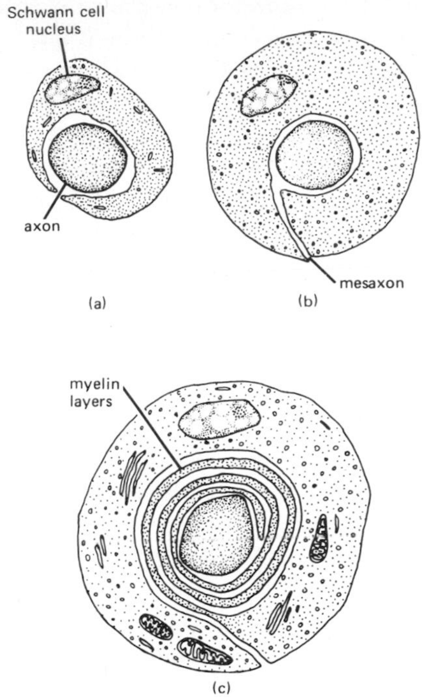

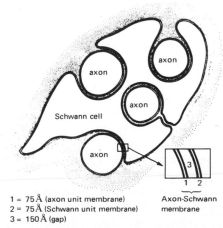

Figure 7-7 Diagrammatic representation of the steps in the formation of myelin. (a,b) The Schwann cell envelops the axon and wraps about the axon. (c) Successive layers of Schwann cell membrane form the compact myelin. [After Geren (1954) and Robertson (1966.]

as myelinated axons do, do not have a thick myelin covering, but they are invested with supportive Schwann cells. Often several unmyelinated axons are contained within one Schwann cell (Figure 7-8).

The function of Schwann cells is not fully understood. They provide an electrically insulating coat around axons that permits a faster rate of impulse conduction, but this is true only for heavily myelinated fibers. It is sometimes suggested that Schwann cells act as nutritive cells, supplying axons with needed metabolites or growth factors. Axons are usually very long processes, and the cell body may not be able to supply all the needs of distant portions of axons, although there is a continual flow of materials down the axon from the soma. There is an intimate relationship between the neuron and its supportive cells. For example, degeneration of an axon that has been transected or otherwise injured

results also in the degeneration of the Schwann cell.

Suggestions have been made that glial cells in the central nervous system act as storage units for memory processes or as a separate integrating and coordinating system (Hydén, 1962, 1965). Evidence for this hypothesis is weak. Questions also arise concerning the mechanisms by which nutrients from the blood reach nerve cells of the central nervous system because blood vessels and neurons are separated by a thick layer of glial cells and supportive tissue (the so-called blood-brain barrier) (see Kuffler and Nicholls, 1965). The structure and functions of glial cells are discussed in Kuffler and Nicholls (1966), Bunge (1968), and Bullock and Horridge (1965).

Bioelectric Potentials: Injury and Resting Potentials

7-6. Early Development of Bioelectric Concepts. Some of the first models of nerve action held that neurons were pipelike structures through which flowed gases or liquids to inflate and deflate muscles. Descartes (1662) elaborately modeled the nervous system as a series of water pipes operating on hydraulic principles. In the eighteenth century hydraulic models

1 = 75 Å (axon unit membrane)
2 = 75 Å (Schwann unit membrane)
3 = 150 Å (gap)

Axon-Schwann membrane

Figure 7-8 The relations of vertebrate peripheral unmyelinated nerve fibers ("C" fibers) to a Schwann cell. The insert shows that both Schwann cell and axon are surrounded by typical unit membranes.

were abandoned because they could not account for the high velocities of nervous conduction seen, for example, in reflex actions. Hall in the eighteenth century suggested that nerves were structured of long rows of touching spheres. The last in line would fly off almost instantaneously when the first in line was struck (note the similarity of this model with that of the conduction of protons in water, Section 2-7). This type of activity would account for the observed velocities of nerve action (see Hoff, 1936). Isaac Newton in 1782 (reprinted 1952) suggested that neurons were solid but transparent fibers which conducted stimuli in the form of optical vibrations.

In the eighteenth century Cavendish (1776) began to associate the shock received upon touching an electric fish with electricity. *Torpedo* (an electric ray) and *Electrophorous* (an electric eel or fish) had been known before the time of Aristotle. Cavendish made several models of *Torpedo* using wood and leather bodies connected to Leyden jars. With the aid of this model, he showed that all of the effects of touching *Torpedo* could be duplicated with electricity. This answered the objections of others to the hypothesis that electricity was the origin of the shocks produced by electric fish and rays (Harmon and Lewis, 1966, have excellent descriptions of neural models up to the present).

Galvani (1791, 1794) demonstrated that electricity could excite frog muscle into contracting, and he introduced the idea that muscles and nerves contained electricity (in that period electricity was thought to be a fluid). Volta, however, argued that the presence of electricity arose, not from the tissues themselves, but from the junctions between dissimilar metals present in the experimental apparatus—such junctions were known to generate electrical currents and, for example, lie at the basis of such instruments as the thermocouple used to measure temperature.

duBois-Reymond (1848, 1852, 1863), after designing and constructing sensitive galvanometers (instruments for measuring electrical currents), was able to show that electrical currents did exist in nerve and muscle. The

currents he measured are now known as injury currents. But galvanometers cannot measure accurately the brief and rapid electrical events that occur in excitable cells and our present knowledge of bioelectrical phenomena is based upon the cathode ray oscilloscope developed by Gasser and Erlanger in 1922. This instrument and its associated electronic circuitry depended on the invention of the triode vacuum tube. From the time of Galvani and Volta to the present we have an example of the stimulating influence of biology on the physical sciences from which developed the formal theories of electricity. Curiosity about the functioning of nerve and muscle was a major force leading to the development of electrical concepts and the instruments needed to measure electrical phenomena.

7-7. Injury Potentials. On the basis of work with squid giant axons and other single neuron preparations, it is thought that the resting potential across the membranes of most axons is the result of the distribution of the major diffusible ion, K^+, which is at high concentration inside and low concentration outside the cell. The active transport of Na^+ maintains this ion in low intracellular concentration in the resting nerve. Upon adequate stimulation the axon membrane undergoes a specific increase in permeability to Na^+, which allows this ion to move rapidly into the axon and which thus lowers the resting potential and actually causes the sign of the potential to change with the inside of the membrane becoming positive with respect to the outside. At the peak of this action potential another specific permeability change of the membrane occurs and K^+ moves rapidly out of the cell, thus tending to restore the transmembrane potential toward its normal value.

In the remainder of this chapter, I shall discuss the classical and modern experiments that led to this concept of potential changes in the nerve (and also muscle) cell. Axonal potentials and the mechanisms underlying their generation are to be considered.

In the nineteenth century Matteuci, duBois-Reymond, Bernstein, and others (see the historical accounts by Brazier, 1959, 1960) discovered that when one metal electrode was placed on a damaged portion of a nerve or muscle and another electrode was placed on nearby undamaged tissue, a potential difference between the electrodes could be measured. The damaged region was electrically negative with respect to the uninjured region. This potential difference was called the **injury potential**.

Bernstein in 1868 measured the conduction velocities of nerve and believed that nerve cells were polarized in the resting condition with the inside negative to the outside. This idea was to be expanded into the theory that the polarization of nerve cell membranes was the result of a differential distribution of ions across a semipermeable membrane (Bernstein, 1902, 1911). According to this classical theory of nerve function, any injury to the neuron that damages the membrane allows an ionic current to flow—**the injury current**—through the damaged portion of the nerve membrane. Bernstein assumed that the potential difference across the membrane was caused by what we have called a Donnan equilibrium, established by a membrane relatively permeable

to K^+ and Cl^- and impermeable to Na^+. Upon damage to the membrane, ions move down their concentration gradients, producing the action currents and allowing the transmembrane potential to be measured. This theory and its extensions to the phenomenon of action potentials was a remarkable creation at a time when electrical events in single neurons could not be studied nor could ionic movements or concentrations be measured.

Until the middle of the twentieth century detailed study of nerve functioning was confined to **compound nerves**—nerves composed of many neurons. The classical preparation was the frog sciatic-gastrocnemius preparation, and the responses of nerve stimulation were often measured in terms of the responses of the muscle. Then two developments made it possible to analyze bioelectrical activities in single neurons.

7-8. The Squid Axon and Microelectrodes. Standard extracellular electrodes employed for studying bioelectrical potentials of whole nerves or muscle are silver chloride coated silver wires, the Ag-AgCl electrode (Figure

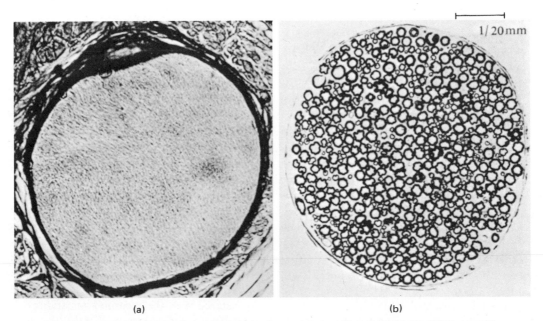

1/20 mm

(a)   (b)

Figure 7-9 Comparison of the diameters of a squid giant fiber (a) and a rabbit nerve (b) composed of many individual neurons. [From J. Z. Young, (1942) *Doubt and Certainty in Science* Oxford University Press, New York.]

6-24). Such electrodes are far too large to be placed in most cells without damaging them, and thus the actual transmembrane potential of an undamaged cell cannot be measured.

Young (1936) introduced the use of giant axons of the squid as experimental material in neurophysiological studies. These axons are many times the size of axons customarily found (see Figure 7-9). Giant fibers serve as fast-conducting pathways (needed for fast movements in locomotion, flight, and so forth) in a variety of organisms, especially in annelids, molluscs, and arthropods. Since the single axons of the squid are sometimes as large as a mm in diameter, thin wire electrodes can be inserted directly into the axon through a cut end, without damaging the axoplasm or membrane. It becomes possible to directly measure electrical differences between the inside and outside of the membrane (Curtiss and Cole, 1940; Hodgkin and Huxley, 1939).

Another development that allowed single cells to be studied was the microelectrode technique introduced into the United States by Graham and Gerard (1946) and Ling and Gerard (1949). Microelectrodes had been used as early as 1925 in Europe to determine the membrane potentials of single cells such as *Amoeba*, but such measurements were not precise because the necessary associated electronic circuitry was not available (Peterfi, in Keller, 1925; Gicklhorn, 1929).

Microelectrodes are pulled from glass tubing until a capillary tip is formed with a diameter as small as 0.5 μ. The microelectrode is then filled with 3 M KCl which serves as a conducting medium between the cellular material and Ag-AgCl electrodes from which copper wires conduct electrical signals to a measuring instrument. Such electrodes have extremely high electrical resistance (on the order of 10 to 40 million ohms) and require special circuitry in order to accurately measure potential differences (Frank and Becker, 1964; Burés et al., 1962; Katz, et al., 1964; Moore, 1963; Schoenfeld, 1964).

Microelectrodes are important tools because they permit a direct measurement of transmembrane potentials and the penetration of a microelectrode into a cell appears to do negligible damage to the membrane. Microelectrodes are also used to stimulate a small region of a cell by applying an electrical current to the KCl-filling solution. In addition, microelectrodes if filled with a solution containing a suitably charged solute can be used to mark a point inside a cell. The application of a brief current pulse to the electrode causes the charged solute to move out from the electrode into the cell. In this way the effects of various ions on the inside of the cell can be tested, or if the solute is a dye, then the cell is stained at that point. The amount of material injected can be determined from a knowledge of the current and voltage applied to the electrode. The name "iontophoresis" or "microelectrophoresis" is given to this procedure of microinjection (Curtis, 1964).

7-9. Resting Potentials. All cells for which measurements have been made exhibit a potential difference between the inside and outside of the membrane. Electrodes placed only on the outside of the cell, or only on the inside, reveal no potential differences. Some values for the resting potentials of a variety of excitable cells and fibers are given in Table 7-1.

Although the transmembrane potential of an excitable cell that is neither stimulated by external agents nor undergoing spontaneous electrical activity is called the resting potential, the cell is at rest only in so far as the membrane and its associated potentials of activity are concerned; metabolically the cell is not at rest. The resting and injury potentials are, essentially, measures of the same phenomenon. They differ in the method used to record them. Injury potentials have lower values than corresponding resting potentials measured with intracellular or microelectrodes because in the former current flows through the damaged membrane and is lost to the recording electrodes by passing through the external conducting solution—a path of lower electrical resistance than the recording apparatus.

7-10. The Basis of the Resting Potential. The ionic distributions between nerve and muscle

Table 7-1 Resting Potentials of Some Excitable Cells*

Preparation	Resting Potential (mV)
Giant Axons	
Loligo (squid)	60
Sepia (cuttlefish)	62
Lumbricus (earthworm)	70
Periplaneta (cockroach)	70
Cambarus (crayfish)	90
Nerve fibers	
Carcinus (crab; leg axon)	71–94
Homarus (lobster; leg axon)	71
Rana (frog; sciatic nerve axon)	60–80
Felis (cat; sympathetic nerve axon)	50–80
(motoneuron axon)	60–80
Nerve cell bodies	
Aplysia (mollusc; visceral ganglion)	40–60
Cambarus (stretch receptor)	70–80
Bufo (toad; dorsal root ganglion)	50–80
(spinal motoneuron)	40–60
Felis (spinal motoneuron)	55–80
Oryctolagus (hare; sympathetic neuron)	65–82
Striated muscle fibers	
Rana (sartorius)	80–90
Oxya (grasshopper; wing muscle)	50–70
Periplaneta (leg muscle)	60
Locusta (locust; wing muscle)	47
Felis (tenuissimus)	55–70
Smooth muscle fibers	
Oryctolagus (uterus)	32–52
Mesocricetus (guinea pig; uterus)	27–66
(small intestine)	51
Man (uterus)	21–31

* Data from many sources; see Bullock and Horridge (1965).

cells and their environments are basically similar to those given for the erythrocyte (Table 6-9) except that internal chloride concentrations are lower because of the presence of a variety of other anions (Table 7-2).

If the resting potentials of nerve or muscle were due to equilibrium potentials of diffusible ions such as K^+ or Cl^-, distributed according to a Donnan equilibrium, then the measured transmembrane potentials should be the same as those calculated from the Nernst equation (Equation 6.28). The equilibrium potential, again, is that potential difference which must exist across the membrane if a given species of diffusible ion is to be in equilibrium. It

Table 7-2 Ionic Concentrations of Squid Giant Axon (*Loligo*), Squid Blood, and Sea Water—and of a Muscle Cell (Frog Sartorius) and Blood Plasma*

SUBSTANCE	SQUID AXOPLASM†	SQUID BLOOD†	SEA WATER†	SARTORIUS MUSCLE†	BLOOD PLASMA†
K^+	400	20	10	124	2.2
Na^+	50	440	460	9.2	120.0
Cl^-	40	560	540	1.5	77.5
Ca^{2+}	0.4	10	10	4.9	2.1
Mg^{2+}	10	54	54	14	1.2
HCO^-	—	—	—	12.4	26.6
ATP^{-4}	0.7	—	—	4.0	—
Isethionate $^-$	250	—	—	—	—
Phosphocreatine $^-$	—	—	—	35.2	—
Phosphoarginine $^-$	1.8	—	—	—	—
Aspartate $^-$	75	—	—	—	—
Glutamate $^-$	12	—	—	—	—
Other amino acids	—	—	—	8.8	7.2
Succinate $^-$	17	—	—	—	—
Lactate $^-$	—	—	—	3.9	3.5
Creatine	—	—	—	7.4	2.2
Protein	—	—	—	0.6	2.2

* Squid data from Koechlin (1955) and Hodgkin (1958). Frog muscle data from Conway (1957) and Boyle and Conway (1941).
† Concentrations are given in millimoles/kg water.

represents the electrical force just necessary to balance the diffusion pressure for a given ion. It represents, from basic thermodynamic principles, the electrical work needed to move a small quantity of ions across a boundary in one direction and, at equilibrium, must be equal to the osmotic work required to move the same quantity of ions in the opposite direction. As shown in Table 7-3 the calculated equilibrium potentials for K^+ and Cl^- are close to the observed values of the resting potentials of nerve and muscle, but the latter are always less than the theoretical. The resting potential is also far from the sodium equilib-

Table 7-3 Ion Ratios and the Observed Resting Potentials and Calculated Ion Equilibrium Potentials across Squid Giant Axon Membranes and Frog Sartorius Membranes

PREPARATION	$[K]_o/[K]_i$	$[Na]_o/[Na]_i$	$[Cl]_i/[Cl]_o$	OBSERVED RESTING POTENTIAL	CALCULATED POTENTIALS* E_K	E_{Na}	E_{Cl}
Squid axon	0.05	8.8	0.07	−65	−75	+55	−67
Frog muscle	0.017	13	0.02	−90	−103	+64	−99

* Equilibrium potentials were calculated from the data of Table 7-2, using the Nernst equation for 18°C:
$E_a = 58 \log([+]_o/[+]_i) = 58 \log([-]_i/[-]_o)$.

Table 7-4   Ion Fluxes across Frog Sartorius Muscle Membrane*

$[Na]_o$	$[Na]_i$	Na INFLUX†	Na EFFLUX	$[K]_o$	$[K]_i$	K INFLUX	K EFFLUX
120 mM	9.2 mM	3.5	3.5	2.5 mM	140 mM	5.4	8.8

* Data from Hodgkin and Horowicz (1959).
† Fluxes are given as 10^{-12} M/cm^2 − sec.

rium potential, which would require that the inside of the cell be positively charged. Bernstein's classical theory required revision when it was found, through tracer studies, that the membrane of muscle and nerve cells is permeable to sodium (Levi and Ussing, 1948; Harris and Burn, 1949). Both Na$^+$ and K$^+$ are in a steady flux across these membranes. A comparison of the Na$^+$ and K$^+$ fluxes for frog sartorius muscle is given in Table 7-4.

The sodium distribution cannot be considered an equilibrium distribution, and, as with erythrocytes, an active pump using metabolic energy is hypothesized to account for the outward movement of Na$^+$ against its electrochemical gradient (Hodgkin and Keynes, 1955). The details of the mechanism by which ions are moved are not known, except that a carrier system coupled with ATP and a membrane ATPase are thought to be involved.

The ionic distributions of nerve and muscle are also affected by the presence of impermeable anions. Squid giant axons possess large quantities of the anion isothionate, $CH_2OHCH_2SO_3^-$, which has no known function other than to serve as an impermeable intracellular anion. Isothionate has not been found in other neurons. Other impermeable anions of the squid axon include various organic phosphates (ATP, ADP, and so forth) and amino acids. In many neurons high concentrations of glutamate and aspartate are found. In the next chapter it will be shown that they also serve as important agents in chemical transmission of impulses across some synapses. The nonpermeating anions of frog sartorius muscle include organic phosphates and amino acids. Phosphocreatine is in high concentration. In frog muscle there is also a significant

protein concentration. In no case, however, do the fixed charges of proteins contribute greatly to the anionic content of the cell (Conway, 1950). Although the elements of a Donnan equilibrium system are present in excitable cells, the rest potential is based upon ionic distributions maintained by active transport and is not a true Donnan equilibrium potential.

The energy which a cell must expend in pumping Na$^+$ out of the cell against its electrochemical gradient is an important aspect of the energy economy of the cell. Keynes and Maisel (1954) calculated the energy expenditure of frog sartorius muscle in transporting Na$^+$. They determined that about 15 per cent of the oxygen consumption of a noncontracting muscle was directed toward maintaining the sodium active transport. This assumed 100 per cent efficiency for the energy-coupling reactions—an unlikely situation. But even the use of 20 per cent of a cell's basal metabolic energy to maintain ionic distributions necessary for proper functioning cannot be considered extravagant.

Active transport of sodium in neurons was linked to metabolic energy-producing systems by the use of metabolic poisons that inhibit the transport process. Injections of high energy compounds such as ATP or arginine phosphate into invertebrate axons start the pump after such poisoning (Caldwell et al., 1960). Na-K-ATPases (those cellular ATPase whose activity requires proper concentrations of Na$^+$ and K$^+$) have been isolated from nerve cell membranes (Skou, 1964). The situation in muscle is more complex, in part because of the complex system of membranes associated with skeletal muscle (see Chapter 10) that makes measurements of ion movements more difficult than in nerve fibers, which are basically cylindrical structures bounded by a geometrically simple membrane. Even in muscle, however, it has been shown that the active extrusion of Na$^+$ is the mechanism responsible for maintaining ionic distributions (Conway et al., 1961; Dee and Kernan, 1963).

Most theories of ion movements through nerve and muscle membranes are based on the assumption of independent ionic fluxes, but this is not an accurate picture of the ion movements in these cells. It is not certain how much exchange diffusion occurs for individual ions. Part of the inward K$^+$ flux is linked with cellular metabolism and is coupled with the outward flux of Na$^+$ (Hodgkin and Keynes, 1955). A large part of ion movements in nerve cells is the result of passive diffusion of ions down their concentration gradients. For example, although Na$^+$ efflux is prevented by metabolic inhibitors, such drugs have no effect on passive Na$^+$ influx.

A final question concerns the ability of the sodium active transport process to separate charges, that is, can metabolic energy be used to generate an electrical potential by moving only Na$^+$? This type of electrogenic system would create a transmembrane potential which would cause K$^+$ and other diffusible ions to distribute themselves in such a way that their concentrations were in equilibrium with the potential across the membrane. If the outward movement of each Na$^+$ is accompanied by the movement of an anion, however, the process is electrically neutral. In the latter case any transmembrane potential is produced by the accumulation of K$^+$ inside the cell and by the differences in permeability of the membrane to K$^+$ and Na$^+$. In squid giant axons, inactivation of the sodium pump by metabolic inhibitors does not alter the resting potential, except for a very slow decline that results from the unchecked passive influx of Na$^+$ and the passive efflux of K$^+$. Nor is the rate of Na$^+$ efflux effected by altering artificially the transmembrane potential. This indicates that the active transport of Na$^+$ in squid nerve is not electrogenic. But in frog nerve it has been found that the uphill movement of Na$^+$ causes an increase in the transmembrane potential when such movement is experimentally caused to proceed at very high rates (Connelly, 1959). Therefore, the question of active transport electrogenic activity is not settled and may well depend on the particular preparation under study.

7-11. Electrical Characteristics of Cells. Before proceding further with the discussion of resting and other potentials of excitable cells, a few definitions and descriptions of important electrical parameters require discussion. Electrical **resistance** is a basic property of materials and is the tendency to prevent the flow of electrons or ions. Materials of high resistance are insulators; those of low resistance are conductors. The reciprocal of resistance is the **conductance**—the ability of a material to conduct electrons or ions.

Electrical **current** is the quantity of electrons or ions flowing through a conductor in a given time, and the electrical **voltage** is the driving force providing the energy for the current flow. The relationship between current, resistance, and voltage in at least simpler electrical circuits is given by one expression of Ohm's law:

$$I \text{ (current)} = \frac{E \text{ (voltage)}}{R \text{ (resistance)}} \qquad (7.1)$$

The unit of resistance is the "ohm" (Ω), and conductance has the reciprocal unit "mho" (ohm spelled backward).

When a layer of poorly conducting (dielectric) material is sandwiched between two layers of a highly conducting material, a capacitor is formed. A capacitor can store charge when a potential difference is applied across the two outer plates. Capacitance is the ability to store charge and a capacitance of 1 farad will store 1 coulomb of charge when 1 volt is placed across it. A coulomb is the number of electrons required to neutralize the ions of 1 mole of a univalent metal. Since this is an extremely large quantity, the farad represents a large quantity of capacitance. Therefore capacitance is usually expressed in microfarads (1 μf $= 10^{-6}$ farads) or in picofarads (1 pf $= 10^{-12}$ farads; "pf" is

Table 7-5 Electrical Constants of Some Nerve and Muscle Fibers*

PREPARATION	FIBER DIAMETER (μ)	R_m (ohm-cm^2)	R_i (ohm-cm)	R_o (ohm-cm)	C_m (μF/cm^2)	τ (msec)	λ (mm)
Squid (*Loligo*) giant axon	500	700	30	22	1.1	0.7	2.5
Cuttlefish (*Sepia*) giant axon	200	9,000	30	22	1.2	6.2	2.5
Lobster (*Homarus*) leg nerve	75	2,290	60	22	1.3	2.3	1.6
Frog (*Rana*) sartorius muscle	75	4,000	200	87	2.5	10	0.7

* Data from Prosser and Brown (1961); Falk and Fatt (1964).

pronounced as "puffs"). The capacity of a system depends on the thickness, surface area, and dielectric constant of the nonconducting material.

These various electrical characteristics are of interest because a cell membrane can be modeled as a layer of highly resistive material placed between two conducting layers (the extracellular and intracellular electrolyte-containing fluids). The cytoplasm has a slightly higher electrical resistance than the external medium, but the membrane resistance is much greater than either. The thin bimolecular leaflet of lipid is the source of the high electrical resistance in membranes (Cole, 1940; Katz, 1948; Falk and Fatt, 1964). These references describe the methods used to measure membrane capacitance.

The values of some electrical constants of some membranes are given in Table 7-5. Note that although the membrane is very thin, less than 100 Å, it has a high resistance (R_m) compared with the resistance of the extracellular medium (R_o) or the intracellular resistance (R_i). The membrane also has a high capacitance (C_m). The high resistance of the membrane is another indication of the relatively low permeability to ions. Muscle presents a special problem because of a series of membranous invaginations running transversely to the long axis of the fiber. The capacitance value given in the table is probably that of the surface membrane.

The characteristics of a capacitor lend important properties to biological membranes (as well as to electronic circuits used to measure electrical potentials and currents). When a capacitor is connected to a voltage source through a resistance (Figure 7-10a), time is required for current to flow through the resistance and charge the capacitor. As the capacitor charges, more and more of the applied voltage appears across the plates of the capacitor and less across the resistance, therefore, the current flow through the resistor decreases with time as does the rate of capacitor charging (Figure 7-10b). Note that current does not flow through a capacitor, the applied voltage establishes a charge across the capacitor. Capacitance, thus, has time effects on an electrical system. The **time constant** τ, of a capacitor is the time (in milliseconds) required to charge the capacitor to about 63 per cent of its maximum. The time constant is related to the resistance and capacitance of an electrical circuit by

$$\tau = RC \qquad (7.2)$$

Time constants (and space constants) are important factors in the behavior of excitable cells, and they will be further discussed after the nature of the action potential has been described.

Although the relatively high capacitance of biological membranes is an indication of their low permeability to ions, the physiological membrane shows a selectivity with respect to the rates of passage of various ions. The transmembrane flux of ions depends both on chemical concentration gradients and on the electrical potential differences across the

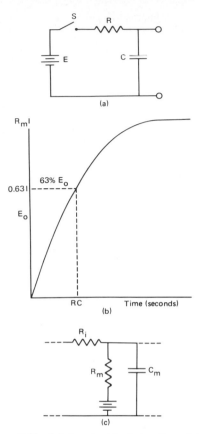

Figure 7-10 (a) An electrical circuit containing resistance, R, and capacitance, C. When the switch, S, is closed, the voltage applied to the circuit changes suddenly from zero to the value E. At this instant the voltage at the capacitor end of R is zero and the full voltage E is applied across R. As current flows through the resistance, the capacitor charges, and the voltage at the capacitor end of R increases. This lowers the voltage drop across R, and the current through it decreases. The result is a decrease in the rate of charging of C with time. The relationship between capacitor voltage, E_0 and the time, t, for its buildup is $E_0 = Ee^{t/RC}$. The time constant, τ, is equal to RC. (b) The graphic expression of the relation between the voltage across C and the time. (c) The electrical model of a membrane can be considered as series of RC elements. The time constant RC is the time in seconds required to charge a capacitor to $0.63\ E_0$.

membrane. Ion flux is therefore expressed as the product of a permeability factor and an electrical potential factor. The relationship is in a form of Ohm's law:

$$I = \left(\frac{1}{R}\right) E = gE = JzF \qquad (7.3)$$

where g, the ionic conductance, is the reciprocal of the resistance to ion movement and has the units of mhos. As previously defined J is the ion flux; z the ion valence: and F the Faraday. The conductance is a measure of the ease with which ions pass through the membrane under the influence of electrical forces and chemical concentration differences. Membrane permeability in most cases is synonomous with membrane conductance because rapid changes of one are accompanied by rapid similar changes in the other (Katz, 1966).

The electrochemical potential of a membrane system can be defined by

$$\Delta\mu_a = z_a F \left(E_m - \frac{RT}{zF} \log_e \frac{[a]_o}{[a]_i}\right) \qquad (7.4)$$

where a refers to any ion in the system. Substituting from the Nernst equation (Equation 6.28):

$$\Delta\mu_a = z_a F\ (E_m - E_a) \qquad (7.5)$$

E_m is the transmembrane potential, and E_a is the equilibrium potential of the ion, a.

Substituting into Equation 7.3 gives

$$I_a = z_a F = g_a\ (E_m - E_a) \qquad (7.6)$$

I_a is the current flow of the ionic species a. The ion current is zero when $E_m = E_a$. That is, at equilibrium, there is no net flow of ions across the membrane.

The Nernst equation applies only to the situation when an ion is in equilibrium across the membrane. It cannot apply to Na^+ or other ions that are not at equilibrium distribution. For the conditions when a cell is not in ionic equilibrium but in a steady state condition, another model has been developed to describe the transmembrane potential. The **constant field hypothesis** (Goldman, 1943; Hodgkin and Katz, 1949) is based on the following assumptions:

1. The electrical field is constant everywhere in the membrane (in an earlier model for liquid junction potentials derived by Plank, it was assumed that the electrical field decreased logarithmically with distance into the boundary or membrane).

2. The membrane is homogeneous.
3. The movements of different ionic species are independent.
4. Ion movements through the membrane are due to diffusion.
5. In most cases ions have a lesser solubility in the membrane than in aqueous solution, therefore permeability constants are used which take into account the partition coefficients of ions.

Considering that only K^+, Na^+, and Cl^- ions are present, the constant field equation (sometimes called the Goldman, the Goldman-Hodgkin-Katz, or GHK equation) is

$$E_m = \frac{RT}{z} \ln \left(\frac{P_K[K]_i + P_{Na}[Na]_i + P_{Cl}[Cl]_o}{P_K[K]_o + P_{Na}[Na]_o + P_{Cl}[Cl]_i} \right)$$
(7.7)

Potassium permeability is often used as a standard reference, with P then representing the relative permeabilities of other ions (Hodgkin, 1958; Harris and Martins-Ferreira, 1955).

When ions are moving in an electrical field, the ion fluxes are determined by multiplying the concentration of the ion by a factor representing the effect of the electrical field. From constant field assumptions this factor is $(EF/RT)/1 - \exp [-EF/RT]$. According to Katz (1966) this factor is 3.7 for inward movements of Na^+ and K^+ and is 0.102 for the outward movement of these ions. From this information and the values of influx and efflux (for example, those of Table 7-4), it is possible to determine Na^+ and K^+ permeability coefficients by relationships of the form

$$P_a = \frac{\text{efflux}_a}{[a]_i \text{ (factor)}}$$
(7.8a)

$$P_a = \frac{\text{influx}_a}{[a]_o \text{ (factor)}}$$
(7.8b)

Comparison of the permeability coefficients for K^+, calculated from both influx and efflux data for frog skeletal muscle, show that they agree closely: 6.2×10^{-7} and 5.8×10^{-7}, respectively. Na^+ permeability, which can be determined only from passive influx data because Na^+ efflux is by active transport, is about 7.9×10^{-9} cm/sec. Thus muscle membrane is about 75 times more permeable to K^+ than to Na^+ under resting conditions.

From the values of permeability coefficients obtained in this manner, the ratios of permeabilities needed for Equation 7.7 can be obtained. These results are from tracer studies and substantiate the conclusions reached on the basis of electrical measurements; therefore, the model and its assumptions are not far wrong. But the assumptions of the constant field hypothesis are certainly oversimplified. For example, in both muscle and nerve it has been shown that ion movements are not independent. In the giant fiber of the squid there is an interference between the inward and outward movements of K^+, and it is assumed that K^+ ions must move through narrow channels in single file. Similar results have been found for Na^+ channels in lobster nerve (Moore et al., 1967).

Most models for ion movements through membranes assume some type of narrow pore in the membrane perpendicular to the length of the membrane. Such pores are still hypothetical, and it is not known how ions actually move through membranes. By measuring the size of molecules that can pass through a membrane and by measuring the fluxes of THO and other tracers, it is possible to calculate the equivalent pore size (or apparent pore radius), that is, the hypothetical maximum size of pore which would fit with the observed sizes and fluxes of materials penetrating a membrane. Pores, if present, would have to be about 7 Å in diameter (Goldstein and Solomon 1960; Hays and Leaf, 1962; Pappenheimer et al., 1951; Staverman, 1951).

It is usually assumed that the physiological membrane is identical with the unit membrane observed in the electron microscope. However, there is no direct evidence that this is so, and it is possible that only a part, and perhaps an unobservable part, of the unit membrane is acting as the physiological surface barrier.

7-12. Note on Electrical Conventions. It is the usual convention to take the potential of the inside of the membrane relative to the outside as the transmembrane potential. The presence of a potential difference across the membrane leads us to say that the membrane is polarized. Increasing the potential difference across the membrane, either by making the inside more negative, the outside more positive, or both, leads to the condition of hyperpolarization. The membrane potential becomes greater numerically, that is, more negative. When the membrane potential is lowered, that is, becomes less numerically or approaches closer to zero, the membrane is depolarized. Such depolarization can result from increasing the internal potential, that is, making it less negative, from decreasing the positivity of the outside, or both.

Often potentials are given amplitude without regard to their electrical sign. The statement that the resting potential is below the potassium equilibrium potential means that the value of the former (say -70 mV) is numerically smaller than that of the latter (say -75 mV). But as far as relative levels of potential, the resting potential is 5 mV less negative, that is, it is above the potassium equilibrium potential.

Electrical current is considered to move in the direction that positive charges would take. Therefore, an inward flow of current may represent either positive charges moving into the cell or negative charges moving out of the cell. In considering electron currents, the direction of current movement is opposite to that of actual electron movement because electrons are negatively charged. Inward flow of positive ions, or outward flow of negative ions, tends to depolarize the membrane from its resting potential level.

In recording potential changes, it is usual to have depolarizations from the resting potential deflect upward. In recording current flows a downward deflection indicates inward current flow, whereas upward deflections represent outward current flows.

Bioelectric Potentials: The Conducted Action Potential

7-13. Stimulation and Recording. The resting potential, as previously defined, is the transmembrane potential of the unstimulated excitable cell and is a potential dependent on the K^+ distribution. Excitable cells upon adequate stimulation produce a potential change—the action potential (also termed the spike or nerve or muscle impulse)—which is conducted along

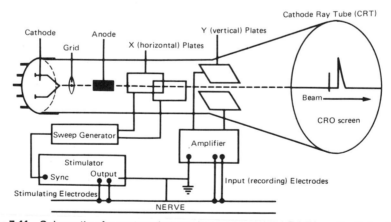

Figure 7-11 Schematic of a system that can be used to measure nerve potentials. A nerve is placed in a small chamber containing a small pool of physiological solution. By closing the chamber, the nerve is suspended in a water-saturated atmosphere that keeps it moist and viable. The nerve is laid across platinum recording and stimulating electrodes. Stimuli are applied through the electronic square wave stimulator while potential changes picked up by the recording electrodes are sent into an amplifier before being displayed on the face of the cathode ray oscilloscope.

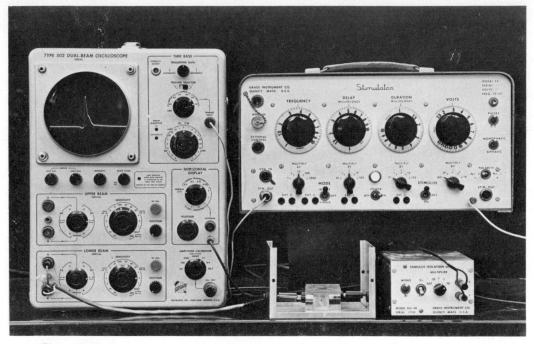

Figure 7-12 Instrumentation for measuring action potentials of nerves such as the frog sciatic. A nerve is in place in the moist chamber and its compound action potential is displaced on the face of the oscilloscope. Compare with Figure 7-11.

the axonal region of a neuron or along the muscle plasma membrane.

Action potentials are very rapid changes in the transmembrane potential, lasting only a few thousandths of a second, and it was not until the development of the cathode ray oscilloscope that these potential changes could be readily measured. The cathode ray oscilloscope has the advantage over other electrical measuring instruments of using an electron beam that has no inertia and that is, therefore, capable of following accurately the extremely rapid potential changes found in excitable cells. A typical system for measuring bioelectrical potentials is shown schematically in Figure 7-11. The oscilloscope contains a cathode ray tube in which a beam of electrons is generated by a cathode. The beam is accelerated toward the front of the tube by the anode or gun. The face of the tube is coated with a phosphor that phosphoresces upon impact of the electrons. A pair of metal plates—the vertical plates—lie above and below the path of the electron beam. Potential differences placed

across this pair of plates will cause a deflection of the beam of negatively charged electrons. Because the strength of the potential required to deflect the beam is much higher than that of ordinary bioelectric potentials, the oscilloscope contains a vertical amplifier that electronically increases the strength of the incoming signal. Ordinarily input signals are applied to the vertical amplifier input connections.

Because it is usually necessary, or at least desirable, to determine the time course of biological potentials, the oscilloscope has arrangements for producing a horizontal time base. The oscilloscope tube contains a pair of horizontal plates on either side of the tube and a sweep circuit that produces a rapidly rising potential difference across these plates. This potential causes the electron beam to move horizontally across the face of the tube. The rate of rise of the sweep potential is variable, and this rate of rise determines how fast the electron beam moves horizontally. Once the beam has reached the far right of the tube, the sweep potential falls rapidly and drives the electron beam back to the starting left edge of the tube. This operation can be adjusted to occur as many times a second as desired by the investigator. Details of oscilloscope circuitry and operation, as well as discussions of bioelectric potential measurements, are found in Donaldson (1958); Burés et al. (1962); and Whitfield (1959).

Although excitable cells may be stimulated by heat, chemical, physical, or physicochemical stimuli, the physiologist in the laboratory ordinarily uses electrical stimulation because electrical currents and potentials are not normally harmful to cells. Also the parameters of electrical stimulation, for example, the strength, duration, frequency, and shape of the stimulus, are easily controlled by modern electronic stimulators. A typical stimulus used for many biological studies with excitable cells is a brief square wave of electrical current (see Figure 1-3). In many cases such stimuli can be applied through small platinum wire electrodes; in other cases they are delivered to the tissue through Ag-AgCl or saturated KCl electrodes. Figure 7-12 shows a typical system used to stimulate and record the potentials of nerves such as the sciatic of the frog.

7-14. Biphasic and Monophasic Action Potentials. The nature of the recorded action potential depends upon the positioning of the recording and stimulating electrodes and upon the type and condition of the preparation used. Early investigators used two recording electrodes placed on the outside of a nerve (Figure 7-13). The application of an adequate stimulus resulted in a wave of electrical activity passing along the nerve. This activity was recorded as a biphasic action potential. Each point reached by the potential becomes electrically negative with respect to the regions on either side. Each part of the nerve also recovers almost immediately and regains its normal resting potential.

Initially, before the stimulation of the nerve, no potential difference is recorded between the electrodes (Figure 7-13a). After stimulation, the action potential passes along the nerve until it reaches the first electrode (elec-

trode 1, Figure 7-13b). This electrode becomes negative with respect to the second (2) electrode. According to physiological convention such negativity of the first or reference electrode is shown as an upward deflection on the oscilloscope. As the action potential travels further along the nerve, the membrane under electrode 1 recovers and regains its normal resting potential. At this time no difference of potential is recorded between the electrodes (Figure 7-13c). When the action potential reaches electrode 2, the membrane under this electrode becomes negative with respect to that under electrode 1, and the wave of the action potential is recorded again. Because of the arrangement of inputs to the oscilloscope, this second wave appears as a downward deflection (electrode 1 is now

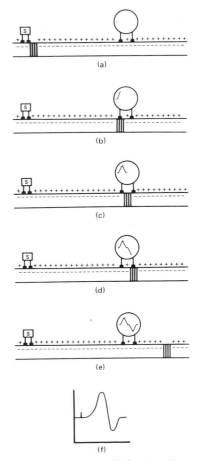

Figure 7-13 Recording a biphasic action potential. For description see text.

positive with respect to electrode 2, Figure 7-13d). Once the potential of the membrane under electrode 2 has been restored to the normal resting potential, again no potential difference between the electrodes is seen.

The shape of the recorded potentials will depend on the distance between the two recording electrodes and the rate of conduction of the action potential along the nerve. Because many nerves are short, it is impossible to achieve a sufficient separation of the recording electrodes so that the two waves are separated (see Figure 7-13f). Therefore, accurate measurement and observation of the details of the action potential is not feasible.

By the simple expedient of crushing or otherwise damaging the nerve under one electrode, a monophasic action potential can be recorded (Figure 7-14). In this case, the membrane under one electrode is damaged and cannot conduct an action potential; this electrode remains over inert tissue and serves only as a reference point.

In each of these two cases the absolute values of the transmembrane potential are not recorded—only relative potential changes between the two electrodes. Note that in the arrangement for recording a biphasic action potential, the initial potential difference between the electrodes is zero; the action potential rises to a peak and then falls. In recording the monophasic action potential with external electrodes, initially there is a difference of potential between the two electrodes—the injury potential—and the action potential seems to fall to zero and then return to the injury potential base line.

Bernstein's classical hypothesis of nerve activity assumed that initially the membrane is permeable only to K^+. He considered the action potential was the result of a stimulus opening up the membrane so that it became permeable to all ions. Under these conditions the transmembrane potential would fall to zero.

However, Hodgkin and Huxley (1939) and Curtis and Cole (1940, 1942), using single giant axons from the squid with one wire electrode inside and another electrode outside the axon, showed that during the course of the

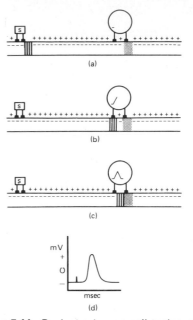

Figure 7-14 By destroying a small region of the nerve membrane (shaded area) the same experimental method used in Figure 7-13 produces a monophasic action potential. (a) Before stimulation an injury potential is recorded (not zero potential). (b) As impulse reaches active electrode a change in potential is recorded—membrane potential falls to zero and then returns to injury level as impulse passes beyond active electrode (c). Form of the monophasic action potential shown in (d).

action potential there was a transient reversal of polarization with the inside of the cell becoming positive with respect to the outside (Figure 7-15). This reversal of polarization, not simply a depolarization to zero potential, required some alteration of Bernstein's ideas. The nature of the ion movements and permeability changes underlying the action potential were brought to light with the use of the voltage clamp technique.

7-15. The Voltage Clamp Method. The activities of the membrane associated with the development of an action potential and its conduction along the excitable fiber cannot at this time be described in terms of molecular events occurring in the membrane. Although tracer studies, using ions, allow measurement of ionic fluxes in the resting cell and although

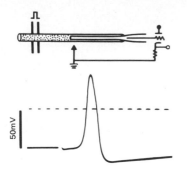

Figure 7-15 (Upper) Schematic outline of recording arrangement with squid giant axon. Wire electrode is inserted into axon, second recording electrode is in external medium. Square wave impulses delivered to axon from a pair of stimulating electrodes. (Lower) Initially the resting potential is measured and following stimulation a monophasic action potential is recorded. Time marks (1 msec) are set at zero potential level. Note that potential falls to zero level and then reverses polarity. [After I. Tasaki, 1959.]

experimental alterations of the ionic composition of the external and, in some cases, the internal media permit an analysis of some of the permeability properties of the membrane and of the basic ionic requirements for action potentials, the analysis of the ionic and potential changes during activity are extremely difficult to measure because the action potential is a transient and extremely rapid event.

The voltage clamp technique was developed as a means of measuring membrane currents and ionic events underlying the activity of excitable cells. It was introduced by Cole (1949) and Hodgkin et al. (1952); and was perfected by Hodgkin and Huxley (1952a, b, c, d). Discussions of the method and its results are found in monographs by Hodgkin (1964) and Katz (1966) as well as in Ruch et al. (1965); Moore and Cole (1963). According to the latter authors the definition of the method should be that an axon held under voltage clamp conditions has a transmembrane potential that at all times has a known and controlled value. The method allows measurements of membrane currents while the transmembrane potential is held constant at any desired level.

When an action potential is conducted along an axon, the internal potential varies with time and distance, and time-variant currents flow through the internal, external, and membrane substances. According to the cable model of the axon (Section 7-19; Figure 7-22) these currents flow through a large number of resistances and capacitances, and

the mathematical analysis of such a situation is impossibly complex.

In the voltage clamp method, as used with long axons, a long wire electrode is inserted inside the giant axon. This electrode acts to electrically connect all internal parts of the fiber and prevents current flow along the fiber. Conduction is effectively prevented and the nerve can be treated as an isolated region of membrane instead of as a conducting cable. An electronic feedback system is used to automatically supply the current required to hold the transmembrane potential at any desired level. A highly schematic and simplified sketch of a voltage clamp system is shown and described in Figure 7-16. The ability to control the transmembrane potential now permits detailed quantitative analysis of the time and voltage dependencies of the ionic conductances.

7-16. Sodium and Potassium Ionic Currents. If, under voltage clamp conditions, the membrane potential of a squid giant axon is suddenly reduced to zero, that is, the membrane is suddenly and completely depolarized, a flow of current is seen which consists of three components (Figure 7-17a).

First, there is an initial and extremely brief outward surge of current (in voltage clamp records a downward deflection indicates inward current flow; upward deflections represent outward current flow). This initial outward surge of current is due to the discharge of the membrane capacitance, that is, as the membrane is suddenly depolarized, the charge

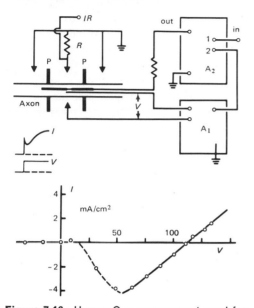

Figure 7-16 Upper: One arrangement used for clamping the membrane potential of a squid giant axon along rectangular time courses. A_1 is a low-gain differential amplifier; A_2 is a high-gain differential amplifier. The axon is placed across three pools of sea water separated by two narrow partitions, P, (vasoline, plastic, or other seals are used as insulators). A pair of metal wire electrodes are placed intracellularly; one is used to measure the transmembrane potential, V; the other is used to pass currents through the membrane. The two lateral pools are grounded. The middle pool is also grounded through a low-value resistance, R. A current, I, passes through R and through the axon membrane in the middle pool when a current is applied to the long internal electrode. The small potential drop $(=IR)$ across the resistance is amplified and is a measure of the membrane current. The two amplifiers and other circuitry are arranged in a feedback system so that the transmembrane potential can be held at any desired level by automatic adjustments in the current passing through the membrane. Lower: Relation between the membrane depolarization and the membrane current at the peak of the inward current surge. The insert shows that when a voltage is suddenly applied to the membrane there are both inward and outward surges of current (see text). [Redrawn by permission from I. Tasaki (1959) "Conduction of the nerve impulse" in *Handbook of Physiology*, Sect. 1, "Neurophysiology," Vol. 1, pp. 75–121. American Physiological Society, Washington, D.C.]

held by the membrane is lost. The use of clamped voltage, rather than clamped current, is preferred in the first place because under conditions of constant voltage, the membrane capacitance can play no role in current movements. A capacitance can charge or discharge only when an applied potential is changing. Cole and Curtis (1939) had shown that the membrane capacitance did not change during activity.

The second component of the current flow is directed inward, which means that either cations are entering the cell or that anions are leaving the cell. The direction of this component does not follow Ohm's law relations because the positive current flow is into the axon, although the inside potential has been reduced from about -60 mV to zero mV.

Finally, the inward surge of current is followed by an outward current surge that continues to flow as long as the membrane potential is held constant. Tracer studies showed that this outward current flow is due to the movement of K^+. Since this occurs during the time when normally an axon would be returning from the peak of the action potential to the resting potential, the recovery phase of the action potential is attributed to outward K^+ movement.

The transient inward surge of current was shown to be due to Na^+ influx. It is to be noted that the inward current flow is not maintained as is the outward current surge. Therefore, time is not available to use tracer methods for analyzing the system to see which ion is moving. However, by depolarizing a membrane by various increments, a series of current records are obtained as shown in Figure 7-18. It can be seen that both inward and outward current sequences are found until at a displacement of the membrane potential somewhere between 104 and 117 mV (for the squid giant axon) the inward surge disappears and is replaced by an early outward current flow. The inward current changes to an outward current at a membrane potential equal to the calculated Na^+ equilibrium potential. This is proof that the inward current surge is due to Na^+. At membrane potentials above

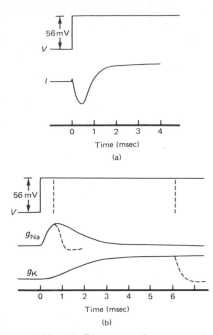

Figure 7-17 (a) Diagrammatic representation of the current flows through the squid axon as measured by the voltage clamp technique. Inward (downward deflections) and outward (upward deflections) current flows result when the membrane is suddenly depolarized by 56 mV and held at this level. The outward flow is due to K^+ movement; the inward flow is due to Na^+ movement. (b) Diagrams of the time course of Na^+ conductance (g_{Na}) and of K^+ conductance (g_K). The sodium conductance decreases if the potential is restored to its normal resting level (dotted lines indicate related potential and current changes). The sodium conductance also decreases if the applied potential is maintained, producing the phenomenon of "sodium inactivation." After the sodium conductance has been inactivated, the membrane must be repolarized for a few milliseconds before a second voltage pulse will be effective in increasing the sodium conductance. The curve of potassium conductance shows that it remains at its high level as long as the voltage pulse is applied and falls (dotted lines) if the potential is restored to its normal value. Both sodium inactivation and potassium decline follow an exponential time course. The curves shown are diagrammatic only, but illustrate the findings of Hodgkin and Huxley (1952a,b,c,d).

the Na^+ equilibrium potential, Na^+ would be expected to flow out of the axon. At a membrane potential displacement equal to the

Na^+ equilibrium potential, no current will flow, because by definition the equilibrium potential of an ion is that potential at which no net movement of the ion occurs. That Na^+ is responsible for the inward current surge can also be demonstrated by replacing the external Na^+ by choline or other cations. Under these conditions the current surge is reduced or lost (Figure 7-19). The inward movement of Na^+, which again is a transient event, is responsible for the rising phase of the action potential.

The amplitudes of the ionic currents depend on the amount of displacement of the membrane potential. As already stated a suddenly applied, constant depolarization produces an increased Na^+ conductance, but this conductance falls off rapidly although the depolarization is maintained. The drop in Na^+ conductance is called the **sodium inactivation**. In order to reactivate Na^+ conductance, the membrane must be repolarized briefly before a second depolarizing pulse is administered. The inactivation of the sodium conductance is responsible, at least in part, for the refractory period of the excitable cell—that period of time when a second stimulus following a previous stimulus can elicit no response of the cell. Under normal conditions the Na^+ conductance declines about ten times faster than does the K^+ conductance.

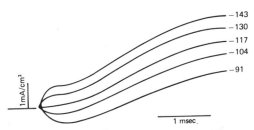

Figure 7-18 Membrane currents at different displacements of the membrane potential. Outward current flows are indicated by upward deflections. Between 104 and 117mV the inward current surge disappears and is replaced by an early outward current surge. This transition occurs at about the level of transmembrane potential equivalent to the Na^+ equilibrium potential. This is used as a proof that the inward current flow is due to the movement of Na^+. [Redrawn from the data of Hodgkin et al. (1952).]

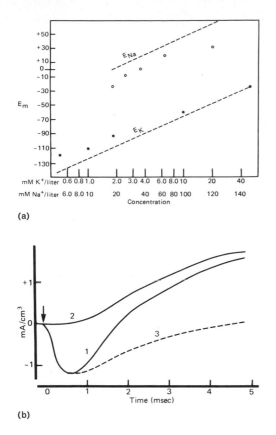

(a)

(b)

Figure 7-19 (a) Changes in the resting trans-membrane potential of frog sartorius muscle produced by alterations in external K^+ concentration (lower curve) and in the magnitude of the action potential produced by alterations of the external Na^+ concentration (upper curve). Points are experimentally measured potentials. The straight lines are plots of the equilibrium potentials of the two ions. At high values of external K^+, the transmembrane and equilibrium potentials change in a similar manner; at lower external K^+ concentrations (in the normal range) the equilibrium potential for K^+ changes more rapidly than does the transmembrane potential. [K^+ data from Adrian (1956); Na^+ data from Nastuk and Hodgkin (1950).] (b) Separation of the squid axon membrane current flows into their separate components by the replacement of the external Na^+ by choline (which is relatively incapable of passing through the membrane yet provides a normal concentration of external cations). Curve 1: normal currents found when nerve is placed in sea water. Curve 2: current recorded when choline replaces external Na^+. Curve 3: difference between curves 1 and 2 yields the Na^+ current. [From the data of Hodgkin and Huxley (1952a).]

Voltage clamp records show no signs of threshold phenomena. The Na^+ and K^+ conductance changes are graded responses as the amount of depolarization is altered. But the excitable cell exhibits a threshold depolarization that must be reached before the inward current surge becomes regenerative and leads to an action potential. In the normal excitable cell there is an antagonism between the inward Na^+ conductance and the outward K^+ conductance, and not until a sufficient depolarization has been reached does the Na^+ conductance become greater than the K^+ conductance. As the Na^+ conductance brings the transmembrane potential closer to the Na^+ equilibrium potential, the increasing K^+ conductance initiates a return to the resting level of potential. The Na^+ conductance can only decrease.

7-17. Action Potentials Recorded from Single Cells. When detailed analyses are to be made of action potentials, the use of micro-electrodes with single fibers or the use of giant axon preparations is required. In this section I shall summarize the results of voltage clamp techniques and tracer studies with respect to the various phases of the action potential.

Figure 7-15b shows the form of the action potential recorded by an intracellular glass micropipet from squid giant fiber. A major feature of this potential is the **overshoot** of the spike. During the action potential, the membrane does not simply depolarize to zero, but there is a transient reversal of polarity with the inside of the membrane becoming positive with respect to the outside.

Adequate stimulation of the axon results in a depolarization of the membrane, which in turn causes an increase in the inward Na^+ conductance. At a given level of membrane depolarization (about 15 per cent of the resting potential), the membrane becomes highly permeable to Na^+, which flows into the cell. The inward movement of Na^+ causes the transmembrane potential to fall rapidly toward zero potential. Na^+ has become the major diffusible ion, and the membrane potential tends to arrive at the Na^+ equilibrium potential, which for the squid axon is about +55 mV (Table 7-3). Thus the rising phase of the action potential overshoots the zero potential level, and the membrane potential reverses sign.

At the peak of the spike there is initiated another change in membrane permeability and an increased K^+ conductance results. The K^+ efflux down its concentration gradient tends to bring the transmembrane potential back to the value of the K^+ equilibrium potential (ca. -75 mV). As the K^+ conductance has increased, the Na^+ conductance has been inactivated as described in the previous section.

Following the rapid spike phase of the action potential, there is an exponential return to the resting level of membrane potential. In some nerves after-potentials are seen during the recovery period. The negative after-potential is a period when the rate of change of potential toward the resting level slows; the positive after-potential (seen in Figure 7-15) is a phase during which the potential falls slightly below the resting potential level and then rises. The K^+ and Na^+ active transport processes may play some role in producing these potentials as these active mechanisms operate to restore Na^+ to the outside and K^+ to the inside of the cell. But the more likely source for these potentials is the high K^+ conductance that is still in effect during this period.

It is not known what structural alterations or events occur in the membrane to bring about the specific increases and then decreases in ionic permeabilities. These activities are dependent on the value of the transmembrane potential, but the relationship at a mechanistic level is unknown.

The amount of Na^+ that must enter the axon during the rising phase of the spike represents the electrochemical equivalent of the coulombs needed to displace the transmembrane potential from its resting level to that of the peak of the spike. Similarly, the amount of K^+ leaving the axon during the falling phase of the action potential represents the number of coulombs required to bring the potential back to the resting level. The entry of 4 pmole of Na^+ across one square centimeter of membrane surface adequately accounts for the observed peak of the action potential (compare the measured ion movements given in Table 7-6 with the quantities calculated from the electrical properties of the membrane in the last columns of the table).

The amount of charge needed to change the voltage across a one-microfarad capacitor by 120 mV is 0.12×10^{-6} coulombs. This is equivalent to 1.2×10^{-12} mole of univalent cation. There is, obviously, more than enough Na^+ and K^+ movement to cause the observed potential changes. Part of the excess movement is accounted for by the fact that during the falling phase of the action potential there is an exchange of Na^+ and K^+ when the permeabilities of both ions are still higher than normal.

The quantity of ions moving during a single impulse is very small compared with the total ionic concentrations of the axoplasm and the external medium. For example, the outward movement of 4 pmole of K^+ represents the loss of only about one-millionth of the total internal K^+. Theoretically an axon could discharge about 5×10^5 impulses before requiring the recharging of the K^+ battery by active transport.

In order to portray accurately what is occurring with respect to ion movements during an impulse, tracer studies must be used to measure both influx and efflux of ions. In *Sepia* axons, for example, the Na^+ influx is about 10.3 pmole/cm², and the Na^+ efflux is about 6.6 pmole/cm². The net movement of Na^+ during the action potential is, therefore, an influx of about 3.7 pmole/cm² (Keynes, 1951). The calculations shown in Table 7-6 were made assuming a transmembrane potential, V, of 120 mV (this is the total change in potential during the impulse). The capacities were taken to be 1 μF for unmyelinated axons and 13 pF for myelinated axons.

The Hodgkin-Huxley hypothesis that the action potential depends on specific movements of Na^+ and K^+ because of specific changes in membrane permeability is often referred to as the **sodium-potassium form of the membrane theory**. Although the results of

Table 7-6   Net Movements of Na$^+$ and K$^+$ Associated with a Single Impulse*

PREPARATION	FIBER DIAMETER (μ)	TEMP. (°C)	Na$^+$ ENTRY (pmole/cm^2)‡	K$^+$ LOSS (pmole/cm^2)‡	CV/F† (pmole/cm^2)‡
Crab (*Carcinus*) axon	30	17	—	2	1.2
Cuttlefish (*Sepia*) axon	200	17	3–4	3–4	1.2
Squid (*Loligo*) axon	500	20	3–4	3–4	1.2
	500	6	—	9	1.2
Frog (*Rana*) myelinated nerve	10	20	5×10^{-5}	4.5×10^{-5}	1.6×10^{-5}

* Data from Hodgkin (1964a).
† The product of the capacitance, C, and the voltage, V, of a system, divided by the Faraday constant, F, gives the amount of ions moved in the system.
‡ 1 pmole $= 10^{-12}$ mole $= 6 \times 10^{11}$ ions.

experiments on squid giant fibers may apply to many excitable cells—the hypothesis has been successfully applied to frog ventricular muscle (Brady and Woodbury, 1960) and to the nodes of myelinated neurons (see Section 7-25) —there are some excitable cells which show differences. For example, Hagiwara and Takahashi (1967) found that the resting potentials of skeletal muscle fibers from salt water elasmobranchs are dependent on Cl$^-$, not K$^+$. The resting potentials of marine teleosts are K$^+$-dependent as are most excitable cells so far examined. The spike potentials of marine elasmobranch skeletal muscle fibers show considerable overshoot; spikes from muscle fibers of marine teleosts show none. The relative importance of Cl$^-$ and K$^+$ in muscles is still not clear.

7-18. Perfused Axons.   If the resting potential of excitable cells is based on the K$^+$ concentration gradient across the membrane, varying the external concentration of K$^+$ should result in potential changes predictable by the Nernst equation.

At higher concentrations, the effects of varying [K$^+$]$_o$ accord well with theory, but at lower concentrations, the potential does not fall as rapidly as predicted. Part of this discrepancy is due to K$^+$ not being the only diffusible ion in the system. In muscle, for example, the resting potential appears to be based on both K$^+$ and Cl$^-$ distribution. Furthermore, the K$^+$ permeability itself changes with changing transmembrane potential, decreasing with increasing potential. At high [K$^+$]$_o$ the membrane is depolarized and K$^+$ permeability is high. Since the transmembrane potential depends on the K$^+$/Na$^+$ permeability ratios, the Nernst equation fails as K$^+$ permeability falls (Stämpfli, 1959; Baker et al., 1962; Hodgkin, 1964).

If Na$^+$ in the external medium is replaced with some inert cation such as choline or with a nonelectrolyte such as sucrose, little change is found in the resting potential level. But decreasing Na$^+$ concentration externally results in a decreased amplitude of the action potential upon stimulation. This is further proof that Na$^+$ is the ion responsible for the generation of the spike of the action potential.

Although it is relatively easy to alter the external medium of a cell, experimental difficulties are normally experienced when it is desired to replace or alter the internal ions in axons or muscle fibers. Baker and Shaw (1961); Baker et al. (1961, 1962); Oikawa et al. (1961) developed methods for squeezing out the axoplasm of giant fibers of the squid and replacing it with perfusion fluids of desired composition. Axoplasm may be extruded from the cut end of an axon by stroking it with a

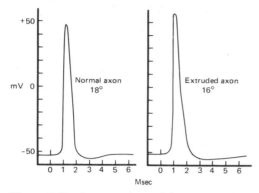

Figure 7-20 A comparison of the action potentials produced by normal and extruded axons of the squid shows that extrusion does not significantly alter the properties of the membrane with respect to action potential generation. The extruded axon was filled with potassium sulfate solution and potentials were measured by means of an intracellular electrode. [From data of Baker et al. (1961).]

glass rod or by using a miniature glass roller. During the firm squeezing required to remove the axoplasm it has been found that the membrane is not damaged, at least as evidenced by the ability to produce a normal action potential (Figure 7-20).

The emptied membrane may be filled with various solutions and their effects on the action potential tested. Internal solutions isosmotic with normal axoplasm and containing K^+ permit the production of normal action potentials upon stimulation of the membrane. The nature of the anions present seems unimportant. Both KCl and K-isethionate solutions allow the production of similar action potentials. This points out that the isethionate is not playing a direct role in excitation. Replacing internal K^+ with Na^+ blocks the action potential. This effect is reversible if Na^+ is not left inside the membrane for too long a period.

Although extrusion and perfusion remove more than 99 per cent of the axoplasm, fibers remained excitable for several hours and conducted large numbers of normal-appearing action potentials. Evidence of this nature seems to disprove the cytoplasmic adsorption theory of Ling and others (see Section 6-15)

because only the membrane is left to serve as a source of impulse generation and conduction.

The resting potential disappears in the perfused axon if the internal K^+ concentration is made equal to the external K^+ concentration. Cl^- concentration has no effect on the resting potential of squid nerve fibers.

7-19. Characteristics of Excitation. As already stated the production of an action potential requires an adequate or threshold stimulus that can alter the resting potential in such a way as to cause depolarization of the membrane. As a general rule, if a stimulus can depolarize the membrane of an excitable cell by about 15 per cent, a transient change in permeability to Na^+ occurs and the Na^+ influx results in the rising phase of the spike and a transient reversal of membrane polarization.

Initial depolarization of the membrane is accompanied by **local currents** and **local potentials** that are endogenic potentials (see Figure 7-4) of graded intensity and decremental spread. The presence of such local currents has led to the cable or core conductor model of excitable cells. The cell is pictured as an elongated cylinder filled with a conducting axoplasm or sarcoplasm, which is separated from the exterior conducting medium by an

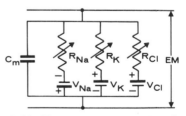

Figure 7-21 Electrical circuit model of an excitable membrane. The variable resistances, R, represent the changing ionic conductances of the membrane. The potential sources (or batteries), EM, represent the concentrations of major ions. C_m is the membrane capacitance. A membrane is assumed to be composed of a series of such resistance-capacitance elements. The model as shown is for a squid giant axon. In other excitable cells the major ions or the particular ionic conductances of the membrane may differ.

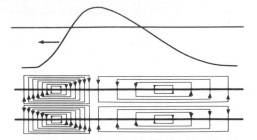

Figure 7-22 Schematic representation of the relation between the action potential development along an axon and the resultant flows of electrical current through the axon cylinder, the external medium, and across the membrane. Current density is greatest at that region of the membrane, where the spike is developing. The outward flow of current at points removed from the actual site of the spike is responsible for the conduction of the action potential because the effect of outward current flows is to cause the Na^+ conductance changes that lead to depolarization of the membrane. If such current flow is great enough, the Na^+ conductance reaches the irreversible level at which the events leading to the action potential cannot be stopped.

insulating membrane. The membrane is considered to impose a capacitance on the system, so that an excitable cell behaves like a capacitor capable of being charged on the application of a potential difference across the membrane. Since some current does flow through the membrane in the resting condition, it must be considered as a leaky capacitor.

The excitable cell can be modeled by an electrical circuit (Figure 7-21). The R's represent the resistance channels for Na^+, K^+, and Cl^- and are equivalent to the permeabilities of these ions. A battery is indicated, representing the voltage sources, EM, that serve to maintain the charge across the membrane. These are equivalent to the equilibrium potentials of the ions and therefore the concentration differences of each ion across the membrane. The Cl^- battery is usually considered to be kept charged by a Donnan distribution (again, using this term with the realization that Na^+ active transport is responsible for maintaining the system). Keynes (1963) has presented evidence that in muscle Cl^- is also actively transported. The K^+ battery is charged indirectly by the activity of the Na^+

pump and by exchange diffusion. The Na^+ battery is kept charged by the active transport of Na^+ out of the cell. The membrane capacitance, C_m, is the overall charge-storing ability of the membrane.

When two electrodes from a stimulator are placed on an excitable cell, it is found that only one acts as the source of stimulation when a current pulse is applied to the cell. This is the cathode (negative electrode). Current flow is toward the cathode from all regions of the preparation. Upon stimulation, potentials and currents arise in the region of the electrodes—the electrotonic potentials and currents. These potentials arise from current flows extrinsic to the membrane and are decremental. Their nature and spread is dependent on the resistance and capacitance of the membrane.

In older terminology the change in excitability caused by pulses from stimulating electrodes and the passage of stimulating current was termed "electrotonus." The increased excitability under the cathode was called "catelectrotonus"; and the change at the anode was "anelectrotonus." The effects of stimulating currents at the anode are such as to require larger currents for stimulation than are needed at the cathode. Note that these current flows result from the application of an external electrical stimulus. The flow of current under the cathode is outward from the cell, leading to a decreased transmembrane potential. This outward current flow cannot as yet be related to the movement of particular ions. If the depolarizing effect of the stimulus is great enough it can cause the permeability changes which lead to the sequence of events producing the action potential. The direction of electrotonic current flows are shown in Figure 7-22.

In order to cause a response, the stimulus must be of sufficient strength and duration and must also have a sufficient rate of change. We shall first consider square wave stimuli whose rate of change of strength is nearly instantaneous.

When measuring the strength of a stimulus, it is the current flow through the membrane

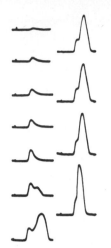

Figure 7-23 In this series of recordings of a nerve action potential the stimulus strength increases from the upper left recording and the resultant compound action potential increases in magnitude as the thresholds of more and more fibers is reached.

which is important. Although a stimulator may be set at a given voltage, the flow of current through the electrodes and the preparation will vary depending on the resistance of the medium between the electrodes, the resistance of the tissue, and the resistance of the electrodes themselves. Although most stimulators used in physiological research are constant-voltage types, that is, the output voltage is constant, constant-current stimulators are now appearing, which by means of negative feedback circuits maintain the current at constant levels despite variations in the resistance of the preparation or the electrodes.

There is a minimal value of stimulus strength —the threshold, liminal, or adequate stimulus —required to produce an action potential. As indicated in Figure 7-23, at low stimulus strengths, the depolarization is not great enough to cause a change in Na^+ permeability adequate to create an action potential. As the stimulus strength increases, there comes a point where the action potential is produced. If a single fiber is studied, it is found that the action potential is an all-or-none event. If the conditions of the fiber remain the same, increasing stimulus strengths above threshold will not produce a greater response (Adrian,

1914, 1932). It should be noted that the all-or-none principle does not mean that different magnitudes of action potentials cannot be produced in a given axon. It only states that under a given set of physiological conditions, the size of the action potential does not depend on the strength of the stimulus once threshold is reached. The principle applies to the action potential conducting region of most nerve and muscle cells.

There is also a minimal duration required if the stimulus is to produce a response. In Section 1-10, the strength-duration relation was discussed in the context of systems analysis. The equivalent circuit of a portion of an axon membrane (Figure 7-21) can be used as a model to derive other equations describing the strength-duration relationship. If the area of membrane affected by the stimulating current is small, it can be represented by a single resistance-capacitance circuit element. According to core conductor theory, the requirement for a threshold stimulus is that it displace the resting potential of this patch of membrane by a small, fixed amount. The change in the transmembrane potential is defined by

$$\Delta E_m = I_s r_m (1 - \exp\{-(t/\tau)\}) \qquad (7.9)$$

where I_s is the portion of the stimulating current flowing through the membrane resistance, r_m, at the stimulating electrode; τ is the membrane time constant; $r_m C_m$, and t is the stimulus duration time. The cell will produce a response if E_m reaches the critical threshold value, E_t. Setting $\Delta E_m = E_t$ and solving for I_s in Equation 7.9 gives

$$I_s = E_t r_m (1 - \exp\{-[t/\tau]\}) \qquad (7.10)$$

which relates the necessary current strength and the time it must flow in order to cause a response. When the duration is long, the strength of the stimulating current required is minimal and

$$I_{min} = E_t / r_m \qquad (7.11)$$

Substituting Equation 7.11 into Equation 7.10 and considering the stimulus duration as extremely small with respect to τ, it can be shown that

$$I_s = I_{min}\,\tau/t \qquad (7.12)$$

That is, for stimuli of short durations, a constant amount of charge stimulates the fiber, and all of the applied current enters the capacity of the membrane.

Chronaxie, the time required for stimulation at twice rheobase strength (see Section 1-10), is directly proportional to the membrane time constant:

$$c = \tau \ln 2 \qquad (7.13)$$

Both the current strength and the duration of stimulus current flow must be great enough to charge the membrane capacitors and to depolarize the membrane. The shape of the strength-duration curve can be directly related to these so-called cable properties of the excitable cell (see Woodbury, 1965).

Two stimuli, each of itself too brief to cause excitation, may summate to produce a response if they are applied close together in time. The first stimulus produces a small change in the membrane polarization, the second short stimulus can add to this change. When the sum of the two responses is great enough to reach the critical depolarization value, the membrane produces an action potential.

Summation of subthreshold stimuli, that is, stimuli whose strengths are below threshold is also possible. This is called **latent addition** of stimuli. If a second subthreshold stimulus is applied to an excitable cell before the effects of a first ineffective stimulus have disappeared, the two may summate to produce a response. Summations of these types are possible because capacitance properties of the membrane cause the membrane to return to normal relatively slowly after the application of a subliminal stimulus.

All excitable cells have the property of **accommodation**. They adapt or accommodate to a change produced by a long-lasting stimulus. A constant electrical current is an effective stimulus upon its initial application, but during continued application loses its effectiveness. This decrease in excitability is due to the inactivation of g_{Na}—the sodium conductance—which has the effect of increasing the threshold voltage (toward zero). The increase in threshold voltage is greater than the actual membrane depolarization brought about by the applied current. Sustained depolarization also tends to increase g_{Na}.

Stimuli of slowing rising strength may not set up an action potential even though they reach intensities many times greater than threshold. If the rate of change of stimulus strength is not great enough, a sufficient charge will not build up due to the leaky nature of the membrane capacitance. In order to produce the train of events leading to an action potential, the membrane capacitance must be charged at some minimal rate.

Sinusoidal alternating currents of low frequency are usually ineffective stimuli, because the rate of change of current is too slow. High frequency alternating currents are also usually ineffective because the cycles of current change are too brief to permit charging of the membrane capacitance to the point where the transmembrane potential is displaced sufficiently for excitation. It is perhaps unfortunate that normal household alternating currents of 50 or 60 cycles per second are in the most effective range of frequencies for the excitation of nerve cells and are, therefore, the most dangerous.

Rushton (1937) developed relationships describing the spread of electrotonic currents along the excitable fiber. The membrane potential, E_x, at some point at distance, x, from the stimulating electrode where the membrane potential is E_o can be determined from

$$E_x = E_o \exp\left(-\frac{x}{[r_m/(r_i + r_o)]^{1/2}}\right) \quad (7.14)$$

The quantity in the denominator is the **space constant**, λ, which is an index of the distance over which there is an electrotonic spread of current when a given potential is applied as the stimulus. The space constant (also called the characteristic length or length constant) has the dimensions of centimeters. Some values are shown in Table 7-5.

We can summarize by saying that the electronic current flows generated by a stimulating

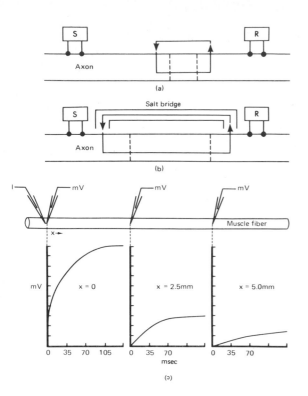

Figure 7-24 (a) When a nerve is blocked by narcotics, cold, or membrane destruction, if the area of blocked membrane is large enough, an action potential is incapable of crossing the gap. If a salt bridge (b) is added so that currents can flow around the damaged area, an action potential results across the gap. This is evidence that local current flows provide for the conduction of the impulse (R = recording electrode, S = stimulating electrode). (c) According to cable theory, the potential and currents measured at points at increasing distances from the site of stimulation should decrease. That this is so is shown by the data provided here, recorded from a muscle fiber.

circuit can lead to the formation of local currents and potentials through the membrane. The effect of these currents is to lower the membrane polarity at sites of outward current flow. Local currents can be shown to exist in excitable cells by experiments such as that shown in Figure 7-24 and such experiments also show that these are decremental currents —they decrease with distance from the point of stimulation. Local currents are also known to exist because the measured currents are

greater than those due to the production of electrotonus by the stimulating electrode. As we shall see, local currents and potentials are responsible for the development and the propagation of the action potential.

The effective stimulus of the excitable cell is one which produces a sufficiently high outward current density to allow a great enough depolarization of the membrane. Graham and Gerárd (1946), using microelectrodes, showed that the passage of outward current was effective in stimulating muscle fibers when currents as low as 1×10^{-10} coulombs were used. No excitation was obtained with inward flowing currents hundreds of times greater.

Cable theory, developed from the study of the behavior of the first undersea telephone cables, is a useful tool for describing certain properties of excitable cells such as the spread of electrotonic currents, space constants, or membrane capacitance; but of course the cell structurally and functionally is very different from a telephone cable through which electrons are moving. Discussions of cable theory and of the measurements of cable constants can be found in Cole (1965); Cole and Hodgkin (1939); Falk and Fatt (1964); Hodgkin and Rushton (1946); and Lorente de Nó (1947).

7-20. Refractory Periods. During the rise of the spike and the initial rapid decline of the action potential, the axon is in its **absolute refractory period**—a time during which further stimulation has no effect on the fiber. Refractory periods refer to declines in the excitability of a cell—a decline in its capabilities for responding to stimuli. Once the inward movement of Na$^+$ has been initiated and the depolarization of the membrane has proceeded beyond the threshold level, the action potential—based on the inward Na$^+$ conductance—becomes a self-sustaining, self-amplifying, all-or-none event which stimulation cannot influence. Since by definition the response of an excitable cell is a spike potential, it is apparent that during the spike a further stimulus can have no effect. Not until the membrane has partially returned to its normal polarized state can another stimulus cause an action potential.

During the period of the after-potentials, or at least during the time when the return to the resting potential level is following an exponential time course, greater than normal threshold strengths of stimulation can cause another response. This period is the **relative refractory period**. The durations of the absolute and relative refractory periods depend upon the particular excitable cell and the nature of its action potential.

Because of the refractory period there is a limit to the number of action potentials which an axon can carry in a given time period. The frequency of discharge is limited to an interval greater than the absolute refractory period during a continuous train of stimuli. Mammalian neurons, with relative refractory periods of about 0.5 msec, can discharge impulses at a maximal frequency of about 1000 per second. *Carcinus* leg axons have a refractory period of about 1 msec and their maximal frequency of impulse conduction is about 500 per second. These maximal possible discharge rates are not those normally found in the organism. Although auditory neurons in mammals may conduct impulses at about 1000 per second, the normal operating range for the average mammalian neuron appears to be 5 to 100 impulses per second. Only rarely under normal conditions does the discharge rate reach 200 or more impulses per second.

An interesting exception to high frequency impulse conduction is found in the Gymnotid electric fish of South America. These fish emit electrical impulses and detect disturbances in the associated electrical field with special sensory receptors whose underlying mechanism is still not known (Chapter 8). The discharge of the electric organ is continuous throughout life and in some species reaches frequences of about 1600 per second. Since each electrical discharge is initiated by a nerve impulse, the nerve cells must be capable of carrying action potentials at these high frequencies. A fish such as *Stenarchus albifrons*, which emits 1,000 discharges per second, in three years would conduct over 10^{11} action potentials (Lissman, 1961).

The durations of the refractory periods and the presence or absence of afterpotentials

depend upon the particular properties of the membrane of the excitable cell. These properties determine the shape and time course of the recorded action potential. As Figure 7-25 shows, action potentials of different excitable cells may vary considerably in shape and duration. The plateau regions of the action potentials of cells such as cardiac muscle, provide for a long refractory period during which the cell is inexcitable. This is a feature required by heart muscle cells, which must beat in a synchronous, rhythmic fashion if

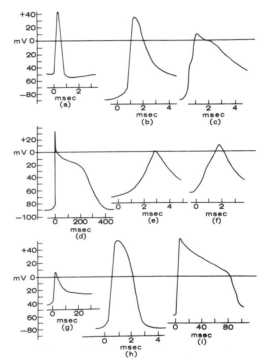

Figure 7-25 Action potentials recorded with intracellular electrodes from a variety of excitable cells. (a) Squid nerve fiber. (b) Frog sartorius muscle. (c) Frog sartorius muscle fiber recorded at an end-plate. (d) Conducting fiber of the dog heart during spontaneous activity. (e) Crab (*Carcinus*) muscle fiber. (f) Cockroach (*Perinplaneta*) muscle fiber. (g) Stick insect (*Carausius*) muscle fiber. (h) Electric eel (*Electrophorous*) electroplax. (i) Crab (*Carcinus*) muscle fiber in Ringer's solution containing tetraethylammonium ions instead of sodium ions. [After G. Hoyle (1957). Comparative Physiology of the Nervous Control of Muscular Contraction. By permission, Cambridge University Press.]

proper blood movement is to be achieved (Chapter 12). The long refractory period ensures that inadvertent or extraneous stimulation does not affect the rhythmic contractions of the cells.

7-21. Heat and Metabolism of Nerve. Studies of the metabolic dependence of action and resting potentials are best performed on nerve cells, because in muscle the action potential is accompanied by the contractile event with its high heat production. Frog nerve, at rest, consumes about 50 mm^3 O$_2$ per gram per hour and produces about 0.5 calories per gram per hour.

Measurement of the heat production during the brief duration of the action potential is extremely difficult since even a train of impulses lasting for one second raises the temperature by only 6×10^{-6} °C. Hill (1932, 1933) and his colleagues developed sensitive galvanometers and small thermopiles suitable for making such measurements. They found an early transient phase of heat production and a prolonged period of heat production during the recovery phase. The latter is thought to be associated with the metabolic events that produce an accelerated extrusion of Na$^+$ and intake of K$^+$ during recovery. This conclusion is based upon experimental results which show that anoxia or metabolic inhibitors cause a decrease or the absence of the recovery heat of nerve. The initial heat signals a chemical reaction or change occurring immediately after, or during, the changes in permeability which lead to the action potential.

With improved instrumentation Abbot et al. (1958) repeated the earlier measurements of heat production and found that following the initial heat production there is a brief period of heat absorption. It has also been found that the electric organs of eels and fishes cool when the organ discharges continuously on open circuit (Aubert et al., 1961; Aubert and Keynes, 1961). As yet there is no satisfactory relationship known between heat production or absorption and the metabolic events of the action potential. Small increases in oxygen

consumption do occur during activity in axons (Brink et al., 1952).

The action potential of the squid giant fiber appears to be independent of any activity of the metabolically driven transport of Na$^+$, but cyanide reduces the magnitude of the action potentials of vertebrate myelinated neurons (Schoepfle and Bloom, 1959). Hodgkin (1964) points out that the ease with which the muscle action potential can be abolished by fatigue may indicate a close relationship between metabolic and electrical events in this type of cell.

In the absence of oxygen, frog nerves slowly lose their ability to conduct impulses. In an atmosphere of pure N$_2$ the resting heat production falls slowly over a period of two hours. After this there is a steady evolution of heat but at a rate one-fourth that of the normal resting rate in oxygen. On readmitting O$_2$ to the preparation, the heat production rises rapidly to overshoot the resting level of heat production for about one hour. Thus, neurons may possess some oxygen reservoir and may also show an oxygen debt similar to that found in muscle.

Usually reduced metabolic activity is not immediately reflected in a changed resting potential. Agents that block metabolism probably affect the action potential by acting on Na$^+$ and K$^+$ permeability changes. Procaine, which blocks nerve conduction, has little or no effect on the resting potential (Bishop, 1932; Bennett and Chinbury, 1946).

7-22. Models of Conductance Pathways. In Chapter 1 the importance of models was discussed, and at the beginning of the present chapter some early models of electrical phenomena found in living systems were mentioned. One of the first electrochemical models was the iron wire model of Lillie (1925, 1936). An iron wire immersed in concentrated nitric acid develops an oxidized coat that protects the wire against dissolution. If the wire is scratched while in dilute nitric acid, the oxide surface is broken and the wire dissolves. In nitric acid of proper concentration, a local reaction occurs upon scratching, and the wire immediately recovers as a new surface is formed. A wave of dissolution and reformation of iron oxide proceeds down the wire. Although an iron wire immersed in dilute nitric acid is far from being a nerve cell, the activities of this model were similar in some respects to those of neurons, and it was studied in great detail (Bonhoefer, 1948; Akiyama, 1955). The iron wire model helped in the development of present models of nerve activity with respect to the development and conduction of action potentials. It is interesting to note that engineers are now attempting to develop a complex and highly miniaturized computer using networks analogous to those found in the central nervous system. Miniature iron fiber and nitric acid systems are used as the nerve elements.

In the 1930's mathematical models were introduced into nerve studies (Katz, 1939; Rashevsky, 1936). These models attempted to describe excitation, propagation, strength-duration relationships, and so forth. In 1943 McCullock and Pitts using the all-or-none behavior of action potentials as a basis, initiated the treatment of nervous systems by discrete mathematics (Boolean algebra and set theory) rather than by continuous functions. These models are used to analyze learning processes and the activities of nerve nets (Chapter 11).

These early attempts at neuronal modeling

finally led to the mathematical models of Hodgkin and Huxley, derived from voltage clamp experimentation with living axons. These workers put their results into a series of mathematical equations and used computer techniques to examine what happened to ion currents and potentials under various conditions. Figure 7-26, for example, shows a theoretical reconstruction of the action potential and the various ionic conductances which accompany it. The similarities between the calculated and observed action potentials are clear when Figure 7-26 is compared with Figure 7-15.

A major need today is for better models of the pathways through which ions enter and leave, not only excitable cells, but all cells. This problem has been examined from the physical-chemical point of view (Eisenman et al., 1967) based on work with artificial membranes. Hodgkin and Huxley derived an interesting model for the mechanisms underlying the conductance changes in squid axons and although the model is hypothetical and has no known molecular basis, it does present ideas on the nature of membrane activities which relate time and voltage changes to ion conductance changes.

It is assumed that a sodium channel is opened when three particles of a certain probability, m, move into a given region of the membrane. A single particle of probability

Figure 7-26 Theoretical action potential and membrane conductance changes obtained by computer solution of the Hodgkin-Huxley equations derived from voltage clamp experiments on squid giant axon. There is a close agreement between the theoretical and observed curves. [After Hodgkin and Huxley (1952d).]

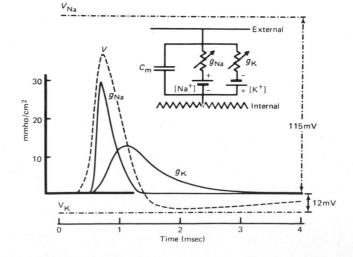

$(1 - h)$ can close the channel. Note that the nature of the channel is not specified; whether it is an actual porelike hole through the membrane or some type of carrier system is not known. The probability that three activating and no inhibiting particles are present is $m^3 h$. And it can be shown that

$$g_{Na} = \bar{g}_{Na} m^3 h \qquad (7.15)$$

where g_{Na} is the Na$^+$ conductance and $\bar{g}_{Na}$ is the maximal Na$^+$ conductance. Although it is easier to think of m and h as molecules that can attach to specific sites on the membrane, they can represent any simultaneous events taking place during changes in Na$^+$ conductance, for example, membrane protein conformational changes or lipid-protein alterations.

The probability that a given molecule is at the proper site depends on the membrane potential. It may be supposed that m and h are charged particles whose orientation or position depends on the transmembrane potential. The positioning of the particles responsible for opening or closing channels for Na$^+$ influx depends also on their kinetics of reaction and the equilibria established under various conditions between molecules at effective sites and molecules at ineffective sites. For example, the values of m and h are given by

$$\frac{dm}{dt} = \alpha_m (1 - m) - \beta_m m \qquad (7.16a)$$

$$\frac{dh}{dt} = \alpha_h (1 - h) - \beta_h m \qquad (7.16b)$$

where the α's and β's are rate constants dependent on Ca^{2+} concentration, temperature, and membrane potential—factors that greatly influence the Na$^+$ conductance.

Similar considerations apply to K$^+$ conductance except from the data of voltage clamp experiments and the mathematical models which fit this data, it appears that a K$^+$ channel is opened when four particles attach to a specific site. These ideas are illustrated in Figure 7-27.

The Hodgkin-Huxley models apply to the squid axon and other excitable cells may not follow this model. The perfused axon behaves in a similar manner to the normal living

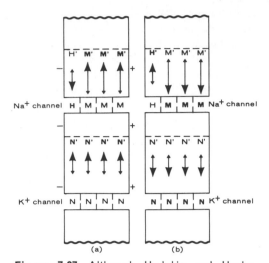

Figure 7-27 Although Hodgkin and Huxley were careful to make no statements about molecular events underlying the generation of action potentials in the squid giant axon, it is possible to derive hypothetical models for ion pathways in the membrane. One such model is illustrated above as an example of how the mathematical description of a physiological mechanism can lead to ideas concerning possible physical mechanisms. Sodium ions can pass through the membrane only if 3 M molecules and 1 H molecule are at proper sites (Na$^+$ channel). Similarly, a K$^+$ channel is formed when 4 N molecules are in position. Boldface letters represent equilibrium positions of molecules between effective and ineffective sites. Arrows represent rates of the reactions. In the polarized membrane (a) the transmembrane potential is near the resting level. When ineffective sites (primed letters) equals effective sites, equilibrium is to the right for M and to the left for H, and the Na$^+$ channels are closed. Since the equilibrium of N is far to the right, the K$^+$ channels are also closed. In a depolarized membrane (b) depolarization changes the rate constants of all reactions and equilibria are shifted to other side. This causes an opening of the sodium channels until H molecules are moved out of position (Na inactivation). The N molecules move into proper position to open K$^+$ channels, which remain open during entire course of depolarization. [After Ruch et al. (1965).]

axon (Chandler et al., 1965; Chandler and Meves, 1965). Recent evaluations of neuronal models and model development include articles on core conduction (Clark and Plonsey, 1966); threshold phenomena (Fitzhugh, 1955,

1961); excitation processes (Franck, 1952, 1956); electrodiffusion models (Cole, 1965); and applications of the Hodgkin-Huxley model (Noble, 1966).

The use of drugs with highly specific effects on membrane activities is aiding in the problem of ion conductances. Tetrodotoxin (TTX) is a powerful neurotoxin that specifically inhibits Na^+ conductance in neurons (Mosher et al., 1964; Nakamura et al., 1965; Narahashi et al., 1964). This substance has a molecular weight of about 319 and is obtained from the poisonous puffer fish.

TTX was used, for example, in experiments designed to obtain an estimate of the number of Na^+ channels in nerve membrane (Moore et al., 1967). A known quantity of TTX was applied to lobster axons and the uptake of the drug was measured. Light and electron microscope studies were used to determine the surface area of membrane exposed to the drug. It was then possible to estimate the number of Na^+ channels present. Since the amount of TTX taken up by the cells was less than 1.6×10^{-11} moles and the axonal membrane area was $0.7 \times 10^{-4}\ \mu^2$; it was calculated that there were less than 13 Na^+ channels present per μ^2 of membrane. This experiment assumed that since TTX specifically inhibits only Na^+ conductance, its uptake from solution represented an irreversible binding of the drug only at Na^+ channel sites.

Chandler and Meves (1965) using voltage clamp data had estimated that there were less than 100 Na^+ channels per μ^2 of membrane. On the basis of molecular dimensions, Na^+ channels appear to be rarities in the lobster axon. TTX blocks Na^+ conductance only when placed on the outside of the membrane; no effects are observed when it is perfused into giant axons (Narahashi et al., 1966). Concentrations as low as 10^{-8} molar are effective in blocking Na^+ conductance in nerve and muscle. The activity of TTX on neuromuscular transmission has also been studied (Chapter 8). It is of interest that TTX has no effect on the nerve or muscle cells of those fish which normally possess it.

Saxotoxin is another specific inhibitor of Na^+ conductance. Procaine and cocaine, which also block nerve action potentials, do so by inhibiting the mechanisms leading to increases in K^+ conductance during the falling phase of the action potential. Through the use of specific drug inhibitors of this type, it is hoped that better models for the pathways of ion movements will be developed.

Conduction of Action Potentials

7-23. Local Circuit Theory. The propagation of the action potential along the axonal membrane is due to the activity of local circuit currents which are established by the inward movement of Na^+ at the region of a developing action potential. The surface of the active region of an excitable cell, that is, the region where an action potential is present, becomes negative with respect to the inactive regions (Figure 7-22) and a positive current flows from the inactive to active zones. Simultaneously the inner core of the active region becomes more positive than inactive regions of the core; as a result positive current flows from active to inactive regions. These flows of local current, in the immediate vicinity of the action potential, are large enough to cause the depolarization of membrane adjacent to the point where the action potential is located, that is, where the Na^+ conductance has been activated. Local currents cannot maintain a given region in an active state for long periods of time because of the refractory period caused by the transient nature of the increased Na^+ conductance.

That the action potential is propagated by local currents can be shown by any of several experimental arrangements. For example, if a region of an axon is made inexcitable by the use of an anesthetic such as chloroform, the blocked (nonconducting) zone can be bypassed by the local currents through a salt-bridge, and action potentials will appear on the other side of the block (Figure 7-24b). Cold blocks and drug blocks have also been used to render a small region of membrane nonconducting. If the blocked region is small

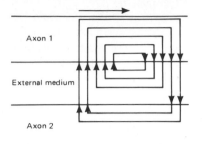

Figure 7-28 An illustration of how local currents set up by the passage of an action potential along one axon in a nerve may spread out and effect other neighboring axons. Such local currents are usually not great enough to produce an action potential in other axons, but they can lower the threshold of these axons. Current amplitude is attenuated by its passage through the extracellular materials separating neighboring axons from one another and thus is only strong enough to produce conduction in the axon responsible for the current flow.

enough, the action potential can jump the block because the local currents flow through the external conducting medium and reach conducting membrane.

Under laboratory conditions, stimulation of an isolated axon results in an action potential that travels in both directions away from the point of stimulation because the local currents spread in each direction away from the active zone. In the intact nervous system impulses normally travel in only one direction because synapses—junctions between neurons—act as one-way valves and in most cases axons are not directly stimulated by external stimulating agents.

When many nerve fibers are bundled together into nerve trunks, there can be interaction between nerve fibers as a result of local current flows. Impulses are not normally transferred to other fibers in such bundles but the local currents from one excited axon can affect the excitability of neighboring fibers. Katz and Schmitt (1940) using isolated axons from the crab, *Carcinus maenus*, demonstrated that such interactions did exist (Figure 7-28). Current flows from an excited axon can invade other fibers and reduce the thresholds of these fibers by 10 to 20 per cent.

The condition for conduction of an impulse is a difference in potential between adjacent portions of the surface of a fiber and it is a requirement that the height of the action potential should be greater than the threshold stimulus. The ratio of the magnitude of the normal action potential to the magnitude of the threhold stimulus is the **safety factor**. For example, during the relative refractory period, the threshold for stimulation may be raised by a factor of five, while the magnitude of the action potential may be lowered by one-half. In order to ensure that nervous activity can occur under these far from optimal conditions, the magnitude of the normal action potential should be about 10 times greater than the normal threshold stimulus. Tasaki (1959) discusses these, and other aspects, of nerve impulse generation and conduction.

7-24. Conduction in Myelinated Fibers. To this point we have assumed that local currents spread through all portions of the axonal membrane and that the impulse is generated at each point along the surface, unless a small region is narcotized. This is true of unmyelinated fibers and most muscle cells, but is not the case in vertebrate myelinated fibers. Conduction in these axons is discontinuous as first proposed by Lillie (1925). The impulse is said to jump from node to node— **saltatory conduction**. The myelin sheath acts as a good insulator, and only at the node where myelin is absent do local currents flow through the membrane in sufficient strength to create the conditions needed for an action potential. At the internodes, it is not known whether sufficient Na^+ channels exist to produce the needed depolarization. The nature of the membrane structure at the node is shown in Figure 7-29.

Proof of saltatory conduction comes from several types of experiments. Kubo and Ono showed that electrical stimuli applied at various points along a myelinated fiber had the lowest thresholds at the nodes (see Tasaki, 1959). Lillie, on the basis of the iron wire model, showed that an electrical current was carried along by the activity at nodes when

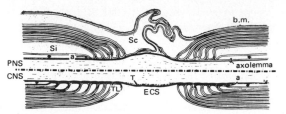

Figure 7-29 Diagrammatic comparison of the structure of the node of Ranvier in the central nervous system (CNS) and in the peripheral nervous system (PNS). In the CNS the myelin sheath disappears leaving the axon exposed to the extracellular space (ECS). In the peripheral nervous system Schwann cells form an outer collar (Sc) about the axon. b.m., basement membrane; TL, terminal loops of myelin; T, thickened layer of dense material in axoplasm; Si, inner collar; a, axoplasm. [After R. P. Bunge (1968). "Glial cells and the central myelin sheath." *Physiological Reviews* **48**: 197-251. By permission.]

lengths of glass tubing were used to partially cover the wire. He hypothesized that a similar type of activity occurred in the myelinated axon.

Although cooling a whole fiber slows the propagation of the action potential, cooling only an internode has no effect on the duration of the longitudinal currents associated with the impulse (Hodler et al., 1951). Blocking agents such as cocaine or urethane show no effect when placed at the internodes, but suppress action potentials when applied to the nodes. Tasaki and Takeuchi (1941, 1942) first definitively showed that saltatory conduction occurs in myelinated fibers.

The myelination of axons provides a faster conduction rate and may also conserve energy for the neuron. If the action potential can be generated only at nodes instead of along the entire surface of the axon, less energy is required to restore normal conditions after the passage of an impulse since less Na^+ and K^+ will have moved in or out of the fiber. Heavily myelinated fibers with regularly spaced nodes are found only in the vertebrates. Heavily myelinated axons are found in some invertebrates but the distribution of nodes is irregular.

The internodal length of vertebrate myelinated axons increases with increasing fiber diameter. In a series of measurements on bullfrog sciatic nerve fibers, it was found that the internodal length, L, is related to the diameter, d, of the axon by

$$L = (0.146 \times 10^3)d \qquad (7.17)$$

d is given in microns. It was also found that the velocity of conduction, v, equalled $2.5d$. The average conduction time for one internodal length, the ratio L/v, equalled 0.059. Thus, internodal conduction time is approximately constant and independent of fiber diameter.

7-25. Voltage Clamp Studies of Nodes. Myelinated fibers present difficulties as far as the analysis of action potentials of single cells is concerned. Although Tasaki (1952) and Woodbury (1952) recorded the potentials of myelinated fibers with microelectrodes, these fibers are readily damaged and do not survive well after microelectrode puncture. Huxley and Stämpfli (1951) recorded longitudinal currents in myelinated fibers across a vaseline seal on an internode. The vaseline seal—a layer of vaseline around the fiber—electrically isolates a normal node from a depolarized one. By applying a potential that made the longitudinal current zero at the moment of measurement, such longitudinal currents could be calculated. Sucrose solutions have been used in order to make the external recording resistance as high as possible, thus permitting the measurement of potentials across the node during the flow of longitudinal current (Stämpfli, 1954). All of these methods have drawbacks either due to cell damage inflicted by the technique or the inability to make accurate measurements.

Dodge and Frankenhaeuser (1958, 1959) developed methods for measuring the potentials of myelinated fibers using external electrodes. Since that time voltage clamp measurements have been made on nodes and models similar to those proposed for squid axons have been derived (Frankenhaeuser, 1965; Frankenhaeuser and Huxley, 1964).

A sketch of the type of apparatus used is shown in Figure 7-30. Vaseline seals are used to separate and electrically isolate various parts of the fiber. A single internode passes through the seals. The amplifier input is connected across one of these seals and its output is applied as a negative feedback across the other seal. Longitudinal current flow due to depolarization of an adjacent node is prevented. The time course and magnitude of the potential changes developed in order to oppose the applied current are recorded through a second amplifier connected across the feedback amplifier output. The advantage of this method is that no damage is done to cells by the penetration of microelectrodes, also extremely small cells can be studied.

Most of the studies of the electrical properties of nodes have been performed on myelinated nerves from the African clawed frog, *Xenopus laevis*, which has larger nerve fibers than other frogs. Frogs of the genus *Rana* present several problems as experimental animals. Among other factors, the magnitudes of resting and action potentials depend on the time of year at which they are measured. It is known that the properties of both nerve and muscle cells differ in winter and summer frogs

(this is true of many cold-blooded animals which live in a variable climate). The past history of an experimental animal with respect to environmental temperature is of some importance (see, for example, Bishop and Gordon, 1967). As already pointed out in Section 1-12, conformation, especially to temperature, is part of the physiological makeup of organisms. As one example of this type of change, recorded action potentials were 104 to 124 mV in February for myelinated axons of *Rana pipiens*. In May these potentials ranged from 89 to 108 mV.

7-26. The Compound Action Potential. When a whole nerve such as the frog sciatic is placed in an experimental arrangement like that shown in Figure 7-12, the recorded action potentials occur as a series of waves, each wave representing a fiber group with a particular range of conduction velocities (Figure 7-31). This is the **compound action potential**— an action potential recorded by external electrodes from whole nerves or from central nervous system tracts. Early experiments by Bishop and Heinbecker (1930) and Erlanger and Gasser (1937) showed that the compound action potential arises because a compound nerve is composed of a heterogeneous collection of individual neurons with different conduction velocities, thresholds, spike durations, and so forth.

The nature of the recorded potential depends upon the placement of the recording electrodes

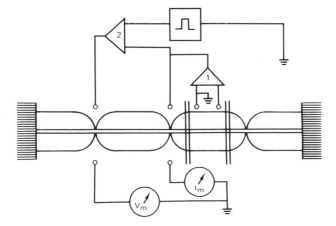

Figure 7-30 One type of apparatus used to analyze node potentials by voltage clamp methods. A single myelinated fiber is placed in a chamber. Vaseline seals are used to isolate various regions of the fiber, and a single internode passes through the seal. The triangles represent operational amplifiers. I_m measures membrane current; V_m measures membrane voltage. [Courtesy of Dr. L. E. Moore.]

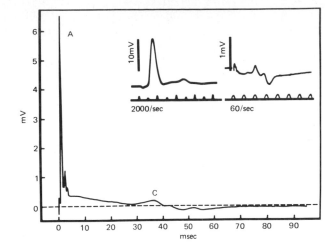

Figure 7-31 Compound action potential of the saphenous nerve of the cat. Left inset shows components of A fiber potential. Right inset shows components of C fiber potentials. [After Gasser (1938), (1941).]

as well as on the nature of the nerve (Figure 7-32). The compound action potential arises because of the fact that the larger the diameter of a fiber, the faster its rate of impulse conduction. The largest group of fibers of a compound nerve have the highest conduction rates, and their action potentials are seen first on the oscilloscope because these potentials reach the recording electrodes first. If the distance between the stimulating and recording electrodes is great enough, other action potentials (from smaller nerve fibers) will be seen.

In the frog sciatic nerve, three major classes of nerve fibers, based on size, are recognized. These are called simply A, B, and C fibers. The A fibers are the largest and are the myelinated fibers of somatic nerves including both sensory and motor neurons. B fibers are smaller, thinly myelinated processes of the autonomic nervous system (motor neurons to visceral organs and blood vessels). C fibers are small, unmyelinated fibers belonging to the sympathetic division of the autonomic nervous system or to dorsal spinal roots. A similar size classification is used for mammalian nerves. Often the A fibers are subdivided into families of differently sized neurons—designated by Greek letters in order of decreasing size: α, β, γ, and δ.

Gasser and Grundfest (1939) concluded that the velocity of the nerve impulse is directly proportional to the diameter of invertebrate and myelinated vertebrate axons. This linear relationship is obtained by using only axon

diameter and not the thickness of the myelin sheath. Hodgkin (1954) concluded that unmyelinated fiber conduction should be proportional to the square root of the fiber diameter when conduction rates are measured in a large volume of external solution. Pumphrey and Young (1938) found that in squid giant axons, the velocity was proportional to the diameter raised to the 0.6th power (Figure 7-33).

Table 7-7 lists some properties of different sized mammalian nerve fibers. It can be seen

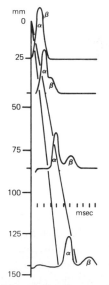

Figure 7-32 The shape of an action potential depends on the positioning of electrodes used to record it. [After H. S. Gasser and J. Erlanger (1937). Electrical Signs of Nervous Action. Philadelphia: University of Pennsylvania Press.]

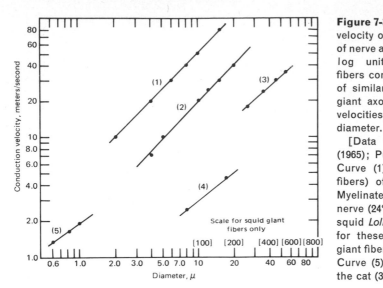

Figure 7-33 Relationship between the velocity of conduction and the diameter of nerve axons (both coordinates are in log units). Mammalian myelinated fibers conduct faster than other fibers of similar diameter. Squid and other giant axons achieve high conduction velocities by a greatly increased fiber diameter.

[Data from Bullock and Horridge (1965); Pumphrey and Young (1937).] Curve (1), Peripheral myelinated (A fibers) of the cat (35°C). Curve (2), Myelinated (A fibers) of frog sciatic nerve (24°C). Curve (3), Giant fibers of squid *Loligo* (23°C; note scale change for these fibers). Curve (4), Median giant fibers of annelid *Neanthes* (24°C). Curve (5), Unmyelinated (C fibers) of the cat (37°C).

that the larger the fiber diameter, the faster the rate of conduction, the shorter the duration of the spike, and the shorter the refractory period. Mammalian nerve fibers generally conduct impulses faster than comparable sized fibers of other animal groups.

On the basis of Rushton's core-conductor analysis of excitable fibers, it is to be expected that the conduction velocity would increase with increasing fiber diameter. The space constant depends upon the internal and external resistances (Equation 7.14), and increasing the diameter of the fiber reduces the internal resistance because a larger path is opened to current flow. A lower internal resistance increases the value of the space constant, that is, for a given magnitude of potential, local currents spread over a longer length of fiber. Presumably a thick myelin sheath increases conduction rate by presenting an insulating sheath that prevents current loss to the external medium. Rushton's analysis also indicates that the space constant and thus the rate of conduction would decrease if the external medium's electrical resistance were increased. Katz (1948) found that upon replacing part of the electrolyte of the external medium with nonelectrolytes, thus increasing resistance to current flow, the conduction rate was in fact decreased.

Schwann cells are not influenced in any direct way by the action potentials of the axons with which they are associated. Microelectrode studies show that during the action potential development in an axon, there are no potential changes in the Schwann cell. Nor do induced changes in the Schwann cell affect the axon (Villegas et al., 1963, 1968).

Stimulation of a compound nerve produces no result until the stimulus reaches threshold strength. As the strength of the stimulus is gradually increased above threshold, there is a gradually increasing response (in terms of magnitude of the action potential) until at some stimulus strength—the maximal stimulus—the action potential reaches a maximal size and increased stimulus strengths cause no further increase in response. This is an example of **spatial summation** and results from the additive effects of the potentials of many individual neurons within the nerve. Different fibers have different thresholds, and not until the threshold strengths of all fibers has been reached with the maximal stimulus do all fibers respond. The compound action potential is the result of the summing of many individual action potentials. Each individual neuron is following the all-or-none law, but due to the geometry of the preparation one sees an increasing size of compound action potential with increasing stimulus strengths.

Table 7-7 Some Properties of Mammalian Nerve Fibers*

			C FIBERS	
	A FIBERS	B FIBERS	SYMPATHETIC	DORSAL ROOT
Fiber diameter (μ)	20–1	< 3	—	0.4
Conduction velocity (meters/sec)	100–< 5	14–< 3	< 2	< 2.4
Spike duration (msec)	0.4–0.5	1.2	2.0	2.0
Negative after-potential				
per cent of spike height	3–5	none	3–5	none
duration (msec)	12–20	—	50–80	—
Positive after-potential				
per cent of spike height	0.2	1.5–4.0	1.5	—
duration (msec)	40–60	100–300	300–1,000	—
Absolute refractory period (msec)	0.4	1.2	2.0	—
Period of latent addition (msec)	0.2	0.2	2.5	—

* By permission from M. A. B. Brazier (1960), *The Electrical Activity of the Nervous System.* (New York: The Macmillan Company).

The recorded action potentials from frog sciatic nerve are in the range of about 5–20 mV although individual action potentials may measure 50–100 mV. But in a whole nerve current is shunted through the connective tissue sheaths and other materials in which the neurons are embedded, and as a result the recording electrodes do not pick up the full currents and the action potentials appear lower in magnitude than they actually are.

Table 7-8 lists some comparative values of resting and action potentials, as well as fiber diameters and conduction velocities. These are selected values taken from Bullock and Horridge (1965) and Prosser and Brown (1961). It is difficult to obtain good comparisons of this nature because of the differences in experimental methods and conditions used for various animals and their excitable cells. In some cases the values given are averages. In most cases the diameter given includes the surrounding sheath.

7-27. The Acetylcholine Hypothesis. Nachmansohn (1959) believes that the liberation and destruction of acetylcholine (ACh) are im-

portant steps in the generation and conduction of the action potential. ACh is involved in the transmission of signals at neuromuscular junctions and at many synapses (Chapter 8), and Nachmansohn considers that the conduction of an impulse also requires ACh.

Nachmansohn's hypothesis is based, in part, upon the fact that anticholinesterases (inhibitors of acetylcholinesterase, AChE, the enzyme responsible for the hydrolysis and destruction of ACh) prevent impulses in nerve and muscle. The hypothesis states that upon depolarization ACh is released from the membrane. The released ACh combines with a receptor protein and the complex alters membrane permeability. The AChE present in the membrane hydrolyzes some of the ACh and this destruction of ACh, in turn, reduces membrane permeability to Na^+, and the repolarization process is initiated. Inhibition of AChE should allow ACh to accumulate in the membrane and repolarization should be greatly prolonged.

Feng and Hsieh (1952) using tetraethyl pyrophosphate, a specific inhibitor of AChE, found that the activity of this enzyme can be completely abolished in frog nerve and muscle

Table 7-8   Comparison of Some Properties of Excitable Cells

PREPARATION	DIAMETER (μ)	CONDUCTION VELOCITY (m/sec)	RESTING POTENTIAL (mV)	PEAK SPIKE POTENTIAL (mV)	TEMP. (°C)
Cat (*Felis*)					
A fibers	20	110	—	—	37
	15	80	—	—	
	10	50	—	—	
	6	30	—	—	
C fibers	< 1	0.2–0.6	—	—	
Spinal motoneuron	12	67	55–80	80–110	
Frog (*Rana*)					
A fibers	20	40	—	—	24
	15	30	—	—	
	12	25	—	—	
	10	20	—	—	
	8	15	—	—	
Sciatic nerve axon	16	31	60–80	100–130	20
Squid (*Loligo*) giant axon	260	18	60	120	23
	500	33	—	—	18
Earthworm (*Lumbricus*)					
Median giant axon	70	30	70	100	22
Crab (*Carcinus*) leg axon	30	4.4	71–94	116–153	21

without reducing the magnitude of the action potential.

At the present time most investigators in this area see no true role of ACh in the development or conduction of action potentials in neurons. However, so little is known about the actual molecular activities underlying these phenomena, ACh may prove to have some role, even if indirectly, in them.

This chapter has been concerned with the action potentials and the local currents and potentials associated with the axonal region of neurons and with the membrane of muscle, primarily striated muscle. The next potentials to be discussed are those associated with the dendritic region of excitable cells. These potentials and the mechanisms by which signals are passed from one neuron to another or from a neuron to an effector cell will comprise the subject matter of Chapter 8.

References and Readings

Abbot, B. C., A. V. Hill, and J. V. Howarth (1958). "The positive and negative heat production associated with a nerve impulse." *Proc. Roy. Soc.* (London) **B148**: 149–187.

Adrian, E. D. (1914). "The all-or-none principle in nerve." *J. Physiol.* (London) **47**: 460–474.

Adrian, E. D. (1932). **The Mechanisms of Nervous Action.** Philadelphia: University Pennsylvania Press.

Adrian, R. H. (1956). "The effect of internal and external potassium concentration on the membrane potential of frog muscle." *J. Physiol.* (London) **133**: 631–658.

Akiyama, I. (1955). "The silver nitrate and iron system as an electrochemical model of nervous conduction." *Gunman J. Med. Sci.* **4**: 41–46.

Aubert, X., A. Fessard, and R. D. Keynes (1961). "The thermal events during and after the discharge of the electric organs of *Torpedo* and *Electrophorus*." In: **Bioelectrogenesis.** (C. Chagas and A. Paes de Cavalho, eds.), p. 136. New York: American Elsevier Publishing Company.

Aubert, X. and R. D. Keynes (1961). "Temperature changes in the electric organ of *Electrophorus electricus* during and after its discharge." *J. Physiol.* (London) **158**: 17P.

Baker, P. F., A. L. Hodgkin, and T. I. Shaw (1961). "Replacement of the protoplasm of a giant nerve fibre with artificial solutions." *Nature* **190**: 885–887.

Baker, P. F., A. L. Hodgkin, and T. I. Shaw (1962a). "Replacement of the axoplasm of giant nerve fibres with artificial solutions." *J. Physiol.* (London) **164**: 330–354.

Baker, P. F., A. L. Hodgkin, and T. I. Shaw (1962b). "The effects of changes in internal ionic concentrations on the electrical properties of perfused giant axons." *J. Physiol.* (London) **164**: 355–374.

Bass, A. D., ed. (1959). **Evolution of Nervous Control from Primitive Organisms to Man.** Washington, D.C.: American Association for the Advancement of Science.

Bennet, A. L. and K. G. Chinbury (1946). "The effects of several local anaesthetics on the resting potentials of isolated frog nerve." *J. Pharmacol.* **88**: 77.

Bernstein, J. (1868). "Über den Zeitlichen Verlauf der negativen Schwankung des Nervenströms." *Pflüg. Arch. ges. Physiol.* **1**: 173.

Bernstein, J. (1902). "Untersuchungen zur Thermodynamik der bioelektrischen Ströme. *Pflüg. Arch. ges. Physiol.* **92**: 521–562.

Bernstein, J. (1911). **Elektrobiologie.** Braunshweig: Vieweg Verlag.

Bishop, G. H. (1932). "The action of nerve depressants on potentials." *J. Cell. Comp. Physiol.* **1**: 177.

Bishop, G. H. (1956). "The natural history of the nerve impulse." *Physiol. Rev.* **36**: 376–399.

Bishop, G. H. and P. Heinbecker (1930). "Differentiation of axon types in visceral nerves by means of the potential record." *Am. J. Physiol.* **94**: 170–200.

Bishop, L. G. and M. S. Gordon (1967). "Metabolism in anuran amphibians." In: **Molecular Mechanisms of Temperature Adaptation.** (C. L. Prosser, ed.), pp. 263–280. Washington, D.C.: American Association for the Advancement of Science.

Bloom, W. and D. W. Fawcett (1962). **A Textbook of Histology.** 2nd ed. Philadelphia: W. B. Saunders Company. 720 pp.

Bodian, D. (1952). "Introductory survey of neurons." *Cold Spring Harbor Symp. Quant. Biol.* **17**: 1–13.

Bodian, D. (1962). "The generalized vertebrate neuron." *Science* **137**: 323–326.

Bonhoeffer, K. F. (1948). "Activation of passive iron as a model for excitation of nerve." *J. Gen. Physiol.* **32**: 69–91.

Bonhoeffer, J. F. (1953). "Modelle der Nervenerregung." *Naturwissenschaften* **40**: 301–311.

Boyle, P. J. and E. J. Conway (1941). "Potassium accumulation in muscle and associated changes." *J. Physiol.* (London) **100**: 1–63.

Brady, A. J. and J. W. Woodbury (1960). "The sodium-potassium hypothesis as the basis of electrical activity in frog ventricles." *J. Physiol.* (London) **154**: 385–407.

Brazier, M. A. B. (1959). "The historical development of neurophysiology." In: **Handbook of Physiology.** Sect. 1, Vol. 1, pp. 1–58. Washington, D.C.: American Physiology Society.

Brazier, M. A. B. (1960). **The Electrical Activity of the Nervous System.** New York: The Macmillan Company, 273 pp.

Brink, F., D. W. Bronk, F. D. Carlson, and C. M. Connelly (1952). "The oxygen uptake of active axons." *Cold Spring Harbor Symp. Quant. Biol.* **17**: 53–67.

Bullock, T. H. and G. A. Horridge (1965). **Structure and Function in the Nervous Systems of Invertebrates.** 2 volumes. San Francisco: W. H. Freeman & Company, Publishers.

Bunge, R. P. (1968). "Glial cells and the central myelin sheath." *Physiol. Rev.* **48**: 197–251.

Burés, J., M. Petrán, and J. Zachar (1962). **Electrophysiological Methods in Biological**

Research. Praha: Czechoslovak Academy of Sciences (New York: Academic Press, Inc.). 515 pp.

Cajal, R. S. y (1909–1911). **Histologie du systé nerveux de l'homme et des vertébrés.** 2 volumes. Paris: A. Maloine. Reprinted by Institute Ramón y Cajal, Madrid, 1952.

Cajal, R. S. y (1934). "Les preuves objectives de l'unité anatomique des cellules nerveuses." *Trav. Lab. Invest. Biol. Univ. Madrid* 29: 1–137.

Caldwell, P. C. (1968). "Factors governing movement and distribution of inorganic ions in nerve and muscle." *Physiol. Rev.* 48: 1–64.

Caldwell, P. C., A. L. Hodgkin, R. D. Keynes, and T. I. Shaw (1960). "The effects of injecting energy-rich phosphate compounds on the active transport of ions in the giant axons of *Loligo*." *J. Physiol.* (London) 152: 561–590.

Cavendish, H. (1776). "An account of some attempts to imitate the effects of the *Torpedo* by electricity." *Trans. Roy. Soc.* (London) 66: 196–225.

Chandler, W. K., A. L. Hodgkin, and H. Meves (1965). "The effect of changing the internal solution on sodium inactivation and related phenomena in giant axons." *J. Physiol.* (London) 180: 821–837.

Chandler, W. K. and A. L. Hodgkin (1965). "The effect of internal sodium on the action potential in the presence of different internal anions." *J. Physiol.* (London) 181: 594–611.

Chandler, W. K. and H. Meves (1965). "Voltage clamp experiments on internally perfused giant axons." *J. Physiol.* (London) 180: 788–820.

Clark, J. and R. A. Plonsey (1966). "A mathematical evaluation of the core conductor model." *Biophys. J.* 6: 95–112.

Cole, K. S. (1940). "Permeability and impermeability of cell membranes for ions." *Cold Spring Harbor Symp. Quant. Biol.* 8: 110–122.

Cole, K. S. (1941). "Rectification and inductance in the squid giant axon." *J. Gen. Physiol.* 25: 29–51.

Cole, K. S. (1949). "Dynamic electrical characteristics of the squid axon membrane." *Arch. Sci. Physiol.* 3: 253–258.

Cole, K. S. (1965a). "Electrodiffusion models for the membrane of the squid giant axon." *Physiol. Rev.* 45: 340–379.

Cole, K. S. (1965b). "Theory, experiment, and the nerve impulse." In: **Theoretical and Mathematical Biology.** (T. H. Waterman and H. J. Morowitz, eds.), pp. 136–172. Waltham, Mass.: Blaisdell Publishing Co.

Cole, K. S. and H. J. Curtis (1939). "Electrical impedance of the squid giant axon during activity." *J. Gen. Physiol.* 22: 649–670.

Cole, K. S. and A. L. Hodgkin (1939). "Membrane and protoplasm resistance in the squid giant axon." *J. Gen. Physiol.* 22: 671–687.

Connelly, C. M. (1959). "Recovery processes and metabolism of nerve." In: **Biophysical Science—A Study Program.** (J. Oncley, ed.), pp. 475–484. New York: John Wiley & Sons, Inc.

Conway, E. J. (1950). "Calculation of the idiomolar value and its electrostatic equivalent in normal mammalian skeletal muscle." *Irish J. Med. Sci.* 6: 216–224.

Conway, E. J. (1957). "Nature and significance of concentration relations of potassium and sodium ions in skeletal muscle." *Physiol. Rev.* 37: 84–132.

Conway, E. J., R. P. Kernan, and J. A. Sadunalsky (1961). "The sodium pump in skeletal muscle in relation to energy barriers." *J. Physiol.* (London) 155: 263–279.

Curtis, D. R. (1964). "Microelectrophoresis." In: **Physical Techniques in Biological Research.** (W. L. Nastuk, ed.), Vol. 5, Part A, pp. 144–192. New York: Academic Press, Inc.

Curtis, H. J. and K. S. Cole (1940). "Membrane action potentials from the squid giant axon." *J. Cell. Comp. Physiol.* 15: 147–157.

Curtis, H. J. and K. S. Cole (1942). "Membrane resting and action potentials from the squid giant axon." *J. Cell. Comp. Physiol.* 19: 135–144.

Davis, F. A. and D. Nachmansohn (1964). "Acetylcholine formation in lobster sensory axons." *Biochem. Biophys. Acta* 88: 384–389.

Dee, E. and R. P. Kernan (1963). "Energetics of sodium transport in *Rana pipiens*." *J. Physiol.* (London) **165**: 550–558.

Descartes, R. (1662). **De homine figuris et latinitate donatus a Florentio Schuyl.** Leyden: Leffen and Fraciscum Movardum.

Dodge, F. A. and B. Frankenhaeuser (1958). "Membrane currents in isolated frog nerve fibres under voltage clamp conditions." *J. Physiol.* (London) **143**: 76–90.

Dodge, F. A. and B. Frankenhaeuser (1959). "Sodium currents in the myelinated nerve fibre of *Xenopus laevis* investigated with the voltage clamp technique." *J. Physiol.* (London) **148**: 188–200.

Donaldson, P. E. K. (1958). **Electronic Apparatus for Biological Research.** New York: Academic Press, Inc. 718 pp.

DuBois-Reymond, E. (1848). **Untersuchungen Über Thierische Elektricität.** Berlin: Reimer.

DuBois-Reymond, E. (1852). **On Animal Electricity** (trans. Bence Jones). London: Churchill.

DuBois-Reymond, E. (1863). **Über das Desetz des Muskelströmes.** Berlin: Unger.

Eisenman, G., J. P. Sandblom, and J. L. Walker (1967). "Membrane structure and ion permeation." *Science* **155**: 965–974.

Erlanger, J. and H. S. Gasser (1937). **Electrical Signs of Nervous Activity.** Philadelphia: University of Pennsylvania Press. 221 pp.

Falk, G. and P. Fatt (1964). "Linear electrical properties of striated muscle fibres observed with intracellular electrodes." *Proc. Roy. Soc.* (London) **B160**: 69–123.

Feng, T. P. and W. M. Hsieh (1952). "Conduction in muscle after complete irreversible inactivation of cholinesterase." *Chinese J. Physiol.* **18**: 81–92.

Feng, T. P. and W. M. Hsieh (1952). "Conduction in nerve after complete irreversible inactivation of cholinesterase." *Chinese J. Physiol.* **18**: 93–102.

Fitzhugh, R. (1955). "Mathematical models of threshold phenomena in the nerve membrane." *Bull. Math. Biophys.* **17**: 257–278.

Fitzhugh, R. (1961). "Impulses and physiological states in theoretical models of nerve." *Biophys. J.* **1**: 445–466.

Fitzhugh, R. (1963). "Thresholds and plateaus in the Hodgkin-Huxley nerve equation." *J. Gen. Physiol.* **43**: 767–796.

Franck, U. F. (1952). "Elektrochemische Modelle zur saltatorischen Nervenleitung. II. Modellversuche in den elektrischen Organen elektrischer Fische." *Z. Naturforsch.* **7**: 220–230.

Franck, U. F. (1956). "Models for biological excitation processes." *Prog. Biophys.* **6**: 171–206.

Frank, K. and M. C. Becker (1964). "Microelectrodes for recording and stimulation." In: **Physical Techniques in Biological Research.** (W. L. Nastuk, ed.), vol. 5, Part A, pp. 23–88. New York: Academic Press, Inc.

Frankenhaeuser, B. (1957). "A method for recording resting and action potentials in the isolated myelinated nerve fibre of the frog." *J. Physiol.* (London) **135**: 550-559.

Frankenhaeuser, B. (1960). "Sodium permeability in toad nerve and in squid nerve." *J. Physiol.* (London) **152**: 159–166.

Frankenhaeuser, B. (1965). "Computed action potential in nerve from *Xenopus laevis*." *J. Physiol.* (London) **180**: 780–787.

Frankenhaeuser, B. and A. F. Huxley (1964). "The action potential in the myelinated nerve fibre of *Xenopus laevis* as computed on the basis of voltage clamp data." *J. Physiol.* (London) **171**: 302–315.

Galvani, L. (1791). **De Biribus Electricitatus in Moto Musculari, Commentarius.** Bologna: Typographia Instituti Scientarum.

Galvani, L. (1794). **Dell'uso e dell'attivita dell'arco Conduttore Nelle Contrazione die Muscoll.** Bologna: Thammaso D'Aquino.

Gasser, H. S. (1941). "Classification of nerve fibers." *Ohio J. Sci.* **41**: 145–159.

Gasser, H. S. (1960). "Effect of the method of leading on the recording of the nerve fibre spectrum." *J. Gen. Physiol.* **43**: 927–940.

Gasser, H. S. and J. Erlanger (1922). "A study of the action currents of nerve with a cathode ray oscilloscope." *Am. J. Physiol.* **62**: 496.

Gasser, H. S. and J. Erlanger (1926). "The role played by the sizes of constituent fibers of a nerve trunk in determining the form of its action potential." *Am. J. Physiol.* **80**: 522–547.

Gasser, H. S. and H. Grundfest (1939). "Axon diameters in relation to spike dimensions and conduction velocity in mammalian fibres." *Am. J. Physiol.* **127**: 393–414.

Geren, B. B. (1954). "The formation from the Schwann cell surface of myelin in the peripheral nerves of chick embryos." *Exp. Cell Res.* **7**: 558–562.

Gicklhorn, J. (1929). "Die Herstellung von Mikroelektroden." In: **Elektrostatik in der Biochemie.** (W. Ostwald, ed.), pp. 252–258. Berlin: Sonderausgabe Kolloidchemische Behefte.

Goldman, D. E. (1943). "Potential, impedance, and rectification in membranes." *J. Gen. Physiol.* **27**: 37–60.

Goldstein, D. A. and A. K. Solomon (1960). "Determination of equivalent pore radius for human red cells by osmotic pressure measurements." *J. Gen. Physiol.* **44**: 1-17.

Golgi, C. (1898). "Sur la structure des cellules nerveuses." *Arch. Ital. Biol.* **30**: 60–71.

Graham, J. and R. W. Gerard (1946). "Membrane potentials and excitation of impaled single muscle fibers." *J. Cell. Comp. Physiol.* **28**: 99–117.

Hagiwara, S. and K. Takahashi (1967). "Resting and spike potentials of skeletal muscle fibres of salt-water elasmobranchs and teleost fish." *J. Physiol.* (London) **190**: 499–518.

Harmon, L. D. and E. R. Lewis (1966). "Neural modeling." *Physiol. Rev.* **46**: 513–591.

Harris, E. J. and G. P. Burn (1949). "The transfer of sodium and potassium ions between muscle and the surrounding medium." *Trans. Faraday Soc.* **45**: 508–528.

Harris, E. J. and H. Martins-Ferreira (1955). "Membrane potentials in the muscles of the South American frog, *Leptodactylus ocellatus*." *J. Exp. Biol.* **32**: 539–546.

Harrison, R. G. (1907). "Observations on the living developing nerve fiber." *Proc. Soc. Exp. Biol. Med.* **4**: 140–143.

Hays, R. M. and A. Leaf (1962). "Studies on the movement of water through the isolated

toad bladder and its modification by vasopressin." *J. Gen. Physiol.* **45**: 905–919.

Held, H. (1929). "Die Lehre von dem Neuronen und vom Neurencytium und ihr heutiger Stand." *Fortschr. Naturw. Forsch.* **8**: 1–44.

Hill, A. V. (1932). "A closer analysis of the heat production of nerve." *Proc. Roy. Soc.* (London) **B111**: 106.

Hill, A. V. (1932). **Chemical Wave Transmission in Nerve.** New York: Cambridge University Press. 74 pp.

Hill, A. V. (1933). "The three phases of nerve heat production." *Proc. Roy. Soc.* (London) **B113**: 345–364.

Hodgkin, A. L. (1939). "The relation between conduction velocity and the electrical resistance outside a nerve fibre." *J. Physiol.* (London) **94**: 560.

Hodgkin, A. L. (1954). "A note on conduction velocity." *J. Physiol.* (London) **125**: 221–224.

Hodgkin, A. L. (1958). "Ionic movements and electrical activity in giant nerve fibres." *Proc. Roy. Soc.* (London) **B148**: 1–37.

Hodgkin, A. L. (1964a). **The Conduction of the Nerve Impulse.** Liverpool: Liverpool University Press. Springfield, Ill.: Charles C. Thomas. 108 pp.

Hodgkin, A. L. (1964b). "The ionic basis of nerve conduction." *Science* **145**: 1148–1154.

Hodgkin, A. L. and P. Horowicz (1959). "The influence of potassium and chloride ions on the membrane potential of single muscle fibres." *J. Physiol.* (London) **148**: 126–160.

Hodgkin, A. L. and P. Horowicz (1959). "Movements of Na and K in single muscle fibres." *J. Physiol.* (London) **145**: 405–432.

Hodgkin, A. L. and A. F. Huxley (1939). "Action potentials recorded from inside a nerve fibre." *Nature* **144**: 710–711.

Hodgkin, A. L. and A. F. Huxley (1952a). "Currents carried by sodium and potassium ions through the membrane of the giant axon of *Loligo*." *J. Physiol.* (London) **116**: 449–472.

Hodgkin, A. L. and A. F. Huxley (1952b). "The components of membrane conductance in the giant axon of *Loligo*." *J. Physiol.* (London) 116: 473–496.

Hodgkin, A. L. and A. F. Huxley (1952c). "The dual effect of membrane potential on sodium conductance in the giant axon of *Loligo*." *J. Physiol.* (London) 116: 497–506.

Hodgkin, A. L. and A. F. Huxley (1952d). "A quantitative description of membrane currents and its application to conduction and excitation in nerve." *J. Physiol.* (London) 117: 500–544.

Hodgkin, A. L., A. F. Huxley, and B. Katz (1952). "Measurement of current-voltage relations in the membrane of the giant axon of *Loligo*." *J. Physiol.* (London) 116: 424–448.

Hodgkin, A. L. and B. Katz (1949). "The effect of sodium ions on the electrical activity of the giant axon of the squid." *J. Physiol.* (London) 108: 37–77.

Hodgkin, A. L. and R. D. Keynes (1955). "Active transport of cations in giant axons from *Sepia* and *Loligo*." *J. Physiol.* (London) 128: 28–60.

Hodgkin, A. L. and W. A. H. Rushton (1946). "The electrical constants of a crustacean nerve fibre." *Proc. Roy. Soc.* (London) B133: 444–479.

Hodler, J., R. Stämpfli, and I. Tasaki (1951). "Über die Wirkung internodaler Abhulung auf die Erregungsleitung in der isolierten markhaltigen Nervenfasten des Frosches." *Pflüg. Arch. ges. Physiol.* 253: 380.

Hoff, H. E. (1936). "Galvani and the pre-Galvanian electrophysiologists." *Ann. Sci.* 1: 157–172.

Hoyle, G. (1957). **Comparative Physiology of the Nervous Control of Muscular Contraction.** New York: Cambridge University Press. 147 pp.

Hunt, C. C. and A. K. McIntyre (1960). "Analysis of fibre diameter and receptor characteristics of myelinated cutaneous afferent fibres in the cat." *J. Physiol.* (London) 153: 99–112.

Huxley, A. F. (1964). "Excitation and conduction in nerve: quantitative analysis." *Science* 145: 1154–1159.

Huxley, A. F. and R. Stämpfli (1949). "Evidence for saltatory conduction in peripheral nerve fibres." *J. Physiol.* (London) 108: 315–339.

Huxley, A. F. and R. Stämpfli (1951). "Direct determination of membrane resting potential and action potential in single myelinated fibres." *J. Physiol.* (London) 112: 476–495.

Hydén, H. (1960). "The neuron." In: **The Cell.** (J. Brachet and A. E. Mirsky, eds.), Vol. 4, part 1, pp. 215–234. Academic, N.Y.

Hydén, H. (1962). "A molecular basis of neuro-glial interaction." In: **Macromolecular Specificity and Biological Memory.** (F. O. Schmitt, ed.), pp. 55–69. Cambridge, Mass.: Massachusetts Institute of Technology Press.

Hydén, H. (1965). "Activation of nuclear RNA of neurons and glia in learning." In: **Anatomy of Memory.** (D. P. Kimble, ed.), pp. 178–239. Palo Alto, Cal.: Science and Behavior Books.

Kappers, C. U. (1929). **The Evolution of the Nervous System.** Haarlem, Netherlands: deErven F. Bohn.

Kappers, C. U., G. C. Huber, and E. C. Crosby (1936). **The Comparative Anatomy of the Nervous System of Vertebrates, Including Man.** 2 volumes. New York: The Macmillan Company.

Katz, B. (1939). **Electric Excitation of Nerve.** New York: Oxford University Press. 151 pp.

Katz, B. (1948). "The effect of electrolyte deficiency on the rate of conduction in a single nerve fiber." *J. Physiol.* (London) 106: 411.

Katz, B. (1966). **Nerve, Muscle, and Synapse.** New York: McGraw-Hill Publishing Co. 193 pp.

Katz, B. and O. H. Schmitt (1940). "Electric interaction between two adjacent nerve fibres." *J. Physiol.* (London) 97: 471–488.

Katz, G., G. Webb, and A. Sorem (1964). "Recording and display." In: **Physical Techniques in Biological Research.** (W. L. Nastuk, ed.), Vol. 5, part A, pp. 374–448. New York: Academic Press, Inc.

Keller, R. (1925). "Data of T. Peterfi on microelectrodes." In: **Die Elektrizität der Zelle,** 2nd ed. Maehrisch-Ostrau: Verlag Julius Kittls Nachfolger Keller and Co.

Keynes, R. D. (1951). "The ionic movements during nervous activity." *J. Physiol.* (London) 114: 119–150.

Keynes, R. D. (1963). "Chloride in the squid giant axon." *J. Physiol.* (London) 169: 690–705.

Keynes, R. D. and G. W. Maisel (1954). "The energy requirement for sodium extrusion from a frog muscle." *Proc. Roy. Soc.* (London) B142: 383–392.

Koechlin, B. A. (1955). "On the chemical composition of the axoplasm of squid giant nerve fibers with particular reference to its ion pattern." *J. Biophys. Biochem. Cytol.* 1: 511–530.

Kuffler, S. W. and J. G. Nicholls (1965). "How do materials exchange between blood and nerve cells in the brain?" *Perspectives Biol. Med.* 9: 69–76.

Kuffler, S. W. and J. G. Nicholls (1966). "The physiology of neuroglial cells." *Ergebn. Physiol.* 57: 1–90.

Le Gros Clark, W. E. (1963). "The problem of tracking fiber connections in nervous systems in relation to the functional specificity." *Harvey Lect.* 58: 157–179.

Levi, H. and H. H. Ussing (1948). "The exchange of sodium and chloride ions across the fibre membrane of the isolated frog sartorius." *Acta Physiol. Scand.* 16: 232–249.

Levi-Montalcini, R. (1965). "The nerve growth factor: its mode of action on sensory and sympathetic cells." *Harvey Lect.* 60: 217–260.

Lillie, R. S. (1925). "Factors affecting transmission and recovery in the passive iron wire nerve model." *J. Gen. Physiol.* 7: 473–507.

Lillie, R. S. (1936). "The passive iron wire model of protoplasmic and nervous transmission and its physiological analogues." *Biol. Rev.* 11: 181–209.

Ling, G. N. and R. W. Gerard (1949). "The membrane potential and metabolism of muscle fibers." *J. Cell Comp. Physiol.* 34: 413–438.

Lissman, H. W. (1961). "Ecological studies on Gymnotids." In: **Bioelectrogenesis.** (C. Chagas and A. Paes de Carvalho, eds.), pp. 215–226. New York: American Elsevier Publishing Company, Inc.

Lorente de Nó, R. (1947). "Correlation of nerve activity with polarization phenomenon." *Harvey Lect.* 42: 43–105.

Lowry, O. H. (1963). "The chemical study of single neurons." *Harvey Lect.* 58: 1–19.

McCulloch, W. S. and W. H. Pitts (1943). "A logical calculus of the ideas immanent in nervous activity." *Bull. Math. Biophys.* 5: 115–133.

Moore, J. W. (1963). "Operational amplifiers." In: **Physical Techniques in Biological Research.** (W. L. Nastuk, ed.), Vol. 6, part B, pp. 77–98. New York: Academic Press, Inc.

Moore, J. W. and K. S. Cole (1963). "Voltage clamp techniques." In: **Physical Techniques in Biological Research.** (W. L. Nastuk, ed.), Vol. 6, part B, pp. 263–321. New York: Academic Press, Inc.

Moore, J. W., T. Narahashi, and T. I. Shaw (1967). "An upper limit to the number of sodium channels in nerve membrane?" *J. Physiol.* (London) 188: 99–105.

Mosher, H. S., F. A. Fuhrman, H. D. Buchwald, and H. G. Fischer (1964). "Tarichatoxin-tetrodotoxin: a potent neurotoxin." *Science* 144: 1100–1110.

Nachmansohn, D. (1959). **Chemical and Molecular Basis of Nerve Activity.** New York: Academic Press, Inc. 235 pp.

Nakamura, Y., S. Nakajima, and H. Grundfest (1965). "The action of tetrodotoxin on electrogenic components of squid giant axons." *J. Gen. Physiol.* 48: 985–996.

Narahashi, T., N. C. Anderson, and J. W. Moore (1966). "Tetrodotoxin does not block excitation from inside the nerve membrane." *Science* 153: 765–767.

Narahashi, T., J. W. Moore, and W. R. Scott (1964). "Tetrodotoxin blockage of sodium conductance increase in lobster giant axons." *J. Gen. Physiol.* 47: 965–974.

Nastuk, W. L. and A. L. Hodgkin (1950). "The electrical activity of single muscle fibers." *J. Cell. Comp. Physiol.* 35: 39–74.

Newton, I. (1704, reprinted in 1952). **Optics.** New York: Dover Publications, Inc.

Noble, D. (1966). "Applications of Hodgkin-Huxley equations to excitable tissues." *Physiol. Rev.* 46: 1–50.

Oikawa, T., C. S. Spyropoulos, I. Tasaki, and T. Teorell (1961). "Methods for perfusing the giant axon of *Loligo pealii.*" *Acta Physiol. Scand.* **52**: 195–196.

Pappenheimer, J. R., E. M. Renkin, and L. M. Borrero (1951). "Filtration, diffusion, and molecular sieving through peripheral capillary membranes, a contribution to the pore theory of capillary permeability." *Am. J. Physiol.* **167**: 13–46.

Prosser, C. L. and F. A. Brown (1961). **Comparative Animal Physiology,** 2nd ed. Philadelphia: W. B. Saunders Company. 688 pp.

Pumphrey, R. J. and J. Z. Young (1938). "The rates of conduction of nerve fibers of various diameters in cephalopods." *J. Exp. Biol.* **15**: 453–466.

Rashevsky, N. (1936). "Physico-mathematical aspects of excitation and conduction in nerves." *Cold Spring Harbor Symp. Quant. Biol.* **4**: 90–97.

Robertson, J. D. (1955). "The ultrastructure of adult vertebrate peripheral myelinated nerve fibers in relation to myelinogenesis." *J. Biophys. Biochem. Cytol.* **1**: 271–278.

Ruch, T. C., H. D. Patton, J. W. Woodbury, and A. Towe (1965). **Neurophysiology,** 2nd ed. Philadelphia: W. B. Saunders Company. 538 pp.

Rushton, W. A. H. (1937). "The initiation of the propagated disturbance." *Proc. Roy. Soc.* (London) **B124**: 210–243.

Schoenfeld, R. L. (1964). "Bioelectric amplifiers." In: **Physical Techniques in Biological Research.** (W. L. Nastuk, ed.), Vol. 5, part A, pp. 277–352. New York: Academic Press, Inc.

Schoepfle, G. M. and F. E. Bloom (1959). "Effects of cyanide and dinitrophenol on membrane properties of single nerve fibres." *Am. J. Physiol.* **197**: 1131.

Skou, J. C. (1964). "Enzymatic aspects of linked transport of Na^+ and K^+ through the cell membrane." *Prog. Biophys.* **14**: 131–166.

Stämpfli, R. (1959). "Is the resting potential of Ranvier nodes a potassium potential?" *Ann. N.Y. Acad. Sci.* **81**: 265–284.

Staverman, A. J. (1951). "The theory of measurement of osmotic pressure." *Rec. des Travaux Chim. des Pays-Bas.* **70**: 344–352.

Tasaki, I. (1959). "Conductance of the nerve impulse." In: **Handbook of Physiology.** Vol. 1, Sect. 1, Neurophysiology, pp. 75–122. Washington, D.C.: American Physiology Society.

Tasaki, I. and T. Takeuchi (1941). "Der am Ranvierschen Knoten entstehende Aktionsstrom und seine Bedeutung fur die Erregungsleitung." *Pflüg Arch. ges. Physiol.* **244**: 696.

Tasaki, I. and T. Takeuchi (1942). "Weitere Studien über den Aktionsstrom der Markhaltifen Nervenfaser und uber die elektrosattatorische Ubertragung des Nervenimpulses." *Pflüg. Arch. ges. Physiol.* **245**: 764.

Thomas, R. C. and V. J. Wilson (1966). "Marking single neurons by staining with intracellular recording electrodes." *Science* **151**: 1538–1539.

Villegas, R., L. Villegas, M. Gimenez, and G. M. Villegas (1963). "Schwann cell and axon electrical potential differences." *J. Gen. Physiol.* **46**: 1047–1064.

Villegas, J., R. Villegas, and M. Gimenez (1968). "Nature of the Schwann cell electrical potential. Effects of the external ionic concentrations and a cardiac glycoside." *J. Gen. Physiol.* **51**: 47–64.

Whitfield, I. C. (1959). **An Introduction to Electronics for Physiological Workers,** 2nd ed. London: Macmillan and Co., Ltd. 263 pp.

Woodbury, J. W. (1952). "Direct membrane resting and action potentials from single myelinated nerve fibers." *J. Cell Comp. Physiol.* **39**: 323–339.

Woodbury, J. W. (1965). "Action potential: properties of excitable membranes." In: **Neurophysiology.** (T. C. Ruch, H. D. Patton, J. W. Woodbury, and A. L. Towe, eds.), pp. 26–72. Philadelphia: W. B. Saunders Company.

Young, J. Z. (1936). "The structure of nerve fibres and synapses in some invertebrates." *Cold Spring Harbor Symp. Quant. Biol.* **4**: 1–6.

Young, J. Z. (1942). **Doubt and Certainty in Science.** New York: Oxford University Press, Inc.

8-1. Functions of the Dendritic Zone. Of the various potentials listed in Figure 7-4, we have now discussed the conducted action potential and the local potentials and currents of the axonal region. These are the potentials responsible for conducting information rapidly, and often over long distances, in organisms. The all-or-none spike is a feature of all neurons so far examined excepting only the retinula cells of *Limulus* and the rod and cone cells of the vertebrate retina (cells which are not considered as neurons by some workers). The conducted spike is also found in most muscle cells.

According to the discussion of information flow systems and feedback systems of Chapter 1, organisms must possess also (a) mechanisms for receiving information about the internal and external environment; (b) mechanisms for transmitting information from one neuron to another or to an effector cell; and (c) sites for integrating and coordinating information and responses. The dendritic regions of various neurons play a part in all of these activities.

In Chapter 7, the dendritic zone was considered to be composed of either sensory nerve endings or regions of synaptic contact (dendrites, soma, or initial part of the axon) between neurons. Such a classification is convenient because the potentials of these functional regions are similar in many respects but yet are distinct from the action potential. Such a classification does have difficulties because it cannot be inferred, for example, that the somal membrane of all neurons is devoid of spike activity. The soma of the giant nerve cells of *Aplysia* does develop action potentials (Arvanitaki and Chalazonitis, 1955), and there are other cases where this is probably true. Since the classification is convenient it will be used here, but with the proviso that the dendritic zone may include certain regions of the somal membrane, not necessarily all. The classification is a functional, not a morphological, one.

The potentials of axonal and dendritic regions are distinguished in any of several ways. Action potentials are **endogenic**—they result from antecedent activity in the same neuron. Dendritic potentials are **exogenic**—they are initiated in a neuron in response to

Chapter 8

Synaptic and Generator Potentials

extracellular events. Dendritic potentials are often called **transducer potentials** because they represent conversion of various forms of stimulatory energy into bioelectric energies. Both action and dendritic potentials are active potentials, responses of the cell to stimulation.

Dendritic potentials at receptor endings are called **generator potentials**; those at synaptic sites are **synaptic potentials**. A comparison of some of the properties of the action potential and synaptic potential is given in Table 8-1. The different properties of these potentials is a result of membrane differences in the region that produces each. The synaptic zone is generally electrically inexcitable, and axonal membrane is generally electrically excitable. Because of the all-or-none, nondecremental nature of nerve spikes, the activity

of the nervous system was first compared to the action of a digital computer—an on-off type of device (see Bishop, 1956). As we shall see, the dendritic zone potentials add the features of an analog computer type of behavior to the nervous system.

The introduction of microelectrode technique that made possible intracellular recording of potentials from smaller cells than giant fibers led to the discovery that the smaller and more localized synaptic and generator potentials are graded and decremental. The greater the stimulus strength, the greater is the magnitude of these potentials. Nor are these potentials conducted; they decline in strength with distance from their point of origin. The relationship between a synaptic and an action potential in the same neuron is not one-to-one

Table 8-1 Some Characteristics of the Membranes and Potentials of the Axonal and Synaptic Regions of Nerve Cells

Axonal	Synaptic
1. Electrically excitable	1. Electrically inexcitable
Initiating Action	
2. Sequential increase in Na^+ and then K^+ conductances; Na^+ inactivation.	2. Two types: (a) increased conductance of all ions, or (b) specific increase of K^+ and/or Cl^- conductance.
3. Rate of potential generation determined by membrane potential.	3. Rate of potential generation not determined by membrane potential.
Electrical Response	
4. All-or-none spike	4. Graded response depending on stimulus strength.
5. Starts with graded depolarization (effect of local currents) and usually develops overshoot.	5. Two types: (a) depolarizing (b) hyperpolarizing
Results of Differences	
6. Spike always in polarizing direction	6. Potential may be either positive or negative
7. Pulsatile; with short duration not dependent on stimulus.	7. May be prolonged while stimulus lasts.
8. Decrementless propagation	8. Nonpropagated potential.
9. Relatively inert to chemicals	9. Sensitive to chemicals. Responses are: (a) evoked by activators readily. (b) readily depressed or blocked by inhibitors.

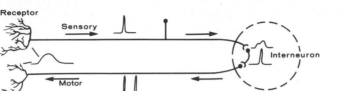

Figure 8-1 Schematic diagram of the different functional regions found in neurons. A neuronal chain consisting of a sensory neuron, interneuron, and motor neuron is shown. This is the pattern of a reflex arc. As shown, spikes are found in the axonal (conducting) regions of neurons, whereas smaller, longer durationed, and summating receptor or synaptic potentials are found at synapses or receptor endings (the dendritic regions of neurons).

generally, that is, one arriving action potential at a synapse produces a synaptic potential that is usually not large enough to create an action potential in that neuron.

Figure 8-1 diagrams, in highly schematic fashion, the different types of potentials that can exist in the various functional regions of a neuron—a two-neuron-one-effector-cell pathway is shown. The neuron can be divided into four functional regions (see, for example, Kandel and Spencer, 1968): (1) the input component, consisting of subsynaptic membrane—that membrane region directly affected by activity in a preceding neuron. This is the site of generation of synaptic potentials which may be either excitatory or inhibitory—either depolarizing or hyperpolarizing. (2) The integrative component, which is usually the initial segment of the axon—only if net depolarization exceeds the threshold value is a spike initiated. (3) The conductile region—the axonal region along which a spike is conducted. (4) The output component—the arrival of a spike at the terminal ends of an axon can initiate activity in a following neuron or effector cell either by the release of a specific chemical substance or by the flow of electrical currents. Regions 1 and 2 correspond to the dendritic zone as described above; regions 3 and 4 are part of the axonal region of the neuron.

In the remainder of this chapter, we shall consider the nature of the dendritic zone and the mechanisms that produce its potentials. Much more is known about the generation of potentials in the synaptic region than in the receptor regions of neurons.

Synapses

8-2. Definition of a Synapse. Once the neuron theory was accepted by physiologists, it was a necessary and consequent assumption that nerve cells were related not by continuity of their protoplasm but by contiguity or functional contact. Although this idea was fostered by the histological studies of Cajal and others, it was not until the development of the electron microscope that such cellular relationships could be studied in their morphological detail. On the basis of physiological evidence, the famous neurophysiologist, Sir Charles Sherrington, came to the conclusion that functional contacts existed between neurons and he named these functional entities **synapses** (from the Greek συναπτω, to clasp; Foster and Sherrington, 1897). Sherrington supposed that the properties of synapses derived from the characteristics of the membranes of neurons.

In Sherrington's (1906) classic studies of integrative action in the central nervous system, he found a fatigability, a sensitivity to anesthetics and oxygen depletion, a one-way conduction of impulses, and a delay in information flow in reflex arcs. These features he attributed to the synaptic region because nerve trunks, that is, axons, did not exhibit these characteristics. However, in Sherrington's time, Cajal and others believed these to be axonal properties. The history of the development of the neuronal and synaptic theories has been described by Eccles (1957); Grundfest (1959); Liddel (1960); McLennan (1963).

The synapse is defined as a functional connection between distinct neurons accomplished through contact or near contact of their membranes (Bullock and Horridge, 1965). The definition can be made more general to include functional connections between any two excitable cells, since the junction between a neuron and an effector cell, for example the myoneural junction, has similar characteristics to many nerve-nerve junctions.

There are some difficulties with this definition. They arise primarily from a lack of physiological or morphological information. The variety of known synapses with their different features that are being discovered is another complicating factor. Some cells are known to have functional relationships, but whether they are separate or syncytial systems is not known—a situation that will improve as the techniques of electron microscopy are refined. In other cases excitable cells in contact with one another have not yet been shown to have any functional relationships. In the central nervous system, for example, contacts between neurons and supporting cells (oligocytes, astrocytes, and so forth) are known, but it is doubtful that they are functionally related, at least in terms of information transmission by impulses (see Section 8-22).

Finally, we may note that the definition of a synapse as given above does not include any statement as to required structures or mechanisms. Although features such as chemical transmission, one-way transmission, or fatigability are common to many synapses; they are not found in all functional contacts between excitable cells.

The concept of the synapse does require definition of several general morphological

features of the contact. The neuron contributing the axon or axon terminals, that is, the source of the incoming action potential, is the **presynaptic neuron**: the cell contributing the dendritic sites is the **postsynaptic neuron**. The membrane of the presynaptic neuron that is applied to the synaptic area of the postsynaptic neuron is the **presynaptic membrane**. The area of postsynaptic membrane—the membrane of the postsynaptic neuron affected by the presynaptic neuron—that is directly under the presynaptic membrane is the **subsynaptic membrane**. These relationships are diagrammed in Figure 8-2.

The presynaptic site is usually the ending of an axon terminal, although some synaptic connections are made along the axon, for example in giant fiber systems in crustaceans and annelids. The postsynaptic membrane may be that of a dendrite, the soma membrane, the axon hillock, or in a few cases on the axon itself. In invertebrates most synapses are between axon terminals and fine dendrites in the central nervous system (making a tangle of fine fibrous processes with neuroglial cells and nerve cell bodies interspersed in a structure known as the **neuropile**. Most synapses of the vertebrate central nervous system are between axon terminals and the somal membrane. The postsynaptic membrane may also be that of a muscle or other effector cell. In most, but not all, synapses information is carried from presynaptic to postsynaptic cell.

8-3. General Types of Synapses. Many types of synapses are known based on both morphological and physiological criteria. A few morphological types are shown in Figure 8-3. In this section only some grosser anatomical

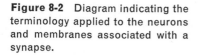

Figure 8-2 Diagram indicating the terminology applied to the neurons and membranes associated with a synapse.

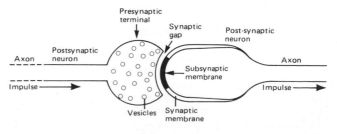

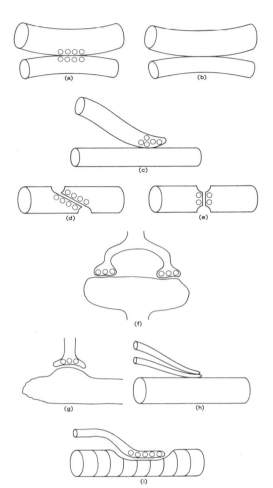

Figure 8-3 Schematic representations of some types of synaptic contacts. (a) Axon-axon type, with synaptic vesicles on both sides of synapse. (b) Axon-axon type, with no synaptic vesicles. (c) Axon terminal ending on small dendrite, often found in the invertebrate neuropile. Synaptic vesicles found only in axon. (d) Septal synapse found in the earthworm. Synaptic vesicles on both sides of synapse. This is an axon-axon contact. (e) Crustacean septal synapse with restricted area of contact between axons. (f) *Bouton terminaux* endings typical of axon-dendrite synapses in vertebrate central nervous system. (g) Spine synapses between axon and dendrite found in vertebrate cerebral cortex. The postsynaptic region is specialized. (h) Serial synapse, axon-axon-dendrite. Found in spinal cord, cerebral cortex, and plexiform layer of retina in vertebrates. (i) Neuromuscular endings found in vertebrate striated muscle with postsynaptic grooves and infolding of membrane.

features of synapses will be considered; later sections will discuss the ultrastructural details of some synaptic connections.

A common type of synapse involves the **bouton terminaux**, prominent in motoneurons of the ventral horn of the spinal cord and medulla of vertebrates. This ending is characterized by a knoblike enlargement of the axon terminal (Figure 8-3). The bouton is one of several synaptic types possessing swellings or enlargements of the axon terminal. The bouton is typical of bud or foot endings. Endings which cover a large area of the postsynaptic cell are known as cup or calix endings. Also found are club endings with a thick terminal axon connection, although swelling is absent.

The **calyciform synapse** in the chick ciliary ganglion (a sympathetic ganglion of the autonomic nervous system) is an unusual synapse physiologically (Section 8-16). Its structure is shown in Figure 8-4.

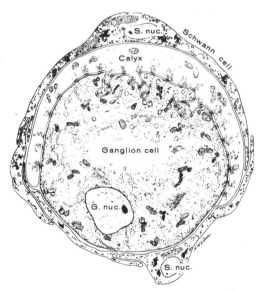

Figure 8-4 Calyciform synapse in the ciliary ganglion of the chick. This schematic drawing incorporates the principal details revealed by the electron microscope. The calyx is shown bordering on a large area of the ganglion cell surface. Active sites are indicated as regions of thickened membranes and clusters of synaptic vesicles. [By permission from A. J. de Lorenzo, (1960) *Journal Biochemical and Biophysical Cytology* 7: 31-36.]

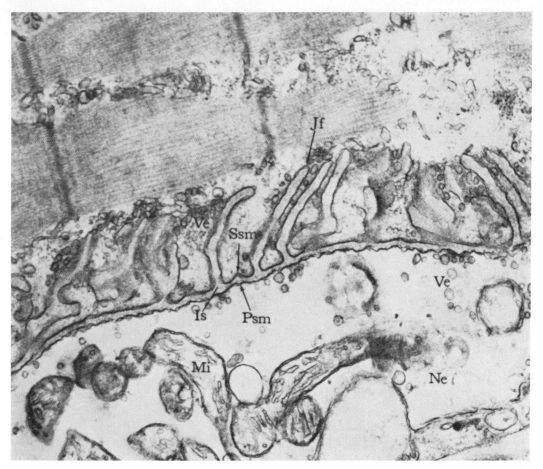

Figure 8-5 Detail of a vertebrate motor end plate, showing the junction between a motor nerve ending and the striated muscle. The cytoplasm of the nerve ending (Ne) contains several mitochondria (Mi) and small synaptic vesicles (Ve). The axoplasm is bordered by a membrane, usually called the presynaptic membrane (Psm). The nerve ending inserts into the postsynaptic region (Ssm) of the muscle plasma membrane which has a complex system of narrow, longitudinal infoldings, the junctional folds (Jf). The synaptic cleft (Is) is occupied by an amorphous substance that is structurally identical with the basement membrane. The sarcoplasm also contains vesicles (Ve) near the junctional folds. [By permission from J. A. G. Rhodin (1963) *An Atlas of Ultrastructure* © 1963 by W. B. Saunders Company, Philadelphia.]

The vertebrate myoneural junction or motor end plate has been extensively studied because of its relatively large size and because it is simpler than central nervous synapses in having only one motor axon terminal making contact. The motor end plate is characterized by an infolding of the postsynaptic membrane (Figures 8-5, 8-6, and 8-7). Some of the myoneural junctions of invertebrates have also been studied (Figure 8-8).

Table 8-2 lists the salient features of some of the better studied synapses. An examination of this table will point out the types of known connections between neurons; the animal groups that have been studied; and the mechanisms of synaptic transmission. Summaries of synaptic types are found in Bodian (1942, 1962); Eccles, (1964); DeRobertis (1964); and Bullock and Horridge (1965).

8-4. Number and Distribution of Synaptic Endings. In some cases where neurons and

Table 8-2 Morphological Characteristics of Some Synapses

PREPARATION[*]	TYPE AND STRUCTURE OF SYNAPSE	TRANSMISSION MODE AND PHYSIOLOGICAL ACTIVITY
Coelenterate nerve net[1]	Axon-to-axon (en passant) or axon-soma. Two axons in lateral contact. Vesicles on both sides. Synaptic gap: 180–220 Å.	Electrical (?), short delay. Two-way transmission (?)
Septal segmental junctions in earthworm giant fibers[2]	Axon-to-axon abutment. Unit membranes apposed over large area. Vesicles (few) on both sides. Synaptic gap: ≈ 100 Å.	Electrical. Two way transmission. Septa with low electrical resistance.
Septal segmental junctions in crayfish giant fibers[2]	Axon-to-axon abutment. Unit membranes apposed over small area. Vesicles (few) on both sides. Synaptic gap: ≈ 100 Å.	Electrical. Two way transmission. Septa with low electrical resistance.
Giant fiber to motoneuron in crayfish[2]	Axon-to-minute-dendrite. Vesicles (few) on both sides, either side, or absent.	Electrical. Rectifying junction with one-way transmission.
Calyciform synapse in chick ciliary ganglion[3]	Enlarged axon ending about most of cell body. Presynaptic vesicles only. Synaptic gap: 300–400 Å.	Chemical (cholinergic) and electrical. One-to-one transmission with parallel paths.
Cat cerebral cortex synapses[4]	Axon-soma and axon-dendrite. Dense regions along postsynaptic sides of membrane or on both sides. Vesicles presynaptic only. Synaptic gap: 200–300 Å.	Transmission unknown.
Inhibitory axon to muscle receptor organ cell of crayfish[5]	Axon-soma and axon-dendrite. Apposed membranes. Vesicles presynaptic only. Synaptic gap: 200 Å.	Transmission not known. No ACh. Inhibitory junction.
Bouton-terminaux in mammalian spinal cord[6]	Axon terminal to soma and dendrites. Swelling of axon endings abut on soma membrane. Vesicles presynaptic only. Synaptic gap: 120 Å.	Chemical transmission. Excitatory (?); much spatial summation.
Vertebrate motor endplate	Axon aborization terminating on muscle membrane. Many presynaptic vesicles. Muscle membrane highly infolded. Synaptic gap: 500–1,000 Å.	Chemical transmission, ACh. One-to-one impulse transmission.
Insect leg motor endplate[7]	Axon in groove of muscle. Repeated axon-muscle membrane contacts, en passant. Vesicles presynaptic only. No muscle membrane infolding. Synaptic gap: ≈ 120 Å.	Chemical (?). Graded postsynaptic responses; temporal summation.
Neuromuscular inhibitory synapse of crayfish muscle receptor organ[5]	Axon to muscle. Vesicles on both sides. Gap very narrow.	Chemical (?) Inhibitory activity.

[*] References indicated by superscripts: (1) Horridge et al. (1962); (2) DeLorenzo (1959, 1960); (3) DeLorenzo (1960a); (4) DeRobertis (1964); (5) Peterson and Pepe (1961); (6) Palay (1958); (7) Edwards et al (1958).

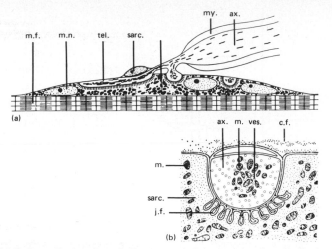

Figure 8-6 (a) Schematic drawing of a motor end plate seen in a longitudinal section of the muscle fiber. ax., axoplasm with its mitochondria; my., myelin sheath; tel., teloglia; sarc., sarcoplasm with its mitochondria; m.n., muscle nuclei. The terminal nerve branches lie in synaptic gutters or troughs. (b) Schematic drawing of a synaptic gutter, or trough seen in cross section. ves., synaptic vesicles; j.f., junctional folds; c.f., collagen fibers (after Robertson). [By permission from R. Couteaux (1960) "Motor end-plate structure" *The Structure and Function of Muscle* (G. H. Bourne, editor), Vol. 1, pp. 337–380. New York: Academic Press, Inc.].

synaptic processes are relatively large, measurements have been made of the numbers and distribution of synaptic endings. In large motoneurons of the vertebrate spinal cord, Haggar and Barr (1950) calculated that there are as many as 1,200 to 1,800 endfeet per cell and that 38 per cent of the postsynaptic surface is covered with synaptic contacts. The size of the individual boutons varies between 0.3 and 4.5 μ^2. The area of surface contact per bouton varies between 1 and 2 μ^2, although in a few cases it is as high as 100 μ^2.

Minkler (1940) found 23 terminals per 100 μ^2 in human motoneurons and 14.5 per 100 μ^2 in sensory neurons of the spinal cord. Silver staining techniques used to visualize neurons and their connections have been improved and Minckler's findings have been confirmed. Wyckoff and Young (1956) estimated vertebrate motoneurons to possess 15 to 20 endfeet per 100 μ^2 of postsynaptic surface. Since the total surface area of these cells is about 10,000 μ^2, there are not less than 1,500 end feet per cell.

Hydén (1960) calculated that on isolated neurons of Deiter's nucleus there were 15 to 20 synaptic knobs per 100 μ^2. The total surface area of this cell is about 50,000 μ^2, so there

are about 10,000 synaptic contacts per cell.

From these figures it is evident that synaptic connections on a given postsynaptic cell may represent a complex network of junctions. The endings on a given postsynaptic neuron are usually of diverse types, although in a few cases the endings appear to be homogeneous. The complex patterning of synaptic connections and resultant action potentials are responsible for the integrative features of nervous systems. As previously stated, overall a nervous system does not function on the basis of all-or-none activity; this is the mechanism of conduction only.

Whereas the general distribution of synaptic connections on some larger neurons is known, little has been done with similar analyses of smaller neurons or with neurons from invertebrates. A major deterrent to such studies in any animal is the small size of synaptic contacts and the complexity of fine interconnections exemplified by the neuropile.

8-5. Ultrastructure of Synapses. The electron microscope has brought to light details of synaptic structure that aid in understanding synaptic function. In a majority of synapses so far studied there is a gap—the **synaptic cleft**—

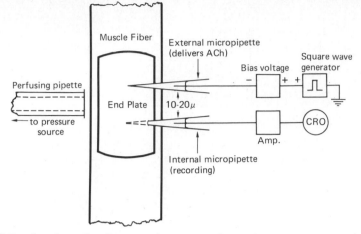

Figure 8-7 A schematic diagram of one experimental arrangement used to study transmembrane potentials in a muscle end plate. Electrical pulses applied to the external micropipet electrophoretically apply acetylcholine to the end plate region. The internal micropipet is used to record the resulting transmembrane potential changes. [*Annals of The New York Academy of Sciences*, Vol. 81, Art. 2, Fig. 1, pg. 318, W. L. Nastuk. © The New York Academy of Sciences, 1959. Reprinted by permission.]

between the pre- and postsynaptic membranes. This gap is about 100 to 200 Å in most synapses, although in the vertebrate myoneural junction it may be as large as 1,000 Å.

At some synapses the membranes show regions of closer proximity and even a fusion of the outer layers of the unit membranes of the pre- and postsynaptic cells. These **tight junctions** have been found, for example, in certain teleost spinal neurons (Bennett et al., 1963) and in synapses associated with giant axons in crayfish (Hama, 1961). Tight junctions are associated with synapses which transmit information by electrical mechanisms.

DeRobertis and Bennett (1954) demonstrated the presence of **synaptic vesicles** in neurons of the earthworm neuropile. Simultaneously Palade and Palay (1954) reported the presence of small membrane-bounded vesicles in the axon endings of several central nervous system synapses and in the neuromuscular junction of vertebrates.

These vesicles are bounded by a 40 to 50 Å thick unit membrane. The spherical or ovoid-shaped particles have a major diameter in the range of 200 to 650 Å. In the myoneural junction the vesicles are about 500 Å in diameter (Birks et al., 1960). These vesicles, at least in some cases, are the source of chemical substances used to transmit the impulse across a synaptic cleft and they have been related to the quantal release of transmitter (del Castillo and Katz, 1954; see Section 8-8).

Originally, because vesicles were associated with chemical transmission, it was thought that their presence at a synaptic ending would be evidence of such transmission. And it was further thought they would be found only on the presynaptic side of the junction. However, vesicles are found at electrically transmitting junctions (see Table 8-2) and in some cases, for example, in junctions between coelenterate neurons, are found on both sides of the junction (Horridge et al., 1962). The distribution of vesicles varies from synapse to synapse. In the myoneural junction, at the motoneuron-electroplaque junction in the electric organ of the eel, and in many other synapses, there is an orderly distribution of vesicles close to the presynaptic membrane. In some synapses, for example, central synapses in the cerebral cortex, or rod and cone synapses in the retina, the vesicles fill the axon endings homogeneously.

The number of vesicles also differs according to the synapse. In the adrenal medulla are found about 82 vesicles per μ^2 of tissue section (DeRobertis, 1964). This is equivalent to about 1,600 vesicles per μ^3. In human motor end plates a population density of about 250 vesicles per μ^2 is found—corresponding to a total number of vesicles per junction of about 3×10^6 (De Harven and Cöers, 1959).

Although in most typical synapses the presence of vesicles is taken as an indication of chemical transmitter activity, vesicles must also play other roles. Microvesicles are found not only at nerve endings but also in other regions of neurons.

Mitochondria are also found at synaptic endings. In boutons the number varies from about 4 to 9 per ending, and these are higher concentrations than in other similar sized parts of the neuron. In some species rod and

cone cells lack mitochondria, an important observation since it has often been hypothesized that mitochondria are essential to synaptic transmission (Bodian, 1942; De-Robertis and Franchi, 1956). Where present, mitochondria are considered to provide energy for the synthesis or the release of chemicals contained in the vesicles and needed for synaptic functioning.

In some synapses thin intersynaptic filaments seem to provide an anchoring mechanism for the pre- and postsynaptic membranes (DeRobertis et al., 1961). In some vertebrate central nervous system synapses a subsynaptic web of filaments is found. This web attaches to the subsynaptic membrane and projects

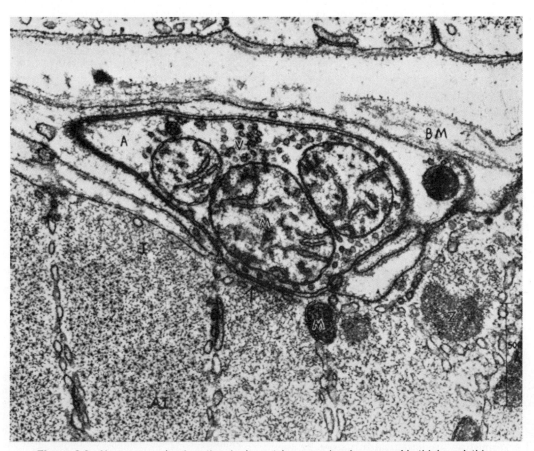

Figure 8-8 Neuromuscular junction in locust leg muscle. A, axon; AI, thick and thin contractile elements in A-1 region of sarcomere (transverse section); BM, basement membrane; M, mitochondria; V, presynaptic vesicles; Z, Z line of muscle fiber [From P. N. R. Usherwood, (1967) "Insect neuromuscular mechanisms" *American Zoologist* 7: 553–582.]

inward for a variable distance into the post-synaptic cell's cytoplasm. Neurofilaments, neurofibrils, and synaptic webs may all participate in holding together the pre- and postsynaptic cells. In some cases it has been found that treatment such as centrifugation will cause the postsynaptic membrane to break away from its own cell before it releases from the presynaptic terminal—an indication that the postsynaptic membrane is more firmly attached to the presynaptic membrane than to the remainder of its own cell membrane (Whittaker and Gray, 1962).

The electron microscope reveals patches of increased density and thickening on some synaptic membranes, and at these points there is often a greater concentration of synaptic vesicles. These specialized regions, resembling desmosomes, may be sites for extruding transmitter substances, or, less likely, for the adhesion of synaptic membranes (Figure 8-9).

8-6. Chemical Versus Electrical Transmission. Paralleling the opposed morphological hypotheses of separate versus continuous neural elements, there arose a similar dichotomy of ideas to explain synaptic transmission. Electrical transmission implies a functional continuity in that transmission is by a continuation of processes similar to those responsible for axon impulse propagation. Chemical transmission implies that the mechanisms responsible for impulse conduction stop at the presynaptic membrane—that a chemical substance (transmitter) is released by the presynaptic terminals—and that the transmitter specifically reacts with the postsynaptic membrane to produce a potential change that can finally lead to the formation of a postsynaptic impulse in the axonal region of the cell.

Historically, before the development of these ideas on electrical and chemical transmission, some physiologists thought that conduction was due to chemical processes and transmission was electrical in nature. In this case also there would be a discontinuity of mechanisms at the synapse. As described in Chapter 7, however, the conduction of

impulses is by local electrical currents, not by chemical means.

As far as synaptic transmission is concerned, as has been the case with so many biological arguments, both sides were partially correct, because both chemically and electrically transmitting synapses have now been found.

Before much was known about the structure or potentials of the synaptic region, most physiologists believed that electrical transmission was the mechanism for synaptic activity. But in 1904 Elliot suggested that sympathetic neurons released a chemical similar to adrenalin because smooth muscle activity was initiated by these neurons, and such activity closely resembled that produced when adrenalin was secreted by the adrenal glands. In 1906 Dixon proposed that muscarine-like substances were released by parasympathetic neurons (reviewed by Dale, 1914, 1936).

Chemical transmission was established as one mechanism of synaptic functioning when

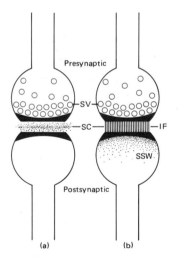

Figure 8-9 Schematic drawings of some types of synaptic membrane contacts. Membrane thickenings are exaggerated for illustrative purposes. (a) Type of synaptic contact often found on dendritic spines. The synaptic cleft contains a small amount of dense material. (b) Type of synapse found in the brain (cortex) of the rat. IF, intersynaptic filaments; SC, synaptic cleft; SV, presynaptic vesicles; SSW subsynaptic web of filaments.

Otto Loewi (1921, reviewed in 1933) demonstrated that a stimulated vagus nerve released a substance that inhibited cardiac muscle activity. The transmission from the nerve endings to cardiac muscle cells had to be chemical in nature because the perfusion fluid collected from a frog heart whose vagus had been stimulated could be used to inhibit the beat of another isolated frog heart. The vagus normally slows contraction of cardiac cells.

The Vagusstoff of Loewi was subsequently identified as acetylcholine, ACh (the structures of various chemical transmitters are given in Table 8-3). Dale and Vogt (1936) proved that ACh is released in the vertebrate myoneural junction during activity, and it has subsequently been shown that ACh acts as the transmitter at this synapse. Loewi demonstrated that sympathetic neurons to the heart —fibers which have an antagonistic action on the heart as compared with the vagus fibers— released a transmitter which he named accelerating substance; others called it sympathin. This cardioaccelerator was identified as noradrenaline, thus substantiating Elliot's earlier guess (von Euler, 1946).

Only in the case of the vertebrate myoneural junction and some endings of the autonomic nervous system has it been possible to positively identify the transmitter substances. Other synapses release such small quantities of transmitter or are so much less sensitive to transmitter action, that chemical analysis is impossible. Acetylcholine and noradrenalin are the only two firmly established transmitters, although, as we shall see, several other compounds are suspected of this function in various synapses and have much evidence in their favor.

The results of Loewi and other workers led to the belief that all synapses were chemically transmitting. But this overgeneralization was disproven when Furshpan and Potter (1959) found a giant fiber synapse in the crayfish abdominal nerve cord which operated by electrical transmission of impulses. Furukawa and Furshpan (1963) demonstrated the presence of an electrically transmitting, inhibitory ending on the large Mauthner cell of the goldfish cerebral cortex. Electrical transmission has now been found in a variety of synaptic junctions, although chemical transmission is still the most commonly found mechanism.

The feasibility of electrical transmission at most synapses appears dubious because of the presence of the synaptic cleft. This gap is filled with the extracellular medium and it would have an electrical resistance many times lower than that of the postsynaptic membrane. Therefore, electrical currents established by an incoming action potential would tend to flow through the lower resistance pathway of the gap, rather than through the postsynaptic membrane. Only if currents flow through the latter could permeability changes be produced that could lead to the generation of a synaptic potential. In addition, the contact area of the presynaptic membrane is so much smaller than the total area of the postsynaptic membrane (at least in most known synapses) that it appears unlikely that enough current could flow from pre- to postsynaptic neurons to effectively change the potential of the latter.

On the basis of cable theory and from a knowledge of the leakage resistance at synapses ($R_m = 2,000$ ohm-cm^2) and leakage capacitance ($C_m = 1\mu f$), it is possible to calculate the probability of electrical transmission (Katz, 1966). An impulse traveling along a $5\ \mu$ diameter axon faces an input impedance of about 20 megohms. Activation of the membrane ahead of the impulse requires that sufficient current must flow into it to lower the resting potential by about 15 per cent of its normal value. At this level excitation occurs and the resulting change in potential is higher than the local potentials by a factor of ten and excitation provides sufficient current flow to excite the next region of the axon.

With the introduction of a synaptic gap, the potential is attenuated by a factor of a thousand (Figure 8-10), if the properties of the synaptic membrane are at all similar to those of the axonal region. This argument depends, however, on the assumption that axonal and dendritic membranes are similar, but as already stated they have obvious differences

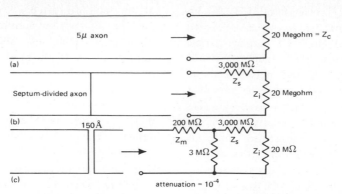

Both resistance and impedance in an electrical circuit tend to oppose the flow of current. The measure of this opposition is the impedance, Z. From the cable properties of axons, the impedance may be defined by

$$Z = \sqrt{R_m R_i / 2\pi^2 r^3} \sqrt{1 + 4\pi^2 f^2 R_m^2 C_m^2}$$

Symbols (and typical values for axons)
R_m (membrane resistance) = 2,000 ohm/cm^2
R_i (internal resistance) = 200 ohm/cm
C_m (membrane capacitance) = 1 μF/cm^2
r (fiber radius)
f (frequency of alternating current at which impedance is measured) = 250 cycles per second

Figure 8-10 (a) The input impedance of a typical axon 5μ in diameter is about 20 megohms (MΩ). Sufficient current must flow to lower the resting potential by about 20 mV just ahead of the action potential, if the membrane is to be activated and the impulse conducted. The increase in sodium conductance at excitation produces sufficient current to excite the next region of the membrane. (b) If the axon were divided by a septum whose properties are similar to those of the surface membrane (in so far as specific electrical resistance is concerned), then 3,000 MΩ are placed across the line in front of the 20 MΩ cable impedance. The effectiveness of the local currents are reduced to less than 1 per cent of normal and conduction is blocked. Note that a similar effect is obtained by cold blocking or narcotizing a sufficient length of membrane (see Figure 7-32). (c) If the case of two separate axons, separated by a gap of about 150 Å, is considered, the situation with respect to current flow is now worsened. There are two cable structures connected by an electrical network of high loss. There is a series impedance of the terminal presynaptic membrane, a parallel resistance of the gap, and another series impedance of the postsynaptic membrane. Even considering that the presynaptic membrane's resistance falls from 2,000 to 40 ohm/cm^2 upon activation, there is still an attenuation of current by a factor of 10^{-4} (the attenuation is equal to (3 MΩ/200 MΩ) (20 MΩ/3,000 MΩ). Thus, the possibilities for excitation by current flow in this situation are unlikely. Unless the cells are much larger (as for some giant fiber synapses) or the membrane electrical properties are different, chemical transmission is required.

that may extend to their electrical characteristics. If the potential is attenuated, then it can have no effect on the synaptic membrane.

However, there are synapses at which electrical transmission, although unproven, is likely to occur. The terminal membrane impedance falls with the inverse square of the fiber diameter. In some giant fiber synapses, the attenuation of potential across a septum would only be by a factor of ten, and slight modifications of membrane properties could easily bring about the conditions needed for electrical transmission. In fact, electrically transmitting synapses are not uncommon at giant fiber synapses (Table 8-2). The necessary modifications to allow potentials and currents across the postsynaptic membrane can include fusion of membranes, the presence of minute cytoplasmic bridges, the presence of conducting tubules or fibrils between cells, increased membrane porosity, or molecular rearrangements to reduce membrane resistance. As we have already seen, membrane fusion has been observed in some giant fiber synapses.

Mechanisms of Chemical Transmission

8-7. Steps in Chemical Transmission. The basic steps thought to occur in chemical transmission are

1. The release of a chemical transmitter in quantal units upon the arrival of an action potential at an axon terminal (or in a few cases at some other portion of the axon.)
2. Diffusion of the transmitter substance across the synaptic gap and its attachment to specific receptor sites on the outer surface of the subsynaptic membrane.
3. Permeability changes in the subsynaptic membrane brought about by the complexing of the transmitter with the membrane molecules.
4. The initiation of ionic current flows in the dendritic region of the postsynaptic cell.
5. Generation of either an excitatory postsynaptic potential (EPSP) or an inhibitory postsynaptic potential (IPSP). The excitatory potentials of the myoneural junction are the end plate potentials (EPP) sometimes called postjunctional potentials (PJP). These synaptic potentials may be depolarizing (and usually therefore stimulatory) or they may be hyperpolarizing (and therefore inhibitory in that they prevent the lowering of the membrane resting potential).
6. If the synaptic potentials are great enough to create sufficiently strong local currents, a spike is generated in the appropriate region of the postsynaptic cell.
7. A mechanism is present, of enzymatic nature, to destroy the transmitter quickly so that normal subsynaptic resting potentials are restored and the region is ready to respond to a new incoming spike.

The evidence for these steps is presented in the following sections.

8-8. Transmitter Release. In Section 8-6 we saw some reasons for believing that the structure of most synapses precludes direct electrical transmission of a nerve impulse from one cell to another. In chemically transmitting synapses the actual synaptic area is so small and the gap so relatively large that any significant current flow from pre- to postsynaptic neuron is prevented. In those synapses large enough for the insertion of intracellular electrodes, that is, in a certain ganglion between giant axons in the squid, it has been shown that there is no electrical coupling between neurons (Bullock and Hagiwara, 1957). A presynaptic action potential produces, by itself, no change in the membrane potential of the postsynaptic cell nor do applied electrical stimuli to the postsynaptic neuron cause any potential changes in the presynaptic neuron.

The vertebrate myoneural junction has been extensively studied with respect to chemical transmission mechanisms because it is relatively large. ACh is found in high concentration in the motor axon terminals. Repetitive stimulation of the motoneuron causes the release of measurable amounts of ACh into the perfusion fluid of experimental preparations. This one piece of evidence that ACh is the transmitter is also supported by the finding of the enzyme, choline acetyltransferase [E.C. 2.3.1.6], only in the motoneuron terminals. This is the enzyme needed to synthesize ACh.

Activity of the muscle in releasing ACh was ruled out by experiments in which repetitive stimulation of a denervated muscle showed no release of ACh (Dale and Vogt, 1936). Also, stimulation of the motoneuron in the presence of curare, a drug which prevents the attachment of ACh to the muscle membrane, still allows impulses to reach the axon terminals and normal quantities of ACh to be produced, although the muscle membrane does not respond (Katz, and Miledi, 1965; Krnjević and Mitchell, 1961).

Although chemical transmission is associated with synaptic vesicles, few facts are known concerning the mechanisms involved in transmitter synthesis, accumulation in vesicles, or release. DeRobertis (1964) and Whittaker (1964), using density gradient centrifugation and electron microscope observations of cellular fractions, were able to isolate and identify vesicles from central nervous system axon terminals. They contained the ACh of the nerve cell. Choline acetyltransferase appeared to be part of the vesicular apparatus. Only vesicles in the presynaptic neuron contain ACh.

Just prior to the discovery of synaptic vesicles Fatt and Katz (1950, 1952) described spontaneous potentials recorded from the motor end plate with microelectrodes. These potentials—**miniature end plate potentials (MEPP)**—are similar to normal end plate potentials except for their smaller magnitude (ca. 0.05 mV) and their random occurrence in the absence of any presynaptic action potentials. They are suppressed by curare and enhanced in strength and duration by cholinesterase inhibitors (see Section 8-9).

These potentials have been related to momentary increases in membrane ionic conductance and associated inward pulses of ion current. Such potentials have now been found in synapses in both vertebrate and invertebrate central nervous systems as well as in all types of vertebrate myoneural junctions.

Although miniature potentials arise in the motor end plate or postsynaptic region, their cause lies in the spontaneous release of ACh by the presynaptic terminal. Spontaneous activity disappears some days after a motoneuron has been cut and has degenerated. Botulinum toxin, which irreversibly stops ACh release, also causes the disappearance of the MEPP (Brooks, 1956). The frequency of discharge is controlled by the membrane potential of the nerve terminal and not by the muscle fiber potential (del Castillo and Katz, 1954).

The release of ACh is in quantal units, and the MEPP represents a spontaneous release of a quantum of ACh, caused perhaps by a spilling over of excess transmitter from the presynaptic terminal. The term quantum is used here in the sense of some small certain amount of ACh released from a fixed number of vesicles. No specific function has, as yet, been related to this spontaneous release of ACh.

Upon stimulation of the presynaptic neuron, the EPP becomes larger because increased numbers of vesicles are releasing transmitter.

It is assumed that each nerve impulse arriving at an axon terminal releases a given amount of ACh from some given number of vesicles. Summation of the EPP will result at higher frequencies of arriving impulses and a consequent greater release of ACh. The discovery of the MEPP and of synaptic vesicles containing transmitter and their relationships to quantal transmitter release contribute some of the most convincing evidence to date for the nature of chemical transmission.

The permeability changes to Na^+ and K^+ associated with the nerve impulse are not necessary for transmitter release. Tetramethylammonium ions (TEA) iontophoretically injected into the presynaptic axon of a squid giant fiber synapse produce a prolonged postsynaptic potential and spike. When tetrodotoxin is used to bathe such a synapse, there is no modification of the postsynaptic potentials although tetrodotoxin prevents the permeability changes to Na^+ and K^+ associated with the spike.

It is suggested that Ca^{2+} currents may be required to release transmitter. Many types of experiments have shown that Ca^{2+} is an essential factor for transmitter release. Mg^{2+} inhibits this activity (del Castillo and Katz, 1954; Katz and Miledi, 1965). If the Ca^{2+} concentration is lowered and Mg^{2+} is added (5 to 10 mM Mg^{2+}; normal Mg^{2+} concentration at the neuromuscular junction is about 1 mM) to an experimental preparation, the quantity of ACh released is reduced to low levels and this is reflected in a reduction of the EPP in steps—another indication that quantal units of transmitter are released (Boyd and Martin, 1954).

8-9. Action of Transmitter on Subsynaptic Membranes. Once a transmitter is released by the presynaptic terminal, it must diffuse across the synaptic gap and bond to specific sites on the subsynaptic membrane. The diffusion is no problem. For example, in the case of the neuromuscular junction, it is estimated that ACh is released from 100 to 300 presynaptic sites and must cross a distance less than 1 μ.

In the normal mammalian striated muscle

fiber, only the end plate region of the membrane is sensitive to ACh, although after chronic denervation of the muscle, the whole fiber membrane becomes sensitive to ACh. The slow fibers of frog skeletal muscle have ACh sensitivity over a large region of their membrane under normal conditions. The fast fibers of frog skeletal muscle are like mammalian muscle cells in respect to their ACh sensitivity.

ACh—a quaternary ammonium base (Table 8-3)—is a strong base and exists as a cation at physiological pH. ACh might act to depolarize the postsynaptic membrane simply by thermodynamic effects similar to those of K^+. But it has been shown that the prolonged depolarization of the end plate brought about by the application of the drug eserine could not depend on thermodynamic effects because the amount of ACh needed is several orders of

Table 8-3 Some Synaptic Transmitters and their Analogs*

NAME (AND MOLECULAR WEIGHT)	STRUCTURAL FORMULA
Acetylcholine (146.07; as the chloride, 181.7)	$CH_3-\overset{\overset{O}{\|\|}}{C}-CH_2-CH_2-\overset{+}{N}-(CH_3)_3$
*Carbachol (147)	$NH_2-\overset{\overset{O}{\|\|}}{C}-CH_2-CH_2-\overset{+}{N}-(CH_3)_3$
*Succinylcholine (290)	$CH_2-\overset{\overset{O}{\|\|}}{C}-O-CH_2-CH_2-\overset{+}{N}-(CH_3)_3$
Noradrenalin (= norepinephrine) (169)	$HO-\langle\!\!\!\!\!\!\!\!\overset{OH}{\bigcirc}\!\!\!\!\!\!\!\!\rangle-CHOH-CH_3(NH_3)$
*Adrenalin (epinephrine) (183)	$HO-\langle\!\!\!\!\!\!\!\!\overset{OH}{\bigcirc}\!\!\!\!\!\!\!\!\rangle-CHOH-CH_2(NH)(CH_3)$
*Dopamine (153)	$HO-\langle\bigcirc\rangle-CH_2-CH_2-NH_2$ (with HO- at two positions)
γ-Aminobutyric acid, GABA (103.1)	$HOOC-CH_2-CH_2-CH_2-NH_3$
Glutamic acid (147.13)	$HOOC-CH_2-CH_2-CH(NH_2)COOH$ $\uparrow$ glutamic decarboxylase
Aspartic acid (133.1)	$HOOC-CH_2-CH(NH_2)-COOH$
5-Hydroxytryptamine (= serotonic) (175)	$HO-\langle\bigcirc\rangle\text{(indole)}-C-CH_2-CH_2-NH_2$

* Analogs are indicated by asterisks in the table. These transmitters are discussed in the text, especially in Section 8-13. The neurochemical relations of some of these transmitters are considered in Chapter 11.

Table 8-4 Drugs Acting on Presynaptic Neurons and Drugs Acting on the Central Nervous System Generally*

SUBSTANCE AND STRUCTURE (WHERE KNOWN)	COMMENTS
Drugs acting on transmitter release	
Botulinus toxin	Inhibits transmitter release at neuro-muscular junctions, autonomic ganglia, and cholinergic autonomic neuroeffectors.
Procaine (see below)	Inhibits release of transmitter at cholinergic neuromuscular junctions in addition to other more specific effects (see below).
Tetraethylammonium (TEA), (see Table 8-5)	No drugs specific for the promotion of transmitter release are known. TEA and carbachol have this action in addition to their more specific effects (see other tables indicated).
Carbachol (see Table 8-3)	
Drugs acting on transmitter synthesis	
Hemicholinium, HC-3	A synthetic compound that prevents choline uptake at axon terminals and thus inhibits ACh synthesis.
CNS stimulants and convulsants	
Strychnine:	By blocking all inhibitory activity and pathways, strychnine and picrotoxin cause a high level of CNS activity and muscle responses, which are usually convulsive. Only pathways which include inhibitory neurons are acted on.
Picrotoxin:	
Caffeine:	Caffeine is a general CNS stimulant, representative of a class of xanthine derivatives which have this activity because they inhibit the destruction of cyclic AMP. High levels of intracellular cyclic AMP lead to high levels of metabolic activity.

Table 8-4 (continued)

Substance and Structure (Where Known)	Comments
CNS and local anesthetics Procaine: Cocaine: 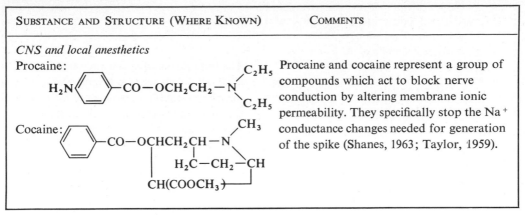	Procaine and cocaine represent a group of compounds which act to block nerve conduction by altering membrane ionic permeability. They specifically stop the Na^+ conductance changes needed for generation of the spike (Shanes, 1963; Taylor, 1959).

* Figure 8-2 indicates possible sites for chemicals to effect synaptic activity. For further references see Goodman and Gilman (1965).

magnitude greater than that actually available at the junction. It is more reasonable to think that ACh brings about a depolarization of the membrane because of its ability to create a reversible change in permeability to ions. In order to do so, it must attach to a receptor site—a chemical grouping on a molecule of the postsynaptic membrane. This idea is bolstered by the fact that only small amounts of ACh are required to cause a depolarization of the membrane. This has been shown by micro-injection experiments in which amounts as small as 10^{-16} moles ACh can produce depolarization (Nastuk, 1953; del Castillo and Katz, 1956).

Further evidence for a reaction between ACh and chemical groups on the membrane is the specificity of the reaction. Quaternary ammonium compounds make the best inhibitors of synaptic transmission and also some of the best cholinomimetic agents (substances whose effects at synapses mimic those of ACh). The effects of substances antagonistic to ACh fit well into a Michaelis-Menten type of competitive inhibition relationship (Jenkinson, 1960).

Nothing is known about the nature of the attachment site. The receptive substance has been studied in the electric organs of eels, which consist primarily of neuromuscular junctions (Chargas, 1959). Chargas et al. (1958) prepared extracts from these organs thought to contain the receptive site substance. Ehrenpreis (1960) found some correlation between the binding of drugs by this preparation and their effects at the intact neuromuscular junction.

The permeability change brought about by ACh attachment to the subsynaptic membrane must be reversed; otherwise, continued excitation (either depolarization or hyperpolarization of the membrane) would occur. A hydrolyzing enzyme for ACh is found in high concentration at the motor endplate and in ganglia of the central nervous system of vertebrates. This is acetylcholine esterase, AChE [E.C. 3.1.1.7., acetylcholine hydrolase: acetylcholine + H_2O → choline + acetate]. This enzyme destroys ACh soon after it has complexed with the subsynaptic receptor and thus restores normal permeability and transmembrane potential.

AChE is a rapidly acting enzyme and hydrolyzes ACh in a few milliseconds after its attachment. At the neuromuscular junction, destruction of ACh must occur within the refractory period of the muscle: about 5 msec in frog skeletal muscle and about 1 msec in

Table 8-5   Some Drugs Which Act at Postsynaptic Sites

Substance and Structure (Where Known)	Comments

Atropinic drugs (blockers of ACh activity)
Atropine:

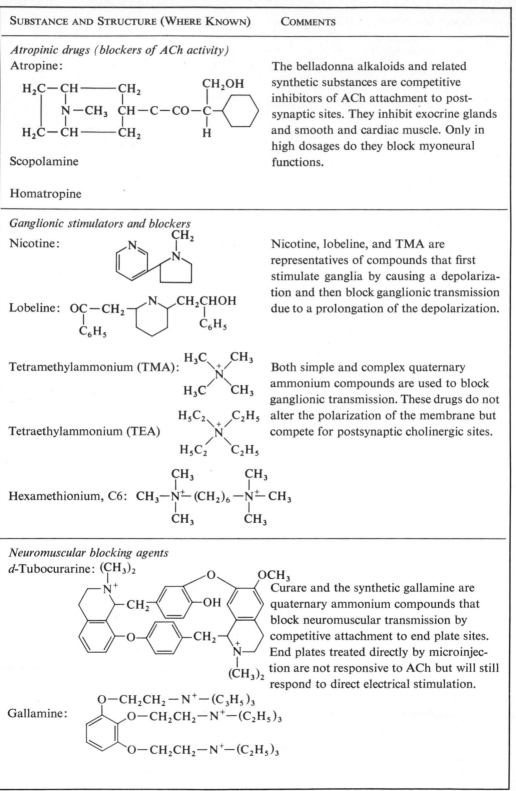

Scopolamine

Homatropine

The belladonna alkaloids and related synthetic substances are competitive inhibitors of ACh attachment to post-synaptic sites. They inhibit exocrine glands and smooth and cardiac muscle. Only in high dosages do they block myoneural functions.

Ganglionic stimulators and blockers
Nicotine:

Lobeline:

Nicotine, lobeline, and TMA are representatives of compounds that first stimulate ganglia by causing a depolarization and then block ganglionic transmission due to a prolongation of the depolarization.

Tetramethylammonium (TMA):

Tetraethylammonium (TEA)

Hexamethionium, C6:

Both simple and complex quaternary ammonium compounds are used to block ganglionic transmission. These drugs do not alter the polarization of the membrane but compete for postsynaptic cholinergic sites.

Neuromuscular blocking agents
d-Tubocurarine:

Gallamine:

Curare and the synthetic gallamine are quaternary ammonium compounds that block neuromuscular transmission by competitive attachment to end plate sites. End plates treated directly by microinjection are not responsive to ACh but will still respond to direct electrical stimulation.

Table 8-5 (continued)

Substance and Structure (Where Known)	Comments
Neuromuscular blocking agents—continued Decamethionium, C10: $(CH_3)_3 - \overset{+}{N} - (CH_2)_{10} - \overset{+}{N} - (CH_3)_3$	Another group of compounds block neuro-muscular transmission by causing a sustained depolarization. Curare and C10 are antagonistic. Electrical currents and low temperatures intensify C10 activity while reducing those of curare.

mammalian skeletal muscle. It has been calculated that at one end plate, 8×10^9 molecules of ACh could be split during the refractory period. This compares with the estimate that about 1×10^6 molecules of ACh are liberated per impulse (Krnjević and Mitchell, 1961). Thus the rate of activity of the enzyme is sufficient to destroy any ACh liberated.

Histochemical methods for the localization of AChE (Koelle and Friedenwald, 1949; Barrnett, 1962) show that AChE is highly concentrated at the endplate and in low concentration in the remainder of the muscle membrane. However, AChE is found in both muscle and nerve terminal cytoplasm, as well as in the neuromuscular junction gap. The meaning of this distribution in terms of chemical transmission is not known.

Before considering the permeability and potential changes that are brought about by transmitter action, a brief consideration of the types of drugs used experimentally to influence synaptic transmission will be helpful.

8-10. Drug Actions at Synapses. Tables 8-4, 8-5, and 8-6 list some of the drugs that affect synaptic transmission, their structural formulas, and their sites and modes of action. In nearly all types of physiological research, the use of a chemical to specifically enhance or inhibit a particular phase of cellular activity is a most useful tool. By simplifying the experimental preparation's responses, a simpler model can be obtained. The use of drugs also yields clues about the nature of chemical groups at reactive sites.

As shown in the tables drugs affecting synaptic activity may be divided into several classes depending on their site of action. Some drugs block or enhance the synthesis of transmitter or the release of transmitter. Others act at the postsynaptic region either by competing for sites normally occupied by transmitter (inhibitory drugs) or by inhibiting the activity of the transmitter's hydrolytic enzyme and thus potentiating the transmitter depolarization (Figure 8-11).

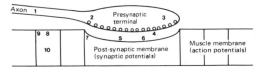

Figure 8-11 Schematic of a motor axon and muscle end plate indicating the sites of action of various drugs.
1. Axon action potentials blocked by tetrodotoxin.
2. ACh synthesis inhibited by hemicholinium, blocks postsynaptic response.
3. ACh release blocked by procaine, botulinium toxin, low $[Ca^{2+}]$, high $[Mg^{2+}]$.
4. ACh release stimulated by high $[Ca^{2+}]$.
5. Curare alkaloids block postsynaptic activity by competitively combining with cholinergic membrane sites.
6. Depolarization of postsynaptic membrane by succinylcholine, decamethionium, $[K^+]$.
7. Low $[K^+]$ or $[Na^+]$ lowers postsynaptic current flow and blocks spike generation.
8. Veratrine, Ca^{2+}, initiate muscle action potentials.
9. Quinine blocks muscle action potential conduction.
10. Metabolic poisons, low $[Ca^{2+}]$ interfere with energy production, block both contraction and active transport of ions.

Table 8-6 Drugs that Inhibit Acetylcholine Esterase (Anticholinesterases)

Substance and Structure	Comments
Physostigmine: 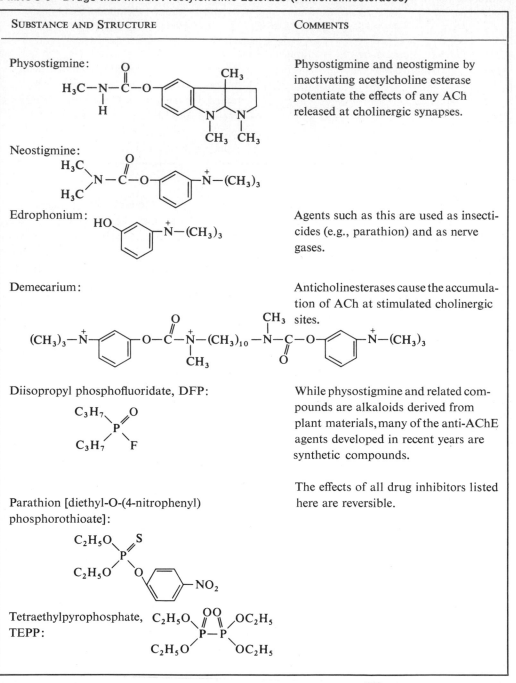	Physostigmine and neostigmine by inactivating acetylcholine esterase potentiate the effects of any ACh released at cholinergic synapses.
Neostigmine:	
Edrophonium:	Agents such as this are used as insecticides (e.g., parathion) and as nerve gases.
Demecarium:	Anticholinesterases cause the accumulation of ACh at stimulated cholinergic sites.
Diisopropyl phosphofluoridate, DFP:	While physostigmine and related compounds are alkaloids derived from plant materials, many of the anti-AChE agents developed in recent years are synthetic compounds.
Parathion [diethyl-O-(4-nitrophenyl) phosphorothioate]:	The effects of all drug inhibitors listed here are reversible.
Tetraethylpyrophosphate, TEPP:	

When a drug combines with a cholinergic receptor (one that is normally activated by ACh), it may have either of two actions: (1) it may produce the same effect as does ACh— this is a cholinomimetic drug; or (2) it may produce no direct effect except that by occupation of the receptor sites it prevents the action of endogenous ACh—this is a cholinergic blocking agent. Some drugs produce the two actions in sequence. For example, nicotine

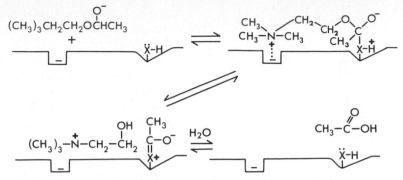

Figure 8-12 A hypothetical model for the attachment and hydrolysis of ACH by acetylcholinesterase at the postsynaptic membrane. An anionic site is used for the attachment of ACh; this involves the positively charged N of ACh. At a second site, the esteratic site, the electrophilic atoms of C of the ACh carboxyl group react with a protonated acidic group ($-\ddot{X}-H-$). Choline is split off from the ACh and the acetylated enzyme reacts with water to produce acetic acid and the regenerated enzyme.

Some reagents can irreversibly inhibit acetylcholinesterase by attaching to one or the other of the two sites. Reversible inhibition is caused by agents that combine with both sites and are then hydrolyzed by the enzyme, for example, this is the case with neostigmine. Other agents combine with the esteratic site and are then hydrolyzed and released, for example, DFP.

first mimics the action of ACh and then produces synaptic blocking.

Nerves of the vertebrate parasympathetic nervous system that secrete ACh are known as **cholinergic neurons**. In the sympathetic nervous system neurons secreting noradrenalin are termed **noradrenergic**. These names are now often applied to any neuron secreting either ACh or noradrenalin.

The drugs that are best known are those that act on peripheral neurons and the effectors of organisms. Much less is known concerning the mode of action of centrally acting agents nor is much known about transmitters other than ACh (see Section 8-13). Many of the blocking agents, as well as the cholinomimetic agents, are quaternary amines, which makes it appear that positively charged nitrogen atoms are an essential part of the compound needed for reaction with the receptor site. Figure 8-12 gives one model for the action of an ACh inhibitor. Note that in this model two sites are required: one for the attachment of ACh and another for the substrate-enzyme complex during the hydrolysis of ACh.

Curare (the purified form is *d*-tubocurarine) is one of the earliest known inhibitors of neuromuscular transmission. Curare competes for receptor sites on the postsynaptic membrane. Increasing dosages of curare progressively lower the end plate potential, finally preventing spike formation (Figure 8-13). Since lower dosages block transmission without complete elimination of the EPP, the curarized nerve-muscle preparation is extremely useful for studying the EPP in the absence of the overshadowing action potential.

Drugs such as eserine, prostigmine, or tensilon bring about ACh potentiation. They inhibit AChE, and therefore, any ACh depolarization of the end plate becomes long lasting while ACh is attached to the subsynaptic membrane.

8-11. Excitatory and Inhibitory EPP's and PSP's. The attachment of a transmitter molecule to the subsynaptic membrane brings about a permeability change and a subsequent flow of ionic currents that can lead to a change in the transmembrane potential. ACh at the neuromuscular junction causes a potential change that is decremental, that is, the potential change decreases in magnitude with increasing distance from the end plate as measured with microelectrodes (Figure 8-14). The figure also includes an electrical model of the synaptic membrane and some potentials produced from a hardware analog.

285

established capable of depolarizing an appropriate part of the cell membrane where an action potential can be initiated.

Although the permeability changes in the membrane that result from attachment of a transmitter cannot be defined in terms of known membrane structures, in some cases the changes in ionic conductances that result in the development of a synaptic potential are known. The EPP of the vertebrate neuromuscular junction arises from an increased conductance to Na^+ and a *simultaneous* increased conductance to K^+ (Takeuchi and Takeuchi, 1960). The inward movement of Na^+ and the outward movement of K^+ is responsible for the change in level of the transmembrane potential from the resting potential level that is the synaptic potential. Although these results from studies of the vertebrate striated muscle neuromuscular junction are sometimes used as a basis for generalizations about all synapses, there is no reason for believing that other ions are not involved at other transmission sites. Very few synapses have been studied specifically for ion movements during activity. An electrical model for the vertebrate muscle end plate membrane is shown in Figure 8-15.

The conductance changes produced in the postsynaptic membrane by the transmitter are independent of the membrane potential, a situation different from that found in the axonal membrane where the magnitude of the

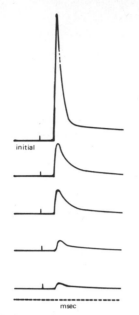

Figure 8-13 Intracellular recordings from a muscle fiber showing end plate potentials during washout of *d* tubocurarine from the end plate region. The motor nerve was stimulated every 3 sec (time markers represent 1 msec intervals). The bottom record shows the potential recorded in presence of curare, top record shows spike generated after the curare is washed out. [Data from Nastuk (1955).]

As previously stated, the EPP and PSP are local potentials that are graded in magnitude according to the number or strength of incoming stimuli. They must be of a certain magnitude before a sufficient current flow is

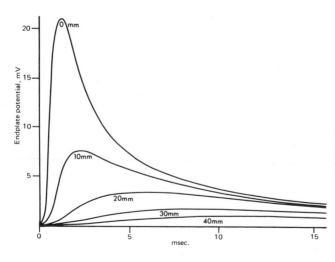

Figure 8-14 Intracellular recordings of the end plate potentials measured in a curarized muscle fiber at different distances from the end plate. [Redrawn from the data of Fatt and Katz (1951).]

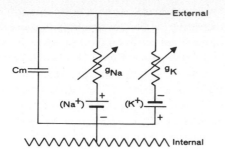

Figure 8-15 An electrical model for the vertebrate motor end plate. The EPP results from an increased conductance to both K^+ and Na^+ ions. The resting transmembrane potential is maintained by K^+ and Na^+ (note opposite signs). Upon stimulation the conductances of both ions are simultaneously increased. Other synapses may depend upon the movement of chloride ions as well as sodium or potassium ions.

Na^+ conductance depends on the value of the transmembrane potential. The excitatory postsynaptic potential, a depolarizing potential that can lead to the production of a spike, and the end plate potential of vertebrate skeletal muscle arise from ionic current flows as diagrammed in Figure 8-15. If these current flows become great enough, a spike potential can develop in the appropriate region of the membrane. Figure 8-16 also shows the time relationships between the postsynaptic current flow and the development of the EPSP of the motor neuron of the cat (Curtis and Eccles, 1959).

If the transmembrane potential is held at given levels and a stimulus applied to the presynaptic neuron, it is possible to measure the magnitude of the excitatory postsynaptic potential. The size of the postsynaptic potential varies in an approximately linear fashion with the level of the initial transmembrane potential (for example, see Takeuchi and Takeuchi, 1960). The EPSP or the EPP is a change in potential from the normal or from the preset transmembrane potential.

At the postsynaptic membrane there is a net inflow of current and a subsequent depolarization of the membrane; above a certain level of potential, a net current flows outward, and there is a change in sign of the postsynaptic or end plate potential. This **reversal of potential**

occurs when the transmembrane potential of a muscle fiber is displaced by voltage-clamp methods to about -15 mV (the normal resting potential is about -65 mV). The null point of the EPP does not correspond to the equilibrium potential of any one of the major ions present, and from this it is inferred that more than one type of ion channel is opened in the membrane.

Since the ionic conductances and associated membrane potential changes are different for the generation of a synaptic potential as compared with the generation of an action potential, it is concluded that these phenomena occur at different membrane sites with different properties.

The EPP's of vertebrate muscle end plates are all excitatory depolarizing potentials, but many insect and crustacean muscle fibers are innervated by both excitatory and inhibitory end plates. Inhibitory synapses are as common as excitatory synapses in nervous systems. Although the excitatory postsynaptic potential tends to move in the direction of a sodium equilibrium potential (and is prevented from so doing by the simultaneous K^+ and/or Cl^- increased conductance) and is therefore a

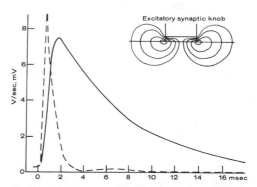

Figure 8-16 The inset diagramatically shows the current flows in the subsynaptic membrane of the cat motor neuron that generate the excitatory postsynaptic potential. Current flow is inward at the active subsynaptic membrane and outward through the surrounding membrane. The graph shows the time relationships (in msec) between the current flow (V/sec) (dashed line) and the EPP (mV) (solid line). [Redrawn and modified from the data of Curtis and Eccles (1959).]

depolarizing potential; the inhibitory post-synaptic potential, IPSP, tends to approach a potassium or chloride equilibrium potential. In most cases this means that the IPSP is a hyperpolarizing potential because the potassium and chloride equilibrium potentials are greater than the resting potential. The IPSP prevents the formation of an action potential.

Generally inhibitory postsynaptic potentials are based on mechanisms that either hyperpolarize the membrane or maintain it below the threshold value of an effective depolarizing stimulus. These mechanisms are based on increased conductances of K^+ and/or Cl^-, while the concomitant sodium conductance remains unaltered.

In the mammalian heart ACh released by the vagus nerve produces hyperpolarization of the cardiac muscle cells and only K^+ conductance is increased. In spinal motoneurons of mammals and in some insect and crustacean end plates increased Cl^- conductance predominates at inhibitory endings (Coombs et al., 1955).

At a given synaptic region, the EPSP's and IPSP's at various subsynaptic regions summate to determine whether a threshold depolarization is reached that can produce a spike. The role of inhibitory and excitatory synapses and the integration of activity that occurs at synapses will be considered in Chapter 11.

8-12. Properties of Chemically Transmitting Synapses. Synaptic delay is a feature of all chemically transmitting synapses. Synaptic delay was originally discovered in reflex arcs, where impulses took longer to travel over a pathway of neurons than would be expected from the rate of impulse conduction along the axons. The junctions between neurons seemed the likely site for the delay in transmission.

Mg^{2+} in concentrations of 5 to 10 mM reversibly blocks transmission in the vertebrate neuromuscular junction, whereas conduction in the nerve and muscle membranes is unimpeded. If the Ca^{2+} concentration is increased, a higher Mg^{2+} concentration is needed to block transmission. The effects of

Ca^{2+} and Mg^{2+} are in a sense antagonistic. Increasing the Ca^{2+} concentration of an otherwise normal perfusion fluid causes an increase in the magnitude of the EPP when the axon is stimulated. Katz and Miledi (1963, 1964, 1965, 1967) in a series of experiments with frog neuromuscular junctions found that the increased Ca^{2+} concentration resulted in an increase in the amount of ACh released by the presynaptic terminal, perhaps by increasing the number of available attachment sites on the inner surface of the presynaptic membranes to which vesicles, it is hypothesized, must attach before transmitter can be released. Ca^{2+} and Mg^{2+} could combine with and alter the conformation of membrane proteins, thus exposing or hiding chemical sidegroups on these molecules.

Localized placement of a recording microelectrode filled with calcium chloride solution made it possible to show that in a region of the junction, blocked by low Ca^{2+} and high Mg^{2+}, the spike was normal in the axon terminal and remained unchanged when Ca^{2+} was added to the region by microinjection from the microelectrode. Thus the action of Ca^{2+} was on the transmitter system, not on the depolarization process responsible for the spike and its conduction down the neuron. Both the depolarization and the accompanying local increase of Na^+ on the inside of the presynaptic membrane may play a role in activating the Ca^{2+} effect on transmitter release.

In order to measure accurately the delay at the neuromuscular junction, Katz and Miledi used local application of Ca^{2+} from a micropipet in an otherwise low Ca^{2+} blocked preparation to ensure that the end plate responses occurred at one limited region. Under these experimental conditions any delay in transmission was found to be caused by the properties of the transmitter release system, not by the diffusion time of transmitter across the junction nor by the reaction time of the transmitter. The synaptic delay at 20°C ranged from 0.4 to 2.5 msec.

An interesting distribution of delay times appeared when experiments were conducted at

Table 8-7   Some Synaptic Delay Times*

PREPARATION	SYNAPTIC DELAY (msec)	MODE OF TRANSMISSION
Sea anemone (*Metridium senile*), through-conduction path in nerve net.	2.5	Chemical (?)
Earthworm and crayfish, giant axons, segmental septa	0.05	Electrical, two-way transmission
Squid (*Loligo*), giant fiber synapse in stellate ganglion	0.5	Chemical
Crayfish, giant axon to motoneuron synapse	0.1	Electrical, one-way rectifying
Frog nerve-muscle junction (twitch muscle)	0.8	Chemical
Frog nerve-muscle junction (slow muscle)	1.2	Chemical
Cat, motoneuron in spinal cord	0.3	Chemical
Squid fibers in contact (artificial junction)	1.5	Electrical
Frog, motoneuron	1.1	Chemical
Cat, motor end plate	0.2	Chemical

* For references see: Bullock and Horridge (1965); Eccles (1964).

5°C. In this case delays ranged from 6 to about 40 msecs. When the delay times were arranged in a distribution histogram, the major peak in the distribution was at 9 msec; minor peaks were found at 18, 27, and 36 msec. Whether this distribution of delay times in multiples of the main peak is by chance, or whether it is related to the quantal release of transmitter or some other phenomenon is unknown.

The synaptic delay times of some synapses are given in Table 8-7. The mode of transmission is also shown, and it can be noted that in general a longer synaptic delay is found at chemical synapses as compared with electrical synapses. However, comparisons of such data found in the research literature are difficult because synaptic delay is measured in different terms by various workers and for preparations under different conditions. In many cases synaptic delay is defined as the time elapsing between the first sign of a presynaptic impulse or volley of impulses in the axon terminal and the first sign of a postsynaptic response, that is, the first indication of a postsynaptic potential. The time at which a spike is generated after postsynaptic potential development is variable, although this

Figure 8-17 Diagrammatic representation of the changes in the postsynaptic potential or end plate potential that follow repetitive stimulation. There is an initial period of facilitation in which the potential increases in magnitude. This is followed by a period of depression in which the magnitude of the potential falls.

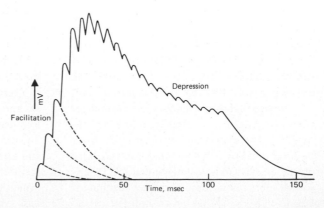

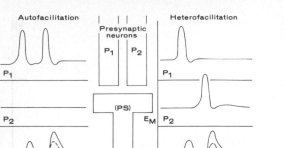

Figure 8-18 Representation of auto- and hetero-facilitation. Two presynaptic fibers (P_1 and P_2) are shown synapsing with a single postsynaptic structure (PS). On the left is shown autofacilitation, an increase in successive responses to activity in one presynaptic fiber. On the right is shown heterofacilitation, the increase in postsynaptic response to the action of one presynaptic response to the action of one presynaptic fiber augmented by previous activity in another presynaptic fiber. The dashed curves indicate responses of postsynaptic structure to the second impulse in the absence of facilitation.

has in some cases been used in the measurement of synaptic delay.

Facilitation of synaptic transmission is common in many synapses. **Facilitation** is a successive incremental increase in response (Figure 8-17). The mechanisms underlying facilitation are not clear. Facilitation is part of the phenomenon of cellular excitability and is an integrative action demonstrated only under suitable experimental conditions by visible responses. Facilitation is shown by the additional effect of a second stimulus, over and above the summated effects of a first and second stimulus (Bullock and Horridge, 1965).

Facilitation in frog slow muscle fiber end plates was studied by using Mg^{2+} to block transmission (Hubbard, 1963). Brief trains of repetitive stimulation caused the amplitude of successive EPP's to increase to a level about twice that resulting from a single control stimulus. After the stimulus train, the facilitation decayed slowly and was replaced by a slight depression after about 0.5 sec. A later phase of **post tetanic potentiation** (PTP) appeared after about 1 sec and after reaching a

peak then decayed over a period of 5 secs. PTP is the enhancement of excitability following a long period of high frequency (tetanic) stimulation. PTP and facilitation both increase with increasing frequency of stimulation (Braun and Schmidt, 1966; Braun et al., 1966). Both phenomena are also increased if the Mg^{2+} concentration is raised above normal.

Facilitation is generally thought to result from an increased mobilization of transmitter from a reserve pool to the releasable state, but no firm evidence is yet available to support this idea. The PTP is thought to result from an accumulation of Na^+ in axon terminals during repetitive stimulation. Increased Na^+ does increase the amount of transmitter released, and ACh is also raised in internal concentration as the intracellular Na^+ concentration increases (Birks, 1963; Birks and Cohen, 1965).

Facilitation can be part of the more general phenomenon of **summation**—the addition of responses to yield a larger response. When increased response depends on the repetition rate or time between incoming stimuli, the process is **temporal summation**. When summation results from stimuli entering the system from different sources, for example, when impulses arrive at a postsynaptic region from two or more presynaptic neurons simultaneously, the addition of response is **spatial summation**. On the other hand, repeated stimulation may lead to a progressive decline in response; this is defacilitation or antifacilitation. The increase in successive responses to activity in one presynaptic neuron is autofacilitation. The increase in response brought about by the action of one presynaptic neuron followed by activity of another presynaptic neuron is heterofacilitation. These different concepts are represented diagrammatically in Figure 8-18.

There is no refractory period associated with synaptic potentials; therefore, a presynaptic impulse can cause a postsynaptic response at any time. Excitatory postsynaptic potentials can sum to a certain extent, thereby increasing membrane depolarization. Inhibitory postsynaptic potentials cannot sum—they can prolong but not increase the potential change —the so-called ceiling effect (Kuffler and Eyzaquirre, 1955). Summation of EPSP's can actually be inhibitory because prolonged above-threshold depolarization will cause Na^+ inactivation in axonal regions of the membrane.

Synapses are easily fatigued—rendered inoperative by high frequency stimulation. Their fatigability results from the high order of chemical metabolism required to effect synaptic transmission. Repetitive stimulation can cause fatigue through any of several mechanisms including: (1) reduction in transmitter release due to exhaustion of stored transmitter; (2) a buildup of metabolic inhibitory endproducts; (3) the use of all available stores of chemical intermediates needed for transmitter synthesis; (4) an increase in the Na^+ concentration or a decrease in the K^+ concentration in the presynaptic or postsynaptic cell. Whatever mechanism may be operating, chemical transmission is more sensitive to repetitive stimulation than are axons or muscle cells and their conducted action potentials. The synapse acts as a safety device in the neuromuscular system, protecting it from overloads of required response.

Grundfest (1957, 1959) considers that all dendritic membranes are inexcitable by electrical stimulation. This conclusion is based on experimental results from many types of muscle and gland cells, from electroplaques of electric organs, and from receptor endings such as the Pacinian corpuscle (see Section 8-22). These cells cannot be stimulated by electrical currents applied to regions involved with the production of synaptic or generator potentials. This is another line of evidence used to support the concept that membranes in different regions of an excitable cell are different in molecular structure and thus in their properties. The validity of this generalization awaits detailed examination of more synaptic and receptor regions.

In some cases it has been found that the activity of inhibitory neurons includes causing a decrease in the amount of transmitter released by excitatory endings connecting to the same postsynaptic cell. For example, this occurs in the crustacean neuromuscular system where both inhibitory and excitatory axons synapse with a skeletal muscle cell (Dudel and Kuffler, 1961; see also Chapter 11). Such activity is **presynaptic inhibition**. The mechanisms by which inhibitory neurons can influence presynaptic excitatory neuron activity remain unclear. Suggestions are made that some ACh (or other transmitter) acts at presynaptic sites to modify the permeability of the presynaptic terminal membrane in such a way that release of transmitter is impeded. There is also the possibility that extremely fine terminal branches of axons may synapse on another presynaptic neuron—thus acting as a feedback inhibitor (Eccles, 1964; Florey, 1961). This type of activity in which a presynaptic neuron is excitatory as far as the postsynaptic neuron is concerned but inhibitory with respect to its own activity is a contradiction of the axiom that any single neuron is either excitatory or inhibitory in its action, not both (see Section 8-13).

8-13.   Chemical   Transmitters. McLennan (1961) and Terzuolo and Edwards (1962) among others have proposed several criteria that should be satisfied before a compound is classified as a transmitter. These criteria include (1) the substance must be found in sufficient amounts in the presynaptic neuron; (2) there must be an enzyme system for synthesizing the substance in the presynaptic terminals; (3) stimulation of the presynaptic neuron must cause the release of the substances, preferably in quantity sufficient to be detectable in the extracellular fluid about a synapse; (4) there should be an inactivating enzyme system present in the postsynaptic structure; (5) the action of the substance when applied by microinjection should mimic the normal activity of the synapse; and (6) drugs which potentiate or block the action of the neurons should similarly affect the action of the injected substance.

At present very few transmitters are positively identified by all the above criteria (Table 8-3 lists the proven and some tentative transmitters). Transmitters are difficult to identify because synapses generally are minute, and the amount of chemical released even during volleys of impulses is very small and beyond the resolution of available microchemical quantitative analyses. ACh is the most widely distributed transmitter known among the animal phyla and also is the only one for which some details are known concerning its cellular synthesis and distribution.

In previous sections it was pointed out that differences between inhibitory and excitatory synaptic connections depend on the nature of the subsynaptic membranes. This conclusion is drawn from the fact that ACh acts as both an excitatory transmitter, for example, in vertebrate skeletal muscle, and an inhibitory transmitter, for example, in vertebrate cardiac muscle. Also some terminals of a presynaptic neuron may act as inhibitory, whereas others may act as excitatory. Dale's law states that a given cell can secrete only one type of transmitter, and since there are, as yet, no known violations of this concept, then if the same neuron can produce both excitatory and inhibitory responses, these effects must depend not on the nature of the transmitter but on the nature of the subsynaptic membrane and its response to the transmitter. Both Dale's law and the status of a single presynaptic neuron

with respect to excitatory and inhibitory action are based on very little evidence.

There is, of course, some supportive evidence that Dale's law holds at certain synapses. The crustacean neuromuscular junction, for example, depends for its activity on two different transmitters from two different neurons—one excitatory (producing glutamic acid), the other inhibitory (producing gamma-aminobutyric acid).

The ACh content and distribution of the superior cervical ganglion of the cat were studied using preparations perfused with physiological salines containing inhibitors such as hemicholinium (HC-3) and anticholinesterases such as eserine. The solutions contained glucose and choline when necessary in order to supply an energy source and the necessary material for ACh synthesis (Birks and MacIntosh, 1961). By varying the solutions and other experimental conditions, it was possible to obtain a picture of ACh content and distribution in resting and stimulated ganglia. The results are summarized in the highly hypothetical diagram of Figure 8-19.

ACh is thought to exist in three major compartments. The stationary ACh (about 40 μg) is in an extrasynaptic compartment and is inaccessible for release at the synaptic

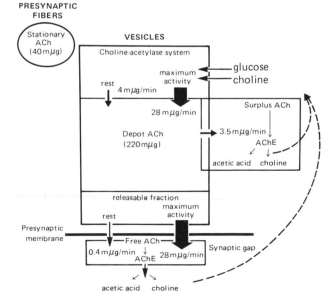

Figure 8-19 A hypothetical model of the distribution of ACh and ACh metabolism in the cat superior cervical ganglion. The different compartments are described in the text.

membrane. The other two compartments are in diffusional contact and are located in the presynaptic terminals because part of this ACh is that released for transmitter action. Depot ACh is the major compartment (containing about 220 μg) and is thought to be the ACh of the synaptic vesicles. Surplus ACh, outside the vesicles, is accessible to hydrolysis by AChE since inactivation of this enzyme, for example by eserine, brings about an accumulation of surplus ACh. However, this compartment of transmitter is not available for release.

Increasing the choline concentration of the perfusion fluid does not influence the rate of ACh synthesis in this preparation, and it appears that the choline split off from released ACh is not fed back into the axon terminal for resynthesis. The model does not attempt to indicate the mechanisms by which a nerve impulse initiates transmitter release nor how repetitive stimulation facilitates transmitter release. Obviously, many gaps remain in our knowledge of ACh.

Another proven transmitter, noradrenalin, is found in postganglionic sympathetic neurons and in basal ganglia of vertebrates. It is also present in some central ganglia of insects and annelids but is lacking in other phyla, at least in nervous tissues. The closely related compound adrenalin is released by the adrenal glands, and although its action on smooth muscle and other tissues is similar to that shown by noradrenalin, it is not a synaptic transmitter substance.

5-hydroxytryptamine (serotonin; 5-HT) is found in the nervous tissues of the mammalian brain and in central ganglia of annelids, molluscs, and sipunculids. In most cases, it has not yet satisfied all criteria needed to establish it as a transmitter. An increased synthesis and release of 5-HT has been found when isolated frog and mouse spinal cords are stimulated (Andén et al., 1964). The transmitter that controls the rate of relaxation of molluscan catch muscles is 5-HT (Chapter 10).

Difficulty in identifying a transmitter may arise from the fact that a substance can activate postsynaptic neurons when applied to them but need not be the physiological transmitter. Or substances may be associated with nervous tissue or be produced by neighboring tissues and, while possessing the ability to influence postsynaptic potentials, are not the physiological transmitters. For example, 5-HT stimulates both the vertebrate and molluscan hearts but is not a physiological transmitter in the former. Although adrenalin and noradrenalin stimulate smooth and cardiac muscle in vertebrates, these substances are found in other tissues as well and have other actions. All these compounds are found in one or more extranervous tissues of many animals from coelenterates to mammals.

Gamma-aminobutyric acid (GABA) is the inhibitory transmitter at the crustacean inhibitory neuromuscular junction. GABA makes up about 0.5 per cent of the wet weight of the inhibitory axon to the opener muscle of the lobster walking leg (Kravitz et al., 1963). This is an extremely high percentage for one substance in a cell. Takeuchi and Takeuchi (1966a, b) found that microinjection of GABA onto crayfish muscle fibers produced potential changes with a reversal at about -60 mV, similar to that of the physiological transmitter. L-Glutamate produced depolarizing potential changes at sites on the membrane, where excitatory junction potentials are maximal. From these and other results—all showing the close mimicry of glutamate to the excitatory transmitter and GABA to the inhibitory transmitter—came the conclusion that these are the normal transmitters.

As an interesting sidelight, it is speculated that the difference between inhibitory and excitatory neurons in the crustacean neuromuscular system depends on gene repression and activation (Strumwasser, 1965). GABA is formed from L-glutamate through the enzyme glutamic decarboxylase, and it has been suggested that the difference between the two types of neurons resides in the gene controlling the synthesis of this enzyme. If the gene is repressed in the excitatory neuron, this would account for the fact that only glutamate is present in the terminals of its axon. In the inhibitory neuron the gene is not repressed, and the enzyme or enzyme template for the formation of glutamic decarboxylase is present and moves down the axon to the terminals where GABA is produced. This is the first instance where differences in nerve activity, even although tentatively, can be based on the fundamental cellular control mechanism—the gene.

The uses of GABA and glutamate in the neuromuscular system just described exemplify the use of separate transmitters to bring about excitation or inhibition in an effector cell. Suggestions are made that in the vertebrate central nervous system, for which information is lacking concerning the actual transmitters, acidic amino acids such as glutamate, aspartate, or cysteine may play the role of transmitters. These amino acids are present in relatively high concentrations in both vertebrate and invertebrate neurons. In central nervous systems it is not known whether excitation and inhibition are brought about by specific transmitters or by the integration of impulses at different loci of synaptic membranes. It is known that the commonly accepted transmitters such as ACh, noradrenalin, 5-HT, or GABA are absent in most vertebrate central nervous system synapses. Extracts of mammalian central nervous system tissues yields substances that exhibit transmitter activity when injected into test preparations, but none of the commonly accepted transmitters are present in the extracts (see Florey, 1954; McLennan, 1961). A polypeptide (Substance P) has been extracted from brain tissue and can produce inhibitory effects in mammalian central nervous systems, but whether or not it is a physiological transmitter is unknown (von Euler and Gaddum, 1931; Erdös, 1963).

Electrically Transmitting Synapses and Ephapses

8-14. Nature of Electrical Transmission. The electrically transmitting synapse, in which current flow through the presynaptic membrane affects the postsynaptic membrane, must possess sufficient area of synaptic contact so that the electrical resistance between the two neuronal membranes is as low as possible. The postsynaptic membrane of the electrically transmitting synapse does not act as a generator of electrical currents and potentials as does the membrane of the chemically transmitting synapse. The postsynaptic membrane acts as a channel for current flow. Since no series of chemical reactions or any diffusion of transmitter is needed, synaptic delay at the electrical synapse is usually low, less than 0.1 msec. All known electrical synapses are between neurons, none has been found between a neuron and an effector cell.

Katz (1966) points out that from a consideration of the cable and other electrical properties of a neuromuscular junction, electrical transmission is impossible. For example, a frog muscle fiber of average diameter, ca. 150 μ, presents a load (input impedance) of about 50,000 Ω to the brief current pulse of the motoneuron spike. In order to excite the muscle membrane, the resting potential must be raised from -90 mV to about -50 mV. This requires according to Ohm's law a current of about 0.8×10^{-6} amps. But if it is assumed that the synaptic surface covers about 2.3×10^{-5} cm^2 and the outward current density of the spike is about 1 mamp/cm^2, the total current is only 2.3×10^{-8} amps—far less than that needed to produce any significant change in the potential of the muscle membrane. The actual situation is worse because of the large gap separating the two cells and the fact that the postsynaptic membrane has a large input impedance.

If the resistivity of the gap is about 100 ohm-cm, the potential change across the gap produced by an impulse would be only 40 μV, and the current entering the muscle only about 10^{-11} amps. From calculations such as these, based on assumptions that appear approximately correct, electrical transmission is seen to be impossible in junctions separated by a large gap. The case is similar for nerve-nerve junctions as was shown in Figure 8-10.

It may be noted that in the chemically transmitting synapse, specifically those where

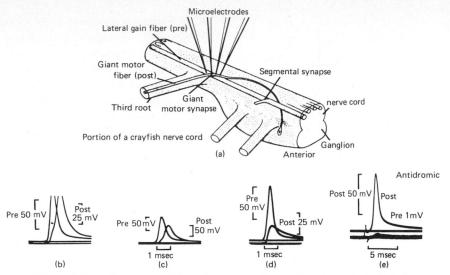

Figure 8-20 Schematic representation of a portion of a crayfish abdominal cord containing one ganglion. The path of one giant motor axon is shown from its cell body in the ventral part of the ganglion until it leaves the third ganglionic root on the opposite side of the cord. Only its synapse with the lateral giant prefiber is shown; it also synapses with the two medial giant fibers centrally where the fibers cross the motor axon. A septal synapse between two segments of the lateral giant fiber is also indicated. In (b) to (d) are shown some responses obtained with simultaneous intracellular recording from pre- and postfibers. (a) Orthodomic impulse transmission at giant synapse; (b) (c) recorded from same synapse at different amplifications, post spike origin indicated by arrow in (b). (e) Upper trace is postfiber antidromic spike potential, which produces negligible potential change in prefiber (lower trace). [Redrawn by permission from E. J. Furshpan and D. D. Potter (1959). "Transmission at the giant synapses of the crayfish". *Journal of Physiology* (London) **145**: 289–325.]

ACh is responsible for transmission, the effective current produced by the release of ACh is about 3×10^{-6} amps—greater by a factor of three than that needed theoretically to sufficiently depolarize the postsynaptic membrane.

In the electrically transmitting synapse it is usual to find a tight junction and a large area of contact between the pre- and postsynaptic membranes. It may also be that membranes at electrical synapses have different electrical characteristics than those at chemically transmitting synapses, perhaps a lower resistance to current flow. In the following sections the structure and nature of some of the electrical synapses which have been studied will be described.

8-15. The Crayfish Giant-Motor Synapse. Furshpan and Potter (1959) first discovered a synapse that operated on the basis of electrical transmission—the junction between a giant

axon and a motor axon in the crayfish nerve cord (Figure 8-20). This preparation is relatively easy to study because microelectrodes can be positioned in both pre- and postsynaptic neurons.

Recording from such a preparation reveals that both normal impulses and subthreshold electrical pulses spread across the synapse and result in measurable potential changes in the postsynaptic neuron—a situation not found in chemically transmitting junctions. However, presynaptic hyperpolarization causes appreciable hyperpolarization of the membrane of the presynaptic neuron. This synapse acts therefore as an electrical rectifier of low resistance to positive current flowing from the presynaptic neuron but interposes a high resistance to electrical current flow in the opposite direction (Figures 8-20, and 8-21). In this case, although transmission is by electrical means, there is still only a one-way flow of information.

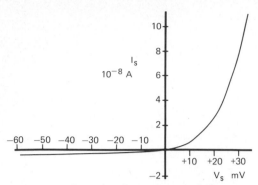

Figure 8-21 Current-voltage characteristic curve of the giant-to-motor synapse of the crayfish. Positive values of V_s indicate that the prefiber side of the synapse was electrically positive with respect to the postfiber side. When prefiber side is electrically negative with respect to postfiber side, no current flows. This is also the characteristic behavior of an electrical rectifier.

Morphological studies of this axon-axon synapse reveal that there is a close juxta-positioning of the two membranes. Small bulbous processes of the motor axon fit into presynaptic processes (Hama, 1961; Robertson, 1961). The membranes of the ball and socket joint approach each other closely and fuse at some points (see Figure 8-4).

To illustrate the dangers of biological generalization from only a few observations, giant fiber synapses are found in the squid stellate ganglion between the endings of a large central axon and a giant motor axon that supplies the musculature of the mantle—the muscle responsible for the jet-propelled swimming of the squid. Superficially this junction resembles that of the crayfish giant-motor connection. But Hagiwara and Tasaki (1958) found no evidence for direct electrical transmission, nor is any type of cable transmission found in either direction across the synapse. Examination of this structure in the electron microscope revealed the presence of vesicles in the presynaptic neuron (Hama, 1962), and there is a complete separation of membranes. This synapse then is a chemically transmitting one between a giant axon and a motor axon (Figure 8-22).

8-16. Segmental Synapses in the Crayfish and Earthworm. The giant fiber system of the crayfish contains several types of electrically transmitting synapses. Although the giant-motor synapse is a highly developed structure, much simpler synapses, morphologically speaking, are found which operate by electrical transmission. In the longitudinal nerve cords of both crustaceans and annelids there are giant axons segmented by the transverse septa that are part of the metameric structure of these organisms. Impulses propagate in either direction along these giant axons at a high velocity, indicating that the septa have little influence on current flows. These synapses have no rectifying properties. Most of the analyses of such synapses have been performed on crayfish preparations because the earthworm axons are too short relative to the space constant of the fibers to obtain suitable recordings.

As shown in Figure 8-23 the spread of impulses through the septate region is due to cable transmission. Since the crustacean septate axon membrane has a relatively high

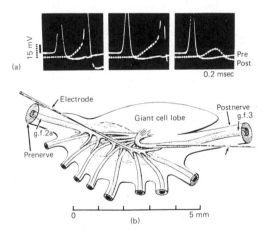

Figure 8-22 A chemically transmitting synapse between second- and third-order giant fibers in the squid. (a) Presynaptic spikes (solid line) and postsynaptic responses (broken line) are shown as recorded following a prolonged repetitious stimulation. There is a long delay between the onset of pre- and post- activity. (b) Diagrammatic representation of the preparation, indicating position of microelectrodes. [Redrawn and modified from Bullock and Hagiwara (1957) and Hagiwara and Tasaki (1958).]

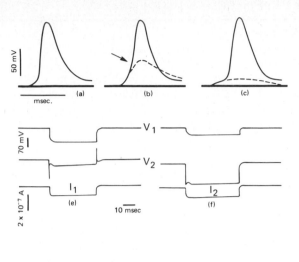

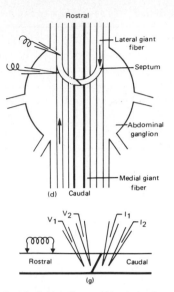

Figure 8-23 Septal and commisural synapses of the crayfish. (d) shows the positioning of microelectrodes used to obtain the intracellular responses of (a) to (c). (a) Rostrally traveling impulse in the left lateral giant fiber just below the oblique septum. (b) Rostrally traveling impulse in the left lateral giant fiber just above the oblique septum. (c) Caudally traveling impulses on the lateral giant fiber. Dotted lines represent time courses of the potentials when impulse transmission was blocked by hyperpolarizing the postsynaptic fiber. (g) Position of electrodes used to record responses of (e) and (f). Electrodes are used for voltage recording (V) or current passing (I). (e) Response when hyperpolarizing current pulses through I_1. (f) Response when hyperpolarizing current pulses through I_2. [Redrawn from Eccles (1964); following Watanabe and Grundfest (1961); Kao (1960).]

electrical resistance (ca. 0.2 to 0.4 megohms) there is some attenuation of the spike on passing from one segment to the next. The septate axons of annelids appear to have a lower membrane resistance because there is less spike attenuation (Kao, 1960).

Morphological studies of the annelid septate system show that the membranes of the two axons are in close apposition—the total combined structure being about 200 Å wide— just about the expected thickness of two unit membranes. (Hama, 1959). The structure is symmetrical, correlating with the lack of rectification in this system.

8-17. The Mauthner Cell. In the medulla of higher fish and of tailed amphibians is found a pair of Mauthner cells (M-cells) which conduct impulses between the brain and the spinal cord (Figure 8-25). M-cells of the goldfish have been intensively studied and possess both electrical and chemically transmitting syn-

apses. Each mode of transmission, in addition, has both excitatory and inhibitory endings (Table 8-8).

The M-cell is supplied with presynaptic endings from a variety of neurons including the contralateral (the opposite side, as opposed to ipsilateral, the same side) M-cell. Because of its position and the complexity of its connections, the M-cell is a major integrating and coordinating center in the nervous system.

When the club endings of the eighth cranial nerve transmit the excitation produced by eighth nerve stimulation, they do so by electrical transmission that gives rise to graded, short-latency excitatory postsynaptic potentials on the distal lateral dendrite of the M-cell (this dendrite is extremely large, making it readily accessible to microelectrode recording). The postsynaptic potentials in this region are large, declining in magnitude as they are monitored further away from the dendrite toward the soma and axon hillock.

Table 8-8 Types of Synapses on the Mauthner Cell

M-CELL PROCESS	FORM AND SIGN OF TRANSMISSION		PRESYNAPTIC ELEMENTS*
Distal lateral dendrite	Electrical	+	8th cranial nerve (club endings)
Axon hillock	Electrical	−	8th cranial nerve (axon cap endings)
Soma	Chemical	+	8th cranial nerve via interneurons
Soma	Chemical	−	8th cranial nerve (contralateral)

* These represent only a few of the presynaptic elements and are given here because the 8th nerve is often the stimulated element in experimental studies.

Furshpan and Furukawa (1962) found that the synaptically generated spikes of the M-cell arose in the axon hillock or adjacent axon, whereas the soma and large dendrite were incapable of spike production.

GABA applied by microinjection to an M-cell produces inhibitory effects at the axon hillock, soma, and adjacent dendrites. These are regions where inhibitory synapses are located. The inhibition is the result of an increased Cl⁻ conductance, but whether GABA is the physiological inhibitory transmitter is unknown (Diamond, 1963).

Of interest is the presence of inhibitory electrical synapses. It has been known for some time that under certain conditions, action currents of one axon can inhibit or reduce the excitability of neighboring fibers (see Figure 7-28; and Katz and Schmitt, 1940). Such effects can be experimentally induced by plac-

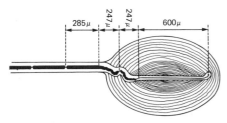

Figure 8-24 Diagrammatic representation of the Pacinian corpuscle and its dimensions. The laminated capsule is shown with the inner unmyelinated receptor ending. Before its entrance into the capsule, the acon becomes myelinated (several nodes and internodes are shown in the diagram). [Redrawn and modified from Quilliam and Sato (1955).]

ing a bundle of axons in an electrically insulating medium during stimulation. They are absent under normal conditions, where the neuron is surrounded by a large volume of conducting tissue space. In the axon cap region of the M-cell, where there is a dense network of glial and neuronal fibers, the extracellular volume is small and the electrical resistance is high. An electrode placed in this area measures a high potential from adjacent neurons. The volley of impulses reaching the M-cell at this locus affects the M-cell transmembrane potential because the incoming action currents instead of spreading out into a low resistance extraneuronal space are concentrated in the dense, electrically insulated cap region. These currents, passing through the cell membrane, can raise its potential by as much as 18 mV. Current enters the M-cell at the sites where it is most excitable, and raises its threshold, thus acting as inhibitory current flows. In the same region are located chemical synapses, which produce a longer lasting inhibition.

Furshpan and Potter (1962) examined these activities by appropriate application of microelectrodes to the M-cell. In a series of elegant experiments they also correlated potential changes with structural sites inside and outside the cell by subsequently observing sites of iron salt deposition from the steel tip of the microelectrodes used for the electrical observations. The axon cap region is invaded by fibers of the ipsilateral and contralateral eighth nerves and by fibers of the contralateral M-cell. Either orthodromic or antidromic stimulation of the M-cell results in an extracellularly recorded spike that is followed by a positive wave about 1 msec in duration. A similar positive wave is recorded outside the unstimulated M-cell. The positive waves are extracellular because placement of the electrodes within the axon hillock recorded much smaller potential changes. This wave of positivity was called the extrinsic hyperpolarizing potential (EHP). It was inhibitory since no spikes are generated in the axon hillock when the EHP exceeds a value of about 10 mV. Also the threshold of the hillock is increased to stimulatory volleys applied to the eighth nerve.

The EHP differs in several respects from the IPSP's recorded in the same region. A normal IPSP shows negative potentials when recorded intracellularly, and there is an accompanying membrane conductance change. No such changes are found associated with the EHP. The hyperpolarization of the EHP resembles the blockage of electrotonic spread produced by the anode of an external stimulating electrode (Section 7-19). Stimulation of both eighth nerves as well as the contralateral M-cell results in EHP formation. Only stimulation of the ipsilateral eighth nerve leads to excitation under appropriate conditions.

Correlation is found between the experimental conditions leading to the production of EHP's and of IPSP's, and it is assumed that both are produced by impulses arriving over the same presynaptic fibers. Some fibers of the axon cap region have normal synapses on the axon hillock, and these chemically transmitting junctions produce a longer lasting inhibition of M-cell spike production.

Electrical inhibition such as that demonstrated in the axon cap region of the Mauthner cell may also be present in other neurons because Bodian (1937) observed similar axon cap structures around the axon hillocks of several other neuronal types.

8-18. The Chick Ciliary Ganglion and *Aplysia* **Giant Cells.** Two other large cells which, like the Mauthner cell, are centers of coordination and integration, deserve mention. These are the chick ciliary ganglion cell, which possesses both chemical and electrical synapses, and

the large ganglion cells of the sea hare, *Aplysia*, which has only chemical synapses. These cells have been intensively studied because their size permits both intra- and extracellular microelectrode recording and stimulation.

In the chick ciliary ganglion cell a single presynaptic terminal forms a calyx that covers a large part of the surface of the ganglion cell (Figure 8-5). Schwann cells, in turn, cover the calyx and remainder of the ganglion cell. Martin and Pilar (1963a, b) found both orthodromic and antidromic electrical transmission across the single synapse of the ganglion cell. The electrical currents pass across the very large surface area in a manner similar to the way in which currents pass across septate axons or other large nonrectifying electrically transmitting junctions. In addition, typical synaptic vesicles are present and synaptic transmission by chemical means also occurs. The latter is cholinergic. The electrical transmission delays or blocks the formation of spikes. Antidromic impulses can generate slow depolarizations in the postsynaptic neuron because such impulses generate spikes in the presynaptic neuron, which then releases transmitter to activate the postsynaptic neuron.

The cells of the visceral ganglion of *Aplysia* have both excitatory and inhibitory synapses and can fire repetitively even at low frequencies of stimulation. In both of these cells ACh is the synaptic transmitter. In *Aplysia* ACh acts as both the excitatory and the inhibitory transmitter. Inhibition can also arise as the result of excessive depolarization because of prolonged or heightened EPSP production.

From the brief discussions of some of the more studied synaptic systems, it should be evident that the output of a postsynaptic neuron is the result of a complex mixture of inhibitory and excitatory events whose mechanisms often are based on both chemical and electrical transmission at synaptic sites.

8-19. Ephapses. Arvanitaki (1942) designated as ephapses any false or artificial junctions between excitable cells. An ephapse can be formed when an axon is brought into contact with another axon such that a site is produced where impulses cross over from one cell to the other or cause a local response in the other. An ephapse may also result when a nerve trunk is transected. Some ephapses occur where there is a natural contact between fibers that do not normally function as transmitting sites. The transmission at an ephapse must be electrical in nature. Unfortunately some authors now use the term ephapse to include any electrically transmitting synapse (see, for example, Grundfest, 1959).

Ephaptic transmission is an interesting phenomenon, in part because there is a variation in ephaptic delay times, in polarization, in facilitation, and so forth. These variations result from differing geometries of contact or from differing properties of the contacting membranes. Historically, one of the first examples of ephaptic transmission was that used by Galvani to demonstrate that the stimulation of one nerve caused a response in a second nerve laid across the first, as measured by the contraction of a muscle attached to the second nerve.

Generator (Receptor) Potentials

8-20. Introduction. In this section the bioelectrical activities of the receptor neuron will be considered. The receptor cell is the first link in the information flow chain that allows the organism to react properly to its environment. The receptor neuron is a transducer—transforming changes of the internal or external environment into electrical signals (generator potentials), which eventually are transformed into information-containing trains of nervous impulses. The transducer region of a receptor neuron must function on the basis of a sensitive membrane capable of the biogenesis of electrical potentials, but much less is known about the underlying mechanisms of this activity than about the other activities of excitable cells.

Here I shall discuss only the genesis of generator potentials and their nature; in later chapters the specific types and functions of receptor cells will be considered in relation to their role in animal regulatory activities.

8-21. Classification of Receptors. All cells have the ability to change in response to environmental changes. These responses may be either active or passive. Changing the ionic concentration of the fluid bathing a nerve cell causes an alteration in the membrane resting potential—a response predicted by and based upon the laws governing ionic movements and the physicochemical properties of the cell membrane. If an electrical current is applied to the nerve, the change in membrane potential at some point is enough to change the physicochemical characteristics of the membrane in the axonal region and a new phenomenon—the action potential—results. This first type of response is passive; the second is an active response and is a secondary reaction or change of the cell.

When we speak of cellular irritability, we are considering primarily active responses, and it is the change in the environment capable of causing an active response that is called a stimulus. An essential feature of cellular response is that it be reversible; otherwise, it can lead to cell destruction.

The receptor neuron is a cell that has differentiated so that it possesses the ability to respond to one specific type of stimulating agent—its response at some point being converted into an action potential that can be conducted into the coordinating and integrating centers of the nervous system. Specificity of response is actually relative because the receptor neuron has come to possess a low threshold to one type of environmental agent—very high levels of other agents may also cause responses. A familiar example is found in the retina of the human eye. The cells of the retina respond to relatively low levels of visible radiation but will also respond to strong pressures exerted on the eye (for example, by pressing with a finger upon the eyeball — with the eye closed to prevent damage — visual sensations can be obtained).

Primary sense cells are neurons with at least one centripetal axon (an afferent fiber that carries impulses toward the central nervous system). Primary sense cells are the only ones found in invertebrates and make up a majority of the sensory cells of vertebrates. These will be referred to here as receptor cells or neurons. **Secondary sense cells** are found only in vertebrates, and they are cells, usually not neurons, which are acting as excitatory mediators between the stimulating agent of the environment and the conducting neuron. Secondary sense cells include the cells of taste buds and the neuromast cells of the acoustico-lateralis system.

Sensory receptors may be simple unmyelinated nerve endings, or they may be complex anatomical structures such as the vertebrate eye. All degrees of structural complexity are found in sensory receptors throughout the animal phyla.

Various classifications of receptors are used. Sherrington (1906) based his classification on the location of the receptor and the source of the stimulating agent. **Proprioceptors** in muscles, tendons, and joints sense the movements and positions of muscles and appendages relative to each other. **Labyrinthine receptors** (sometimes included in the proprioceptor group) sense the position of the body in space and include statocyst or labyrinth receptors. **Interoceptors** sense changes in visceral organs and body fluids—internal conditions of the body. **Exteroceptors**, located in the skin, sense changes in the immediate external environment of the organism. **Teleceptors** sense changes in the more remote parts of the environment and include such organs as the eyes and ears.

In more common usage is a receptor classification based on the modality of the stimulating agent. **Thermoreceptors** respond to temperature changes; **mechanoreceptors** respond to tactile stimuli, to sound, to other vibrations, or to pressure changes; **chemoreceptors** include neurons sensitive to chemical changes in the internal or external environment and the cells for taste and smell; **photoreceptors** respond to changes in radiant energy; **osmoreceptors** sense changes in osmotic pressure; **pressoreceptors** (or **baroreceptors**) sense the pressures of body fluids or other pressure changes; **nocioreceptors** are deep pain sensors, responding to any damaging stimulating agent; **electroreceptors** sense changes in the geometry of electrical

fields (these are found in the electrolocating system of electric fish).

8-22. The Pacinian Corpuscle and Crustacean Stretch Receptor Organ. Most receptor terminals are minute and usually surrounded by other structures so that the analysis of events accompanying transducer activity is extremely difficult. In only a few receptor organs is there a relative simplicity of structure that lends itself to detailed study of the mechanisms underlying cell activity. One is the stretch receptor organs found in crustaceans. That in the crayfish has received the most attention. Another is the Pacinian corpuscle, a deep pressure receptor in vertebrates that responds

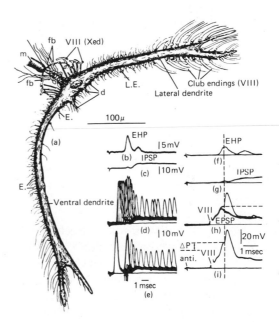

Figure 8-25 Diagrammatic representation of the Mauthner cell of the goldfish. Impulses in the contralateral M-axon evoke potentials in the axon cap (b) and the axon hillock (c). (d) and (e) are intracellular recordings illustrating that the EHP and later IPSO produce depression or block of antidromic impulses invading that M-cell from its axon. (f) and (g) correspond to (b) and (c) but are from another M-cell. (h) shows superimposed traces of EPSP's of M-cells evoked by gradually increasing stimuli to the ipsilateral eighth cranial nerve. (i) shows that the threshold level of EPSP's is increased because of its superposition upon the conditioning EHP of (f).

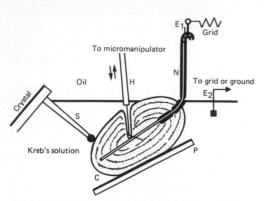

Figure 8-26 One experimental arrangement used for stimulating and recording from a Pacinian corpuscle. A piezoelectric crystal is used to apply mechanical stimuli through a glass stylus (S). A microelectrode (H) mounted on a micromanipulator is used to record from the unmyelinated nerve ending. A wire electrode E_1 records from the myelinated axon. Electrode E_2 serves as a reference electrode. The capsule (C) of the Pacinian corpuscle rests on a plate (P) in a physiological solution. [Modified from W. R. Loewenstein and R. Rathkamp (1958) "The sites for mechano-electric conversion in a Pacinian corpuscle" *Journal of General Physiology* **41**: 1245–1265.]

selectively to mechanical compression. Here I shall discuss the results of experiments on the latter receptor, which serve as a good example of the workings of sensory neurons. The stretch receptor organ will receive further attention in Chapter 11.

Figure 8-24 diagrams the structure and dimensions of a Pacinian corpuscle (Loewenstein, 1958, 1961, 1965). It contains a single myelinated axon which enters the large laminated connective tissue capsule. Inside the capsule the axon loses its myelin sheath and runs as a bare fiber for most of the capsule's length. It is this bare axon which acts as the mechanoelectrical transducer. Figure 8-26 diagrams one arrangement for stimulating and recording from this preparation. Mechanical stimuli are used and displacements as small as 0.2 μ are sufficient to create a measurable response.

8-23. Generator Potentials. The generator potential produced in the Pacinian corpuscle by appropriate stimulation is a graded, non-

propagated, exogenic potential, similar in appearance to the synaptic potentials discussed in the first part of this chapter. All generator potentials so far measured have been depolarizing potential changes.

The generator potential of the Pacinian corpuscle is a highly localized potential. When small regions of the receptor membrane are stimulated, the resultant potential change decays exponentially with distance from the site of stimulation (Figure 8-27). Experiments have also shown that the transducer region of the nerve membrane is incapable of spike initiation. The generator potential is accompanied by a generator current that can initiate a spike in an appropriate region of the axon. Increasing the stimulus spread increases the amplitude of the generator potential.

Figure 8-28 illustrates the sequence of events

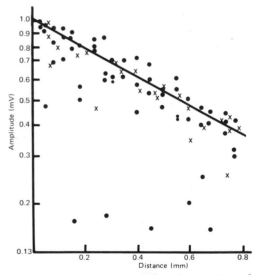

Figure 8-27 A membrane spot of about 20 μ of a decapsulated nonmyelinated nerve ending of a Pacinian corpuscle is stimulated with a series of equal mechanical impulses delivered by a crystal-driven stylus. The resulting generator potentials (circles) are left off the membrane surface at varying distances from the stimulated site with a microelectrode. A current is applied to the surface of this spot with two concentric microelectrodes and the resulting passively spreading electrotonic potentials (crosses) are recorded as before. [Redrawn from data of Loewenstein, 1961.]

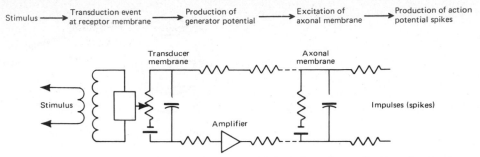

Figure 8-28 (upper) The sequence of events which leads from the application of a stimulus to a receptor ending to the generation of a spike in the sensory axon. (lower) Schematic of the various regions of a sensory neuron. The stimulus is coupled to the ending through some type of transducer mechanism (shown here as a transformer). The transducer membrane has resistance and capacitance as do other membranes and, in addition, an amplifying mechanism for increasing the response so that a spike can be generated in the axonal region.

that leads from the effective stimulus to the initiation of spikes in the myelinated region of the axon. An electrical model of the transducer membrane is also shown. It has been found that the strength of the stimulus (I_s) determines the amplitude of the generator potential (A) which, in turn, determines the frequency (F) of spike output along the sensory axon. In some cases an intermediary event may be placed between a stimulating agent and the transducer action. An example is the photic breakdown of visual pigment in retinal cells, which initiates the proper transducer action and the production of a generator potential (see Chapter 17). High-frequency stimulation of the Pacinian corpuscle depresses the generator potential, and this effect is also a highly localized phenomenon, appearing restricted to only that area of membrane being stimulated.

8-24. Ionic Mechanisms. The small size of most receptor terminals precludes direct investigation of the ionic changes responsible for generator potential production. But indirect answers to this question have been obtained, based partially on the clues given by studies on other types of bioelectric potentials.

It is thought that the stimulation of a transducer membrane produces a nonselective change in ionic permeabilities of the membrane. This would tend to drive the transmembrane potential toward zero, that is, in the direction of the Na^+ equilibrium potential.

But because Ka^+, Cl^- and other ions are also permeable the potential would not be expected to actually reach the level of the Na^+ equilibrium potential. If the stimulating agent produces an increase in the channels for all ions, the greater the number of openings, the greater would be the potential change across the membrane. Stimuli of higher strength, by opening more channels, thus increase the magnitude of the generator potential. As a corollary, the degree of polarization achieved by a given number of open channels (proportional to stimulus strength) would vary directly with the magnitude of the initial transmembrane potential.

The steady state potential toward which the transducer action drives the membrane potential can be determined by measuring the amplitude of generator potential produced by equal strength stimuli delivered to the membrane maintained at different transmembrane potentials by voltage clamp techniques. The results of such experiments with crayfish stretch receptor cells show that there is a linear decrease in the amplitude of the generator potential with increasing initial transmembrane potentials. Extrapolation shows that the generator potential arrives at zero when the resting potential does—zero potential corresponding to no one of the equilibrium potentials of the normal ionic constituents of tissues or the extracellular medium. In the crayfish stretch receptor it seems then that stimulation produces an increased permeability to all ions.

Measurements of this type are not possible on the minute axon terminals of the Pacinian corpuscle. However, assuming that Na$^+$ ions are normally farthest removed from equilibrium and would contribute most (but not all) to the development of the generator potential, the removal of Na$^+$ from the external medium should reduce but not completely abolish the generator potential.

Initial experiments in which the Pacinian corpuscle was immersed in a Na$^+$-free medium were disappointing because although spike potentials were abolished, there were no changes in the generator potential. It was then found that the capsule surrounding the transducer membrane region of the axon acts as a diffusion barrier, preventing changes in the ionic composition of the extracellular fluid directly surrounding the bare nerve ending. When Na$^+$-free or Na$^+$-deficient solutions are perfused into the periterminal space through a small blood capillary that penetrates into the capsule along with the axon, then there is found a diminution of the generator potential as the sodium ion concentration decreases (Diamond et al., 1958).

Loewenstein points out that the generator potential has other peculiarities. Studies of the temperature dependence of the amplitude and rate of rise of the generator potential yield ΔH values of about 16,000 cal/mole, corresponding to a Q_{10} of about 2. These values are higher than similar ones for the action potential or currents at the node of Ranvier. Drug action is also peculiar. Tetrodotoxin in concentrations of 5 to 10×10^{-6} M abolishes the action potentials but not the generator potentials of Pacinian corpuscles and of crustacean stretch receptors (Loewenstein et al., 1963).

8-25. Transducer Input and Output. Nothing is known about the mechanisms whereby the stimulating agent alters membrane permeability in a receptor. In most cases the relations between stimulus and response are not well defined. The transducer region is small and

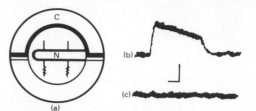

Figure 8-29 The decapsulated nerve ending of a Pacinian corpuscle is compressed in a chamber consisting of two piezoelectric half cylinders (a). (b) The generator potential produced in response to unequal pressure distribution caused by compression of one half cylinder. (c) The response to uniform pressure. Horizontal and vertical marks represent 1 millisecond and 1 millivolt, respectively. High hydrostatic pressure failed to produce a response indicating that the ending is responsive to distortional strain not hydrostatic stress. The response in (b) also illustrates the off-response produced when the stimulus ends. [Redrawn after Loewenstein (1965).]

normally not directly accessible to the external stimulus. For example, in the Pacinian corpuscle the mechanical energy driving the transducer must first pass through a fluid-filled lamellar capsule. Therefore, the stimulus, although accurately measured at its source, undergoes both time and amplitude alterations before it acts on the transducer membrane (Skalak and Loewenstein, 1966). Experimental results with the Pacinian corpuscle and the Lorenzinian ampulla of elasmobranchs show that these receptors are sensitive only to distortional strain, not hydrostatic stresses (Figure 8-29).

The capsule of the Pacinian corpuscle acts as an elastic storage and filter element. It stores kinetic energy during the compression phase and releases it during the decompression phase, therefore giving rise to an off response (Figure 8-29). It also cuts off low mechanical frequencies. In neither the Pacinian corpuscle nor crayfish stretch receptor is the generator potential a perfect analog of the applied stimulus. If the stimulus is prolonged, the amplitude of the generator potential decreases. This decrease and the consequent decrease in receptor output with prolonged stimulation is the adaptation typical of most excitable cells.

Phasic receptors are those in which adaptation reduces the generator potential to zero during prolonged stimulation. Examples include the Pacinian corpuscle and some mechanoreceptors associated with hair follicles. **Tonic receptors** are those in which adaptation reduces the generator potential to some low value of depolarization but not to zero. Examples are muscle stretch receptors, tendon stretch receptors, pressoreceptors in the carotid sinus of mammals, and many cutaneous touch and thermal receptors.

Phasic receptors signal only the beginning and ending of a stimulation. Tonic receptors continuously signal a stream of impulses whose frequency is used as information by the central nervous system. Phasic receptors also have a continuous background level of firing. If they adapted to lack of stimulation this would effectively transmit information. The mechanism underlying adaptation in receptors is not known. Adaptation is often used to refer to changes in frequency of spike production, but since this frequency depends on generator potential amplitude, no confusion arises from this use of the term.

Electric Organs

8-26. General Nature of Electric Organs. Although electric organs are effectors found in certain fishes and are derived usually from embryonic muscle cells, they are introduced here for several reasons. The cells of electric organs have lost all contractile machinery but retain either or both the typical muscle fiber excitable membrane and the end plate type of membrane. The hypothesis that there exist electrically inexcitable and electrically excitable electrogenic membranes has been derived primarily from the study of these organs (Grundfest, 1957, 1959, 1966). Significant information about impulse generation and transmission has resulted from the study of electric organs because their output is in the form of bioelectrical potentials and currents and the cells are relatively large. They are of interest also because in some fishes there has

developed a special type of receptor cell that responds to the electrical field produced by the fish's electric organ—the only known cases of receptor membranes responding to electrical stimuli (it might be noted that responses to electric shock are caused by direct action of electrical potentials on axonal and muscle membranes).

Historically, the discharges of electric fish were the first bioelectrical phenomena observed by man, although centuries were to pass before the shocks and unpleasant sensations associated with the handling of these fishes were to be related to electricity. The ancient Egyptians were familiar with the Nile catfish, *Malapterurus*; the Greeks and Romans knew the Mediterranean electric ray, *Torpedo*. Early explorers of the new world brought back to Europe the South American fresh water eel, *Electrophorus electricus* (see Keynes, 1957).

There are about five hundred species of fish known to possess electric organs although only a few have been studied. Electric organs are found in marine elasmobranchs, especially in the families Torpedinae; in fresh water teleosts, Gymnotidae and Mormyridae; and in one family of marine teleosts, the Uranoscopidae, which includes *Astroscopus*, the stargazer found along the American Atlantic coast. The functions and evolution of electric organs are discussed by Lissman (1958).

In all fishes the electric organs are derived from muscle cells. These may be modified

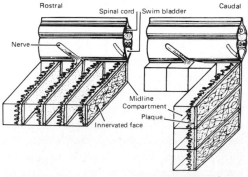

Figure 8-30 Schematic representation of the series and parallel arrays of electroplates found in the main electric organ of the electric eel *Electrophorus*. [After Grundfest (1960).]

Table 8-9   Discharge of Electric Organs and Response Patterns of Their Electroplaques*

ANIMAL	DISCHARGE AMPLITUDE (V)	FORM	FRE-QUENCY	RESPONSE† AMPLITUDE (mV)	TYPE	DURATION PSP	SPIKE
Torpedo nobilians	60	monophasic	repetitive	80	1	5	none
Narcine brasillensis							
main organ	30	monophasic	repetitive	80	1	5	none
accessory organ	0.5	monophasic	repetitive	80	1	5	none
Raia clavata	4	monophasic	repetitive	80	1	25	none
Astroscopus y-graecum	7	monophasic	repetitive	80	1	5	none
Electrophorus electricus	600	monophasic	repetitive	100	2	2	2
Eigenmannie virescens	1	monophasic direct + current	250/sec	100	2	1	2
Stemopygus elegans	1	monophasic direct current	50/sec	100	2	2	10
Gymnotus carapo	1	triphasic	50/sec	100	3	1.5	1
Sternarchus albifrons	1	monophasic direct + current	750/sec	100	3		
Gnathonemus compressirostris	10	diphasic	variable	100	4		0.2
Mormyrus rume	12	diphasic	variable	100	4		4
Gymnarchus niloticus	low	monophasic	300/sec	?	?		
Malapterurus electricus	300	monophasic	repetitive	100	4		

* From H. Grundfest. (1960). "Electric organ" (Biology). In *McGraw-Hill Encyclopedia of Science and Technology*, **8**: 427–433. By permission.

† Response types: (1) electrically inexcitable, producing only PSP on innervated surface; (2) responses are both PSP's and spikes; only at unnervated surface; (3) Opposite, innervated surface also is electrically excitable, producing a spike; innervated surface develops both a PSP and a spike; (4) the synaptic junction is at some distance from the major surface of the electroplaque on one or several stalks of the caudal surface, both surfaces produce spikes.
Repetitive frequency is during stimulation.

skeletal or branchial muscle cells as in elasmobranchs or modified ocular muscles as in *Astroscopus*. It was at first thought that the cells of the electric organ of *Malapterurus* were derived from secretory cells in the skin, but Johnels (1956) showed that these also are derivatives of embryonic muscle cells. The thin, flattened cells of electric organs are known as **electroplaques** (also as "electroplates," "electroplaxes," or simply "plates"). Each cell is embedded in a transparent gelatinous material. A connective tissue barrier surrounds each cell, and therefore, each unit is a separate compartment (Figure 8-30). One face of each electroplaque is innervated, whereas the other surface is noninnervated and usually is highly infolded and bearing papillae. The innervation varies according to species (Figure 8-31).

The electroplaques are stacked in columns, the number and arrangement depending on the species. In electric rays the organ is arranged in columns of electroplaques running dorsoventrally. The columns run longitudinally in

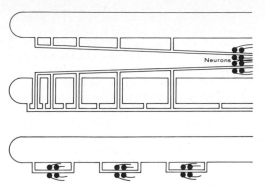

Figure 8-31 Schematic diagrams of some different types of innervation found in electric organs of mormyrid fishes and in *Malapterurus*. The electroplates are innervated by one or more stalks that arise on the caudal surface. In *Malapterurus* there is a single stalk that arises from the center of the caudal face of the electroplate. In some species the stalks penetrate the body of the electroplate.

the main organ of the electric eel. In the eel the organs make up about 40 per cent of the mass of the animal. All the viscera lie under the bones of the skull and first 20 vertebrae; the electric organs lie under the remaining 230 vertebrae (about 4/5ths of the body length).

The resting and action potentials of electroplaques fall within the normal range of values for these potentials in any excitable cell (see Table 8-9). The number of electroplaques per column, the number of columns, and the surface area of each electroplaque determine the magnitude of the electric organ discharge. Electroplaques in a column are connected in series electrically, similar to a series of batteries. Columns are connected in parallel electrically. Increasing the number of columns in an organ therefore increases the current output.

Long columns with many electroplaques are typical of fresh water fishes because a high voltage is needed to overcome the electrical resistance of the fresh water. A large number of short columns is typical of marine fishes because the electrical conductivity of salt water allows large currents to flow with relatively lower voltages.

The main organ of *Electrophorus* (there are two smaller electric organs in this eel—the

organ of Sachs and the organ of Hunter—Couceiro and Akerman, 1948) contains about 120 columns arranged in parallel; each column contains from 6,000 to 10,000 electroplaques. The organ produces a maximum discharge of about 600 volts and is the most powerful bioelectric generator known.

In contrast, the giant marine ray, *Torpedo nobilianae*, has about 1,000 electroplaques in each of 2,000 vertically placed columns. The discharge voltage is only about 60 volts, but extremely large currents are produced. A discharge of 6,000 watts (representing about 100 amperes) was once measured from another large ray, *T. occidentalis*; the normal maximal discharge is about 1,000 watts.

As shown in Table 8-9, many fish have electric organs that produce periodic low amplitude, low voltage discharges. These function in electrolocation through a complex sensory system (Section 8-28). The two accessory organs of *Electrophorus* are used for this purpose.

8-27. Mechanism of Discharge. If there were no asymmetry in the electroplaque system, excitation could lead only to a cellular membrane depolarization that would produce no

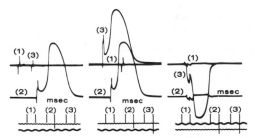

Figure 8-32 Records of potentials from the electroplate of the eel showing that there is an asymmetry of the two faces. At the bottom are shown the positions of the microelectrodes; at the top are shown the potentials recorded from these positions. The heavy wavy line represents the noninnervated face, the light wavy line the innervated face of each electroplate. No action potentials are recorded until the electrodes are across the innervated as well as the noninnervated face, when electrodes are positioned from direction of noninnervated face. [After Keynes and Martins-Ferreira (1953).]

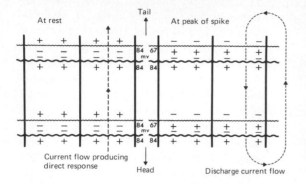

At rest

Tail

At peak of spike

Current flow producing direct response

Head

Discharge current flow

Figure 8-33 Diagram illustrating the additive discharge of electroplates. Heavy wavy line represents noninnervated face; light wavy line represents innervated face of each plate. At rest there is no net potential difference across the electroplates. At the peak of the spike, following stimulation, all the potentials are in series and the head of the eel becomes positive with respect to its tail. Only the innervated face of the electroplate can respond with a potential change. [After Keynes and Martins-Ferreira (1953).]

electrical discharge. Microelectrode studies showed that in the electric eel the asymmetry arose from differences in the innervated and noninnervated face of each electroplaque (Keynes and Martins-Ferreira, 1957). The experiments are illustrated in Figure 8-32. Only the innervated face of the eel electroplaque is depolarized upon stimulation. As shown in Figure 8-33 this leads to a sudden electrical coupling of the outside, noninnervated surfaces and a summing of all the potentials of these surfaces.

The innervated surface of the eel electroplaque responds to both electrical nervous stimulation, indicating that some regions of the membrane have the properties of motor end plate membrane whereas other regions are similar to the muscle plasma membrane in being responsive to electrical stimulation. The innervated surface is sensitive to ACh and the nerves innervating all electric organs studied have been found to be cholinergic. The non-innervated face is not excitable.

The electroplaques of Torpedinae are different in that the innervated surface is not electrically excitable and is thus similar in this respect to end plate membrane. Direct electrical stimulation produces no response; only nervous excitation is effective. The normal responses are reduced by tubocurarine and atropine, substances that also inhibit motor end plate activity. Denervated electroplaques respond to application of ACh. Thus this surface has the properties of a typical chemical synapse. There is, in fact, no action potential produced, only a postsynaptic type of potential. Most marine fish have this type of

electroplaque membrane surface, including *Astroscopus*. Freshwater teleosts have electroplaque membranes similar to those of *Electrophorus*.

As indicated by the data of Table 8-9, there is some variability in the nature of electroplaque surfaces. In *Gymnotus* and other species, both surfaces are electrically excitable, producing spikes; the innervated surface produces a PSP in addition. *Malapterurus* is an unusual fish whose electric organ surrounds the body, lying in the skin. Although in most fishes the innervated face of the electroplaque temporarily becomes negative with respect to the noninnervated face (Pacini's rule), *Malapterurus* is the exception. Although electric organs in which both faces of the electroplaques can depolarize are found in low-voltage fishes, *Malapterurus* again is the exception. In the latter, the amplitude of the spikes of the two surfaces vary markedly.

The discharge of the electric organ is the result of a summation of the individual potentials or currents of the electroplaques. The electric organs are highly synchronized. All the electroplaques along the body of an eel that may be six to eight feet long discharge simultaneously (within a period of 3 msec). In the eel such synchronization is achieved by the morphology of the nerves innervating the electroplaques. These nerves, which run from the spinal cord out to the electric organ, progressively shorten from head to tail, thus decreasing the distance to be traversed by impulses at the caudal end of the animal. In addition, synapses near the head have a greater delay, thus slowing the transmission of impulses slightly. It seems likely that a variety of mechanisms have evolved to bring about coordination in electric organ discharge, and more studies with other species of fish are needed.

8-28. Functions of Electric Organs. Although the larger discharges of electric eels and rays function in defense and can be used to stun and capture prey, it was only recently discovered that the smaller repetitive discharges of most fish, serve as a detection and location finding mechanism.

By means of conditioning experiments *Gymnarchus niloticus* was shown to be sensitive to changes in the electrical field about it. Changes as small as 0.03 mV could be detected (Lissman and Machin, 1958; Machin and Lissman, 1960). The fish could sense the presence of magnets, electrical currents, electrical conductors as well as nonconductors placed in its habitat. Such a sensory system allows *Gymnarchus* to detect other fish in its environment, but the electrical impulses are so small that prey are not frightened away as long as they do not possess the specialized electrodetection system.

Gymnarchus produces a continuous stream of electrical discharges at rates ranging from 65 to 2,000 per second depending on the species. In a majority of electric organs, one surface of the electroplaque is innervated directly; in others innervation occurs on stalks extending from the caudal electroplaque surface. The latter type of innervation is found in the African fresh water electric fishes and in the American knife fishes. The nerve impulse produces a PSP in the stalk that triggers a spike. The spike propagates into the electroplaque. The stalked caudal surface depolarizes first, followed by a depolarization of the nonstalked rostral surface. The result is a diphasic action potential. These spikes have extremely short durations, about 0.3 msec, and are adapted to serve as part of the electrolocation system.

Gymnarchus varies the amplitude of the pulses on contacting a strange object. The Mormyrid fish vary both amplitude and fre-

quency of the pulses. The patterned discharges of the organs at the end of *Gymnarchus'* tail produce an electric field about the body of the fish, with the tail becoming negative to the head at each discharge. The configuration of the electrical field about the fish varies as objects of differing electrical conductivity are encountered. The fish maintains its body in a straight rigid position while swimming, presumably to maintain a constant electrical field about itself.

The electroreceptor cells in mormyrid fish are the **mormyromast cells**. These cells are electrically excitable and their generated potentials are passed on to neurons by both electrical and chemical mechanisms (Bennett, 1965; Dijkgraaf, 1963; Hagiwara et al., 1962; Murray, 1965). The **ampullae of Lorenzine** of elasmobranch fishes possess some cells which act as electroreceptors in these organisms (Murray, 1965). Both of the above cells are found in the ampullary lateral line organs, a major cutaneous sensory system of fishes generally. Much more remains to be learned about this fascinating system.

References and Readings

Altamirano, M., C. W. Coates, H. Grundfest, and D. Nachmansohn (1953). "Mechanisms of bioelectric activity in electric tissues. I. The response to indirect and direct stimulation of electroplax of *Electrophorus electricus.*" *J. Gen. Physiol.* **37**: 91.

Andén, N. E., A. Carlsson, N. A. Hillarp, and T. Magnusson (1964). "5-Hydroxytryptamine release by nerve stimulation of the spinal cord." *Life Sci.* **3**: 473–478.

Arvanitaki, A. (1942). "Effects evoked in an axon by the electrical activity of a contiguous one." *J. Neurophysiol.* **5**: 89–108.

Arvanitaki, A. and N. Chalazonitis (1955). "Potentiels d'activité du soma neuronique géant (*Aplysia*)." *Arch. Sci. Physiol.* **9**: 115–144.

Barrnett, R. J. (1962). "The fine structural localization of acetylcholinesterase at the myoneural junction." *J. Cell Biol.* **12**: 247–262.

Bennett, M. V. L. (1961). "Modes of operation of electric organs." *Ann. N.Y. Acad. Sci.* **94**: 458–509.

Bennett, M. V. L. (1965). "Electroreceptors in Mormyrids." *Cold Spring Harbor Symp. Quant. Biol.* **30**: 245–262.

Bennett, M. V. L., E. Aljure, Y. Nakajima, and G. D. Pappas (1963). "Electrotonic junctions between teleost spinal neurons: electrophysiology and ultrastructure." *Science* **141**: 262–264.

Birks, R. I. (1963). "The role of sodium ions in the metabolism of acetylcholine." *Canad. J. Biochem. Physiol.* **41**: 2573–2597.

Birks, R. I. and M. W. Cohen (1965). "Effects of sodium on transmitter release from frog motor nerve terminals." In: **Muscle: Proceedings of a Symposium at the University of Alberta, June, 1963,** pp. 403–420. Long Island City, N.Y.: Pergamon Press, Inc.

Birks, R. I., H. E. Huxley, and B. Katz (1960). "The fine structure of the neuromuscular junction of the frog." *J. Physiol.* (London) **150**: 134–144.

Birks, R. I. and F. C. MacIntosh (1961). "Acetylcholine metabolism of a sympathetic ganglion." *Canad. J. Biochem. Physiol.* **39**: 787–827.

Bishop, G. H. (1956). "The natural history of the nerve impulse." *Physiol. Rev.* **36**: 376–399.

Bodian, D. (1937). "The structure of the vertebrate synapse. A study of the axon endings on Mauthner's cell and neighboring centers in the goldfish." *J. Comp. Neurol.* **68**: 117–159.

Bodian, D. (1942). "Cytological aspects of synaptic function." *Physiol. Rev.* **22**: 146–169.

Bodian, D. (1962). "Introductory survey of neurons." *Cold Spring Harbor Symp. Quant. Biol.* **17**: 1–13.

Boyd, I. A. and A. R. Martin (1954). "Spontaneous subthreshold activity at mammalian neuromuscular junctions." *J. Physiol.* (London) **132**: 61–73.

Braun, M. and R. F. Schmidt (1966). "Poten-

tial changes recorded from the frog motor nerve terminal during its activation." *Arch. ges. Physiol.* **287**: 56–80.

Braun, M., R. F. Schmidt, and M. Zimmerman (1966). "Facilitation at the frog neuromuscular junction during and after repetitive stimulation." *Arch. ges. Physiol.* **287**: 41–55.

Brooks, V. B. (1956). "An intracellular study of the action of repetitive nerve volleys and of botulinum toxin on miniature endplate potentials." *J. Physiol.* (London) **134**: 264–277.

Bullock, T. H. and S. Hagiwara (1957). "Intracellular recording from the giant synapse of the squid." *J. Gen. Physiol.* **40**: 565–577.

Bullock, T. H. and G. Horridge (1965). **Structure and Function in the Nervous System of Invertebrates,** 2 volumes. San Francisco: W. H. Freeman & Company, Publishers.

Chagas, C. (1959). "Studies on the mechanism of curare fixation by cells." In: **Curare and Curare-like Agents.** (D. Bovet, F. Bovet-Nitti, G. B. Marino-Bettólo, eds.), pp. 327. New York: American Elsevier Publishing Company.

Chagas, C., E. Penna-Franca, K. Nishie, and E. J. Garcia (1958). "A study of the specificity of the complex formed by gallamine triethiodide with a macromolecular constituent of the electric organ." *Arch. Biochem. Biophys.* **75**: 251–259.

Coombs, J. S., J. C. Eccles, and P. Fatt (1955). "The specific ion conductances and the ionic movements across the motoneuronal membrane that produce the inhibitory postsynaptic potential." *J. Physiol.* (London) **130**: 326–373.

Couceiro, A. and M. Akerman (1948). "Sur quelques aspects du tissue électrique de l'electrophorus électricus." *Anais de Acad., Bras. de Ciencias* **20**: 383.

Couteaux, R. (1955). "Localization of cholinesterases at neuromuscular junctions." *Int. Rev. Cytol.* **4**: 335–375.

Couteaux, R. (1958). "Morphological and cytochemical observations on the post-

synaptic membrane at motor endplates."
Exp. Cell Res. (Suppl.) **5**: 294–322.

Curtis, D. R. and J. C. Eccles (1959). "The time courses of excitatory and inhibitory synaptic actions." *J. Physiol.* (London) **145**: 529–546.

Dale, H. H. (1914). "The action of certain esters and ethers of choline, and their relation to muscarine." *J. Pharmacol. Exp Therap.* **6**: 147–190.

Dale, H. H. (1935). "Pharmacology and nerve endings." *Proc. Roy. Soc. Med.* **28**: 319–332.

Dale, H. H. and M. Vogt (1936). "Release of acetylcholine at voluntary motor nerve endings." *J. Physiol.* (London) **86**: 353–380.

DeHarven, E. and C. Cöers (1959). "Electron microscope study of the human neuromuscular junction." *J. Biophys. Biochem. Cytol.* **6**: 7–10.

del Castillo, J. and B. Katz (1954a). "The effect of magnesium on the activity of motor nerve endings." *J. Physiol.* (London) **124**: 553–559.

del Castillo, J. and B. Katz (1954b). "Quantal components of the end-plate potential." *J. Physiol.* (London) **124**: 560–573.

del Castillo, J. and B. Katz (1956). "Biophysical aspects of neuro-muscular transmission." *Prog. Biophys.* **6**: 121–170.

DeLorenzo, A. J. (1959). "The fine structure of synapses." *Biol. Bull.* **117**: 390.

DeLorenzo, A. J. (1960). "Electron microscopy of electrical synapses in the crayfish." *Biol. Bull.* **119**: 325.

DeLorenzo, A. J. (1960a). "The fine structure of synapses in the ciliary ganglion of the chick." *J. Biophys. Biochem. Cytol.* **7**: 31–36.

DeLorenzo, A. J. (1966). "Electron microscopy: tight junctions in synapses of the chick ciliary ganglion." *Science* **152**: 76–78.

DeRobertis, E. D. P. (1964). **Histophysiology of Synapses and Neurosecretion.** Long Island City, N.Y.: Pergamon Press, Inc. 244 pp.

DeRobertis, E. D. P. and H. S. Bennett (1954). "Submicroscopic vesicular components in the synapse." *Fed. Proc.* **13**: 35.

DeRobertis, E. D. P. and H. S. Bennett (1955). "Some features of the submicro-scopic morphology of synapses in frog and earthworm." *J. Biophys. Biochem. Cytol.* **1**: 47–58.

DeRobertis, E. D. P. and C. M. Franchi (1956). "Electron microscope observations on synaptic vesicles in synapses of the retinal rods and cones." *J. Biophys. Biochem. Cytol.* **2**: 307–318.

DeRobertis, E. D. P., A. Pellegraino de Iraldi, G. Rodriguez, and C. J. Gomez (1961). "On the isolation of nerve endings and synaptic vesicles." *J. Biophys. Biochem. Cytol.* **9**: 229–235.

Diamond, J. (1963). "Variation in the sensitivity to gamma-amino-butyric acid of different regions of the Mauthner cell." *Nature* **199**: 773–775.

Diamond, J., J. A. B. Gray, and D. R. Inman (1958). "The relation between receptor potentials and the concentration of sodium ions." *J. Physiol.* (London) **142**: 282–294.

DiCarlo, V. (1967). "Ultrastructure of the membrane of synaptic vesicles." *Nature* **213**: 883–834.

Dijkgraaf, S. (1963). "The functioning and significance of the lateral-line organs." *Biol. Rev.* **38**: 51–105.

Dudel, J. (1962). "Effect of inhibition on the presynaptic nerve terminal in the neuromuscular junction of the crayfish." *Nature* **193**: 587–588.

Dudel, J. (1965a). "The mechanisms of presynaptic inhibition at the crayfish neuromuscular junction." *Arch. ges. Physiol.* **284**: 66–80.

Dudel, J. (1965b). "The action of inhibitory drugs on nerve terminals in crayfish muscle." *Arch. ges. Physiol.* **284**: 81–94.

Dudel, J. and S. W. Kuffler (1961). "Presynaptic inhibition at the crayfish neuromuscular junction." *J. Physiol.* (London) **155**: 543–562.

Eccles, J. C. (1957). **Physiology of Nerve Cells.** Baltimore: Johns Hopkins Press.

Eccles, J. C. (1964). **The Physiology of Synapses.** Berlin: Springer-Verlag. 316 pp.

Edwards, G. A., H. Ruska, and E. de Harven (1958). "Electron microscopy of peripheral nerves and neuromuscular junctions in the wasp leg." *J. Biochem. Biophys. Cytol.* **4:** 107–114.

Ehrenpreis, S. (1960). "Isolation and identification of the acetylcholine receptor protein of electric tissue." *Biochem. Biophys. Acta* **44:** 561–577.

Erdös, E. G., ed. (1963). "Structure and function of biologically active peptides: bradykinin, kallidin, and congeners." *Ann. N.Y. Acad. Sci.* **104:** 1–464.

von Euler, U. S. (1946). "A specific sympathomimetic ergone in adrenergic nerve fibers (sympathin) and its relations to adrenaline and nor-adrenaline." *Acta Physiol. Scand.* **12:** 73–97.

von Euler, U. S. and J. H. Gaddum (1931). "An unidentified depressor substance in certain tissue extracts." *J. Physiol.* (London) **72:** 74–87.

Fatt, P. and B. Katz (1950). "Membrane potential changes at the motor end-plate." *J. Physiol.* (London) **111:** 46P–47P.

Fatt, P. and Katz, B. (1951). "An analysis of the end-plate potential recorded with an intra-cellular electrode." *J. Physiol.* (London) **115:** 320–370.

Fatt, P. and B. Katz (1952). "Spontaneous subthreshold activity at motor nerve endings." *J. Physiol.* (London) **117:** 109–128.

Florey, E. (1954). "An inhibitory and an excitatory factor of mammalian central nervous system, and their action on a single sensory neuron." *Arch. Int. Physiol.* **62:** 33–35.

Florey, E. (1961). "Comparative physiology: Transmitter substances." *Ann. Rev. Physiol.* **23:** 501–528.

Florey, E. and H. McLennan (1955). "Effects of an inhibitory factor (Factor I) from brain on central synaptic transmission." *J. Physiol.* (London) **130:** 446–455.

Foster, M. and C. S. Sherrington (1897). **A Textbook of Physiology.** "Part III, The Central Nervous System." London: Macmillan & Co., Ltd.

Furshpan, E. J. and T. Furukawa (1962). "Intracellular and extracellular responses of the several regions of the Mauthner cell of the goldfish." *J. Neurophysiology* **25:** 732–771.

Furshpan, E. J. and D. D. Potter (1959). "Transmission at the giant synapse of the crayfish." *J. Physiol.* (London) **145:** 289–325.

Furukawa, T. and E. J. Furshpan (1963). "Two inhibitory mechanisms in the Mauthner neurons of goldfish." *J. Neurophysiol.* **26:** 140–176.

Goodman, L. S. and A. Gilman, eds. (1965). **The Pharmacological Basis of Therapeutics,** 3rd ed. New York: The Macmillan Company. 1785 pp.

Grundfest, H. (1957). "The mechanisms of discharge of electric organs in relation to general and comparative electrophysiology." *Prog. Biophys.* **7:** 1–74.

Grundfest, H. (1959). "Synaptic and ephaptic transmission." In: **Handbook of Physiology.** (J. Field, ed.), Sect. 1, Vol. 1, pp. 147–197. Washington, D.C.: American Physiology Society.

Grundfest, H. (1960). "Electric organ." (Biology). In: **McGraw-Hill Encyclopedia of Science and Technology, 8:** 427–433. New York: McGraw-Hill Book Company, Inc.

Grundfest, H. (1964). "Bioelectrogenesis." In: **Encyclopedia of Electrochemistry.** (C. A. Hampel, ed.), pp. 107–138. New York: Reinhold Publishing Corporation.

Grundfest, H. (1966). "Electrophysiology and pharmacology of different components of bioelectric transducers." *Cold Spring Harbor Symp. Quant. Biol.* **30:** 1–14.

Haggar, R. A. and M. L. Barr (1950). "Quantitative data on the size of synaptic endbulbs in the cat's spinal cord." *J. Comp. Neurol.* **93:** 17–35.

Hagiwara, S., K. Kusano, and K. Negishi (1962). "Physiological properties of electroreceptors in some gymnotids." *J. Neurophysiol.* **25:** 430–449.

Hagiwara, S. and I. Tasaki (1958). "A study of the mechanism of impulse transmission across the giant synapse of the squid." *J. Physiol.* (London) **143:** 114–137.

Hama, K. (1959). "Some observations on the fine structure of the giant nerve fibers of the earthworm, *Eisenia foetida*." *J. Biophys. Biochem. Cytol.* **6:** 61–66.

Hama, K. (1961). "Some observations on the fine structure of the giant fibers of the crayfishes (*Cambarus viriulus, Cambarus clarkii*) with special reference to the submicroscopic organization of the synapses." *Anat. Rec.* **141**: 275–294.

Hama, K. (1962). "Some observations on the fine structure of the giant synapse in the stellate ganglion of the squid, *Doryteuphis bleekeri.*" *Z. Zellforsch.* **56**: 437–444.

Horridge, G. A., D. M. Chapman, and B. MacKay (1962). "Naked axons and symmetrical synapses in an elementary nervous system." *Nature* **193**: 899–900.

Hubbard, J. I. (1963). "Repetitive stimulation at the neuromuscular junction and the mobilization of transmitter." *J. Physiol.* (London) **169**: 641–662.

Hydén, H. (1960). "The Neuron." In: **The Cell.** (J. Brachet and A. E. Mirsky, eds.), Vol. 4, part 1, pp. 215–324. New York: Academic Press, Inc.

Jenkinson, D. H. (1960). "The antagonism between tubocurarine and substances which depolarize the motor end-plate." *J. Physiol.* (London) **152**: 309–324.

Johnels, A. G. (1956). "On the origin of the electric organs of *Malapterurus.*" *Quart. J. Microscop. Sci.* **97**: 455–464.

Kandel, E. R. and W. A. Spencer (1968). "Cellular neurophysiological approaches in the study of learning." *Physiol. Rev.* **48**: 65–134.

Kandel, E. R. and L. Tauc (1966). "Anomalous rectification in the metacerebral giant cells and its consequences for synaptic transmission." *J. Physiol.* (London) **183**: 286–304.

Kao, C. Y. (1960). "Postsynaptic electrogenesis in septate giant axons. II. Comparison of medial and lateral giant axons of crayfish." *J. Neurophysiol.* **23**: 618–635.

Kao, C. Y. and H. Grundfest (1957). "Postsynaptic electrogenesis in septate giant axons. I. Earthworm medium giant axon." *J. Neurophysiol.* **20**: 553–573.

Katz, B. (1958). "Microphysiology of the neuromuscular junction." *Johns Hopkins Hosp. Bull.* **102**: 275–312.

Katz, B. (1966). **Nerve, Muscle, and Synapse.** New York: McGraw-Hill Book Company, Inc. 193 pp.

Katz, B. and R. Miledi (1963). "A study of spontaneous miniature potentials in spinal motoneurons." *J. Physiol.* (London) **168**: 389–422.

Katz, B. and R. Miledi (1964). "Localization of calcium action at the nerve-muscle junction." *J. Physiol.* (London) **171**: 10P–12P.

Katz, B. and R. Miledi (1965). "The effect of calcium on acetylcholine release from motor nerve terminals." *Proc. Roy. Soc.* (London) **B161**: 496–503.

Katz, B. and R. Miledi (1967a). "Modification of transmitter release by electrical interference with motor nerve endings." *Proc. Roy. Soc.* (London) **B167**: 1–7.

Katz, B. and R. Miledi (1967b). "The release of acetylcholine from nerve endings by graded electric pulses." *Proc. Roy. Soc.* (London) **B167**: 23–38.

Katz, B. and O. H. Schmitt (1940). "Electric interaction between two adjacent nerve fibres." *J. Physiol.* (London) **97**: 471–488.

Katz, B. and S. Thesleff (1957). "On the factors which determine the amplitude of the 'miniature end-plate potential'." *J. Physiol.* (London) **137**: 267–278.

Kelley, J. S. (1965). "Antagonism between Na^+ and Ca^{2+} at the neuromuscular junction." *Nature* **205**: 296–297.

Keynes, R. D. (1957). "Electric organs." In: **The Physiology of Fishes.** (M. E. Brown, ed.), Vol. 2, pp. 323–343. New York: Academic Press, Inc.

Keynes, R. D. and H. Martins-Ferreira (1953). "Membrane potentials in the electroplates of the electric eel." *J. Physiol.* (London) **119**: 315–351.

Kiyoshi, K., D. R. Livengood, and R. Werman (1967). "Correlation of transmitter release with membrane properties of the presynaptic fiber of the squid giant synapse." *J. Gen. Physiol.* **50**: 2579–2602.

Koelle, G. B. and J. S. Friedenwald (1949). "A histochemical method for localizing cholinesterase activity." *Proc. Soc. Exp. Biol.* **70**: 617–622.

Kravitz, E. A., S. W. Kuffler, and D. D. Potter (1963). "Gamma-amino-butyric acid and other blocking compounds in Crustacea. III. Their relative concentrations in separated motor and inhibitory axons." *J. Neurophysiol.* **26**: 739–751.

Krnjević, K. and R. Miledi (1958). "Failure of neuromuscular propagation in rats." *J. Physiol.* (London) **140**: 440–461.

Krnjević, K. and J. F. Mitchell (1961). "The release of acetylcholine in the isolated rat diaphragm." *J. Physiol.* (London) **155**: 246–262.

Kuffler, S. W. and C. Eyzaguirre (1955). "Synaptic inhibition in an isolated nerve cell." *J. Gen. Physiol.* **39**: 155–184.

Kuno, M. (1964). "Quantal components of excitatory synaptic potentials in spinal motoneurons." *J. Physiol.* (London) **175**: 81–99.

Kurokawa, M., T. Sakamoto, and M. Kato (1965). "A rapid isolation of nerve-ending particles from brain." *Biochim. Biophys. Acta* **94**: 307–309.

Liddell, E. G. T. (1960). **The Discovery of Reflexes.** Oxford: Clarendon Press. 174 pp.

Lissmann, H. W. (1958). "On the function and evolution of electric organs in fish." *J. Exp. Biol.* **35**: 156–191.

Lissmann, H. W. and K. E. Machin (1958). "The mechanism of object location in *Gymnarchus niloticus* and similar fish." *J. Exp. Biol.* **35**: 451–493.

Loewenstein, W. R. (1958). "Generator processes of repetitive activity of a Pacinian corpuscle." *J. Gen. Physiol.* **41**: 825–845.

Loewenstein, W. R. (1959). "The generation of electric activity in a nerve ending." *Ann. N.Y. Acad. Sci.* **81**: 367–387.

Loewenstein, W. R. (1961). "Excitation and inactivation in a receptor membrane." *Ann. N.Y. Acad. Sci.* **94**: 510–534.

Loewenstein, W. R. (1965). "Facets of a transducer process." *Cold Spring Harbor Symp. Quant. Biol.* **30**: 29–43.

Loewenstein, W. R. and M. Mendelson (1965). "Components of receptor adaptation in a Pacinian corpuscle." *J. Physiol.* (London) **177**: 377–397.

Loewenstein, W. R., C. A. Terzuolo, and Y. Washizu (1963). "Separation of transducer and impulse generating processes in sensory receptors." *Science* **142**: 1180–1181.

Loewi, O. (1921). "Über humorale Übertragbarkeit der Herznervenwirkung." *Pflüg. Arch. ges. Physiol.* **189**: 239–242.

Loewi, O. (1933). "Problems connected with the principle of humoral transmission of the nerve impulse." *Proc. Roy. Soc.* (London) **B118**: 299–316.

Machin, K. E. and H. W. Lissman (1960). "The mode of operation of the electric receptors in *Gymnarchus niloticus*." *J. Exp. Biol.* **37**: 801–811.

Martin, A. R. (1966). "Quantal nature of synaptic transmission." *Physiol. Rev.* **46**: 51–66.

Martin, A. R. and G. Pilar (1963a). "Dual mode of synaptic transmission in the avian ciliary ganglion." *J. Physiol.* (London) **168**: 443–463.

Martin, A. R. and G. Pilar (1963b). "Transmission through the ciliary ganglion of the chick." *J. Physiol.* (London) **168**: 464–475.

Martin, A. R. and G. Pilar (1964). "Quantal components of the synaptic potential in the ciliary ganglion of the chick." *J. Physiol.* (London) **175**: 1–61.

McLennan, H. (1961). "Inhibitory transmitters—a review." In: **Nervous Inhibition.** (E. Florey, ed.), pp. 350–368. Long Island City, N.Y.: Pergamon Press, Inc.

McLennan, H. (1963). **Synaptic Transmission.** Philadelphia: W. B. Saunders Company. 134 pp.

Minckler, J. (1940). "The morphology of the nerve terminals of the human spinal cord as seen in block silver preparations, with estimates of the total number per cell." *Anat. Rec.* **77**: 9.

Murray, R. W. (1965). "Receptor mechanisms in the Ampullae of Lorenzini of elasmobranch fishes." *Cold Spring Harbor Symp. Quant. Biol.* **30**: 233–243.

Nachmansohn, D. (1963). "Choline acetylase." In: **Cholinesterases and Anticholinesterase Agents.** (G. B. Koelle, ed.), pp. 40–54. *Handb. Exp. Pharmak.* (*Suppl.*) **15.** Berlin: Springer-Verlag.

Nachmansohn, D. and A. L. Machado (1943). "The formation of acetylcholine. A new enzyme 'choline acetylase'." *J. Neurophysiol.* **6**: 397–403.

Nastuk, W. L. (1953). "The electrical activity of the muscle cell membrane at the neuromuscular junction." *J. Cell Comp. Physiol.* **42**: 249–272.

Nastuk, W. L. (1955). "Neuromuscular transmission: fundamental aspects of the normal process." *Am. J. Med.* **19**: 663–668.

Nastuk, W. L. (1959). "Some ionic factors that influence the action of acetylcholine at the muscle end-plate membrane." *Ann. N.Y. Acad. Sci.* **81**: 317–327.

Palade, G. E. and S. L. Palay (1954). "Electron microscope observations of interneuronal and neuromuscular synapses." *Anat. Rec.* **118**: 335.

Palay, S. L. (1958). "The morphology of synapses in the central nervous system." *Exp. Cell Res.* (*Suppl.*) **5**: 275–293.

Palay, S. L. and G. E. Palade (1955). "The fine structure of neurons." *J. Biophys. Biochem. Cytol.* **1**: 69–88.

Peterson, R. P. and F. A. Pepe (1961). "The fine structure of inhibitory synapses in the crayfish." *J. Biophys. Biochem. Cytol.* **11**: 157–169.

Quilliam, T. A. and M. Sato (1955). "The distribution of myelin on nerve fibers from Pacinian corpuscles." *J. Physiol.* (London) **129**: 167–176.

Robertson, J. D. (1961). "Ultrastructure of excitable membranes and the crayfish median-giant synapse." *Ann. N.Y. Acad. Sci.* **94**: 339–389.

Salmoraghi, G. C. and F. E. Bloom (1964). "Pharmacology of individual neurons." *Science* **144**: 494–499.

Shanes, A. M. (1963). "Drugs and nerve conduction." *Ann. Rev. Pharmacol.* **3**: 185–204.

Sherrington, C. S. (1906). **Integrative Action of the Nervous System.** New Haven, Conn.: Yale University Press. 411 pp.

Skalak, R. and W. R. Loewenstein (1966). "Mechanical transmission in a Pacinian corpuscle. An analysis and a theory." *J. Physiol.* (London) **182**: 346–378.

Strumwasser, F. (1965). "Nervous function at the cellular level." *Ann. Rev. Physiol.* **25**: 451–476.

Szabo, T. and A. Barets (1963). "Les organes spécifiques de la ligne latérale du *Gymnarchus nilotocus*." *Comp. Rend. Acad. Sci.* (Paris) **257**: 1798–1800.

Takeuchi, A. (1958). "Neuromuscular transmission of fish skeletal muscles investigated with intracellular microelectrodes." *J. Cell Comp. Physiol.* **54**: 211–220.

Takeuchi, A. (1963). "Effects of calcium on the conductance change at the end-plate membrane during the action of transmitter." *J. Physiol.* (London) **167**: 141–155.

Takeuchi, A. and N. Takeuchi (1960). "On the permeability of the end-plate membrane during the action of transmitter." *J. Physiol.* (London) **154**: 52–67.

Takeuchi, A. and N. Takeuchi (1966a). "A study of the inhibitory action of γ-aminobutyric acid on neuromuscular transmission in the crayfish." *J. Physiol.* (London) **183**: 418–432.

Takeuchi, A. and N. Takeuchi (1966b). "On the permeability of the presynaptic terminal of the crayfish neuromuscular junction during synaptic inhibition and the action of γ-amino-butyric acid." *J. Physiol.* (London) **183**: 433–449.

Taylor, R. E. (1959). "The effect of procaine on electrical properties of squid axon membrane." *Am. J. Physiol.* **196**: 1071–1078.

Terzuolo, C. A. and C. Edwards (1962). "Excitation and synaptic transmission." *Ann. Rev. Physiol.* **24**: 325–356.

Terzuolo, C. A. and Y. Washizu (1962). "Relation between stimulus strength, generator potential, and impulse frequency in stretch receptor of Crustacea." *J. Neurophysiol.* **25**: 56–66.

Thesleff, S. (1955). "The mode of neuromuscular block caused by acetylcholine, nicotine, decamethonium, and succinylcholine." *Acta Physiol. Scand.* **34**: 218–232.

Thies, R. E. (1965). "Neuromuscular depression and the apparent depletion of transmitter in mammalian muscle." *J. Neurophysiol.* **28**: 527–542.

Twarog, B. M. (1966). "Catch and the mechanism of action of 5-hydroxytryptamine on molluscan muscle: a speculation." *Life Sci.* **5**: 2101–1213.

Watanabe, Y. and H. Grundfest (1961). "Impulse propagation at the septal and commisural junctions of crayfish lateral giant axons." *J. Gen. Physiol.* **45**: 267–308.

Whittaker, V. P. (1963). "Identification of acetylcholine and related esters of biological origin." In: **Cholinesterases and Anticholinesterase Agents.** (G. B. Loelle, ed.),

pp. 1–39. *Handb. exp. Pharmak.* (*Suppl.*) **15.** Berlin: Springer-Verlag.

Whittaker, V. P. (1964). "Investigations on the storage of biogenic amines in the central nervous system." *Prog. Brain Res.* **8**: 90–117.

Whittaker, V. P. and E. G. Gray (1962). "The synapse: biology and morphology." *Brit. Med. Bull.* **18**: 223–228.

Wyckoff, R. W. G. and J. Z. Young (1956). "The motoneuron surface." *Proc. Roy. Soc.* (London) **B144**: 440–450.

9-1. Introduction. In some tissues there is a need for all of the cells to function in a coordinated, often simultaneous, manner. Such a situation is found, for example, in cardiac muscle where, in order to develop a strong efficient blood-pumping action, all of the muscle cells of a heart or heart chamber must contract together. This type of coordinated activity is also typical of many smooth muscles that produce peristaltic waves of contraction in various regions of the gastrointestinal tract or which function in the walls of blood vessels, in the uterus, and so forth.

These are tissues in which typically each cell is not connected to a motoneuron terminal, rather action potentials spread rapidly from cell to cell throughout the mass of the tissue. Cellular contacts between these excitable cells serve as low resistance pathways to electrical currents. These contacts could be called synapses except for the uncertainty that exists in many cases concerning the actual functions of observed contacts. Not all of the cellular junctions necessarily operate in electrical transmission.

Before the development of the electron microscope and the thin-sectioning methods required for high resolution, it was thought that electrical conduction through masses of cells could be accounted for by assuming actual protoplasmic continuity between the cells. The heart, for example, was considered to be an anatomical syncytium. But it has been shown that while many cellular masses act as functional syncytia, all of the cells are bounded by their plasma membranes and there is no continuity of protoplasm although there is a contiguity. The same situation that was found for the nervous system.

In many cases it has been found that layers of epithelial cells, such as those found in the skin or lining various parts of the gastrointestinal or excretory tubules also possess specialized regions of contact which provide for a rapid movement of materials through the cell mass.

Epithelial linings and surfaces are often involved with the active transport of ions—an activity which can lead to the generation of bioelectric potentials across the epithelial membrane. Again, it should be noted that

Chapter 9

Mass Cellular Contacts; Spontaneous and Other Potentials

although ease of electrical current flow or material flow between cells is a common phenomenon in many tissues, the nature of the membranes involved is still unclear at the molecular level.

In this chapter also we shall consider spontaneous potentials, which are often found in excitable cells and which arise without the need for external stimulation. Since these potentials are often the source of stimulation for masses of cardiac or smooth muscle cells, their mechanism of generation will be described at this time, rather than in later chapters dealing specifically with the functioning of these tissues. The spontaneous activity is often of a rhythmic regular nature.

The purpose of this chapter then is to complete the discussion of the various bioelectric potentials found in cells and the types of contacts for electrical current flow or material movement found in cells. The orientation of the chapter is primarily upon the mechanisms at the cellular and molecular levels that might account for these activities; in later chapters the roles of these activities in various animal systems will be considered. Much of the discussion is based on cardiac muscle cells from vertebrates and on epithelial surfaces, especially frog skin because these have been the most intensively studied tissues with respect to spontaneous potentials, potentials arising from active transport, or mass cellular contacts.

Cell Contacts and Spontaneous Potentials

9-2. Cardiac Muscle Cell Junctions. The need for coordinated stimulation and contraction of cardiac muscle cells has already been mentioned. The details of the circulatory performance of cardiac muscle is given in Chapters 13 and 14; the contractile mechanisms of cardiac muscle are described in Chapter 10. Here only the nature of the rapid electrical conduction through vertebrate cardiac muscle and the mechanisms and nature of spontaneous potential generation will be considered.

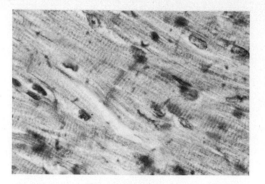

Figure 9-1 Longitudinal section of human cardiac muscle showing the intercalated discs.

Basically, the mammalian heart consists of two pairs of chambers—the atria and the ventricles—separated by a ring of connective tissue. The masses of cardiac muscle tissue, the myocardium, is composed of branching, striated cardiac muscle cells (Figure 9-1). In addition to the transverse striations, which are typical of cardiac and striated skeletal muscle, the cardiac muscle cell, observed in the light microscope, is seen to possess denser transverse bands—the intercalated discs—at the abutting ends of cells. In the electron microscope these are seen to be due to an infolding of each muscle cell membrane (sarcolemma) and an interdigitation of the two membranes (Figure 9-2). In the region of the intercalated disc, the myofibrils of the cells spread out and the cytoplasmic material appears denser. These facts account for the ability to resolve the discs as dark bands in the light microscope. Before the development of electron microscope techniques it was thought that the myofibrils ran across the intercalated disc region, making the cardiac cells one continuous syncytium: this has been shown not to be the case.

The intercalated disc has been shown to possess at least four different structural arrangements (Muir, 1965). There are dense plaques into which the myofibrils are inserted (note Figure 9-2). There are regions where an intercellular gap exists between the membranes. There are regions of desmosomal contact, and there are regions where nexi are present (see Section 3-14).

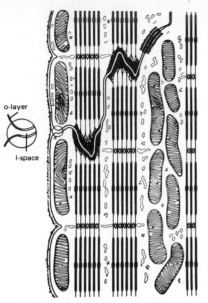

Figure 9-2 Schematic drawing of intercalated disc of mouse cardiac muscle. [By permission from F. S. Sjöstrand and E. Andersson-Cedergren (1960). "Intercalated discs of heart muscle". In: The Structure and Function of Muscle (G. H. Bourne, ed), Vol. 1, pp. 421–445.]

Desmosomes are found not only in the region of the intercalated disc but also between Purkinje fibers, specialized muscle cells that conduct action potentials through the heart. The intercellular material, as well as the cytoplasm adjacent to the membranes, appears dense, and tonofibrils are seen in the cytoplasm. Desmosomes are common in the myocardium of lower vertebrates, which lack Purkinje conduction systems, and are less prevalent in the cardiac tissue of mammals and birds.

The nexus is a region where the outer layers of each of two opposing unit membranes appears to have fused, and there is no intercellular gap. It is thought to be a region of low electrical resistance between cells. In addition to the nexi found at the intercalated disc, such junctions have also been described along the length of cardiac muscle cells and are called "longitudinal connections" (Sjöstrand et al., 1958; Barr et al., 1965).

Action potentials spread readily through the mass of cardiac cells, and transmission is thought to occur at the nexus of the intercalated disc. Whereas the resistance of the rest of the cardiac fiber membrane is about 500 ohm/cm², that of the membrane of the intercalated disc is about 1 ohm/cm². The folding of the membrane, which develops only after birth in mammals, increases the available area for the passage of electrical current between cells.

That the cells of cardiac tissue are electrically connected can be shown by the sucrose gap technique. Barr et al. (1965) placed a strip of frog atrial muscle across a sucrose gap. Sucrose is a nonconducting nonelectrolyte and prevents the passage of electrical currents in the external medium (see Figure 9-3). When a suitable resistance was placed across the gap, an action potential initiated at one end of the strip was transmitted across the gap. In order to produce an action potential in cells across the gap, current had to flow through the cell membranes as well as through the external resistance, that is, a complete circuit had to be established for current flow. Since the external conducting pathway was limited to the resistor, the cells must have provided the pathway for opposite current flow.

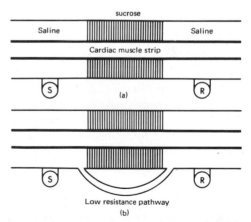

Figure 9-3 Schematic representation of Barr's sucrose gap technique. A strip of cardiac muscle is placed in a nonconducting sucrose solution and the spread of action potentials is prevented. When an appropriate resistance is placed between two regions of the muscle, strip potentials spread across the gap. This indicates that the action potentials are conducted by current flows similar to those described for axons (see Chapter 7).

That the nexus was involved and not des-mosomes was shown by treating an atrial strip with hypertonic, instead of isotonic, sucrose. Hypertonic sucrose blocks conduction and electron microscope examination of the treated strips revealed that the cells underwent osmotic shrinkage, which caused the membranes at the nexus to pull apart. No such separation occurred at the desmosomes, which, as previously stated, are sites of strong attachments between cell membranes. Thus conduction was blocked when the nexus, not the desmosome, was destroyed.

9-3. Excitation and Conduction in the Vertebrate Heart.

In considering the electrical activities of the heart, two general questions arise: (1) what is the origin of the rhythmic beat of the heart, and (2) how does excitation spread so that all the muscle cells of a chamber or pair of chambers are excited to contract nearly simultaneously?

Cardiac rhythms arise from activity within the organ itself, not from extrinsic neurons. A **pacemaker** is a cell or group of cells within a tissue exhibiting spontaneous electrical activity, which can spread in the form of action potentials and trigger contractile or other events. Cardiac pacemakers are of two types: **myogenic**, in which the spontaneous electrical activity arises in specialized muscle cells of the myocardium; and **neurogenic**, in which the electrical activity arises in nerve (or ganglion) cells lying in or on the cardiac musculature. Both types of pacemakers may have their activity modified by extrinsic neurons of the central nervous system, but the rhythmic activity does not originate in the central nervous system.

In mammals and birds the pacemaking impulses arise in the sinoauricular node (SA-node), a small mass of muscle cells located in the right atrium near the entrance of the superior vena cava. The spikes generated by the pacemaker are conducted rapidly through the myocardium. In lower vertebrates this is accomplished by intercellular conduction alone. In mammals and birds, a specialized conduction system aids in the spread of exci-

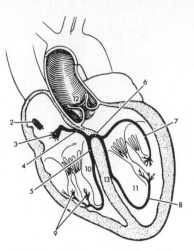

Figure 9-4 Conduction system of the mammalian heart. 1, right atrium; 2, sinoauricular node; 3, atrioventricular node; 4, bundle of His; 5, right bundle branch; 6, left bundle branch; 7, superior division; 8, inferior division; 9, Purkinje fiber system; 10, right ventricle; 11, left ventricle; 12, aorta with aortic valve; 13, intraventricular septum.

tation. It might be noted that nothing is known about the spread of excitation through cardiac muscle in other phyla.

The conduction system of the mammalian heart is diagrammed in Figure 9-4. From the SA-node impulses travel rapidly over the cells of the thin-walled atria, exciting the cardiac muscle cells and causing contraction. Impulses reach another node, the atrioventricular (AV-node), perhaps by a specialized conduction system. Recent evidence indicates that there is a specialized pathway between the two nodes because high levels of K^+, which prevent conduction and excitation along ordinary atrial fibers, do not stop impulse conduction between the nodes (Paes de Carvalho et al., 1959; Vasselle and Hoffman, 1965). Nodal tissue is composed of thin, spindle-shaped cells that contain few myofibrils. Other cardiac cells also exhibit spontaneity under various conditions. The AV-node acts as a reserve pacemaker and is able to take over control of the heart if impulse generation in the SA-node is inhibited, although its rate of potential generation is slower.

From the AV-node conduction spreads

rapidly throughout the thick-walled ventricles via a specialized conduction system of Purkinje fibers. From the AV-node conduction is along the atrioventricular bundle of fibers (bundle of His). The bundle divides into two branches that run down either side of the intraventricular septum. The branches break up into a complex network of individual Purkinje fibers that spread through the ventricular myocardium. Purkinje fibers have a larger diameter than normal cardiac cells (50 to 70 μ compared with 15 μ) and their cytoplasm contains fewer myofibrils and more glycogen than normal fibers. The nature of the junctions between Purkinje fibers and normal cardiac fibers is not known. Once excitation has reached each part of the atria, and ventricles conduction occurs among the individual cells of that region, presumably through the nexus as already described.

9-4. Spontaneous Potentials in Cardiac Muscle. A spontaneous potential is one that arises from some internal activity of a cell. The important feature of this potential is not its freedom from environmental influences but its internally determined timing (Bullock and Horridge, 1965). The system that produces spontaneous potentials in a cell has its own intrinsic mechanisms that initiate the generation of the potential. Many cells exhibit spontaneous generation of potentials, cardiac muscle mechanisms are described here only because more is known about this activity in these cells.

The methods used to locate a cardiac pacemaker and to determine its myogenic or neurogenic origin also yield information about the nature of the spontaneous activity. Several types of studies are used including microscopic observations of cell types, surgical removal of suspected pacemaker cells, cauterization, and local application of drugs or cold.

Microscopic observations can determine whether or not ganglion cells are present. If they are absent, the heart is myogenic. But in many hearts it is difficult to determine the presence of ganglion cells or to differentiate them from other cells.

Local warming or cooling of small regions of a heart can be used to locate the pacemaker because it is more sensitive to temperature changes, as reflected in alterations of heart rate, than are the normal cardiac cells.

Surgical removal of small pieces of the heart can be used to identify the pacemaker zone, since its excision will cause the heart to stop beating, at least temporarily until another pacemaker zone takes over the beat. A heart can be identified as neurogenic if removal of ganglion cells stops its beat. Ligation, by preventing the spread of conduction, can give an indication of the region where the pacemaker is located.

The type of pacemaker can be determined by the use of drugs, after cardiac connections to the central nervous system are transected. Ether, in low concentrations, inhibits ganglion cells but not muscle cells. ACh stimulates ganglion cells, causing an increased heart rate. But ACh inhibits innervated myogenic hearts and has little or no effect on noninnervated myogenic hearts.

All adult vertebrate hearts are myogenic. The hearts of other animal groups are discussed in Chapter 12.

Analysis of the potentials of cells of cardiac muscle, recorded with microelectrodes, shows that these potentials vary in different types of cells. The spike potential of a normal cardiac muscle cell has a rapid spike rise and a long, relatively slowly declining plateau. The cells are slower to begin the recovery processes leading back to the resting potential (Figure 9-5a). The plateau is caused by a prolongation of the period of high Na^+ conductance, while K^+ conductance remains low. As previously stated, the resting and action potentials of cardiac muscle cells depend on the same ionic mechanisms found in the squid giant fiber (Noble, 1962; Trautwein, 1963).

The potentials recorded from pacemaker cells exhibit a different form (Figure 9-5b). The resting potentials of pacemaker cells are lower than those of other cardiac cells, although whether a true resting potential can be said to exist in these cells is debatable because

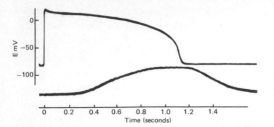

Figure 9-5(a) Cellular transmembrane potential and muscular tension of isolated frog ventricle. Note delay between the upstroke of the action potential and the beginning of contraction (lower curve). Relaxation begins after the fast phase of repolarization of the membrane. [Redrawn from data of Lee and Woodbury in Woodbury (1962).]

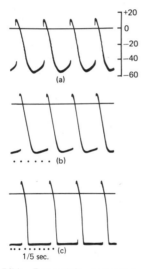

Figure 9-5(b) Potentials recorded from Purkinje fibers. (a) Recording from a pacemaker cell. Note large diastolic depolarization and gradual transition to the upstroke of the action potential. This represents the pacemaker or spontaneous potential. (b) Recording from a cell a short distance from the pacemaker cell above. (c) Recording from an atrial cell. Rate of all three cells is determined by the time required for pacemaker potential to reach threshold. [Redrawn from data of Hutter and Trautwein (1956).]

the cell membrane never reaches a stable condition. The rising phase of the spike is slow, and there is no plateau. The activity of a pacemaker cell begins as a slow depolarization—the **pacemaker potential**—or prepoten-

tial. Since this slow depolarization begins as soon as the cell has recovered from a previous action potential, there cannot be said to exist any true resting potential. When a certain level of depolarization is reached by the pacemaker potential, a spike is generated. In the frog sinus venosus, the site of the amphibian heart pacemaker, a spike is generated when depolarizations of from 3 to 15 mV have been reached (Hutter and Trautwein, 1956).

The rate of development of the pacemaker potential varies in different nodal cells, and this is a mechanism whereby one or a few cells act as the true pacemakers. Those nodal cells with a slower development of the prepotential have their spontaneous activity blocked by the rapidly conducted spikes generated in those cells with a faster rate of depolarization.

Although it is often stated that all cardiac cells can act as pacemakers under appropriate conditions, it has been shown that in the rabbit heart such activity can occur only within certain areas of cardiac tissue. These include cells located near the junction of the sinus node and the atrial muscle, in the sino-atrial ring, in the AV-node, and in the bundle of His. Pacemaker activity is an early development in cardiac cells as shown by tissue culture studies of chick cardiac fibers separated by treatment with hydrolytic enzymes. These cells can contract and consist of pacemaker and follower cells. The pacemakers initiate the contractions in the follower cells that are in contact with a pacemaker (Harary and Sato, 1964; Smith and Berndt, 1964).

The pacemaker potential is due to a relatively high Na^+ conductance compared with the K^+ conductance. In fact, the latter declines throughout diastole—the period of relaxation of cardiac muscle which occurs simultaneously with the period when repolarization of the cardiac cells is taking place. This decrease allows the Na^+ conductance to be the determining factor in the membrane potential level and causes the slow prepotential depolarization that leads to the threshold level at which Na^+ conductance proceeds in a regenerative fashion.

Noble (1962) applied the Hodgkin-Huxley

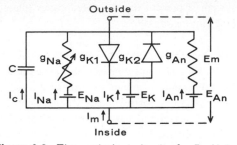

Figure 9-6 The equivalent circuit of a Purkinje fiber is modified from that of the squid giant axon (see Figure 7–21) by the inclusion of two rectifiers for K$^+$ conductance connected to the K$^+$ battery. The symbol g_{k_1} represents anomalous rectification (outward electrochemical gradients cause an outward movement of positive current and thus a decrease in K$^+$ movement); g_{k_2} falls instantaneously with depolarization; g_{k_2} represents normal rectification (a greater K$^+$ conductance when positive current moves out of the cell). This conductance rises with depolarization.

equations to cardiac muscle and from computer analyses obtained curves predicting the shapes of action and pacemaker potentials. The equations and curves predict accurately the expected shapes of the potentials and also indicate that in such a system pacemaker activity should exist. The relation of the K$^+$ conductance is complex and shows several different parts. The equivalent circuit of a Purkinje fiber (Figure 9-6) differs from that for the squid axon in that the potassium conductance is composed of two elements, g_{k_1} and h_{k_2}. The first conductance represents anomalous rectification—the K$^+$ current falls instantaneously with depolarization, that is, an outward electrochemical gradient which is expected to cause an outward movement of positive current, results instead in a decrease of the outward movement of K$^+$ following a decrease in permeability to K$^+$. The second term represents a delayed rectification and is seen when the membrane potential has been displaced to the point where the increased K$^+$ conductance begins. The depolarization now causes an increased K$^+$ conductance. This is the increase in outward potassium movement that serves to repolarize the fiber after the Na$^+$ spike.

Pacemaker activity thus appears to depend on a relatively high resting Na$^+$ conductance and a slow decline in K$^+$ conductance in the diastolic phase of the cardiac cycle. It has been hypothesized that the conductances of the ions depends on cellular metabolism and also on the ATPase-dependent active transport system. The ATPase complex could be responsible for increasing the buildup or the lowering of particular ion concentrations (see, for example, Duncan, 1961).

The level of the resting potential, the rate of pacemaker depolarization, the rate of spike rise, and the magnitude of the spike are all factors that determine the final nature of the pacemaker activity. These various phases are controllable by cholinergic and adrenergic neurons. This control system for regulating heart rate according to the needs of the organism will be described in Chapter 13.

9-5. Spontaneous Potentials and Excitation of Smooth Muscle. Smooth muscle is found in sheets of contractile tissue surrounding the viscera and blood vessels. Smooth muscle (whose contractile and structural features are considered in Chapter 10) lacks the organized structure of cardiac or striated skeletal muscle. Like cardiac muscle, smooth muscle often exhibits spontaneous activity, although as with cardiac tissues, the activity is coordinated and often controlled by the action of excitatory and inhibitory neurons. In addition, the electrical and contractile properties of smooth muscle are very much under the control of hormonal influences as well (see Chapter 10). Only some of the properties of vertebrate smooth muscle will be given here. Vertebrate smooth muscle is chosen because smooth muscle of the invertebrate groups often has most of the characteristics of striated muscles.

Because of the observed coordinated activity of the cells contained in layers of smooth muscle and the absence of complete innervation, mechanisms must be present for the rapid conduction of excitation from cell to cell. The nexus or tight junction, already described, has been found in a variety of smooth muscles and is considered to be the site of intercellular electrical transmission (Dewey and Barr, 1962; Burnstock et al., 1963).

From microelectrode studies with guinea pig intestinal smooth muscle, it has been shown that certain muscle cells act as pacemakers, producing slow depolarizations which lead to spike formation. The accompanying waves of contraction over the tissue (peristalsis) depend in intensity upon the frequency of the spikes. The peristaltic wave starts from the same region for several periods, but then a new pacemaker takes over. Such shifts of pacemaker zones are frequent in intestinal smooth muscle.

In the uterus, contraction is preceded by a series of action potentials which, in turn, are preceded by a slow pacemaker depolarization. These pacemaker potentials are not conducted but are local potentials. Since both the uterine and the intestinal smooth muscle masses lack innervation to all cells, they must be considered as a functional syncytium with excitability transmitted by electrical means (Bülbring, 1954, 1957).

Smooth muscle is difficult to study because the cells are small, even for microelectrode implantation. The few measurements of intracellular Na^+ and K^+ concentrations that have been made, indicate that ionic distributions in these cells are similar to those in striated muscle and nerve cells, and it has also been shown that a Na^+-K^+-activated ATPase

system is present in their membranes (Daniel and Robinson, 1960).

9-6. Neuroglial Systems. Before leaving the discussion of mass contacts and potentials in excitable cells, a further mention of the neuroglial system is worthwhile. Although Schwann cells of peripheral axons are electrically isolated from their associated neurons (Villegas et al., 1963) and although neuroglia do not possess the machinery for generating or conducting action potentials, some neuroglia have been shown to be affected by the electrical activity of neighboring neurons. As shown in Figure 9-7, repetitive volleys of impulses in the optic nerve axons of *Necturus* cause a slow, nonconducted change in the glial cell membrane potential (Orkand et al., 1966; Kuffler et al., 1966). Tight junctions have been found between some neuroglial cells, and the type of slow potential changes just described could extend throughout a system of neuroglia by local currents. To what purpose, if any, this type of electrical activity is put, is not known.

It has been suggested that the glial mantle may protect adjacent neuronal regions from the activities of synaptic groupings of neurons (Palay, 1966). That glial cells, at least in one instance, are not associated with neuronal functioning directly was shown for a leech ganglion, where the removal of all the glial cells did not affect ganglionic potentials or functioning (Nicholls and Kuffler, 1964).

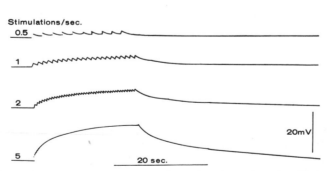

Figure 9-7 The effect of repetitive volleys of impulses in optic nerve fibers of *Necturus* upon membrane potential of associated glial cell, recorded with an intracellular electrode. Amplitude of glial cell depolarization increases with increasing frequency of nerve volleys from 0.5 to 5/sec. At this point the effects produced by each volley fuse and approach the plateau depolarization of about 17 mV. [After Orkand et al. (1966).]

Trophic influences between neuroglia and neurons seem important. The term trophic (from the Greek word meaning to nourish) means more than that one cell supplies nutrients for another. It implies that chemical substances required for the support or survival of one cell are furnished by another cell. Although evidence exists for trophic relationships between neurons and neuroglia, as well as between neurons and the organs they innervate, no trophic substances have as yet been identified. At one time it was hypothesized that glial cells possess a high Na^+ concentration and serve as storage sites for this ion required by axons for action potential generation. But it now appears that this is incorrect because the glial cell interspaces do permit a rapid movement of large molecules and therefore the glial cells cannot act as a barrier between the neuron and the extracellular fluids. This was shown by examining neuroglial tissues in the electron microscope after they had been perfused with ferritin (an iron-containing protein now used as a marker in electron microscope studies). The ferritin readily penetrated through the glial cells (Rosenbluth and Wissig, 1964).

Neurons and neuroglia exist in what might be called a symbiotic relationship. Tissue culture of neurons is not successful unless neuroglia are present. When an axon is cut and begins to degenerate, the associated neuroglial cells also degenerate. The number of glial cells associated with a peripheral motoneuron increases when the activity of the neuron is high for long periods of time. When motoneurons to an organ are transected, the organ in many cases degenerates. As we shall see in some cases the contractile properties of a muscle depend on the type of neuron innervating the muscle (Chapter 10).

9-7. Epithelial Interconnections. In Chapter 6 the transport of materials such as amino acids, sugars, and water across epithelial surfaces was discussed from the viewpoint of the membrane active transport system and the carrier systems involved. The electron microscope has, in recent years, revealed that complicated pathways of intercellular communication exist in a wide variety of epithelial tissues and many types of junctional complexes have been found (Farquahar and Palade, 1963).

When speaking of the permeability of epithelial surfaces, we are concerned with a membrane composed of interconnected cells; materials transported across this system move across the outer cell membrane, through the cell itself, and then out through the inner cell surface and into the circulation or tissues of the organism.

Loewenstein et al. (1965) found that in renal tubule cells and salivary gland cells (*Chironomus*); in the urinary bladder (toad); and in sensory epithelia (elasmobranchs) the membrane permeability is so high that the cells are functionally interconnected in so far as ions, water, and other small molecules are concerned.

The high permeabilities of the tissues studied by Loewenstein depend on the presence of low concentrations of Ca^{2+} and Mg^{2+}. If the concentrations of these ions are raised experimentally, the permeability of the epithelial junctional membranes is drastically reduced. These two ions play a role in membrane stabilization in all tissues. But by independent mechanisms in epithelial tissues they also affect the membrane permeability of both the junctional and perijunctional membranes. The latter are the membrane that insulate the cell from the exterior medium (Loewenstein et al., 1967).

Depending on the particular tissue, this intercellular system may play a role in the distribution of water, ions, hormones, or metabolites. The interconnectivity of epithelial cells and junctional activities are exemplified by the work of Diamond on glandular epithelium described in Chapter 6.

Epithelial layers are also used for rapid electrical conduction in sensory epithelia of some vertebrates, primarily in the lateral line organs of teleost fish and in the sensory epithelia of elasmobranchs. One of the better examples of the role of epithelial layers in the conduction of excitation comes from the work of Passano (1963); Mackie (1965);

Mackie et al. (1967) on coelenterates. Conduction systems (both epithelial and neuronal) and behavioral activity in this phylum is receiving a large amount of attention. In siphonophores (class Hydrozoa) it has been shown that nerve- and muscle-free stretches of epithelium covering the swimming bell are capable of conducting depolarizations in response to stimulation. The conduction velocities are in the range of 20 to 50 cm/sec (see Figure 9-8) and the potentials are of an all-or-none nature with a 2 to 3 msec refractory period. Conduction can be in any direction. Obviously some part of the epithelial cell membrane possesses the mechanisms required for the generation and propagation of potentials. The epithelial system provides a motor pathway for rapid effector responses needed for escape.

Potentials Across Epithelial Surfaces

9-8. Frog Skin Potentials. Dubois-Reymond in 1848 observed that frog skin maintained a potential difference between the inside and the outside—the inside normally being positive to the outside. Although the potentials found across epithelial surfaces such as skin, gastrointestinal tract linings, or kidney tubules differ in their mechanism of generation from the activity potentials of excitable cells, they yield important information concerning the mechanisms underlying bioelectric phenomena.

Galeottie in 1904 postulated that Na^+ or Li^+ was needed to maintain the potential difference across frog skin and he hypothesized that the potential arose from unequal rates of Na^+ diffusion in the opposite directions through the

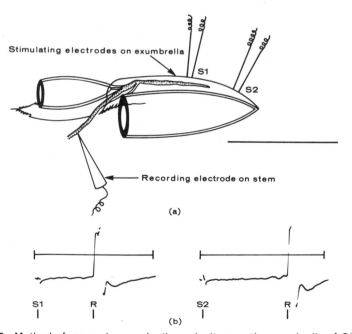

Figure 9-8 Method of measuring conduction velocity over the exumbrella of *Chelophyes*. The time intervals represented by distances S1–R, S2–R, (b), represent conduction time from points S1 and S2 on the exumbrella to the stem muscle whose response, R, is recorded with a suction electrode. The difference between the two gives the conduction time in the strip of exumbrellar epithelium between the two stimulating points. [By permission from G. O. Mackie (1965) "Conduction in the nerve-free epithelia of siphonophores" *American Zoologist* **5**: 439–454.]

skin. Such diffusion differences he attributed to the morphological arrangement of the skin.

Huf (1935) found that Cl^- was transported to the inside of the skin and assumed that this represented the movement of NaCl. Krogh (1937, 1938) while studying water balance and ion balance in frogs found that in salt-depleted frogs, Na^+ was taken up even from solutions as dilute as 10^{-5} M NaCl. Ussing (1949) observed that in isolated frog skin there was a transport of Na^+ inward against a steep concentration gradient. Cl^- movement was passive resulting from the electrochemical differential between inside and outside produce by the Na^+ active transport.

The passive fluxes of ionic species not interacting with other particles are given by

$$\frac{J_{in}}{J_{out}} = \left(\frac{c_o}{c_i}\right) \exp\left[\frac{EF}{RT}\right] \tag{9.1}$$

where E is the potential difference across the membrane; c_o and c_i are the external and internal concentrations of the ion, respectively; F is the Faraday constant; R is the gas constant; and T is the absolute temperature. This relation describes the movement of chloride ions across frog skin under nearly all experimental conditions.

But the flux ratio of Na^+ differs from the theoretical, in many cases by factors of 100 or more. Na^+ movement, on this basic, cannot be considered passive. Na^+ fluxes also depend on metabolic energy, since metabolic inhibitors such as dinitrophenol reduce Na^+ inward movement (Table 9-1). Note the large outward movement of Na^+ in the metabolically inhibited animal and the differences between the observed and calculated flux ratios in the normal animal.

Koefoed-Johnsen and Ussing (1953) considered the possibility that Na^+ was transported by solvent drag. In a porous membrane with solvent flow, the flux ratio equation contains an additional term describing the effect of solvent drag (see also Katchalsky and Curran, 1965):

$$\ln\left(\frac{J_{in}}{J_{out}}\right) = \ln\left(\frac{c_o}{c_i}\right) + \frac{ZFE}{RT} + \frac{\Delta_w}{D}\int_0^{x_o} \frac{1}{A}\,dx$$

$$(9.2)$$

Δ_w is the rate of volume flow of water through unit area of the membrane; D is the diffusion coefficient of the solute; A is the fraction of unit area of membrane available for flow as a function of x, the distance from the outer surface of the membrane; and x_o is the total thickness of the membrane.

Since solvent drag is a function of water flow —which is readily measurable—and since both the diffusion coefficients and the pore shape integral are known (the latter is constant for all transported ions if they pass through the same pores); it is possible to estimate the drag on Na^+ ions in frog skin by determining the flux ratios of one or more test substances that are not subject to active transport and that have diffusion coefficients

Table 9-1 Representative Values of Na^+ Across Frog Skin*

PREPARATION	FLUX (μmole/cm^2/hour) J_{in}	J_{out}	E (mV)	J_{in}/J_{out} OBSERVED	CALCULATED
Normal	0.34	0.093	+62	0.011	3.66
DNP-treated	0.25	1.57	−11	0.16	0.15

* Data from Ussing (1965). The inner bathing solution was Ringer's; the outer solution was 1/10 Ringer's.

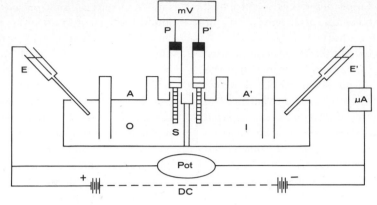

Figure 9-9 Schematic of the arrangement used to record from and maintain a voltage clamp on frog skin preparations.

similar to that of Na^+. Andersen and Ussing (1957) used deuterium and tritium-labeled water as well as thiourea (labeled with either ^{14}C or ^{35}S) and acetamide labeled at either the C-1 or the C-2 position. Using one solute labeled in two different ways makes measurement of both influx and efflux possible (Levi and Ussing, 1949). The measured flux ratios of these solutes showed that solvent drag is not a factor in their transport, and presumably Na^+ also would not be transported by this mechanism.

9-9. Short-Circuited Frog Skin. Ussing and Zerahn (1951) initiated the use of short-circuited frog skin preparations (see Figure 9-9) as a means of proving that the potential difference across the skin was due to the active transport of Na^+. When the potential difference across the skin—placed between two solutions identical in composition and concentration—is reduced to zero by an adjustable, opposing external voltage; then there are no concentration or electrical potential differences to act as driving forces for ion movements. This is a voltage clamp system with the voltage stabilized at zero. Under these conditions any net flux of ions must be the result of active transport.

The electrical current generated by the skin due to active transport of Na^+ must equal the current generated in the external battery circuit, and this can be measured by a sensitive microammeter or galvanometer placed in the external circuit. The ion fluxes are followed by tracer studies. The results of experiments with this type of preparation showed that Na^+ was actively transported and that the potential difference across the frog skin was due to this transport. When the isolated skin is placed between two Ringer's solutions of identical composition, a potential of about 50 mV is recorded, the inside being negative with respect to the outside. Some observed fluxes are given in Table 9-2 from measurements made on the skin of *Rana temporaria*.

The net Na^+ flux is seen to equal the value of the short-circuit current. Normally the skin is moving Na^+ from outside to inside and equal numbers of Na^+ and Cl^- ions must be transported. Na^+ is actively transported, whereas Cl^- moves passively down its electrochemical gradient. In the short-circuit system, reducing the potential across the membrane to zero by an external potential source prevents Cl^- influx. The Cl^- which would normally move in with the Na^+ gives up electrons to the measuring electrodes, and a flow of current is recorded as the electrons move through the circuit to the inside, where they neutralize the transported Na^+.

Replacement of the external Na^+ by K^+

Table 9-2.   Sodium Fluxes and Short-Circuit Currents of Frog Skin*

EXP. NO.	NA_{in}^{+}†	NA_{out}^{+}	NET NA^{+} TRANSPORTED	CURRENT†
1	20.1	2.4	17.7	17.8
2	47.9	2.5	45.4	44.3
3	11.1	1.5	9.6	9.9

* Data from Ussing (1965).
† Fluxes and currents are given as microamperes per square centimeter.

or choline$^+$ reduces or abolishes the potential. Only Li$^+$ ions can partially substitute for Na$^+$ and be actively transported, an indication of the specificity of the transport mechanism.

9-10. Localization of the Transport Process. Microelectrode studies can in some cases be used to determine the source of a membrane potential. Early studies by Ottoson et al. (1953) on frog skin indicated that the potential

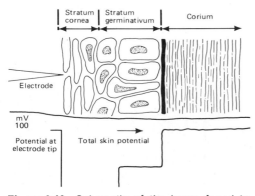

Figure 9-10 Schematic of the layers found in frog skin. Also indicated are potential changes recorded as a microelectrode penetrates into the skin and its various layers. A positive potential of about 50 mV is recorded as the electrode penetrates one of the large epithelial cells of the stratum germinativum. The positivi · suddenly increases as the electrode emerges at the other side of the cell and remains constant from this point on. These epithelial cells are therefore held responsible for the total skin potential. [After Hoshiko (1961).]

was generated in one step close to the basement membrane; later Engbaek and Hoshiko (1957) showed that two potential steps were located in the epithelium of the skin.

Frog skin is composed of several thin cellular layers (Figure 9-10). Facing the external medium (the corneum is the outer surface of the skin) is an ectodermal epithelium consisting of several layers. In the outermost layer are keratinized cells. Next comes a stratum spinosum, followed by a stratum germinativum. Beneath the ectodermal layers is the mesodermal chorion of connective tissue cells and protein fibers, muscle cells, blood vessels and chromatophores. Between the corium (inner surface of the skin) and the stratum germinativum is a basement membrane some 200 to 300 Å thick.

Ottoson thought that the potential arose close to the basement membrane. Engbaek and Hoshiko considered that the potential arose at the inner and outer surfaces of the stratum germinativum. Na$^+$ and Cl$^-$ ions to reach this layer would have to pass through the interspaces of the more superficially positioned cells.

Ussing and Windhager (1964) using electrophoretic deposition of carmine from a micropipet to mark the levels at which potential steps are found, came to the conclusion that the first potential step is located just under the cornified layer (see Figure 9-11). By pushing the electrode deeper into the skin and observing the potential recorded at each increment of

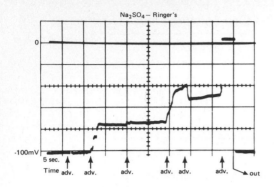

Figure 9-11 Potential profile through frog skin epithelium, recorded with indifferent electrode on the inside. The microelectrode first records total skin potential, on impalement, a short lasting break in the record results, corresponding to negative potentials observed in most skins during penetration of the stratum corneum. Upon further impalement a stable potential plateau is found which does not change upon further impalement. [After Ussing and Windhager (1964).]

movement, a potential profile is obtained that shows that the potential is developed in a series of steps and that all of the cells of the epithelium contribute to ion movements and the generation of the trans-skin potential.

Na^+ enters the first cell layer, just under the cornified layer, through a Na^+-selective membrane—one that is permeable to Na^+ (and Li^+) but not to other cations (it is also permeable to all small anions). The inner-facing membranes of this cell layer are permeable to K^+ but not to free Na^+. The Na^+ pump is located at this inner membrane and maintains the cellular Na^+ concentration at low levels.

Na^+ enters the outer living cell layer by passive diffusion across the cell membrane. The outer membrane does not contain enough K^+-Na^+-activated ATPase to account for the required level of active transport according to Koefoed-Johnson and Ussing (1958) based on the transport of 3 ions for every molecule of ATP used (Rotunno et al., 1966). They feel that the pump is a sodium-potassium exchange pump that does not of itself contribute to the potential. It maintains a low intracellular Na^+ and a high intracellular K^+ concentration. The measured potential would be the result of the sum of a Na^+ diffusion potential at the outer surface and a K^+ diffusion potential at the inner surface. If the skin is thought of as a sodium battery partly shunted by the flow of passive ions, it should be possible to approach the electromotive force of the battery by increasing the resistance of the shunt. This was done experi-

mentally either by using a slowly permeable anion such as sulfate instead of chloride ions in the external medium or by treating the outside of the skin with very low concentrations of copper ions, which reduce the chloride permeability of the membrane. Under both of these experimental conditions it was found that, as predicted, very high potentials were obtained with the outer skin boundary behaving as an ideal sodium electrode, whereas the inner side of the skin behaved as a potassium electrode.

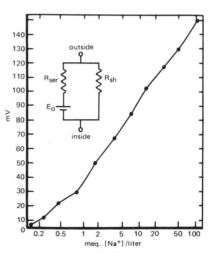

Figure 9-12 The graph illustrates the dependence of the potential difference across frog skin upon external sodium concentration. Sulfate is used as the major anion to prevent shunting by anion penetration. The insert presents an electrical model of the frog skin. [Data from Koefoed-Johnsen and Ussing (1958).]

Figure 9-12 shows the equivalent electrical circuit of frog skin. The resistance of the skin through the active transport pathway is R_s. This pathway is that of Na^+ movement from the sodium-selective outer face of the first cell layer to the stratum germinativum cells facing the basement membrane. Connections between the cells of the various rows is made through desmosomes, which are numerous in this epithelium. Tight junctions are also present (Farquahar and Palade, 1964). The intercellular spaces are open toward the inside and closed toward the outside of the skin and provide a partial pathway for the movement of Na^+ to the inside. This pathway is therefore a shunt by which Na^+ ions, as well as other diffusable ions, may lower the skin potential from the high values that would occur if no such shunt existed. The shunt is represented by resistance R_{sh} of Figure 9-11.

Cereijido and Curran (1965) and Cereijido and Rotunna (1967) have developed a slightly different model for frog skin. They feel that there are two Na^+ compartments because exchange studies show that only 37 per cent of the Na^+ is available for transport. According to their scheme all cells of the epithelium are involved in sodium transport, moving the sodium through the layers of cells into the body fluids. As yet the nature of the sodium compartmentation is not known, presumably it represents two different forms of sodium, not a cellular compartmentation by membranes.

9-11. Toad Bladder. Another preparation that has been studied with respect to Na^+ transport is the toad bladder, which is a simpler structure than skin, the wall of the bladder consisting of a single layer of mucosal cells (the inner side), some connective tissue, and a serosal (outer surface) mesothelial layer (Peachey and Rasmussen, 1961). An average difference of potential exists across the bladder of about 51 mV, the mucosal surface being negative with respect to the serosal surface. By short-circuiting isolated bladder, it was found that the net flux of Na^+

was equal to the short-circuit current; therefore, showing that only Na^+ is actively transported (Leaf et al., 1958).

The neurohypophyseal hormone, vasopressin, increases the flow of water across the bladder, without the hormone there is little net movement of water (Bentley, 1958). An effective pore radius of 8.4 Å was calculated for the bladder in the absence of hormone, while an effective pore radius of 40 Å was calculated for the bladder in the presence of the hormone. The hormone increases the permeability of the mucosal side of the bladder although it is effective only when placed in contact with the serosal side. (Hays and Leaf, 1962).

The Na^+-transport mechanism in both frog skin and toad bladder represents a system used in osmoregulation in amphibians. In frog skin it is a mechanism for moving needed Na^+ ions from the dilute fresh water medium in which the animals live into the body against a concentration gradient. In the toad, the system acts as a mechanism for conserving water, which is reabsorbed from the urinary bladder back into the body fluids. The active transport of Na^+ creates an osmotic gradient along which water flows from the bladder.

These mechanisms and their control will be discussed in more detail when the topic of osmoregulation is considered (Chapter 14). However, it may be noted that both mechanisms are under hormonal control, as indicated by the effects of vasopressin on the activity of toad bladder.

Na^+ and K^+ ions are commonly found to be actively transported in various epithelial tissues and in organs associated with osmoregulation including kidney tubules, salt glands of marine birds, specialized cells in the gill region of crustaceans and fishes, amphibian skin, and so forth. Most amphibia can also actively transport Cl^- across the skin, although this activity is lost when the skin is removed from the animal for experimental studies (see Zadunaisky et al., 1963). The active transport of Cl^- and of H^+ ions is an important aspect of the secretion of HCl by the vertebrate gastric mucosa (Wilbrandt, 1960).

References and Readings

Andersen, B. and H. H. Ussing (1957). "Solvent drag on non-electrolytes during osmotic flow through isolated toad skin and its responses to antidiuretic hormone." *Acta. Physiol. Scand.* **39**: 228–239.

Barr, L., M. M. Dewey, and W. Berger (1965). "Propagation of action potentials and the structure of the nexus in cardiac muscle." *J. Gen. Physiol.* **48**: 797–823.

Bentley, P. J. (1958). "The effects of neuro-hypothyseal extracts on water transfer across the wall of the isolated urinary bladder of the toad, *Bufo marinus*." *J. Endocrinol.* **17**: 202–209.

Bülbring, E. (1954). "Membrane potentials of smooth muscle fibres of the Taenia coli of the guinea pig." *J. Physiol.* (London) **125**: 302–315.

Bülbring, E. (1957). "Changes in configuration of spontaneously discharged spike potentials from smooth muscle of the guinea pig's taenia coli." *J. Physiol.* (London) **135**: 412–435.

Bullock, T. H. and G. A. Horridge (1965). **Structure and Function in the Nervous Systems of Invertebrates,** 2 volumes. San Francisco: W. H. Freeman & Company, Publishers.

Burnstock, G., M. E. Holman, and C. L. Prosser (1963). "Electrophysiology of smooth muscle." *Physiol. Rev.* **43**: 482–527.

Cereijido, M. and P. F. Curran (1965). "Intracellular electrical potentials in frog skin." *J. Gen. Physiol.* **48**: 543–557.

Cereijido, M. and C. A. Rotunna (1967). "Transport and distribution of sodium across frog skin." *J. Physiol.* (London) **190**: 481–497.

Daniel, E. E. and K. Robinson (1960). "The relation of sodium secretion to metabolism, in isolated sodium-rich uterine segments." *J. Physiol.* (London) **154**: 445–460.

Dewey, M. M. and L. Barr (1962). "Intercellular connections between smooth muscle cells: The nexus." *Science* **137**: 670–672.

Duncan, C. L. (1961). "Spontaneous activity in the isolated nerves of pulmonate molluscs." *Comp. Biochem. Physiol.* **3**: 42–51.

Engbaek, L. and T. Hoshiko (1957). "Electrical potential gradients through frog skin." *Acta Physiol. Scand.* **39**: 348–355.

Farquahar, M. G. and G. E. Palade (1963). "Junctional complexes in various epithelia." *J. Cell Biol.* **17**: 375–412.

Galleotti, G. (1904). "Concerning the EMF which is generated at the surface of animal membranes on contact with different electrolytes." *Z. Physik. Chem.* **9**: 542–562.

Harary, I. and E. Sato (1964). "Studies in vitro on single beating heart cells." *Biochim. Biophys. Acta* **82**: 614–616.

Hays, R. M. and A. Leaf (1962). "Studies on the movement of water through the isolated toad bladder and its modification by vasopressin." *J. Gen. Physiol.* **45**: 905–919.

Huf, E. (1935). "Versüche uber die Zusammenhang zwischen Stoffwechsel, Potentialbildung Funktion der Froschhaut." *Pflüg. Arch. ges. Physiol.* **235**: 665–673.

Hutter, O. F. and W. Trautwein (1956). "Vagal and sympathetic effects on the pacemaker fibers in the sinus venosus of the heart." *J. Gen. Physiol.* **39**: 715–733.

Jha, R. K. and G. O. Mackie (1967). "The recognition, distribution, and ultrastructure of Hydrozoan nerve elements." *J. Morphol.* **123**: 43–61.

Katchalsky, A. and P. F. Curran (1965). **Nonequilibrium Thermodynamics in Biophysics.** Cambridge, Mass.: Harvard University Press. 248 pp.

Koefoed-Johnsen, V., H. Levi, and H. H. Ussing (1952). "The mode of passage of current through isolated frog skin." *Acta Physiol. Scand.* **25**: 150–163.

Koefoed-Johnsen, V. and H. H. Ussing (1953). "The contributions of diffusion and flow to the passage of D_2O through living membranes." *Acta Physiol. Scand.* **28**: 60–76.

Krogh, A. (1937). "Osmotic regulation in the frog (*Rana esculentia*) by active reabsorption of chloride ions." *Scand. Arch. Physiol.* **76**: 60–73.

Krogh, A. (1938). "The active absorption of ions in some freshwater animals." *Z. vergl. Physiol.* **25**: 235–250.

Kuffler, S. W., J. G. Nicholls, and R. Orkand (1966). "Physiological properties of glial cells in the central nervous system of amphibia." *J. Neurophysiol.* **29**: 768–787.

Leaf, A., J. Anderson, and L. D. Page (1958). "Active sodium transport by the isolated toad Bladder." *J. Gen. Physiol.* **41**: 657–668.

Levi, H. and H. H. Ussing (1948). "The exchange of sodium and chloride ions across the fibre membrane of the isolated frog sartorius." *Acta Physiol. Scand.* **16**: 232–249.

Loewenstein, W. R., M. Nakas, and S. J. Socolar (1967). "Junctional membrane uncoupling: permeability transformations at a cell membrane junction." *J. Gen. Physiol.* **50**: 1865–1892.

Loewenstein, W. R., S. J. Socolar, S. Higashino, Y. Kanno, and N. Davidson (1965). "Intercellular communication: renal, urinary bladder, sensory, and salivary gland cells." *Science* **149**: 295–298.

Mackie, G. O. (1965). "Conduction in the nerve-free epithelia of siphonophores." *Am. Zool.* **5**: 439–454.

Mackie, G. O., L. M. Passano, and M. Pavans de Ceccatty (1967). "Physiologie du comportment de l'Hydromeduse *Sarsia tubulosa* Sars: Les systemes a conduction aneurale." *Compte Rend. Seances Acad. Sci. D*, **264**: 466–469.

Muir, A. R. (1965). "Further observations on the cellular structure of cardiac muscle." *J. Anat.* **99**: 27–46.

Nicholls, J. G. and S. W. Kuffler (1964). "Extracellular space as a pathway for exchange between blood neurons in central nervous system of the leech: the ionic composition of glial cells and neurons." *J. Neurophysiol.* **27**: 645.

Noble, D. (1962). "A modification of the Hodgkin-Huxley equations applicable to Purkinje fibres action and pace-maker potentials." *J. Physiol.* (London) **160**: 317–352.

Orkand, R. K., J. G. Nicholls, and S. W. Kuffler (1966). "The effect of nerve impulses on the membrane potentials of glial cells in the central nervous system of amphibia." *J. Neurophysiol.* **29**: 788.

Ottoson, D., F. Sjöstrand, S. Stenström, and G. Svaetichin (1953). "Microelectrode studies on the e.m.f. of the frog skin related to electron microscopy of the dermo-epithelial junction." *Acta Physiol. Scand.* **29** (*Suppl.* 106): 611–624.

Paes de Carvalho, A., W. C. DeMello, and B. F. Hoffman (1959). "Electrophysiological evidence for specialized fiber types in the rabbit atrium." *Am. J. Physiol.* **196**: 483.

Palay, S. L. (1956). "Synapses in the central nervous system." *J. Biophys. Biochem. Cytol.* **2**: 193–202.

Palay, S. L. (1966). "The role of neuroglia in the organization of the central nervous system." In: **Nerve as a Tissue.** (K. Rodahl, ed.), pp. 1–10. New York: Harper & Row.

Passano, L. M. (1963). "Primitive nervous systems." *Proc. Nat. Acad. Sci.* (U.S.) **50**: 306–313.

Peachey, L. D. and H. Rasmussen (1961). "Structure of the toad's urinary bladder as related to its physiology." *J. Biophys. Biochem. Cytol.* **10**: 529–553.

Rosenbluth, J. and S. L. Wissig (1964). "The uptake of ferritin by toad spinal ganglion cells." *J. Cell Biol.* **23**: 307–325.

Rotunno, C. A., M. I. Pouchan, and M. Cereigjido (1966). "Location of the mechanism of active transport of sodium across the frog skin." *Nature* **210**: 597–599.

Sjöstrand, F. S. and E. Andersson-Cedergren (1960). "Intercalated discs of heart muscle." In: **Structure and Function of Muscle.** (G. H. Bourne, ed.), Vol. 1, pp. 421–445. New York: Academic Press, Inc.

Sjöstrand, F. S., E. Andersson-Cedergren, and M. M. Dewey (1958). "The ultrastructure of the intercalated discs of frog, mouse, and guinea pig cardiac muscle." *J. Ultrastruct. Res.* **1**: 271–287.

Smith, T. E. and W. O. Berndt (1964). "The establishment of beating myocardial cells in long term culture in fluid medium." *Exp. Cell Res.* **36**: 179–191.

Trautwein, W. (1963). "Generation and

conduction of impulses in the heart as affected by drugs." *Physiol. Rev.* **15:** 277.

Trautwein, W. and K. Uchizono (1963). "Electron microscopic and electrophysiologic study of the pacemaker in the sino-atrial node of the rabbit heart." *Z. Zellforsch.* **61:** 96–109.

Ussing, H. H. (1949). "Transport of ions across cellular membranes." *Physiol. Rev.* **29:** 127–155.

Ussing, H. H. (1965). "Transport of electrolytes and water across epithelia." *Harvey Lect.* **59:** 1–30.

Ussing, H. H. and B. Andersen (1955). "The relation between solvent drag and active transport of ions." *Proc. 3rd Internat. Congr. Brussels, 1956*, pp. 434–440.

Ussing, H. H. and E. E. Windhager (1964). "Nature of shunt path and active sodium transport path through frog skin epithelium." *Acta Physiol. Scand.* **61:** 484–504.

Ussing, H. H. and K. Zerahn (1951). "Active transport of sodium as the source of electric current in the short-circuited isolated frog skin." *Acta Physiol. Scand.* **23:** 110–137.

Vassalle, M. and B. F. Hoffman (1965). "The spread of sinus activation during potassium administration." *Circ. Res.* **17:** 285–295.

Villegas, R., L. Villegas, M. Gimenez, and G. M. Villegas (1963). "Schwann cell and axon electrical potential differences." *J. Gen. Physiol.* **46:** 1047–1053.

Wilbrandt, W. (1960). "Permeabilität und Stofftransporte." *Fortschr. Zool.* **12:** 28–127.

Woodbury, J. W. and W. E. Crill (1961). "On the problem of impulse conduction in the atrium." In: **Nervous Inhibition.** (E. Florey, ed.), pp. 124–135. Long Island City, N.Y.: Pergamon Press, Inc.

Woodbury, J. W. (1962). "Cellular electrophysiology of the heart." In: **Handbook of Physiology,** Sect. 2, Circulation. (W. F. Hamilton, ed.), Vol. 1, pp. 237–286. Washington, D.C.: American Physiological Society.

Zadunaisky, J. A., O. A. Candia, and D. J. Chiarandini (1963). "The origin of the shortcircuited current in the isolated skin of the South American frog *Leptodactylus ocellatus.*" *J. Gen. Physiol.* **47:** 393–402.

10-1. Introduction. In previous chapters the basic properties of excitable cell membranes were shown to provide mechanisms for receiving and conducting information in animals. This information is acted upon through the agency of effector cells and effector organs—primarily muscle and glands.

Contractility and movement are basic properties of all animal cells as evidenced by such phenomena as cytoplasmic streaming; amoeboid movement; chromosome, spindle fiber, and membrane movements in mitosis; movements of cilia and flagella; and muscular contraction.

Muscle cells are specialized for contractile ability and perform a wide variety of functions including movement of the animal through its environment, maintenance of animal posture and body orientation, circulatory movements such as the heart beat and changes in blood vessel diameter, digestive and food-gathering activity (movement of mouth parts, food swallowing, propulsion of food through the gastrointestinal tract, and so forth), reproductive activities, and movements of secretory and excretory products in glands and excretory systems. Muscles control the activity of chromatophores in cephalopod molluscs. Modified muscle cells, as we have already seen, function as electric organs in certain fish. Muscles also play a role in sensory reception, where they may move and guide eye or ear movements or may be part of the sensory system.

Specialization of contractile structures began early in the evolution of animals. Cilia and flagella are found in most animal classes. Contractile stalks, "myonemes," are found in protozoans such as *Stentor* and *Vorticella*. Contractile epithelial cells are found about the oscula of sponges and in the body wall of coelenterates. Many of the contractile cells of coelenterates contain a muscular tail portion only (Hoyle, 1957, reviews neuromuscular systems throughout the animal kingdom). All higher metazoans possess true muscles cells.

Today it is thought that all contractile events in cells have their basis in the reactions of contractile proteins, similar to the actin and myosin of vertebrate skeletal muscle, with ATP, and divalent cations such as Ca^{2+} and

Chapter 10

Contractility of Muscle and Cells

Mg^{2+}. Part of this chapter will present the evidence for believing in a common molecular mechanism for all contractile events.

Lehninger (1962) expressed the opinion that all contractile proteins evolved from a family of enzymes associated with oxidative-phosphorylation. Mitochondria can swell and contract by the nonosmotic inflow or outflow of water and this ability is based on the presence of mechanoenzymes that can divert energy away from the phosphorylation of ADP to mechanical energy for altering protein conformation. Such a change in structure (and volume) of proteins is not an uncommon feature of these macromolecules. There are many similarities between muscle contractile proteins and mitochondrial mechanoenzymes with respect to their reactions with ATP, divalent cations, drugs, and pH.

Similar proteins may be present in membranes, and it has been suggested that ion movements through membranes are brought about by electrostatic interactions with particular membrane proteins that can contract and allow the ion access to a water filled pathway through the membrane. Figure 10-1 gives one highly simplified model of such a contractile reaction. Crane (1966) and Booij (1966) discuss these ideas.

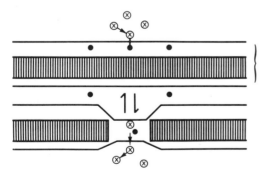

Figure 10-1 A hypothetical model for membrane contraction and penetration by water-soluble solutes. A material, X, might attach to specific sites on the membrane which is then stimulated to contract. The contraction includes the opening up of a water channel through the lipid layer (the shaded region), which would allow water-soluble materials to pass through by diffusion.

Contractile mechanism theories are based primarily on evidence obtained from the study of vertebrate striated skeletal muscle and a major part of this discussion of contractility must center about this highly specialized cell type. Vertebrate striated muscle cells have many characteristics that make them especially suitable for study. The high degree of structural organization makes it easier to follow structural changes during contractile activity, thus yielding clues about the underlying contractile mechanisms. Most of the mass of the cell is made up of the contractile proteins, thus providing a good source of material in quantities suitable for biochemical analysis. The output of the cell in the form of shortening, tension development, or work is readily measurable, especially since many vertebrate striated muscle cells are large and relatively easy to manipulate. It is possible to relate output to input energies, thus providing a starting point for thermodynamic as well as metabolic studies.

Since the rabbit and frog possess suitable muscles for analysis and are animals readily obtainable and maintainable in the laboratory, a large amount of work has been done with muscles from these animals. But the extensive use of the frog gastrocnemius and sartorius muscles for studies on mechanical properties and of the rabbit psoas muscles for studies of the biochemical properties has, perhaps, made it appear that all muscles are similar to these— a conclusion that comparative studies are showing to be false. As we shall see, the basic molecular mechanisms of contractility may be similar, but the actual arrangement and details vary considerably in different contractile cells.

Structure and Properties of Striated Skeletal Muscle

10-2. Classification of Muscles. Muscles are often classified as striated, smooth, or cardiac, but such a division is based primarily on muscles from vertebrates and ignores relationships based on functional characteristics.

There is, at present, no good single classification of muscles from vertebrates and invertebrates.

Prosser (1960) placed muscles into either of two groups:

1. Muscles with origins and insertions on exo- or endoskeletons or on skin. These are generally **phasic muscles**—ones with rapid, brief contraction cycles. They include those responsible for appendage and body movements and are often arranged in antagonistic pairs. One of the pair causes movement in one direction; the other member of the pair produces movement in the opposite direction. In some cases a phasic muscle pulls against an opposing elastic ligament.

2. Muscles arranged around hollow structures, lacking strict origins and insertions so that one portion of the muscle inserts on another portion. These are generally **tonic muscles**—ones that contract slowly and can hold for a long period of time. This type is found in gastrointestinal and urogenital tracts and in circulatory vessels. They sometimes appear in paired groups as in the circular and longitudinal muscles of the body walls of annelids and holothurians and in the vertebrate intestinal tract. Often they are nonstriated muscles.

The vertebrate muscle classification of striated, smooth, and cardiac muscles is based primarily on histological characteristics. Bozler (1936) introduced the following scheme of classification which attempted to correlate the anatomy, histology, and physiology of many muscles as well as the type of innervation of the muscles.

(=fibers) that possess a regular cross-banding and also longitudinal striations when observed in the light miscoscope. The fibers are multinucleate, that is, each adult fiber is developed from a syncytium of embryonic cells. Striated muscle fibers are unbranched, and in nearly all cases they are attached to bones via tendons.

Innervation is by motor units. A **motor unit** consists of a single branching terminal motor neuron innervating a group of muscle fibers. The number of fibers innervated by the axon varies depending on the particular muscle. It is often indicated by the innervation index: the ratio of number of muscle fibers to the number of neurons entering the muscle. For example, in the cat the innervation index ranges from 3 for the occular muscles (one axon for every three muscle fibers) to 200 for some limb muscles (one axon for every 200 muscle fibers).

Vertebrate striated muscle has monoterminal, mononeuronal innervation, that is, one motor axon ending is found on each fiber and only one neuron innervates a given fiber. Some muscles are polyneuronal. Such is the case, for example, in crustacean leg muscles (see Chapter 11). Other muscles are multiterminal with either one or several different axons contributing several endings on each muscle fiber.

Smooth muscle is unstriated, although faint longitudinal bands are sometimes seen. The fibers possess a single, centrally located nucleus. **Visceral smooth muscle** is found in the gastrointestinal and urogenital tracts. It is usually excited by spontaneous action potentials that spread through the mass of tissue

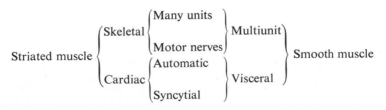

The scheme applies only to vertebrate muscles. The terms will be defined in the following paragraphs.

Striated skeletal muscle is composed of cells

(see Chapter 9) and that produce coordinated contractions. Although the production of action potentials is through spontaneous activity, there may also be innervation by the

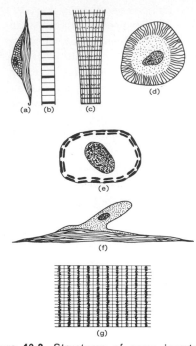

Figure 10-2 Structures of some invertebrate muscle fibers. (a) Coelenterate smooth muscle fiber from *Pelagica*. (b) Striated muscle fiber from *Pelagica*. (c) Annelid striated muscle fiber from the polychaete *Syllis*. (d) Tranverse section through unstriated muscle fiber from the leech *Hirudinea*. There is a cortex of lamellar fibrils and a medulla of nonfibrillar sarcoplasm containing the nucleus. (e) Transverse section through a striated muscle fiber from the arm of the octopus. Note double layer of peripheral fibers and central nucleated sarcoplasm. (f) Giant muscle cell of the nematode *Ascaris*. (g) Whole muscle fiber of the insect *Cyclochila*. Thin transverse lines represent M-line region of the A-band. Short I-band is bisected by the Z-lines. [Adapted from Hoyle (1957) after various sources.]

autonomic nervous system to control the rate of activity as required. **Multiunit smooth muscle** is found in precapillary sphincters of the circulatory system, nictating membranes, intrinsic muscles of the eye, and in piloerector muscles. It has an innervation similar to that of striated skeletal muscle—a motor axon exciting groups of cells. While smooth muscle is usually characterized as a slow-contraction type, multiunit smooth muscle is phasic rather than tonic.

Cardiac muscle has characteristics of both skeletal muscle and smooth muscle. Its cells are cross-striated and contain a single nucleus. The cells are often branched. The heart is a functional syncytium (Chapter 9). Cardiac muscle cells resemble visceral smooth muscle in that their contraction is initiated by spontaneously arising action potentials with control by the autonomic nervous system. Its contraction is relatively rapid.

To point out the variations that occur in the anatomy and physiology of muscle cells and that lead to difficulties in classifying muscles the following statements may be considered. A high rate of contraction-relaxation is usually correlated with long muscle fibers that are closely striated and that contain only small amounts of connective tissue. However, multiunit smooth muscle is also very fast as are many smooth muscles of the invertebrates. Except in cardiac muscle, vertebrate striated fibers are not branched, but many insect striated fibers are branched. Muscle fibers of the tunicate heart are striated on one side and nonstriated on the other (Bozler, 1927). The visceral muscles of insects and other invertebrates are usually striated. Some apparently spirally striated fibers in the

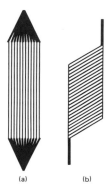

Figure 10-3 (a) Parallel-fibered muscle fiber. When fibers of this type of muscle contract, the whole muscle shortens by an amount equivalent to the amount of shortening of the fibers. (b) Pennate arrangement of fibers in a muscle. Such a muscle shortens as a whole to a much smaller extent that the shortening of its fibers. The pennate arrangement allows a greater force to be developed and such muscles are used for short powerful movements. The force exerted by a muscle is a function of its cross sectional area, not of its length.

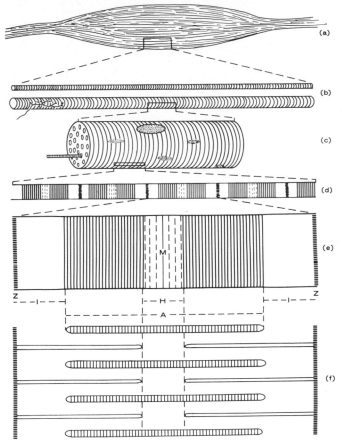

invertebrates have a helical arrangement of fibers which gives the appearance of striations. Visceral smooth muscle fibers of vertebrates are short (with lengths between 0.1 and 0.5 mm); nonstriated muscles of bivalve molluscs may reach lengths of 1 to 2 cm. While vertebrate smooth muscle fibers are unbranched, the short nonstriated fibers of some invertebrates, for example, holothurian body wall muscles, are profusely branched.

Following the suggestion of Prosser (1960) the visceral nonstriated muscles of vertebrates will be called smooth muscles. Other muscles lacking striations will be called nonstriated. Figure 10-2 presents some of the anatomical variations found in muscle cells (Hanson and Lowy, 1960; Hoyle, 1967).

10-3. Ultrastructure of Striated Skeletal Muscle. Whole muscles, bundles of muscle fibers, and individual fibers are surrounded by a network of collagen fibers and connective

tissue. Most muscles at their ends blend into bands of tendon that provide attachment to skeletal structures. Fibers vary from 10 to about 100 μ in diameter and range from a millimeter to as much as 20 centimeters in length, depending on the muscle. The length of a muscle is not an indication of fiber length because often fibers do not run the entire length of the muscle or are not arranged parallel to the long axis of the muscle (Figure 10-3). As shown in the figure, pennate muscles are capable of developing high forces with short degrees of shortening; muscles with parallel fibers undergo a greater degree of shortening while developing less total force. As we shall see in a later section, the speed of muscle shortening is related to the percentage of shortening.

Each fiber is surrounded by a membrane— the muscle plasma membrane or **sarcolemma**. In the past confusion arose over the meaning of this term since part of the sarcolemma

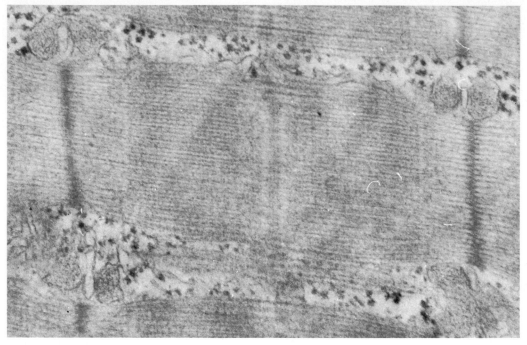

Figure 10-5 Electronmicrograph of a fast fiber from the rectus abdominis muscle of the frog *Rana pipiens*. The dense zones running vertically are Z-lines bisecting the I-band regions. Outside the fibrillar area is the lighter appearing sarcoplasm containing mitochondria and other bodies. At each Z-line is seen the triad system composed of elements of the sarcoplasmic reticulum and the transverse tubular system. Scale line equals 0.5 μ. Magnification = 49,500X. [Courtesy of Dr. Robert Hikida.]

was thought to consist of connective tissue. The electron microscope has shown that this is not the case. Lying outside the sarcolemma there is a 500 Å wide basement membrane, followed by connective tissue containing reticular fibers (Bennett, 1960).

The fiber, in turn, is built up of many parallel threadlike structures—the **myofibrils** (Figure 10-4). These are 1 to 3 μ in diameter and are barely visible in the light microscope. Myofibrils are arranged in closely packed groups of 4 to 20 or more. Each group is separated from its neighbors by spaces 0.2 to 0.5 μ wide filled with muscle cytoplasm—the **sarcoplasm**. Figure 10-5 shows the appearance of a fast muscle fiber from the frog.

The mitochondria (=sarcosomes) of striated muscle cells are larger than those of other cells and generally fewer in number. They are distributed between groups of fibrils either in longitudinal rows or in horizontal planes at the level of the I bands, A-I junctions, or triads of the sarcomere. Because sarcosomes are the sites of oxidative energy metabolism, their presence in relatively large numbers in a muscle has usually been taken as an indication of a muscle that performs more work (Slater, 1960).

Muscles are sometimes divided into groups dependent on their color. Red muscles and white muscles are found, but generally a mammalian muscle is composed of a mixture of red and white fibers. Red and white muscles are exemplified by the dark and white meats of domestic fowl. The redness of a muscle depends upon its fibers' content of myoglobin, the oxygen storage pigment (Chapter 2). Although it is generally true that the fibers of red muscles contain more sarcoplasm than those of white muscles and also more sarcosomes, such is not always the case. Red color has often been taken to indicate that a muscle undergoes more continuous usage than does a white muscle, but many exceptions to this generality are known (see Walls, 1960). The histological appearance of a muscle is not always correlated with its activity. As an example, the flight (breast) muscles of domestic fowl are primarily composed of white fibers containing few sarcosomes, yet these are muscles capable of sustained activity (Bennett and Porter, 1953).

Within the sarcoplasm is also found the **sarcoplasmic reticulum**—a membranous network of tubules and cisternae analogous to the endoplasmic reticulum of other cells.

The sarcoplasmic reticulum consists of a complicated arrangement of sarcotubules, vesicles, and cisternae (Andersson-Cedergren, 1959; Bennett, 1960; Porter and Palade, 1957; Sjöstrand, 1959).

Terminal cisternae of the sarcoplasmic reticulum form **diad** or **triad** structures associated with another tubular system, the **transverse tubular system**. The latter is initiated by invaginations of the sarcolemma and extends inward encompassing the myofibrils, generally as a system of tubules that provides a pathway between the external medium and each sarcomere of the myofibril. The arrangement of these structures depends on the particular

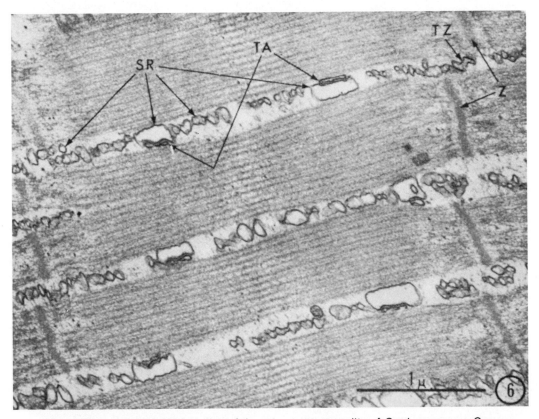

Figure 10-6 A longitudinal section of the extensor carpopodite of *Carcinus maenas*. One Z tubule (TZ) appears between the Z-lines (Z) of two adjacent myofibrils. Several diads are located near the ends of the myofibrillar A-bands. The smaller element of each of these is an A tubule (TA); the larger is part of the SR. Other parts of the SR lie adjacent to the central portions of the A-bands and next to the I-bands of the myofibrils (36,000X). [By permission from L. D. Peachey (1967) "Membrane systems of crab fibers." *American Zoologist* **7**: 505–513.]

Figure 10-7 Longitudinal section through a crayfish phasic abdominal muscle fiber. Note relatively short sarcomeres (2 μ). Myofibrils are separated by sarcoplasmic reticulum (S) and diads (arrows). [By permission from H. L. Atwood (1967) "Crustacean neuromuscular mechanisms" *American Zoologist* 7: 527–551.]

muscle and animal. Figures 10-5, 10-6, and 10-7 illustrate the nature of these structures in the frog, crab, and crayfish.

The amount of this reticular material is correlated with the contractile activity of the fiber. Slow muscles, those which undergo slower contractions, possess fibers with a poorly developed sarcoplasmic reticulum and few diads or triads. Fast muscle fibers have an extensive reticulum with many triads or diads. The role of the two reticular systems in excitation-contraction coupling, the mechanism which converts membrane action potentials into a contractile response, is discussed in a later section of this chapter.

The myofibrils are composed of **myofilaments**—fibrous elements composed of the muscle's contractile proteins.

10-4. Structure of the Sarcomere. As indicated in Figures 10-4 and 10-8, the pattern of cross-striations that gives striated muscle its name is caused by the presence of crossbands in the myofibrils. The fibrils are in close alignment so that the pattern of each fibril lies in register with those of neighboring fibrils. Such banding appears to be an early feature of muscle cells during animal evolution because it is found even in coelenterate muscle-epithelial cells (see Figure 10-2). The bandings of the myofibril are due to the arrangement of protein filaments within the fibril.

The dense and less dense bands of the fibril repeat along the fibril's length and are areas of higher and lower refractive index, respectively. In polarized light one band appears dark and is the **A-band** (anisotropic band).

The other major band appears lighter in the polarizing microscope and is the **I-band** (isotropic band). The birefringence of the fiber (a measure of the structuring of the bands) is uniaxial, with the optical axis parallel to the length of the fiber. Isotropism in the polarized light microscope indicates a less ordered structure or a structure whose arrangement of elements is masked by isotropic substances.

The terms light and dark for the major bands of the sarcomere are not good ones since the darkness or lightness of a band depends upon the conditions of observation. In the light microscope the bands are invisible if the fiber is examined in ordinary light with a wide condenser aperture. Stopping down the condenser brings the bands into view, but their relative densities depend on the focussing. By convention A-bands are made to appear dark and I-bands light, by focussing low. In polarized light the A-bands are ordinarily dark when compared with the I-bands, but again this depends on the conditions used. The appearance of the bands will also depend on the nature of any stains used (see A. F. Huxley,

1957, for a discussion of these points).

Each I-band is bisected by a narrow dark line (as seen in the light microscope), the **Z-line** (from the German, *Zwischenscheibe*, central membrane). It was thought for some time that these were membranous structures, but in the electron microscope they are seen to be the regions where the thin filaments meet (Garamvölgi, 1963; H. Huxley, 1965). Zig-zag patterns of protein filaments, with a basketweave appearance are found in some Z-line regions (Reedy, 1964). Filaments of very fine dimensions are found in other Z-line regions. Other muscles have no Z-line region (Figure 10-9).

The distance between two successive Z-lines is the **sarcomere**—often called the smallest function unit of muscle. In many striated muscles the region between two successive M-lines is better thought of as the basic functional unit. The M-line is a dark thin band bisecting the A-band. It lies in the center of a central lighter zone, the H-zone (Hensen's zone).

These bands of the sarcomere result from the regular alignment and register of two types

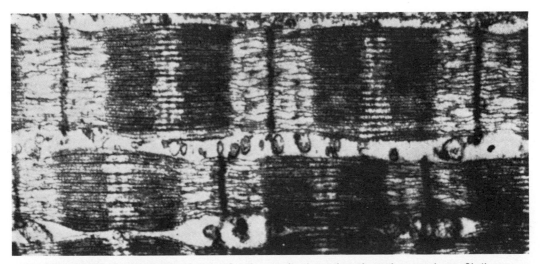

Figure 10-8 Electron micrograph of a longitudinal section through several myofibrils in a glycerol-extracted fixed rabbit psoas muscle. Between the fibrils are sarcoplasmic elements. The fibrils show the same bands as they do in the light microscope. The bands are caused by the presence of thick filaments in the A-band and thin filaments in the I-band extending into the A-band. Magnification = 53,000X. [By permission from H. E. Huxley. "The contraction of muscle" *Scientific American* **199** (5): 66–86. © 1958 W. H. Freeman and Company, San Francisco.]

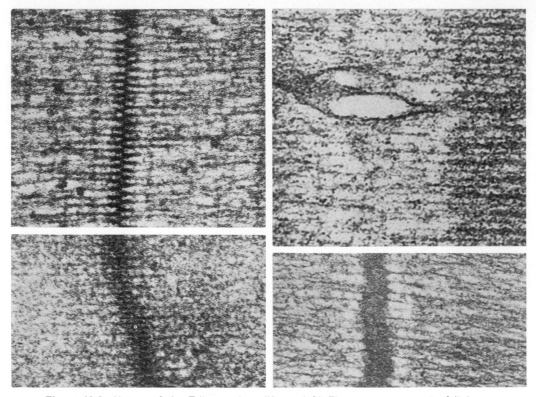

Figure 10-9 Nature of the Z-line region. (Upper left) Zig-zag arrangement of linkages between actin filaments from adjacent sarcomeres of fish tail muscle. (Upper right) Z-region with little structure and no density. Some thin filaments are crosslinked, others appear to go straight across. Antennular muscle of copepod larva. (Lower left) Overlapping arrangement of actin filaments with lateral cross connections. Garter snake ribs to body wall muscle. (Lower right) Alternating attachments of thin filaments but broad band with numerous cross connections. Locust, *Schistocerca*, extensor tibiae. (120,000X) [By permission from G. Hoyle (1967) "Diversity of striated muscle." *American Zoologist* **7**: 435–449.]

of protein filaments. As shown in Figures 10-10 and 10-11, the A-band contains a set of thick filaments that run the length of this band. In rabbit psoas muscle these thick filaments are 1.5 μ in length and about 110 Å in diameter. They are composed of molecules of the contractile protein myosin and are primarily responsible for the anisotropy of the A-band. The length of the thick (or myosin) filaments, and therefore of the A-band, varies according to the particular muscle and animal examined. In insect flight muscles the I-band is often extremely short. And the thick filaments extend to the Z-line, perhaps being attached to the Z-line by other protein filaments (the C-filaments). Most of the sarco-

mere length in this case is made up of the A-band.

The H-zone is the portion of the A-band where, during the relaxed condition, only thick filaments are found. At the M-line region there appear to be interconnecting bridges between each thick filament and its six neighbors (in many muscles there is a hexagonal packing of the thick filaments). These bridges, probably protein in nature, could account for the greater optical density of the M-line region.

A set of thin filaments that contain the protein actin is found in the I-bands. The thin filaments are about 50 Å in diameter, and they extend from the Z-line, through the I-band, and into the A-band region up to the

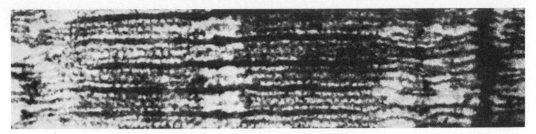

Figure 10-10 Longitudinal section through a glycerol-extracted fixed rabbit psoas muscle. Two thin filaments are seen lying between two thick filaments. The cross bridges of the myosin filaments are readily seen. Magnification = 147,000X. [By permission from H. E. Huxley "The contraction of muscle." *Scientific American* **199** (5): 66–86. © W. H. Freeman and Company, San Francisco.]

H-zone. The isotropy of the I-band results, partially at least, from the dense array of thin filaments. A third contractile protein, tropomyosin, is part of the thin filament structure. Its function is still uncertain although it may be involved in the relaxation process (see Sections 10-9 and 10-30).

In rabbit psoas muscle, the classical object of muscle ultrastructure and biochemical studies, there are six actin filaments surrounding each myosin filament in the A-band: a 2:1 ratio of actin to myosin (Figure 10-10). Ratios of 3:1 have been found in blowfly flight muscle; 4:1 in locust flight muscle; and 5:1 in insect and crustacean skeletal muscles. The two sets of filaments are the basis for a model of contraction to be discussed in Section 10-11 (see Hanson and Huxley, 1955). The ultrastructure of the vertebrate sarcomere has been reviewed by H. E. Huxley (1960, 1965).

10-5. T-filaments. Knowledge of the ultrastructure of striated muscle depends on techniques in electron microscopy and x-ray diffraction analysis. Whereas the thick and thin filaments described above lie well within the range of resolution of the electron microscope and thin-sectioning techniques, suggestions have been made that other filaments and structures exist in the sarcomere. For example, Hoyle and his co-workers, after examining a variety of invertebrate and vertebrate striated muscles, came to the conclusion that a super-thin filament runs the length of many sarcomeres. These filaments, 25 Å in diameter, were

observed by these workers in all bands of the myofibril and were seen to bridge the gap between actin and myosin filaments produced when a muscle fiber was stretched. It was suggested that they served as elastic supportive elements of the myofibril (McNeil and Hoyle, 1967; Walcott and Ridgway, 1967).

The size of these filaments places them close to the limit of resolution of the electron microscope, and their existence is questioned by other workers. However, this type of study points out the possibility of structures other than the thick or thin filaments being present in the sarcomere and playing roles in the

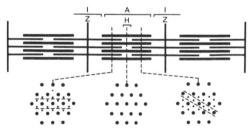

Figure 10-11 Schematic representation illustrating the positioning of thick and thin filaments in the sarcomere. At the bottom are shown the distributions of protein filaments observed in cross sections. Only thin actin filaments are present in the I-band. The thin filaments extend into the A-band. Thick filaments are present only in the A-band. Only thick filaments are present in the H-zone of the A-band. In the A-band it is seen that six actin filaments surround each myosin filament. This is the pattern found in rabbit psoas muscle, and other arrangements are found in different animals.

contractile process. The structures of the Z-line region are not clearly understood, and small filaments attaching to actin filaments were seen in this region (Knappeis and Carlson, 1956). Possibly they were smaller actin filaments. There is still much to be learned about the ultrastructure of the striated muscle cell.

Before describing the current model upon which muscle contractility is based, it is necessary to describe briefly the nature and reactions of the major protein constituents of muscle.

Biochemistry of the Contractile Proteins

10-6. Myosin. Three proteins make up the bulk of the dry mass of striated muscle cells: myosin, 54 per cent; actin, 20 to 25 per cent; and tropomyosin, 11 per cent. The properties of the contractile mechanism depend upon the characteristics and reactions of these three proteins. Unfortunately, actin and myosin are extremely complex macromolecules both structurally and functionally—a fact which is not surprising in light of the complex and often rapid contractile

activities in which they play a role; activities that must be closely controlled as well. The basic properties of actin or myosin, extracted from a wide variety of sources, are very similar.

Myosin undergoes a variety of reactions with itself, with other proteins, with ATP, and with divalent cations; at least part of its biochemical properties depend upon the ionic strength of the medium. Myosin is an ATPase enzyme, and this discovery was of importance since it related a functional activity of the main contractile protein with ATP, thought to be the direct energy source for muscular contraction (Szent-Györgyi, 1951, 1953, reviews the older literature on myosin and its ATPase activity). In addition myosin can combine with actin to form the complex protein actomyosin.

Because of the ready self-aggregation of myosin molecules in solution (and also of a tendency for myosin to rapidly denature and precipitate out of solution), it has proven difficult to obtain a reliable estimate of the molecular weight of myosin. Values ranging from 400,000 to 800,000 have been reported. Probably the best value is 490,000 (Driezen et al., 1967). These results are for myosin

Table 10-1   Molecular Weights of Some Myosins and Actins*

Protein and Source	Molecular Weight	Method of Measurement
Myosins		
Rabbit skeletal muscle	490,000	Ultracentrifugation
Lobster skeletal muscle	600,000	Ultracentrifugation
Dog cardiac muscle	534,000	Ultracentrifugation
	503,000	Light scattering
Cod skeletal muscle	510,000	Ultracentrifugation
Pigeon leg muscle (red)	517,000	Ultracentrifugation
Pigeon breast muscle (white)	517,000	Ultracentrifugation
Actins		
G-Actin (variety of sources)	~60,000	
F-Actin (rabbit skeletal)	~3,000,000	(depends on state of polymerization)

* The data given here were collected from Perry (1967); Gergely (1966). These references may be consulted for original data and references.

Table 10-2 Dimensions of Some Contractile Proteins and Their Subunits*

PROTEIN (MOLECULAR WEIGHT)		LENGTH (Å)	WIDTH (Å)
Myosin (490,000)	overall dimensions	1520	20
	tail dimensions	150–250	40
Light meromyosin (135,000)		800	
Heavy meromyosin (350,000)		500	
	globular region	200	40–50
	tail region	400	20
G-Actin (60,000)			60

* Data are selected values from the literature as reported in Perry (1967); Gergely (1966); Huxley (1969).

extracted from rabbit psoas muscle. Some generally accepted values for the molecular weights of myosins and actins obtained from different preparations are given in Table 10-1. Table 10-2 lists the accepted dimensions of myosin, actin, and their subfragments. Perry (1967) has reviewed the biochemistry of myosin.

Myosin can be hydrolyzed into a variety of subfragments whose characteristics depend on the agents and conditions used to break bonds in the molecule (Figure 10-12). The major subfragments are light meromyosin (LMM) and heavy meromyosin (HMM). HMM possesses the ATPase and the actin-combining power of the myosin. LMM has no specialized biological activities of this type. Treatment of LMM with alcohol leads to the formation of a soluble fraction, LMM-1. LMM probably contains LMM-1 and additional peptides from other parts of the myosin molecule, but the

relationships are still not clear. It should be noted that the subfragments result from the breakage of peptide bonds of the myosin. They are not subunits from which a polymeric myosin is built up (this would be accomplished by bonds other than peptide bonds). Although the term subunits is often used to refer to the meromyosins, protomyosins, and the like, here subfragments will be used. Subunits of myosin can be produced by the use of dissociating agents such as high concentrations of urea, guanidine, or extremes of pH—treatments that are generally used to break hydrogen bonds.

Driezen et al. (1966, 1967) using 5 M guanidine isolated two types of subunits from myosin. Myosin appeared to be composed of 2 f subunits (molecular weight 215,000) and three g subunits (molecular weight 20,000). It is thought that the f subunits contain the sulfhydryl groups that are known to be needed

Figure 10-12 Illustrating the various subunits obtained by various treatments of the myosin molecule.

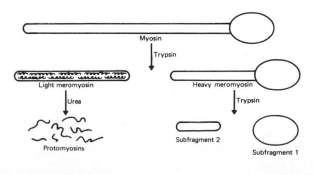

for myosin's ATPase activity. These subunits make up the elongate helical core of myosin and extend into the globular head region (Figure 10-11).

The shapes of the meromyosins provide a particular shape for the myosin molecule itself. On the basis of molecular weight, there is one HMM to one LMM in myosin. Since isolated HMM can combine with actin, it is thought that the bridges on the myosin molecule seen in the electron microscope are polypeptides of the HMM subfragment. These bridges are used to combine myosin and actin during the contractile process (Section 10-12). The filaments of myosin in rabbit psoas muscle are estimated to each contain about 400 myosin molecules (Huxley, 1963). The cross-bridges are 180 Å long and 40 Å in diameter. The myosins are arranged in a staggered fashion so that the globular heads fall on a helix of 429 Å pitch. Each cross-bridge is separated from its neighbors by 143 Å. These relationships are illustrated in Figure 10-16.

Pepe (1967a, b), on the basis of electron microscope observations and antibody staining reactions, proposed a model for the myosin filament in which myosin molecules are placed tail end (the LMM segment) to tail end in the so-called L-region of the sarcomere, also called the pseudo-H-zone. There are 12 molecules in this region arranged in triangular cross section. In the region of the cross-bridges eighteen myosin molecules occupy the cross section and most of the heavy meromyosins project outward forming the bridges. These bridges are arranged approximately in a double helix with pairs of bridges projecting in opposite directions. The thick filaments are seen to taper near their ends and contain fewer molecules. The M-line according to this model consists of projecting linkages between adjacent myosin filaments, but the projections are another protein not myosin. Analysis of the spatial arrangements of bridges in living frog sartorius muscle (analyzed by x-ray diffraction) indicates that the linkages move during contraction (Huxley et al., 1965). The significance of these structures for contraction will be considered in Section 10-11. These

models have been given here so that some concept of the complexity of the myosin and myosin filaments can be appreciated.

A-band filaments vary in dimensions in different muscles. The diameter of A-filaments in rabbit psoas muscle is about 110 Å (the filaments taper toward each end); in the opener and closer muscles of the crayfish, *Cambarus clarkii*, they are 180 Å in diameter (Peterson, 1963); and in the Kamchatka crab they are 260 to 300 Å in diameter (Gilëv, 1966). Such variation is one indication that the number and arrangement of myosin molecules must vary according to the particular muscle. The significance of such variation is not known.

10-7. Actin.   Actin exists in two forms. Globular actin (G-actin), is a monomer form that can aggregate to yield fibrous actin (F-actin). The molecular weight of G-actin is about 60,000 and the molecule is spherical with a diameter of about 55 Å. In the presence of salts G-actin undergoes the polymerization to form F-actin.

One of the difficulties of studying G-actin has been the inability to prevent the polymerization because salts are usually required in the solutions needed for physical-chemical studies. However, the reaction does not occur in potassium iodide solutions.

There is one mole of ATP tightly bound per mole of G-actin. During polymerization the ATP is hydrolyzed:

$$n \text{ (G-actin-ATP)} \underset{\text{KI inhibits}}{\overset{\text{low salt}}{\rightleftharpoons}} \text{(G-actin-ADP)}_n + n\text{P}_i$$

The I-bands contain actin filaments formed of a double-stranded F-actin helix with about 13 subunits per turn of the helix (A. F. Huxley, 1964). It is not considered that the G-actin–F-actin transformation plays a direct role in muscle contraction.

10-8. Actomyosin.   Purified solutions of actin and myosin are readily prepared (for the classical methods see Szent-Györgyi, 1951). When the two proteins are mixed striking changes occur in the physical as well as biological properties. The most obvious of these is a greatly increased viscosity. In the absence of external ATP, solutions of acto-myosin (AM) are gellike, presumably due to the combination of myosin and actin through the actin-combining sites on the HMM portion of the myosin. Such combination is enhanced in rate by the presence of Ca^{2+} or Mg^{2+}. At high ionic strengths (>0.3) the addition of ATP to actomyosin solutions leads to the dissociation of the complex. This reaction does not involve the hydrolysis of ATP because inorganic phosphate is also effective. At low ionic strengths (0.05 to 0.15) the actomyosin complex is insoluble. The addition of ATP at low ionic strengths leads to syneresis—the contraction of colloidal particles usually due to the elimination of water from the spaces around the particles. Under these conditions the actomyosin molecules become denser and rapidly settle out of solution. This phenomenon is **superprecipitation** and has often been used as a model system for studying the effects of various agents on the contractile properties of actomyosin. During this reaction ATP is hydrolyzed.

The control of contraction and relaxation rests on a series of complex interactions of the contractile proteins, ATP, Ca^{2+}, and Mg^{2+} (Section 10-14). In discussing the effects of ions such as calcium and magnesium, only free ions, not bound calcium or magnesium, are considered. Actin, for example, contains firmly bound calcium as part of its structure, and this calcium is not directly involved in the contractile process.

Addition of actin to myosin alters the nature of the ATPase activity of the protein. Purified myosin, in the presence of Ca^{2+} and Mg^{2+} concentrations similar to those found in muscle during activity, has a relatively low ATPase activity. But when combined with actin, the ATPase activity is much higher under the same ionic conditions.

Magnesium plays a dual role in muscle activity. It is required for actomyosin-ATPase activity, which is needed for contraction; and it is required for dissociation of the actomyosin complex. Magnesium breaks the cross-bridges that hold the two proteins together at least briefly during contraction. Mg^{2+} is present in sufficient concentration in muscle (~ 10 to 20 millimolar) to optimally activate both of these reactions. If dissociation of actomyosin occurs, the actomyosin-ATPase activity is halted and the free myosin-ATPase activity is inhibited by the Mg^{2+}.

The relaxed condition of the muscle is caused by the presence of dissociated contractile proteins in the relatively high free-magnesium concentration. In resting muscle free Ca^{2+} is minimal ($<10^{-7}$ M in frog sartorius). The addition of free calcium ions (10^{-6} M or greater) to muscle fibers or to various model systems is found to counteract the dissociation of actomyosin produced by the presence of Mg^{2+}. This reaction may result from the competition between Mg^{2+} and Ca^{2+} for sites on the proteins. Once actomyosin is formed, the Mg^{2+} can activate the actomyosin-ATPase and contraction results. Systems that increase or decrease Ca^{2+} concentration in the muscle could act as controls over the contraction-relaxation cycle. Such a system is found in the sarcoplasmic reticulum and will be discussed in Section 10-14.

To summarize: when the concentration of free Mg^{2+} is greater than 2×10^{-6} M (which it is in many skeletal muscles), there is a dissociation of actomyosin. As a result ATP hydrolysis is prevented, thus preventing contraction—the muscle is in the relaxed state. Addition of minute quantities of Ca^{2+} to the system overcomes the contraction inhibition by allowing the actomyosin complex to be formed with a subsequent hydrolysis of ATP and muscle contraction. This scheme is based on several assumptions, none of which are proven except by circumstantial evidence. It is assumed that ATP hydrolysis is directly involved at some stage of the contractile event. It is assumed that in the relaxed muscle actin and myosin exist as separate proteins, whereas in the contractile state they have associated (at least momentarily) to form actomyosin. These are likely possibilities and will be assumed true in the following discussions.

ATP obviously plays several roles in the

muscle contractile machinery. Since it is involved in both the contractile reaction and in the actomyosin dissociation reaction, as well as in the G-actin polymerization reaction, the state of the muscle is greatly influenced by the amount and state of ATP. Muscle has several natural as well as experimentally induced states that can be explained on the basis of the properties of the actin and myosin filaments and their reactions with ATP. Muscle is a relatively rigid structure due partially to the rigid nature of the myosin filaments. Since these are multistranded coils of myosin molecules, the thick filament is a strong structural entity. Resting striated muscle is stretched relatively easily because in the resting state the cross-bridges between actin and myosin are not formed, and a stretch can readily pull the two sets of filaments apart. Upon stimulation, the muscle becomes more difficult to stretch because the actin and myosin have crosslinked through the mediation of ATP to form a strong latticework. To stretch the muscle and pull the filaments apart, the cross linkages must be broken. The different responses to stretch of the relaxed and contracted muscle is one piece of evidence indicating that actomyosin is part of the contractile machinery.

ATP can not only aid in the formation of actomyosin, it is also a plasticizer that can loosen the cross linkages between actin and myosin at higher concentrations. Excess amounts of ATP in model systems result in the plasticity of the model. If ATP is completely removed from a muscle, the state of **rigor** ensues. In this state stretching a muscle tears it, because the cross-bridges are attached and the resultant atcin-myosin lattice prevents any movements of the filaments relative to one another without destruction of the system. In the rigor condition it is more difficult to extract the muscle proteins, indicating that the less soluble actomyosin is present (Bate-Smith and Bendall, 1947). Myosin may be extracted from normal muscle by stirring a muscle mince for 10 minutes in a buffered 0.6 M KCl solution. The removal of actomyosin requires several hours of stirring. These extraction

times are greatly extended when a muscle in rigor is used.

Actomyosin extracted from smooth muscle is composed entirely (arterial wall) or partially (cow uterus) of a protein called **tonomyosin**, which is soluble at lower ionic strengths than actomyosin extracted from rabbit skeletal muscle (Needham and Williams, 1963a, b). Tonomyosin has similar Ca^{2+} requirements for activity as actomyosin, but its Mg^{2+} requirements are 10 times greater (Rüegg et al., 1965). That actomyosin-like proteins are found in a variety of cells is one reason for assuming that contractility generally is based upon similar mechanisms. For example, such a protein is found in the outer membrane of liver cells and may be responsible for membrane movements and activities.

10-9. Tropomyosin B and Paramyosin. Bailey (1948) was the first to extract from vertebrate skeletal and cardiac muscle a protein called variously tropomyosin or natural tropomyosin. This protein has a molecular weight of about 53,000 and is a rod-shaped molecule 400 Å long by 15 to 20 Å in diameter. The molecular weights from different animal groups range from 50,000 to 153,000. Tropomyosin is found as a contaminant of highly purified actomyosin preparations and is associated with another protein, troponin, believed to be associated with Ca^{2+} binding and release in the muscle. (Ebashi and Kodama, 1965). Tropomyosin appears to be part of the thin filaments and may be associated with the formation of actomyosin (Gergely, 1966; Pepe, 1966). Tropomyosin in vertebrate muscles is also called tropomyosin B.

Tropomyosin A or **paramyosin** is found in many invertebrate smooth muscles, especially in the slow or catch muscles of molluscs (see Hanson and Lowy, 1964; also Section 10-30). It has an amino acid composition similar to tropomyosin B. The distribution of tropomyosins in several types of muscles and the properties of these muscles are given in Table 10-3.

The molecular weight of paramyosin from the clam, *Venus mercenaria*, is 220,000 (Lowey

Table 10-3 Distribution of Tropomyosins and Paramyosins*

ANIMAL AND MUSCLE	TYPE OF MUSCLE	TROPOMYOSIN	PARAMYOSIN
Molluscs			
Oyster (tonic adductor)	Nonstriated, paramyosin	+	+
Oyster (less tonic adductor)	Nonstriated, paramyosin	+	+
Pecten (tonic adductor)	Nonstriated, paramyosin	+	+
(striated adductor)	Striated	+	−
Mytilus (ABRM)	Nonstriated, paramyosin	+	+
(adductor)	Smooth, mixed	+	+
Helix (foot)	Smooth, paramyosin	−	+
Sepia (mantle)	Smooth, helical	+	−
Octopus (arm)	Not known	+	−
Annelids			
Lumbricus (body wall)	Nonstriated, helical	+	+
Arenicola (body wall)	Nonstriated, helical	+	
Arthropods			
Lobster (abdomen)	Striated	+	
Vertebrates			
Tropomyosin has been found in all muscles, striated, smooth, and cardiac. Paramyosin is not found in vertebrate muscle.			

* For references see Hanson and Lowy (1960; 1964).

et al., 1963) but the size varies according to species. It appears that paramyosin is a dimer consisting of two α-helices packed side by side. Paramyosin filaments are characterized by a repeating structure with dimensions of 5×145 Å (Bear, 1944; Hall et al., 1945). An electron-micrograph of paramyosin is given in Figure 10-13. Thin and thick filaments from the adductor of *Crassostrea angulata* are shown in Figure 10-14. The thick filaments in this case are paramyosin filaments 1.5 μ long and 120 Å in diameter.

The amino acid composition of tropomyosin is unusual in that proline and tryptophan are lacking, whereas dicarboxylic acids are present in high concentration (Kominz et al., 1954). Although the amino acid composition of some myosins, for example, dog heart myosin (Iyengar and Olson, 1965) and rabbit myosin (Kominz et al., 1954) have been determined, as yet very little is known about primary, secondary, or tertiary structures in the contractile proteins.

10-10. Other Proteins Associated with Contractility. Aside from the three major proteins associated with contractile function and some of the enzymes associated with energy metabolism in muscle, very little is known about other muscle proteins that are present in smaller amounts in muscle and that may play roles in contractility.

The superprecipitation of natural actomyosin is inhibited by chelating agents such as EDTA or EGTA, which remove divalent ions from solution, but reconstituted actomyosin (prepared by mixing purified actin and myosin solutions) is very erratic in this respect. Ebashi et al. (1964) found a protein component of muscle that restores the EDTA-induced inhibition of reconstituted actomyosin as well as that of trypsin-treated actomyosin. This is the protein troponin, mentioned in the preceding section. This was the first indication that this protein was involved in Ca^{2+} binding and activity in muscle.

Maruyama (1965a) discovered a protein that

influences the network formation of F-actin. This protein, β-actinin, controls the length of F-actin filaments formed in solution. Whereas normally, in the absence of this protein, the polymerization of G-actin leads to very long

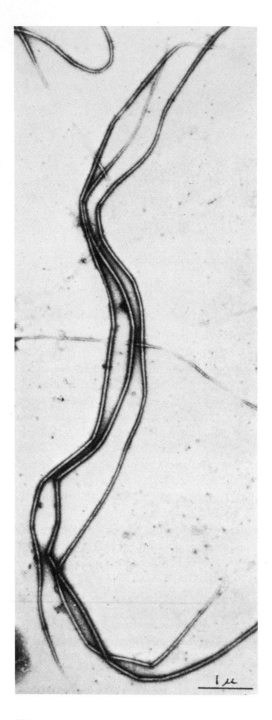

$1\,\mu$

F-actin filaments, the presence of β-actinin limits the filament length to about $1\,\mu$. This happens to be the length of the actin filaments on either side of the Z-line in rabbit psoas muscle, and therefore, this protein may play a physiological role in regulating actin filament length. Ebashi and Ebashi (1965) isolated another protein, α-actinin, which increases the rate of actin polymerization and may control the network formation of F-actin in muscle.

There obviously exists in muscle a variety of proteins associated with the main contractile event. And there are also proteins which regulate the formation and interaction of the major protein filaments.

The study of contractile proteins from nonmuscle cells is limited by the small amount of such protein present in these nonspecialized cells (nonspecialized for contraction). It has been very difficult to extract and purify such proteins from the mass of other materials present.

Blood platelets physiologically are responsible for initiating clot contraction—the extent of the contraction depending on the number of platelets present. Blood platelets are relatively easy to collect and purify in large numbers and, lacking a nucleus, protein preparations free of nucleoproteins can be prepared from these cells. A contractile protein, thrombosthenin, is present in relatively high concentration in platelets (Bettex-Galland and Luscher, 1965). It is extractable by the same solution used for muscle actomyosin. It superprecipitates at ionic strengths of about 0.1 in the presence of ATP and Mg^{2+}, and it is similar to other actomyosin-like ATPase enzymes in the conditions required for activity.

A protein, dynein, has been isolated from the cilia of *Tetrahymena pyriformis* and is

Figure 10-13 Electronmicrograph showing three paramyosin filaments isolated from the anterior byssus retractor muscle of *Mytilus edulis*. The ends of the filaments taper. Negatively stained preparation made from glycerol-extracted muscle. Magnification = 15,000X. [By permission from J. Lowy and J. Hanson (1962) "Ultrastructure of invertebrate smooth muscle" *Physiological Reviews* 42 (Suppl.): 34-47.]

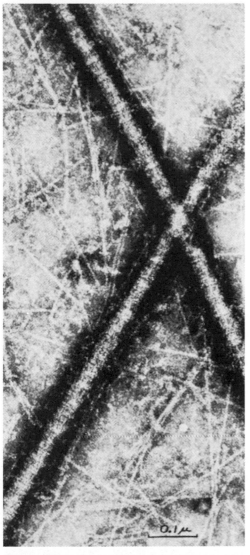

Figure 10-14 Electron micrograph showing the two kinds of filaments isolated from the contractile apparatus of the opaque part of the adductor muscle of *Crassostrea angulata*. The numerous actin-containing filaments are variable in length, because they are broken. Some lie alongside the two paramyosin filaments, which bear projections. One of the paramyosin filaments shows a tapered end. Preparation made from glycerol-extracted muscle and negatively stained with potassium phosphotungstate. Magnification = 152,000X. [By permission from J. Lowy and J. Hanson (1962) "Ultrastructure of invertebrate smooth muscles" *Physiological Reviews* **42** (Suppl.): 34-47.]

thought to be part of the contractile mechanism of these cellular organelles. It exhibits ATPase activity similar to that of striated muscle actomyosin (Gibbons and Rowe, 1965). Two fractions of this protein have been prepared by ultracentrifugation. One fraction consists of rodlike particles 70 to 90 Å in diameter. These are linear polymers of a smaller globular unit. The monomer has a molecular weight of about 600,000. Both fractions possess similar ATPase activity.

As mentioned in Section 10-1, contractile proteins are often referred to as mechano-enzymes, and because of the widespread nature of contractile events, including the activities of membranes, a wide variety of such proteins must exist. The ones isolated and studied up to this time are very similar to the actomyosin of striated skeletal muscle.

The Mechanism of Muscular Contraction

10-11. The Sliding Filament Hypothesis. From a variety of light and electron microscope observations, as well as from the results of x-ray diffraction studies, Hanson and Huxley (1955) proposed the sliding filament model of muscular contraction. This model, which is generally accepted today, states that contraction depends on the presence of two sets of filaments in the contractile cell and that by the actions of cross-bridges connecting the two sets of filaments for at least part of the contractile cycle, the actin filaments are caused to slide past the myosin filaments thus producing a shortening of the sarcomere or the development of tension.

Lateral extension of the myosin molecules are seen to project outward from the thick filaments in the electron microscope. These cross-bridges are presumed to operate in a cyclic manner; alternately attaching and detaching from the actin filaments. During their time of attachment, they move in such a manner as to pull the actin filaments past the myosin and deeper into the A-band. This reaction is mediated by ATP, which is hydrolyzed

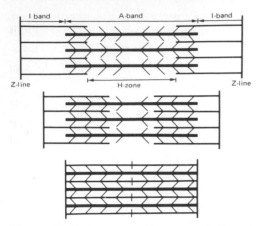

Figure 10-15 Diagrammatic representation of the nature of contraction according to the sliding filament hypothesis. As shown in the middle and lower illustrations, shortening is the result of the inward movement of actin filaments into the A-band, drawing the Z-lines of each sarcomere inward.

at some point in the cycle. Such a movement of cross-bridges is difficult to model in molecular terms, and although some complex models have been formulated, (for example, Davies, 1963) there is yet no satisfactory explanation for the observed movement of filaments (see, however, Section 10-12).

The sliding filament model, although based on structures visible only in the electron microscope or by x-ray diffraction analysis, has confirmation in certain light microscope observations. As shown in Figure 10-15, during contraction the actin filaments slide past the myosin filaments into the H-zone region. Early light microscope studies had shown that during contraction so-called contraction bands appear. These new dark bands are the result of the inward movement of the Z-lines, pulled, through attachment to the actin filaments, toward the A-band. As contraction becomes maximal there is a pileup of the Z-line material at the borders of the A-band (Hodge, 1956). Also it can be seen that during shortening, the A-band remains of constant length, whereas the I-bands disappear at maximal shortening as the actin filaments move into the A-band.

In the early days of muscular contraction

studies it was thought that shortening of a muscle resulted from a shortening of the contractile proteins themselves. At about this time, it had been shown that keratin could shorten and lengthen and that this activity was based on structural alterations between the α-helix and the extended form of the molecule (see Chapter 2). However, x-ray diffraction studies showed that in frog muscle and in mussel (*Mytilus edulis*) muscle there was no change in the axial spacing of the fibers during shortening. Since axial spacing is a measure of the atomic arrangements in a molecule or fiber, a lack of change in the spacing meant that during contraction the protein molecules themselves could not be shortening or coiling.

10-12. Operation of the Cross-Bridges. The actin and myosin filaments in the A-band are separated by a gap of about 130 Å, and early electron microscope studies showed that the cross-bridges, extending from the myosin molecules linked the two sets of filaments together. Since cross-bridges were seen in the H-zone of relaxed or stretched sarcomeres, where actin filaments were absent, it was known that the cross-bridges were part of the myosin molecule structure. The dimensions of the cross-bridges were found to be 40 to 50 Å in width and about 120 Å long. They were considered to be formed of the HMM portion of the myosin molecule because shadow-casting techniques (see Section 3-3) showed that isolated HMM molecules possessed a globular region about 40 to 50 Å wide by about 200 Å long and a tail region about 400 Å long. The cross-bridges of the sarcomere filaments were thought to consist of the globular head region of the HMM whose tail region lay parallel to the backbone of the filament. Since HMM possessed both the ATPase and the actin-combining activities of myosin, it made sense that this region should be the one forming the cross-bridges that interacted with the actin filaments during contraction.

A major problem concerns the mechanism by which the cross-bridges bring about a sliding of the actin filaments. It must be assumed that at some time during the

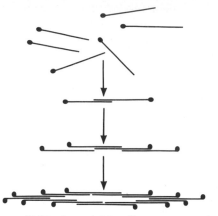

Figure 10-16 A model for the arrangement of components in the myosin filament. Light mero-myosin forms the backbone of the filament, and heavy meromyosin forms the movable cross-bridge. The orientation of myosin molecules must be different on each side of the center in order to permit actin filaments to move inward from each side of the sarcomere (see Figure 10-17).

contractile process the bridges of the myosin filaments attach to the actin. Sliding of the actin filaments could be achieved by a cyclic back and forth movement of the cross-bridges, making and breaking contact with sites on the actin filaments and sliding them inward. Or there might be some internal changes in the actin filaments, which enable them to move along rigidly fixed cross-bridges. The former hypothesis is favored.

A simple schematic of the arrangement of myosin molecules forming the myosin filament is shown in Figure 10-16. Myosin molecules

must be arranged with a different orientation on either side of the center so that actin filaments from either side of the sarcomere can be moved inward during contraction.

Figure 10-17a shows the necessary relations between myosin filaments and actin filaments if a sliding of filaments from either side of the sarcomere is to occur. Figure 10-17b shows the dimensions and arrangement of cross-bridges on the myosin filaments. The cross-bridges are positioned helically about the myosin filament. It is doubtful that the cross-bridges could be rigidly fixed in position and still be capable of connecting to and moving the actin filaments.

During contraction, the filament lattice maintains a constant volume (this is also true of the whole muscle). As the sarcomere shortens, the filaments move farther apart, thus increasing the interfilament spacing. In frog skeletal muscle the interfilament spacing increases by about 18 per cent as the sarcomere shortens from 2.8 μ to 2.0 μ. In the resting muscle the distance between centers of actin and myosin filaments is about 210 Å. This distance increases to about 250 Å during shortening. 250 Å is too large a distance for interactions between protein molecules to occur unless the cross-bridges are flexible and can continue to bridge this gap (Elliot et al., 1965). The cause of interfilament spacing changes lies in the long-range electrostatic forces existing between the protein filaments (Rome, 1967, 1968). Any factor that changes the degree of overlap between actin and myosin filaments

Figure 10-17 (a) Showing the arrangement of myosin molecules in the thick filament in more detail. LMM forms the backbone of the thick filament, and HMM forms the cross-bridge. The orientation of myosin molecules is different on each side of the center so that actin filaments can move from both sides of the sarcomere. (b) Model of the myosin filament showing the helical arrangement of cross-bridges along the filament.

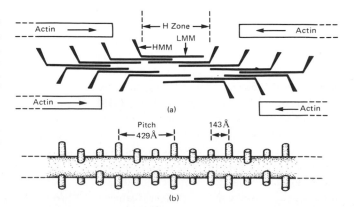

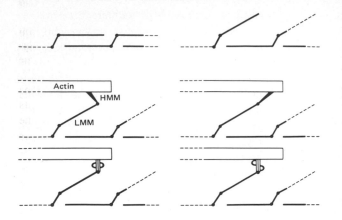

Figure 10-18 (Upper) A model for the arrangement of components in the myosin filament. LMM forms the backbone of the filament, and while HMM, through its S_2 component, forms a movable joint at the HMM–LMM junction. The globular head, formed by the S_1 component of HMM, can attach to actin over a range of different interfilament spacings while maintaining the same orientation. (Middle) Sliding of the actin filaments may be accomplished by movement of the globular head, swinging the attached actin filament inward or (Lower) by relative movements of two subunits of the globular head.

(such as shortening) will change the value of the electrostatic forces between the filaments. Such forces are thought to provide a cushion along which the filaments slide, a necessity for providing a low internal friction between filaments so that muscles can contract rapidly and efficiently.

The spacing between attachment sites on actin filaments and the spacing of cross-bridges on myosin filaments are not the same. Since these sites are not in alignment on the two filaments, rigid cross-bridges appear impossible. Thin filaments are composed of a double helical array of actin molecules. It is a nonintegral helix with subunits repeating at intervals of about 55 Å along either chain. The chains of the helix are staggered with respect to one another by 27.3 Å. The pitch of the helix is 720 Å. These dimensions may be compared with the spacing of cross-bridges on myosin filaments shown in Figure 10-17.

It has been proposed that the cross-bridges can move at two joints (Figure 10-18). Under these conditions cross-bridges could attach to actin filaments with their nonaligned attachment sites and remain attached even when the interfilament spacing changed. As indicated in Figure 10-18 the linear portion of the HMM segment of the myosin molecule lies parallel to the backbone of the thick filament but can also extend outward at various angles. The globular head of the HMM segment can also move in order to maintain a proper orientation for attachment to the sites on the actin filament.

To produce movement of the actin filaments, the globular portion of the HMM subfragment might either tilt (Figure 10-18, lower left) or undergo a more complicated sliding action (Figure 10-18, lower right). Such models satisfy two necessary conditions for shortening. The force for shortening must be produced as a result of precisely determined structural changes in the protein complex and be associated with the hydrolysis of ATP; and this mechanism must be capable of operating over changing interfilament distances.

The mechanisms just described are hypothetical and remain to be proven or disproven. X-ray diffraction techniques are best suited for analyzing the changes that occur during shortening.

10-13. Alternative Models of Contraction. A number of observations seem to contradict the sliding filament model, but most of these are explained away as quickly as they arise. I shall discuss some of the evidence that at first seemed to contradict this model and some of the other difficulties with the model.

The term **contraction** refers to the overall activity of a muscle upon stimulation and includes both the shortening or the tension developing phase and the relaxation phase. When a muscle is allowed to shorten, the contraction is **isotonic** because the tension of the muscle remains relatively constant throughout the activity. When a muscle is not allowed to shorten, for example if it is held to a spring or similar device, the contraction is **isometric** (constant length) and the muscle develops tension. In the body muscles must undergo a contraction that is neither purely isotonic nor purely isometric because, athough most muscles actually shorten, they do so against the pull of elastic ligaments or antagonistic muscles.

In an isotonic contraction, according to the sliding filament hypothesis, the actin filaments must move past the myosin filaments into the H-zone of the A-band. The maximal shortening that can be developed depends upon the relative length of the I- and A-bands. If the two bands are of equal length, the maximal amount of shortening possible is about 50 per cent of rest length, because the I-band filaments could move completely into the A-band. This is the situation in most vertebrate skeletal muscles.

At the other extreme are many insect flight muscles in which the I-band is extremely short and the amount of shortening is very small because the thin filaments are not long enough to advance very far into the A-band. These are muscles which oscillate rapidly between shortening and relaxation, each cycle is rapid and of small spatial extent (see Section 10-32).

An exception to the relationship between sarcomere band lengths and maximal possible shortening was found in certain muscles of the barnacle, *Balanus nubilis*. These muscles can shorten down to a very small fraction of their rest length, a seeming invalidation of the sliding filament hypothesis. However, it is now known from electron microscope studies that this can occur because myosin filaments of adjacent sarcomeres overlap. The thick filaments pass through perforations in the Z-line region (Hoyle and McAlear, 1963) during contraction.

Within the error of experimental technique, it has been found that muscles shorten to a degree predicted by the lengths of the A- and I-bands on the basis of the sliding filament model. As well, they may have some specialized morphological arrangement that permits greater shortening.

The sliding filament hypothesis does not, as

yet, satisfactorily explain contraction of smooth muscles, where little evidence for the existence of a double set of filaments has been found. But this lack of evidence depends more on the difficulties of studying smooth muscle cells than the actual lack of a double filament arrangement. There is suggestive evidence that smooth muscle (Alexander, 1967; Lane, 1965), invertebrate nonstriated muscle (Bagby, 1966; Lowy et al., 1966), and cilia (Satir, 1967) all operate on principles compatible with the sliding filament model.

An isometric contraction should develop tension proportional to the number of cross-bridges involved in the contractile event. It has long been known that stretching a muscle decreases the amount of tension it can develop when stimulated. Such stretching decreases the number of possible contacts between the thin and thick filaments by reducing the length along which they could interact. The greater the number of chemical links established between the actin and myosin filaments, the greater should be the tension developed in a stimulated muscle. Elegant studies by Gordon et al. (1964) showed that in a small region of a single sarcomere, this is exactly the situation. The tension developed is directly proportional to the degree of overlap of the A- and I-band filaments (see Section 10-25). The results of these workers have been the best corroborative evidence for the sliding filament model at the sarcomere level of structure (see Figure 10-31).

Although all tension development should cease when a fiber is stretched to a point where no cross-bridge formation is possible, under such conditions of stretch there is always some small, unexplained amount of tension found upon stimulation. This tension could exist because some sarcomeres of the fiber are not fully stretched and thus are still able to develop a slight amount of tension. Stretching a muscle fiber is not necessarily going to stretch out fully all the thousands of sarcomeres present.

Mechanically, it is difficult to see how the cross-bridges, arranged generally perpendicular to the long axis of the sliding filaments, can efficiently cause a sliding or resist shearing forces. Hoyle (1967), for example, feels that the sliding filament model might require the inclusion of other filaments, such as the T-filaments, to account for all the activities during contraction. Morales (1965) proposed a model in which contraction occurs as the result of myosin molecules sliding past other myosin molecules in the thick filaments. Other models involving electrostatic forces, and electrical forces have also been proposed (see Katchalsky, 1954).

A major difficulty with all of these models is the lack of knowledge concerning the actual nature of the contractile proteins as they exist in the muscle and the nature of the energy reactions used to produce the contractile event.

10-14. Excitation-Contraction Coupling. There must be some link between the passage of an action potential along the muscle membrane and the onset of contractile activity in the fibrils. This linkage is referred to as **excitation-contraction coupling**.

Striated muscle cells in vertebrates are generally innervated by only one motor axon terminal, and a nerve impulse passing down the motor axon causes a synaptic potential at the end plate that in turn initiates an action potential that spreads over the muscle membrane. This action potential has reached its peak at about the time that latency relaxation is occurring in the muscle (Figure 10-19). The latent period is that time interval between the delivery of a stimulus to the muscle and the beginning of the visible contraction. During this period the muscle may lengthen slightly before shortening commences.

Although any treatment that causes a sufficient depolarization of the muscle membrane can result in a contraction, there is no easy way of explaining how the potential change itself could directly activate the contractile elements, especially those located deep within the fiber. Nor can there be any direct influence by electrical currents established in the muscle by a depolarization because it has been shown that contraction results when a uniform depolarization of the fiber surface—conditions under which no current flows are established—

is produced by immersing a muscle fiber in high [K+] solutions (Kuffler, 1949).

Nor can the simple diffusion of some substance released by the surface membrane during depolarization cause contraction. The fibers of most vertebrate skeletal muscles are at least 100 μ in diameter—a distance too great for diffusion to operate at the rate at which a muscle is activated. To produce an effective mechanical force, all parts of the fiber should enter the active state simultaneously—an effect which diffusion could not accomplish over these distances. These statements apply only to vertebrate fast striated muscles. In the so-called slow fibers and in the muscles of invertebrates as well as in nonstriated muscles, such mechanisms can operate because of a different type of innervation and other morphological differences.

By using microelectrodes that stimulated only very small selected regions of a sarcomere, it was shown that the passage of small localized currents caused contraction only when the region in the vicinity of the Z-line was stimulated (A. F. Huxley, 1957; Huxley and Taylor, 1958). The resulting contraction spread out over the two half I-bands on either side of the stimulated Z-line; but did not spread elsewhere along the fiber. No response was obtained when the microelectrode was placed in the

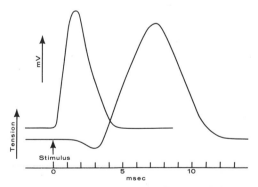

Figure 10-19 The temporal relations of the action potential and muscle tension development in a twitch muscle. As indicated the action potential is nearly over before the muscle begins its contraction phase. The initial dip in the muscle contraction is the latency-relaxation period.

A-band region. These results are for frog skeletal muscle. When similar experiments were repeated with crab muscles it was found that the excitable region was not at the Z-line but near the A-I boundary. When the membrane is depolarized at this point, only the adjacent half-I-band contracts.

With the knowledge of these physiological differences between the two types of muscle, the electron microscope was used to see if any detectable morphological differences existed at the Z-lines and A-I junctions. In frog muscle the terminal cisternae of the sarcoplasmic reticulum of the triad system were found at the Z-line only. In crab muscles equivalent structures were found only at the A-I boundary. Therefore, these structures seemed implicated in the excitation-contraction coupling mechanism.

Heilbrunn and Wiercinski (1947), Niedergerke (1955), and others showed that microinjection of Ca^{2+} into a fiber resulted in a reversible contraction. Mg^{2+} or other ions, or ATP had no effect. Microinjection of Ca^{2+} was effective only at the Z-line of frog semitendinosus muscle in producing a contraction. And Ca^{2+} was effective only at the A-I boundary of crab muscle. This was further evidence that Ca^{2+} was involved in the contractile triggering mechanism.

In some manner the passage of an action potential over the membrane of the muscle triggers the release of Ca^{2+} from the sarcoplasmic reticulum. The release of Ca^{2+} throughout the muscle fiber causes a rapid activation of the myofilaments. The T-system of the fiber forms direct connections between all parts of the sarcomere and its outer surface, and the action potential can reach inner parts of the fiber and the parts of the sarcoplasmic reticulum located there. These membranous systems are discussed by Smith (1966).

An indication that the T-system penetrates through all parts of the muscle fiber comes from the use of ferritin as an electron microscopic stain (Ferritin is a protein used for the storage and control of iron. It is found in the liver, spleen, bone marrow, and intestinal mucosa. Ferritin is used as an electron stain and tracer substance because of the presence of the electron-dense iron and the large size of the molecule. The iron, in the form of ferric hydroxides forms a central core of about 100 Å in diameter, surrounded by a protein shell. The protein portion of the molecule, called apoferritin, has a molecular weight of about 465,000). It was found that when ferritin was placed into a solution bathing a muscle fiber it penetrated deeply into the fiber. Since the molecule is too large to pass through the muscle membrane, it could only have moved deeply into the fiber through the T-system formed by invagination of the surface membrane.

The terminal cisternae of the sarcoplasmic reticulum can accumulate calcium ions and can release these ions when an action potential passes over the membrane. During the stimulation of toad muscles there is a transient appearance of Ca^{2+} in the sarcoplasm as evidenced by spectrophotometric techniques (Jöbsis and O'Connor, 1966). This calcium appears at the time of the onset of latency-relaxation and at the time of the volume increase of the fiber. Ca^{2+} moves from the I-band to the A-band during activity. At the A-band it is picked up by longitudinal elements of the sarcoplasmic reticulum. After several minutes this Ca^{2+} is returned to the terminal cisternae. It appears that the longitudinal elements actively uptake Ca^{2+}, whereas the terminal cisternae store and release it as necessary. Other studies have shown that the uptake of Ca^{2+} by this system can reduce the Ca^{2+} concentration of the muscle fiber to below 2×10^{-8} molar, sufficient to cause relaxation of the actomyosin system.

As stated in Section 10-8, during relaxation Ca^{2+} concentration is low in the muscle fiber. Upon stimulation, the release of Ca^{2+} and its rapid diffusion into the myofilament spaces causes the activation of myosin-ATPase. This is accomplished it would appear not directly but by the action of Ca^{2+} upon troponin, which is present in the thin filaments. Troponin acts as a safety mechanism. Although its mode of functioning is not as yet known, it may, upon the presence of Ca^{2+}, allow the myosin crossbridges to interact with the actin, simultaneously permitting the actomyosin-ATPase to hydrolyze ATP.

Research in this area is active for much remains to be discovered about the mechanisms responsible for the uptake and release of Ca^{2+}, the actual role of the T-system and the sarcoplasmic reticulum, the molecular basis for the activity of troponin, and the nature of the spread of the action potential through the T-system (see Ebashi and Endo, 1968; Sandow, 1965). Similar systems to those discussed above have been found in crustacean muscle (Selverston, 1967); in barnacle muscle; and in mouse muscle (Edwards and Lorkovic, 1967).

Energetic and Thermal Aspects of Muscular Contraction

10-15. The Energy Source for Contraction. Muscle, like other cells, depends basically upon the glycolytic pathway and the TCA cycle-cytochrome system to supply energy in the form of ATP for its activities. In muscle there is a great dependence on the glycolytic system to provide energy for contraction under anoxic conditions—which often occur when a muscle is engaged in vigorous activity and oxygen cannot be supplied rapidly enough for aerobic metabolism to supply energy. These schemes of energy metabolism have been discussed in Chapter 4 and require no further detailed consideration here (see also Jöbsis, 1964).

A more important question concerns the nature of the direct energy source for muscular contraction. Since metabolic pathways result in the production of ATP and since actomyosin is an ATPase enzyme, it is usually considered that ATP is the direct energy source for the contractile process. However, this assumption has been very difficult to prove by direct measurements. Although in the following discussion it will be assumed that ATP is the direct energy source, it should be noted that at present the actual role of ATP or its high energy in the contractile process is not known. The mechanism by which chemical energy is transformed into the mechanical energy of contraction is still a mystery.

10-16. Phosphagens and ATP. A discussion of the energetics of muscular contraction and the nature of the evidence for assuming that ATP is the direct energy source is best introduced by considering the history of theories of muscular contraction. The attempts to discover the energy source of contraction led not only to the discovery of many important muscle constituents for which roles had to be found but were also the beginnings of the detailed analysis of metabolic pathways. The energetics of muscular contraction have been the topic of many recent reviews (Carlson, 1963; Wilkie, 1960, 1966). Many aspects of the development of muscle theory are presented from an interesting point of view by Ernst (1958).

In 1907 Fletcher and Hopkins showed that lactic acid production accompanies muscular fatigue and death rigor under anaerobic conditions. By 1914 it had been demonstrated that muscle lactic acid was derived from the breakdown of muscle glycogen. Meyerhof in the early 1920's showed that the work done, the tension developed, or the heat produced by a muscle were all proportional to the lactic acid production under anaerobic conditions. During this period A. V. Hill (see Section 10-18) found that during the contraction cycle there is an initial phase of heat production that is not affected by the presence of oxygen. These various facts formed the basis for the lactic acid theory of muscular contraction—basically the idea that the formation of lactic acid from carbohydrate was the only energy providing reaction for contraction.

But in 1930 Lündsgaard found that muscles poisoned with iodoacetic acid (IAA) contract normally without producing any lactic acid; therefore, lactic acid was not needed for contraction. We know now that IAA specifically blocks the glycolytic pathway by inhibiting the enzyme glyceraldehydephosphate dehydrogenase.

Phosphagens such as phosphocreatine (CP) were discovered by Fiske and SubbaRow (1929) and by Eggleton and Eggleton (1927) (see Section 5-7). Tension development was shown to be proportional to the amount of creatine phosphate breakdown and it was found that CP was broken down and resynthesized during a contraction cycle under anaerobic conditions. The creatine phosphate theory of muscular contraction arose at this time and assumed that CP was the direct energy source for vertebrate muscle contraction. Arginine phosphate was thought to play this role in invertebrate muscles.

In 1929 Fiske and SubbaRow, and independently Lohman, discovered another organic phosphate compound in muscle, later identified as ATP. ATP, like CP, has a high heat of hydrolysis and ATP was also a required factor in glycolysis. Because ATP was found to be hydrolyzed by actomyosin, it was decided that ATP, not CP, was the direct energy source. It was not until the mid 1960's that the roles of these two phosphate compounds were established, at least in one or two muscles.

10-17. Interactions of Muscle Organophosphates. By 1936 it was shown that in addition to the hydrolysis of ATP into ADP and inorganic phosphate there also occurred in muscle the reaction:

$$ADP + CP \rightleftharpoons ATP + C$$

catalyzed by the enzyme creatine kinase [ATP: creatine phosphotransferase; E.C. 2.7.3.2]. This reversible reaction could serve to replenish the supply of ATP by rephosphorylating any ADP produced during contraction. Also free creatine could be phosphorylated at the expense of ATP produced in energy metabolism. This particular reaction is a complicating factor in establishing which compound is actually used during contraction because creatine kinase is extremely rapid in its catalytic activity, and, if ATP is split during contraction, the ADP formed is almost instantaneously rephosphorylated.

Biochemical experiments also showed that AMP can be used as a substrate for rephosphorylating ADP, but it was later found that the enzyme myokinase [ATP:AMP phosphotransferase; E.C. 2.7.4.3; adenylate kinase] is present in muscle and can form ADP and ATP, thus allowing the creatine kinase reaction to proceed. Myokinase appears to have no direct role in the contractile event. Since the creatine kinase reaction requires the presence of some ADP, the concentration of ADP in muscle could play a role in the control of the creatine kinase activity and of the contractile process, as it does in mitochondrial and sarcosomal oxidative phosphorylation (see Chapter 4; also Slater, 1960; Needham, 1964).

It was the discovery of these various organophosphates and the need to explain their roles and methods of production that led to the elucidation of the metabolic pathways now recognized to function in energy metabolism.

As in other types of physiological studies, the use of specific inhibitors has proven of value in assessing the roles of creatine phosphate and ATP in muscle activity. Dinitrofluorobenzene (DNFB) specifically inhibits creatine kinase, thus preventing the possibility of rephosphorylation of any ADP produced during contraction (Infante and Davies, 1965; Dydynska and Wilkie, 1966). As previously mentioned IAA may be used to prevent ATP formation through the glycolytic pathway; fluoride is also sometimes used for this purpose. Treatment of a muscle with pure nitrogen gas serves to provide anaerobic conditions and to block oxidative phosphorylation. Dinitrophenol (DNP) an uncoupler of oxidative-phosphorylation reduces CP levels in muscle and also prevents further ATP production through the cytochrome system.

The action of DNP is not completely understood, and there are indications that it may directly effect part of the contractile mechanism since relaxation is inhibited in its presence although contraction is not. Except for DNP, the enzyme inhibitors listed above produce no direct effects on the contractile mechanism, and a stimulated muscle undergoes normal contraction cycles in their presence until all stores of ATP and CP are exhausted.

The role of CP appears to be that of a storage molecule for high-energy phosphate groups. It is present in relatively large quantities, as a storage molecule should be, for example, ~ 30 μmoles/gram in frog sartorius muscle. During contraction, under conditions when insufficient oxygen enters the muscle to provide optimal operation of oxidative-phosphorylation pathways, any ADP produced by ATP hydrolysis is immediately rephosphorylated by the creatine kinase system. During the recovery period following contraction, oxidative phosphorylation can efficiently rephosphorylate all ADP to ATP and thus indirectly rephosphorylate any creatine present. This is the period of the so-called oxygen debt, when sufficient oxygen must be supplied to rephosphorylate all ATP used during contraction.

ATP has been shown to participate in the contractile event in a direct manner in at least a few muscles. Its energy is probably used to achieve some conformational change in the actomyosin structure that can lead to the sliding of the thin filaments. Note that as stated in Chapter 4, the hydrolysis of ATP by actomyosin is not sufficient to provide energy for contraction because simple splitting of ATP in solution would release the energy of ATP as useless heat. ATP must attach in some manner to the contractile proteins and produce a change in them. ATP bears four negative charges, whereas ADP bears only three, and it has been suggested by several workers that such a difference in charge might produce electrostatic effects that could alter the contractile proteins. The importance of electrostatic charges to the sliding of filaments has already been indicated in Section 10-12.

ATP is compartmented in the muscle fiber and perhaps CP also. Since glycolysis occurs in the cytoplasm and oxidative phosphorylation in the sarcosomes, the flow of high-energy phosphates is complicated, and complex controls exist over the entire system. It might also be noted that other ATPase enzymes, besides actomyosin, are found in muscle. In order to study ATP hydrolysis by the contractile proteins, appropriate controls must be maintained over sarcosomal, sarcoplasmic reticulum, and sarcolemmal ATPases.

The lactic acid produced by glycolysis during muscular contraction is, in most cases, transported back to the circulatory system and moved to the liver, where it is converted back to glucose or glycogen. An exception to this is found in frog muscles, where lactic acid is converted back to glucose in the muscles themselves. Little is known about the fates of metabolic products in the invertebrate muscles.

10-18. Heat Production. In the early part of this century, interest arose in energy exchanges, especially those associated with heat machines, and thermodynamic analysis was firmly established. It became inevitable that biologists should begin to think of muscles as machines because muscles, unlike most other tissues, perform measurable mechanical work presumably by the transduction of chemical energy. Since the liberation of heat is associated with energy transformations, measuring the heat production during a contractile cycle is one method for determining the general nature of the succession of chemical and physical events underlying contraction.

A. V. Hill in Great Britain initiated a series of experiments in which the heat production of muscle under various conditions was measured. The quantitative relations between the time course of heat production and of total heat production to the work done, the load, or the amount of shortening of the muscle are of concern to the physiologist. Any theory of contraction must take into account the facts concerning muscle heat production. Nearly all knowledge of heat production in muscle comes from work with excised amphibian muscle.

Hill and his colleagues developed sensitive galvanometers to record the electrical currents produced by thermocouples (in the form of thermopiles—stacks of thermocouples) placed along a muscle. The electrical current varies according to temperature, which in turn is affected by the amount of heat produced by the muscle. Muscular contractions are recorded simultaneously. The thermopile does not detect all of the heat produced by a muscle, and various correction factors must be introduced which places some limitation on the accuracy.

The contraction of a muscle is accompanied by the liberation of heat in two major phases. The **initial heat** is liberated during the contraction-relaxation cycle (Figure 10-20). The **recovery heat** is liberated in the period

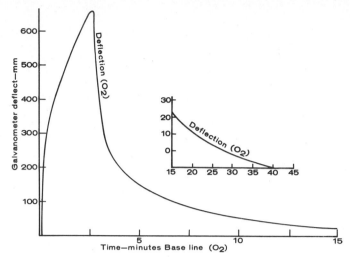

Figure 10-20 The heat production of a frog sartorius muscle during a series of twitches. The total heat produced is given by the area of the curve above its base line. The insert shows the later part of the heat production curve. [Redrawn from data of A. V. Hill (1949a).]

immediately following the contraction cycle. There is also a resting heat production—the basal metabolism of the muscle cell, which represents the normal metabolism that must be maintained to keep the cell in a living functional state.

If a muscle is stimulated to perform under anaerobic conditions, only the initial heat appears. The amount and the time course of initial heat production is independent of the presence of oxygen. Under anaerobic conditions, there is no recovery heat. Such heat results from the processes of glycolysis and oxidative-phosphorylation that restore the muscle to its normal state following contraction. Although the rate of recovery heat liberation is much slower than that of the initial heat, the recovery heat proceeds over a much longer period of time (sometimes for several minutes). Thus, the absolute magnitudes of initial and recovery heats are approximately equal.

Measurements of heat production or work output cannot yield quantitative information about the underlying chemical or physical changes unless the number of different chemical reactions proceeding simultaneously; the heat of reaction, ΔH, for each reaction, and the moles of reactant in each reaction, are known. The liberation of heat says very little about the nature of the underlying process. Heat production depends on the ratio of the ΔH to the ΔG of each reaction, and thus on

the nature of the entropy changes. A reaction that gives off heat in the forward direction does not absorb an equivalent amount of heat in the reverse direction (see Chapter 4; also Wilkie, 1960).

When a reaction is driven in the reverse direction by free energy supplied to it, usually more heat is liberated. At the present time there is not enough information available to relate initial heat of muscular contraction to specific mechanisms. But the nature of the heat liberation under various conditions helps in gaining clues as to the nature of the mechanisms and in indicating the nature of further experimentation needed.

The initial heat is divided into several stages: the **activation heat** (= **maintenance heat** in sustained contractions); the **shortening heat** liberated during the actual shortening of a muscle; and the **relaxation heat** produced at the end of an isotonic contraction when a muscle has done work by lifting a load.

10-19. Shortening Heat. Fenn in 1923 found that when a muscle was permitted to shorten so that it lifted a load and performed work, the amount of heat liberated was greater than that liberated during an isometric contraction. The additional heat liberated is the shortening heat.

In a classic paper A. V. Hill (1938) reported that the shortening heat is a simple linear function of the degree of shortening of a muscle and is independent of the load the

363

Figure 10-21 Total heat production of a frog sartorius muscle during isotonic tetanic contractions at 0°C. Curves a to d, the muscle was allowed to shorten different distances under a constant load of 1.9 g. (a) isometric, (b) 3.4 mm, (c) 6.5 mm, (d) 9.6 mm. Curves e to i, the muscle was allowed to shorten a constant distance of 6.5 mm under different loads. (e) isometric, (f) 31.9 g, (g) 23.7 g, (h) 12.8 g, (i) 1.9 g. With a constant load, the magnitude of the steep rise of the curves (the shortening heat) increased with the degree of shortening permitted by the experimental arrangement. Even an isometric tension shows some heat of shortening presumably due to the stretching of the series elastic components of the muscle. The displacements of curves b, c, and d from curve a, are proportional to the amount of shortening and represent the extra heat due to shortening. The maintenance heat is represented by the constant slope portion of the curves and is relatively constant for all conditions illustrated. [Replotted from data of A. V. Hill (1938).]

muscle lifts, the velocity of shortening, the work done, or the temperature. Shortening heat may be defined by

$$H_s = ax \qquad (10.1)$$

where a is the thermal constant related to the maximum tension, P_o, a muscle can develop at its rest length; and x is the distance the muscle shortens, in centimeters.

Frog sartorius muscle has been most often used for heat production experiments. This is a thin muscle that can readily be supplied with oxygen by aeration of the perfusion fluid. The muscle is functional at 0°C, where its slower response allows a better temporal resolution of the contractile events. The muscle is parallel fibered, and all fibers run the length of the muscle so that stimulation at any point causes a response in all fibers.

Figure 10-21 shows heat production curves recorded for the frog sartorius undergoing isotonic contractions (these are tetanic or sustained contractions produced by repeated high frequency stimulation of the muscle). The steep initial slopes of the curves represent the shortening heats when the muscle is allowed to shorten to various lengths. The later, less steep slopes represent the maintenance heats. Note that even in an isometric contraction there is some shortening heat. This is heat produced by the shortening of the contractile elements against the inert elastic components of the muscle including the sarco-

lemma and tendons. This demonstrates that the externally recorded or observable shortening (or tension development) is a reflection of internal unobservable changes in the muscle. Although no external shortening may appear when a muscle is stimulated, there may still be activity of the contractile filaments of the sarcomere.

The ratio a/P_o is a constant. Although both a and P_o depend on temperature, their ratio does not. a/P_o is 0.25 g/cm² for frog sartorius (see Table 10-4). The introduction of cross-sectional area permits comparison of this ratio in different muscles.

During an isometric contraction no work is done (a muscle can do work only during an isotonic contraction, where shortening of the muscle can lift a load), and the curves of Figure 10-20 show that the maintenance heat is constant for different loads.

The difference between the heat production of an isotonic and an isometric contraction is the shortening heat. The fact that shortening heat is independent of load indicates that when a muscle does do more work, energy must be produced by the muscle. This is the **extra energy liberation**, and the phenomenon is often called the Fenn effect (Fenn, 1923, 1924).

The rate of extra energy liberation, h, during an isotonic contraction is defined by

$$h = av \qquad (10.2)$$

Table 10-4 Some Thermal and Mechanical Constants of Muscles*

MAXIMAL SHORTENING VELOCITIES (MUSCLE LENGTHS PER SECOND)	
Toad sartorius (10°C)	1.5
Frog sartorius (27°C)	10
Rabbit uterus (37°C)	0.2
Locust flight muscle (30°C)	13
Mytilus ABRM (18°C)	0.3

MAXIMAL TETANUS TENSION (P_o)	
Frog sartorius muscle (0°C)	1.5 to 2.0 kg/cm²
Frog sartorius, single fibers (22°C)	3.5 kg/cm²
Rabbit skeletal muscle (37°C)	5.0 kg/cm² (Mammalian skeletal muscle is generally faster and can develop more tension than other animal muscles.)

HEAT PRODUCTION OF FROG MUSCLE	
Resting	6.3×10^{-5} cal/g-sec
Tetanic	2.0×10^{-1} cal/g-sec
Shortening heat	400 g-cm/cm²

HILL'S CONSTANTS		
a/P_o	0.32 (toad sartorius)	0.1 (smooth muscle)
	0.26 (frog sartorius)	
b	0.26 (toad sartorius)	
	0.33 (frog sartorius)	

* These data are given only to indicate the types of values found for these muscle characteristics. Skeletal muscle is usually faster in shortening than smooth muscle. Lower values of a/P indicate a better efficiency of the muscle. The data are taken from Hill (1938, 1964a); Ramsay (1960); Wilkie (1960); Csapo (1960).

v is the velocity of shortening. During shortening, with a load P, the work rate is vP gm-cm per second; and the total extra energy rate above the maintenance heat production is $(P + a)v$ gm-cm per second. By plotting the experimental values of this total energy rate against the load, a straight line is obtained with slope $-b$. The equation for this line is

$$(P + a)v = b(P_o - P) \qquad (10.3)$$

The symbol b is a constant having the signifi-

cance of an absolute rate of energy liberation and with the dimensions of centimeters per second, thus depending on muscle length. The equation states that the total energy liberation rate when work is done is proportional to the deficit of the load below the maximum and that the rate for extra heat production is proportional to the speed of shortening.

The reference length (sometimes called the rest length) of a muscle is about the maximum length of the muscle as it exists in the body of

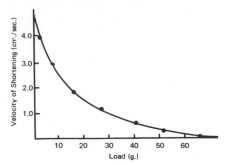

Figure 10-22 The force velocity curve for isotonic contractions of frog sartorius muscle. [Redrawn from data of A. V. Hill (1938).]

the animal. It is under a resting tension, l_o, at this length. At reference length maximum isometric tension is developed. All muscles are under a slight stretch in the animal; the excised muscle is therefore shorter than the reference length.

The more rapidly a muscle shortens, the less the load it can lift. The relation between velocity of shortening and the load lifted by a frog sartorius muscle is shown in Figure 10-22. Since the velocity of shortening during the contraction is constant, P is equivalent to the tension developed by a single isometric contraction of the muscle. Hill showed that the curve of Figure 10-22 can be expressed by the equation:

$$(P + a)(v + b) = \text{constant} \quad (10.4)$$

In an isometric tetanus no shortening occurs and the tension developed is P_o, therefore:

$$(P + a)(v + b) = b(P_o + a) \quad (10.5)$$

which refactored and rewritten is

$$(P + a)v = b(P_o - P) \quad (10.6)$$

identical to Equation 10.3.

Although this equation—the **characteristic equation of muscle**—is derived on an empirical basis and has no mechanistic meaning, it is still a useful one. Note that it can be derived by two independent types of measurements—mechanical and thermal. And, for example, a thermal constant a, can be derived from mechanical measurements because the force-velocity curve of a muscle is hyperbolic with asymptotes at $P = -a$ and $v = -b$.

The results and relationships described above came first from the analysis of brief tetani. Experimental work by Hill and others showed that similar results are obtained when single twitches are examined. In a single twitch the initial heat is made up of two components: the shortening heat and the activation heat. The latter is the same heat found in a tetanic contraction, where it is called the maintenance heat and is the sum of the activation heats of the individual contractions that make up the tetanus.

In recent years several workers have reported that shortening heat is actually dependent on load or work (see, for example, Carlson et al., 1963; Wilkie, 1966). But other results seem to restore the independence of shortening heat on load or amount of shortening (A. V. Hill, 1964a, b, c).

The source of the shortening heat is not known. A. V. Hill (1966), who is famous for making challenges to biochemists, asked them to discover the chemical basis for shortening heat. Davies et al. (1967) in partial answer to this challenge designed appropriate experiments and found that there is no concurrent hydrolysis of ATP at the time of the liberation of shortening heat, nor was any CP hydrolysis found at this time (Infante et al., 1965).

Shortening heat might represent heat liberated by the formation of new cross-bridges between actin and myosin (Davies, 1963). Another suggestion is that it arises as a result of a lateral expansion of the myofilament lattice (Peachey, 1968). The filament lattice, as already mentioned, remains at constant volume during shortening and therefore, as the sarcomere shortens, there must be a lateral expansion of the lattice. During such an expansion the myosin cross-bridges would have to extend across a wider interfilament space to make contact with the actin filaments. This type of expansion would be accompanied by entropy changes and possibly the liberation of heat.

10-20. Activation Heat. Activation heat production is initiated before shortening is observed in a stimulated muscle. A. V. Hill (1949) used toad semimembranosus muscles in his

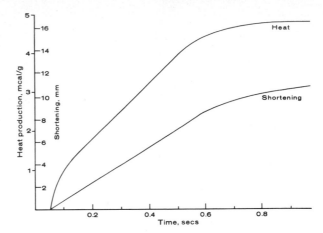

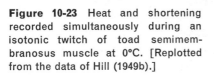

Figure 10-23 Heat and shortening recorded simultaneously during an isotonic twitch of toad semimembranosus muscle at 0°C. [Replotted from the data of Hill (1949b).]

analysis of the activation heat. They have a slower response time than frog muscles and therefore a better temporal resolution of results can be obtained. Figure 10-23 shows simultaneous records of shortening and heat production during an isotonic twitch. There is a brief rapid output of heat, preceding the initiation of shortening. The heat production continues during shortening, but at a slower rate. Thus, it appears that there are two components of the initial heat: the shortening heat and the activation heat. The activation heat of the twitch is of the same nature as the maintenance heat found during tetanic contractions.

The activation heat may be analyzed by comparing the heat productions and shortening of both preloaded and afterloaded muscles. A **preloaded** muscle is arranged to bear a load before it is stimulated and starts to shorten. It is slightly stretched by the load before stimulation. An **afterloaded** muscle is set up experimentally so that before stimulation it is at rest length and does not begin to bear a load until after shortening has begun.

The afterloaded muscle shortens less than the preloaded muscle and has a smaller shortening heat production. It was found experimentally that the shortening heat was independent of load and determined only by the amount of shortening. The activation heat can be calculated by subtracting the heat production of an afterloaded muscle from that of a nonafterloaded muscle. Since both shorten-

ing and heat production are measured for the two muscles it is possible to determine the shortening heat (Figure 10-24). Shortening heat in these muscles amounts to 5.25 gm-cm per cm. Recent measurements using a different method have given comparable results (Gibbs and Ricchiuti, 1965; Gibbs et al., 1966).

The source of activation heat is not known. The amount of ATP or CP split during the early stages of contraction is insufficient to account for the magnitude of the activation heat which amounts to about 40 per cent of the total initial heat (Davies et al., 1967; Jöbsis and Duffield, 1967). It might represent heat liberated during the release of calcium from the sarcoplasmic reticulum—the contractile triggering event. Or it might be due to length changes of the actin filaments.

10-21. The Active State. When a muscle is stimulated, it is obvious that a series of internal changes is initiated as the muscle goes from inactivity to activity. This new state of activity is called the **active state** (D. K. Hill, 1949). It is a conceptual model only, one that aids in studying the changes in activity level of the muscle. The nature of the changes are not known, although many associated phenomena have been observed.

As already mentioned, there is a slight drop in tension during the latency-relaxation period of an isometric twitch, followed by the onset of mechanical activity (Figure 10-25). At 0°C, stimulation of frog sartorius muscle produces

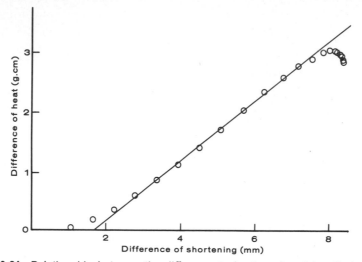

Figure 10-24　Relationship between the difference in heat produced by afterloaded and not afterloaded muscles and the difference in shortening. Slope of the linear portion of the curve gives the shortening heat, which is 5.25 g-cm/cm^2. [From data of Hill (1949b).]

no outward manifestation of response for about 7 msec. Then the tension drops slightly. After another 7 msec the tension begins to rise again. A. F. Huxley (1957) suggested that the drop in tension during latency-relaxation was because of a lengthening of the actin filaments prior to cross-bridge formation. Such a lengthening is difficult to detect in most muscles because most of the resting tension is due to the presence of inert elastic elements, and any small tension drop would go undetected.

D. K. Hill (1953) found a change in the transparency of a muscle during the initial stages of contraction, there being a transitory period of increased light transmittance through the muscle. There is a later change in the strength of the birefringence of polarized light that might be accounted for on the basis of water moving from the myofibrils into the sarcoplasm (Bozler and Cottrell, 1937). Following the latency-relaxation phase, there is a decrease in the amount of light scattered by the muscle. It should be noted that the role of water in muscular contraction is not known, although water makes up about 70 per cent of the mass of muscle.

The beginning of activity is accompanied by an increase in the resistance of the muscle to stretch. Hill (1949) found that during a rapid stretch the contractile system reaches its full peak of activity before the tension reaches its peak. Hill defined the active state as the tension that the contractile elements exert when they are neither shortening nor lengthening.

The active state decays with time, and Ritchie (1954) developed one method for measuring the decay. Frog sartorius muscles are released at various times after the start of an isometric twitch and allowed to shorten slightly. The tension at this shorter length is recorded. The nature of the results for frog sartorius and some other muscles are shown in Figure 10-26. In all cases the tension outlasts the active state, although muscles differ markedly in the extent to which this occurs (Hanson and Lowy, 1960).

Brown (1934, 1941, 1957) showed that the application of hydrostatic pressures of a few hundred atmospheres to a muscle during the early part of a twitch caused an increase in the peak tension developed, even when the pressure was removed before the muscle reached its peak tension. This activation was called the **alpha process**. Increased pressure might cause a lengthening of either set of filaments. This would result in a greater degree

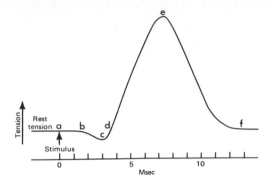

Figure 10-25 Diagrammatic representation of an isotonic twitch showing the various periods of the contraction cycle. Durations approximately correspond with those found for frog muscle at room temperature but may vary according to temperature, muscle, or nature of transducing instruments.

a to b: quiescent period of latent phase; a period between the application of the stimulus and the first observable signs of contractile activity.

b to c: relaxation phase of the latency-relaxation period; tension falls below the resting level.

c: the beginning of active contraction; tension begins to rise.

c to e: period of tension development.

e to f: period of relaxation; tension falls to resting level.

of filament overlap and a more rapid approach to the fully active state and a maximum of cross-bridge formation. The use of hydrostatic pressure is another means for determining the time course of the development and decay of the active state.

The application of pressures to various physiological systems is a valuable experimental tool, especially since pressure and volume changes can be treated by absolute reaction rate theory and related to basic thermodynamic variables (Johnson et al., 1954).

Another change accompanying activation is a transient increase in muscle volume, amounting to about 10^{-6} ml per gram (Abbot and Baskin, 1962; Baskin, 1964). This volume change reverses rapidly.

Evidently a variety of changes accompany the onset of contraction. The volume and light transmitting changes probably indicates alterations in the state or compartmentation of water, but little is known about these activities.

10-22. Relaxation and Relaxation Heat. It is usually assumed today that relaxation is a comparatively passive activity on the part of the contractile machinery. It is a return to an inactive state, and little energy expenditure is needed at this time. If a muscle has lifted a load, then the relaxation heat consists of the mechanical work dissipated as heat while the load is lowered.

Relaxation is brought on by the cessation of stimulation and the removal of Ca^{2+} by the sarcoplasmic reticulum as already discussed. During relaxation there is an alteration in the cross-bridges linking the action and myosin filaments. Usually relaxation is slow compared to the rate of rise of shortening or tension development. However, this is not the case in many striated twitch muscles, where the relaxation period is not much longer than the shortening phase.

Mechanical Properties of Muscle

10-23. Muscle Responses to Single Stimuli. The gastrocnemius muscle and the sartorius muscle of the frog have been favorite experimental objects in both research and teaching laboratories when the properties of muscle are to be studied, especially the mechanical properties. Figure 10-27 shows one type of student setup for measuring and recording muscle contractions. The classical recording instrument is the revolving drum or kymograph, while today various types of transducers are used which convert movement or tension development into electrical signals that can be observed on an oscilloscope or rapid penwriting instrument. The transducer-type of instrumentation is favored because of its greater sensitivity and freedom from friction. In the laboratory, electrical stimuli are commonly used to excite muscle because they cause little damage and are readily quantitated with respect to strength, duration, and frequency.

A muscle, such as the frog gastrocnemius, is a twitch muscle—capable of responding with a single all-or-none contraction of the type shown in Figure 10-25. In the case of frog

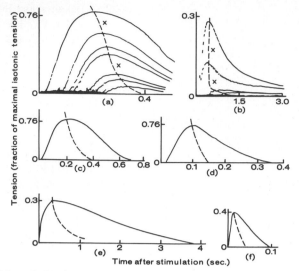

Figure 10-26 (a) and (b) Active state curves from experimental tension-time records. The active state is maximal even in a single twitch. After stimulation ends, the active state decays with time and at the peak of an isometric twitch, the tension exerted by the contractile elements represents the degree of activation remaining. (Hill, 1949b). (a) Tension development in frog sartorius muscle (0°C) following quick releases at different times during a twitch. Beginning of each curve is time of stimulation. Curve X—X drawn through peaks of contraction shows decline in active state. (b) Similar records for the pedal retractor muscle of *Mytilus edulis* (14°C). Note that tension outlasts active state. (c) to (f) When a muscle is released by a small amount at various times after the start of an isometric twitch and tension redevelops at the shorter lengths, the peak of each curve lies along the active state curve (Ritchie, 1954). Isometric twitches and active state curves are for (c) frog sartorius muscle (0°C). (d) Locust (*Schistocerca*) flight muscle (11°C). (e) *Mytilus edulis* pedal retractor muscle (14°C). (f) Tymbal muscle of the cicada *Platypleura* (30°C). In each case tension outlasts the active state although muscles differ in the extent to which this happens. [Adapted from Hanson and Lowy (1960) data from various sources.]

muscles, the simple twitch has a duration of about 0.1 second.

There are three main phases of the twitch: (1) the latent period, lasting about 0.01 seconds; (2) the contraction period of about 0.04 seconds; and (3) the relaxation period of about 0.05 seconds duration. Only with extremely sensitive and inertia-free instruments will the latency-relaxation phase be seen.

The twitch of a single muscle fiber is an all-or-none event (see Section 7-19 for a definition of all-or-none events). Stimuli below threshold strength produce no contractile response. In a whole muscle, such as the gastrocnemius, increasing the strength of the stimulus from subthreshold to threshold will produce a minimal response. Further increases of the stimulus strength will produce greater and greater con-

tractions until finally a maximal stimulus strength is reached that produces a maximal contractile response in the muscle. At maximal stimulus strength all fibers are responding since the thresholds of all fibers have now been reached. This sequence of events is the result of **spatial summation of contraction** and represents the fact that different fibers have different thresholds. Since the fibers are arranged in parallel in the muscle, at maximal stimulus strength all fibers contract, and the effects of their separate contractions summate to produce the total response of the muscle.

10-24. Muscle Responses to Repeated Stimuli. The twitch is a single discrete contractile event. Twitches are produced as long as stimuli are applied far enough apart in time so that the relaxation of one contraction cycle is completed before the next stimulus arrives in the muscle. If a series of stimuli are applied so that a very brief interval of time elapses between the relaxation of the muscle and the application of the next stimulus, the result is often a **treppe** (or **staircase effect**) in which each successive contraction of the muscle, for the first half-dozen or so, is slightly greater than the preceding contraction. This effect is probably due to the prolongation of the active state, which does not completely decay before the next stimulus enters the muscle. The prolongation of the active state might be caused by the movement of K^+ out of the fibers. The staircase is especially prominent in vertebrate cardiac muscle (Hadju, 1953).

When two maximal stimuli are applied so close together that the second enters the muscle before the first contraction cycle is over,

a greater contraction can result than that produced by a single stimulus. This is an example of **temporal summation of contraction**. The second stimulus, if it enters the muscle before the active state has decayed, will produce an amount of new active state material that can sum with the remainder of the previous active state and therefore produce a greater contraction. These responses are not contradictory to the all-or-none law, which states that a maximal response or none at all is obtained upon the application of an adequate stimulus only as long as the tissue is in the same condition. In the case described here, the second stimulus enters the muscle when it is in a different condition than when the first stimulus was applied.

If two stimuli are applied too closely together, the second stimulus will have no effect because the membrane of the muscle will be in

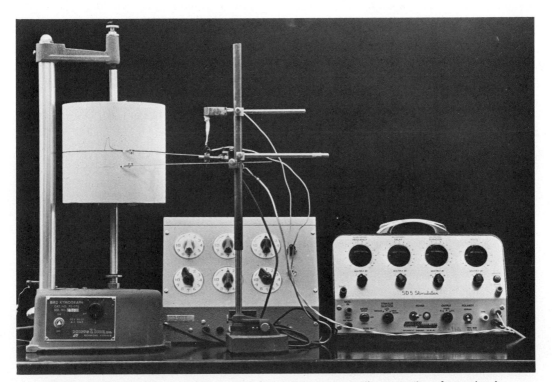

Figure 10-27 One type of student setup for studying contractile properties of muscle. A kymograph (a revolving drum) is used to record contractions of the muscle. Either an electric spark is used to write on a special electrically conducting paper or classically a stylus attached to the muscle lever is used to scratch away soot layered over the paper. Stimuli to the muscle are delivered through a square wave electronic stimulator.

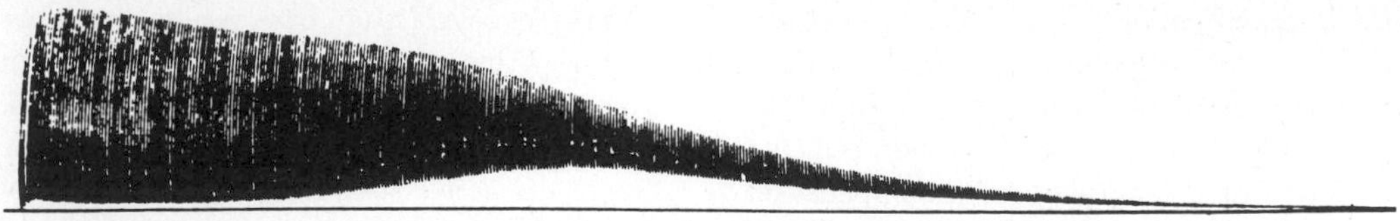

Figure 10-28 Contraction curve resulting from stimulation of a frog gastrocnemius muscle at a frequency of one per second. A staircase effect is seen in the first half dozen contractions. Contracture effects are also seen. The falling off of the contraction height indicates the onset of fatigue until finally the muscle can no longer respond.

its refractory period and will not be capable of producing the contractile-triggering action potential. For frog muscle, stimuli spaced about 0.004 seconds or less will be in the refractory period of the muscle.

If a train of adequate stimuli are applied to a muscle, an incomplete tetanus results when the stimuli are spaced such that the muscle incompletely relaxes between stimuli. When the frequency of stimulation of frog gastrocnemius is raised to about 30 to 50 per second, a complete tetanus is produced. A complete tetanus is a sustained contraction of the muscle due to the fusion of many successive twitches with no time for relaxation to be initiated between stimuli.

The tension developed in a tetanic contraction may be four or more times greater than that of a single twitch. The tetanic contraction is the greatest response a muscle can produce. These are all examples of temporal summation. In terms of the active state—the phenomenon of tetanus represents the condition in which the maximal active state of the muscle is reached and is maintained by continuous stimulation.

If tetanic stimulation is maintained on an excised muscle, the muscle will finally enter into the state of **contracture**—the inability to relax even when stimulation ceases. Then, if the stimulation is continued, the muscle enters the state of fatigue (Figure 10-28). Fatigue is the inability to maintain the contracted state and occurs in excised muscles under any conditions of prolonged stimulation. It occurs most rapidly when tetanic stimulation is applied and will require a longer time to develop if single stimuli are administered successively. Fatigue is brought about by the build-up of toxic materials that in excised muscle are not

removed as they are from muscles in the organism in which the circulatory system is functioning. In the excised muscle there is also a decrease in the amount of ATP and CP available for contraction. Washing a fatigued muscle in Ringers solution containing glucose restores the contractile activity for a brief period.

In the intact animal muscles probably never reach this fatigue condition because the myoneural junction is more susceptible to fatigue than is the muscle and the junction would cease transmitting impulses first. Also in the intact animal the circulatory system can remove toxic materials and supply nutrients. The nature of the toxic materials responsible for fatigue is unknown. Although lactic acid is often spoken of as the fatigue-causing material, muscles will continue to contract even in high concentrations of lactic acid (Ernst, 1958).

If two subliminal stimuli, neither of which can produce a response individually, are applied to a muscle very close together in time, the muscle will respond. This is the **summation of subliminal stimuli** and is caused by the properties of the excitable membrane, not the contractile machinery. Each stimulus produces a certain degree of depolarization in the membrane, and their summed depolarization, if great enough, will lead to the formation of an action potential.

When discussing summation in muscle, it is necessary to separate out those processes acting on the contractile mechanism directly and those acting on the excitable membrane. Since the contractile response and the duration of the active state is longer in time than the postsynaptic or excitable membrane response, summation of the active state can be accomplished by repetition of stimuli spaced relatively

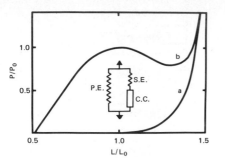

Figure 10-29 Muscle length tension diagram. (a) The resting or passive length-tension curve for an unstimulated muscle. (b) The tension developed during tetanic contraction at different initial muscle lengths. This is the active curve, representing the tension developed following stimulation of the muscle. The insert shows a model of the muscle composed of a contractile element, a series elastic element, and a parallel elastic element.

far apart in comparison with that affecting the membrane.

10-25. The Length-Tension Curve. We can now consider some of the mechanical events associated with muscle contraction—the relations between length, tension, work done, efficiency, velocity of shortening, and so forth —and determine how these phenomena fit into the picture of the sliding filament model and muscle structure.

During an isometric contraction the amount of tension developed depends on the length of the muscle. By fixing a muscle firmly at one end and attaching a transducer to the other, the muscle can be slackened or stretched as desired and the tension at various lengths recorded.

At the reference length of a muscle, there is a resting tension, and as the muscle is stretched passively (without stimulation), the tension increases. A muscle opposes stretch by a force that increases slowly at first and more rapidly with increased stretch. By measuring the tension at a series of lengths, the passive length-tension curve can be plotted (Figure 10-29). This elastic property of muscle depends on the sarcolemma and the elastic connective tissues that surround the muscle and muscle fibers, not on the contractile filaments. The passive

stretch curve is similar to that found in any inert elastic body.

When a muscle is slackened or stretched and then stimulated, the tension developed at various lengths varies as shown in Figure 10-29, curve b. This is the active length-tension curve. By subtracting the passive tension from the total active tension, the tension developed because of the active elements is obtained.

As the curves show, the maximal tension developed by an active muscle is developed at rest length, and the active tension curve does not follow the relationship that an inert elastic body does.

Ramsey (1960) showed that at extreme slackness, when a frog sartorious muscle is allowed to shorten to about 20 per cent of its rest length (Figure 10-30), the tension falls to zero and a "delta state" is reached, where irreversible damage has been done to the muscle fiber. This is caused by a complete disruption of the filament lattice of the muscle. The actin filaments become irreversibly tangled in the A-band under conditions of extreme contraction. Stretches of 30 per cent or less are reversible as far as their effects on the length-tension relation is concerned. At stretches beyond about 200 per cent of rest length, the sarcolemma tears and the tension falls irreversibly to zero.

According to the sliding filament model, decreased overlap of the filaments at lengths above the reference length might explain the decrease in tension; but there is no simple

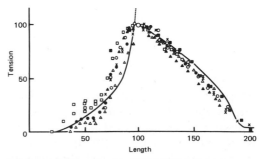

Figure 10-30 The length-tension diagram as recorded for whole frog muscle. [From data of Ramsey (1955).]

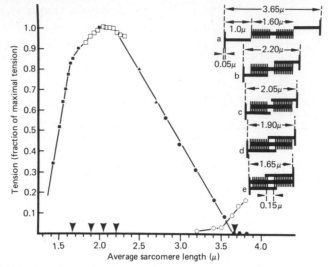

Figure 10-31 The length-tension diagram for single sarcomeres of individual frog semitendinosus muscle fibers. The lengths of sarcomeres along a fiber vary considerably during
contraction. To overcome this difficulty, a method of length clamping, somewhat analogous
to voltage clamping for measuring nerve potentials, is used to mechanically hold a short
central segment of the fiber at constant length (central sarcomeres are used since they are
generally more constant in length than sarcomeres at the fiber ends). An interference
microscope is used to measure sarcomere lengths accurately.

The tension developed at different degrees of overlap of sarcomere filaments is measured
and plotted as percentage of maximal tension. The curve shown is the result of measurements on many different fibers. Different points are used to indicate a few of the different
fibers used. The open circles represent passive tension obtained when a fiber is simply
stretched. The active tension developed by the same fiber when stimulated is shown by
solid circles.

The diagram on the right shows the degree of filament overlap at the different lengths
indicated by arrows on the graph's abscissa. (a) no overlap; (b) maximum overlap of thin
filaments with bridges on one half of the thick filaments; (c) thin filaments meet at center of
A-band; (d) double overlap of thin filaments; (e) maximal shortening with Z-lines brought
up to ends of thick filaments.

The figures are drawn to scale with the following dimensions: thick filaments, $1.60\,\mu$ long;
thin filaments, $2.05\,\mu$ long; Z-line, $0.05\,\mu$ thick; region of thick filaments without bridges,
$0.15\,\mu$ long. [From data of Gordon et al. (1964).]

explanation for the decreased tensions with
activity at shorter lengths. The increasing
diameter of the sarcomere as it shortens and
the consequent separation of the filaments
might provide a partial explanation.

Gordon et al. (1964) observed the bands of
a single sarcomere in the interference microscope while stretching the fiber and recording
its tension. The tension developed could be
related to the degree of overlap of the filaments
in the sarcomere (Figure 10-31). Maximum
isometric tension was found to be directly
proportional to the number of cross-bridges
that could be formed.

From the first studies of muscle energetics,
it was thought that a muscle stored energy,
as a spring does, when stretched. Such a spring
would liberate energy as it reshortened. A
viscous element was added to the model to
explain the observed energy relations of the
muscle, which seemed to indicate that a muscle
when shortening had to overcome the viscosity
of its own medium—the sarcoplasm. Several
viscoelastic models were used in the attempt
to explain the behavior of muscle (see discussions by Ramsey, 1960; Abbott and Brady,
1964; A. F. Huxley, 1957; and H. E. Huxley,
1960). These models, which included an assort-

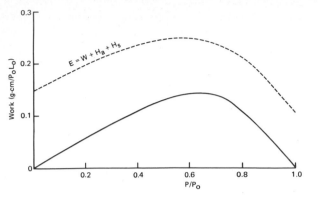

Figure 10-32 The work, heat, and total energy of a muscle as a function of load. Upper curve is total energy, the sum of work done plus heats of activation and shortening. Lower curve shows the variation of work with load. Load, P, is normalized in terms of maximal load or tension, P_0. Energy is expressed in terms of g per cm per maximum tension multiplied by length at which tension is exerted. The data shown are typical for frog muscle where $P_0 L_0 = 266$ g per cm/muscle.

ment of springs and damped and undamped viscous elements, have been generally unsatisfactory in producing useful theories of muscular contraction. They fail, not only because a muscle is not a collection of springs and damped viscous elements, but because a muscle does many more things than such mechanical systems. Although a muscle does have some of the properties of elastic bodies in that at rest a muscle resists stretching or compression, the generation of extra energy when a muscle shortens and must do work is not explainable on the basis of any simple viscoelastic system. Nor, as already pointed out, does a muscle's elasticity follow Hooke's Law when the muscle is stimulated.

These types of models were useful in that they yielded some clues as to the nature of components which were necessary in the muscle. The elastic behavior of the muscle requires some form of series elastic elements and undamped series elastic components. The latter might be represented by the thinner filaments that connect the actin filaments to the Z-line. Parallel elastic elements must also be present and might be due to the sarcolemma and connective tissues or structures such as T-filaments (see Street and Ramsey, 1965).

The early tension changes that occur during latency-relaxation have been studied by Sandow (1944) and Abbott and Ritchie (1951). Figure 10-24 shows the nature of these tension changes in frog muscle. Such tension changes are measurable only in the isometric twitch. No equivalent changes have been found during the latent period of isotonic contractions.

10-26. Work Load and Efficiency of Muscular Contraction. Work can be done by a muscle during an isotonic contraction, where the muscle can shorten and lift a load. This is the external work. The external work may be defined by

$$W = Px \qquad (10.7)$$

where P is the load and x is the distance through which the load is lifted. According to the length-tension curve (Figure 10-29 or Figure 10-31), the distance a muscle can shorten depends on the load, that is, x is a function of P. The product of the abscissa and ordinate at any point on the length-tension diagram is the work that can be done at a given load.

The work done by a muscle is optimal at some given load (Figure 10-32). When $P = 0$, the muscle does no work since there is no load to lift. At the other extreme, when $P = P_0$ (the maximal isometric tension), the load is too great for the muscle to lift and since $x = 0$, no work is done. Between these two extremes, there is some optimal load at which the muscle does maximal work. For frog sartorius muscle the maximal work is done at a load approximately equal to $2/3 P_0$.

The characteristic equation of muscle states that the velocity of shortening depends on the difference between the actual force on the muscle and the maximal force it can develop. The force-velocity curves for some muscles are shown in Figure 10-33 (a similar curve was given in Figure 10-22 for frog sartorius muscle). As the load on the muscle is increased, the shortening velocity decreases. Maximal shortening velocity is obtained when the muscle is at its reference length, l_o. But as the velocity of shortening increases, the load that can be raised decreases until at maximal shortening velocity no work can be done (see Abbott and Wilkie, 1953).

Since the heat liberated by a muscle during shortening is independent of the load, the passive internal viscosity cannot be playing any role in controlling the velocity of shortening. Otherwise, there would be an increased heat liberation with shortening. In some manner the load on the muscle controls the chemical reaction rates and the velocity of shortening. As noted above, these are some of the reasons why viscoelastic systems cannot properly model the muscle.

A prestretched muscle has a faster velocity of shortening than an unstretched one because less time and energy must be spent in stretching the series-elastic components. They are already stretched by the application of the external force. A preloaded muscle can exert greater tension or do more work than an after-loaded muscle. In the latter case, the muscle itself must expend energy in stretching the series-elastic components.

The total energy liberated by a muscle during a contraction can be represented by the sum of the heat produced and the external work done. The efficiency of muscular contraction is of interest to physiologists, although efficiency is difficult to express in any unambiguous terms. Mechanical efficiency is the ratio of work performed to the total energy

output of the muscle. That is, the ratio of work done to the sum of the initial heat and the external work. The efficiency of frog sartorius muscle, on this basis, varies from about zero when small loads are lifted to about 50 per cent when maximal external work is performed. Muscles efficiencies average about 30 per cent in these terms.

Because in a mechanochemical system such as muscle there is always energy wasted as heat, the efficiency of interest is the thermodynamic efficiency, the efficiency with which muscle transforms chemical into mechanical energy. The thermodynamic efficiency is equal to the work done divided by the free energy available from the chemical reactions underlying the contractile process. Because these reactions are not known, their free energy changes are unknown and the thermodynamic efficiency cannot be calculated. Wilkie (1960) and Podolsky (1960) discuss these problems.

At the present time many of the things done by muscle are only inexactly modeled. Whereas the sliding filament hypothesis aids in outlining the general nature of the contractile event, the lack of detailed information about the actual molecular mechanisms involved and the manner in which chemical energy is coupled to the mechanical activity results in a lack of good models for the contractile system.

In the next part of the chapter some model systems and muscles other than those of amphibians will be discussed, and the phenomena discussed in the last few sections will be amplified.

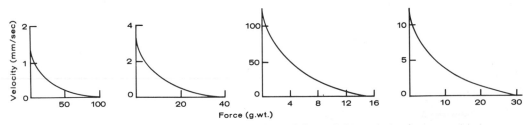

Figure 10-33 Some force-velocity curves. From left to right: anterior byssus retractor muscle of *Mytilus edulis*; pharynx retractor muscle of *Helix pomatia*; cross-striated part of adductor muscle of *Pecten*; flight muscle of locust *Schistocerca*. [Adapted from Hanson and Lowy (1960) from various sources.]

Muscle Models and Other Contractile Systems

10-27. The Glycerol-Extracted Muscle Fiber. The study of the mechanical properties of muscle have centered primarily upon amphibian muscle; biochemical studies have been done mainly on rabbit muscles. Because of the complexity of the intact muscle cell, models are sought that eliminate some of the variables associated with contractile studies of the whole muscle. An important model is the glycerol-extracted muscle fiber first used by Szent-Györgyi (1949) in studies on rabbit psoas muscle. When a muscle was extracted in 50 per cent glycerol at low temperature, it was thought that the external membrane was destroyed, that metabolic machinery was destroyed or removed, and that only a contractile skeleton was left (Perry, 1956). Such a system is useful because the effects of stimulation of the membrane no longer have to be considered. Muscles may be kept for several years in glycerol at $-20°C$ without losing contractile ability. This type of preparation gives a convenient source of experimental material, and the method of storage avoids protein denaturation and bacterial decomposition of the tissue.

As soon as a glycerol-extracted fiber is placed in solutions containing ATP, it will contract. The requirements for contraction are as follows: ATP or other nucleotide triphosphate must be present in concentration of at least $10^{-7}\ M$; the pH must be physiological (approximately in the range of 6 to 8); the actomyosin system must still be capable of hydrolyzing ATP; and at least trace amounts of Ca^{2+} must be present. If ATPase activity is blocked, for example by inhibitors such as the Hg-containing Salyrgan, contraction is prevented. Because the factors required for contraction of this model system are in the range needed for the normal physiological system, it is believed that the glycerol model contraction is based on the same mechanisms used by the living muscle.

Glycerol-extracted muscles exert tensions similar to those produced by living muscle. For example, rabbit psoas muscle has a maximum tension development of about 5 kg/cm²; the glycerol-extracted psoas muscle produces a maximum tension of about 4 kg/cm². This is another indication that the response of the glycerol system mimics that of the living system.

Although contraction is readily produced by the addition of ATP, Ca^{2+}, and Mg^{2+} to the glycerol-extracted fiber, relaxation does not follow the shortening or tension development. In order to obtain relaxation, either a proper ratio of CP/ATP must be used in the bathing medium; or a proper adjustment of ionic strength and pH must be made (Carew, 1962); or relaxing factor preparations extracted from living muscle must be added (Hasselbach, 1964, reviews relaxing factor systems).

The relaxing factor is a component of the sarcoplasmic reticulum and operates through modifications of the Ca^{2+} available to the myofilaments. Glycerol-extracted fibers have been used in many studies of muscle structure and in the examination of the Ca^{2+} release and uptake system of excitation-contraction coupling (Costantin et al., 1965; Costantin and Podolsky, 1967; Elison et al., 1965; Eisenberg and Eisenberg, 1968; Pease et al., 1965).

Depolarization of frog twitch muscle membranes causes a release of Ca^{2+} into the sarcoplasm and a Ca^{2+}-dependent increase in respiration. The T system might be the storage site for Ca^{2+}. And it has been shown that the store can be replenished by Ca^{2+} entering from the extracellular medium (Van der Kloot, 1967). In any given muscle the question arises whether the Ca^{2+} needed to trigger the contractile filaments is derived from an intracellular store or an extracellular store of the ion. Experimental results with different muscle fibers suggest that differences in this respect occur and may depend on the size of the fiber. Thin fibers will require no specialized arrangement for getting Ca^{2+} to all the filaments by diffusion; but in thicker muscle fibers the limitation of the rate of diffusion requires a more complex system—the T-system and sarcoplasmic reticulum. In thinner fibers, including smooth muscle, Ca^{2+} appears to be controlled by the outer limiting membrane.

The glycerol-extracted fiber has been ana-lyzed with regard to its mechanical properties and it has been found that the length-tension and velocity-load relationships of the model are similar to those of the living muscle. The localization of actin and myosin filaments was made with model fibers (see Huxley, 1964) and, in fact, it is assumed that the filament array seen in the model fiber is the same as exists in the living muscle.

The glycerol-extracted model has been suc-cessfully used with a wide variety of contractile tissues in order to analyze responses of the contractile machinery to various chemical and physical stimuli. Protozoan amoeboid move-ment and contractile stalk activity; mitotic events; as well as striated, smooth, and cardiac muscle cells have all been studied through glycerol models (Weber, 1958; Hoffmann-Berling, 1960, review this work). The similari-ties of response of all of these systems to ATP, Ca^{2+}, and other stimuli have led to the con-clusion that contractility is based in all cases on the reactions of actomyosin-like system.

However, there are indications that glycerol-extracted models are not as simple as was once thought. Under some conditions respira-tion can occur in rabbit glycerol-extracted psoas fibers (Wilson et al., 1959); respiratory activity and several intact enzymes systems have been found in cardiac glycerol-extracted fibers after several months of storage (Naylor and Merrillees, 1964); and after a few months of storage a transmembrane potential can still be measured in glycerol-extracted muscle fibers. It appears that it is not the glycerol treatment itself that is responsible for any destruction of cellular membranous elements that may occur, but rather the osmotic shock as fibers are transferred from one solution to another following glycerol-extraction (Eisen-berg and Gage, 1967).

The glycerol model, as any model, must be used with care when extrapolating results obtained with such preparations back to the living normal system, and there is still much to be learned about the nature of this prepara-tion. Although not as much is removed from glycerol-extracted fibers as was once thought,

the selective destruction of various membrane components of the model by appropriate solu-tions presents the opportunity to examine muscle cells at various levels of structural integrity—and the model becomes even more useful.

10-28. Actomyosin Threads. Another type of model system used to study the effects of chemical and physical agents on the contractile system is the actomyosin thread. The use of superprecipitation of actomyosin as a system for studying the properties of the contractile protein has already been mentioned.

If a purified solution of actomyosin is prepared and dissolved in 0.6 M KCl and then squirted from a fine capillary pipet moved back and forth beneath the surface of a con-tainer of distilled water (Figure 10-34), salt diffuses from the string of actomyosin very rapidly and the actomyosin precipitates out in the form of a thread. Actomyosin is insoluble at ionic strengths below about 0.1.

Such a thread can be treated by drying so that the molecules are oriented in parallel fashion. Such a thread will shorten in solutions of ATP, producing a tension of a few hundred grams per square centimeter. The system imper-fectly mimics many of the properties of intact muscle and glycerol models. It is difficult to compare this system with the normal physio-logical one because the mechanism by which

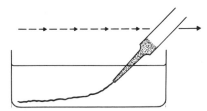

Figure 10-34 Arrangement for the preparation of actomyosin threads. Actomyosin dissolved in 0.6 M KCl is gently released from a capillary pipet held under a dilute solution of KCl (0.05 M) with a trace of Mg^{2+} (0.0005 M). The actomyosin loses its salt and gelatinizes to a thread that settles to the bottom. After a few hours the threads, which originally are soft and fragile, harden and can be manipulated.

the actomyosin threads is probably not that of normal muscle. However, the lack of organization of the molecules in the model (or in the actomyosin sheet, Hayashi and Rosenbluth, 1952) approaches, perhaps, that of smooth muscle. In any case these models serve a useful purpose in illustrating the possibilities of the actomyosin-ATP reaction in contractility.

10-29. Slow and Fast Fibers. The type of muscle considered up to this point has been the tonic, fast fiber characterized by the possession of a propagated action potential and a rapid twitch contraction. Although there is a range of contraction times for fast muscle fibers even within the same muscle, some fibers have been found that are characterized by contraction times much slower than that of the twitch fiber. These are the slow fibers whose contraction is generally not all-or-none and that usually lack a propagated action potential. Increasing information about the two fiber types indicates that, in mammals, it is truer to speak of a continuum of fiber types, not just two classes.

On the basis of morphological evidence, Kruger (1952) classified striated muscle fibers as either *Fibrillenstruktur* or *Felderstruktur* in nature. The former are typical twitch fibers possessing a well-defined array of fibrils (Peachey and Huxley, 1962). Felderstruktur fibers are the slow fibers, having only junctional potentials and with their contractile material appearing in cross-section to be arranged in large ribbonlike areas with little sarcoplasmic reticulum in the interfibrillar spaces and lacking an M-zone.

The slow fiber is innervated by small motoneurons (5 to 8 μ in diameter); fast fibers are innervated by larger axons (12 to 20 μ in diameter). The larger motoneurons terminate on typical motor end plates, and the fast muscle fiber is monoterminally, mononeuronally innervated. The small neurons to the slow muscle fibers have grape endings, and the slow fiber innervation is polyterminal (Figure 10-35). That region of the slow fiber membrane underneath a nerve ending responds with a graded

postjunctional potential that produces a localized contraction.

Among the vertebrates slow muscle fibers were first found in certain frog skeletal muscles. Some muscles appear to be wholly constituted of fast fibers, for example, the sartorius; others are composed only of slow fibers, for example, rectus abdominus; whereas most muscles are a mixture of both types of muscle fibers.

Slow fibers have now been found in the extraocular muscles of many mammals including man, monkeys, guinea pig, rabbit, and cat (see Matyushin, 1963, 1967). Slow and fast fibers have been found in teleosts (Barets, 1955). Slow muscle systems are prominent in the possession of slow fibers (see Chapter 11). However, in many invertebrate systems, for example, crustacean skeletal muscle, the so-called slow system depends not on the muscle fiber but on the nature of the neuron innervating it.

The characteristics ascribed above to slow fibers are not always found. For example, those of birds do have propagated action potentials, whereas those of mammalian ocular muscles possess M-bands. All functional, as well as morphological, characteristics of a muscle fiber must be considered before it is placed in one or the other of these categories.

When calcium solutions are microelectrophoretically applied to frog slow fibers that have had their sarcolemmas removed (Constantin and Podolsky, 1964; Constantin et al.,

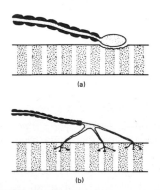

Figure 10-35 (a) Typical motor end plate of a vertebrate twitch muscle. (b) Multiple endings on a slow muscle fiber.

1967), a slow contraction results. This points out that the slow properties of the fiber are a result of the nature of the contractile machinery itself, not of the sarcolemma or the excitation-contraction coupling system.

Red and white muscle fibers are, in some cases, correlated with slow and fast properties. As already stated the terms red and white as applied to muscles are an indication of biochemical differences between fibers that may be associated with contractile differences.

Bajusz (1964) found that denervation of a muscle has different results on the red and white types of fibers. White fibers degenerate and atrophy much faster than do the red fibers when the motoneuron to a mixed muscle is transected. Experiments in which cross-innervation is performed between a tonic and a phasic muscle showed that such experimental procedures changed the nature of the fibers and altered the myoglobin content (McPherson and Tokunga, 1967). It has been proposed that the type of neuron innervating a muscle fiber controls the biochemical nature of the fiber and also its contractile properties (see Buller et al., 1960). Cross-innervation, denervation, and tenotomy (cutting of muscle tendons) all seem to have effects on the chemical nature of a muscle (Vbrová, 1963). These are further examples of the tonic influences of neurons discussed previously (Section 9-6).

The differences between muscle fiber types are reviewed by Hnik (1962). There is a correlation between the rate of ATP splitting and the speed of muscular contraction (Bárány, 1967). The activity of red fiber ATPase is slower than that of white fiber ATPase. The capabilities for tension development are greater in white fibers than in red fibers (Sexton and Gersten, 1967).

10-30. Comments on Some Crustacean Muscles.
The barnacle *Balanus nubilis* possesses giant muscle fibers whose diameters are on the order of 1 mm (Hoyle and Smyth, 1963). These fibers are large enough to be canulated and internally perfused, similar to squid giant axons. Unlike frog twitch muscles, the giant fibers of the barnacle respond to stimulation

only with graded contractions. The development and duration of the active state is much longer in these fibers than in frog muscle.

The maximum force developed under isometric conditions depends on the strength of the stimulating current at durations below 3 msec. At stimulus durations of 3 msec alteration of the current strength up to 250 mA does not evoke any further contraction, and the tension development does not amount to more than 30 per cent of the maximum under tetanic stimulation. Further tension is developed upon the application of repetitive stimuli or by increasing stimulation duration to at least 10 msec.

Although twitch muscles of the frog are triggered into contractile activity by the release of intracellular-bound calcium ions, it is thought that in some muscles the activation of contraction is, partially at least, controlled by the entrance of Ca^{2+} from the extracellular medium. This appears to be the case, for example, in frog cardiac muscle (Niedergerke, 1955) and some slow fibers of the frog (Shanes, 1961). Twitch muscles usually possess a well-developed sarcoplasmic reticulum and T-system and contain enough intracellular Ca^{2+} to account for contractile triggering (Sandow, 1965).

Contracture of barnacle muscle in K^+ solutions occurs only in the presence of Ca^{2+} or Sr^{2+}. These are the only divalent ions which will support contracture, and they are also the only ions that activate the contractile elements when applied intracellularly. In barnacle muscle the action potential has also been found to depend upon an increase in permeability to Ca^{2+} (Hagiwara, 1965; Hagiwara and Nakajima, 1966). Another type of evidence indicating that Ca^{2+} enters barnacle muscle during excitation is that although the intracellular free Ca^{2+} concentration is only about 1 mM/kg; 5 to 7 mM/kg of EGTA [ethylene glycolbis(β-aminoethyl ether)-N,N'-tetraacetate] are required to supress the Ca^{2+} activation of the contractile elements. EGTA is a selective sequestering agent (binding agent) for Ca^{2+}.

In muscles of the crayfish it has been found

that both Ca^{2+} and Cl^- are required for the initiation and maintenance of tension (Reuben et al., 1967). Skeletal muscles of crustaceans vary widely in their properties. Both phasic and tonic muscle fibers are known, for example, many abdominal muscles in which such fibers are segregated into two parallel sets of muscles. In the appendages of decapod crustaceans, the fibers have heterogeneous properties and innervation. In some cases both tonic and phasic muscle fibers are present, in other cases the nature of the neural innervation is responsible for tonic or phasic responses (Chapter 11). All-or-none twitch fibers of crustaceans have a well-developed transverse tubular system. Barnacle giant fibers also have such a system although it is generally better developed in decapod crustaceans.

10-31. Molluscan "Catch" (Paramyosin) Muscles.

Molluscs have a variety of muscle fiber types (see Hoyle, 1964; Hanson and Lowy, 1960). In addition to typical striated muscle fibers, molluscs may also have: obliquely striated fibers in which bands of contractile material are spiraly wrapped about a central core of sarcosome-rich sarcoplasm; obliquely striated muscles that have no specialized core but only a central region, where merging bands of spiraling contractile filaments meet; nonstriated fibers that contain crosslinked filaments but that do not have organized myofibrillar groupings; and nonstriated muscles characterized by the presence of large paramyosin filaments.

The latter are often catch muscles, so named because they appear to have some mechanism that allows them to remain in the contracted state for long periods of time (sometimes for days) with very little energy expenditure. They are used primarily to hold the shells of lamellibranch molluscs tightly closed. The large filaments containing paramyosin may be up to 30 μ in length and 1200 Å in diameter. The paramyosin (also called tropomyosin A because of its similarities to tropomyosin B from vertebrate and other muscles) is probably located in the central core of the large filament surrounded by a sheath of myosin molecules with

their projecting cross-bridges (see Millman, 1967). Catch muscles also contain thin filaments—about 50 Å in diameter and of undetermined length—which are composed of actin. Some tropomyosin B may be contained in these thin filaments (see Figures 10-13 and 10-14).

In addition to the adductor muscles of lamellibranchs, paramyosin is also found in the byssal and pedal retractor muscles of the edible mussel, *Mytilus edulis*, and in the foot retractor muscles of some snails. The most studied nonstriated muscle is the anterior byssus retractor muscle (ABRM) of *Mytilus*. This muscle contains fibers that run for several centimeters parallel to the length of the muscle and is one of the best preparations for experimental study of nonstriated muscle; however, the ABRM is a highly atypical nonstriated muscle.

Although the ABRM is composed of all nonstriated fibers, most adductor muscles of bivalve molluscs consist of two parts: one is white and opaque and can produce a prolonged contraction. This is the catch portion of the muscle. The other part is translucent and has the nature of a phasic muscle. Often this part of the muscle is composed of striated fibers.

The catch muscle is of interest because of the presence of paramyosin and because of the muscle's ability to maintain a sustained contraction with very little energy expenditure (Parnas, 1910; von Uexküll, 1912) even in the absence of an intact innervation. The slow adductor muscle of *Venus verrucosa* uses only 0.0056 ml O_2 per hour while maintaining 3 kg of tension. On the same basis a frog sartorius muscle would use 60 ml O_2 per hour (Ritchie, 1928; Whalen and Collins, 1963, discuss work and oxygen consumption in frog sartorius muscle).

The ABRM responds to stimulation in either of two ways (Winton, 1937). Stimulus pulses cause a relatively rapid phasic-type contraction, whereas direct current stimulation leads to a prolonged contraction with a slow relaxation phase (Figure 10-36). The tonic type of contraction is elicited by the application of ACh (in concentrations as low as 10^{-6} M)

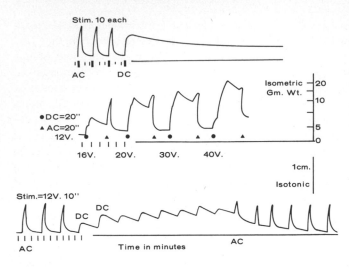

Stim. 10 each

AC   DC

●DC=20"
▲AC=20"
12V.

16V.   20V.   30V.   40V.

Isometric — 20
Gm. Wt. — 10
— 5
— 0

1cm.

Isotonic

Stim.=12V. 10"

DC
DC

AC

AC

Time in minutes

Figure 10-36 (Upper) When the anterior byssus retractor muscle (ABRM) of *Mytilus edulis* is stimulated with alternating current (AC), the contraction is followed by a relatively rapid relaxation. When stimulated with direct current (DC), the contraction is followed by a slow relaxation. (Middle); AC stimulation during slow relaxation following DC results in a much faster relaxation rate. (Lower) Reversal of current is shown not to affect the DC response. [Redrawn from Winton (1937).]

to catch muscle fibers. Phasic contractions result when 5-HT ($10^{-9} M$) is applied. Twarog (1954, 1966) suggests that these are the transmitters of the motoneurons and relaxing neurons, respectively. Figure 10-37 illustrates the effects on the contraction of stimulation of the inhibitory nerve and also the application of 5-HT.

Several mechanisms have been advanced to explain the mechanism underlying the sustained contraction of the catch-type muscle. None is entirely satisfactory. One early suggestion that there were spontaneous action potentials produced in the muscle cells or in intrinsic ganglia and that a continuous stream of impulses maintained the muscle in the shortened state was disproven by the use of tetracaine. This drug, which abolishes electrical activity in the ABRM, does not abolish the tonic contraction (see Johnson and Twarog, 1960). Nor does such a hypothesis explain the low expenditure of energy. The role of excitatory neurons and inhibitory (for slow relaxation) neurons is not yet known nor do all tonic muscles possess a dual innervation.

Johnson and Szent-Györgyi (1960) revived the hypothesis that the catch mechanism depends on the properties of paramyosin fibers. Working with glycerol-extracted ABRM fibers these workers found that at low ionic strengths the fibers are stiff at pH's slightly below 6.5. At higher pH's the fibers are in a relaxed condition or less stiff condition. Purified para-

myosin crystallizes out of solution at a pH slightly below 6.5, and it was hypothesized that a tonic contraction results when the muscle pH changes to below 6.5 and thus sets the paramyosin rigidly into position.

But other pieces of experimental evidence are against this hypothesis. For example, both tonic and phasic contractions of the ABRM proceed at about the same rate; if a tonic contraction were accompanied by a crystallization of paramyosin, one would expect the shortening velocity to be much lower because of the increased viscosity of the intrafibrillar material. In addition, x-ray diffraction studies of living fibers have shown that there are no detectable changes in the spacings or intensities

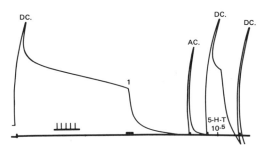

DC.
DC.
DC.
AC.
1
5-H-T
10^{-5}

Figure 10-37 Tonic contraction of the ABRM of *Mytulis edulis* is followed by relaxation when the inhibitory nerve is stimulated (at point 1). Such relaxation occurs also when 5-hydroxytryptamine (5-HT) is applied to the muscle. In the presence of 5-HT a direct current stimulus is not followed by a slow relaxation. [After Hoyle and Lowy (1956.)]

of the diffraction pattern when tonically contracted muscles are compared with those in the relaxed state (Millman and Elliot, 1965). If crystallization or other molecular changes had occurred, changes in the spacings of the paramyosin filaments would be expected.

Some investigators feel that paramyosin is not the key to the sustained contraction (see Millman, 1967). They believe that a sliding filament system is in operation as in other muscles but with the addition of a control system capable of varying the rate of cross-linkage breaking, that is, the relaxation process. According to this proposal there is a one-component system of actin filaments sliding past thick myosin-paramyosin filaments, and paramyosin serves only as a strengthening element. The evidence for these suggestions lies partially in electron microscope studies which show that the thick filaments of the catch muscle are discontinuous. To serve as a catch mechanism, they should be continuous. There is also a sliding of filaments during contraction. It has also been stated that all molluscan muscles contain some paramyosin, although not all are of the tonic variety (see Lowy et al., 1964).

The type of model just described lacks detailed mechanisms to explain the sustained contraction. Although 5-HT might be responsible for causing the removal of ATP from the actomyosin system, thus causing relaxation, no such sequestering mechanism has been found. The low energy requirement is also not explained on this basis, although it is possible that a slow relaxation time of the contractile system might mean that little ATP is utilized in sustaining a recycling of crosslink formation between filaments. Obviously at present there are no complete models for explaining how these muscles can maintain a prolonged contraction with low energy input.

10-32. Smooth Muscle. The properties of molluscan catch muscles are, in some respects, simply those of many nonstriated muscles exaggerated. Although the nonstriated muscles of some invertebrates and the multiunit nonstriated muscles of vertebrates are character-

ized by a phasic-type contraction, smooth muscle generally is thought of as tonic in nature—with a slow relaxation time compared with typical striated muscle fibers. Smooth muscle is also typified by its ability to generate spontaneous potentials, although coordination and control by the nervous or endocrine systems is also usually present.

Smooth muscle has been called the headache muscle because of the difficulties encountered when its contractile or bioelectrical properties are to be studied (Csapó, 1960). Smooth muscle is laid down in sheets, interspersed with connective tissue. In the blood vascular system the cells are arranged spirally about the vessel wall (Chapter 13). In both cases, the isolation of single cells for analysis is extremely difficult. Furthermore, the spindle-shaped cells are small. Average dimensions for mammalian smooth muscle cells are as follows: 50 to 150 μ in length by 2 to 5 μ in width at the central region. The small size of these cells usually precludes single cell studies of contractile and electrical properties. It was for these reasons that the long-fibered, nonstriated ABRM was chosen for study, although it is an atypical nonstriated muscle fiber.

The lack of organized structure, at least at the microscopic level, makes it impossible to follow structural changes during contractile activity as is done with striated muscle, and thus clues about the contractile mechanism from this source are lacking. Although myofilaments are sometimes visible in the electron microscope, any myofibrillar arrangement is minute and lacking the organization of striated muscle.

Actomyosin is extractable from smooth muscle and presumably forms a sliding filament system. However, smooth muscle contains less actomyosin than a corresponding quantity of striated muscle (6 to 10 mg per gram wet weight as compared with 70 mg per gram wet weight, Needham, 1964). Also smooth muscles contains less ATP and other high energy phosphate compounds. The ATPase activity of smooth muscle actomyosin is lower than that of striated muscle. Because of the less organized structure and the smaller

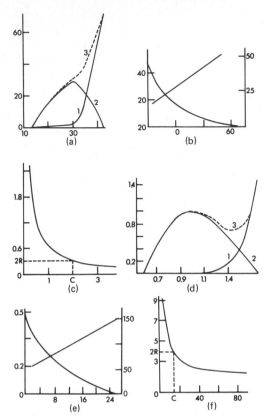

Figure 10-38 A comparison of the properties of smooth and striated muscles. (a) to (c). The length-tension relations, the velocity-load relations, and the strength-duration relations of uterine smooth muscle. (d) to (f) The same relations for frog skeletal muscle. Curves 1, 2, and 3 of (a) and (d) represent the resting tension, the total tension produced by electrical stimulation, and the difference between the two, that is, the active tension developed by the muscle, respectively. The parabolic curves of (b) and (e) represent the relation between load (abscissa) and velocity of shortening (left ordinate); the straight line relationships of (b) and (e) represent the relationship between load and $(P_0 - P)$/velocity (right ordinate). [Modified from Csapó (1962) after various sources.]

amounts of contractile protein of smooth muscle, the contraction of smooth muscle is generally slower, and a smaller tension is developed than in striated muscle. However, the mechanical properties are qualitatively similar (Figure 10-38) despite differences in structure and mode of innervation.

Smooth muscle cells have a poorly developed

sarcoplasmic reticulum and lack T-systems. (Smith, 1966). Many of the classical non-striated muscles of invertebrates possess at least a limited T-system or its analog. Although the contraction of smooth muscle is triggered by Ca^{2+}, the influx of this ion is through the sarcolemma with subsequent diffusion throughout the sarcoplasm. This may partially account for the slower responses of smooth muscle compared with striated muscle.

It is of interest that tetrodotoxin does not block spike initiation in mammalian smooth muscle cells. Nor does TTX block spike initiation in barnacle muscle fibers. Since the latter cells are known to have an action potential dependent on Ca^{2+} conductance changes in the membrane, Ca^{2+} may also be involved with impulse generation in smooth muscle.

Smooth muscle is characterized by a high sensitivity to chemical agents. In the organism the activity of smooth muscle is greatly influenced by the endocrine system. In addition, smooth muscle activity is under the influence of mechanical stimuli such as stretch. The responses to stretch of smooth muscle cells are due to inherent properties of the muscle cells and are not due to associated neurons or other types of receptor cells (Burnstock et al., 1963). This is an important property of smooth muscle because it permits the maintenance of tension or an increased tension in organs such as the stomach, intestine, bladder, or uterus, which must propel materials along the lumen. As the organ lumen fills with material, an intraluminal pressure is created that leads to a contractile response.

Smooth muscle generally is stimulated by acetylcholine, which increases the force of contraction. Since the acetylcholine effect is not blocked by ganglionic blocking agents, the compound presumably acts on the smooth muscle membrane directly. Adrenalin has both inhibitory and excitatory actions on smooth muscle, depending both on the particular muscle studied and on the animal species. The nature and site of adrenalin action on smooth muscle are not known (Daniel, 1964). Noradrenalin has similar actions on smooth muscle as adrenalin, but higher concentrations of noradrenalin are needed to elicit similar responses.

Uterine muscle has been extensively studied with respect to hormonal influences (Bozler, 1938, 1941; Csapó, 1961, 1964; Marshall, 1959). During the estrous cycle, uterine smooth muscle goes through period phases of activity and nonactivity (Reynolds, 1965; Turner, 1960, describe the estrous cycle; see also Chapter 11).

Uterine muscle from an animal in diestrous shows little spontaneous activity and is not sensitive to chemical, electrical, or mechanical stimulation. But during estrous there is an increase in spontaneous electrical activity and in sensitivity to stimulation. This condition can be induced in ovariectomized or immature mammals by the application of estrogen. Estrogen activates the synthesis of actomyosin and the production of high energy organophosphates (Csapó, 1961).

In addition to its effects on the contractile machinery of the smooth muscle cell, estrogen also influences the level of the resting transmembrane potential. In an immature animal, the resting potential of the myometrium is about −35 mV. Little spontaneous activity is seen. This is explained by accommodation, the fact that continuous depolarization of a membrane results in lowered ability to generate action potentials. Estrogen treatment brings the potential to about −50 mV, a level where spontaneous activity and development of action potentials occur.

Progesterone raises the membrane potential to about −65 mV, thus diminishing the excitability of the muscle. Not all regions of the myometrium are active during progesterone domination, and the contractions of the uterine muscle under this condition is weak and uncoordinated as compared with the estrogen-dominated muscle. Progesterone has no significant effect on the contractile elements of the smooth muscle cell as does estrogen. Its activity is based primarily on induced changes of the cell excitability (Figure 10-39).

During estrogen-domination not only is the activity of the muscle increased, but the force generated by the contractile elements is greatly augmented. Estrogen operates on both the membrane excitability and the contractile filaments.

The hormone oxytocin also acts on the myometrium of the uterus as well as on the musculoepithelial cells of the mammary glands. It stimulates these cells by causing a depolarization of the cell membrane and by increasing the frequency of spontaneously generated action potentials. If the muscle is already active, oxytocin increases both the force and the frequency of contraction (Marshall, 1964).

In mammals both oxytocin and vasopressin affect the adenohypophysis. Oxytocin causes a release of prolactin, the hormone responsible for stimulating milk production. Vasopressin stimulates the release of adrenocorticotropic hormone (ACTH) from the anterior lobe. In the animal, therefore, the activities of these various hormones regulate the activities and conditions of the uterine muscle and other reproductive structures. This regulation depends on the stage of the estrous cycle as well as on whether or not copulation has occurred,

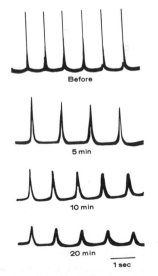

Figure 10-39 The effect of progesterone on the electrical activity of the uterus. Upper trace, before addition of progesterone. Lower traces show increasing effect with time of the addition of 10 μg/ml progesterone. [Redrawn from data of Kuriyama and Csapó (1958).]

385

and on the age and general condition of the animal.

Very little is known concerning the physiology of vascular smooth muscle. Part of this lack of information stems from the difficulties of obtaining suitable experimental preparations. Part is based on the variety of responses of smooth muscle found in different regions of the circulatory system or even within the same circulatory vessel. Vascular smooth muscle responds to nerve transmitters, hormones, metabolites, and metabolic by-products, and it is difficult to separate out the actions of these many agents. For example, *in vitro* studies show that ACh may constrict, relax, or have no effect on vascular smooth muscle depending on the particular region of the circulatory system in which the muscle is located. Nor is it certain that excised preparations behave similarly to those of the intact animal. In some cases ATP causes a contraction of excised smooth muscle, in others it causes a relaxation. Vascular smooth muscle responses also depend upon the degree of stretch or tension applied to the muscle. As already stated, this is a common phenomenon with smooth muscle. The properties of vascular smooth muscle will be discussed further in relation to the functioning of the circulatory system (Chapters 12 and 13).

10-33. Insect Fibrillar Muscle. All insect muscles are striated, although a variety of histological and physiological types are known (Edwards, 1960). Of particular interest because of their unusual mechanical properties are the fibrillar flight muscles of certain insects and the tymbal muscles of the sound-producing organs of some cicadas.

Many insects have wing beat frequencies in the range of 100 to 300 beats per second, and a few approach frequencies of 2,000 per second. If a muscular contraction, initiated by an action potential, accompanied each wing stroke, a contraction cycle of less than 1 millisecond would be required—a duration less than that of most action potentials and one difficult to explain on the basis of ordinary contractile processes in striated muscle.

It has been found that the high wing beat frequency of certain insects results from a specialized mechanical arrangement of the thorax–flight muscle–wing system and from the properties of the flight muscles. In this section only the general physiological nature of fibrillar muscles will be discussed. The control of insect flight will be considered in a later chapter. Also fibrillar flight mechanisms will be described only at a very general level. Flight systems are complex and extremely varied in different insect species (see Pringle, 1957; 1967; 1968).

Insect flight muscles have been classified into two functional groups (Roeder, 1951). **Synchronous muscles** are found in the orders Odonata (dragonflies), Lepidoptera (moths, butterflies), and Orthoptera (grasshoppers, locusts)—insects with relatively low wing beat frequencies. Each wing beat in this case is accompanied by a muscle twitch initiated by a single impulse (or sometimes a short burst of impulses). **Asynchronous muscles** are found in the orders Diptera (flies, mosquitos), Hymenoptera (bees, wasps), Coleoptera (beetles), and many Hemiptera (true bugs). These are insects with high wing beat frequencies and with the best developed flight abilities. Insects with fibrillar muscles (the term is roughly synonymous with asynchronous) are able to hover in the air, make rapid starts and stops, or fly backward. Fibrillar muscle is characterized by its oscillatory activity. Although each period of mechanical activity is initiated (and usually terminated) by nerve impulses, the contractile activity once begun does not depend upon nerve impulses.

Insect striated muscles differ from vertebrate striated muscles in the nature of their connections to the skeletal system. Myofibrillar elements run through the Z-line and connect to the exoskeleton through **tono-fibrillae**—specialized extensions of certain epidermal cells (Auber, 1963; Auber and Couteaux, 1962, 1963). There is no intervening tendon (Korschelt, 1938); in fact, insect muscles generally contain little connective tissue.

Insect flight muscles also differ from striated

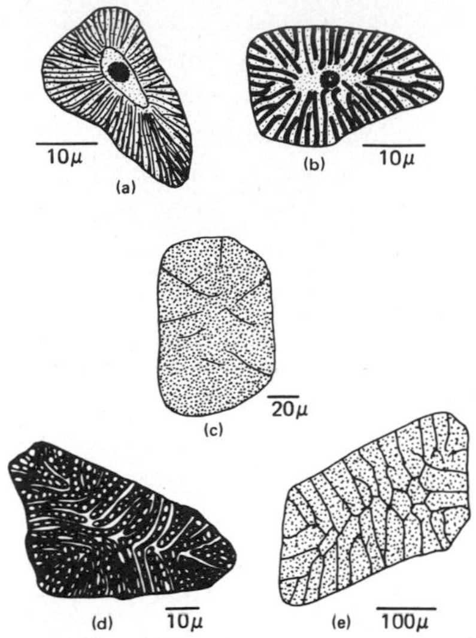

Figure 10-40 Some muscle types found in insects. (a) Tubular leg muscle of *Vespa*. (b) Tubular flight muscle of *Libellula* (Odonata). (c) Close packed flight muscle of *Chortoicetes terminifera*. (d) Lamellar flight muscle of *Cyclochila australasiae* (Cicadidae). (e) Fibrillar flight muscle of *Musca domestica*. [Redrawn from J. W. S. Pringle (1957) " Insect Flight ". By permission Cambridge University Press, New York. 132pp.]

muscle generally in that the thick filaments of the A-band pass through the I-band and connect to the Z-line material. The thick filaments narrow to smaller filaments, the **C-filaments,** in the I-band (Garamvölgyi, 1965). The C-filaments are very extensible and serve as part of the elastic component of the flight muscle. Fibrillar muscles possess very short I-bands and, on the basis of the sliding filament model, would not be expected to undergo very great shortenings. In *Calliphora* (blowfly) maximal shortening is about 2 to 3 per cent of rest length; while in *Bombus* (bumblebee) maximal shortening is less than 1 per cent of rest length (Boettiger, 1957). Full movement of the wings is produced by what amounts to an isometric contraction, and the insect indirect flight system operates on the basis of short contractions producing maximal power.

The more primitive orders of insects possess **direct flight muscles**. The muscles supplying power to drive the wings are directly connected to the wing articulation. In the Odonata the direct flight muscles are tubular muscles in which the nuclei are arranged in a linear row down the center of the fiber in a cytoplasmic space lacking myofibrils (see Figure 10-40).

In all other insect orders the flight muscles are **indirect**. They are not attached directly to the wing articulation but instead create movements of the elastic thorax and its associated structures, which then transmit the movement to the wings. Indirect flight muscles may be tubular or they may be close-packed or fibrillar (Figure 10-40). Close-packed muscles are a histological type forming the power producing flight muscles of Orthoptera, Lepidoptera, and other synchronous flight insects. The fibrillar muscles are the self-oscillatory muscles of Diptera and other high-frequency wing beat insects. Cicadas possess another type of flight muscle (also found in their tymbal organs) known as lamellar muscle. Because any given order of insects may have a diverse distribution of these types of muscles, generalizations are not very factual.

As far as the biochemistry of insect fibrillar muscles is concerned, it has been found that actin, myosin, and tropomyosin are present in proportions similar to those in vertebrate striated muscle, and the properties of these proteins are generally the same in both groups (Maruyama, 1965b). One important difference is that insect fibrillar muscle actomyosin-ATPase activity, in the presence of Ca^{2+}, is increased by stretching the muscle (Rüegg and Tregear, 1966). This may partially explain the very important characteristic of fibrillar muscle: under tension the active state of the muscle increases and the muscle can shorten without the need for nervous stimulation.

Boettiger (1951) found that electrical stimulation of fibrillar muscles in flies did not affect the frequency of contraction although abnormally high frequencies of muscle action potentials were produced. Further, if one end of the fibrillar muscle was detached from the wing articulation, it

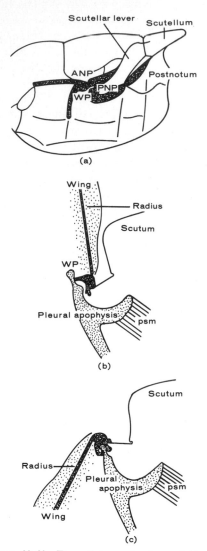

Figure 10-41 The click mechanism of the fly wing. (a) Diagrammatic lateral view of the thorax of *Sarcophaga bullata*. (b) and (c) Diagrammatic sections of the wing base showing the position of the articular pieces at the start of the downstroke (b) and upstroke (c). ANP, anterior notal process; PNP, posterior notal process; WP, pleural wing process; psm, pleurosternal muscle. [Redrawn from J. W. S. Pringle (1957) "Insect Flight". By permission Cambridge University Press, New York. 132pp.]

the flight muscles were not caused by high frequency stimulation but rather depended on the attachment of a suitable load.

The following description of the flight mechanism in insects with high wing beat frequencies is very much simplified and generalized both physiologically and anatomically. The anatomy and physiology of insect indirect flight is both complex and highly diversified in different insect species (see Pringle, 1957). The wings in dipterans and other high wing beat frequency insects are inserted at a junction between the lateral pleurum and the dorsal scutum and attached to skeletal processes that form a scutellar lever system (Figure 10-41). This lever system has two stable positions, up and down, and its operation is sometimes referred to as the click mechanism.

Boettiger and Furshpan (1952) found that when blowflies were anesthetized with carbon tetrachloride, the wings assumed only one of two extreme positions, either fully up or fully down. This click action was caused by the anatomical arrangements of the articulating lever system and by the action of various pleurosternal muscles, which are stimulated by low levels of carbon tetrachloride. The general nature of the click mechanism is shown in Figure 10-42.

The major indirect flight muscles, responsible for the power-producing action that

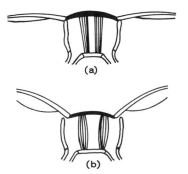

Figure 10-42 Highly simplified diagram of the click mechanism of indirect flight. The muscles shown are the dorsoventral indirect flight muscles. Not shown are the dorsal longitudinal flight muscles. (a) Bottom of the downstroke. (b) Top of the upstroke.

would go into a smooth tetanic contraction at frequencies of 10 to 20 stimuli per second—not the situation found in the intact system. This was evidence that the oscillations of

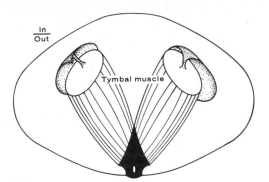

In
Out

Tymbal muscle

Figure 10-43 The nature of the sound-producing tymbal organ of cicadas.

depresses the wings, are the **dorsal longitudinal muscles** that run through the thoracic box and exert their pull at the hinged joint between the postnotum and scutellum (Figure 10-41). When these muscles contract, they arch the elastic tergum and cause the lever system to move beyond its midpoint toward a position of stability. During this movement the edge of the wing snaps over the edge of the pleurum while the pleurum advances toward the edge of the scutum, thus depressing the wing. Figure 10-41b shows the position of the wing and lever system at the end of the upstroke. Figure 10-41c shows the wing position and arrangement of the lever system at the end of the downstroke.

When the wings snap downward accompanied by the movements of the lever system, the load is quickly removed from the dorsal longitudinal muscles. Since they are no longer exerting force on the pleurum, this elastic skeletal plate rapidly returns to its original position. Simultaneously the lever system returns to its original position, and the wing is moved upward. These activities place a quick stretch on the dorsal longitudinal muscles and they respond to the stretch by an increase in active state and another contraction. The rapid oscillation of the wings depends therefore on the elastic properties of the tergum, the properties of a complex lever system, and the ability of the indirect flight muscles to be stimulated by stretch. Nervous

impulses are needed only to initiate the wing beat and at intervals to ensure that some active state is present in the muscles.

The upward movement of the wings is aided by another set of muscles, the **dorsoventral complex**. Part of this complex is composed of fibrillar muscle that acts antagonistically to the dorsal longitudinal muscles. The complex also undergoes cyclic contractions caused by releases from tension and subsequent stretches that activate the muscles.

Other muscles in the thorax are used to maintain the mechanical arrangements of the skeletal components of the flight machinery and to cause wing movements about the articulatory axis.

The muscles of the sound-producing organ, the tymba, of cicadas are similar to the flight muscles described above. The tymbal organ consists of a stiff, curved membrane covering a resonance chamber. Within the chamber are tymbal muscles (Figure 10-43). A single nervous impulse from the motor neuron causes the tymbal muscles to contract isometrically. This action buckles in the membrane. A click mechanism now allows the muscles to shorten and lose tension. This causes the membrane to bulge outward again, stretching the muscle, increasing its active state, and causing it to shorten again. An oscillatory cycle is established in which one action potential develops enough active state for several cycles of contraction and relaxation to occur. The frequency of sound emitted by the organ—the sound is a result of the inward and outward movements of the stiff membrane causing compressions and rarefractions in the resonating chamber—is higher than the frequency of nerve impulses in most cicadas. In *Platypleura capitata* one nerve impulse elicits four sound pulses, and a stimulus frequency of 50 per second sets up a muscle rhythm of about 320 per second (Pringle, 1957). There is a great diversity in both the structure and functional arrangements of tymbal organs of different species.

Insect fibrillar muscle has been extensively studied using glycerol-extracted preparations (Pringle, 1967, should be consulted for an analysis of this work and the mechanisms underlying fibrillar muscle activity).

10-34. Ciliary Activity. Cilia are cellular organelles often classified into two types: (1) flagella—relatively larger organelles occurring singly or in small numbers on a cell and (2) true cilia—relatively smaller organelles usually present in large numbers on the cell surface, for example, *Paramecium caudatum* has about 2,500 cilia on its surface. A true cilium has the typical 9:2 fiber arrangement described in Section 3-11 and also has a basal granule from which the two central fibers arise. Flagella are found in protozoans (class Flagellata), the choanocyte cells of sponges, the solenocyte and flame-bulb end cells of some invertebrate nephridia (Chapter 14), the gastroderm of coelenterates, and the sperm cells of most animal groups.

Cilia are found in all animal phyla, although in nematodes and arthropods they serve no motor functions. Throughout the animal kingdom cilia are found to be part of the structure of certain sensory organs including the visual receptor cells and many types of sensory hairs, otocysts, and so forth. It has now been shown that true cilia are present in some sensory organs of at least one nematode (Roggen et al., 1966). I shall discuss cilia here only with respect to their contractile properties.

Ciliary activity can occur only in an aqueous medium, and cilia are therefore found on cell surfaces that are bathed by a fluid or covered with an aqueous film. If an organism is small, surface cilia can produce a rapid movement of the organism through its medium. Larger organisms, for example, Ctenophora, can be moved slowly through their medium by cilia only if their body density is about the same as that of the medium. If the inertia is too great, surface cilia can move the medium past the organism, rather than the organism through the medium. External cilia, which are often present in complex structural arrangements, for example, in some molluscs, can be used to provide a current of water that brings nutrients and

oxygen to the organism and removes waste products, sperm or ova, or other materials from the animal. Ciliated epithelium is found in respiratory, excretory, digestive, circulatory, genital, and nervous systems of various animal groups. Respiratory tracts are often lined wholly or in part with cilia whose function is to lubricate and clean the respiratory passages by removing particulate matter and distributing mucous. Cilia are the means by which sperm or ova are transported in many urogenital systems. Ciliary epithelium of the mammalian brain ventricles serves to circulate cerebrospinal fluid. Cilia are found in some endocrine organs and function to move glandular secretions to point where they are released.

Not only do cilia have the property of contractility, but they must also possess a conduction system. The mechanisms and ciliary structures responsible for these two functions are not known. It would appear that the inner fibers are the contractile elements because in some organisms the two central fibers are missing in modified cilia, and these cilia can conduct stimulation but cannot contract. However, in other cilia the two central fibers appear to conduct excitation, whereas the outer filaments are the contractile elements. Because the cilia are covered by extensions of the cell membrane, it is

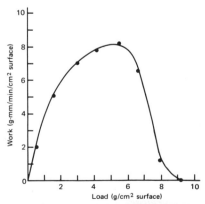

Figure 10-44 A work load curve for ciliary activity. Note its similarity to the work load curve of striated muscle (Figure 10-32). [From the data of Maxwell (1905).]

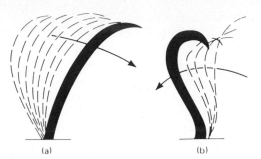

Figure 10-45 (a) Effective stroke of cilium from human nasal epithelium. (b) The recovery stroke.

possible that in many cases this acts as the conducting structure.

Glycerol-extracted cilia beat in ATP solutions (Hoffmann-Berling, 1958). Cilia contains a protein with ATPase activity; dynein has already been described (Section 10-10). A flagellar ATPase has also been isolated and is thought to play a role in flagellar contraction (Claybrook and Nelson, 1968). Closely related to cilia are the contractile stalks, myonemes, of some protozoans. Studies of the contractile stalk of *Vorticella* reveal that these also contain ATPase enzymes. Most hypotheses of ciliary activity are based on the reactions of an actomyosin-like protein reacting with ATP and Ca^{2+}.

Cilia are relatively strong organelles. L. Hill (1928) found that the cilia of bullfrog gullet could easily move a 5 gram weight and could slowly move even 10 and 15 gram weights. A work-load curve can be obtained for cilia (Figure 10-44) by allowing a ciliated surface to move a weight up an incline. Increased work by cilia leads to increased oxygen consumption by the cells (Gray, 1928).

Very little is known about the mechanisms used either to produce ciliary contraction or to control and coordinate ciliary beating on epithelial surfaces. The cilia of most metazoans beat only in one direction, and the direction of beat is permanently determined. Twitty (1928) removed epithelial cells and then grafted them back in position but with reversed polarity. The cells continued their original beat direction, now reversed relative to that of the surrounding cells. Although a cilium may beat in only a single plane, it can

still achieve an effective water movement in either direction by altering the form of the beat. Such changes might result from the initiation of contraction at a different part of the ciliary base.

The effective stroke of a cilium is the power-producing forward beat. The nasal cilia of humans undergo a rapid, stiffly-sweeping, pendular movement (Figure 10-45a). The recovery stroke is a bending back again of the base of the cilium and then a progressive flexing movement toward the tip of the cilia. A wide variety of ciliary movements are known. Some cilia, for example, cilia of the frog pharynx, simply bend back and forth with a flexing at the base. Others, especially the locomotor cilia of protozoans, undergo a three-dimensional movement with the tip of the cilium tracing an inverted funnel in a counterclockwise motion. The cilia of protozoans are usually capable of reversal of beat direction.

Ciliated surfaces usually show metachronism. There is an orderly succession of beat initiation of cilia located in a spatial sequence (Figure 10-46). Each cilium along one axis is slightly out of phase with cilia in front and in back in the direction of metachronic wave propagation. At right angles to this wave direction, cilia beat isochronically (in phase) giving an optical picture of waves passing across the ciliated surface. Knight-Jones (1954) pointed out that four basic patterns of ciliary movements could exist. If the direction

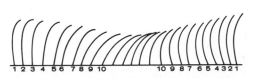

1 2 3 4 5 6 7 8 9 10   10 9 8 7 6 5 4 3 2 1

Figure 10-46 (Upper) The nature of the continuous wave of ciliary activity over an epithelial surface. (Lower) The nature of ciliary wave propagation. One through 10, the active stroke; 10 through 1, during the recovery strokes. [After Proetz (1941).]

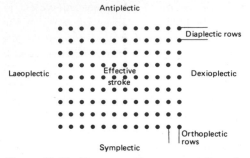

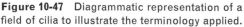

Figure 10-47 Diagrammatic representation of a field of cilia to illustrate the terminology applied.

of the effective stroke of the cilia is in the same direction as the passage of the metachronal wave, then the metachronism is symplectic; if the direction is opposite, the metachronism is antiplectic. When the direction of the effective stroke is perpendicular to the direction of wave passage, the metachronism is diaplectic. If the effective beat is to the right or to the left of the direction of passage of the wave, then the metachronism is dexioplectic or laeoplectic, respectively (Figure 10-47).

There are two major theories concerning the mechanism by which ciliary activity is coordinated. The neuroid theory (Englemann, 1868; Parker, 1905) proposes that nervelike impulses are transmitted from cell to cell. The mechanical theory (Verworn, 1890) proposes that the action of one cilium mechanically stimulates the next one into activity (Fawcett, 1961, discusses these and other aspects of ciliary activity). There are objections to both theories. No center for stimulatory activity has been shown as needed by the neuroid theory, nor are any nervous activities as slow as the rate of wave travel in ciliary surfaces. The mechanical theory has difficulties because temperature, viscosity, or ionic changes have different effects of rate of ciliary stroke and the passage of the metachronal wave. It is probable that both mechanisms are used by different animals.

According to Gray (1928) some cilia are normally unaffected by external agents, others are normally active but can be inhibited by nervous or hormonal influences, whereas a third type are normally quiet but can be stimulated into activity. Most nervous controls appear to be inhibitory.

However, the lateral cilia on the gills of *Mytilus* stop their movements only when isolated from the gills, although all other ciliary types continue to beat. 5-Hydroxytryptamine was found to activate the lateral cilia (Gosselin, 1961). Although it was at first proposed that 5-HT was released by the branchial nerve (Aiello, 1957), Gosselin and O'Hara (1961) obtained evidence that the 5-HT responsible for maintaining the beat of these lateral cilia was produced by nonnervous tissues. Schor (1965) found that 5-HT and ATP had a synergistic effect on the cilia of mussel gills. The effects of the two substances combined was far greater than would be expected from their separate effects.

Acetylocholine increases the ciliary activity of the frog pharynx. Normally the pharyngeal cilia are quiescent, but stimulation of certain cranial nerves increases activity that persists for 10 minutes or more after cessation of the stimulus (Lucas, 1932a, b; Seo, 1931).

In the ciliate protozoan, *Opalina*, both the membrane potential and the ciliary beat direction are sensitive to ionic and electrical changes (Kinosita, 1954). The orientation of the cilia of *Paramecium caudatum* is dependent on the presence of the proper amounts of ATP, Ca^{2+}, and Zn^{2+} (Naitoh, 1969). *Paramecium* are sensitive to both electrical stimulation and calcium concentrations (Grebeci, 1965). The membrane potential of *Paramecium* averages about 20 mV, inside negative. Depolarization of the membrane leads to ciliary beat reversal (Yamaguchi, 1960).

The cilia of some protozoans were thought to be under the control of a neuromotor center that sent impulses out through a set of neuromotor fibrils. However, even after complete microdissection of this fibrillar system, coordinated movements in *Eupolotes* continue uninterrupted (Okajima, 1966). The ciliary systems of protozoans are complex and respond to a variety of external agents. This is not surprising, since these are the locomotor organelles which the organism must use in avoiding harmful factors and moving toward favorable conditions.

The control of flagellar movement has been reviewed by Machin (1963). Bradfield (1955) discusses the protein fibers of flagella and cilia. Bacterial flagella do not have the 9:2 fiber arrangement of animal cilia and flagella, rather they are composed of a triple-stranded helix with a hollow center (Swanbeck and Forslind, 1964). Sleigh (1962); Kinosita and Murakami (1967); and Rivera (1962) review cilia and ciliary control.

10-35. Amoeboid Movement. Protoplasmic streaming (or cyclosis) is commonly found in cells and represents a movement of the protoplasm within the cell in the absence of distortions of the plasmalemma. In some cells streaming is rapid enough to be directly observable in the microscope; other cells show a much slower activity and a mixing motion rather than a steady current flow of protoplasm. Streaming probably serves as an intracellular transport mechanism. The molecular mechanisms underlying streaming are not known. Amoeboid movement in many respects is similar to protoplasmic streaming, and both may share a common molecular basis (Wolpert, 1965).

Amoeboid movement involves changes in cell shape, deformations of the plasmalemma, the extension and retraction of pseudopods, and often locomotion of the cell. Locomotory activity—found in the rhizopod protozoans, in the plasmodium of Myxomycetes (slime molds), in amoeboid leucocytes, and in wandering cells of metazoans—requires that the pseudopod attach to the substrate, an activity that requires Ca^{2+} in the medium. In most Foraminifera, heliozoans, radiolarians, and vertebrate macrophages of the reticuloendothelial system, amoeboid movement serves as a feeding mechanism, and the pseudopods do not attach to the substrate although they do extend, flex, and retract. Pseudopods are found in a variety of shapes depending on species (Schaeffer, 1920), and their number on a cell is also a species variable.

The theories of amoeboid movement are still in an unsatisfactory state, and only a very general picture of the mechanisms thought to underlie this contractile phenomenon are given here. The early theories of amoeboid movement considered that the sole driving force for activity was produced either by surface tension forces or by sol-gel transformations (Mast, 1926). Neither by itself is satisfactory in explaining amoeboid movement. Sol-gel transformations of the

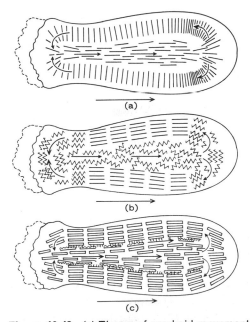

Figure 10-48 (a) Theory of ameboid movement according to R. D. Allen. A semiliquid endoplasm streams up the center of the cell pulled forward by contraction of the cortical gel near the head. The region in which endoplasm moves out to each side at the anterior end is the fountain zone. (b) According to R. J. Goldacre, contraction at the tail, where gel is liquefying into endoplasm, accounts for forward movement of endoplasm. Wavy lines represent contracted molecules of endoplasm. (c) Sliding molecule model or gel-endoplasm shearing is a third theory for ameboid movement. Chemical bridges on the inner edge of the gel push forward individual molecules of endoplasm. The flow of these molecules carries along the endoplasm nearer the center. The endoplasm (as in the top and center diagrams) turns to gel at the head and gel turns to endoplasm at the tail. [From T. Hayashi (1961) "How cells move" *Scientific American* **205** (3): 184-204. Copyright © 1961 by Scientific American, Inc. All rights reserved.]

protoplasm accompany amoeboid movement and are presumably caused by alterations in the shapes of protein molecules within the cytoplasm (Marsland, 1956; Marsland and Brown, 1936). The surface tension of a cell is not high enough to provide the forces observed in amoeboid movement (Harvey and Marsland, 1942). Most theories today are based on some form of contractile event. Seravin (1964) discusses the state of these various theories.

Allen and his co-workers postulate a contractile process at the forward end of the cell, specifically in the fountain zone region (see Figure 10-48a). In the shear zone, particles move with high velocities, as determined by exposing the cell to centrifugal forces, and this zone appears to have a low viscosity. Endoplasm, according to this model, is recruited from the ectoplasm in the recruitment zone of the posterior part of the cell, and the endoplasm is thought to actively contract in the fountain zone. The tension developed displaces the endoplasm anteriorly. The contraction is conducted posteriorly causing the endoplasm to advance. The contraction squeezes water and solutes from the anterior end of the cell, forming the clear hyaline cap (see Allen, 1960, 1961, and 1964).

This model has been criticized by Rinaldi and Jahn (1964). These workers postulate a sliding molecule model of contraction (Figure 10-48c) based on work with foraminiferans. These protozoans have very slender pseudopods, and filaments of undetermined nature are seen that could form the basis of a sliding mechanism in the cell (Jahn and Rinaldi, 1959). It is, of course, possible that the mechanisms underlying amoeboid movement differ in the two groups of protozoans.

Figure 10-48b shows another model for amoeboid movement. Here it is suggested that contractile events occur in the posterior region of the cell and push forward the endoplasm. Amoeboid movement in amoebas is accompanied by a spike potential along the plasmalemma (Kamiya, 1964). Reversible sol-gel changes follow, with solation occurring at the anterior end of the amoeba (Marsland, 1964). But again, the driving force for these changes is not determined. The contraction of material at the posterior end of an amoeba would drive material forward and allow it to form a pseudopod. But although contraction of the cortical gel at the posterior end of the cell is supposed to occur, the ectoplasm in this region has a lower viscosity than that at the anterior end.

Which of these models is correct awaits further observations and experiments with amoeboid cells. It is extremely difficult to analyze molecular events in these minute single cells. In fact, the analysis of all types of cellular contractile events is now dependent on suitable methods for observing and measuring molecular changes, especially of the proteins involved in these events.

References and Readings

Abbott, B. C. and R. J. Baskin (1962). "Volume changes in frog muscle during contraction." *J. Physiol.* (London) **161**: 379–391.

Abbott, B. C. and A. J. Brady (1964). "Amphibian muscle." In: **Physiology of the Amphibia.** (J. A. Moore, ed.), pp. 329–370. New York: Academic Press, Inc.

Abbott, B. C. and R. A. Chaplain (1966). "Preparation and properties of the contractile element of insect fibrillar muscle." *J. Cell Sci.* **1**: 311–330.

Abbott, B. C. and J. M. Ritchie (1951). "Early tension relaxation during a muscle twitch." *J. Physiol.* (London) **113**: 330–335.

Abbott, B. C. and D. R. Wilkie (1953). "The relation between velocity of shortening and the tension length curve of skeletal muscle." *J. Physiol.* (London) **120**: 214.

Adrian, R. H. (1956). "The effect of internal and external potassium concentration on the membrane potential of frog muscle." *J. Physiol.* (London) **133**: 631–658.

Aiello, E. L. (1957). "The influence of the branchial nerve and of 5-hydroxytryptamine on the ciliary activity of *Mytilus gill.*" *Biol. Bull.* **113**: 325.

Aiello, E. L. and G. Guideri (1964). "Nervous control of ciliary activity." *Science* **146**: 1692–1693.

Alexander, R. S. (1967). "Role of calcium in the plasticity of venous smooth muscle." *Am. J. Physiology* **213**: 287–294.

Allen, R. D. (1960). "The consistency of ameba cytoplasm and its bearing on the mechanism of ameboid movement." *J. Biophys. Biochem. Cytol.* **8**: 379–397.

Allen, R. D. (1961). "A new theory of amoeboid movement." *Exp. Cell Res.* **8** (Suppl.), 17–31.

Allen, R. D. (1964). "Cytoplasmic streaming and locomotion in marine Foraminifera." In: **Primitive Motile Systems in Cell Biology.** (R. D. Allen and N. Kamiya, eds.), pp. 407–432. New York: Academic Press, Inc.

Andersson-Cedergren, E. (1959). "Ultrastructure of motor endplate and sarcoplasmic components of mouse skeletal muscle fiber as revealed by three-dimensional reconstruction from serial sections." *J. Ultrastr. Res.* **1** (Suppl.), 1–191.

Atwood, H. L. (1967). "Crustacean neuromuscular mechanisms." *Am. Zool.* **7**: 527–551.

Auber, J. (1963). "Ultrastructure de la myo-epidermique chez les Diptéres." *J. Microscop. Sci.* **2**: 325–336.

Auber, J. and F. Couteaux (1962). "L'attache des myofilaments secondaires au niveau de la strie Z dans les muscles de Diptéres." *Compt. Rend.* **254**: 3425–3426.

Auber, J. and F. Couteaux, (1963). "Ultrastructure de la strie Z dans les muscles de Diptéres." *J. Microscop.* **2**: 309–324.

Bagby, R. M. (1966). "The fine structure of myocytes in the sponges *Microciona prolifera* (Ellis and Solander) and *Tedania ignis* (Duchassing and Michelotti)." *J. Morphol.* **118**: 167–181.

Baguet, F. and J. M. Gillis (1967). "The respiration of the anterior byssus retractor muscle of *Mytilus edulis* (ABRM) after a phasic contraction." *J. Physiol.* (London) **188**: 67–82.

Bailey, K. (1948). "Tropomyosin: a new asymmetric protein component of the muscle fibril." *Biochem.* **43**: 271–278.

Bajusz, E. (1964). "'Red' skeletal muscle fibers: relative independence of neural control." *Science* **170**: 938–939.

Bárány, M. (1967). "ATP-ase activity of myosin correlated with speeds of muscle shortening." *J. Gen. Physiol.* **50**: 197–218.

Barets, A. (1955). "Caracteristiques morphologiques des deux types d'innervation motrice du muscle lateral des téleostéens." *Compte. Rend.* **169**: 1420–1422.

Baskin, R. J. (1964). "Volume changes in isolated myofibrils." *Biochim. Biophys. Acta* **88**: 517–527.

Baskin, R. J. and S. Gaffin (1965). "Oxygen consumption in frog sartorius muscle. I. The isometric twitch." *J. Cell. Comp. Physiol.* **65**: 19–26.

Baskin, R. J. and P. J. Paolin (1965). "Muscle volume changes and relation to the active state." *Science* **148**: 971–972.

Baskin, R. J. and G. M. Wiese (1964). "Contraction-band formation in barnacle myofibrils." *Science* **143**: 134–136.

Bate-Smith, E. C. and J. R. Bendall (1947). "Rigor mortis and adenosine triphosphate." *J. Physiol.* (London) **106**: 177.

Bear, R. S. (1944). "X-ray diffraction studies on protein fibres. II. Feather rachis, porcupine quill tip and clam muscle." *J. Am. Chem. Soc.* **66**: 2043–2050.

Bennett, H. S. (1960). "The structure of striated muscle as seen by the electron microscope." In: **Structure and Function of Muscle.** (G. H. Bourne, ed.), Vol. 1, pp. 137–181. New York: Academic Press, Inc.

Bennett, H. S. and K. R. Porter (1953). "An electron microscope study of sectioned breast muscle of the domestic fowl." *Am. J. Anat.* **93**: 61–106.

Bettex-Galland, M. and E. F. Luscher (1965). "Thrombosthenin, the contractile protein from blood platelets and its relation to other contractile proteins." *Adv. Protein Chem.* **20**: 1–35.

Boettiger, E. G. (1951). "Stimulation of the flight muscles of a fly." *Anat. Rec.* **111**: 443.

Boettiger, E. G. (1957). "Triggering of the contractile process in insect fibrillar muscle." In: **Physiological Triggers.** (T. H. Bullock, ed.), pp. 103–116. Washington, D.C.: American Physiology Society.

Boettiger, E. G. (1960). "Insect flight muscles and their basic physiology." *Ann. Rev. Entomol.* **5**: 1–16.

Boettiger, E. G. and E. Furshpan (1952). "The mechanics of flight movements in Diptera." *Biol. Bull.* **102**: 200–211.

Booji, H. L. (1966). "Thoughts about the mechanism of membrane movement." In: **Intracellular Transport.** (K. B. Warren, ed.), pp. 301–317. New York: Academic Press, Inc.

Boulpaep, E. (1963). "Permeability of heart muscle to choline." *Arch. Intern. Physiol. Biochim.* **71**: 623–625.

Bozler, E. (1927). "Untersuchungen zur Physiologie der Tonusmuskeln." *Z. vergleich. Physiol.* **7**: 407.

Bozler, E. (1936). "Electrical stimulation and conduction in smooth muscle." *Cold Spring Harbor Symp. Quant. Biol.* **4**: 260–266.

Bozler, E. (1938). "Electrical stimulation and conduction of excitation in smooth muscle." *Am. J. Physiol.* **122**: 614–623.

Bozler, E. (1941). "The mechanical properties of resting smooth muscle." *J. Cell. Comp. Physiol.* **18**: 385–391.

Bozler, E. and C. L. Cottrell (1937). "The birefringence of muscle and its variation during contraction." *J. Cell. Comp. Physiol.* **10**: 165.

Bradfield, J. R. G. (1955). "Fiber patterns in animal flagella and cilia." *Symp. Soc. Exp. Biol.* **9**: 306–334.

Brady, A. J. (1964). "Excitation and excitation-contraction coupling in cardiac muscle." *Ann. Rev. Physiol.* **26**: 341–356.

vom Brocke, H. H. (1966). "The activating effect of calcium on the contractile system of insect fibrillar flight muscle." *Pflüg. Arch. ges. Physiol.* **290**: 70–79.

Brown, D. E. S. (1934). "The effect of rapid changes in hydrostatic pressure upon the contraction of skeletal muscle." *J. Cell. Comp. Physiol.* **4**: 257–281.

Brown, D. E. S. (1936). "The effect of rapid compression upon events in the isometric contraction of skeletal muscle." *J. Cell. Comp. Physiol.* **8**: 141–157.

Brown, D. E. S. (1941). "The regulation of energy exchange in contracting muscles." *Biol. Symp.* **3**: 161–190.

Brown, D. E. S. (1957). "Temperature-pressure relation in muscular contraction." In: **The Influence of Temperature on Biological Systems.** pp. 83–110. Washington D.C.: American Physiology Society.

Brown, D. E. S., F. H. Johnson, and D. A. Marsland (1942). "The pressure, temperature relations of bacterial luminescence." *J. Cell. Comp. Physiol.* **20**: 151–168.

Buller, A. J., J. C. Eccles, and R. M. Eccles (1960). "Differentiation of fast and slow muscles in the cat hind limb." *J. Physiol.* (London) **150**: 399–416.

Buller, A. J., J. C. Eccles, and R. M. Eccles (1960). "Interactions between motoneurons and muscles in respect to the characteristic speeds of their responses." *J. Physiol.* (London) **150**: 417–439.

Burnstock, G., G. Campbell, M. Bennett, and M. E. Holman (1963). "The transmission of inhibition from autonomic nerves to the smooth muscle of the Guinea Pig Taenia Coli." *Nature* **200**: 581–582.

Burr, J. H. and H. McLennan (1960). "The apparent extracellular space of mammalian skeletal muscle. A comparison of the inulin space in normal and dystropic mouse tissues." *Can. J. Biochem. Physiol.* **38**: 829–835.

Caldwell, P. C. and G. Walster (1963). "Studies on the micro-injection of various substances into crab muscle fibers." *J. Physiol.* (London) **169**: 353–372.

Carew, E. B. (1962). "A contraction cycle in glycerinated fibers controlled by ionic strength." *J. Gen. Physiol.* **45**: 357.

Carlson, F. D. (1963). "The mechano-chemistry of muscular contraction, a

critical revaluation of *in vivo* studies."
Prog. Biophys. **13**: 261–314.

Carlson, F. D., D. J. Hardy, and D. R. Wilkie (1963). "Total energy production and phosphocreatine hydrolysis in the isotonic twitch." *J. Gen. Physiol.* **46**: 851–882.

Carsten, M. E. and A. M. Katz (1964). "Actin: a comparative study." *Biochim. Biophys. Acta* **90**: 534–541.

Chaplain, R. A. (1966a). "Indication for an allosteric effect of ADP in actomyosin gels from insect indirect fibrillar flight muscle." *Arch. Biochem. Biophys.* **115**: 450–461.

Chaplain, R. A. (1966b). "The allosteric nature of substrate inhibition of insect actomyosin ATP-ase in presence of magnesium." *Biochem. Biophys. Res. Comm.* **22**: 248–253.

Claybrook, J. R. and L. Nelson (1968). "Flagellar adenosine triphosphatase from sea urchin sperm: properties and relation to motility." *Science* **162**: 1134–1136.

Connell, J. J. and I. M. Mackie (1964). "Molecular weight of rabbit and cod myosins." *Nature* **201**: 78–79.

Costantin, L. L., C. Franzini-Armstrong, and R. J. Podolsky (1965). "Localization of calcium-accumulating structures in striated muscle fibers." *Science* **147**: 158–160.

Costantin, L. L. and R. J. Podolsky (1967). "Depolarization of the internal membrane system in the activation of frog skeletal muscle." *J. Gen. Physiol.* **50**: 1101–1123.

Costantin, L. L., R. J. Podolsky, and L. W. Tice (1967). "Calcium activation of frog slow muscle fibres." *J. Physiol.* (London) **212**: 261–272.

Crane, R. K. (1966). "Organization of an epithelial cell brush border." In: **Intracellular Transport.** (K. B. Warren, ed.), pp. 71–102. New York: Academic Press, Inc.

Csapó, A. (1960). "Molecular structure and function of smooth muscle." In: **Structure and Function of Muscle.** (G. H. Bourne, ed.), Vol. 2, pp. 229–264. New York: Academic Press, Inc.

Csapó, A. (1961). "The *in vivo* and *in vitro* effects of estrogen and progesterone on the myometrium." In: **Mechanism of Action of Steriod Hormones.** (C. A. Villee and L. L. Engel, eds.), pp. 126–145. Long Island City, N.Y.: Pergamon Press, Inc.

Csapó, A. (1962). "Smooth muscle as a contractile unit." *Physiol. Rev.* **42** (Suppl.): 7–33.

Daniel, E. E. (1964). "Effect of drugs on contractions of vertebrate smooth muscle." *Ann. Rev. Pharmacol.* **4**: 189.

Davies, R. E. (1963). "A molecular theory of muscle contraction: calcium-dependent contractions with hydrogen bond formation plus ATP-dependent extensions of part of the myosin-actin cross-bridges." *Nature* **199**: 1068–1074.

Davies, R. E., M. J. Kushmerick, and R. E. Larson, (1967). "(Professor A. V. Hill's further challenge to biochemists) ATP, activation, and the heat of shortening of muscle." *Nature* **214**: 148–151.

Driezen, R., D. J. Hartshorne, and A. Stracher (1966). "The subunit structure of myosin. I. Polydispersity in SM quanidine." *J. Biol. Chem.* **241**: 443–448.

Driezen, P., L. Gershman, P. Trotta, and A. Strachner (1967). "Myosin: subunits and their interactions." *J. Gen. Physiol.* **50** (Suppl.), 85–118.

Dydynska, M. and D. R. Wilkie (1966). "The chemical and energetic properties of muscles poisoned with fluorodinitrobenzene." *J. Physiol.* (London) **184**: 751–769.

Ebashi, S. ed. (1965). **Molecular Biology of Muscular Contraction.** Tokyo: Igaku Shoin.

Ebashi, S., and F. Ebashi (1965). "α-Actinin, a new structural protein from striated muscle, I. Preparation and action on actomyosin-ATP interaction." *J. Biochem.* (Tokyo) **58**: 7–12.

Ebashi, S., F. Ebashi, and K. Maruyama (1964). "A new protein factor promoting contraction of actomyosin." *Nature* **203**: 645–646.

Ebashi, S. and M. Endo (1968). "Calcium ions and muscle contraction." *Prog. Biophys.* **18**: 123–183.

Ebashi, S. and A. Kodama (1966). "Interaction of troponin with F-actin in the presence of tropomyosin." *J. Biochem.* **59**: 425–426.

Edwards, G. A. (1960). "Insect micromorphology." *Ann. Rev. Entomol.* **5**: 17–34.

Edwards, C. and H. Lorkovic (1967). "The roles of calcium in excitation-contraction coupling in various muscles of the frog, mouse, and barnacle." *Am. Zool.* **7**: 615–622.

Eggleton, P. and G. P. Eggleton (1927). "The inorganic phosphate and labile form of organic phosphate in the gastrocnemius of the frog." *Biochem. J.* **21**: 190.

Eisenberg, B. and R. S. Eisenberg (1968). "Transverse tubular system in glycerol-treated skeletal muscle." *Science* **160**: 1243–1244.

Elison, C., A. S. Farhurst, J. N. Howell, and D. J. Henden (1965). "Calcium uptake in glycerol-extracted rabbit psoas fibers. I. Biochemical properties and conditions for uptake." *J. Cell. Comp. Physiol.* **65**: 133–140.

Elliot, G. F., J. Lowy, and B. M. Millman (1965). "X-ray diffraction from living striated muscle during contraction." *Nature* **206**: 1357–1358.

Englehardt, V. A. and M. N. Ljubimowa (1939). "Myosin and adenosine triphosphatase." *Nature* **144**: 668–669.

Englemann, T. W. (1868). "Über die Flimmerbewegung." *Z. Med. Naturw.* **4**: 321–478.

Ernst, E. (1958). **Die Muskeltätigkeit.** Budapest: Hungarian Academy of Sciences. New York: Academic Press, Inc. 355 pp.

Fawcett, D. W. (1961). "Cilia and Flagella." In: The Cell. (J. Brachet and A. E. Mirsky, eds.), Vol. 2, pp. 217–297. New York: Academic Press, Inc.

Fenn, W. O. (1923). "A quantitative comparison between the energy liberated and the work performed by the isolated frog sartorius muscle." *J. Physiol.* (London) **58**: 173–203.

Fenn, W. O. (1924). "Relation between work performed and energy liberated in muscular contraction." *J. Physiol.* (London) **58**: 373–395.

Fiske, C. H. and Y. SubbaRow (1929) "Phosphocreatine." *J. Biol. Chem.* **81**: 629–679.

Gans, C. and W. Bock (1965). "The functional significance of muscle architecture: a theoretical analysis." *Ergeb. Anat. u. Entwicklungsges.* **38**: 115–142.

Garamvölgyi, N. (1963). "Observations préliminaires sur la structure de la strie Z dans muscle alaire de l'abeille." *J. Microscop.* **2**: 107–112.

Garamvölgyi, N. (1965). "The arrangement of the myofilaments of insect flight muscle." *J. Ultrastruct. Res.* **13**: 409–424.

Gergely, J. (1966). "Contractile proteins." *Ann. Rev. Biochem.* **35** (Part 2), 691–722.

Gibbons, I. R. and A. J. Rowe (1965). "Dynein: a protein with adenosine triphosphatase activity from cilia." *Science* **149**: 424–426.

Gibbs, C. L. and N. V. Ricchiuti (1965). "Activation heat in muscle: method for determination." *Science* **147**: 162–163.

Gibbs, C. L., N. V. Ricchiuti, and W. F. H. M. Mommaerts (1966). "Activation heat in frog sartorius muscle." *J. Gen. Physiol.* **49**: 517–535.

Gilëv, V. P. (1966). "Further investigations of the thick filaments of crab muscles." *Biochim. Biophys. Acta* **112**: 340–345.

Gordon, A. M., A. F. Huxley, and F. J. Julian (1964). "The length-tension diagram of single vertebrate striated muscle fibers." *J. Physiol.* (London) **171**: 28P–30P.

Gosselin, R. E. (1961). "The cilioexcitatory activity of serotonin." *J. Cell. Comp. Physiol.* **58**: 17–25.

Gosselin, R. E. and G. O'Hara (1961). "An unsuspected source of error in studies of particle transport by lamellibranch gill ciliary." *J. Cell. Comp. Physiol.* **58**: 1–9.

Gray, J. (1923). "The mechanism of ciliary movement. III. The effect of temperature." *Proc. Roy. Soc.* (London) **B95**: 6–15.

Gray, J. (1928). **Ciliary Movement.** New York: Cambridge University Press.

Gray, J. (1929). "Mechanisms of ciliary movement." *Am. Naturalist* **63**: 68–81.

Grebeci, A. (1965). "Membrane calcium and

the anodal galvanic taxis in *Paramecium caudatum.*" *2nd Int. Conf. Protozool.*, London. p. 242.

Hadju, S. (1953). "Mechanism of staircase and contracture in ventricular muscle." *Am. J. Physiol.* **174:** 371–380.

Hagiwara, S. (1965). "Relation of membrane properties of the giant muscle fiber of a barnacle to internal composition." *J. Gen. Physiol.* **48:** 55–58.

Hagiwara, S. and S. Nakajima (1966). "Effects of intracellular Ca ion concentration upon the excitability of muscle fiber membrane of a barnacle." *J. Gen. Physiol.* **49:** 807–818.

Hall, C. E., M. A. Jakus, and F. O. Schmitt (1945). "The structure of certain muscle fibrils as revealed by the use of electron stains." *J. Appl. Phys.* **16:** 459–465.

Hammerle, P. and F. Cammeron (1966). "ATP-induced ciliary movements in glycerinated *Tetrahymena pyriformis.*" *J. Protozool.* **13:** 26.

Hanson, J. and H. E. Huxley (1955). "The structural basis of contraction in striated muscle." *Symp. Soc. Exp. Biol.* **9:** 228–264.

Hanson, J. and J. Lowy (1960). "Structure and function of the contractile apparatus in the muscles of invertebrate animals." In: **The Structure and Function of Muscle.** (G. H. Bourne, ed.), Vol. 1, pp. 265–335. New York: Academic Press, Inc.

Hanson, J. and J. Lowy (1964). "The structure of molluscan tonic muscles." In: **Biochemistry of Muscle Contraction.** (J. Gergely, ed.), pp. 400–409. Boston: Little, Brown and Company.

Harvey, E. N. and D. M. Marsland (1932). "The tension at the surface of *Amoeba dubia* with direct observations on the movement of cytoplasmic particles at high centrifugal speeds." *J. Cell. Comp. Physiol.* **2:** 75–87.

Hasselbach, W. (1964). "Relaxing factor and the relaxation of muscle." *Prog. Biophys.* **14:** 167–222.

Hayashi, T. (1961). "How cells move." *Sci. Am.* **205** (3): 184–204.

Hayashi, T. and R. Rosenbluth (1952). "Con-traction-elongation cycle of loaded spread actomyosin fibers." *J. Cell. Comp. Physiol.* **40:** 495–506.

Heilbrunn, L. V. and F. J. Wiercinski (1947). "The action of various cations on muscle protoplasm." *J. Cell. Comp. Physiol.* **29:** 15–32.

Hill, A. V. (1938). "The heat of shortening and the dynamic constants of muscle." *Proc. Roy. Soc.* (London) **B126:** 136–195.

Hill, A. V. (1939). "The mechanical efficiency of frog's muscle." *Proc. Roy. Soc.* (London) **B127:** 434–451.

Hill, A. V. (1949a). "Work and heat in a muscle twitch." *Proc. Roy. Soc.* (London) **B136:** 120.

Hill, A. V. (1949b). "The heat of activation and the heat of shortening in a muscle twitch." *Proc. Roy. Soc.* (London) **B136:** 195–211.

Hill, A. V. (1964a). "The effect of load on the heat of shortening of muscle." *Proc. Roy. Soc.* (London) **B159:** 297–318.

Hill, A. V. (1964b). "The effect of tension in prolonging the active state in a twitch." *Proc. Roy. Soc.* (London) **B159:** 589–595.

Hill, A. V. (1964c). "The variation of total heat production in a twitch with velocity of shortening." *Proc. Roy. Soc.* (London) **B159:** 595–605.

Hill, A. V. (1966). "A further challenge to biochemists." *Biochem. Z.* **345:** 1–8.

Hill, D. K. (1940). "The anaerobic recovery heat production of frog's muscle at $0°$ C." *J. Physiol.* (London) **98:** 460–466.

Hill, D. K. (1949). "Changes in transparency of muscle during a twitch." *J. Physiol.* (London) **108:** 292–302.

Hill, D. K. (1953). "The effect of stimulation on the diffraction of light by striated muscle." *J. Physiol.* (London) **119:** 501–512.

Hill, L. (1928). "The ciliary movement of the trachea studied *in vitro*: A measure of toxicity." *Lancet* **215:** 802–805.

Hnik, P. (1962). **The Denervated Muscle.** Prague: Czechoslovak Academy of Sciences.

Hodge, A. J. (1956). "The fine structure of striated muscle." *J. Biophys. Biochem. Cytol.* **2** (Suppl.) 131–142.

Hoffmann-Berling, H. (1958). "Der Mechanismus eines neuen, von der Muskelkonverschiedenen Kontraktions zyklus." *Biochim. Biophys. Acta* **27**: 247–255.

Hoffmann-Berling, H. (1960). "Other mechanisms producing movement." In: **Comparative Biochemistry.** (E. Florkin and M. Mason, eds.), Vol. 2, pp. 341–370. New York: Academic Press, Inc.

Hoyle, G. (1957). **Comparative Physiology of the Nervous Control of Muscular Contraction.** New York: Cambridge University Press. 147 pp.

Hoyle, G. (1964). "Muscle and neuromuscular physiology." In: **Physiology of Mollusca.** (K. M. Wilbur and C. M. Yonge, eds.), Vol. 1, pp. 313–351. New York: Academic Press, Inc.

Hoyle, G. (1967). "Diversity of striated muscle." *Am. Zool.* **7**: 435–450.

Hoyle, G. and J. Lowy (1956). "The paradox of *Mytilus* muscle: A new interpretation." *J. Exp. Biol.* **33**: 295–310.

Hoyle, G. and J. H. McAlear (1963). "Mechanism of supercontraction in a striated muscle fiber." *Science* **143**: 712–713.

Hoyle, G. and T. Smyth (1963). "Neuromuscular physiology of giant muscle fibers of a barnacle, *Balanus nubilis* Darwin." *J. Comp. Biochem. Physiol.* **10**: 291–314.

Huxley, A. F. (1957). "Muscle structure and theories of contraction." *Prog. Biophys.* **7**: 255–318.

Huxley, A. F. (1964). "The links between excitation and contraction." *Proc. Roy. Soc.* (London) **B160**: 486–488.

Huxley, A. F. and H. E. Huxley eds. (1964). "A discussion on the physical and chemical basis of muscular contraction." *Proc. Roy. Soc.* (London) **B160**: 433–542.

Huxley, A. F. and R. E. Taylor (1958). "Local activation of striated muscle fibers." *J. Physiol.* (London) **144**: 426–441.

Huxley, H. E. (1960). "Muscle cells." In: **The Cell.** (J. Brachet and A. E. Mirsky, eds.), Vol. 4, pp. 365–481. New York: Academic Press, Inc.

Huxley, H. E. (1963). "Electron microscope studies on the structure of material and synthetic protein filaments from striated muscle." *J. Mol. Biol.* **7**: 281–308.

Huxley, H. E. (1964). "Evidence for continuity between the central elements of the triads and the extracellular space in frog sartorius muscle." *Nature* **202**: 1067–1071.

Huxley, H. E. (1965). "The mechanism of muscle contraction." *Sci. Am.* **213**: 18–27.

Huxley, H. E. (1969). "The mechanism of muscular contraction." *Science* **164**: 1356–1366.

Huxley, H. E., W. Brown, and K. C. Holmes (1965). "Constancy of axial spacing in frog sartorius muscle during contraction." *Nature* **206**: 1358.

Ikeda, K. (1959). "Studies on the origin and pattern of miniature electrical oscillation in the insect muscle." *Japanese J. Physiol.* **9**: 484–497.

Infante, A. A. and R. E. Davies (1965). "The effect of 2,4-dinitrofluorobenzene on the activity of striated muscle." *J. Biol. Chem.* **240**: 3996–4001.

Infante, A. A., D. Klaupiks, and R. E. Davies (1965). "Phosphorylcreatine consumption during single-working contractions of isolated muscle." *Biochim. Biophys. Acta* **94**: 504–515.

Iyengar, M. R. and R. E. Olson (1965). "The amino acid composition of dog-heart myosin." *Biochim. Biophys. Acta* **97**: 371–373.

Jahn, T. L. and R. Rinaldi (1959). "Protoplasmic movement in the foraminiferan *Allogromia laticollaris*, and a theory of its mechanism." *Biol. Bull.* **117**: 100–118.

Jewell, B. R. and J. C. Rüegg (1966). "Oscillatory contractions of insect fibrillar muscle after glycerol extraction." *Proc. Roy. Soc.* (London) **B164**: 428–459.

Jöbsis, F. F. (1964). "Basic processes in cellular respiration." In: **Handbook of Physiology.** (W. O. Fenn and H. Rahn, eds.), Sec. 3, Respiration, Vol. 1, pp. 63–124. Washington, D.C.: American Physiology Society.

Jöbsis, F. F. and J. C. Duffield (1967). "Force, shortening, and work in muscular contraction; relative contributions to overall energy utilization." *Science* **156**: 1388–1392.

Jöbsis, F. F. and M. J. O'Connor (1966). "Calcium release and reabsorption in the sartorius muscle of the toad." *Biochem. Biophys. Res. Comm.* **25**: 246–252.

Johnson, F. H., H. Eyring, and M. J. Polissar (1954). **The Kinetic Basis of Molecular Biology.** New York: John Wiley & Sons, Inc. 874 pp.

Johnson, W. H. and B. M. Twarog (1960). "The basis for prolonged contraction in molluscan muscle." *J. Gen. Physiol.* **43**: 941–960.

Kamiya, N. (1964). "The motive force of endoplasmic streaming in the ameba." In: **Primitive Motile Systems in Cell Biology.** (R. D. Allen and N. Kamiya, eds.), pp. 257–277. New York: Academic Press, Inc.

Katchalsky, A. (1954). "Polyelectrolyte gels." *Prog. Biophys.* **4**: 1–59.

Kinosita, H. (1954). "Electrical potentials and ciliary response in *Opalina*." *J. Fac. Sci. Tokyo Univ.* (*Zool.*) **7**: 1–14.

Kinosita, H. and A. Murakani (1967). "Control of ciliary motion." *Physiol. Revs.* **47**: 53–82.

Knappeis, G. G. and F. Carlsen (1956). " The ultrastructure of the Z disc in skeletal muscle." *J. Cell. Biol.* **13**: 323–335.

Knight-Jones, E. W. (1954). "Relations between metachronism and the direction of ciliary beat in metazoa." *Quart. J. Microscop. Sci.* **95**: 503–521.

Kominz, D. R., A. Hough, P. Symonds, and K. Laki (1954). "The amino acid composition of actin, myosin, tropomyosin, and the meromyosins." *Arch. Biochem. Biophys.* **50**: 148–159.

Korschelt, E. (1938). "Cuticularsehe und Bindegewebssehne. Eince vergleichend morphologische-histologische Betrachtung." *Z. Wiss. Zool.* **150**: 494–526.

Kruger, P. (1952). **Tetanus und Tonus der quergestreiften Skelettmuskeln der Wirbeltiere und des Menschen.** Leipzig: Akademische Verlag.

Kuriyama, H. and A. Csapó (1961). "A study of the parturient uterus with the microelectrode technique." *Endocrinology* **68**: 1010–1025.

Lane, B. P. (1965). "Alterations in the cytologic detail of intestinal smooth muscle cells in various stages of contraction." *J. Cell. Biol.* **27**: 199–213.

Lehninger, A. L. (1962). "Respiration-linked mechanochemical changes in mitochondria." In: **Horizons in Biochemistry.** (M. Kasha and B. Pullman, eds.), pp. 421–435. New York: Academic Press, Inc.

Lorkovic, H. and C. Edwards (1968). "Threshold for contracture and delayed rectification in muscle." *Life Sci.* **7**: 367–380.

Lowey, S., J. Kucera, and A. Holtzer (1963). "On the structure of the paramyosin molecule." *J. Mol. Biol.* **7**: 234–244.

Lowy, J. and J. Hanson (1962). "Ultrastructure of invertebrate smooth muscle." *Physiol. Rev.* **42** (Suppl.): 34–47.

Lowy, J., J. Hanson, G. F. Elliott, B. M. Millman, and M. W. McDonough (1966). "The design of the contractile systems." In: **Principles of Biomolecular Organization.** (G. E. W. Wolstenholme and M. O'Connor, eds.), pp. 229–258. Boston: Little, Brown and Company.

Lowy, J., B. M. Millman, and J. Hanson (1964). "Structure and function in smooth tonic muscles of lamellibranch molluscs." *Proc. Roy. Soc.* (London) **B160**: 525–536.

Lucas, A. M. (1932a). "Coordination of ciliary movement. I. Methods of study and the relation of ciliary coordination to ciliary inhibition." *J. Morphol.* **53**: 243–263.

Lucas, A. M. (1932b). "Coordination of ciliary movement. II. The effect of temperature on ciliary wavelength." *J. Morphol.* **53**: 265–276.

Lündsgaard, E. (1930). "Untersuchungen über Muskelkontraktionen ohne Michsaurebildung." *Biochem. Z.* **217**: 162.

Machin, K. E. (1963). "The control and synchronization of flagellar movement." *Proc. Roy. Soc.* (London) **B158**: 88–104.

Marshall, J. M. (1959). "Effects of estrogen and progesterone on single uterine muscle fibers in the rat." *J. Physiol.* (London) **197**: 935.

Marshall, J. M. (1964). "The action of oxytocin on uterine smooth muscle." In:

Pharmacology of Smooth Muscle. (E. Bül-bring, ed.), Vol. 6, pp. 143–155. Long Island City, N.Y.: Pergamon Press, Inc.

Marsland, D. A. (1956). "Protoplasmic contractility in relation to gel structure. Temperature-pressure experiments on cytokinesis and amoeboid movement." *Int. Rev. Cytol.* **5**: 199–227.

Marsland, D. A. (1964). "Pressure-temperature studies on amoeboid movement and related phenomena: an analysis of the effects of heavy water on the form, movement and gel structure in *Amoeba proteus.*" In: **Primitive Motile Systems in Cell Biology.** (R. D. Allen and N. Kamiya, eds.), pp. 173–187. New York: Academic Press, Inc.

Marsland, D. A. and D. E. S. Brown (1963). "Amoeboid movement at high hydrostatic pressure." *J. Cell. Comp. Physiol.* **8**: 167.

Maruyama, K. (1965a). "A new protein-factor hindering network formation of F-actin in solution." *Biochim. Biophys. Acta* **94**: 208–225.

Maruyama, K. (1965b). "The biochemistry of the contractile elements of insect muscle." In: **Physiology of Insecta.** (M. Rockstein, ed.), Vol. 2, pp. 451–482. New York: Academic Press, Inc.

Mast, S. O. (1926). "Structure, movement, locomotion and stimulation in Amoebae." *J. Morphol.* **41**: 347–425.

Matsumoto, Y. (1967). "Validity of the force-velocity relation for muscle contraction in the length region, $l \leq l_o$." *J. Gen. Physiol.* **50**: 1125–1137.

Matyushin, D. P. (1963). "Varieties of tonic muscle fibers in the oculomotor apparatus of the rabbit." *Byull. Eksperim. Biol. Med.* **55**: 3–6.

Matyushin, D. P. (1967). "Contractions and their relationships to action potentials in the phasic fibers of the external eye muscles of adult and newborn animals." *Biofizika* **12**: 462–469.

Maxwell, S. S. (1905). "The effect of salt solutions on ciliary activity." *Am. J. Physiol.* **13**: 154–170.

McNeill, P. A. and G. Hoyle (1967). "Evi-

dence for superthin filaments." *Am. Zool.* **7**: 483–498.

McPherson, A. and J. Tokunaga (1967). "The effects of cross-innervation on the myoglobin concentration of tonic and phasic muscles." *J. Physiol.* (London) **188**: 121–129.

Millman, B. M. (1967). "Mechanism of contraction in molluscan muscle." *Am. Zool.* **7**: 583–591.

Millman, B. M. and G. F. Elliott (1965). "X-ray diffraction from contracting molluscan muscle." *Nature* **206**: 824–825.

Morales, M. (1965). "On the mechanochemistry of contraction." In: **Molecular Biophysics.** (B. Pullman and M. Weissbluth, eds.), pp. 397–410. New York: Academic Press, Inc.

Naitoh, Y. (1964). "Time change of the membrane potential of *Opalina* after changing the external osmotic pressure." *J. Fac. Sci. Tokyo Univ.* (*Zool.*) **10**: 311–321.

Naitoh, Y. (1969). "Control of the orientation of cilia by adenosinetriphosphate, calcium and zinc in glycerol-extracted *Paramecium caudatum.*" *J. Gen. Physiol.* **53**: 517–529.

Naylor, W. G. and N. C. R. Merrillees (1964). "Some observations on the fine structure and metabolic activity of normal and glycerinated ventricular muscle of toad." *J. Cell Biol.* **22**: 533–550.

Needham, D. M. (1964). "Proteins of the contraction mechanism." In: **Pharmacology of Smooth Muscle.** (E. Bülbring, ed.), Vol. 6, pp. 87–95. Long Island City, N.Y.: Pergamon Press, Inc.

Needham, D. M. and J. M. Williams (1963a). "Salt-soluble collagen in extracts of uterus muscle and in foetal metamyosin." *Biochem. J.* **89**: 546–552.

Needham, D. M. and J. M. Williams (1963b). "Proteins of the uterine contractile mechanism." *Biochem. J.* **89**: 552–561.

Niedergerke, R. (1955). "Local muscular shortening by intracellularly applied calcium." *J. Physiol.* (London) **128**: 12P–13P.

Okajima, A. (1966). "Ciliary activity and coordination in *Euplotes eurystomus.* I. The effect of microdissection of the neuro-motor fibres." *Comp. Biochem. Physiol.* **19**: 115–131.

Parker, G. H. (1905). "The movement of the swimming plates of ctenophores with reference to the theories of ciliary metachronism." *J. Exp. Zool.* **2**: 407–423.

Parnas, J. (1910). "Energetik glatter Muskeln." *Pflügers Arch. ges. Physiol.* **134**: 441.

Peachey, L. D. (1967). "Membrane systems of crab fibers." *Am. Zool.* **7**: 505–513.

Peachey, L. D. and A. F. Huxley (1962). "Structural identification of twitch and slow striated muscle fibers of the frog." *J. Cell Biol.* **13**: 177–180.

Pease, D. C., J. D. Henden, and H. N. Howell (1965). "The calcium uptake in glycerol-extracted rabbit psoas muscle fibers. II. Electron microscopic localization of uptake sites." *J. Cell. Comp. Physiol.* **65**: 141–154.

Pepe, F. A. (1966). "Some aspects of the structural organization of the myofibril as revealed by antibody staining methods." *J. Cell Biol.* **28**: 505–525.

Pepe, F. A. (1967a). "The myosin filament. I. Structural organization from antibody staining observed in electron microscopy." *J. Mol. Biol.* **27**: 203–225.

Pepe, F. A. (1967b). "The myosin filament. II. Interaction between myosin and actin filaments observed using antibody staining in fluorescent and electron microscopy." *J. Mol. Biol.* **27**: 226–236.

Perry, S. V. (1956). "Relation between chemical and contractile function and structure of the skeletal muscle cell." *Physiol. Rev.* **36**: 1–76.

Perry, S. V. (1967). "The structure and interactions of myosin." *Prog. Biophys.* **17**: 325–381.

Peterson, R. P. (1963). "A note on the structure of crayfish myofilaments." *J. Cell Biol.* **18**: 213–218.

Porter, K. R. and G. E. Palade (1957). "Studies on the endoplasmic reticulum. III. Its form and distribution in striated muscle fibers." *J. Biophys. Biochem. Cytol.* **3**: 269–300.

Pringle, J. W. S. (1957). **Insect Flight.** New York: Cambridge University Press. 134 pp.

Pringle, J. W. S. (1965). "Locomotion: flight." In: **The Physiology of Insecta.** (M. Rockstein, ed.), Vol. 2, pp. 283–329. New York: Academic Press, Inc.

Pringle, J. W. S. (1967). "The contractile mechanism of insect fibrillar muscle." *Prog. Biophys.* **17**: 1–60.

Pringle, J. W. S. (1968). "Comparative physiology of the flight: motor." *Adv. Insect Physiol.* **5**: 163–227.

Proetz, A. W. (1941). **Essays on the Applied Physiology of the Nose.** St. Louis, Mo.: Annals Publishing Company.

Prosser, C. L. (1960). "Comparative physiology of activation of muscles, with particular attention to smooth muscles." In: **The Structure and Function of Muscle.** (G. H. Bourne, ed.), pp. 387–434. New York: Academic Press, Inc.

Prosser, C. L. and F. A. Brown (1961). **Comparative Animal Physiology.** 2nd ed. Philadelphia: W. B. Saunders Co. 688 pp.

Rack, P. M. H. (1966). "The behavior of mammalian muscle during sinusoidal stretching." *J. Physiol.* (London) **183**: 1–14.

Ramsey, R. W. (1960). "Some aspects of the biophysics of muscle." In: **The Structure and Function of Muscle.** (G. H. Bourne, ed.), Vol. 2, pp. 303–358. New York: Academic Press, Inc.

Reedy, M. (1964). "Discussion on the physical and chemical basis of muscular contraction." *Proc. Roy. Soc.* (London) **B160**: 458–460.

Reedy, M. K., K. C. Holmes, and R. T. Tregear (1966). "Induced changes in orientation of the crossbridges of glycerinated insect flight muscles." *Nature* **207**: 1276–1280.

Reichel, H. (1960). **Muskelphysiologie.** Berlin: Springer-Verlag. 276 pp.

Reuben, J. P., P. W. Brandt, H. Garcia, and H. Grundfest (1967). "Excitation-contraction coupling in crayfish." *Am. Zool.* **7**: 623–645.

Reuben, J. P., P. W. Brandt, L. Girardier, and H. Grundfest (1967). "Crayfish muscle: permeability to Na induced by Ca depletion." *Science* **155**: 1263–1266.

Reynolds, S. (1965). **Physiology of the Uterus,** 2nd ed. New York: Hafner Publishing Co., Inc. 619 pp.

Rinaldi, R. A. and T. L. Jahn (1964). "Shadowgraphs of protoplasmic movement in *Allogromic laticollaris* and a correlation of this movement to striated muscle contraction." *Protoplasma* 58: 369–390.

Ritchie, A. D. (1928). **The Comparative Physiology of Muscular Tissue.** New York: Cambridge University Press. 111 pp.

Ritchie, J. M. (1954). "The duration of the plateau of full activity in frog muscle." *J. Physiol.* (London) 124: 605–612.

Rivera, J. A. (1962). **Cilia, Ciliated Epithelium, and Ciliary Activity.** Long Island City, N.Y.: Pergamon Press, Inc. 167 pp.

Roeder, K. D. (1951). "Movements of the thorax and potential changes in the thoracic muscles of insects during flight." *Biol. Bull.* 100: 95–106.

Roggen, D. R., D. J. Rasky, and N. O. Jones (1966). "Cilia in nematode sensory organs." *Science* 152: 515–516.

Rome, E. (1967). "Light and x-ray diffraction studies of the filament lattice of glycerol-extracted rabbit psoas muscle." *J. Mol. Biol.* 27: 591–602.

Rome, E. (1968). "X-ray diffraction studies of the filament lattice of striated muscle in various bathing media." *J. Mol. Biol.* 37: 331–344.

Rüegg, J. C. and R. T. Tregear (1966). "Mechanical factors affecting the ATP-ase activity of glycerol-extracted insect fibrillar flight muscle." *Proc. Roy. Soc.* (London) **B165**: 497–512.

Rüegg, J. C., E. Strassner, and R. H. Shirmer (1965). "Extraktion und Reinigung von Arterien-Actomyosin, Actin und Extra-globulin." *Biochem. Z.* **343**: 70–85.

Sandow, A. (1944). "General properties of latency relaxation." *J. Cell. Comp. Physiol.* 24: 221–256.

Sandow, A. (1947). "Latency relaxation and a theory of muscular mechanochemical coupling." *Ann. N.Y. Acad. Sci.* 47: 895–929.

Sandow, A. (1965). "Excitation-contraction coupling in skeletal muscle." *Pharmacol. Rev.* 17: 265–320.

Satir, P. (1967). "Morphological aspects of ciliary motility." *J. Gen. Physiol.* 50: 241–258.

Schaeffer, A. A. (1920). **Amoeboid Movement.** Princeton, N.J.: Princeton University Press.

Schor, S. L. (1965). "Serotonin and adenosine triphosphate: synergistic effect on the beat frequency of cilia of mussel gills." *Science* 148: 500–502.

Selverston, A. (1967). "Structure and function of the transverse tubular system in crustacean muscle fibers." *Am. Zool.* 7: 515–526.

Seo, A. (1931). "Studies on the nervous regulation of the ciliary movement." *Japanese J. Med. Sci. Tr. III. Biophysics* 2: 47–75.

Seravin, L. N. (1964). "A critical survey of modern concepts of amoeboid movement." *Tsitologya* 6: 653–667.

Sexton, A. W. and J. W. Gersten (1967). "Isometric tension differences in fibers of red and white muscles." *Science* 157: 199.

Shafiq, S. A. (1964). "An electron microscopical study of the innervation and sarcoplasmic reticulum of the fibrillar flight muscle of *Drosophila melanogaster*." *Quart. J. Micr. Sci.* **105**: 1–6.

Shanes, A. M. (1961). "Calcium influx in frog rectus abdominus muscle at rest and during potassium contracture." *J. Cell. Comp. Physiol.* **57**: 193–202.

Sjodin, R. A. and L. A. Beauge (1967). "Strophanthidin-sensitive transport of cesium and sodium in muscle cells." *Science* 156: 1248–1250.

Sjöstrand, F. (1959). "Fine structure of cytoplasm: the organization of membranous layers." In: **Biophysical Science—A Study Program.** (J. Oncley, ed.), pp. 301–318. New York: John Wiley & Sons, Inc.

Sjöstrand, F. (1962). "The connections between A- and I-band filaments in striated frog muscle." *J. Ultrastruct. Res.* 7: 225–246.

Slater, E. C. (1960). "Biochemistry of sarcosomes." In: **Structure and Function of Muscle.** (G. H. Bourne, ed.), Vol. 2, pp. 105–140. New York: Academic Press, Inc.

Sleigh, M. A. (1962). **The Biology of Cilia and**

Flagella. Long Island City, N.Y.: Pergamon Press, Inc.

Sleigh, M. A. (1966). "The coordination and control of cilia." *Symp. Soc. Exp. Biol.* **20**: 11–31.

Smith, D. S. (1966). "The organization and function of the sarcoplasmic reticulum and T-system of muscle cells." *Prog. Biophys.* **16**: 107–142.

Street, S. F. and R. W. Ramsey (1965). "Sarcolemma: transmitter of active tension in frog skeletal muscle." *Science* **149**: 1379–1380.

Swanbeck, G. and B. Forslind (1964). "A low-angle X-ray diffraction study of bacterial flagella." *Biochim. Biophys. Acta* **88**: 422–469.

Szent-Györgyi, A. (1949). "Free energy relations and contractions of actomyosin." *Biol. Bull.* **96**: 140–161.

Szent-Györgyi, A. (1951). **Chemistry of Muscular Contraction.** 2nd ed. New York: Academic Press, Inc. 162 pp.

Szent-Györgyi, A. (1953). **Chemical Physiology of Contraction in Body and Heart Muscle.** New York: Academic Press, Inc. 133 pp.

Szent-Györgyi, A. G. and W. H. Johnson (1964). "An alternative theory for contraction of striated muscles." In: **Biochemistry of Muscular Contraction.** (J. Gergely, ed.), pp. 485–510. Boston: Little, Brown and Company.

Tagi, K. (1961). "The mechanical and colloidal properties of Amoeba protoplasm and their relations to the mechanism of amoeboid movement." *Comp. Biochem. Physiol.* **3**: 73–91.

Tsao, T. C. (1953). "The molecular dimensions and the monomer-dimer transformation of actin." *Biochim. Biophys. Acta* **11**: 227–235.

Turner, C. D. (1960, 1966, 4th ed.). **General Endocrinology.** Philadelphia: W. B. Saunders Company.

Twarog, B. M. (1954). "Responses of a molluscan smooth muscle to acetylcholine and 5-hydroxytryptamine." *J. Cell. Comp. Physiol.* **44**: 141–164.

Twarog, B. M. (1966). "Catch and the mechanism of action of 5-hydroxytryptamine on molluscan muscle: a speculation." *Life Sci.* **5**: 1201–1213.

Twitty, V. C. (1928). "Experimental studies on the ciliary action of amphibian embryos." *J. Exp. Zool.* **50**: 319–343.

von Uexküll, J. (1912). "Studien über den Tonus. VI. Die Pilgermuschel." *Bio. Z.* **58**: 305–332.

Van der Kloot, W. G. (1967). "Membrane depolarization and the metabolism of muscle." *Am. Zool.* **7**: 661–669.

Vbrová, G. (1963). "Changes in motor reflexes produced by tenotomy." *J. Physiol.* (London) **169**: 513–526.

Vignais, P. V., P. M. Vignais, C. S. Rossi, and A. Lehninger (1963). "Restoration of ATP-induced contraction of pre-treated mitochondria by 'contractile protein'." *Biochem. Biophys. Res. Comm.* **11**: 307–312.

Walcott, B. and E. B. Ridgway (1967). "The ultrastructure of myosin-extracted striated muscle fibers." *Am. Zool.* **7**: 499–504.

Walls, E. W. (1960). "The microanatomy of muscle." In: **Structure and Function of Muscle.** (G. H. Bourne, ed.), Vol. 1, pp. 21–61. New York: Academic Press, Inc.

Weber, H. H. (1958). **The Motility of Muscle and Cells.** Cambridge, Mass.: Harvard University Press. 69 pp.

Whalen, W. J. and L. C. Collins (1963). "Work and oxygen consumption in the frog sartorius muscle." *J. Cell. Comp. Physiol.* **61**: 293–300.

Wilkie, D. R. (1960). "Thermodynamics and the interpretation of biological heat measurements." *Prog. Biophys.* **10**: 260–298.

Wilkie, D. R. (1966). "Muscle." *Ann. Rev. Physiol.* **28**: 17–38.

Wilson, J. A., P. R. Elliot, K. F. Guthe, and D. G. Shappiro (1959). "Oxygen uptake of glycerol-extracted muscle fibres." *Nature* **184**: 1947.

Winton, F. R. (1937). "The changes in viscosity of an unstriated muscle (*Mytilus edulis*) during and after stimulation with alternating, interrupted and uninterrupted direct currents." *J. Physiol.* (London) **88:** 492–511.

Wolpert, L. (1965). "Cytoplasmic streaming and amoeboid movement." *Symp. Soc. Gen. Microbiol.* **15:** 270–293.

Worthington, C. R. (1964). "Impulsive (electrical) forces in muscle." In: **Biochemistry of Muscular Contraction.** (J. Gergely, ed.), pp. 511–519. Boston: Little, Brown and Company.

Yamaguchi, T. (1960). "Studies on the mode of ionic behavior across the ectoplasmic membrane of *Paramecium*. I. Electrical potential differences measured by the intracellular microelectrode." *J. Fac. Sci. Tokyo Univ.* (*Zool.*) **8:** 573–591.

11-1. Introduction. In previous chapters the discussion of nerve and muscle functioning was based primarily on a consideration of the responses of isolated or excised tissues or cells to nonphysiological stimulation. In this chapter I shall be concerned with the basic organization and functions of nervous systems—the organized masses of neurons responsible for initiating and controlling many animal activities. Nervous systems are so complex that their analysis usually entails isolating smaller units of the system and examining their properties. Much of the discussion will center about the vertebrate nervous system about which most is known. However, the important features—both the similarities and differences—of invertebrate systems will also be included.

The most obvious output of the nervous system is that devoted to producing appropriate muscle responses, and another major topic of this chapter will be the mechanisms used to control and gradate muscle contraction in the animal.

Finally, in order to emphasize the interrelations of nervous and chemical control systems, this chapter will also include a discussion of endocrine and neuroendocrine systems. Endocrine control functioning cannot be separated from nervous system operation and, in fact, the endocrine system can be considered as an effector system whose activity is guided by the nervous system.

This chapter, then, is intended to serve primarily as an introduction to the basic properties and organizations of nervous and endocrine systems. Although the control of skeletal muscles is used to exemplify the basic coordinating and integrating activities of nervous systems, and certain reproductive functions are used to exemplify the nature of endocrine system activities, each system, of course, has other functions. The material presented here will form the basis upon which homeostatic mechanisms and behavioral activities can be described in the last two parts of this book.

Chapter 11

Neuromuscular and Neuroendocrine Control Systems

Some Basic Properties of Nervous Systems

11-2. General Functions of Nervous Systems. One of the functions of any nervous system is that of reception—the gaining of information about the environment through the excitation of receptor endings. This information, in the form initially of generator potentials, is converted to action potentials that are conducted by sensory neurons to sites where the information can be acted upon.

Primary sensory information is sent over a variety of pathways. Some lead directly to the excitation of specific effector cells. Others take the information to sites where coordinating, integrating, or delaying operations can occur, which results in more complex responses of the animal to the incoming information.

A basic function of nervous systems is to produce appropriate responses. Responses may be relatively simple as exemplified by the simple reflex arc (although, as we shall see, few reflexes are actually simple) or responses may be in the form of complex patterns of activity as exemplified by learning, thinking, or consciousness—behavioral patterns exhibited especially by higher animals.

Activities of the nervous systems may be looked upon as actions and counteractions. The latter are responses that tend to maintain the status quo of the animal in the face of a changing environment. They include many of the homeostatic regulations to be described in Part III. Others are behavioral responses to be discussed in Part IV. Counteractions are often in the form of reflex actions that are usually of short duration and relatively simple with respect to the neuronal pathways involved. Counteractions often involve visceral effectors—those smooth muscles especially which are involved in circulatory, digestive, and reproductive system operation. All of these responses are compensatory actions in that they restore the animal to some normal state following a disturbance. Often such responses require little activity on the part of higher brain centers but are initiated by activity in reflex pathways of lower parts of the nervous system.

Actions which appear to be initiated by the nervous system itself are found especially in higher organisms, for example, exploratory behavior or the replacement of one mood by another. The spontaneous activity of neurons (Chapter 9) is but one aspect of the ability of nervous systems to produce spontaneous actions without initiation by external stimulation. This means that nervous systems are not always driven by the environment but have mechanisms (of largely unknown nature) that can insulate them from the sensory input. Adaptation (Chapter 8) plays some role in this facet of nervous system functioning as, for example, when the human nervous system quickly learns to ignore the multitude of sensory inputs that result from the wearing of clothes. Although clothes press on the skin and continuously excite pressure and touch receptors, this information, which would be very distracting, is ignored at least as a conscious sensation.

Learned behavior, in which the organism alters its activities as a result of previous experience, is found especially in arthropods, molluscs, and vertebrates. It can be either homeostatic or anticipatory in nature. Learning is a function involving many interacting systems in the organism and is based on the association of at least two different stimuli, therefore, requiring at least two sets of receptors and some mechanism for modifying and coordinating the resultant activity of the nervous system. This appears to be an essential feature of learning in the lowest organisms (Bullock and Horridge, 1965). Learning is more than an adaptive change in behavior in response to a repeated stimulation.

Another important characteristic of nervous systems is **coordination**—the process in which parts of a whole action are combined into a harmonious relationship. Another function is **integration**—the process in which parts are put together to form a whole action, usually the output does not bear a one-to-one relation to the input. In the nervous system, two or more inputs usually converge causing one or more output actions. Or a single input may result in a greater or lesser number of outputs. These are both aspects of integration. Part of the integrative activity depends on the fact that neurons can inhibit activity in other neurons, as well as initiate activity. Although the synapse is one site of integrative activity in the nervous system, the higher brain centers and other organized structures within the nervous system also play a role.

Coordination and integration are poorly understood phenomena of nervous systems. In part this is due to the enormous number of neurons that make up most nervous systems. In part it is due to the even greater number of connections that occur between neurons. And, finally, it is partly due to the changing number and variety of sensory inputs to which the nervous system is constantly subjected. The coordination of homeostatic functions, for example, is difficult to understand because of the often conflicting demands of activities such as water balance, ion and solute regulation, temperature regulation, and pH regulation. In addition, such activities are also partially controlled by endocrine systems, thus adding to the complexity. At present it is impossible to place all of this activity into any clear picture.

The simplest pattern of nervous system organization leading to coordination of response is the reflex arc. But such actions are basically abstractions of nervous system function because they are studied only after the significant part of the nervous system has been isolated by surgical or chemical means.

11-3. Structural Components of Nervous Systems. The central nervous system (CNS) may be defined as an organized collection of neurons specialized for the repeated conduction of an excited state from receptor sites to effectors or to other neurons (Bullock and Horridge, 1965). Parts of the CNS are easily recognizable in higher animal groups, but according to this definition, it is absent in unicellular organisms and sponges, and is difficult to identify or to say it exists in many

coelenterates and ctenophores. Unicellular organisms possess, in some cases, specialized conducting systems but more work is needed to clarify their functions, and such systems will not be considered here (Ehret, 1960; Taylor, 1941).

Nervous tissue generally is organized in many degrees of structural complexity. It is extremely rare to find single isolated neurons, except for some sensory elements. **Nerves** are discrete, connective tissue-sheathed bundles of nerve fibers connecting some CNS structure with a peripheral region of the organism. Some nerves consist only of **efferent fibers**—motor axons carrying impulses away from the CNS to effector cells or to outlying ganglia; some nerves contain only **afferent fibers**—sensory fibers carrying information from sensory receptors to the CNS; most commonly they are **mixed nerves**—containing both sensory and motor fibers. Identifiable nerves are first found in some annelids and sipunculids.

A **plexus** is a tangled layer of nerve fibers with or without nerve cell bodies. A plexus may or may not have synaptic connections between its fibers. The plexus is found in the form of a **nerve net** in coelenterates, ctenophores, and hemichordates, serving in these organisms as the CNS. Nerve nets are diffuse collections of neurons always possessing synaptic connections. Impulses are conducted throughout the net.

Plexuses are also found in specialized regions of higher organisms. As stated in Chapter 9, they are present in the gastrointestinal systems of vertebrates and also in annelids, arthropods, and molluscs. The spontaneous activity of the neurons of these plexuses was described in that chapter. Plexuses are extremely difficult to study because of their diffuse nature and the smallness of the cells.

The term plexus also includes a tangled network of sensory fibers found in the skin of many animals. In lower forms it is often difficult to distinguish between the activities of a plexus or nerve net and the activities of other epithelial cells. In coelenterates, ctenophores, and hemichordates local thickenings in the nerve nets are found, and these clumps of neurons might represent the beginnings of a more organized nervous system.

Ganglia are collections of nerve cells in a nodular form and are surrounded by connective tissue. Both fibers and cell bodies are present. Ganglia form the CNS in all phyla at or above the level of the platyhelminthes.

The central nervous systems and ganglia of vertebrates and invertebrates differ in several structural features. The ganglia of invertebrate animals consist of a fibrous core and a cellular rind. This rind contains most of the nerve cell bodies, and the core contains nerve endings, synaptic regions, and axons. Groups of conducting axons in ganglia and central nervous systems are called **tracts**.

The fiber core of invertebrate ganglia is further divided into tracts and the **neuropile**— a complex arrangement of fine dendrites and axon terminals. The neuropile is an area of synaptic connections. Tracts consist of conduction pathways only with no synapses. A wide variety of sizes, fiber densities, suborganization, and such, however, is found in the structure of neuropiles and ganglia.

Central nervous system organization of vertebrates differs from that of invertebrates. There is a central mass of gray matter that contains cell bodies, axon terminals, dendrites, and synapses. The fibrous white matter surrounds the gray matter and contains pure axon tracts whose heavier myelination results in a creamy white color.

Nervous systems are divided into two major divisions. The **peripheral nervous system** consists of sensory endings, nerves, ganglia, plexuses, and motor endings of neurons. The **central nervous system** consists of ganglia, interconnectives, commissures, and cords. Connectives and commissures are essentially similar to nerves. But, in addition to the conducting fibers they also contain **internuncial neurons** that make connections between various parts of the central nervous system itself. Connectives join CNS ganglia that are on the same side but at different levels along the anterior-posterior axis. Com-

missures join equivalent structures on the two sides of the CNS. When a longitudinal concentration of fibers, nerve endings, and nerve cell bodies develops in an animal, the structure is a nerve cord.

The peripheral nervous system of invertebrates includes sensory nerve cell bodies that are located in the skin or other regions where sensory endings are found. But in vertebrates sensory nerve cell bodies are located within the CNS.

The term **brain** is applied to the most anterior or best developed ganglion of the CNS. If this ganglion is not sufficiently distinctive from other ganglia, it is called a cerebral ganglion.

Peripheral ganglia are found in higher animal phyla, and although in some cases they consist of purely sensory neurons, in most cases they are collections of both sensory and motor neurons. An example of the latter is the dorsal root ganglia of vertebrates. A few ganglia are purely motor neuron collections, for example, the autonomic ganglia of vertebrates.

Bilateral symmetry and the consequent possession of a front or cephalic end are features in the evolutionary development of animals. A complex of exteroreceptors and a progressively greater concentration of nervous elements in the CNS have arisen associated with the cephalic end. This phenomenon is called cephalization, and is first distinct in the annelids although its beginnings are evident in some flatworms. Cephalic ganglia are prominent in the arthropods, cephalopod molluscs, and chordates. Cephalopods possess the best developed brains among the invertebrates and also show the best evidences for complex behavior and long-term memory. Correlated with their highly developed brains, cephalopods also possess an excellent visual system, a high degree of manipulative ability, and often a capability for extremely rapid movement. Hymenopteran insects also have highly developed brains. Honeybees, for example, are noted for their capabilities for complex behavior and the ability to integrate many forms of sensory information so that they can sun-navigate and communicate information. The culmination of cephalization (to this point in time) is, of course, seen in mammals and especially in man, whose brain development had led to phenomena such as abstract thought, conscious behavior, and many other forms of complex behavior.

This section has been primarily a glossary of terms which describe basic functional features of nervous systems. In the following sections specific examples of these structures and their functions will be given.

11-4. Neurons in Nervous Systems. In Chapter 7 it was pointed out that a variety of neuronal types exist. Several different ways of classifying neurons may be used. On the basis of the nature of the processes that arise from the soma, neurons may be classified as **isopolar** (in the light microscope all the processes appear similar) or as **heteropolar** (in the light microscope differences in structure are seen). An example of the latter are the neurons that possess axons and dendrites.

Neurons may also be classified according to the number of processes they possess (Figure 11-1). A **unipolar neuron** has only one process arising from the soma, although

this process may branch. The unipolar neuron with a branching stem is common in the CNS of invertebrates. A majority of the inter-neurons and motoneurons of higher invertebrates are of this type. In fact, the unipolar neuron is the most widespread type of central neuron found in the animal kingdom.

Bipolar neurons possess two main processes, usually arising from opposite ends of a spindle-shaped soma. Nearly all invertebrate sensory cells are of this type. There is usually a short distal sensory process and a long central axonal fiber. The higher the position of an animal on the evolutionary tree, generally the longer is the distal process and the deeper lies the cell body of the sensory neurons.

Multipolar neurons have more than two processes arising from the soma. They are most frequently found as vertebrate motor neurons and interneurons and are usually heteropolar. Multipolar heteropolar neurons are not common among the invertebrates.

Interneurons are classified according to the type of connections they make within the central nervous system. **Projection neurons** send axons for long distances along the CNS. **Commissural neurons** send axons to corresponding structures on opposite sides of the CNS, and **intrinsic neurons** have axons confined to one side of the CNS.

In the CNS projection neurons, as well as sensory and motor fibers, may decussate to the contralateral side. Decussation of axons is the crossing of a median plane of the CNA by an axon. Usually the plane is in the long axis of the CNS, and thus decussation is from right to left or left to right. Decussation is the result of mechanical factors operating during embryonic development. The physiological significance of such axonal crossing over is not clear.

Other classifications of neurons are possible, and in Section 11-8 the relationship between size and function of neurons in the vertebrate nervous system is considered. In previous chapters it was stated that a neuron possesses several different functional regions. These different regions (dendritic zone, axonal region, sites of spontaneous activity, and so

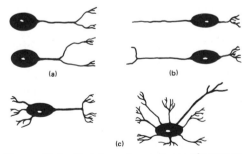

(a)　　　　　　　　(b)

(c)

Figure 11-1 Sketches of some types of neurons, classified according to the nature of their fibrous processes. (a) Unipolar neurons, typical of interneurons and motoneurons in higher invertebrates. (Top) An interneuron; (bottom) a motoneuron. (b) Bipolar neurons. Typical of many sensory neurons with cell bodies in the epithelium. (c) Heteropolar multipolar neurons. Typical of cells found in the vertebrate CNS. The cell on the left is typical of vertebrate motoneurons.

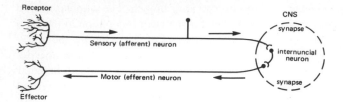

Figure 11-2 Elements of a reflex arc. Shown here is a three-neuron or bisynaptic reflex arc.

forth) can interact in a complex manner and thus add to the capabilities of the nervous system.

11-5. Properties of the Reflex Arc. A reflex arc is defined as a relatively fixed pattern of response or behavior that is always produced by a given stimulus. It is a matter of common experience that when a hand is accidentally brought into contact with a hot object, the hand is quickly jerked away from the source of the stimulus.

The simplest imaginable combination is the **simple reflex arc** consisting of a sensory neuron responsible for reception of information and transmission of information into the CNS. In the CNS the sensory neuron synapses with a motor neuron (or motoneuron), which relays impulses to and excites an effector cell. Seldom, if ever, does a single neuron play a role in sensory reception, the conduction of information, and the activation of an effector cell. Rather one finds that chains of neurons are involved in this information flow system.

But the two-neuron reflex arc, which is also called a monosynaptic reflex arc (since there is only one synaptic junction in the chain) is not typical of reflex arcs. More commonly at least three neurons are present in the chain, one of which is a CNS interneuron (Figure 11-2).

A common reflex that may be represented as a two-neuron reflex is the vertebrate knee jerk. This is elicited by tapping the tendon of the quadriceps femoris muscle just below the knee cap and results in a rapid extension of the lower leg. Many reflex arcs of vertebrate sympathetic ganglia are also monosynaptic.

Most reflex pathways are more complex because a variety of interconnections are made between sensory neurons, interneurons, and motor neurons in the CNS. Further higher centers may also send impulses to the motor neurons controlling a particular effector. When one muscle is stimulated into activity, other muscles must also be activated or inhibited in order to maintain posture or orientation of the animal. Thus apparently simple reflex actions become in most cases relatively complex.

The reflex is a unit of integration within the nervous system as pointed out by several of its properties.

1. The threshold stimulus for the elicitation of the reflex depends on the conditions of the animal—what other stimuli are present, the duration of a given stimulus, and so forth.
2. The gradation of the reflex response is not closely correlated with gradation of a stimulus above threshold.
3. A single afferent impulse does not normally elicit a response. Reflex action is usually the result of temporal summation.
4. There is little correspondence between the rhythm of a repetitive stimulus and the rhythm of the reflex response.
5. A state of depressed excitability, which often is of long duration, follows most reflex actions.
6. In many reflex actions there is a prolongation of motoneuron activity after the stimulus has ceased. This is the after-discharge phenomenon.

That integrative action exists at the reflex level is also shown by the fact that when two or more separate reflexes are stimulated simultaneously, one reflex is completely inhibited, whereas the other proceeds normally. This is particularly the case when reflex actions are antagonistic. The mechanism by which the nervous system switches off one reflex, while another proceeds, is not known.

There is generally no summation of individual reflex actions when several are stimulated simultaneously. It is of interest to note that this is not a property of synapses, where there is usually an algebraic summation of excitatory and inhibitory information.

Most reflex actions are classified as complex and involve a number of neuronal chains. Complex reflexes involve several simple or even complex reflex pathways. Most reflex actions appear to be composed of chains of complex reflexive actions.

Reflexes may be phasic or tonic. The vertebrate knee jerk is a phasic reflex in which the muscle is quickly stretched and as quickly responds with a contraction to counteract the stretch. The nerve impulses that arise from the stimulus are quickly conducted to the CNS as a synchronous volley. The reflex efferent discharge from the CNS likewise passes as a synchronous volley back to the muscle and causes a rapid contraction of all the fibers of the muscle.

If a muscle is stretched slowly, varying numbers of stretch receptors are excited— only a few at first, but more as the muscle is stretched further or if the stretch is maintained. The result is an asynchronous discharge of impulses into the CNS and a resultant asynchronous discharge conducted along the motor nerve to the muscle fibers. A sustained contraction is produced in which,

at any one time, only a relatively few muscle fibers are contracting. This tonic type of reflex is characteristic, for example, of muscle activity used to maintain posture against the force of gravity.

These have been but a few examples of the properties of reflexes. Their nature will be further examined after the organization of the vertebrate nervous system has been discussed. Reflexes are given some emphasis here since they are the functional units of nervous systems about which most is known.

The Vertebrate Nervous System

11-6. The Spinal Cord. A reflex arc such as that diagrammed in Figure 11-2 has its structural components located at particular sites in the nervous system. We shall be primarily considering the nervous systems of mammalian species because most of the physiological and histological analyses have been done with these animals. More complete descriptions of vertebrate nervous systems are found in Ranson and Clark (1959); Gardner (1968). *The Handbook of Physiology*, Section 1 (American Physiological Society, Washington, D.C.) contains much information on vertebrate nervous systems.

The CNS of vertebrates is composed of the brain and spinal cord. Both of these delicate

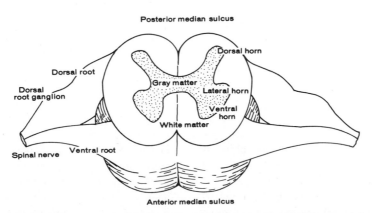

Figure 11-3 Cross-section of spinal cord showing gray matter (H-shaped form) and surrounding white matter. Specific form of gray matter will depend on the level at which spinal cord is observed.

Figure 11-4 Cross-section through the spinal cord to indicate some of the ascending and descending fiber tracts in the white matter. Cross hatched areas are descending tracts (fibers carrying impulses from brain to spinal cord). Only a few tracts are shown on the left side although each tract is duplicated on the two sides of the spinal cord. Ascending fibers arise from neurons within the cord or, in the case of the dorsal columns, may be large 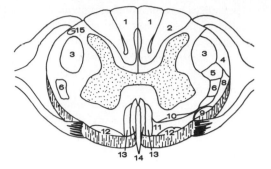 fiber branches of Group I afferents. The first part of the name usually indicates the origin of the fiber, the last part of the name indicates the destination of the fibers. Many of the functions of various fiber tracts are still unknown, nor have all fiber paths been identified.

TRACT	FUNCTION
1. Fasciculus gracilus	Carries impulses from muscle and joint receptors to higher centers.
2. Fasciculus cuneatus	As above.
3. Lateral pyramidal	Carries impulses to primary motoneurons, its origin is in precentral gyrus and tract decussates in medulla.
4. Dorsal spinocerebellar	Carries impulses from leg muscles and trunk between sixth cervical and second lumbar segments, ascends to cerebellum.
5. Rubrospinal tract	Carries impulses for cerebellar reflexes, arises in red nucleus.
6. Lateral spinothalamic	Carries pain and temperature sensory information to thalamus.
7. Spinotectal	Arises from cells of gray column and ascends to corpora quadrigemina.
8. Ventral spinocerebellar	Carries impulses to cerebellum through medulla and pons.
9. Spino-olivary	
10. Tectospinal	Carries information for optic and auditory reflexes. Arises in superior colliculi and ends in motor cells of anterior column.
11. Vestibulospinal	
12. Ventral spinothalamic	
13. Direct pyramidal	Arises from cells in central motor area and at various levels fibers synapse with ventral horn cells.
14. Sulca-marginal fasciculus	
15. Lissaeur's tract	

structures are well protected. They are enveloped in three membranes—the dura mater, arachnoid, and pia mater—and are also surrounded by bones. The brain is located within the cranium; the spinal cord within the flexible vertebral column.

The spinal cord is located in the vertebral canal of the vertebral column and is almost divided into lateral halves by grooves or fissures running longitudinally along the cord.

These are the ventral and dorsal median sulci (Figure 11-3). It may be noted that when referring to the human nervous system, the adjectives anterior and posterior are often substituted for ventral and dorsal, respectively.

The cell bodies of internuncial and motor neurons, together with synaptic regions, lie in an H-shaped zone of the spinal cord—called the gray matter. The lack of myelinated fibers in this region gives it a grayish

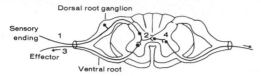

Figure 11-5 Schematic representation of the pathway for somatic reflexes. 1, sensory (afferent) neuron; 2, interneuron (may be absent in monosynaptic pathways); 3, motor (efferent) neuron; 4, interneuron for conveying sensory information to contralateral motoneurons. Note sensory neuron soma in dorsal root ganglion. Cell bodies of motoneurons lie in gray matter. In all diagrams in this text the symbol —● represents cell bodies or dendritic regions of the neuron; —(represents axon terminals.

appearance. Protuberances of the gray matter are known as the dorsal, lateral, and ventral horns (Figure 11-3).

The white matter that makes up the remainder of the spinal cord is partioned by connective tissue septa into regions known as funiculi (singular, funiculus). Some of the fibers found in the white matter carry impulses between various segments of the spinal cord or between spinal cord and brain. Ascending fibers carry impulses from lower to higher levels of the spinal cord or brain, and descending fibers carry impulses from the brain or higher levels of the spinal cord to lower levels. Such fibers are arranged in tracts whose names indicate first the point of origin and second the destination of the fibers. Some of the major tracts are diagrammed in Figure 11-4.

Sensory (afferent) fibers from the peripheral nervous system enter the spinal cord through paired dorsal roots (Figure 11-5). Dorsal root ganglia contain the cell bodies of sensory neurons. Then fibers from these sensory neurons pass into the dorsal horns of the gray matter, where they synapse with interneurons and motor neurons.

Motor (efferent) axons leave the ventral horn of the gray matter and pass into the ventral roots. Cell bodies of motor neurons are located in the gray matter, where synapses between primary sensory neurons or interneurons and the motor neurons occur. These pathways of sensory and motor fibers are

those used for reflex arcs involving skeletal muscles.

The fibers of the dorsal and ventral roots combine to form spinal nerves that then branch to various regions of the body. In the human there are 31 pairs of dorsal roots and 31 pairs of ventral roots.

I stress again that it is highly unlikely that an afferent neuron synapses only with motor neurons; rather it also synapses with interneurons as well which carry impulses to other levels of the spinal cord, to the brain, or to the opposite side of the spinal cord. These various pathways are diagrammed in Figure 11-6.

11-7. The Autonomic Nervous System. The efferent pathway innervating skeletal muscle is a direct one involving only one neuron. Cells in the ventral horn of the gray matter send axons directly to the muscles. In contrast, the efferent pathway for the innervation of smooth muscles of visceral organs, of cardiac muscle, and of endocrine glands involves two neurons and has a different anatomical arrangement.

Some cell bodies in the lateral horns of the gray matter send their myelinated fibers out by the ventral roots and these fibers leave the spinal nerve by the **white ramus**, rather than by the **gray ramus** which is the exit point for skeletal muscle motor neurons. A comparison between the efferent pathways for skeletal muscle and visceral organ innervation is diagrammed in Figure 11-7.

Efferent fibers of the visceral organ system do not go directly to the innervated tissue. Rather the fibers that exit from the spinal cord end in either a **lateral ganglion** lying close to the spinal cord or they may proceed closer to the organ they innervate and end in a **collateral ganglion**. The efferent fibers leaving the spinal cord are **preganglionic fibers**. In the ganglion they synapse with other motor nuerons, the **postganglionic fibers**, whose axons pass to the innervated structure. This system of motor fibers innervating visceral organs is the **autonomic nervous system**. Note that sensory fibers are not

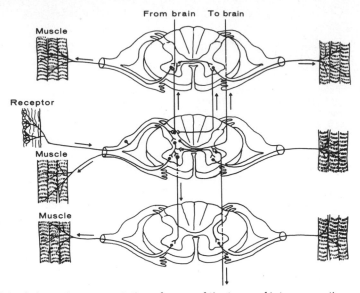

Figure 11-6 Schematic representation of some of the types of interconnections which can be made by interneurons in the spinal cord. A sensory input (shown at second level of spinal cord diagram) not only may cause activity in the muscle from which (or near which) the receptor ending arises but can also cause activity in higher or lower segments of the spinal cord as well as in the brain. Because of the interconnections of interneurons, responses may be multisegmental (motoneurons at more than one level are excited); ipsilateral (motoneurons on the same side, not necessarily the same level of the spinal cord respond); or contralateral (motoneurons on the opposite side from the sensory input respond). The effect of the interneuron may be either excitatory or inhibitory. Thus muscles on the contralateral side may be caused to go into inactivity, rather than responding with a contraction.

anatomically differentiated whether they come from skin, skeletal muscles, or visceral organs. All sensory neurons proceed directly to the dorsal root ganglia and then through the dorsal root into the dorsal horn of the gray matter. The autonomic nervous system includes only motor fibers. But a nerve that innervates a visceral organ is usually a mixed nerve containing both sensory and motor fibers.

The cell bodies that give rise to autonomic system preganglionic fibers lie in four divisions of the central nervous system: midbrain, medulla, thoracolumbar, and the second, third, and fourth segments of the sacral region of the spinal cord (Figure 11-8). That part of the autonomic nervous system originating in the thoracolumbar portion of the spinal cord is the **sympathetic division**; that part originating in the other three segments of the central nervous system is the

parasympathetic system. These two divisions are functionally as well as structurally different.

When we compare autonomic and somatic reflex arcs, we find that the afferent fibers enter the spinal cord through the same channels but the efferent pathways are different. The postganglionic neuron of the efferent autonomic pathway is typically unmyelinated (see Section 11-8).

A physiological difference between autonomic and somatic systems is found in the mode of inhibition produced. Inhibition of somatic reflexes is always accomplished by the action of interneurons upon motor neurons, that is, by one neuron affecting another neuron. This inhibition of neurons within the central nervous system is **central inhibition**. In autonomic reflexes, preganglionic neurons may inhibit postganglionic neurons, but in addition autonomic postganglionic fibers may have an inhibitory action on the effector organ they innervate. An example of this is the inhibition of the heart beat by the parasympathetic system (Chapter 13).

The ratio of preganglionic fibers to post-ganglionic fibers in the sympathetic system is at least 1:20, and the innervation of peripheral organs is often diffuse. Also many connections exist between the sympathetic ganglia. In the parasympathetic system there are sometimes only two postganglionic fibers associated with a preganglionic fiber, and impulse delivery is more localized. Also there is little connection between parasympathetic ganglia lying on or close to the innervated organs.

Many organs receive a double innervation from the autonomic system. This double supply may be antagonistic as exemplified by the sympathetic (speeds up heart rate) and parasympathetic (slows down heart rate) innervation of cardiac muscle. Just as often, however, the two sets of fibers may serve different purposes that cannot be considered antagonistic in the sense of excitatory and inhibitory impulses being delivered to the same muscle.

Functionally, the two divisions of the auto-nomic nervous systems are sometimes characterized by the nature of the transmitter substance released by the postganglionic fiber. All preganglionic fibers release acetylcholine at ganglionic synapses. Acetylcholine is usually released by postganglionic fibers of the parasympathetic division, whereas noradrenaline is released by the postganglionic fibers of the sympathetic division. Sympathetic fibers innervating sweat glands, however, are also cholinergic.

11-8. Mammalian Neurons, Conduction Rates, and Functions. Various sized cells and fibers are found in the nervous system, and the particular function of fibers is often correlated with their size (see also Section 7-26). Each successive level of information processing seems to require neurons with a greater versatility of action, and this is often reflected in the number and variety of fibrous processes they possess. By comparison with primary sensory or motor neurons, the neurons of the cerebral cortex of the vertebrate nervous system are very complex in structure (Figure 7-2), a fact presumably related to their integrating and coordinating functions.

A variety of classifications have been used

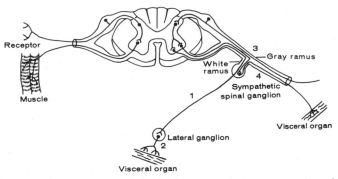

Figure 11-7 Schematic representation of the differences between somatic and autonomic neuron pathways from the spinal cord. A somatic reflex path is shown on the left side of the cord. On the right are shown autonomic pathways (motor). Note that afferent pathways are the same in each case with fibers arriving at the dorsal root and dorsal root ganglion. In the autonomic pathways the preganglionic fiber may either synapse in a spinal ganglion (fiber 3) or may travel out to lateral ganglion on or close to the organ to be innervated (fiber 1). In the latter case the postganglionic fibers are relatively short, and in the former case the postganglionic fiber is long (fiber 4). Spinal ganglia synapses are typical of the sympathetic division; lateral ganglionic connections are found in the parasympathetic division.

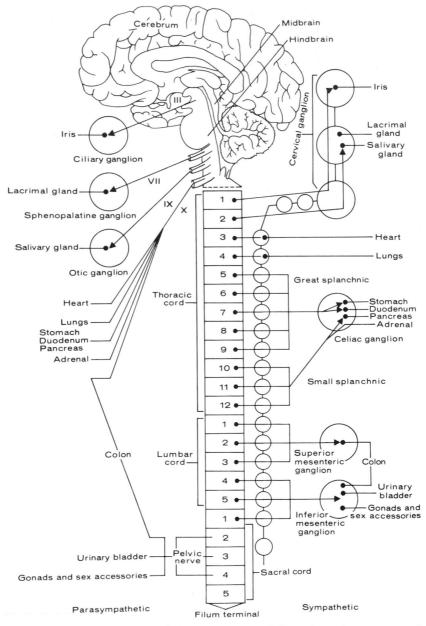

Figure 11-8 Schematic diagram of the arrangement of the autonomic nervous system. For clarity sympathetic outflow to visceral organs is shown on the right, and sympathetic outflow to blood vessels, sweat glands, and smooth muscle fibers of hairs is shown on the left. Note that an important part of the parasympathetic system includes motor fibers in the III, VII, IX, and X cranial nerves. Through the cranial nerves connections are made to higher brain centers, especially the hypothalamus and pituitary glands.

Table 11-1   Classifications of Mammalian Nerve Fibers

FIBER DESIGNATION	DIAMETER	COMMENTS (ORIGIN, DESTINATION, RECEPTOR, ETC.)
SYSTEM OF ERLANGER AND GASSER (see also Table 7-7)		
A-fibers	1-22 μ	Largest myelinated somatic fibers; both afferent and efferent. Subdivided into α, β, γ, and δ subclasses on basis of size.
B-fibers	Less than 3 μ	Myelinated efferent preganglionic fibers of the autonomic nervous system.
C-fibers		Small unmyelinated fibers
sC-fibers	0.3-1.3 μ	Sympathetic efferent postganglionic fibers
dR C-fibers	0.4-1.2 μ	Peripheral axons and axons in dorsal roots.
SYSTEM OF LLOYD		
Group I	12-21 μ	These are A-alpha fibers
Group II	6-12 μ	These are A-beta and A-gamma fibers
Group III	1-6 μ	These are A-delta fibers
Group IV	0.5-1.0 μ	These are C-fibers
FURTHER SUBDIVISIONS USED TODAY (synonyms are given in brackets)		
Group 1A [A-alpha; A-2, endings of Matthews]	12-21 μ	Afferent fibers originating in annulospiral spindle endings of muscles. Stimulated by stretch and connect directly to motoneurons of muscle of origin (synapses in CNS). Involved in myotatic reflexes.
Group 1b [A-alpha, Type B fibers of Matthews]	12-21 μ	Afferent fibers originating in muscle in tendon organs of Golgi. Stimulated by active contraction of muscle and synapse with (a) motoneurons of muscle of origin, causing inhibition and (b) motoneurons of antagonistic muscles, causing excitation.
Group II [A-beta and gamma; A-1 fibers of Matthews]	6-12 μ	Sensory fibers originating in flower spray spindles of extensor and flexor muscles. Stimulated by stretch of muscle and cause inhibition of extensors and facilitation of flexors throughout limb. Also afferent fibers from touch-pressure receptors in skin, causing excitation of flexors and inhibition of extensors through limb.
Group III [A-delta]	1-6 μ	Fibers from receptors (?) of muscle or from skin receptors. Produce excitation of flexors and inhibition of extensors throughout limb. Involved in withdrawal reflexes, and are lateral components in crossed extensor reflexes.
Group IV [C-fibers]		From muscle and skin pain receptors, function as above type.

to separate neurons on functional or structural grounds. The classifications commonly used today are shown in Table 11-1, together with some older classification schemes. Included in the table is a brief description of the origin and destination of various fiber groups and their general functions.

The central nervous system of vertebrates contains an enormous number of neurons. The human brain and spinal cord, for example, are estimated to contain about 10^{10} neurons.

All sensory input to the spinal cord enters through the dorsal roots and the entering fibers range in size from about 0.2 to 20 μ. Unmyelinated fibers of 1 μ or less (Group IV fibers) make up about one half the total number of fibers in the dorsal roots. Gelfan and Tarlov (1963) from actual counts of the neurons and fibers in the seventh lumbar segment of the dog's spinal cord found that the dorsal root contained about 12,000 fibers. In the median part of the dorsal root were 88,000 small and 400 large cells (neurons with cell body diameter of less than 34 μ were classified as small). There were 40,000 small cells and 6,000 large cells in the central gray matter. There were 6,000 cells in the ventral roots of which about 4,500 were large. At the cortex of the gray matter were 45,000 small cells and 800 large cells. The total cell count in this segment of the spinal cord was 375,000.

On the somatic motor output side of the spinal cord, two neuronal types deserve comment. Large cells, the ventral horn cells, also known as alpha motor neurons or Group I efferents, possess thick myelinated axons and are the primary source of efferent impulses to skeletal muscle fibers. But about one third of the ventral root output is from axons of small diameter whose sources are small cell bodies in the ventral horn. These are the gamma motor neurons or gamma efferents. They synapse with fibers from higher levels of the nervous system and provide information to fibers within the spindles of muscles. Spindles are major muscle sensory receptors and control muscular contraction. The ventral horn cells usually make direct synaptic

connection with primary afferents. This control system is discussed in Section 11-16.

11-9. Interneurons. Interneurons in the spinal cord serve several functions. They act, first, as amplifiers of incoming signals and thus intensify their effects. This amplification is brought about by several mechanisms. Cells may be cascaded as shown in Figure 11–9a. Amplification may also be brought about by closed loop (reverberating loop) circuits of neurons (Figure 11–9b). Amplification is also produced because interneurons distribute incoming sensory signals to many groups of motor neurons so that many different muscles may be stimulated as the result of one source of sensory input.

Integration by interneurons can be caused by both inhibitory and facilitory activities. Inhibition of motor neurons (called recurrent inhibition) is produced by a simple feedback

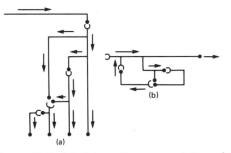

Figure 11-9 (a) Schematic representation of a multiple chain or cascade of neurons. The sequential excitation of parallel chains of interneurons through the collateral axon branches produces a prolonged excitation of the motoneurons and introduces more motoneurons into the activity. Such a circuit could account for after discharges lasting sometimes many seconds in certain reflexes. Bursts of impulses arrive at the motoneurons at intervals determined by the length and complexity of chain interconnections. (b) The closed chain neuron circuit. Collateral branches allow reverberation of impulses through the chain so that bursts of impulses arriving at the motoneuron prolong the period of excitation. The delay varies with the number of synapses involved in each loop of the chain. Such circuits could also produce long lasting discharges in ascending or descending pathways within the central nervous system.

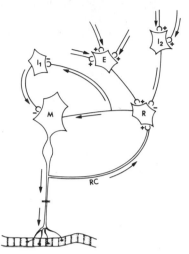

Figure 11-10 Schematic representation of a few of the synaptic connections of a Renshaw cell in the ventral horn of the spinal cord. The basic inhibitory feedback circuit is shown between the recurrent collateral (RC) of a motoneuron (M) and the Renshaw cell (R). Arrows indicate direction of impulses. A negative sign designates an inhibitory synapse, a plus sign designates an excitatory synapse. An excitatory interneuron (E) is shown that has synaptic connections with contralateral, descending, and Group III afferent fibers. The Renshaw cell can be excited by this cell and its impulses will then either inhibit the motoneuron by the direct synaptic connection or can facilitate the motoneuron by inhibiting the inhibitory activity of interneuron (I_1). Activity of the Renshaw cell itself can be inhibited by stimulation from the inhibitory neuron (I_2) which is shown receiving terminals from descending and also sensory fibers.

pathway that involves only the collaterals of the motor neurons and a group of interneurons known as Renshaw cells (Renshaw, 1941, 1946). Impulses passing along a motor neuron pass not only to the muscle but also to a Renshaw cell via an axon collateral. Excitation of the Renshaw cell produces impulses which are used to inhibit the motor neuron (Figure 11-10). Synapses on the Renshaw cell are cholinergic.

By the use of various marking techniques, it has been found that Renshaw cells lie in a focus of activity in the ventromedial region of the ventral horn (Eccles et al., 1954; Thomas and Wilson, 1965; Wilson, 1966).

Cells in this region are small to intermediate in size with short dendrites. As might be expected, this is the region of the ventral horn where the recurrent laterals of motor neurons originate and where there is extensive branching of these collaterals.

The Renshaw cell is also responsible for facilitation of motor neurons. Some motor neurons are kept in an inhibited state by the continuous background discharge of certain interneurons. When the Renshaw cell is excited, its impulses may overcome this inhibition thus causing the discharge of the motor neuron. As indicated in Figure 11-10, the pathways to and from Renshaw cells are complex because synaptic connections are made with other neurons whose fibers may come from ascending, descending, or contralateral sites within the spinal cord.

The purpose of Renshaw cell feedback in normal animals is hard to assess. Facilitation is usually the result of impulses arriving from higher levels of the CNS, whereas motor neuron inhibition is a more direct feedback process. How the two activities are intermingled in the normal animal is not known. Some evidence indicates that Renshaw cell activity produces a pattern of movement such that flexor muscles are facilitated and extensor muscles are inhibited during a given reflex.

The diagrams of the spinal cord and other parts of the nervous system are unsatisfactory in that they cannot portray the large number of neurons and the larger number of synaptic connections made within the CNS. Even a relatively simple pathway such as the inhibitory feedback circuit of the Renshaw cell is greatly modified as a result of the large number of synapses made with other cells. It is the extent of these interconnections within the CNS that poses one problem in the analysis of integrative mechanisms. Even simple reflexes, dissected by surgical or chemical procedures, are complex when studied in the intact animal.

11-10. Convergence and Occlusion. When electrodes are placed on the ventral roots, recordings will show that in monosynaptic

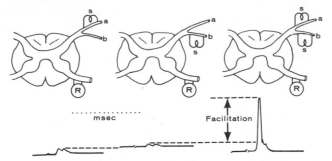

Figure 11-11   To demonstrate facilitation a dorsal root is split into two strands, a and b. Weak stimulation of a and b separately results in the responses shown in the left and middle traces (recorded from the ventral root, R). When the same weak stimulation was applied to both strands, a facilitated response greater than the sum of the separate responses resulted (right trace).

reflexes the amplitude of recorded potentials of Group I fibers increases as the amplitude of stimulation increases. Essentially the same results are obtained in the case of multisynaptic reflexes except that, because of synaptic delay and asynchronous firing, it is the area under the potential curve that is a measure of the number of motor neurons actually caused to fire by the afferent input. By using other experimental conditions it can be shown that more subtle influences operate within the CNS.

For example, if a dorsal root is divided into two strands so that each strand of afferent fibers can be separately stimulated and the results of stimulation are recorded from the ventral root efferent fibers, then the phenomenon of convergence can be demonstrated (Figure 11-11). When either strand is weakly stimulated, a potential is recorded at the ventral root. If both strands are stimulated simultaneously, a potential is recorded that is many times greater than would be expected from only an additive effect.

Such results are interpreted on the basis of the concept of a pool of motor neurons available for excitation. Each group of afferent fibers can cause the discharge of a given number of motor neurons—the synaptic connections are such that each motor neuron develops sufficient synaptic potential to create an action potential. However, some motor neurons are only subliminally excited

by a given afferent input. While a synaptic potential may be developed, it is not great enough to create an action potential. Some motor neurons lie in the field of excitation of both groups of afferent fibers in what is known as the subliminal fringe area. When both dorsal root strands are simultaneously stimulated, the neurons in the subliminal fringe may be sufficiently excited into firing by the summation of subliminal stimuli. Thus, as shown in Figure 11-11, , simultaneous stimulation of both strands can result in a larger number of neurons firing than is indicated by the number of neurons stimulated by each individual strand. This is spatial summation and is a consequence of the convergence of neurons, that is, the fact that morphologically or electrically the array of neurons in the CNS converges. The pool of available motor neurons is fractionated and each reflex uses part of this pool.

Because of the phenomenon just described, recording from the ventral roots during afferent stimulation is not sufficient to indicate the activities occurring in the CNS. The greater the incoming excitation, the greater is the discharge zone (the pool of neurons excited) and the greater is the extent of the subliminal fringe. Even with weak afferent volleys, which would separately cause no motor neuron discharge, repetition may cause a large number of cells to be subliminally excited and result in impulse firing. The discharge zone can never become coextensive with the subliminal fringe because any afferent volley excites only a fraction of the motor neuron pool.

This type of activity was first suggested by Sherrington (1935) and can account also for the properties of sympathetic ganglia. There are no interneurons within these ganglia, and yet long after-discharges and other phenomena are found, which in the spinal cord itself are attributed to interneuronal chains. Convergence is one mechanism that can help account for some of the integrating activity in these ganglia. Sympathetic ganglia have been the object of many experimental studies because the absence of interneurons results in relatively simple reflex arcs. But, consequently they lack certain properties of spinal reflex pathways.

Another phenomenon that can be demonstrated in the CNS is **occlusion**. The experimental arrangement is similar to that used to demonstrate convergence except that strong stimuli are applied to the dorsal root strands (Figure 11-12). Because the fields of excitation of different groups of afferent fibers overlap, the total number of motor neurons excited by the simultaneous stimulation of several afferent sources is less than the sum of the

motor neurons excited by the individual afferent inputs. Occlusion is another CNS activity that depends on the anatomical arrangements between neurons in the CNS and the consequent overlap of electrical fields.

11-11. The Vertebrate Brain. In addition to the spinal cord, the brain is the other important structure in the vertebrate central nervous system. During vertebrate evolution the brain has undergone extensive changes in size, shape, and organization whereas the spinal cord has altered relatively little. If the spinal cord is transected in a mammal, most motor reflexes remain intact. However proprioceptive responses, as well as visual and auditory reflexes, are destroyed. The mammal can live with a transected spinal cord, although consciousness, personality, and other features are lacking. However, the initial effect of spinal cord transection is a condition known as **spinal shock** in which all reflexes are absent and there is a flaccid paralysis of skeletal muscles. The reason for the appearance of spinal shock is not known although it appears to be related to the abrupt removal of descending spinal tracts. After a period of time, in some cases amounting to weeks, reflex

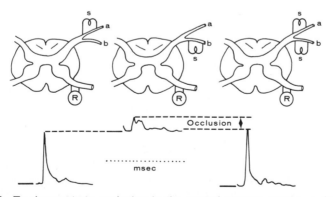

Figure 11-12 To demonstrate occlusion in the central nervous system, a dorsal root is split into two strands, a and b. Strong stimulation of a and b separately resulted in traces shown on left and in the middle (responses recorded from ventral root at R). But when both strands are stimulated simultaneously, the response (right trace) is less than the sum of the responses of each strand separately stimulated. This is because each afferent path shares some neurons, so that stimulation of both results in a smaller response than might be expected.

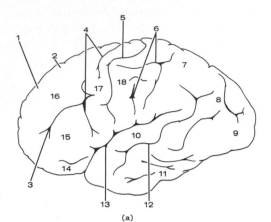

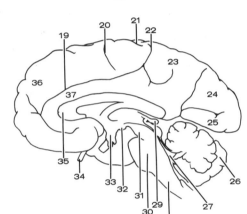

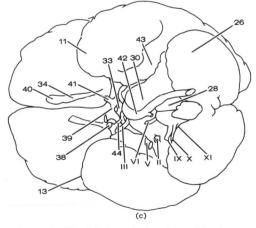

1. Superior frontal sulcus
2. Superior frontal lobe
3. Inferior frontal sulcus
4. Precentral sulcus
5. Central sulcus
6. Postcentral sulcus
7. Superior parietal lobule
8. Angular lobe
9. Lateral occipital
10. Superior temporal lobe
11. Inferior temporal lobe
12. Superior temporal sulcus
13. Lateral sulcus
14. Orbital lobe
15. Inferior frontal lobe
16. Middle frontal lobe
17. Precentral lobe
18. Postcentral lobe
19. Cingulate fissure
20. Precentral fissure
21. Central fissure
22. Postcentral fissure
23. Precuneus lobe
24. Cuneus lobe
25. Lingual gyrus
26. Cerebellar hemisphere
27. Fourth ventricle
28. Medulla oblongata
29. Pineal body
30. Pons
31. Midbrain
32. Mammillary body
33. Hypothalamus
34. Olfactory tract
35. Corpus callosum
36. Frontal lobe
37. Cingulate gyrus
38. Internal carotid artery
39. Optic chiasma
40. Olfactory bulb
41. Optic nerve
42. Basilar artery
43. Hippocampal area
44. Posterior communicating artery

Figure 11-13 (a) An exterior view of the human brain showing some of the major cerebella grooves (sulci) and lobes. (b) Median sagital view of the brain. (c) A ventral view of the brain. Roman numerals indicate cranial nerves (see Table 11-3).

activity begins to appear again, initially in the distal parts of the limbs. Autonomic reflexes require a longer period of time to reappear.

It may be noted that spinal cord transection above the fourth cervical segment results in immediate death because in this region of the spinal cord and medulla oblongata are the centers controlling respiration and other vital functions. If these are destroyed the mammal cannot live.

Although space does not permit a detailed description of the anatomy and physiology of the mammalian brain, a few of the more basic structures and functions will be given here. The general appearance of the human brain is given in Figure 11-13. The primitive vertebrate brain (or the brain in embryological development from the neural tube) can be considered to consist of three primary divisions: the hindbrain (rhombencephalon); the midbrain (mesencephalon); and the forebrain (prosencephalon). These divisions give rise to other structures during the development of the brain. Table 11-2 lists the subdivisions of the adult mammalian brain and gives a general indication of their functions.

Table 11-2 Principle Structures of the Adult Mammalian Brain

PRIMARY DIVISIONS	SUBDIVISIONS	HIGHER DERIVATIVES	GENERAL FUNCTIONS
PROSENCEPHALON (forebrain)	Telencephalon	Cerebral hemispheres	Sensory correlation; centers of association; highest mental abilities.
		Basal nuclei (corpus striatum)	Sensory impulse pathway between cerebral cortex and thalamus; relay fibers for motor impulses.
		Olfactory bulbs	
	Diencephalon	Thalamus Hypothalamus	Visceral regulatory centers; thalamus is concerned with sensory functions. Neurosecretory functions also.
MESENCEPHALON (midbrain)	Midbrain	Tectum (including optic lobes) Cerebral peduncles Collicular regions Pineal body (or epiphysis)	Peduncles contain fiber tracts connecting cerebrum with brain stem and spinal cord. Colliculi are concerned with visual functions.
RHOMBENCEPHALON (hindbrain)	Metencephalon	Pons (part of medulla in mammals)	Serves as bridge between two cerebellar hemispheres with many nerve tracts.
		Cerebellar hemispheres	Centers of motor activity coordination.
	Myelencephalon	Medulla oblongata	Contains nerve tracts connecting higher centers with spinal cord; and contains regulatory centers for vital functions.

The medulla oblongata is an enlarged end of the spinal cord, and all sensory nerves except those concerned with sight and smell pass through it as do all motor nerves. The medulla also contains regulatory centers (a brain center is a functional collection of neurons) for vital functions such as respiration, cardiac control, and vasomotor control. The pons is also part of the hindbrain and serves as a connecting link between the hemispheres of the cerebellum. The cerebellar hemispheres are sites of proprioceptive control over movement and balance. They receive sensory input from the inner ear and semicircular canals—sites of hearing and equilibrium information reception. The cerebellum increases in size and importance during the evolution of vertebrates and reaches its peak in the fast moving birds and mammals. The midbrain, pons, and medulla are often referred to as the brain stem—regions that serve as a bridge between the spinal cord and the cerebral hemispheres in mammals.

The midbrain has not changed structurally a great deal during vertebrate evolution, but its functions have changed markedly. In fish and amphibia the midbrain is a primary structure for the regulation of complex behavior and through the tectum it receives most of the output of the optic nerves. Although in nonmammalian species the midbrain is an important integrating center, in mammals the forebrain has taken over this activity including the reception of visual information.

In mammals, especially the primates, the development of the cerebral hemispheres is enormous, and this region of the forebrain comes to dominate all other brain structures. Whereas in fishes and amphibians the telencephalon is primarily an olfactory center, in mammals the cerebral hemispheres have become centers for the coordination and integration of most sensory information and also are the areas responsible for higher mental processes, consciousness, and so forth. In birds and reptiles the cerebral hemispheres are small, but the corpus striatum at the base of the telencephalon is a primary site for integration of sensory and motor responses.

In mammals each cerebral hemisphere consists of a thick layer of cell bodies and synaptic connections (gray matter) below which lie fiber tracts (white matter) connecting various parts of the cortex to each other and to other regions of the CNS. In the central region of the cerebrum are found relatively discrete bodies of gray matter called **nuclei**. These are generally concerned with one specific type of activity or sensory perception.

As indicated in Figure 11-13, the cerebral hemispheres in mammals possess highly convoluted surfaces. A longitudinal fissure partially divides the cerebrum into two hemispheres. The depressions on the surface of the cerebral hemispheres are called **sulci**, whereas the areas or convolutions between them are called **gyri**. Figure 11-13 shows some of the more prominent and constant of these. The hemispheres are divided by the sulci into lobes, and each lobe theoretically has a specific function or functions. For example, the occipital lobes are concerned with the sensation of vision. However, the anatomical features are not constant, and the assignment of clear-cut functions to each lobe may be only an arbitrary classification. The two hemispheres are connected by tracts or commissures of nerve fibers, the most prominent being the corpus callosum. Figure 11-14 diagrams the sites of sensory and motor activities in the postcentral gyrus.

The function of the cortex has been examined by a variety of techniques: removal or destruction of restricted areas followed by observations of behavioral changes; recording of electrical activity following either physiological or nonphysiological stimulation; observation of motor responses following stimulation; and by histological tracing of fiber pathways. These techniques have shown that there are relatively specific areas for particular sensory input and motor output (Figure 11-14). The gray matter is arranged in columns of cells, each devoted to a given sensation or involved with a particular motor control activity.

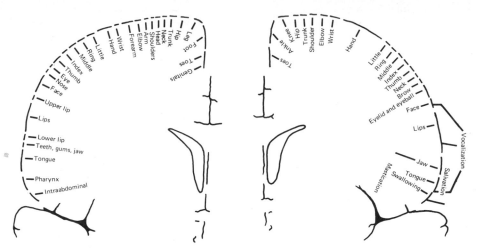

Figure 11-14 Sensory and motor representation of the body in the postcentral gyrus. It can be noted that sensory impulses from a given region of the body impinge close to areas from which motor impulses to that region of the body are sent. The diagrams give some indication of the extent of each sensory and motor area in the cortex. Those parts of the body requiring extremely delicate control, for example, the fingers, have a large area devoted to sensory and motor integration in the cerebrum. [After Penfield and Rasmussen (1950).]

The other portion of the forebrain, the diencephalon, consists of thalamus, hypothalamus, and posterior pituitary, as well as some other appendages of these structures. In higher vertebrates the thalamus functions as an integrative center for all sensory input (the function of the thalamus in fish is still unknown). The thalamus relays sensory information to the cerebral hemispheres and motor information to the spinal cord. The hypothalamus is a collection of nuclei concerned with many homeostatic regulations and will be discussed later in this chapter. The hypothalamus is also a center for neurosecretion, and its cells synthesize factors that cause the release of hormones by the anterior pituitary. Electrical stimulation of certain cells of the hypothalamus produces sensations of hunger, thirst, pain, pleasure, sexual drive, or rage; and the hypothalamus is an integrative center of importance in all vertebrates.

Many areas of the brain have no known function, and this is especially true of the large cerebral hemispheres. Although the development of these structures can be correlated with increases in versatility of response and intelligence, much of their functioning is still mysterious. A familiar example of a cerebellar functioning that is neither sensory nor motor in nature was noted in association with the prefrontal lobes. Removal of these lobes (prefrontal lobotomy) was at one time an operation used to treat conditions such as schizophrenia or anxiety. But, the removal of these brain areas showed they were not essential to sensory or motor functioning and that they were primarily personality determiners.

Another activity of mammals that is not understood is sleeping. This, for unknown reasons, is a vital activity. Animals such as amphibians and fish exhibit states of unresponsiveness that might be termed sleep. This condition, however, is indistinguishable from daily periods of nonactivity found in all organisms. When the brain waves are recorded from the surface of the cortex (the measure of electrical activity of the brain is obtained by the technique of electroencephalography; the recording of brain waves is the electroencephalogram or EEG), differences are found between the sleeping and waking states. During sleep slow waves are recorded, and during wakefulness faster, smaller waves

Table 11-3 Cranial Nerves

CRANIAL NERVE*	SOURCE	COMPONENTS AND FUNCTIONS
Olfactory (I)	Olfactory epithelium; runs to base of brain near optic chiasma.	Afferent fibers—carrying impulses for sense of smell.
Optic (II)	From retina to optic chiasma; optic tracts then run past cerebral peduncles and end near superior colliculi.	Afferent fibers for sense of vision. The optic nerves and tracts are considered cranial not spinal nerves because the retina is part of the CNS.
Oculomotor (III)	Arises ventrally in midbrain; fibers to and from extrinsic eye muscles.	Efferent fibers—activate four eye muscles (superior, anterior, and inferior rectus; and inferior oblique). Afferent fibers from proprioceptive fibers of extrinsic muscles.
Trochlear (IV)	Arises ventrally in midbrain and fibers run upward through brain mass and decussate to arrive at superior oblique muscles of eyeball.	Efferent fibers—innervates a single extrinsic eye muscle. Afferent fibers—some input from proprioceptive organs of eyeball muscles.
Trigeminal (V)	From midbrain at root of pons runs to face and jaws.	A large nerve with three branches; these may be separate nerves with separate ganglia in lower vertebrates. General somatic afferent fibers. Efferent (autonomic) fibers to muscles for mastication. Efferent (somatic) fibers to head and face.
Abducens (VI)	Arises from front of pons and runs to eyeball.	Efferent (visceral) to single muscle of eyeball, posterior rectus muscle.
Facial (VII)	Arises laterally at junction of pons and medulla; runs to muscles of expression of face around eyes, mouth, forehead, scalp.	Efferent (somatic)—general. Efferent (visceral)—Some fibers to salivary glands, lacrimal gland, and tongue taste receptors. Afferent—general sensory fibers and taste.
Vestibulocochlear (auditory) (VIII)	Arises from junction of pons and medulla; runs to inner ear (several branches of the nerve).	Afferent—fibers are associated with impulses used for the sense of hearing and for balance and equilibrium.
Glossopharyhgeal (IX)	Arises from series of rootlets on medulla and runs to mucous membrane and muscles of pharynx; to salivary gland, and tongue (two ganglia along its course).	Efferent (visceral) fibers to salivary gland, some muscles of throat and larynx. Afferent fibers from back of mouth and tongue—impulses from taste buds.
Vagus (X)	From rootlets on medulla; runs to various visceral organs.	Efferent (visceral) fibers to heart, etc. Afferent fibers general sensory elements from visceral organs and some from skin.

Table 11-3 (continued)

CRANIAL NERVE*	SOURCE	COMPONENTS AND FUNCTIONS
Accessory (XI)	From medulla; some fibers go with vagus fibers to pharynx and larynx. Others to trapezius and sterno-cleidomastoid muscle.	Efferent (somatic) to skeletal muscle. Efferent (Visceral) to pharynx. Afferent fibers from many sources.
Hypoglossal (XII)	From medulla; runs to tongue muscles.	Efferent (somatic) fibers to tongue.

* The roman numerals in parentheses are used to identify these nerves in figures in this and other chapters.

are recorded. The significance of these findings is still unknown. The EEG can be used as a clinical tool for diagnosing other brain functions or disorders. For example, epilepsy is diagnosed by electroencephalography, but its mechanism of development and its causes are unknown. Jouvet (1967) has reviewed the physiology of sleep.

In addition to the anatomically discrete fiber tracts which connect different parts of the brain, there is also a **reticular system**, which serves this function (Magoun, 1950). This system is a mass of cells which extends from the base of the midbrain into the thalamus and which originates in the medulla. This anatomically diffuse system receives sensory input from collaterals of many different afferent fibers. Part of the reticular output is used to regulate motor activity. Part of the output is relayed to the cerebral cortex and in some way plays a role in consciousness. This latter system is called the **reticular activating system**. When its activities are interfered with by drugs, sleep, or surgical removal, the animal loses consciousness. When excited, either by strong physiological sensory input or by electrical currents, the animal is aroused. As indicated earlier, although sensory input arrives at the cortex, the nervous system has the ability to ignore this information. Thus, during sleep sensory information reaches the cortex, but there is no conscious reaction. The reticular system must connect with what is called the subconscious mind.

Finally, some mention should be made of the cranial nerves, which differ in several respects from spinal nerves. They are not attached to the brain at regular intervals, as are the spinal nerves to the spinal cord, and they are not formed of ventral and dorsal roots. The cranial nerves also show variation in their sensory and motor components. Some possess ganglia, others do not. Table 11-3 lists the 12 cranial nerves, their occurrence in different vertebrates, and their major autonomic functions. As noted before some parasympathetic fibers (motor axons) may travel in cranial nerves, but these nerves also contain sensory and somatic motor axons.

Vertebrate Neuromuscular Controls

11-12. Components of Muscular Movement. Movement in vertebrates is accomplished by activities in a number of skeletal muscles, and these activities are guided by several interacting control systems. Although space does not permit a detailed discussion of muscular movements, several basic components of such movement must be recognized in order to understand how the basic control systems operate. Hines (1960) and Lockhart (1960) describe human muscle actions and control in some detail.

In most forms of vertebrate skeletal muscle movements, the motion occurs at a joint where two or more bones form a low-friction pivot lubricated by synovial fluid. Muscles are usually arranged so that they are attached on

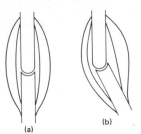
(a)   (b)

Figure 11-15 Arrangement of a typical verte-brate joint. (a) A pair of antagonistic muscles are each attached to opposite sides of a pivot about two bones. The upper bone is indicated as fixed in position, and the bottom bone is movable. (b) During contraction of muscle on right, muscle of left is stretched; and the bone moves in direction shown. During a rapid concentration of the muscle on the right, the left muscle will act as a brake. This vertebrate joint may be compared with crus-tacean joints shown in Figure 11-30.

opposite sides of a joint (Figure 11-15). Individual muscles can exert only pulling forces, and therefore, at least two muscles are needed to provide a range of movement about a joint. At some joints several pairs of muscles are present so that flexion, extension, and rotation can be produced about the joint. Antagonistic muscles usually do not exert diametrically opposed forces, and an im-portant function of direct antagonistic muscles is to obtain precise control over movements by the application of braking forces by one muscle of the pair. Each muscle serves as a brake on its antagonist and such action is produced by appropriate impulses from the CNS.

Because muscular forces are exerted equally at origin and insertion, the movement on one member of a joint requires fixation of the other joint member. Such fixation is produced by contractions of muscles at other joints. When the forearm moves, for example, the muscles of the shoulder must contract in order to fix the humerus in position. This is one reason why even a seemingly simple movement may actually require involvement of many muscles and consequently a large degree of control activity on the part of the CNS.

Muscles are sometimes classified according

to the nature of their actions. One group includes muscles used in locomotion, main-taining posture, standing, and so forth. These are muscles that act against the force of gravity. The term **extensor muscle** is used to describe any muscle that acts against gravity regardless of whether or not it pro-duces flexor or extension activity at a joint. In most cases the name of a muscle is not an indication of its action, for example, the flexor digitorum muscle in the leg is an extensor muscle because its action is to raise part of the body weight against gravitational force. The antagonists of extensor muscles are **flexors**. Flexors also include a second group of muscles that take part in reflex withdrawals of the body from harmful stimuli (Henneman, 1968).

We shall be concerned here with skeletal muscle rather than visceral (autonomic) reflexes. Skeletal muscles are sometimes called **voluntary** because body movements can occur as the result of conscious orders from the brain. On this basis autonomic reflexes are called **involuntary**. However, such terms are not accurate descriptions because it is impossible to selectively move a single skeletal muscle without involuntarily causing contractions in others. Voluntary muscles therefore are basically those used in learned movements. Autonomic reflexes can also be

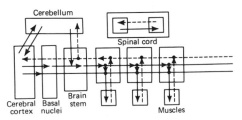

Figure 11-16 An information flow diagram for the vertebrate motor system. Dashed lines indicate afferent (sensory) pathways of informa-tion flow. Solid lines represent efferent (motor) pathways for cortex initiated impulses. The reflex pathway between spinal cord and muscle (indi-cated by insert above spinal cord) is the basic control system for motor activity and is the feed-back system discussed in text with refer-ence to muscle spindle fibers and Golgi tendon organs. See also Figure 11-17.

learned and caused to occur consciously if the necessity arises (Miller, 1969).

As shown in Figure 11-16, there is an exchange of information between the muscle and the spinal column (what I have previously called the spinal reflex); but information is also passed to higher central nervous system structures, and motor impulses are passed down to the muscles from these centers. The cerebral cortex receives all sensory information and can alter or adjust muscular movements. As indicated in Figure 11-16, there is a direct tract—the corticospinal tract—carrying motor impulses from the cerebral cortex to the spinal cord. The cerebellum is a major center for integrating movement in vertebrates, and this part of the brain receives information not only from sensory fibers of the spinal cord but also from the equilibrium receptors of the ear. Thus the cerebellum modifies and controls all movements to be performed. As noted previously, a primary reflex action takes place without intervention from the brain, and these reflexes are means by which the body is quickly removed from harmful environments. Secondary reflex actions, with a delay due to the number of synapses present in the neural pathways (and in many cases due to the use of small diameter neurons with slower conduction velocities) occur as determined by the cerebellar and cerebral actions on the incoming sensory information. In addition the cerebral cortex can initiate muscular

action as the result of emotions or conscious thought. These are muscular activities somewhat removed from the sensory input.

Complex movement requires the participation of several feedback systems. Much of vertebrate motor activity is controlled by visual feedback. In the next section the basic feedback systems used to control muscle length and tension at the spinal cord level will be described. But before we turn to these mechanisms, it is worth mentioning again that other factors are also involved in determining the extent of final muscular activity. As discussed in Chapter 10, the activity of a muscle will depend on the size of the motor units and the number of impulses coming into the system. Muscular activity will also depend on the nature of the muscle fibers themselves—on the ratio, for example, of red to white fibers with their different degrees of activity and different response capabilities. Finally, the initial length, degree of fatigue, and degree of vascularization also play a role in determining the nature of a muscle's response at any given time.

11-13. Feedback Control of Muscular Activity —Muscle Spindles. Lidell and Sherrington showed that stretching a muscle caused it to promptly contract—an action which tends to restore the muscle to its initial length. This reflex action depends upon sensory impulses sent from the muscle itself to the spinal cord and

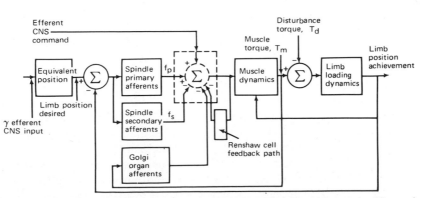

Figure 11-17 Information-flow diagram of skeletal-muscle control system. [From J. H. Milsum (1966) *Biological Control Systems Analysis* McGraw-Hill Book Company, New York. By permission of the publishers.]

Table 11-4   Distribution of Spindles in Some Muscles*

MUSCLE	MUSCLE WEIGHT (G)	NO. OF SPINDLE CAPSULES PER GRAM
Lateral gastrocnemius	7.61	5
Rectus femoris	8.36	9
Tibialis anterior	4.57	15
Semitendinosus	6.41	18
Soleus	2.49	23
Tibialis posterior	0.78	39
Flexor digitorum longus mesial	1.06	45
Vth interossei (Foot)	0.33	88
Vth interossie (Hand)	0.21	119

* Data from Chen et al. (1962) as reported in Henneman (1968).

the resulting efferent volley. A simplified diagram of the components of such a reflex is given in Figure 11-16, and Figure 11-17 gives a feedback diagram of such a system. Neuromuscular systems lend themselves readily to systems analysis (see Contini and Drillus, 1966; Henneman, 1968; Houk and Henneman, 1968; Milhorn, 1966; Stark, 1966).

The feedback transducers of muscle are **stretch receptors** that provide information about the length of the muscle, the degree of tension, or the rate of shortening. There are three types of stretch receptors in vertebrate muscle. There are two types located within the muscle fibers themselves within the muscle **spindles**. The third type—the Golgi tendon organ—is located at the junctions of muscle fibers and their tendons (see Section 11-14).

Muscle spindles are macroscopic fusiform fibers scattered throughout the muscle tissue. They are attached at either end to the ordinary or **extrafusal fibers** of the muscle, and as indicated in Table 11-4 their number per muscle varies according to the muscle. Muscles that require delicate control contain more spindles per unit weight than muscles such as the gastrocnemius, which are power muscles.

Each spindle consists of a connective tissue sheath surrounding 2 to 12 small striated muscle fibers known as **intrafusal fibers**. Two types of intrafusal fibers are recognized in mammalian spindles. **Nuclear bag fibers** are the larger and longer fibers and contain many nuclei within a central baglike region. **Nuclear chain fibers** are shorter and of smaller diameter, and their nuclei lie in a single central row resembling a linked chain when observed in the microscope. The ends of the nuclear chain fibers are attached to the nuclear bag fibers. Many spindles contain 2 nuclear bag fibers and 4 nuclear chain fibers, but the numbers can vary.

The sensory endings are located within an expanded fluid-filled center portion of the spindle and lie on the intrafusal fibers. The innervation and other features of the transducer system are still unclear (Granit, 1966; Marker, 1962).

The innervation of a mammalian skeletal muscle and of the intrafusal fibers is diagrammed in Figure 11-18. Group Ia efferents innervate the ordinary extrafusal muscle fibers. These derive from large ventral horn cells. Each spindle has one primary sensory ending and from 0 to 5 secondary endings. The primary sensory ending is supplied by a Group Ia fiber, whereas the secondary endings are supplied by Group II afferents. Because muscle spindles are attached in parallel with the extrafusal fibers, they are stretched whenever the muscle is stretched. The receptors respond to stretch: the greater the stretch on the muscle, the greater is the afferent signal sent to the spinal cord. The receptors respond

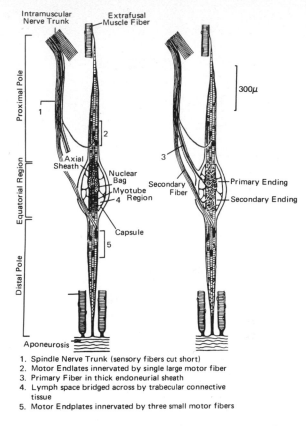

Figure 11-18 The nervous supply of the muscle spindle. On the left are shown only the motor nerve fibers innervating the intrafusal fibers. On the right are shown both efferent and afferent nerve fibers and their endings on the nuclear bag region. Note that only the poles of the spindle fibers are striated and contractile. [Redrawn from D. Barker (1948). "The innervation of the muscle spindle." *Quarterly Journal Microscopical Science* **89**: 143-186.]

1. Spindle Nerve Trunk (sensory fibers cut short)
2. Motor Endlates innervated by single large motor fiber
3. Primary Fiber in thick endoneurial sheath
4. Lymph space bridged across by trabecular connective tissue
5. Motor Endplates innervated by three small motor fibers

to stretch with an increased rate of generator potential development and the generation of action potentials at an increased rate.

Figure 11-19 illustrates the nature of the response of these receptors under different conditions. This system forms the primary feedback control of skeletal muscle and it is basically a length control system.

The intrafusal fibers themselves are innervated by efferent fibers that terminate in two types of endings. Plate endings are discrete motor end plates lying primarily at the poles of the fibers. Trail endings are fine extensive networks of fibers often covering a large area of the spindle surface (Figure 11-20). There is disagreement as to the distribution of these endings (Barker, 1966; Boyd and Davey, 1966). According to one view, plate endings are found only on nuclear bag fibers, and trail endings occur only on nuclear chain fibers. Another hypothesis is that each type of intrafusal fiber receives both plate and trail endings.

The motor innervation of the intrafusal fibers is derived from **gamma** or **fusimotor** fibers and various designations have been used for fibers depending on whether they terminate in plate or trail endings. It has recently been agreed to call fibers to the plate endings the γ-plate fibers, and those to trail endings are called γ-trail fibers (see in Granit, 1966).

Intrafusal fibers are also classified as dynamic or static. Dynamic fibers are innervated by trail endings, whereas static fibers are innervated by plate endings. Dynamic fibers develop local synaptic potentials that result in weak and localized contractions of the intrafusal fiber. Such contractions affect only the primary sensory endings, and it has been shown experimentally that under moderate conditions of contraction only the response of the primary endings changes.

Excitation of static fusimotor fibers elicits a twitch type of contraction and produces a relatively greater tension in the intrafusal fibers, and the support of the primary endings

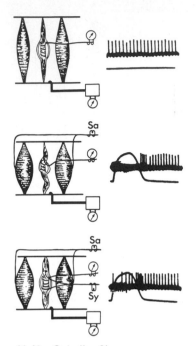

Figure 11-19 Spindle fiber responses under different conditions. As shown in diagrams on left, the spindle fibers are in parallel with normal muscle fibers. Traces on the right indicate recordings from spindle afferent nerve fibers (thick line) and from tension measuring transducer (thin line). (Upper) When muscle is slightly stretched, the spindle fibers are also stretched, and there is a continuous rhythmic discharge from the spindle fibers. (Middle) When the muscle is stimulated and shortens, the spindle fibers are relieved of stretch and the discharge stops. (Lower) When the muscle shortens, but a stimulus is also applied to the fusimotor nerve fibers supplying the spindle fibers with efferent impulses, the afferent discharge is maintained because the spindle fibers are also shortening and thus maintaining some tension. Spindle fibers discharge only when stretched. When not stretched, their output shows a silent period of no discharge. [Modified from Hunt and Kuffler (1951).]

is stretched. At constant muscle length repetitive stimulation of static fusimotor fibers results in an increased output from the sensory receptors (Besou and Laporte, 1966). As indicated in Figure 11-18, only the central portion of an intrafusal fiber contains sensory endings, and this region is noncontractile; only the ends of the fiber are striated and contractile.

Both extension of the whole muscle and contraction of the intrafusal fibers stretch the receptor endings, and the responses of the endings will be determined by the additive effects of these two types of stimuli. The contractions produced by the gamma efferent pathway are too small to affect the overall muscular tension, and they serve only to stimulate the sensory endings. In addition, the number of intrafusal fibers is so small relative to the number of extrafusal fibers that the former can have little effect on total muscular tension.

The activity of individual stretch receptors is studied by recording potentials from dorsal root filaments that have been subdivided until the afferent fiber from a single active receptor is obtained. Distal stimulation of the nerve, while simultaneously recording centrally, allows the conduction velocity of the afferent fiber to be determined. The tension produced by passive stretch or by active contraction is measured by the attachment of an appropriate mechanoelectrical transducer to the tendon of the muscle. The responses from afferent fibers going to primary endings (often called annulospiral endings because of the morphological arrangement) and to secondary endings (often called flower spray endings) are distinguished from the responses of the Golgi tendon organs by their greater sensitivity to stretch and their pause in firing during a twitch contraction.

By simultaneous recording from both alpha and gamma motor neurons to the same muscle, it has been found that gamma activity occurs in parallel with alpha activity in most reflexes. Therefore, the intrafusal fibers generally shorten as the muscle shortens. Whenever intrafusal contraction does not occur, the spindle receptors either slow down their firing rate or stop entirely.

The pattern of innervation of a skeletal muscle is obviously complex, and as stated above, the distribution of small nerve fibers, motor endings, and the types of responses produced in the intrafusal fibers are problems still under study. Overall, the system is responsible for controlling the length of a muscle.

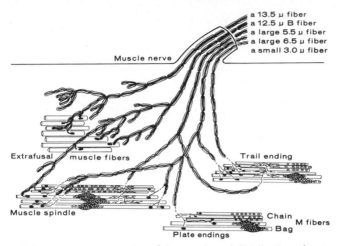

Figure 11-20 Schematic representation of the supply and distribution of motor nerve fibers to mammalian skeletal muscle. Larger nerve fibers supply extrafusal fibers through motor end plates. Smaller fibers (γ fibers, 3.0 to 5.5 μ in diameter) supply either plate or trail endings on the intrafusal fibers. The branching and termination of motor fibers shown is based on innervation patterns observed in teased, silver preparations of deafferentated cat soleus and peroneal spindles. According to this scheme both nuclear bag and nuclear chain fibers may receive plate or trail endings. There is no correlation between the diameter of the γ-stem fibers and their terminal branches. [Redrawn from D. Barker (1966) "The motor innervation of the mammalian spindle" in *Muscular Afferents and Motor Control* (R. Granit, editor), pp. 51–58. First Nobel Symposium, June 1965. John Wiley & Sons, New York.]

In terms of systems analysis, the spindle is a mechanism that measures the difference in the lengths of extrafusal fibers and intrafusal fibers, and whenever the extrafusal fibers are longer, the intrafusal fibers are stretched. This causes an afferent discharge that in turn produces an efferent volley that results in a shortening of the extrafusal fibers. The gamma system, by causing a shortening of the intrafusal fibers, can also lead to a shortening of the extrafusal fibers.

Since muscles in the animal operate usually in antagonistic pairs, the control system must be so arranged that impulses from each member of the muscle pair are comingled in the spinal cord in order for appropriate responses of both muscles to be obtained. The gamma efferent system allows the central nervous system to modify and control the activity of receptors within the muscles.

11-14. Muscle Feedback Control—The Golgi Tendon Organ. Golgi tendon organs are anatomically in series with the contractile elements; this is a situation which is different from that of the spindles, and these receptors respond to changes in muscle tension rather than muscle length (Figure 11-21). A tendon organ is about 500 μ long and is enclosed by a connective tissue capsule that blends into the connective tissue of the muscle-tendon region. It is innervated by Group Ib nerve fibers that branch into small unmyelinated fibers inside the capsule and terminate in sprays of unmyelinated fibers whose granular swollen ends lie on the surface of the tendon fascicles. Distortion of the endings gives rise to generator potentials that in turn lead to the generation of spike potentials.

During a muscular contraction the tendon organs discharge at a rate proportional to the tension developed by the muscle. The afferent output of the tendon organs excites interneurons in the spinal cord, which, in turn, inhibit the motor neurons sending axons to the muscle where the tendon organs are located.

The amount of tension developed at a given

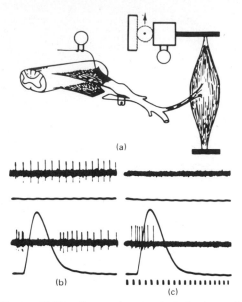

(a)

(b)

(c)

Figure 11-21 Comparison of behavior of spindle fiber (b) and tendon organ (c) during muscle stretch and contraction. (a) Experimental arrangement for recording from dorsal root strand (thick line in records) and from muscle tension transducer (thin line in records). During muscle stretch the spindle fiber continuously discharges, and the tendon organ shows no activity (upper traces). During muscle contraction the spindle fiber stops its discharge, whereas the tendon organ fires. Only moderate stretch was used, and this failed to discharge the high threshold tendon organs. [Adapted from Ruch et al. (1965).]

muscle length depends on the condition of the muscle. It is the function of the tendon organ to measure the tension regardless of the muscle length. In isotonic contractions the tendon organs are only weakly excited, but during isometric contractions tendon organs are strongly excited. It has been found that a single tendon organ in the soleus organ of the cat is excited by the stimulation of any of about 15 motor units. A motor unit consists in this muscle of about 180 muscle fibers of which only 3 to 25 are attached to the tendon organ. Therefore, a tendon organ samples local tension in a muscle, and the response of a tendon organ's firing is determined by the number of active motor units inserting on it and the tension developed by the contracting muscle fibers.

Originally tendon organs were considered only as safety mechanisms to protect a muscle against overload. Since tendon organs have a high threshold to passive stretch, it was thought that only large tensions in the muscle would cause a response in the tendon organs. However, recent experiments have shown that the tendon organ is much more responsive to the tensions produced during active contractions of a muscle than to those produced by passive stretch. The tendon organ is probably operating in a continuous feedback control of muscle tension and activity.

The three stretch receptors of muscle are not involved in conscious proprioception, that is, they do not furnish the CNS with information regarding the position of a joint or limb. The injection of local anesthetics into joints does not affect the operation of stretch receptors although information on the sense of position, which is furnished by other types of receptors, is lost.

Stretch receptors are part of a system that controls the length of a muscle and regulates its activities against external disturbances. The system is complex, and a stream of impulses continuously arrives and leaves a given muscle. During active use of the triceps surae of the cat, for example, as many as 50,000 impulses per second may arrive from the spinal cord. Even during complete relaxation, a few thousand impulses per second are transmitted over the gamma pathway, which is never at rest.

In some of the feedback diagrams used in this section, blocks are represented for afferent and efferent delays in the conduction of information. These delays are caused by the introduction of small diameter nerve fibers or by the introduction of several synaptic connections in the neuronal pathways. The alpha system is a fast conducting pathway with little delay and serves to promote rapid responses to stimuli. The gamma system has the most delay and allows the muscle to shorten without a steady state change in the spindle afferent output. Large signals delivered by the alpha system can send the spindle receptors into saturation of response. This prevents good reflex regulation—a situation partially avoided by having two conducting systems using the same feedback control mechanism. This discussion is based on mammalian spindles, and the situation in other vertebrate groups may be quite different (Cooper, 1960).

There are still arguments, for example, as to whether or not fishes have muscle stretch receptors. Tailless amphibians such as the frog and toad possess spindles that are simpler than those of mammals. A single large nerve fiber enters the frog spindle capsule and divides into myelinated branches that terminate in long strands on the central region of the spindle fibers. Other nerve fibers terminate on typical motor end plates on the spindle fibers outside the central capsullar region. One type only of sensory ending has been observed—a primary or flower spray ending. There appears to be only one type of intrafusal fiber. However, more study is needed, and some workers have suggested that there are differences in the spindles of slow and fast muscles.

11-15. Some Vertebrate Reflexes. Modern neurophysiology is often considered to have started with the work of Sir Charles Sherrington (1906), who initiated the first systematic studies of reflexes and integration in the central nervous system. Sherrington's work was done before any clear ideas had been established about the nature of impulse conduction and, in fact, before it was possible to measure action potentials, synaptic potentials, and so forth.

Sherrington defined the reflex as the unit reaction in nervous integration because every reflex is a complete act of integration. Sherrington recognized that there are qualifications to this statement. For example, in higher animals especially, some events and integrating activities occur in the nervous system without reflex action. These events involve spontaneous and sensory perception phenomena.

Reflexes at the spinal level have the purpose of removing the animal from harmful stimuli, and reflex actions are purposive and adaptive actions at the unconscious level (again, in this section I shall consider only those spinal reflexes involved in skeletal muscle actions).

Because there are many interconnections within the CNS and because large numbers of stimuli constantly impinge on the animal, the activity of one part of the nervous system often modifies that of another part. In studying a particular reflex, it is usually necessary to eliminate as far as possible all other central nervous system activity. For this reason the study of spinal reflexes is done on **spinal animals** whose brain has been removed or destroyed. A familiar student laboratory example is the pithed frog, where the brain has been destroyed with a needle pushed through the foramen magnum. As previously indicated, the spinal animal exhibits spinal shock and a loss of reflex activity. Recovery is rapid in frogs and other nonmammalian vertebrates.

A simple example of reflex action in the spinal frog is seen when the animal is suspended so that the lower legs hang free. The application of small amounts of dilute acetic or hydrochloric acid to the thigh elicits a reflex response in which the frog raises its foot in order to remove the painful stimulus. If the toes on the stimulated side are held so that they cannot be moved, the opposite leg and foot are used to remove the stimulating agent.

Much of Sherrington's work was performed with spinal dogs. Before discussing his earlier work on reflexes, I shall first discuss the stretch or myotatic reflexes (Liddell and Sherrington, 1925). These reflexes are the simplest reflexes found in vertebrates and are monosynaptic. They are best studied in decerebrate animals, whose brain stem has been sectioned thus leaving the medulla oblongata and reticular system intact. Under these conditions there is a hyperactivity of the stretch reflexes; in spinal animals stretch reflexes are sometimes difficult to maintain. A decerebrate animal exhibits **decerebrate rigidity** in which there is a hyper-extension of the neck, arching of the back, and extension of the limbs and tail. Sherrington called this total pattern an exaggerated caricature of reflex standing.

The myotatic reflex depends on the activity of the stretch receptors in the muscles. Such reflexes are composed of both a phasic reflex action and a static reflex action. When the stretch on the muscle is brief, only the phasic component is seen (the best example of this is the knee jerk reflex). The peak of reflex tension in a myotatic reflex occurs at the time of completion of the stretch movement (= phasic reflex action). Following this there is a phase of static action represented by a plateau of gradually declining tension. The degree of tension maintained in the static phase is regulated by the degree of static stretch imposed on the muscle. When the stretch is released, the contraction tension falls instantly to zero. All muscles so far examined show some response to stretch but wide variations are found in the readiness with which a muscle responds.

Stretch reflexes also have an inhibitory component. This can be demonstrated by recording the responses of an extensor muscle when its antagonistic flexor muscle is stretched. An extensor muscle when stretched shows a typical stretch reflex action. If a corresponding flexor muscle is stimulated while the extensor muscle is stretched, the stretch reflex does not occur. Afferent impulses from the flexor muscle prevent the response of the extensor motor neurons to afferent impulses from the extensor muscle itself. The stretch reflex plays an important role in walking. The movement of progression consists of a flexion phase in which the foot moves forward clear of the ground and an extension phase in which the limb is straightened, bringing the foot into contact with the ground and providing a forward push. In the flexion phase the bending of the knee stretches the extensors of the knee, but the reflex is inhibited because the contraction of the physiological flexor muscles soon stops the extensor contraction. At the conclusion of the flexor phase, the stretch reflex is released from inhibition and the contraction of the extensor muscles provides the main drive for the following extension phase. As the knee straightens, the reflex action is limited by the removal of the stretch. The stretch reflex is limited in its field of action. A stretch response occurs only in that muscle (or even part of a muscle) which is stretched; other muscles show no signs of activity.

An early reflex studied by Sherrington was the response evoked by the application of a painful or harmful stimulus to the limb of a spinal animal. The animal withdraws its limb and Sherrington called this type of reaction a **nocioceptive reflex** (= **flexor reflex**). Such reflexes are used not only to remove a limb from harmful stimuli but also play a role in normal running or stepping actions. If the sensory nerve between the muscle receptors and the CNS is cut and the central end stimulated with electrical pulses, the withdrawal of the foot follows the normal pattern found when harmful stimuli are applied. If, however, the motor neurons are cut and the central ends stimulated, no response occurred in any part of the animal and no impulses were detectable in the sensory nerves. It was on the basis of these types of experiments that the reflex pathway was first shown to be organized on the basis diagrammed in Figure 11-2 and Figure 11-5.

When the foot of a spinal dog is raised so that the leg is flexed, the leg muscles respond with an extensor thrust—a myotatic reflex. Going further in his investigations, Sherrington found that if the posterior part of a spinal dog's body were rested upon the hind legs, the legs, which were originally limp, yielded a little and then stiffened to support the body as the weight of the body came upon them. If weights were added to the body the legs yielded a little further, and the contractions of the extensor muscles became a little greater. This activity was called by Sherrington the **spinal arc of plastic tone**—a reflex action designed to maintain a proper degree of tone (= contraction) according to the circumstances and changing needs of the animal. This is a tonic reflex as opposed to a phasic reflex and is used to continuously maintain the posture of an animal against forces such as gravity.

If the leg supporting the weight of the dog's body is painfully stimulated, the leg is immediately flexed—the **flexor** or **withdrawal reflex** already mentioned. As soon as the painful stimulus is removed the extensor reflex returns.

When a leg is withdrawn from a painful stimulus, the spinal animal does not collapse because a stronger extensor reflex is set up in the other leg. As the body weight falls upon one leg, the muscle spindles are more strongly excited, and the muscle responds with a greater contraction to produce a greater tone in the muscle and the limb. Even if the dog is suspended in the air, the flexion of one hind limb is accompanied by an extension of the other. Thus, the two reflex activities are not isolated events but have common connections within the CNS: the ipsilateral, contralateral, and intersegmental interneuronal connections already described with their various combinations of inhibitory and excitatory actions.

Sherrington also discovered phenomena such as facilitation, convergence, and occlusion in the CNS. In spinal reflexes several successive stimuli to many neighboring receptors may result in an enhanced response along the final common pathway. A gentle touch on a dog's skin is usually too weak to elicit a motor response; but if the same touch is drawn along the skin, there will result the motor action in which the dog scratches its skin with a foot— the **scratch reflex**. Sherrington called this type of phenomenon the central excitatory state and also postulated the presence of a central inhibitory state. The summations and facilitations together with their mechanisms have already been described. Sherrington suggested that the hop of a flea was a mechanism which preserved the species from extinction. If fleas crawled over the dog's skin, there would be a continuous recruitment of spatially separate stimuli, and the flea would be destroyed by the scratching foot. By hopping, however, the flea makes detection difficult (Brazier, 1960).

These have been but a few of the many spinal reflexes studied in vertebrates, but they illustrate some of the properties of reflexes. In the next sections the nature of nervous organization and neuromusclar controls in selected invertebrates is considered.

Invertebrate Neuromuscular Systems

11-16. The Coelenterate Nerve Net. The nature of the nervous system and the behavior

of coelenterates have received much attention during the last decade. As stated in Chapter 9, the nervous system of coelenterates is in the form of a nerve net, although conduction is also found in epithelial cells in some species (Mackie, 1965).

It has often been difficult to identify specific nerve cells in coelenterates, but the use of the electron microscope has now allowed such identification, and the nerve cells and processes in the nervous systems of many coelenterates have been identified (Lentz and Barrnett, 1965). The potentials and routes of impulse conduction in various coelenterates have been recorded using microelectrodes. There is also evidence for the presence of neurosecretory cells in some coelenterates, and this is used as supportive evidence for the long-standing hypothesis that regeneration in such forms as hydra is under neuronal control regulated by substances released at nerve endings.

However, there are many differences in nerve cells, nervous system organization, and coordination mechanisms within members of the phylum. And although many similarities between coelenterate and higher nervous systems are being discovered, there are also many differences. It is difficult to determine how coelenterate nervous systems have evolved into higher nervous systems. Coelenterate nervous systems and behavior are discussed in Bullock and Horridge (1965) and in a symposium published in *American Zoologist* 5: 3, 1965 (published by the American Society of Zoologists).

There are two main body plans found in the coelenterates. Polyps, which are generally attached or sedentary animals, and medusae, which are usually free-swimming organisms. Although hydra are common polypoid coelenterates, they are difficult to study because of their small size, and much work has therefore been done with larger sea anemones and various medusae.

The general body plan, including important muscles, of anemones is shown in Figure 11-22. Although the nerve net is sometimes defined as a diffuse network of nerve fibers functionally connected at synapses, many experimental

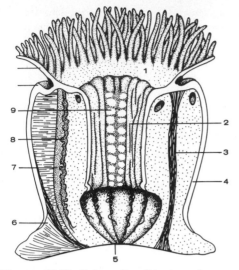

Figure 11-22 Schematic diagram of a sea anemone (hemisection). (1) Peristome on oral disc separates mouth from tentacles; (2) pharynx (3) longitudinal (retractor) muscles; (4) column; (5) pedal disc; (6) basilar muscles; (7) transverse muscles; (8) septal filaments at free edge of septa; (9) siphonoglyphs.

studies indicate that there is more functional organization present than is implied by such a definition. In any neuromuscular control system, there must be organized connections between sensory endings and contractile elements so that discrimination and coordination of responses are made possible.

If a tentacle of a sea anemone is stimulated lightly by scratching with a needle, the tentacle shortens slightly and bends toward the mouth. If stimulation continues, neighboring tentacles begin this activity also. Further continuation of the stimulation causes the edge of the oral disc to rise up all around, and the anemone closes. A zone of muscular activity slowly spreads from the point of stimulation.

If another type of stimulus is employed and a blunt probe is pushed upon the pedal disc, the animal rapidly completely closes. This is a fast response with no indication of a slow spread of excitation such as is seen upon stimulation of a tentacle. This type of response means that there must be present a fast through-conducting system within the nerve net. The probe used in such experiments must be blunt because two discrete stimuli are

required, the first to facilitate the response to the second. In some anemones, for example, *Calliactis*, the fast response system is the sphincter muscle at the oral disc, although conduction is endodermal via the mesenteric nerves.

In the anemone *Mimetridium cryptum* there exist regional differences in the orientation of nerve fibers, average nerve fiber diameters, and density of nerve fibers in the net (Batham, 1965). Fast-contracting muscles are overlaid by a relatively dense nerve net whose fibers are usually more than 2 μ in diameter. Slow-contracting muscles are covered with a thinner nerve net whose fibers are about 1 μ in diameter. Therefore, regional organization may be found in nerve nets. In the sea anemone *Calliactis parasitica* rapid through conduction of impulses has been shown to be due to a network of bipolar nerve cells. This network connects body musculature and mesenteries (Robson, 1965).

Thus, although most anemone muscles contract slowly, there are also muscles which respond with rapid facilitated contractions. As we shall see in later sections, it is typical of nervous systems to possess both fast-conducting and slow-conducting nervous pathways. When mechanical stimuli are applied to the crown or column of an anemone, the animal withdraws symmetrically, but local stimuli can also produce local responses whose effects may slowly spread around the circumference of the animal (Pantin, 1935). In anemones there may be both ectodermal and endodermal muscles, but the mechanisms that coordinate their activities are unknown. In *Metridium senile* slow circular and parietal muscles can produce both local responses and also responses that spread over the animal changing its entire shape. Speed of impulse conduction in the column nerve net is only about one-tenth that in the mesenteries, and the nerve cells are smaller. In some anemones reciprocal inhibition between circular and parietal muscles has been demonstrated (Needler and Ross, 1958).

In scyphomedusae (Figure 11-23) there are eight marginal bodies. When marginal bodies are excised, it can be shown that any one is capable of initiating the swimming contractions

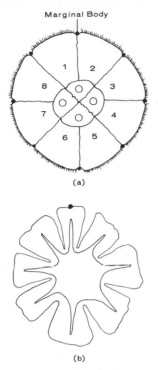

Marginal Body

(a)

(b)

Figure 11-23 (a) Ventral (oral) view of a scyphozo-an medusa showing the eight marginal bodies. Radiating lines represent positions of radial canals. Circles in central region represent gonads. (b) When a medusa has been dissected leaving only one marginal body and a small part of tissue conduction of excitation can still occur.

of the bell. The contractions originate in the region of a marginal body and spread rapidly over the whole bell. Even when all eight marginal bodies are removed, the application of a single electrical impulse can elicit a normal swimming contraction. The electrical impulse can be applied at any point on the margin or subumbrellar surface. This is an indication that there is a conduction system present which connects all of the musculature of the bell. Deep incisions or removal of large regions of the bell fail to interrupt the propagation of the contraction wave (Romanes, 1885). Various types of analyses have shown that the conduction is nervous not muscular.

However, differences are found in the various coelenterates. In scyphomedusans the swimming contraction is initiated by a single through-conduction impulse spreading from

any marginal center across the nerve net. But in hydromedusae local pacemakers cause the muscular contractions, and their activities are coordinated by a through conducted spike that has no direct effect on the muscles. This is a pattern of multiple pacemakers super-imposed on a through conducting system, and there is regional autonomy (see Passano, 1965).

When the scyphistoma of *Aurelia aurita* is stimulated electrically or mechanically at defined sites, it could be shown that each region was neurologically independent because the effects of stimulation were localized in just one specific region of the polyp. Coordination of the different regions during prey capture and during other complex behavioral patterns is possible because the anatomical arrangement of the polyp form allows one region to stimu-late another mechanically. This is the simplest of coelenterate forms, and such a coordinating mechanism is probably not suitable for coe-lenterates with more complex arrangements of body structure.

These are but a few of the recent findings on coelenterate neuromuscular activities, but they are enough to indicate that there is variation within the group's morphological and physio-logical arrangements for muscular control. The nerve net, although the simplest form of nervous system organization, still possesses the capability for providing complex coordi-nated reactions. The coelenterates are of interest also due to their position in the evolution of nervous systems (see Figure 11-24). Lower phyla do not possess nervous systems, but in the coelenterates they are present in a relatively highly developed form.

11-17. The Annelid Nervous System. The simplest annelid nervous systems are similar to those of flatworms. There is a subepidermal plexus in contact with the epidermis. In other annelids this has thickened to form a pair of ventral nerve cords connected in each segment by commissures. At the junctions of nerve cords and commissures are found ganglia. Generally, the annelid nervous system consists of a ventral chain of paired segmental ganglia, an anterior circumenteric nerve ring formed

Figure 11-24 Some movements of the sea anemone *Metridium*. Upper row, from left to right diagrams the form during ingestion, one-half hour after ingestion, and two swaying movements during food seeking. The first three diagrams of the bottom row show stages in antiperistaltic contraction leading to excretion and defecation; the last diagram shows the form during shriveling. [Redrawn after Batham and Pantin (1950).]

of a pair of dorsal cerebral ganglia (= the brain) connected by a cerebral commissure, and a pair of circumesophageal connectives which join the brain to the first ventral ganglia. In oligochaetes a motor system—the enteric nervous system—arises from the brain, circumenteric nerves, or associated ganglia and appears to control muscles of the gut and perhaps also provides control for secretion of enzymes and other materials by the gut. This system may have evolved from the stomatogastric system of polychaetes in which one or more pairs of motor nerves extend from the brain or circumenteric connectives to provide motor control for the eversible pharynx found in some polychaetes.

Several evolutionary trends are seen in the annelid nervous system. There is a tendency for the nervous system to move inward to a more protected position. Whereas in primitive annelids the nervous system is located in the skin, in other annelids it has moved inward into the muscle layers of the body wall. In higher annelids such as the oligochaetes it has moved into the coelom. In the latter organisms muscle cells are found incorporated into the nerve cord sheaths—a finding which is interpreted as indicating a past intramuscular position.

The original paired separate ganglia in each segment of more primitive annelids are found to have moved medially and finally united in higher annelids. Although the nerve cords may unite and be covered by a single sheath, they often each retain a separate histological form

with two neuropiles (see Figures 11-25 and 11-26).

In higher annelids the brain tends to assume a more posterior position than in lower species in which the brain occupies the first segment (= prostomium). In earthworms the brain is usually found in the third segment, whereas in leeches it is in the fourth or fifth segment (Figure 11-26).

Annelids, like many other invertebrate phyla with organized nervous systems, possess a fast-conducting system of giant fibers that function primarily as a rapid escape mechanism. Most earthworms have five giant fibers: a large middorsal fiber, a pair of dorsolateral fibers, and a pair of smaller ventral fibers. Some giant fibers are derived from overgrown neurons, and others are formed by the end-to-end connection of large neurons in each segment. The connections convert the fibers into a through conduction system (see also Chapter 8). The median giant fiber of *Lumbricus* carries impulses about 1,600 times as fast as smaller neurons in the earthworm nervous system. Their length affords another advantage to the animal since the lack of synaptic junctions avoids synaptic delay when fast reflex movements are needed. The giant fiber system, and also the nervous system generally, has many variations in different annelid species (see Figure 11-25).

Ogawa (1939) counted and measured cells and fibers during various stages in the growth of the earthworm *Pheretima* (see Figure 11-27).

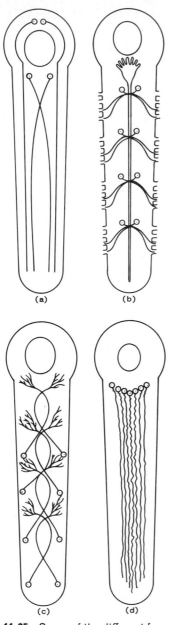

Figure 11-25 Some of the different forms of the rapid through-conducting giant fiber systems of annelids. (a) Giant fibers of *Sigalion* consist of unicellular giant fibers that originate in the brain and anterior regions of the nerve cord. (b) *Neanthes* has lateral giant fibers of multicellular origin that run through two segments. There is also a medial giant fiber system arising from cells associated with the subesophageal ganglion. (c) Decussating smaller giant fibers found in annelids such as *Neanthes*. (d) Giant fiber system of *Halla* with cell bodies positioned anteriorly. There is also a giant fiber system with cell bodies in the posterior part of the animal.

Of interest was the fact that a group of characteristic brain cells increased enormously in number during development, whereas other cells such as those of the stomodeal system increased very little in number. This is one of the few studies in which complete cell counts in a developing organism have been made. Such information would be of interest, especially if correlated with changes in the activity and behavior of the animal. Ogawa made corresponding studies of muscle fibers and epidermal cells.

Much more information is needed concerning neuromuscular control systems and nervous system integration in the annelids. Much of the work that has been done on such activity has been on earthworms, and the discussion to follow will center on these organisms.

When the brain of an earthworm is removed, the animal is hyperactive and restless. Hyperactivity in a decerebrate animal is an indication that the brain normally assumes an inhibitory function over lower regions of the nervous system. In the case of annelids this inhibitory influence appears to be on the subesophageal ganglion, which is important in the control of movements. When this ganglion is removed, the animal is usually almost motionless (removal of the subesophageal ganglion also effectively removes the brain from the nervous system). Decerebrate polychaetes can still crawl, right themselves, copulate, and burrow slowly (Collier, 1939); thus many activities can proceed without the brain. Rapid burrowing and feeding behavior is, however, lost in decerebrate organisms.

When the giant fibers of the earthworm nerve cord are electrically stimulated with single pulses, the longitudinal muscles of the entire body wall contract. The same muscles also exhibit slow facilitated responses—an indication that two neural control systems are present.

No general pattern of locomotion in annelids can be described because a variety of mechanisms are found. In earthworms, movement occurs as a peristaltic wave over the body due to contractions and relaxations of two sets of antagonistic muscles—the circular and longitudinal muscles (Figure 11-28). Peristalsis can

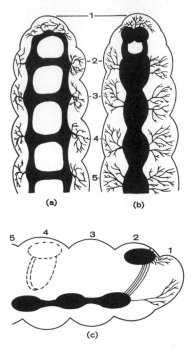

(a)   (b)

(c)

Figure 11-26   (a) In the primitive condition the annelid nervous system has the brain in the prostomium or first segment, while the ventral nerve cord is double. There is a ganglion associated with each nerve trunk in each segment. Commissures connect the ganglia in each segment. (b) In higher annelids the nerve cords tend to fuse, forming finally a single ventral nerve cord. (c) The brain lies in the prostomium in lower annelids and polychaetes, and it moves posteriorly in the oligochaetes and leeches (dashed outline). The dorsally lying brain is connected to the ganglia of the ventral nerve cord by the circumpharyngeal connectives.

be observed to begin as a wave of thinning at the anterior end (the body thins as a result of the contraction of the circular muscles as the longitudinal muscles relax). The wave of activity proceeds caudally—thus moving in a direction opposite to that of the actual progression of the body. There is also a thickening phase as the circular muscles relax and the longitudinal muscles contract; segments of the body when in this thickening phase are in contact with the substratum, and their chaetae are protruded. As indicated in Figure 11-28, segments in the thinning phase move forward and are added to those in the thickening phase.

Friedländer (1888, 1894) showed that when an earthworm is cut into two pieces and the two halves are then joined with pieces of thread, the waves of contraction pass over the cut region as if it were not there at all. This is an indication that intrasegmental reflexes play a role in peristalsis and that purely mechanical stimuli are sufficient to induce contraction in a following segment. There are stretch receptors in each segment which can respond to length or tension changes in the musculature of proceeding segments. Stimulation of these receptors can generate impulses in appropriate motor neurons.

In another type of experiment it was shown that when a worm was cut in half except for the ventral nerve cord and the two halves were pinned down on either side of the cut so that one side could not pull on the other, the peristaltic wave still passed over the cut region. This suggests that another pathway of conduction exists directly through the ventral nerve cord. Thus two alternative pathways for impulse conduction to control peristalsis may exist in earthworms. One may be the through-conducting giant fiber system, the other may be inter- and intrasegmental reflex pathways.

The muscles in each segment of an earthworm exhibit stretch reflexes. When longitudinal muscles are stretched (by stretching the worm lengthwise), these muscles contract. This in turn stretches the circular muscles, and these then contract while the longitudinal muscles relax. A continuous stretch applied to an earthworm induces regular contraction waves along the length of the worm. Such contractions may also be elicited in unstretched worms by tactile stimuli such as those produced by drawing a bristle or fine brush over the body surface. There is a complex feedback system for obtaining proper muscular activity for locomotion, but the details of the system are still obscure.

During locomotion each segment moves forward about 2 to 3 centimeters and the frequency of the peristaltic wave is about 7 to 10 per second. The initiation of peristalsis is by the ventral nerve cord although the pacemaker

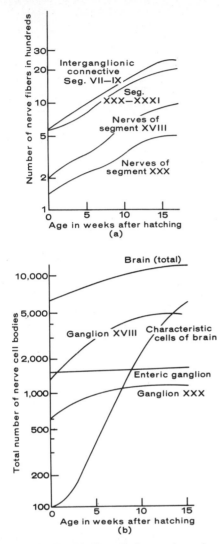

Figure 11-27 (a) Growth in number of nerve fibers from hatching of the earthworm *Pheretima communissima*. (b) Growth in total number of cells. Of interest is the enormous increase in small neurons of the brain known as characteristic brain cells. Such increases may be a factor in developing complexity of behavior. Muscle and epidermal cells generally were found to increase to a greater extent than nerve cells, excepting the characteristic cells. However, nerve cell volumes and fiber diameters showed significant increases during maturation. [Data selected from Ogawa (1939).]

region is not known. Isolated nerve cords show bursts of spontaneous activity, but these have not as yet been related to the normal activity

inducing peristalsis. A slight stretch or tactile stimulus applied to a suspended length of earthworm (consisting of 20 to 40 intact segments) induces a peristalsis that may last for twenty minutes (Collier, 1939). The reflex activity can be inhibited by strong tactile stimulation. Peristalsis in this experimental preparation can also be induced by electrically polarizing the preparation with the anterior end positive. In artificially stretched preparations the conduction of impulses is rapid, suggesting the involvement of the giant fiber system. Normal reflexes are slower.

In polychaetes such as *Nereis* locomotion is by means of appendages called parapodia (Gray, 1968). In general terms creeping is accomplished by movements of the parapodia alone; swimming or fast locomotion involves the combined activity of parapodia and the longitudinal muscles of the body wall. In *Nereis* the contraction wave moves cephalically, and the antagonistic muscle sets are the left versus right muscles. The contraction waves are initiated by spontaneous activities in the central nervous system. Transection of the nerve cord destroys all coordination between segments although each piece still shows all the phases of normal locomotion.

11-18. Arthropod Neuromuscular Systems. The research literature on arthropod nervous and neuromuscular systems is immense, and only some basic principles can be presented here. The arthropods comprise a group with the largest number of animals in the animal kingdom, and there is great diversity in both nervous system organization and in the mechanisms used for muscular control. Bullock and Horridge (1965) should be consulted for details of nervous system organization and function in arthropods; Meglitsch (1967); Snodgrass (1965); and Rockstein (1964–1965) have reviewed insect nervous systems and functions.

The arthropod nervous system is organized in a manner very similar to that described for annelids. However, there is an increased cephalization in arthropods compared with annelids. Arthropods have a distinct head region

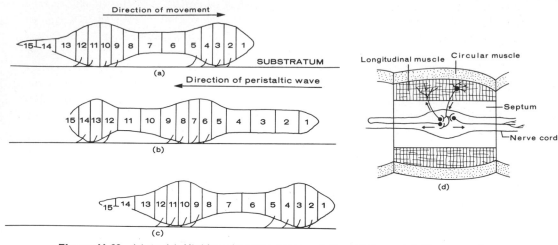

Figure 11-28 (a) to (c) Highly schematic representation of the peristaltic wave of contraction responsible for earthworm locomotion. (a) Segments 1 to 5 and 9 to 12 are contracted (longitudinal muscles contracted) and are in contact with the substratum. Extended chaetae enable worm to grip ground. These segments remain stationary with respect to the substratum. Segments 6 to 8 and 13 to 15 have their longitudinal muscles relaxed and the circular muscles contracted. Arrows indicate that the direction of movement is opposite to that of the contraction wave. (b) Segments 1 to 4 are extended by the contraction of circular muscles as are also segments 10 to 11. This extension moves these segments forward, while the segments with longitudinal muscles contracted remain stationary. (c) The next stage of movement, similar to that of (a). (d) A schematic representation of the distribution of circular and longitudinal muscles in a single segment of the earthworm. Some of the basic neural connections are shown. There are sensory neurons which bring impulses into the ventral nerve cord ganglion. It synapses with motor neurons and also with internuncial neurons that connect the segment with those preceding and following it. The details of the reflexes required for locomotion are still not clear.

and usually the body is further divided into thorax and abdomen. The cephalization in arthropods is seen not only in the greater abundance of cephalic sensory organs and their greater specialization but is also reflected in a more highly developed brain.

Although it is difficult to generalize about the arthropod nervous system, there is a general plan such that the nervous system consists of a brain joined to a ventral nerve cord via circumesophageal connectives. The nerve cord is composed of ganglia joined by longitudinal connectives and transversely by commissures. Although in the arthropod embryo there is a pair of ganglia in each segment, there is a tendency toward fusion of ganglia in the adult especially toward the anterior end. Terminal ganglia are commonly fused also and provide innervation for specialized tail structures. In higher insects and crustaceans

fusion of ganglia is generally complete. As indicated in Figure 11-29, a variety of patterns exist in arthropod nervous systems. In many arthropods a stomadeal system is found which innervates the anterior part of the digestive tract. Giant fiber systems are also present in many arthropods.

The brain is the major anterior or superior ganglionic mass and innervates sensory organs and musculature in the head region. It is also the principal association center for the whole body. The arthropod brain is more highly developed than the annelid brain and may contain as many as 100,000 cells. Generally, crustacean brains contain more neurons than do those of insects or spiders. There are three main regions of the brain. The **protocerebrum** consists of several neuropile masses: paired optic lobes, the median central body, and the median protocerebral bridge. There may also be association neuropiles such as the corpora pedunculata (located in the eyestalks of decapod crustaceans). Each of these regions serves an an integrating center for anterior sensory organs and also as a control center for movements of muscles of the head region. The **duocerebrum** contains neuropile association centers for the first antennae. The **tritocerebrum** is the third region of the brain and supplies neurons to the anterior digestive tract and to structures in the head such as the second pair of antennae (when present). In higher crustaceans about ten nerves from sensory organs of the head run to the brain; motor fibers to head musculature usually occur in separate nerve bundles.

Generally, the CNS of arthropods is similar to that of annelids. A major difference is found in the nature of the brain, which in arthropods is more highly developed, perhaps

a consequence of an increase in complexity of cephalic sensory organs. The arthropod nervous system contains more neurons, although actual cell counts have been made for only one or two species. Arthropod neurons exhibit a variety of types and an even greater variety of axon types. Axons vary in size, nature of branching, and so forth.

The subesophageal ganglion is the first ganglion of the ventral nerve cord and functions as a coordinating center for chewing movements as well as a source of tonic excitation necessary for the partially autonomous activity of more posterior ganglia.

Each segmental ganglia supplies nerves to the appendages on that segment, to the dorsal musculature, to the sensory organs of that segment, and often to the heart in its segment. Dorsal areas and longitudinal nerve

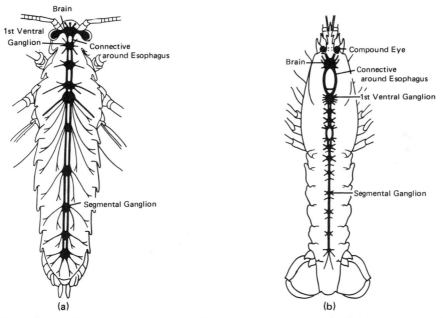

Figure 11-29 The general plan of the arthropod nervous system is a dorsal, anterior brain with circumesophageal connectives and a ventral nerve cord of segmental ganglia, commissures, and nerves, plus a peripheral nervous system. As was true of the annelids, there is diversity in the nervous systems of insects and crustaceans. The evolutionary tendency has been toward a fusion of ganglia. (a) Highly diagrammatic outline of the central nervous system of an insect (cockroach). (b) Highly diagrammatic outline of the central nervous system of a crustacean (crayfish). The similarities between insect and crustacean nervous systems are striking. The anterior portion of the nervous system is highly developed, and the portions of the CNS devoted to processing optic information has become greater than that seen in the annelids.

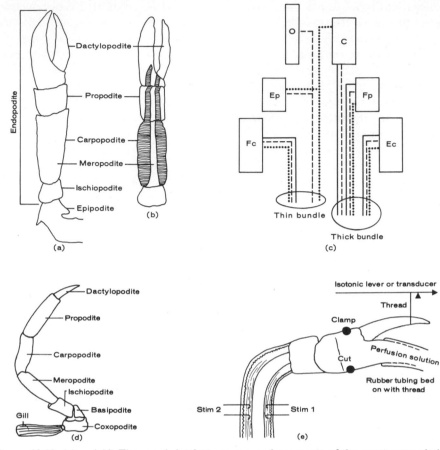

Figure 11-30 (a) and (d) The exoskeletal structures and segments of the crustacean chela and walking leg, respectively. (b) Musculature of the crustacean chela. (c) Nervous innervation of the crayfish walking leg muscles. Solid lines represent excitatory neurons, dashed lines represent inhibitory neurons. O, opener muscle; C, closer muscle; E_p, extensor of propodite; E_c, extensor of carpopodite; F_p, flexor of propodite; F_c, flexor of carpopodite. Note that only relatively few neurons are used to control the muscles of the leg. Each neuron branches to innervate the muscle fibers comprising the whole muscle. (e) Experimental arrangement for studying muscle responses in a crustacean chela. The nerve bundles are easily exposed and isolated.

tracts seem to be associated primarily with motor activities; ventral areas and tracts of the cord tend to be sensory. However, there is much entwining of tracts and fibers throughout the ganglia.

Giant fiber systems occur, especially in lower Crustacea, shrimps, lobsters, scorpions, and some insects. In crustaceans there are one or two pairs of giant fibers. The median pair are formed from a single large axon running from a brain cell to the end of the nerve cord. The lateral pair are formed by end-to-end contact of segmental units with septal synapses located at the transverse membranes (see also Chapter 8). Giant fiber systems, as in the annelids, usually serve as a fast conduction pathway for escape reflexes of arthropods. Insect giant fibers are structurally specialized for a more diverse set of functions. In insects they are usually enlarged interneurons that run in the ventral cord, and they coordinate rapid movements.

The nervous system of arthropods is intimately associated with the endocrine system and, as will be described later in this chapter, neuroendocrine functions have been established for several sites within the arthropod CNS. Thus, the arthropod nervous system exhibits an increase in complexity over that of the annelids in this respect also. It should be stressed that the description of the arthropod nervous system given here is only a general one and many variations are found within the phylum. This observation should be kept in mind when reading the remainder of this section.

The crustacean neuromuscular system is based upon different principles than that of the vertebrates (this is true of arthropods and invertebrate organisms generally). Instead of motor units, arthropods rely upon a few nerves with different effects upon the muscle fibers to achieve a variety of contractile responses. Motor neurons to a structure such as an arthropod limb may branch extensively innervating a large number of muscle fibers and often more than one muscle of the appendage. Although vertebrates possess slow and fast muscle fibers and only in a few known cases rely upon the nature of the motor axon to produce a slow response (for example, muscle fibers of the nictating membrane of the cat's eye; fibers of the mammalian iris), invertebrate muscle innervation is generally based upon the use of different axons to achieve different degrees of contraction. Most invertebrate neuromuscular systems are built upon polyneuronal innervation, that is, more than one axon innervates a given muscle fiber.

Although dual innervation is the general rule, the muscle fibers of some invertebrates are supplied with three or more motor neurons, which means that these muscle fibers are capable of three or more modes of contraction. Two decapod Crustacea have been extensively studied with regard to motor innervation, and much of the remaining discussion will center about these two organisms: a crayfish *Procambarus* and a rock lobster *Panulirus*.

The limbs of decapod crustaceans are often studied with respect to neuromuscular activity because the walking legs as well as the chela contain only a few discrete muscles, and these are innervated by only a few nerves. Figure 11-30 includes diagrams of the structure of chela and walking leg as found in Crustacea (the appendages of insects are similar although the terminology used for the various parts is different). The musculature of a crayfish chela is shown schematically in Figure 11-30b; the innervation of these muscles is shown in Figure 11-30c. The nature of one experimental preparation used to study the effects of stimulation of the various axons on muscle contractility is shown in Figure 11-30e.

It might be noted that due to the presence of a jointed exoskeleton, the attachment and arrangements of muscles about joints in the arthropods differ from those found in the vertebrates (see Figure 11-15 and Figure 11-30). Arthropod muscles are attached to hardened regions of the cuticle, and when a muscle is very powerful, the cuticle is often infolded or ridged to provide a firmer surface for muscle attachment. Muscles are often attached to **apodemes**—the projecting or infolded surfaces of the cuticle. It is usual for a muscle to be confined to one podomere (leg segment) and to operate a joint through mechanical actions on an apodeme or through attachment of the muscle to the inner surface of the cuticle of the adjacent segment to be moved. Membranous hinges between segments of the exoskeleton allow movement.

The flexor muscle of the carpopodite of *Procambarus* or *Panulirus* receives innervation from four axons. However, only 4 per cent of the muscle fibers are innervated by all four axons; 29 per cent are innervated by only three of the axons; 26 per cent by only two axons; and 38 per cent are innervated by only one of the axons (Furshpan, 1955). Thus, the complexity of the neuromuscular system is increased by the differences in innervation of particular muscle fibers within a muscle and the possibilities inherent in the responses of such a system.

It becomes difficult to classify responses of the muscle as fast or slow because the presence of more than two axons results in more than two types of response. Most crustacean muscles are not fast in the sense that a vertebrate muscle twitch is fast. Crustacean muscles generally do not exhibit a twitch response to a single electrical stimulus and a complete spike potential often is not found in the muscle fibers (at least under laboratory conditions). However, the laboratory preparation of a crustacean neuromuscular system is extremely sensitive to fatigue, and this factor and the lack of spikes may be due to the absence of a normal circulatory system. In the normal intact muscle, spikes conceivably could be present.

No spikes are recorded after the stimulation of any one of the four axons nor do single stimuli produce a twitch contraction (van Harreveld and Wiersma, 1939). However, one of the axons when stimulated by two impulses does give rise to a fast contraction. The other three axons require several stimuli per second to cause a response. Facilitation thus plays an important role in the crustacean neuromuscular system. Measurements of the membrane potentials show that each axon upon stimulation produces a different type of end plate potential and a different type of contractile response.

True fast responses caused by all-or-nothing spikes are found only in a few arthropod muscles such as the closer muscle of the chelipeds of crayfish. Other responses are slow responses. True fast responses show no facilitation because they are already maximal responses. Slow responses do facilitate.

As a generality, simultaneous stimulation of all motor axons supplying a muscle fiber results in both electrical and mechanical response summation. Summated junction potentials resulting from the simultaneous stimulation of two or more motor axons are an example of heterofacilitation. Usually a preceding impulse in a given motor axon will result in a summation of electrical response upon the application of second stimulus. This facilitation in response to several stimuli applied to the same axon is an example of autofacilitation.

It has been shown that the size of the junction potential is not necessarily correlated with the degree of mechanical response. There is no interaction between junction potentials elicited by different motor axons (unless they are produced simultaneously), but under these conditions there is often an augmentation of mechanical response. Therefore, in analyzing this type of neuromuscular system, it must be realized that two mechanisms are at work which both can effect the response: there is the transfer of the nerve impulse to the muscle membrane with the formation of an end plate potential and there is also the excitation-contraction coupling system (see Chapter 10). The final activity of a muscle is often dependent on direct effects on the excitation-contraction coupling system and presumably affects in some manner the movement of Ca^{2+} ions.

All crustacean skeletal muscles are innervated by inhibitory axons in addition to excitatory axons. Several muscles may be innervated by branches of the same inhibitory axon—**common inhibition** (Wiersma, 1941). **True inhibitor** is the name given to an inhibitory axon that innervates only one muscle. Double inhibitory innervation is known for the muscles of decapod brachyurans and anomurans.

Impulses arriving over inhibitory axons give rise to small junction potentials that are generally hyperpolarizing. But if the muscle membrane potential is artificially raised or is normally high, the inhibitory potential may be either depolarizing or may not change the membrane potential (Hoyle and Wiersma, 1958b). Inhibitory axons prevent both slow and fast mechanical responses when properly stimulated. The fast responses of the closer muscles of *Procambarus* and *Carcinus*, however, cannot be so inhibited. Generally inhibition appears to be caused by a direct effect on the excitation-contraction coupling mechanism.

The particular response of the musculature of a limb is determined, among other factors, by the frequency of impulses along each motor neuron (both excitatory and inhibitory).

Inhibitory pulses have effects that are long lasting. To inhibit contractions produced by a given frequency of motor neuron excitatory impulses, the impulses of the inhibitory axon need only a frequency of about one-half that of the motor axon. The ratio of the frequency of inhibitory impulses to the frequency of excitatory impulses is the Rc ratio, which is constant over a wide range of frequencies for a given neuromuscular system (Wiersma and Ellis, 1941).

Many of the mechanisms involved in inhibition and excitation of arthropod muscles are still unknown. It may be that insect muscles are innervated similarly to crustacean muscles although inhibitory neurons are missing in many species.

Before leaving the topic of arthropod neuromuscular systems, it is worth mentioning certain escape reflexes. In lobsters and crayfish, for example, frightening stimuli cause the animals to contract suddenly the powerful flexor muscles of the abdomen, an action which drives the animals rapidly backward through the water. This activity is mediated by the rapid conducting giant fiber system. In crayfish are found so-called push button reflexes—a series of coordinated escape responses, body orientations, and cheliped movements that are initiated by activity in single neurons of the CNS (Kennedy et al., 1966).

The cockroach has been intensively studied with regard to its giant fiber system. The cockroach possesses hairs on the anal cerci that are sensitive to air movement and that synapse with giant fibers running the length of the ventral nerve cord to the thoracic ganglia. Slight air movements stimulate the sensory hairs and cause the cockroach to run at full speed. The relationship between giant fibers and neuromuscular apparatus of the running legs is complex and still under study. Reflex arcs involving plastic tonus have also been found in the cockroach. The sensory organs involved are campaniform sensilla located in the cuticle of the legs. If a weight is applied to a leg, the output of the sense organs increases and the frequency of motor impulses to the leg muscles also increases, thus increasing the tone of muscular contractions. It is of interest that the processes of facilitation and recruitment of fibers take place in the muscles themselves, not in the CNS as is the case in vertebrates.

Chemical Control Systems

11-19. Endocrine and Neuroendocrine Systems. In order better to emphasize the close relationship between nervous and chemical control systems, both are included in the discussions of this chapter. Endocrine systems, as previously stated, generally control long term activities of target organs in contrast to the more rapid activities under the control of the nervous system. Endocrine systems are effector organs, in that they are under the control of the nervous system either directly or indirectly. The activity of endocrine systems involves the release of specific chemical substances—**hormones**—which are usually (although not always) carried by the circulating blood to sites where they may act. In general hormonal regulation is found for the following types of activities (Scharrer and Scharrer, 1963):

1. Reproductive activities: control of gametogenesis, development and maintenance of sex ducts and accessory or secondary sexual characteristics, release of sexual behavior (including the release of pheromones), initiation of spawning and oviposition.
2. Growth, maturation, and regeneration: including growth by the addition of segments, for example, annelids; molting and metamorphosis, for example, in crustaceans and other arthropods; regenerative activities, and diapause.
3. Metabolism and homeostasis: regulation of intermediary metabolism (see Chapter 4), maintenance of internal environmental factors including temperature regulation, water and ion balance, blood glucose levels, and so forth.

4. Adaptation to external factors including visual adaptation to light intensities, control of physiological color changes, and so forth.

Hormonal actions are usually longer lasting than those produced by nerve impulses. Also hormonal effects are capable of being exerted throughout the body, whereas nervous actions are usually more localized. Hormonal actions take place wherever cells are found that possess the necessary reaction or combining sites with the chemical hormones. Nearly all systems appear to be regulated by a combination of both hormonal and nervous systems.

In essence the operation of both hormonal and nervous systems are similar in that both cause reactions by means of substances released by cells. Synaptic transmitters usually operate over only short distances and through specific pathways; hormonal actions, because of their distribution by the circulatory system, are more widespread. However, the operation of the autonomic nervous system of vertebrates occurs by the release of transmitters that often pass through intercellular spaces before reaching the target cells, and several parts of the endocrine system release chemicals only into closely attached tissues.

Although endocrine glands were first considered only as ductless glands releasing hormones into the circulation, it is now known that endocrine tissues are found in animals which lack much in the way of circulating fluids and that tissues such as those of the brain or intestinal wall possess endocrine cells. In fact, the first hormonal action to be successfully demonstrated was that of secretin produced by the intestinal wall and released into the intestinal lumen (Bayliss and Starling, 1902).

Both neurosecretion (the release of chemical synaptic transmitters or neurotransmitters) and neuroendocrine secretion (the release of hormones, neurohormones, by nerve cells) are now considered as activities common to all nervous systems. Therefore, the endocrine and nervous systems merge in both functional and morphological aspects. Such a merger is seen, for example, in the case of the adrenal medulla, a classical endocrine organ. The secreting cells (=chromaffin cells) of the adrenal medulla are derived embryologically from neuroblast cells, as are nerve cells. The chromaffin cells cytologically resemble neurosecretory cells; they secrete adrenalin and nor-adrenaline as do most sympathetic neurons; and they are often associated with true neurons. In many respects the chromaffin cells act as postganglionic cells of the sympathetic nervous system.

Many neuroendocrine reflexes are now known. For example, in mammalian temperature regulation (see Chapter 15) lowered body temperatures are sensed by the hypothalamus. Neurosecretory cells of the hypothalamus secrete materials that finally cause the release of thyroxine. The thyroxine, in turn, causes an increased cellular metabolism and an increased heat production that can raise body temperatures. As we shall see, the hypothalamus plays a central role in many neuroendocrine reflexes in vertebrates.

Classically endocrine functions were first determined by the removal of suspected endocrine tissues either by surgical or by chemical means and the analysis of the resulting physiological or biochemical changes. Restoration of the excised tissue or of tissue extracts to the animal to determine whether functional activity was restored is usually the next step in the study of endocrine function. Thus, first elimination and then restoration of excised tissues (sometimes by grafting excised tissues back into the animal) are basic methods in endocrinological studies.

If an extract of excised tissue is found to restore normal activity or to initiate particular activities, the extract may be analyzed in order to isolate and identify the chemical substance responsible for the activity. The use of isotopic tracers has been of great value in determining the pathway of synthesis of a hormone or in determining its routes through the body. Endocrinological methods are described by Eckstein and Knowles (1963).

Vertebrate endocrine systems will be

Table 11-5   Vertebrate Endocrine Glands and Hormones

General location of glands in the vertebrate body.

1. Adrenals
2. Duodenum
3. Pituitary (hypophysis)
4. Neurohyophysis
5. Thyroids
6. Parathyroids
7. Pancreas
8. Gonads (ovary or testes)

GLAND	HORMONES: NAME, ABBREVIATION, CHEMICAL NATURE
Adrenal	
cortex (steroidegenic tissue)	Cortisol, corticosterone, aldosterone, and other (Fig. 2-24; all are steroid hormones)
medulla (chromaffin tissue)	Adrenalin and noradrenaline (catacholamines)
Duodenum and stomach	Secretin and cholecystokinin (proteins)
Hypophysis	
adenohypophysis	
pars distalis (distal lobe)	Adrenocorticotropin, ACTH (large polypeptide)
	Thyrotropin, TSH (glycoprotein)
	Gonadotropins:
	Follicle-stimulating hormone, FSH (glycoprotein)
	Luteinizing hormone, LH; also called insterstial-cell-stimulating hormone, ICSH (glycoprotein)
	Prolactin or luteotropic hormone, LTH (protein)
	Growth-stimulating hormone, GSH; also called somatotropin STH (protein)
pars intermedia (intermediate lobe)	Intermedin or melanocyte-stimulating hormone, MSH (polypeptide)
neurohypophysis	
pars nervosa (neural lobe)	Vasopressin, oxytocin, vasotocin, mesotocin, and others (octapeptides, see Fig. 11-34)
eminentia mediana (median eminence)	Corticotropin releasing factor, CRF (polypeptide?)
	Thyrotropin releasing factor, TRF (polypeptide?)
	Follicle-stimulating hormone releasing factor, FRF (?)
	Luteinizing-hormone releasing factor (LRF) (?)
	Prolactin-inhibiting factor, PIF (?)
	Growth-hormone releasing factor, GRF (?)
Thyroid	Thyroxine, T_x (iodinated derivative of the amino acid)
	Triiodothyrone, T_3 (iodinated polypeptide)
	Calcitonin (polypeptide)
Parathyroids	Parathyroid hormone (protein)
Pancreas (Islets of Langerhans)	Insulin (protein)
	Glucagon (polypeptide)
Gonads	
ovary	Progesterone, estradiol, estrone, estrogen (steroids, see Fig. 2-24)
testis	Androstenedione, testosterone (steroids, see Fig. 2-24)

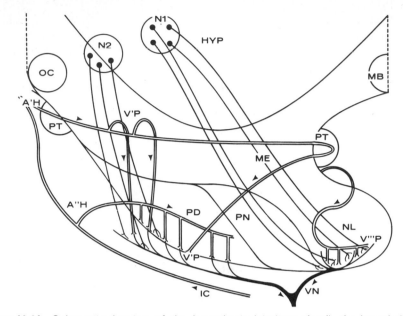

Figure 11-31 Schematic drawing of the hypophysis (pituitary gland), the hypothalamus (HYP), and their circulation. One division of the hypophysis, the adenohypophysis, develops in the embryo from epithelium of the pharynx. It includes the pars tuberalis (PT) lying in contact with the median eminence (ME), the pars intermedia, and the pars distalis (PD). The latter includes a division known as the zona tuberalis containing the portal vessels of the circulation. The second division of the hypophysis, the neurohypophysis, derives from the diencephalon. It includes the median eminence and the neural lobe (NL) or pars nervosa. The circulation of the hypothalamic-hypophyseal region is complex. The median eminence receives its blood supply from branches of the internal carotid arteries (IC) known as the hypophyseal arteries (A′H). This artery also provides blood to the pars tuberalis. Loops from the venous plexus of the pars tuberalis return forming a portal system in the median eminence that can receive neurosecretions from axons in this region. The hypothalamus contains two primary neurosecretory centers (N1 and N2). Axons from N2 pass through the primary venous portal system (V′P) of the median eminence. The pars distalis has a venous plexus supplied also by the hypophyseal artery A″H. The neural lobe receives branches of another hypophyseal artery also derived from the internal carotids. Nerve endings of neurosecretory axons from N1 are found in this region and can deliver neurosecretions to the circulation of this portal system (V‴P). All veins finally enter into the main vein draining the hypophysis (VN). Arrowheads indicate the direction of blood flows. OC, the optic chiasma; MB, mammilary body. N1, paraventricular nuclei and N2, supraoptic nucleus. Neurohormones elaborated in the cell bodies of neurons in these nuclei pass down the axon and reach either the neural lobe or the pars distalis. They are stored in secretory granules in larger nerve terminals until the proper stimulus arrives for their release into the circulation. [Modified from Jenkins (1962).]

discussed first because more is known about them than about those of the invertebrates. General references to endocrinology, including comparative and neuroendocrine aspects, include Gorbman and Bern (1962); Scharrer and Scharrer (1963); Turner (1966); von Euler and Heller (1963). Various aspects of hormone research are found in the annual volumes of *The Hormones* and in *Recent Progress in Hormone Research*.

11-20. Vertebrates: Neuroendocrine Systems. Table 11-5 lists the principle endocrine structures of vertebrates and also the hormones elaborated by these systems. In many cases the full complement of hormones

Table 11-6 Functions of Some Vertebrate Hormones (refer to Table II-5 for sources of hormones and the meanings of abbreviations).

Hormone	Functions
ACTH	Stimulates adrenocortical cells (interrenal cells in cyclostomes, teleosts, and elasmobranchs) to secrete corticosteroid hormones.
Adrenalin Noradrenalin	Elevates blood sugar levels and blood pressure (especially in reptiles, birds, and mammals).
Calcitonin	Decreases blood calcium in mammals
Corticosteroid hormones	Regulate Na^+ and K^+ levels through effects on kidney tubule cells; regulation of carbohydrate metabolism; regulates molting in amphibia and gestation in mammals.
Cholecystokinin	Stimulates release of bile from gall bladder and inhibits gastric secretion.
Gastrin	Stimulates secretion of gastric juice.
Glucagon	Glucagon raises blood sugar levels; in reptiles and birds raises blood pressure.
GSH	Probably generally stimulates growth in all vertebrates; in mammals also raises blood sugar levels.
FSH and LH	Stimulate gamete production and secretion of sex hormones; induce ovulation.
LTH	Maintains blood Na^+ in some freshwater and euryhaline teleosts; induces the water drive (migration to water) in newts; in birds stimulates crop milk production in pigeons and has other influences on reproduction; in mammals acts in mammary growth and lactation and corpus luteum maintenance and secretion.
MSH	Causes pigment disperion in melanophores in amphibia and lower vertebrates.
TSH	Stimulates thyroids to secrete thyroid hormones.
Hormones of pars nervosa	Vasotocin: in amphibians has antidiuretic activity; increases permeability of skin to water; probably antidiuretic activity in reptiles and birds; Oxytocin: in mammals causes milk ejection during suckling, stimulates uterine contractions, stimulates sperm transport. Vasopressin: stimulates water reabsorption by kidney tubules and stimulates smooth muscle contractions—only in mammals (arginine or lysine vasopressins). Oxytocin is also found in Chondrichthyes, lungfish, amphibians, and birds. Mesotocin is found in some fish, lungfish, amphibians and reptiles. Isotocin is found in teleosts. Glumitocin is found in elasmobranchs.
T_3 and T_x	Acts in migration in teleosts and osmoregulation in sticklebacks; in metamorphosis and differentiation in amphibians (molting inurodeles); molting in reptiles and birds; in mammals acts in differentiation, acts in body temperature regulation through calorigenic action.
Parathyroid hormone	Increases blood calcium levels.

produced by a given tissue is still not known, and the detailed chemical structures of many hormones remain to be determined. Table 11-6 lists the major functions of some important vertebrate hormones. All of the endocrine glands, except the parathyroids, are found in all vertebrates, although their structure and functions may differ markedly in

ACTH

(porcine) NH_2-Ser-Tyr-Ser-Met-Glu-His-Phe-Arg-Try-Gly-Lys-Pro-Val-Gly-Lys-Lys-Arg-Arg-Pro-Val-
                        1   5   10   15   20

            -Lys-Val-Tyr-Pro-Asp-Gly-Ala-Glu-Asp-Gln-Leu-Ala-Glu-Ala-Phe-Pro-Leu-Glu-Phe-COOH
                   25   30   35   39

(human)   —Asp-Ala-Gly-Glu-Asp-Gln-Ser-Ala-Glu—
                25 26 27 28 29 30 31 32 33

(bovine)   —Asp-Gly-Glu-Ala-Glu-Asp-Ser-Ala-Gln—
                25 26 27 28 29 30 31 32 33

(sheep)   —Ala-Gly-Glu-Asp-Asp-Glu-Ala-Ser-Glu—
                25 26 27 28 29 30 31 32 33

α-MSH

              CH_3-CO-Ser-Tyr-Ser-Met-Glu-His-Phe-Arg-Tyr-Gly-Lys-Pro-Val-NH_2
                           1   5   10   13

β-MSH

(horse)   Asp-Glu-Gly-Pro-Tyr-Lys-Met-Glu-His-Phe-Arg-Try-Gly-Ser-Pro-Arg-Lys-Asp
             1   5   10   15   18

(human)   Ala-Glu-Lys-Lys-Asp-Glu-Gly-Pro-Tyr-Arg-Met-Glu-His-Phe-Arg-Tyr-Gly-Ser-Pro-Pro-Lys-Asp
             1   5   10   15   20 22

(porcine)   Asp-Glu-Gly-Pro-Tyr-Lys-Met-Glu-His-Phe-Arg-Tyr-Gly-Ser-Pro-Pro-Lys-Asp
            1   5   10   15   18

(monkey)   Asp-Glu-Gly-Pro-Tyr-Arg-Met-Glu-His-Phe-Arg-Tyr-Gly-Ser-Pro-Pro-Lys-Asp
            1   5   10   15   18

(bovine)   Asp-Ser-Gly-Pro-Tyr-Lys-Met-Glu-His-Phe-Arg-Try-Gly-Ser-Pro-Pro-Lys-Asp
            1   5   10   15   18

NEUROHYPOPHYSEAL OCTAPEPTIDE HORMONES (Vertebrates)

Vasotocin   CyS-Tyr-Ileu-Gln-Asn-CyS-Pro-Arg-Gly-NH_2

Oxytocin   CyS-Tyr-Ileu-Gln-Asn-CyS-Pro-Leu-Gly-NH_2

Arginine Vasopressin CyS-Tyr-Phe-Gln-Asn-CyS-Pro-Arg-Gly-NH_2

Lysine Vasopressin   CyS-Tyr-Phe-Gln-Asn-CyS-Pro-Lys-Gly-NH_2

Isotocin   CyS-Tyr-Ileu-Ser-Asn-CyS-Pro-Ileu-Gly-NH_2

Mesotocin   CyS-Tyr-Ileu-Gln-Asn-CyS-Pro-Ileu-Gly-NH_2

Glumitocin   CyS-Tyr-Ileu-Ser-Asn-CyS-Pro-Gln-Gly-NH_2
                      1 2 3 4 5 6 7 8 9

Figure 11-32 The structures of some vertebrate hormones.

different groups. The endocrine system appears to have developed early in the evolution of vertebrates.

The **hypophysis** (=**pituitary**) is the most complex of vertebrate endocrine structures (Figure 11-31). It consists of the adeno-hypophysis (=posterior pituitary) and the neurohypophysis (=anterior pituitary). The latter is derived embryologically from nervous tissue, specifically from the diencephalon, and the former is derived from the tissues of the pharynx. The anatomy and physiology of the hypophysis are reviewed in Daniel (1967); Farrell et al. (1968); McCann et al., (1968). The hypophysis is intimately related to the hypothalamus, which as already stated is a major center for the control and coordination of homeostatic functions.

Hormones are not synthesized by the neurohypophysis itself, rather they are synthesized in the cell bodies of neurosecretory cells located in the supraoptic and para-ventricular nuclei of the hypothalamus. These substances then travel down the axons of the neurosecretory neurons to either the median eminence or the pars nervosa (neural lobe) of the neurohypophysis. Here they are stored until needed in secretory granules in the axon terminals. Neurosecretory substances produced in the hypothalamus also regulate the activities of the adenohypophysis.

The circulation of the hypophysis is complex and consists partly of two portal systems with sinusoids. The median eminence receives its blood supply from branches of the internal carotid artery, and the neural lobe has its own blood supply from another branch. The median eminence and neural lobe are **neurohemal organs**—structures with a rich vascular supply in which nerve endings lie bathed in the blood of the sinuses.

Upon appropriate stimulation the hormones of the neurosecretory axons in the neurohypophysis are released into the blood and carried to all parts of the animal. It is probable that nerve impulses passing down the neurosecretory cell axons stimulate the release of the hormones. The hormones of the neurohypophysis are all octapeptides (Figure 11-32). They include oxytocin and vasopressin (the latter is identical to the substance formerly known as the antidiuretic hormone—a term now used generically for all hormones that influence water balance). The distribution of different octapeptides in vertebrates is indicated in Table 11-6. Physiologically the most important actions of neural lobe octapeptide hormones is in the control of water and salt levels of blood and tissues. Salt regulation is more important in lower vertebrates, and water balance becomes of greater importance in terrestrial vertebrates (Heller, 1963).

Oxytocin also stimulates the contraction of uterine smooth muscle in childbirth and the ejection of milk from mammary glands. Its functions in fish and other lower vertebrates is not yet clear.

The adenohypophysis produces several hormones (Table 11-5), all of which are protein or polypeptides in nature. They are secreted in response to factors released from the median eminence. The latter hormones are probably synthesized by neurosecretory neurons of the hypothalamus although the exact pathway is not known. As shown in Table 11-5, the hormones released by the adenohypophysis are the agents that cause the secretion of hormones by other glands. In addition, some, such as the growth hormone, act generally throughout the body. In mammals the growth hormone appears to function in the regulation of the rate of protein synthesis.

The hypothalamus has sensory neurons that detect the blood pressure level, blood sugar level, blood osmotic pressure, and so forth. These sensory impulses can initiate activity in other neurons and cause the release of various hypophyseal hormones. From this brief discussion it can still be appreciated that synthesis of neurohormones by hypothalamic neurons is but the beginning of complicated chain of neuroendocrine reflex arcs and control systems.

Most of this discussion has been based on mammalian systems. Neurosecretory cells are scattered in various regions of the central nervous system of lower vertebrates, although in higher forms they are generally restricted to the caudal region. In fish neurosecretion is often part of a caudal neurosecretory system that releases materials into a neurohemal organ known as the urohypophysis. This is a structure in the posterior part of the fish which has similarities to the neurohypophysis of the brain.

It may be noted here that evidence for neurosecretory activity comes first from microscopic observations using light and electron microscopy. So-called Gomori stains are useful for detecting the presence of granules that are considered secretory products of the cells. Electron microscopy can be used to identify 1,000 to 3,000 Å granules that are considered to be primary neurosecretory granules. Histological examination is a primary, although not conclusive, method used to identify neurosecretory activity. In all cases of neurosecretion, it is believed that synthesis occurs in the soma of the neuron and that hormonal substances are transported within the axon to the axon terminals where they are stored. Transport within the axon is supported by several lines of experimental evidence. Cytological examination reveals that neurosecretory granules are found all along the length of the axon and transection of an axon leads to a build-up of neurosecretory material at the proximal end of the axon. In addition, there have been direct observations of material flow within axons.

Although neurosecretory axons do not appear to make synaptic contact with other neurons, they are capable of conducting impulses as shown by electrophysiological recording. Such impulses may be the trigger mechanism for release of neurosecretions, in a manner similar to the release of transmitter substances. Other neurons, however, might also trigger this release. It may be noted that the term neurohumor is sometimes used to refer to any substance released by a neuron whether it be a transmitter or a hormone. The release of transmitters that act over short distances usually at postsynaptic membranes is not considered as neuroendocrine activity.

11-21. Vertebrates: Other Endocrine Systems. The discussion here will be brief and represent only a simplified examination of endocrine gland functions. The thyroid gland is found in all vertebrates and its functional unit is a follicle consisting of a layer of epithelial cells. The follicles undergo changes in size depending upon the amount of colloid (= synthesized material) that has been produced. The colloid is composed of thyroglobulin, which contains the hormones thyroxine and triiodothyronine. These hormones are iodinated amino acids. The protein thyroglobulin is rich in tyrosine groups. When this protein is secreted into the lumen of the follicle, iodine that has also been transported by the epithelial layer into the lumen reacts with the tyrosine residues. The iodinated thyroglobulin is then retransported into the cells, where it is broken down releasing the thyroid hormones.

The thyroid also produces calcitonin, whose action is to decrease blood calcium concentrations—an action antagonistic to that of parathyroid hormone. The parathyroids in many species are embedded in thyroid tissue. The release of parathyroid hormone is directly controlled by blood Ca levels. Low concentrations of blood Ca causes the secretion of this hormone.

The actions of thyroid hormone are many. It stimulates metamorphosis in amphibian larvae. Thyroxine also has an effect on growth and development in all vertebrates, although its actions are not clearly understood because other hormones also have this activity. In amphibians, reptiles, and birds the molting of cornified epidermal cells or of feathers is stimulated by thyroxine. Thyroxine also causes the deposition of melanin in bird feathers and of guanine crystals in the skin of fish, giving them a silvery appearance. In addition, thyroxine affects such diverse processes as schooling behavior in fish, the threshold sensitivity of sensory receptors, creatine-creatinine conversion, and water diuresis.

The mechanisms by which thyroxine affects these varied physiological and morphological activities are not known. At the cellular level thyroxine is selectively accumulated by some cells and is picked up by mitochondria. However, its activity in mitochondria is not understood. Thyroxine increases the rate of oxygen consumption and heat production by cells. It has been suggested that the hormone stimulates the synthesis of certain enzymes of oxidative phosphorylation. However, thyroxine is also an uncoupler of oxidative phosphorylation. There are many paradoxes in the actions of thyroxine at both the cellular and the organ levels.

The pancreas, specifically the cells of the islets of Langerhans, produces at least two hormones. Insulin is produced in the α-cells. Glucagon, which is also a protein hormone containing 29 amino acids, is produced by β-cells. These hormones regulate very precisely the blood glucose level. Studies of their activities are complicated by the fact that hormones of the adrenal medulla, pituitary, and thyroid also affect carbohydrate metabolism. Further, in different species different combinations of hormones are active and tissues exhibit different orders of sensitivity to the hormones. Insulin and glucagon can be considered as gastrointestinal hormones because they are synthesized in tissues formed by the outpocketing of the gut wall. In cyclostomes no separate anatomical gland is formed, and the hormones are directly produced by the intestinal wall.

Insulin lowers blood glucose levels by stimulating the deposition of glycogen granules. Glucagon increases blood sugar levels by stimulating the dissolution of glycogen granules and the consequent movement of soluble glucose into the blood. The actions of both hormones is primarily on the liver—a major organ of carbohydrate metabolism. Insulin and glucagon, when released by the pancreas enter the hepatic portal veins and thus reach the liver immediately. Most of the hormone molecules are used by the liver, which also possesses enzymes for inactivating or degrading them. Only an unknown fraction of insulin and probably no glucagon reaches other organs. It is somewhat paradoxical that it has been difficult experimentally to show the action of insulin on glucose in the liver, although its action in causing the formation of muscle glycogen is readily demonstrated. Not all muscle, however, reacts to insulin. For example, in the depancreatized animal, glycogen content increases in cardiac muscle even although insulin is lacking.

Neither insulin nor glucagon release is under nervous or endocrine control. Rather, the blood glucose level directly stimulates the release of the appropriate hormone. This was first shown by Houssay, who transplanted the pancreas of a dog to an atypical site, thus freeing it from its normal vagal innervation. In the new location the pancreas still maintained normal blood sugar levels. It appears, then, that the glucose concentration of the blood entering the pancreas in some manner directly stimulates the release of either insulin or glucagon.

The adrenal glands consist of two hormone producing tissues, which in lower vertebrates may be scattered and not associated with one another. In reptiles, birds, and mammals the chromaffin tissue (named because of its staining properties) is located in the adrenal medulla and synthesizes the catecholamines, adrenalin and noradrenalin.

The steroidogenic tissue of the adrenal cortex of reptiles, birds, and mammals produces a variety of steroid hormones (also known as corticoids). These are listed in Table 11-5. The pituitary hormone adrenocorticotropin (ACTH) is responsible for the maintenance and regulation of the zona reticularis and zona fasiculata of the cortex. These regions produce most of the steriod hormones. However, ACTH has no effect on the third region of the cortex, the zona glomerulosa, which produces the important adrenal cortical hormone, aldosterone. The secretion of ACTH by the pituitary is under a feedback control system since cortisol, produced by the adrenal cortex, inhibits ACTH release. However, ACTH regulation is more complicated than this because the hypothalamus also regulates ACTH.

Some steroid hormones, as well as adrenalin, are involved in the regulation of carbohydrate metabolism. For example, 11-oxy-steroids, the glucocorticoids, prevent glucose utilization by tissues and also inhibit the incorporation of amino acids into proteins. When this occurs, the amino acids are converted into carbohydrate, which moves into the blood thus elevating blood sugar levels. Adrenalin not only stimulates the formation of glucose from liver glycogen but also stimulates glycolysis in tissues generally.

Adrenocortical steroid hormones are also significant factors in the control of water and solute balance. Aldosterone stimulates active sodium transport in the mammalian kidney tubule (Chapter 14) and also effects sodium transport by amphibian skin and urinary bladder. No hormone appears to have only one effect nor are their target sites limited. Generally they affect membrane permeability to water and the rate of monovalent ion transport by the membrane. These are actions exhibited by neurohypophyseal hormones as well.

Gastrointestinal hormones are produced by cells in the wall of the stomach and small intestine. The hormone producing cells appear to be scattered throughout the mucosa and are not organized into compact masses. After transportation through the circulatory system, these hormones are delivered to target sites in the stomach, pancreas, intestine, liver, and gallbladder. They are concerned primarily with digestive processes and aspects of metabolism (see Chapter 15).

This has been but a brief summary of the chief endocrine glands (the activities of the gonads will be considered later in this chapter) of vertebrates, and most of the discussion has been based upon findings from mammalian investigations. The particular regulatory systems in which these various hormones and glands play a role have been or will be discussed further in the appropriate chapters. The mechanisms of hormonal action at the molecular level are, in general, not well understood (see, however, Chapter 4). The feedback systems in which hormones play a part are usually complex and not as yet fully known. It may be noted that cyclic AMP has now been established as an intracellular second messenger, mediating the actions of many hormones. These include insulin, glucagon, the catecholamines, ACTH, vasopressin, angiotensin, thyroid stimulating hormone, and melanin stimulating hormone. One role of cyclic AMP was discussed in Chapter 4 with respect to insulin.

11-22. Invertebrate Neuroendocrine Systems. Neurosecretion is the main source of hormones in the invertebrates (see Hagadorn, 1967). Neurosecretory cells have been found in all metazoan invertebrates including some coelenterates (Lentz and Barrnett, 1965). Comparative aspects of neuroendocrine activity are discussed in Martini and Ganong, 1967; Scharrer and Scharrer, 1963; Bern and Hagadorn, 1965; see also the symposium in *Am. Zool.* **6**:2 (1966). Neurosecretory activity has been inferred primarily from the histological demonstration of supposed neurosecretory granules and, in most invertebrates, the precise chemical nature and functions of neurosecretory substances are unknown.

Although neurosecretion provides the major source of hormonal control, some invertebrate endocrine structures, derived from nonnervous tissue, are known. For example, the salivary glands of cephalopods (Jenkins, 1962) or the ecdysial glands of insects. The crustaceans and insects are the two groups whose hormonal systems have received the most attention among the invertebrate animals. Some arise from nonnervous ectoderm, for example, the Y-organ of crustaceans and the corpora alata and prothoracic glands of insects. Some arise from mesoderm—the androgenic and gonadal glands of crustaceans, for example. Although endocrine structures may arise from endodermal cells in vertebrates, for example, the thyroid, parathyroids, gut epithelia, and islets of the pancreas, no invertebrate endocrine structures have yet been shown to originate from this germ layer. It is sometimes hypothesized that endocrine function was primitively associated with nerve cells and the tissues from which they are derived. Hypothetically only nerve cell bodies originally produced and released neurosecretions. Later these substances came to be transported down the axon to specialized storage regions in the axon terminals, where they formed a supply of regulatory chemicals readily available to the organism as needed. Finally, the endocrine glands developed from other tissues to meet the further requirements of animals.

In the lower invertebrate phyla neurosecretions appear to regulate growth, regeneration, and reproductive activities. Little is known about the role of these substances in so far as mechanisms or feedback pathways are concerned. Nor is anything known about their chemical nature.

In annelids neurosecretory cells are prominent in all three classes. In nereids, the brain produces a juvenile hormone that inhibits the maturation of gametes. In some species there is a transformation (epitoky) from an asexual state (atokous) of the worm into a sexually active reproductive form (heteronereid). This change in state is inhibited by the juvenile hormone (Clarke, 1959; Bobin and Durchon, 1952). The hormone is produced by neurosecretory cells in the subesophageal ganglion. Neurosecretory cells of the sub- and supraesophageal ganglia are involved also in the development of somatic sex characteristics, regeneration, and physiological color changes (Avel, 1947; Hubl, 1959; Scharrer and Scharrer, 1954).

On the basis of cytochemical reactions, at least two types of neurosecretory cells have been found in leeches in the sub- and supraesophageal ganglia and in the ventral nerve cord. At least one of these cell types produces adrenalin or an adrenalin-like material.

Sipunculid worms also have neurosecretory systems and *Sipunculus* possesses a neurohemal organ with finger organs, or papilliform processes of the cerebral ganglion, extending into the hemocoel. The secretory axons invading the finger organs first loop into a sensory organ that extends into a ciliated canal opening to the outside; but the significance of this structural arrangement is not known (Akesson, 1961). Nephridial activity in *Phascolosoma* is affected by brain extracts but not by extracts of the ventral nerve cord. This may be evidence that nephridial functioning is controlled by a neuroendocrine system.

11-23. Crustacean Endocrine Systems. The research literature on arthropod hormonal systems is immense, and only a brief description of crustacean and then insect endocrine activity will be given here. Since much of the work has been done with decapod crustacean endocrine systems, these will be used as the example of crustacean endocrine operation.

In decapod crustaceans neurosecretory cells are found in various parts of the brain; in all ganglia of the ventral nerve cord; and in the optic ganglia. At least a dozen different cell types are found with neurosecretory activity. Figure 11-33 diagrams the location of various endocrine tissues in decapod crustaceans (see also papers in *Am. Zool.* **6**:2; and Welsh, 1961).

The sinus gland is found in nearly all malacostracans. It is not a gland but rather a neurohemal organ—a storage and release site for hormones produced in neurosecretory cells. It is a structure analogous to the neurohypophysis of vertebrates and the corpus cardiacum of insects. The sinus gland contains axons endings of neurosecretory cells from several sources including the medulla terminalis ganglionic X-organ, optic ganglia, brain, and connective and thoracic ganglia. In some species, for example, *Carcinus*, *Pandalus*, it appears that neurons are grouped according to cell type and therefore possibly according to function (Potter, 1958; Carlisle, 1959a). In its simplest form the sinus gland is a thickened disc separated from a blood sinus by a thin membrane. Upon appropriate stimulation hormones are released into the blood. Invagination may result in a more complex structure in which blood channels permeate and diffuse throughout the organ. The hormones of the sinus gland are especially active in the regulation of color changes although other functions are served as well.

The X-organs are primarily collections of neurosecretory cells and are of two types: ganglionic X-organs and sensory pore or pars distalis X-organs (Carlisle and Passano, 1953). In some species the two types are combined to form a complex. When separate from the medulla terminalis, the sensory pore X-organ

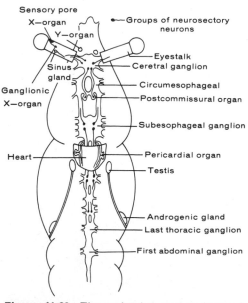

Figure 11-33 The endocrine system (generalized) of crustaceans.

Sensory pore
X-organ
Y-organ
Sinus gland
Ganglionic X-organ
Heart

Groups of neurosectory neurons
Eyestalk
Ceretral ganglion
Circumesophageal
Postcommissural organ
Subesophageal ganglion
Pericardial organ
Testis
Androgenic gland
Last thoracic ganglion
First abdominal ganglion

is a structure lying in a blood sinus near the sensory pore, and it consists of bipolar sensory neurons, elongate cells of epithelial appearance, and lamelated concretions (the onion bodies), which are axon endings of neurosecretory cells from the medulla terminalis ganglionic X-organ and from the brain. These axons form the X-organ connective. Ganglionic X-organs are composed of cell bodies of neurosecretory neurons.

The X-organ–sinus gland complex is involved in the regulation of molting, pigment changes, distal retinal pigment movements (see Chapter 17). It produces hormones that inhibit the ovary (all crustaceans) and some which inhibit the testis in crabs. The removal of the eyestalks results in various metabolic changes such as an increased oxygen consumption, changes in calcium and water levels during molting, and alterations in blood sugar levels. It has been shown that extracts from eyestalks, from postcommissure organs, and from the central nervous system contain **myotropic factors** that influence the contractions of visceral muscles (Gersch, 1959).

The Y-organs are endocrine glands which produce a hormone that initiates molting and which is under the regulation of the X-organ complex. An eyestalk hormone appears to inhibit production of Y-organ hormone.

The postcommissure organs are another neurosecretory complex found in higher crustaceans (Figure 11-33). These contain substances that affect color changes (chromatophorotropic hormone). The postcommissural organ is also associated with a blood sinus and is therefore a neurohemal organ.

The pericardial organs contain neurosecretory cells and also contain axon terminals of neurosecretory cells originating in various ventral ganglia. The organs are stretched across the pericardium in front of the gill veins that carry oxygenated blood into the pericardium. Extracts of these organs increase the frequency and amplitude of the heartbeat (Alexandrowicz and Carlisle, 1953). The hormone action may be due to a polypeptide hormone although 5-hydroxytryptamine is also present (Maynard and Welsh, 1959).

There are anterior ramifications of the pericardial organs found in some species, and these deliver hormones via the blood to respiratory muscles and gills. Therefore, these organs may be active in the regulation of gas transport and gas exchanges (Maynard, 1961).

It can be seen that these neuroendocrine systems appear to play an important role in the control of visceral activities, which in vertebrates are regulated primarily by the autonomic nervous system.

11-24. Insect Endocrine Systems. A generalized pattern of the insect neurosecretory system is given in Figure 11-34. Although many variations in form are found among the many insect species, the general pattern involves neurosecretory cells in the cerebral, subesophageal, and other ganglia. The major neurosecretory system consists of the protocerebrum and corpus cardiacum (corpora cardiaca, plural) together with their connections. The protocerebrum sends neurosecretory axons to the corpus cardiacum, which is often a paired structure just behind the supraesophageal ganglion. The corpora cardiaca

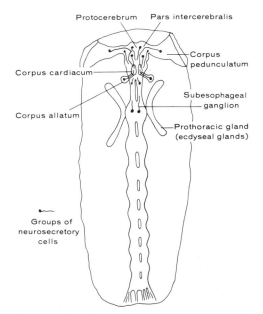

Figure 11-34 The endocrine system (generalized) of insects.

are neurohemal organs, somewhat comparable to the neurohypophysis of vertebrates except that they also contain neurosecretory cells. Axons from the corpora cardiaca and from the supraesophageal ganglia are sent to the corpora alata, which are also paired structures in most insects. They are endocrine glands of nonnervous tissue origin. The corpora cardiaca are involved in control of the heart and secrete an orthodiphenol, which activates the heart indirectly by causing pericardial cells to release a heart accelerating substance (Cameron, 1963; Davey, 1961). This is but one of many regulatory functions of the corpora cardiaca.

The ecdysial glands (also called prothoracic, pericardial, or ventral glands) are also of nonnervous origin and are supplied by nerves originating from neurosecretory cells of the brain. In insects, as contrasted to vertebrates, all endocrine structures appear to be directly innervated by the nervous system. The ecdysial glands release a hormone, ecdysone, which causes molting with metamorphosis. The hormone is a steriod (Butendandt and Karlson, 1954). The action of ecdyson can be modified by a hormone secreted by the corpora alata—neotenin or juvenile hormone. Ecdysone is necessary for molting, but if juvenile hormone is present the postmolt stage is still juvenile. Removal of the corpora allata from an insect larva induces molting and shortens the intermolt period.

Although several hormones have been isolated and a few have been chemically identified, much remains to be determined concerning insect hormones (Novak, 1966). The control of growth and development in insects, which is an important aspect of hormonal functioning, has been discussed by Schniederman and Gilbert (1964).

This completes what has been basically a morphological description of endocrine or suspected endocrine structures in various animal groups. Although some regulatory activities involving hormones are known in some detail, for example, molting in insects, color changes in crustaceans, the exact role and the basic mechanisms of hormones in animal groups is still an area requiring much more investigation. Among the invertebrate animals analysis of hormonal functions is made difficult because of the small size of endocrine structures, which hampers their dissection and isolation. Where possible in the following chapters the role of endocrine secretions in the regulation of physiological variables will be pointed out. The remainder of this chapter will be devoted to a consideration of the endocrine regulation of reproductive activities in some selected animal groups.

Endocrine Systems and the Control of Reproduction

11-25. Mammalian Reproduction. Although this section will be concerned primarily with mammalian reproduction and its control, where significant, the endocrine control of vertebrate reproduction generally will be included. There are many sources of information about vertebrate reproduction including Parkes (1952–1966); Rowlands (1966); and the textbooks of endocrinology already referred to in previous sections.

The gonads of vertebrates have two major functions: (1) to produce gametes (ova in the female ovary and spermatozoa in the male testis) and (2) to produce hormones that stimulate or regulate the development of the reproductive system and that bring about the required sexual behavior in males and females so that fertilization of the ova can occur. Male hormones generically are androgens, and female hormones are estrogens. Through hormonal mechanisms gonadal functioning is usually cyclical in vertebrates so that reproduction occurs only when the environment is suitable for the survival of fertilized eggs or developing embryos.

During embryological development, the vertebrate gonads arise as thickenings of the coelomic epithelium. Primordial germ cells migrate to these so-called genital ridges, and after combining both cell types begin to proliferate. The gonad usually differentiates into a central medulla and a peripheral cortical region. The former zone in most vertebrates also combines with mesenchymal cells. A mesenchymal medulla is lacking only in teleosts and a few other lower vertebrate groups. Initially the germ cells that will give rise to gametes are located in the cortex, but upon sexual differentiation in the female, the germ cells remain in the cortex, which develops greatly, while the medulla regresses; in the male it is the cortex that regresses, and the germ cells migrate into the developing medulla.

The germ cells of the developing ovary proliferate and finally give rise to oogonia, which divide mitotically and produce primary oocytes. This is the process of oogenesis. The primary oocyte divides meiotically to produce secondary haploid oocytes, which finally divide mitotically to produce ova. The secondary oocyte is surrounded by granulosa cells to form the ovarian follicle. Oogenesis in birds and mammals occurs during embryological development but in reptiles, amphibians, and teleosts oogenesis may continue into adult life.

Follicle development is basically similar in all vertebrates, but the size of the mature ovum and the time at which oogenesis stops varies in different vertebrate groups. The size of the ovum depends on the amount of yolk produced by the species for deposition in the egg. Yolk-free mammalian eggs are smaller than the yolk-laden eggs of reptiles and birds. The eggs of amphibians and fish are intermediate in yolk content and size. The amount of yolk or nutrient material deposited during vitellogenesis will depend, among other factors, on the nature of development of the fertilized egg. Mammalian eggs require no yolk because the mother supplies the embryo with nutrients through the circulatory system. Another factor involves the permeability of the shell surrounding the egg. This will depend on the environment in which the egg is placed during development of the embryo (see Chapter 14).

In mammals follicular development proceeds only to a given stage during embryological development and is not initiated again until sexual maturity is reached. At this time the Graafian follicles are formed (see Figure 11-35), and a cyclic rhythm of follicular development and uterine preparation is begun guided by hormonal feedback systems. The resumption of follicular development depends partially upon the secretion of hypophyseal gonadotropins, especially FSH (follicle stimulating hormone). Follicular development in all vertebrate groups tested depends on the release of this substance. Hypophysectomy in adult females always inhibits follicular growth and causes a degeneration of oocytes. Gonadotropins are also needed for the maintenance of mature ova.

During fetal or early postnatal life the hypothalamohypophyseal system determines by its differentiation whether there is to be a steady secretion of gonadotropin that is characteristic of the male or whether there is to be a cyclic secretion of gonadotropin that is characteristic of the female. It has been shown for the rat that testicular hormone in the newborn rat prevents the development of the cyclic gonadotropin release characteristic of the female. The effect is exerted in the central nervous system, and it appears that there is a critical period when hypothalamic neurons are sensitive to androgens and when the cyclic activity can be prevented (see the review by Everett, 1969). This is but one aspect of the very complex problem of the mechanisms which underlie sexual differentiation.

Once ovulation is induced by gonadotropins a controlled cycle of events begins. During the ovarian (or menstrual) cycle, the release of FSH causes the maturation of the ovarian follicle and its contained germ cell (in humans one such follicle matures at each cycle). FSH stimulates the production and release of estrogens, which in low blood concentrations stimulate the hypothalamus to in turn induce the median eminence to release FSHRF (follicle-stimulating hormone releasing factor) and LRF (luteinizing hormone releasing factor). These factors, in turn, cause the release of FSH and LH (luteinizing hormone) by the adenohypophysis. As estrogen levels increase in the blood, an inhibitory effect is

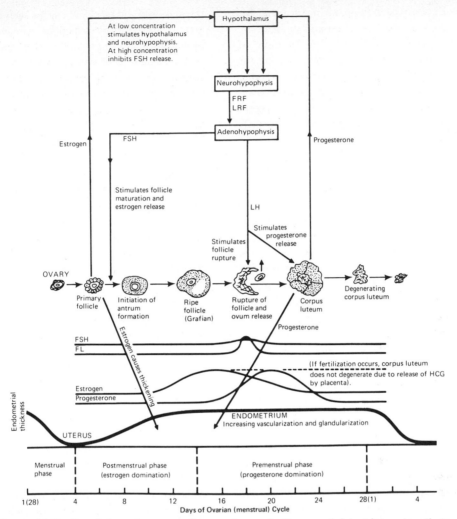

Figure 11-35 Regulation of a mammalian ovarian cycle (times and data relate primarily to the human).

exerted by the hypothalamus, and the level of FSH released decreases. Estrogens also prepare the uterine wall for pregnancy by increasing the thickness of the endometrium.

Under the influence of FSH the follicle ripens, while LH causes it to rupture releasing the ovum. The cells of the ruptured follicle (now forming the corpus luteum) under the influence of LH begin to release progesterone. During the phase of postmenstruation, the ovary and uterus are under estrogen domination, but at the rupture of the follicle and the activation of the corpus luteum, the ovaries and uterus enter into a progesterone-domin-

ated phase. LH plays a role in the ripening of the follicle and is also responsible for ovulation and for the growth and continued maintenance of the corpus luteum. It also stimulates the secretion of the ovarian hormones estrogen and progesterone.

In the progesterone-dominated phase the endometrial wall continues to thicken by cell proliferation, and there is also an increase in the vascularization of the uterus and an increase in its hormone production. Progesterone also stimulates the hypothalamus to trigger the release of LH from the adenohypophysis. Progesterone functions thus include: continuing the work of estrogen in preparing the uterus for receiving the fertilized ovum and maintaining the embryo; inhibiting the maturation of additional Graafian follicles by inhibiting the release of FSH; preventing ovulation of other ova; inhibiting menstruation during pregnancy; and stimulating further development of the mammary glands if these have previously been stimulated by estrogens.

If the ovum is fertilized by a spermatozoan, progesterone continues to be released. About 14 days after fertilization in humans, the placenta begins to release chorionic gonadotropins (CG), which maintain and enlarge the corpus luteum and continue to stimulate its secretion of progesterones and estrogens. Estrogen and progesterone are also secreted by the placenta. CG in humans is a glycoprotein with a molecular weight of about 100,000. Its presence in the urine is used as a test for pregnancy.

If the ovum is not fertilized, the corpus luteum degenerates, and the secretion of progesterone ceases. Estrogen and progesterone, as well as FSH and LH, are reduced to low levels in the blood, and the endometrium degenerates back to its normal thickness. This is the period of actual menstruation and is marked in primates by bleeding and the sloughing off of the endometrial wall. In humans the menstrual cycle is usually dated from the first day of bleeding. The entire cycle lasts about 28 days.

Mammary glands are controlled by at least four hormones. At the onset of puberty estrogens stimulate the growth of the mammary glands. When progesterone and estrogen are both present, the development of the mammary gland secretory cells is stimulated. After parturition the hormone prolactin initiates the production of milk, and oxytocin stimulates its release. Prolactin increases the rate of glucose utilization and also stimulates lipogenesis.

This brief discussion at least points out the types of controls used to regulate the mammalian ovarian cycle. Most of the feedback occurs via the hypothalamus, which is responsive to the concentrations of various chemicals, including hormones, passing

through it in the blood. It can be seen that the actions of hormones such as estrogen and progesterone are many and varied, and many details remain to be worked out in the overall control pattern of reproduction. During the ovarian cycle other hormones and endocrine systems must be coordinated in their activity so that energy metabolism, water balance, ion balance, and so forth, are maintained at proper levels.

The mammalian ovarian cycle as just presented has two phases: the follicular phase, which is common also to all vertebrates, and the luteal phase, which appears to be present only in the mammalian ovary. Even the luteal phase may be modified in different mammalian species.

Ovulation may be spontaneous, or it may be induced reflexively by coitus as in some marsupials, rodents and insectivores. Most carnivores appear to have induced ovulation. In primates the menstrual period occurs because of the lengthy duration of the luteal phase. In other mammals the luteal phase is short enough so that a great thickening of the endometrial wall or a great increase in its vascularization does not have time to occur if the ovum is not fertilized. Thus, a bleeding period is avoided.

The functions of the male testes are also cyclic although far less complex than those of the ovary of the female. Spermatogenesis in all vertebrates is dependent upon the secretion of gonodotropin from the adenohypophysis, and hypophysectomy stops all further sperm formation. However, germ cells that have entered the spermatogenetic cycle are not affected by hypophysectomy—an indication that hormones are not required for this process once it is initiated. FSH in mammals is the spermatogenic hormone. Secretions of the Sertoli cells, which line the testicular walls, may have an endocrine function in regulating the spermatogenic cycle. Androgen production by the testis is initiated by a hormone similar to the luteinizing hormone of the female. The major androgen, testosterone, stimulates the development of the genital tracts in mammals and the development of secondary sexual characteristics. This involves the stimulation of protein synthesis. The results of castration show that testosterone's activities are not limited to sex organs but are widespread throughout the body; there is a decrease in metabolism generally, caused in part by a decreased muscular tone.

Androgens and estrogens are deactivated by the liver. Steroids are combined with glucuronic acid or sulfuric acid forming water-soluble substances that are easily excretable in the urine.

11-26. Regeneration and Metamorphosis. All animals have some ability to renew or restore parts of the body that have been damaged either by accident or through normal physiological processes. Metamorphosis is a reorganization of tissues that occurs postembryologically and is often a preparation of the organism for survival in a different environment. Growth in arthropods is a discontinuous process because of the presence of a rigid exoskeleton, which, although an excellent protective barrier between the external environment and the internal organ systems, does not allow the animal to increase in size until it is shed—the process of molting. All of the activities just described—regeneration, metamorphosis, and molting—are processes controlled by the endocrine systems of animals and deserve some mention here.

Tissue regeneration and tissue differentiation are studied primarily by the cell physiologist because they represent molecular changes brought about in part at least by activities of the nuclear genes. In a sense these activities are associated with or are brought about by mechanisms similar to those used in reproduction and embryology. They are also part of the general phenomena of growth in animals (Needham, 1964, discusses growth in animals; Vorontsova and Liosner, 1960, discuss all aspects of regeneration).

The regenerative abilities of animals differ markedly. Lower forms such as protozoans, sponges, coelenterates, flatworms, and many annelids have the ability to regenerate a new organism from extremely small fragments.

In higher phyla such as the arthropods new limbs can be regenerated to replace lost ones. In mammals regeneration of body parts is limited to the germinal layers of the skin, the mucous membranes of the gastrointestinal tract, and the liver.

In the marine polychaete worm, *Nereis diversicolor*, regeneration and growth are controlled by hormones released from the supraesophageal ganglia. Worms of less than about 60 segments in length can readily regenerate new segments. Removal of some of the segments stimulates neurosecretory cells to release the hormone that activates segment renewal. The ability of the ganglia to initiate regeneration reaches a maximum about 3 days after the loss of segments and then declines. Regenerative ability is lost in older worms—usually those with more than 60 segments. However, such worms can be induced to generate new segments if the ganglia from younger worms are implanted in the older worm's body (Clark and Ruston, 1963; Clark and Sully, 1964). Although the addition of new segments slows considerably once a worm has reached about 60 segments in length, growth by the increase in size of individual segments continues. When animals reach about 90 segments in length, both types of growth stop completely. From these experimental results, together with results on other animals, it is generally hypothesized that regeneration in animals is brought about by the stimulation of nerve endings upon amputation of body parts. Nerve impulses in sensory neurons, in turn, stimulate neurosecretory activity in central ganglia, and the neurosecretory materials initiate regenerative processes.

Metamorphosis has been especially studied in insects and amphibians, although metamorphosis is a feature in the development of crustaceans, echinoderms, molluscs, and other groups. The embryonic development of insects leads to a larval stage, which is often very different in form from the adult. There are three general patterns of development in insects. Some species are ametabolic, that is, they lack metamorphosis. This group includes more primitive insects such as the Collembola.

They hatch from the egg in a form similar to that of the adult. Only growth in size through a series of molts is needed to produce the adult form. In another group, the holometabolic insects, the animal hatches as a nymph, which usually differs in structure from the adult form although it bears the typical three pairs of legs of insects. The nymph increases in size through several molts and then in a final molt progresses through extensive form changes to finally reach the adult or sexually mature form, the imago. This group includes grasshoppers and cockroaches.

The third group is the hemimetabolous insects (including *Diptera*, *Lepidoptera*, *Hymenoptera*, as well as other insect groups). The young hatch from the egg as wormlike larvae with no resemblance to the adult form. The larva grows through several instars (stages separated by a molt) without change of form. Then the larva undergoes a final pupal molt in which the form alters completely. The pupa is encased in a cuticle, and the pupal stage terminates with a final or imaginal molt in which the adult, usually winged, insect emerges from the pupal case.

Metamorphosis in insects is regulated by hormones produced in the brain. The neurosecretory system regulating metamorphosis is similar in some respects to the vertebrate neurohypophyseal system. Neurosecretory cells of the pars intercerebralis of the brain produce brain hormone (ecdysiotropin). Brain hormone does not influence molting directly but is passed in neurosecretory cell axons to the prothoracic gland, where it stimulates the release of ecdysone, the molting hormone. Molting is inhibited by juvenile hormone which must be inactivated before molting can occur.

The bug *Rhodnius prolixus* has been extensively used in studies of molting and metamorphosis (Wigglesworth, 1959, 1965). This hemimetabolous insect has a very long head, which makes it relatively easy to remove various parts of the brain and to determine the effects of such operations on molting or development. If *Rhodnius* nymphs are not fed, they do not molt and can survive for long periods of time even in the fasted condition.

When nymphs are fed a blood meal, they molt at a definite time after feeding (the time varies for each molt of each larval instar, but is always the same for each instar). Feeding stimulates the production of brain hormone, the stimulation being the distension of the abdomen by the blood meal and the consequent activity of sensory neurons. Other insects appear to have different sensory mechanisms for nervous stimulation of the brain neurosecretory cells.

Decapitated animals survive for relatively long periods of time. If an animal is decapitated immediately after feeding, the body fails to molt at the proper time. Decapitation just before normal molting time did not influence the molt. On the basis of histological examination it was shown that the critical time before which decapitation prevented molt was coincidental with the initiation of neurosecretory activity in brain cells.

Rhodnius is also useful in parabiotic experiments in which decapitated insects are joined together so that a mutual blood flow is established. When one insect is decapitated after the critical time, molting was still induced in its parabiotic mate, which had been decapitated before the critical period. Among other things this experiment showed that hormones were responsible for the initiation of molting because only blood-carried chemicals could account for such results.

Ecdysone appears to act by inducing synthesis of messenger RNA. Clever and Karlson (1960) were the first to show that ecdysone acted at the level of the gene and that it caused the formation of chromosomal puffs. Such activity can be used to regulate the synthesis of proteins upon which the development of the animal depends. Ecdysone is a steroid hormone.

Many insects undergo a period of **diapause** —a phase of arrested development or activity that may occur in the larval, pupal, or adult stages of an organism's normal life history. True diapause occurs regardless of the environmental conditions. Diapause occurs when hormone concentrations in the blood fall and ends when threshold levels of brain hormone and other hormones such as ecdysone are reached. Diapause may also be initiated by an increase in inhibitory factors that affect growth. Diapause is a physiological mechanism for survival during adverse conditions. For example, the *Cecropia* moth passes the winter in the pupal stage in diapause. The diapause can be terminated by first chilling the pupa to about 5° and then warming it to about 20°C. Without initial chilling the diapause is not terminated (Williams, 1961). The important structure in controlling this reaction is the brain because only brain extracts (after chilling and warming) can induce the termination of diapause after the injection into diapausing pupa kept at room temperature. Either photoperiod (the alternation of light and dark during a 24-hour period) or temperature are important agents for inducing diapause and presumably act by influencing neurosecretory cells of the brain.

11-27. Crustacean Molting. As indicated in Section 11-26, growth must be coordinated with molting in those animals with rigid exoskeletons. Growth and molting are usually periodic events in the life of arthropods, and these activities are under the control of hormones. Molting only in crustaceans will be discussed in this section because most work has been done with this group. The processes in insects are similar in most respects. Although molting is a prominent feature in the growth of arthropods, it is found in other phyla also (see Davey, 1966). Molting in crustaceans has been reviewed by Carlisle and Knowles (1959) and Passano (1960).

The molting cycle may be divided into four periods: (1) premolt or proecdysis—a period of active preparation for molt; (2) molt or ecdysis—the splitting and shedding of the old, partially reabsorbed cuticle; (3) postmolt or postecdysis—a period of rapid deposition of new chitin, inorganic salts, and a period of tissue growth; and (4) intermolt or interecdysis —a period of time during which the processes normally associated with molting are absent. Some crustaceans, for example, *Carcinus, Maia*, enter a permanent intermolt period (anecdysis); others continue to molt throughout life.

During each period of the molt cycle, various metabolic processes occur. In premolt the cuticle thins as materials are reabsorbed to be used in the formation of the new cuticle. Calcium is needed for the development of a new cuticle, and although marine forms may obtain calcium from sea water, in fresh water crustaceans calcium from the old cuticle is stored in special organs in the stomach—the gastroliths. The hepatopancreas also stores inorganic salts and in addition there is a production of carotenoid pigments in this organ. Glycogen is deposited in the cells of epidermal tissues, and the increase in glycogen concentration means that there is an increased utilization of glucose to form glycogen. Protein synthesis is also accelerated and in general many biochemical reactions occur that prepare materials for the formation of a new cuticle.

During ecdysis the old, partially reabsorbed cuticle is split and shed. The animal immediately increases in size because of an uptake of water from the environment.

In postecdysis chitin is synthesized at the expense of the glycogen stores laid down before the molt. In addition, mucopolysaccharides are synthesized and laid down in the newly forming cuticle. These substances form a matrix upon which calcium is deposited. Before calcification is initiated, the proteins of the new cuticle are polymerized with phenol compounds. It is this phenolization of proteins, combined with the deposition of calcium, which gives the cuticle its rigidity and hardness. When the cuticle is hard enough to permit normal body movements, the animal begins feeding, and the water taken in to swell the body during the molt is replaced by tissue growth.

All of the processes just described are concerned with metabolic reactions or with the transport of materials. All of these activities are normally coordinated and regulated by hormones. Because of the sequence and complexity of the events of molting, there must be elaborate feedback systems to control the production and release of endocrine materials. Several hormones concerned with the initiation of molting, the synthesis of glycogen, and other reactions are produced or controlled by hormones of the eyestalk system. (See Figure 11-33).

Removal of the eyestalks initiates molting—an indication that the eyestalk contains a molt-inhibiting hormone. Removal of the eyestalks also causes an increase in tissue carbohydrate content. The eyestalk system elaborates a hormone that has an inhibitory action on the enzyme UDP-glycogen trans-glucosylase, which is involved in the synthesis of tissue glycogen. This eyestalk hormone causes an increased blood level of glucose because less glucose is used by tissue cells. The Y-organ is the structure that controls the initiation of molting, and the hormone involved is ecdyson. Anecdysis is caused by a molt-inhibiting hormone from the eyestalks of the species which enter this terminal non-molting phase. However, anecdysis is ultimately due to the degeneration of the ecdysial organs (or Y-organs) in crustaceans (this is also true of insects).

Water absorption is also controlled by hormones. The eyestalks of the freshwater crayfish *Procambarus clarkii* contain a factor that maintains normal permeability of the body surfaces to water (Kamemoto et al., 1966). Eyestalk removal results in an increased influx of water. In the semiterrestrial crab *Metopograpsus messor* the thoracic ganglion secretes a hormone that increases the water flow through body surfaces, and this ganglion's activity is controlled by eyestalk substances. It has been shown that the land crab *Gecarcinus lateralis* has a dual hormonal control system for regulating internal water levels. It appears that hormonal systems not only influence the absorption of water for molting but are also used by crustaceans for continuous water balance (see Chapter 14). The use of hormones to control the permeability of surface and cell membranes is a common mechanism of action for these substances.

Still to be elucidated are the exact feedback and control pathways by which the events of molting and growth are synchronized and ordered. Numerous factors influence the initiation of molting, and these include temperature, light, photoperiod, state of reproductive activity, and injury. Some of the hormones influencing molting are also concerned with reproductive activities. For example, the molt-inhibiting hormone of the sinus gland hemal organ prevents females of the crab *Crangon* from molting until the young of this egg-bearing species have hatched. The Y-organ has a gonadotropic influence in both males and females.

In this chapter I have attempted to indicate some of the systems used in the control and coordination of animal activities. Although neuromuscular control systems are reasonably well understood, at least at the level of control of individual muscles by reflex actions, endocrine and neuroendocrine reflexes are less well understood, in so far as their coordinating activities are concerned. In many cases the number and nature of the chemicals controlling particular activities have not yet been determined. The activities of the central nervous systems of animals are also not well understood especially when complex behavior patterns are considered or when activities such as memory, sensations, and the like are discussed. In the next parts of the book, which are concerned with regulatory activities of organ systems and whole animals, the role of nervous and chemical controls will be further considered.

References and Readings

Akesson, B. (1961). "The development of *Golfingia elongata* Keferstein (Sipunculidea) with some remarks on the development of neurosecretory cells in sipunculids." *Ark. Zool. Kungl. Svens. Vetens. Akad.* **13:** 511–531.

Alexandrowicz, J. S. and D. B. Carlisle (1953). "Some experiments on the function of the pericardial organs in Crustacea." *J. Mar. Biol. Ass. U.K.* **32:** 175–192.

Avel, M. (1947). "Les facteurs de la régénération chez les annélides." *Rev. Suisse Zool.* **54:** 219–235.

Barker, D. (1948). "The innervation of the muscle spindle." *Quart. J. Micr. Sci.* **89**: 143–186.

Barker, D. (1966). "The motor innervation of the mammalian muscle spindle." In: **Muscular Afferents and Motor Control.** (R. Granit, ed.), pp. 51–58. First Nobel Symposium. New York: John Wiley & Sons, Inc.

Barrington, E. J. W. (1962). "Digestive enzymes." *Adv. Comp. Physiol. Biochem.* **1**: 1–65.

Batham, E. J. (1965). "The neural architecture of the sea anemone *Mimetridium cryptum.*" *Am. Zool.* **5**: 395–402.

Batham, E. J. and C. F. A. Pantin (1950). "Phases of activity in the sea anemone, *Metridium senile* (L.) and their relation to external stimuli." *J. Exp. Biol.* **27**: 377–399.

Batham, E. J. and C. F. A. Pantin (1954). "Slow contractions and its relation to spontaneous activity in the sea-anemone *Metridium senile* (L.)." *J. Exp. Biol.* **31**: 84–103.

Bayliss, W. M. and E. H. Starling (1902). "The mechanism of pancreatic secretion." *J. Physiol.* (London) **28**: 325.

von Bekesy, G. (1966). **Sensory Inhibition.** Princeton, N.J.: Princeton University Press. 300 pp.

Bern, H. A. and I. R. Hagadorn (1965). "Neurosecretion." In: **Structure and Function in the Nervous System of Invertebrates.** (T. H. Bullock and A. G. Horridge, eds.), Vol. 1, pp. 353–429. San Francisco: W. H. Freeman & Company, Publishers.

Bessou, P. and Y. Laporte (1966). "Observations on static fusimotor fibres." In: **Muscle Afferents and Motor Control.** (R. Granit, ed.), pp. 81–89. New York: John Wiley & Sons, Inc.

Bishop, G. H. (1958). "The dendrite: receptive pole of the neurone." *Electroenceph. Clin. Neurophysiol.* **10** (suppl.): 12–21.

Bobin, G. and M. Durchon (1952). "Étude histologique du cerveau de *Perinereis cultrifera* Grube (annélide polychéte) Mise en évidence d'un complexe cérébro-vasculaire." *Arch. Anat. Micr.* **41**: 25–40.

Boyd, I. A. and M. R. Davey (1966). "The distribution of two types of small motor nerve fibers to different muscles in the hind limb of the cat." In: **Muscular Afferents and Motor Control.** (R. Granit, ed.), pp. 59–68. First Nobel Symposium. New York: John Wiley & Sons, Inc.

Brazier, M. A. B. (1960). **The Electrical Activity of the Nervous System.** New York: The Macmillan Company. 273 pp.

Bullock, T. H. and G. A. Horridge (1965). **Structure and Function in the Nervous System of Invertebrates.** 2 volumes. San Francisco: W. H. Freeman & Company, Publishers.

Burn, J. H. (1963). **The Autonomic Nervous System.** Oxford: Blackwell Scientific Publications. 120 pp.

Burnett, A. L. and N. A. Diehl (1964a). "The nervous system of *Hydra*. I. Types, distribution, and origin of nerve elements." *J. Exp. Zool.* **157**: 217–226.

Burnett, A. L. and N. A. Diehl (1964b). "The nervous system of *Hydra*. III. The initiation of sexuality with special reference to the nervous system." *J. Exp. Zool.* **157**: 237–250.

Burnett, A. L., N. A. Diehl, and F. Diehl (1964). "The nervous system of *Hydra*. II. Control of growth and regeneration by neurosecretory cells." *J. Exp. Zool.* **157**: 227–236.

Burnstock, G. and M. E. Holman (1961). "The transmission of excitation from autonomic nerve to smooth muscle." *J. Physiol.* (London) **155**: 115–133.

Burnstock, G. and M. E. Holman (1961). "Effect of denervation and of reserpine treatment on transmission at sympathetic nerve endings." *J. Physiol.* (London) **160**: 461–469.

Butendandt, A. and P. Karlson (1954). " Über die Isolierung eines Metamorphose-Hormons der Insekten in Gristallisierter Form." *Zeitschr. Naturforsch.* **9**: 389–393.

Cameron, M. L. (1953). "Secretion of an orthodiphenol in the corpus cardiacum of the insect." *Nature* **172**: 349–350.

Carlisle, D. B. (1959a). "Moulting cycles in crustacea." *Symp. Zool. Soc.* (London) **2**: 109–120.

Carlisle, D. B. (1959b). "On the neurosecretory system of the brain and associated structures in *Sipunculus nuda*, with a note on the cuticle." *Gunma J. Med. Sci.* **8**: 183–194.

Carlisle, D. B. (1959c). "Sexual differentiation in Crustacea Malacostraca." *Mem. Soc. Endocrinol.* **7**: 9–16.

Carlisle, D. B. and F. G. W. Knowles (1959). **Endocrine Control in Crustacea.** New York: Cambridge University Press.

Carlisle, D. B. and L. M. Passano (1953). The X-organ of Crustacea. *Nature* **171**: 1070–1071.

Clark, R. B. (1959). "The neurosecretory system of the supra-oesophageal ganglion of *Nepthys* (Annelida: Polychaeta)." *Zool. Jb.* **68**: 395–424.

Clark, R. B. and R. F. G. Ruston (1963). "Time of release and action of a hormone influencing regeneration in the polychaete *Neries diversicolor.*" *Gen. Comp. Endocrinol.* **3**: 524–553.

Clark, R. B. and U. Scully (1964). "Hormonal control of growth in *Nereis diversicolor.*" *Gen. Comp. Endocrinol.* **4**: 82–90.

Clever, U. and P. Karlson (1960). "Production of chromosome puffs in *Drosophila* with ecdysone." *Exp. Cell. Res.* **20**: 623–626.

Collier, H. O. J. (1939). "Central nervous activity in the earthworm. I. Responses to tension and tactile stimulation." *J. Exp. Biol.* **16**: 286–299.

Contini, R. and R. Drillus (1966). "Kinematic and kinetic techniques in biomechanisms." *Adv. Bioengin. Instrum.* **1**: 3–68.

Cooper, S. (1960). "Muscle spindles and other muscle receptors." In: **Structure and Function of Muscle.** (G. H. Bourne, ed.), Vol. 1, pp. 381–420. New York: Academic Press, Inc.

Corning, W. C., D. A. Feinstein, and J. R. Haight (1965). "Arthropod preparation for behavioral, electrophysiological, and biochemical studies." *Science* **148**: 394–395.

Dale, H. (1933). "Nomenclature of fibres in the autonomic nervous system and their effects." *J. Physiol.* (London) **80**: 10–15.

Daniel, P. M. (1967). "The anatomy of the hypothalamus and pituitary gland." In:

Neuroendocrinology. (L. Martini and W. F. Ganong, eds.), Vol. 1, Chap. 2. New York: Academic Press, Inc.

Davey, K. G. (1961). "The mode of action of the heart accelerating factor from the corpus cardiacum of insects." *Gen. Comp. Endocrinol.* **1**: 24–29.

Davey, K. G. (1966). "Neurosecretion and molting in some parasitic nematodes." *Am. Zool.* **6**: 243–249.

Eccles, J. C., P. Fatt, and K. Koketsu (1954). "Cholinergic and inhibitory synapses in a pathway from motor axon collaterals to motoneurons." *J. Physiol.* (London) **126**: 524–562.

Eckstein, P. and F. Knowles, eds. (1963). **Techniques in Endocrine Research.** New York: Academic Press, Inc. 314 pp.

Ehret, C. F. (1960). "Organelle systems and biological organization." *Science* **132**: 115–123.

Erlanger, J. and H. S. Gasser (1930). "The action potential in fibers of slow conduction in spinal roots and somatic nerves." *Am. J. Physiol.* **92**: 43.

von Euler, U. S. (1967). "Adrenal medullary secretion and its neural control." In: **Neuroendocrinology.** (L. Martini and W. F. Ganong, eds.), Vol. 2, pp. 283–334. New York: Academic Press, Inc.

von Euler, U. S. and H. Heller (1963). **Comparative Endocrinology.** 2 volumes. New York: Academic Press, Inc.

Everett, J. W. (1969). "Neuroendocrine aspects of mammalian reproduction." *Ann. Rev. Physiol.* **31**: 383–416.

Farrell, G., L. F. Fabre, and E. W. Rauschkolb (1968). "The neurohypophysis." *Ann. Rev. Physiol.* **30**: 557–588.

Friedländer, B. (1888). "Beitrage zur Kenntnis des Centralnervensystems von Lumbricus. *Z. Wiss. Zool.* **47**: 47–84.

Friedländer, B. (1894). "Altes und Neues zur Histologie des Bauchstranges des Regenwurms." *Z. Wiss. Zool.* **58**: 661–693.

Furshpan, E. (1955). "Studies on certain sensory and motor systems of decapod crustaceans." Ph.D. Thesis, California Institute of Technology, Pasadena.

Gabe, M. (1966). **Neurosecretion.** Long Island City, N.Y.: Pergamon Press, Inc. 872 pp.

Gardner, E. (1968). **Fundamentals of Neurology,** 5th ed. Philadelphia: W. B. Saunders Company. 357 pp.

Gelfan, S. and I. M. Tarlov (1963). "Altered neuron populations in L_7 segment of dogs with experimental hindlimb rigidity." *Am. J. Physiol.* **205:** 606–613.

Gersch, M. (1959). "Neurohormone bei wirbellosen Tieren." *Zool. Anz.* **22** (Suppl.): 40–76.

Goldschneider, A. (1898). **Untersuchungen über den Muskelsinn,** Vol. 2. Liepzig: Gesammelte Abhandlungen von A. Goldschneider.

Gorbman, A. and H. A. Bern (1962). **A Textbook of Comparative Endocrinology.** New York: John Wiley & Sons, Inc. 468 pp.

Grafstein, B. (1968). "Transport of protein by goldfish optic nerve fibers." *Science* **157:** 196–198.

Granit, R. (1955). **Receptors and Sensory Perception.** New Haven, Conn.: Yale University Press. 369 pp.

Granit, R., ed. (1966a). **Muscular Afferents and Motor Control.** New York: John Wiley & Sons, Inc. 466 pp.

Granit, R. (1966b). "Effects of stretch and contraction on the membrane of motoneurons." In: **Muscular Afferents and Motor Control.** (R. Granit, ed.), pp. 37–50. New York: John Wiley & Sons, Inc.

Gray, J. (1968). **Animal Locomotion.** New York: W. W. Norton & Company, Inc. 479 pp.

Hagadorn, I. R. (1967). "Neuroendocrine mechanisms in invertebrates." In: **Neuroendocrinology** (L. Martini and W. F. Ganong, eds.), Vol. 2, pp. 439–484. New York: Academic Press, Inc.

Harris, G. W. (1960). "Central control of pituitary secretion." In: **Handbook of Physiology** (H. W. Magoun, ed.), Sect. 1, Vol. 2, pp. 1007–1038. Washington, D.C.: American Physiological Society.

Heller, H. (1963). "Pharmacology and distribution of neurohypophysial hormones." *Symp. Zool. Soc.* (London) **9:** 93–106.

Henneman, E. (1968). "Organization of the motor system: a preview." In: **Medical Physiology** (V. B. Mountcastle, ed.), Vol. 2, pp. 1675–1680. St. Louis, Mo.: The C. V. Mosby Company.

Hines, M. (1960). "The control of muscular activity by the central nervous system." In: **Structure and Function of Muscle.** (G. H. Bourne, ed.), Vol. 2, pp. 467–516. New York: Academic Press, Inc.

Holmgren, U. (1964). "Neurosecretion in teleost fishes: the caudal neurosecretory system." *Am. Zool.* **4:** 37–46.

Houk, J. and E. Henneman. (1967). "Responses of Golgi tendon organs to active contractions of the soleus muscle of the cat." *J. Neurophysiol.* **30:** 466.

Hoyle, G. (1957). **Comparative Physiology of the Nervous Control of Muscular Contraction.** New York: Cambridge University Press. 147 pp.

Hoyle, G. and C. A. G. Wiersma (1958a). "Excitation at neuromuscular junctions in Crustacea." *J. Physiol.* (London) **143:** 403–425.

Hoyle, G. and C. A. G. Wiersma (1958b). "Inhibition at neuromuscular junctions in Crustacea." *J. Physiol.* (London) **143:** 426–440.

Hoyle, G. and C. A. G. Wiersma (1958c). "Coupling of membrane potential to contraction in crustacean muscle." *J. Physiol.* (London) **143:** 441–453.

Hubl, H. (1956). "Uber die Beziehungen der Neurosekretion zym regenerationsgeschehen bei Lumbriciden nebst Beschriebung eines neuartigen neurosekretorischen Zelltyps im Unterschlundganglion." *Arch. Entw. Mech. Org.* **149:** 73–87.

Hunt, C. C. and S. W. Kuffler (1951). "Further study of efferent small-nerve fibres to mammalian muscle spindles. Multiple spindle innervation and activity during contraction." *J. Physiol.* (London) **113:** 283–297.

Hyman, L. (1940). **The Invertebrates,** Vol. 1. New York: The McGraw-Hill Book Company. 726 pp.

Jenkins, P. M. (1962). **Animal Hormones.** Long Island City, N. Y.: Pergamon Press, Inc.

Jørgensen, C. B. and L. O. Larsen (1967). "Neuroendocrine mechanisms in lower vertebrates." In: **Neuroendocrinology** (L. Martini and W. F. Ganong, eds.), Vol. 2, pp. 485–528. New York: Academic Press, Inc.

Josephson, R. K. (1966). "Mechanisms of pacemaker and effector integration in Coelenterates." *Symp. Soc. Exp. Biol.* **20:** 33–47.

Jouvet, M. (1967). "Neurophysiology of the state of sleep." *Physiol. Rev.* **47:** 117–177.

Kamemoto, F. I., K. N. Kato, and L. E. Tucker (1966). "Neurosecretion and salt and water balance in the Annelida and Crustacea." *Am. Zool.* **6:** 213–219.

Karlson, P., ed. (1965). **Mechanisms of Hormone Action.** New York: Academic Press, Inc. 275 pp.

Kennedy, D., W. H. Evoy, and H. L. Fields (1966). "The unit basis of some crustacean reflexes." *Symp. Soc. Exp. Biol.* **20:** 75–109.

Kennedy, D., W. H. Evoy, and J. T. Hanawalt (1966). "Release of coordinated behavior in crayfish by single central neurons." *Science* **154:** 917–919.

Kiortsis, V. and H. A. L. Trampushi, eds. (1965). **Regeneration in Animals.** Amsterdam: North-Holland Publishing Company.

Knowles, F. and H. A. Bern (1966). "The function of neurosecretion in endocrine regulation." *Nature* **210:** 271–272.

Kuffler, S. W., C. C. Hunt, and J. P. Quilliam (1951). "Function of medulated small nerve fibers in mammalian ventral roots. Efferent muscle spindle innervation." *J. Neurophysiol.* **14:** 29–54.

Kuffler, S. W. and E. M. von Williams (1953). "Small nerve junctional potentials, the distribution of small motor nerves to frog skeletal muscle and the membrane characteristics of the fibers they innervate." *J. Physiol.* (London) **121:** 289–317.

Lentz, T. L. and R. J. Barrnett (1963). "The role of the nervous system in regenerating hydra: The effect of neuropharmacological agents." *J. Exp. Zool.* **154:** 305–328.

Lentz, T. L. and R. J. Barrnett (1965). "Fine structure of the nervous system of *Hydra.*" *Am. Zool.* **5:** 341–356.

Liddell, E. G. T. and C. S. Sherrington (1925). "Further observations on myotatic reflexes." *Proc. Roy. Soc.* (London) **B97:** 267–283.

Lockhart, R. D. (1960). "Anatomy of muscles and their relation to movement and posture." In: **Structure and Function of Muscle** (G. H. Bourne, ed.), Vol. 1, pp. 1–20. New York: Academic Press, Inc.

Mackie, G. O. (1965). "Conduction in the nerve-free epithelia of siphonophores." *Am. Zool.* **5:** 439–454.

Magoun, H. W. (1950). "Caudal and cephalic influences of the brain stem reticular formation." *Physiol. Rev.* **30:** 459–474.

Manning, A. (1967). **An Introduction to Animal Behavior.** Reading, Mass.: Addison-Wesley Publishing Co., Inc. 208 pp.

Marker, D., ed. (1962). **Muscle Receptors.** Hong Kong: Hong Kong University Press, 262 pp.

Martini, L. and W. F. Ganong, eds. (1967). **Neuroendocrinology.** 2 volumes. New York: Academic Press, Inc.

Mathews, P. B. C. (1964). "Muscle spindles and their motor control." *Physiol. Rev.* **44:** 219–289.

Maynard, D. M. (1961). "Thoracic neurosecretory structures in Brachyura. II. Secretory neurons." *Gen. Comp. Endocrinol.* **1:** 237–263.

Maynard, D. M. and J. H. Welsh (1959). "Neurohormones of the pericardial organs of brachyuran Crustacea." *J. Physiol.* (London) **149:** 215–227.

McCann, M., P. S. Dhariwal, and J. C. Porter (1968). "Regulation of the adenohypophysis." *Ann. Rev. Physiol.* **30:** 589–640.

Meglitsch, P. A. (1967). **Invertebrate Zoology.** New York: Oxford University Press. 961 pp.

Mellon, D. (1968). "Junctional physiology and motor nerve distribution in the fast adductor muscle of the scallop." *Science* **160:** 1018–1029.

Milhorn, H. T. (1966). **The Application of Control Theory to Physiological Systems.** Philadelphia: W. B. Saunders Company. 386 pp.

Miller, N. E. (1969). "Learning of visceral and glandular responses." *Science* **163:** 434–445.

Milsum, J. H. (1966). **Biological Control Systems Analysis.** New York: McGraw-Hill Book Company. 466 pp.

Needham, A. E. (1964). **The Growth Process in Animals.** New York: Pitman Publishing Company.

Needler, M. and D. M. Ross (1958). "Neuromuscular activity in the sea anemone *Calliactis parasitica* (Couch)." *J. Mar. Biol. Assoc.* (U.K.) **37**: 789–805.

Novák, V. J. A. (1966). **Insect Hormones.** London: Methuen & Co., Ltd.

Ogawa, F. (1939). "The nervous system of the earthworm (*Pheretima communissima*) in different ages." *Sci. Rep. Tohoku Univ.* **13**: 395–488.

Ortmann, R. (1960). Neurosecretion. In: **Handbook of Physiology.** (H. W. Magoun, ed.), Sect. 1, Vol. 2, pp. 1039–1065. Washington, D.C.: American Physiological Society.

Pantin, C. F. A. (1935). "The nerve net of the Actinozoa. III. Polarity and after-discharge." *J. Exp. Zool.* **12**: 156–164.

Parkes, A. S., ed. (1952–1966). **Marshall's Physiology of Reproduction.** 3 volumes. New York: Longmans, Green & Company.

Passano, L. M. (1960). "Molting and its control." In: **The Physiology of Crustacea** (T. H. Waterman, ed.), Vol. 1, pp. 473–536. New York: Academic Press, Inc.

Passano, L. M. (1965). "Pacemakers and activity patterns in medusae: Homage to Romanes." *Am. Zool.* **5**: 465–482.

Penfield, W. and T. Rasmussen (1950). **The Cerebral Cortex of Man: A Clinical Study of Localization of Function.** New York: The Macmillan Company.

Potter, D. D. (1958). "Observations on the neurosecretory system of portunid crabs." In: **International Symposium Neurosekretion.** (W. Bargmann, B. Hanström, and E. Scharrer, eds.). Berlin: Springer Verlag.

Ranson, S. W. and S. L. Clark (1959). **Anatomy of the Nervous System,** 10th ed. Philadelphia: W. B. Saunders Company.

Renshaw, B. (1941). "Influence of discharge of motoneurons upon excitation of neighboring motoneurons." *J. Neurophysiol.* **4**: 167–183.

Renshaw, B. (1946). "Central effects of centripetal impulses in axons of spinal ventral roots." *J. Neurophysiol.* **9**: 191–204.

Robson, E. A. (1965). "Some aspects of the structure of the nervous system in the anemone *Calliactis.*" *Am. Zool.* **5**: 403–410.

Rockstein, M., ed. (1964–1965). **The Physiology of Insecta.** 3 volumes. New York: Academic Press, Inc.

Romanes, G. J. (1885). "Jelly-fish, star-fish, and sea-urchins: being a research on primitive nervous systems." *Int. Scient. Series* **49**. Appleton, N.Y.

Romer, A. S. (1962). **The Vertebrate Body.** 3rd ed. Philadelphia: W. B. Saunders Company. 643 pp.

Rowlands, I. W., ed. (1966). **Comparative Biology of Reproduction in Mammals.** New York: Academic Press, Inc. 559 pp.

Ruch, T. C., H. D. Patton, J. W. Woodbury, and A. L. Towe (1965). Neurophysiology, 2nd ed. Philadelphia: W. B. Saunders Company. 538 pp.

Scharrer, B. (1967). "The neurosecretory neuron in neuroendocrine regulatory mechanisms." *Am. Zool.* **7**: 161–169.

Scharrer, E. and B. Scharrer (1963). **Neuroendocrinology.** New York: Columbia University Press. 289 pp.

Schneiderman, H. A. and L. I. Gilbert (1964). "Control of growth and development in insects." *Science* **143**: 325–333.

Schwyzer, R. (1963). "Chemical structure and biological activity in the fields of polypeptide hormones." *Pure App. Chem.* **6**: 265–295.

Sherrington, C. S. (1906). **Integrative Action of the Nervous System.** New Haven, Conn.: Yale University Press. 411 pp.

Snodgrass, R. E. (1965). **A Textbook of Arthropod Anatomy.** New York: Hafner Publishing Co., Inc. 363 pp.

Stark, L. (1966). "Neurological feedback control systems." *Adv. Bioengineer. Instrumentation* **1**: 291–360.

Taylor, C. V. (1941). "Fibrillar systems in ciliates." In: **Protozoa in Biological Research**

(G. N. Calkins and F. M. Summers, eds.). New York: Columbia University Press.

Thomas, R. C. and V. J. Wilson (1965). "Precise localization of Renshaw cells with a new marking technique." *Nature* **206**: 211–213.

Turner, C. D. (1966). **General Endocrinology,** 4th ed. Philadelphia: W. B. Saunders Company. 580 pp.

Usherwood, P. N. R. and H. Grundfest (1965). "Peripheral inhibition in skeletal muscles of insects." *J. Neurophysiol.* **28**: 497–518.

Van Harreveld, A. and C. A. G. Wiersma (1939). "The function of the quintuple innervation of a crustacean muscle." *J. Exp. Biol.* **16**: 121–133.

Vorontsova, M. A. and L. D. Liosner (1960). **Asexual Propagation and Regeneration.** New York: Pergamon Press, Inc. 489 pp.

Walsh, E. G. (1964). **Physiology of the Nervous System,** 2nd ed. New York: Longmans, Green & Company. 615 pp.

Washizu, Y. (1960). "Single spinal motoneurons excitable from two different antidromic pathways." *Jap. J. Physiol.* **10**: 121–131.

Welsh, J. H. (1959). "Neuroendocrine substances." In: **Comparative Endocrinology** (A. Gorbman, ed.) New York: John Wiley & Sons, Inc.

Welsh, J. H. (1961). "Neurohumors and neurosecretion." In: **The Physiology of**

Crustacea. (T. H. Waterman, ed.) Vol. 2. New York: Academic Press, Inc.

Wells, G. P. (1950). "Spontaneous activity cycles in polychaete worms." *Symp. Soc. Exp. Biol.* **4**: 127–142.

Wiersma, C. A. G. (1941). "The efferent innervation of muscle." *Biol. Symp.* **3**: 259–290.

Wiersma, C. A. G. and C. H. Ellis (1941). A comparative study of peripheral inhibition in decapod crustaceans. *J. Exp. Biol.* **18**: 223–236.

Wiersma, C. A. G. and S. H. Ripley (1952). "Innervation patterns of crustacean limbs." *Physiol. Comp. Oecol.* **2**: 319–405.

Wigglesworth, V. B. (1959). **The Control of Growth and Form.** Ithaca, N.Y.: Cornell University Press.

Wigglesworth, V. B. (1965). **The Principles of Insect Physiology,** 6th ed. London: Methuen & Co., Ltd. 741 pp.

Williams, C. M. (1952). "The physiology of insect diapause." *Biol. Bull.* **103**: 120–138.

Williams, C. M. (1961). "Insect metamorphosis: an approach to the study of growth." In: **Growth in Living Systems.** (M. X. Zarrow, ed.), pp. 313–320. New York: Basic Books, Inc.

Wilson, V. J. (1966). "Regulation and function of Renshaw cell discharge." In: **Muscular Afferents and Motor Control.** (R. Granit, ed.), pp. 317–329. New York: John Wiley & Sons, Inc.

IN the previous chapters, I have examined the mechanisms by which cells function in activities such as transport, communication, and locomotion. Although the general organization of nervous and endocrine systems were discussed in Chapter 11, it is in this third part of the book that the role of organ systems as they function in homeostasis are considered. The activities of organ systems, of course, depend upon the activities of the cells of which they are composed, although there is superimposed on cellular functioning a supracellular organization and control.

Homeostasis is defined as the regulation of the internal environment, by which is meant the tendency for internal variables such as water content, solute concentrations, pH, body temperature, or respiratory rate to remain at controlled levels. Homeostasis does not imply a strict constancy of such variables. They may change depending on the state of the animal and the stresses imposed on it. The feedback controls governing homeostasis are neither error-free nor instantaneous in action and, therefore, internal variables tend to fluctuate. Also the activities of most organisms, and in fact of cells, occur such that rhythmic peaks of activity are found. Such peaks are part of the phenomenon of biorhythms discussed in Chapter 20. It may also be noted that not all animals control all internal variables. Thus many animals lack mechanisms for temperature regulation or for osmotic regulation. Generally speaking, homeostasis implies that input is equal to output so that some factor tends to remain nearly constant.

Homeostatic mechanisms involve feedback controls (see Chapter 1). In many cases feedback diagrams are not specifically used in the following chapters, and it is left as an exercise for the reader to compose such diagrams. It will become evident that there is a vast complexity in the systems used to regulate the internal environment, especially when the coordination and integration of the various systems under different conditions is considered.

The circulatory system plays a prominent role in homeostatic activities, and in fact the blood in a sense can be considered the internal environment of the animal because the condition of the blood and body fluids determines the conditions of the cell. Circulatory systems themselves require control and regulation over heart rates, heart outputs, blood pressures, and blood composition. Not only are there general controls over circulatory systems, but in addition there are found local controls and regulations so that different regions of the body with their differing needs can be adequately serviced.

A vast amount of material is beginning to accumulate, especially at the morphological level, concerning organ systems of all animals. Here invertebrate systems are described at least in

Part III

Homeostasis: Regulation of the Internal Environment

Chapter 12

Circulatory Systems—Nature and Functions

Chapter 13

Circulatory Systems—Types, Hearts, and Controls

Chapter 14

Water and Solute Regulation

Chapter 15

Nutrition and Body Temperature Regulation

Chapter 16

Animal Respiration

general terms for important animal groups, although there may be a large amount of variation in different species. At best only a glimmering of comparative physiology is introduced here. Most of our physiological knowledge of organ system functioning and homeostasis is derived from work with vertebrates, especially with mammals.

Although cellular physiology tends to point out the basic similarities of cell structures and functions, organ system physiology tends to point out the differences in function of similar appearing systems in different species or to point out how different species may solve problems in quite dissimilar ways. Especially at the organ system level, the relation of the animal to its environment becomes important, and homeostasis is closely tied into questions of adaptation to the environment in which the animal lives. For example, although many animals possess oxygen transport pigments, these molecules may vary considerably in structure and functional characteristics such that they are best suited for the environment in which the animal lives.

Nature of Circulatory Systems

12-1. Importance of Circulatory Systems. Diffusion, aided by intracellular cyclosis, is adequate to distribute materials through the body mass or cells of protozoans, sponges, and other smaller organisms. Diffusion, as explained in Chapter 6, is an inadequate means of distributing materials rapidly over distances greater than a few millimeters. As animals increased in size or became more active, a transport system was needed to ensure that all body cells were supplied with nutrients and oxygen and that metabolic waste products were quickly removed to a place where they could be excreted.

In addition to transport functions, the circulatory system, especially in higher animals, becomes of importance because of its role in homeostasis. Since the circulating fluids come into contact with, or are part of, the interstitial fluids bathing body cells, they can serve as mechanisms aiding in the control of water content, of ions and other solutes, and of pH. The blood of birds and mammals serves as a medium for heat exchange between the inner and outer regions of the body and between the body and the external environment. Thus the circulatory system becomes a basic component of temperature regulating mechanisms.

The circulatory system carries important nutrients such as glucose or amino acids to body cells. It also is a pathway for the transport of many hormones secreted by endocrine tissues. Another function of the circulatory system is to carry antigens and cells, which act as a defense against the invasion of the organism by microorganisms or foreign toxic particles.

The circulatory system itself must be closely controlled, and a variety of mechanisms exist for this purpose. There are, for example, controls over flow rate, fluid volume flow, direction of blood flow, distribution of blood flow in different regions of the organism, circulatory rhythms, and composition of the blood. Some of the most complicated biochemical systems known are those that bring about blood clotting and thus protect the circulatory system and the animal from fluid losses following injury.

Chapter 12

Circulatory Systems—Nature and Functions

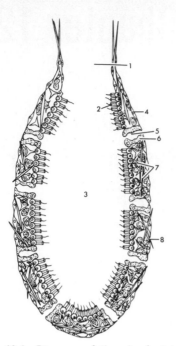

Figure 12-1 Diagram of the simplest type of sponge, the asconoid type. 1, Osculum; 2, layer of choanocytes; 3, spongocoel; 4, epidermis; 5, pore through porocyte; 6, porocyte; 7, mesenchyme; 8, amoebocyte. Most sponges have a more complicated structural organization (See Figure 12-2). Water flow is through the pore in the porocyte into the spongocoel and out through the osculum. [Redrawn from L. H. Hyman (1940) *The Invertebrates: Protozoa through Ctenophora.* By permission of the McGraw-Hill Book Company, New York.]

The statements just made are broad generalizations, and the actual transport and regulatory functions of a given animal's circulatory system depend on factors such as the size of the animal, the range of activities, and the particular species. For example, molluscs have a whole range of structural complexities of the circulatory system from complex systems with excellent pumping organs in the highly active cephalopods to a minimum of vessels and a rudimentary heart in sessile, inactive scaphopods.

The circulatory system of mammals and birds is the most complex structurally and functionally and is a type that has the greatest number of functions because these animals are not only active and require a large supply of oxygen and nutrients, but also they possess the widest range of homeostatic mechanisms. Because the circulatory system of vertebrates, especially of mammals, has been most intensively studied, the discussion of operational details of circulatory systems must be based primarily on these animals.

12-2. Types of Transport Systems. A circulatory system is not the only mechanism for moving materials in or through organisms or cells. Diffusion, as already noted, plays a role in intracellular movements and is also the mechanism for distributing materials between the circulating fluid and the body cells.

In less structured animals such as protozoans and sponges, circulation often consists of a movement of the external medium past the cell or cells of the organism. Sessile animals, especially, use cilia or flagella to move their medium past or through their bodies. The sessile ciliated protozoans often use masses of cilia to provide fresh supplies of oxygen and nutrients in a stream of water flowing past them. The flagellated choanocyte cells of sponges bring in a current of water through openings in specialized porocyte cells. This water then passes through the spongocoel and out through the osculum (Figures 12-1 and 12-2). The choanocyte cells are also digestive cells, but in addition, wandering amoeboid cells of the body wall may have the function of picking up food particles from the currents of water and then transporting them to other cells of the body wall.

Coelenterates move currents of water through specialized channels of the gastrovascular system by means of cilia. Many molluscs depend on highly organized rows of cilia to move nutrient-containing water through the mantle cavity, where the food particles are collected and then ingested. This system also provides oxygen for the gills. Even land vertebrates possess ciliated tracts, which either remove dust and debris from respiratory passages, aid in the movement of food particles in the digestive system, or transport reproductive products in the reproductive system. These examples are given in order to point out that

Figure 12-2 Current flows through various types of sponges. From left to right are shown body wall plans of the ascconoid type, the syconoid type, early stage, and the syconoid type, final stage. 1, Mesenchyme; 2, choanocyte layer; 3, incurrent pore; 4, prosopyles; 5, radial canal; 6, incurrent canal; 7, osculum; 8, spongocoel; 9, internal ostium; 10, dermal pore. Heavy line represents choanocyte layer; stippled areas, mesenchyme. Arrows indicate directions of water flows. [Redrawn from L. H. Hyman (1940). *The Invertebrates: Protozoa through Ctenophora.* By permission of the McGraw-Hill Book Company, New York.]

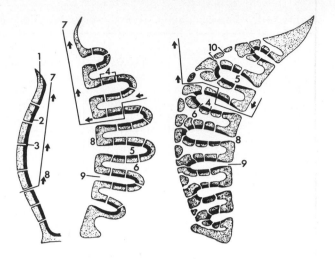

the circulatory system proper is not the only means for transport of materials in organisms.

12-3. Compartmentation of Body Fluids. Before discussing the nature and operation of circulatory systems, we must know something about the different fluid compartments found in animals. The fluids of the body can be divided into two major compartments: the intracellular and the extracellular fluids (see Table 12-1). Intracellular water ranges from 3 to 85 per cent of the total water content of the organism. Here, however, we are primarily concerned with the extracellular fluid. The nature of the extracellular fluid compartments depend first upon the body plan of the animal (see Figure 5-8 on page 143) and upon the developmental processes that occur during embryology.

In the lower invertebrate phyla of metazoans, the Porifera, Coelenterata, and Ctenophora, the body wall is relatively simple in structure. In these animals there is a lack of body spaces and of specialized vascular channels. Thus, the extracellular fluid is found in one compartment—the interstitial fluid. The latter term will be reserved for the layer of fluid that directly surrounds the body cells of an animal.

In higher phyla a space may occur between the endodermal and ectodermal layers. This is the primary body cavity or blastocoel (or hemocoele). This compartment may be composed of blood. The term blood will be used

for fluid wholly or partially contained in a system of vessels—the vascular system. Lymph, found only in vertebrates, is another fluid compartment bounded by the walls of lymphatic vessels.

During embryological development in the Platyhelminthes and higher phyla a third germ layer, the mesoderm, appears—usually a derivative of the endoderm. In higher phyla the mesoderm may form a cavity, the secondary body cavity or coelom. This cell-bounded body space or its remnants can form other fluid compartments.

In the Platyhelminthes and Nemertinea there is no coelom but the beginnings of a vascular system are found in the hemocoel. In some members of both phyla, tube systems are formed from mesenchymal cells, and these channels contain a fluid that can be considered blood (Martin and Johansen, 1965). In the Nemertinea especially is found a two-compartment system of extracellular fluid: the interstitial fluid and the blood. Fluid compartments are formed when cell layers (or membranes) intervene to prevent a free mixing of fluids.

In arthropods and molluscs the hemocoel is filled with a fluid often called the **hemolymph** because in these animals the circulatory system is open and there is a mixing of the vascular fluid and the interstitial fluid. Blood from arteries empties into small spaces (lacunae) or large spaces (sinuses) in the tissues and there mixes with other extracellular fluids. The term

Table 12-1. The Distribution of Body Water as a Percentage of the Total Water*

ANIMAL[†]	CELL WATER	HAEMOCOELE WATER + COELOM	COMMENTS
Cryptochiton[1]	49.5	50.5	Coelom small
Aplysia[1]	15	85	,, ,,
Achatina[1] (pulmonate)	53	47	,, ,,
Margaritifera[1] (lamellibranch)	45	55	Coelom moderate
Cambarus[2]	?	25%	Coelom small
Echinus[3]	3	97	All coelom, no haemocoele

ANIMAL[†]	CELL WATER	BLOOD IN CIRCULATION	PLASMA	COELOM + INTERSTITIAL FLUID	COMMENTS
Man[4]	80	12	5.6	14	Coelom small
Octopus[1]	66	7	—	27	Coelom moderate
Salmo[5]	80	Small	—	15	,, ,,
Cyprinus[7]	78	4	2.5	19.2	,, ,,
Mycteroperca[7]	82.5	4.5	3.2	14.2	
Squalus[6]	81	9.5	—	17.7	,, ,,
Raia binoculata[6]	82	10.2	7.9	10	
Petromyzon[7] in fresh water	68	11	7	25	

* From W. T. W. Potts and G. Parry (1964). *Osmotic Regulation in Animals*. Long Island City, N.Y.: Pergamon Press, Inc. Reprinted by permission.
† References: (1) Martin et al. (1958); (2) Prosser, ed. (1950); (3) Undocumented guess; (4) Smith (1956); (5) Houston (1959); (6) Thorson (1958); (7) Thorson (1961).

hemolymph is sometimes preferred in order to distinguish a circulating fluid that is not separated from the interstitial fluid by a membrane (see Maynard, 1960); but many workers simply use the term blood. Even in the closed mammalian circulatory system there are sites, for example, in the liver and spleen, where blood flows into tissue sinuses instead of through capillaries and thus directly bathes the tissue cells.

In some adult animals the coelomic space is large and filled with coelomic fluid, but in most animals the coelom is reduced to small spaces about the gonads, excretory system, or pericardium. The volume of coelomic fluid varies greatly in different animals, and the presence of a large hemocoel is usually correlated with a small coelomic space. Annelids have a relatively large coelomic cavity. They also possess a closed circulatory system. Therefore, their body fluids are found in three major compartments: the blood, the interstitial fluid, and the coelomic fluid.

A closed circulatory system—one that is formed of a continuous circuit of blood vessels—is found in the vertebrates, some annelids, cephalopod molluscs, some echinoderms, nemerteans, and trematodes. An open system is found in most arthropods, many molluscs, and the ascidians.

In vertebrates the fluid compartments are blood, lymph, interstitial fluid, and a small

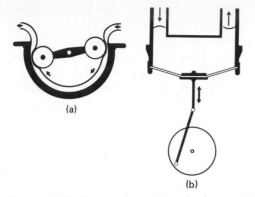

(a)

(b)

Figure 12-3 Types of positive displacement pumps. (a) Rotary pump in which rollers on a rotating arm propel fluid through a flexible tube. (b) Reciprocating pump in which the back and forth movement of a piston or diaphragm moves fluid in a direction controlled by the presence of valves. In the rotary pump it can be seen that backward movement of fluid is prevented by the action of the oncoming roller which closes the tube under it. [After Brecher and Galletti (1963).]

volume of coelomic fluid. In addition other specialized fluid compartments may be present. For example, vertebrates have cerebrospinal fluid in the nervous system (Davson, 1964); perilymph and endolymph are found in the ear chambers; and the aqueous and vitreous humors are found in the eye.

This brief discussion of some body spaces and their fluids is intended only to point out that the water content of an animal is not homogeneously distributed. Various barriers are present which divide the water content into a number of fluid compartments whose water and solutes may not mix freely. Generalization is difficult because of the many differences in fluid compartment found even within phyla or classes. Hyman (1940–1959) reviews the germinal layers and embryonic development of the various invertebrate groups. Circulatory systems of a wide variety of organisms are described in Grassé (1948–).

12-4. Components of Circulatory Systems. In order to function efficiently a circulatory system must possess certain structural and functional features. Circulatory systems operate by providing a driving force to propel the vascular

fluid in a relatively smooth and continuous manner to all parts of the organism. In most circulatory systems the driving force is provided by muscular contractions of a pumping organ or heart.

Hearts are analogous to mechanical positive displacement pumps that may operate on either of two principles (Figure 12-3). In some invertebrates and lower chordates heart action is analogous to that of a rotary pump, which produces a forward movement of fluid by an action similar to peristalsis. This is typical of many tube hearts of arthropods, *Limulus*, some annelids, and tunicates.

In many molluscs, decapod crustaceans, and vertebrates the heart action is more like that of a reciprocating pump, characterized by a pulsatile activity during which blood is directed in a one-way flow by appropriately positioned valves. In either case the heart operates by converting the potential energy of chemical compounds into kinetic energy for fluid movement measured as a pressure gradient between the heart and the blood vessels of the vascular system.

Valves are a basic feature of nearly all circulatory systems and are required to maintain a one-way flow of blood. Valves are structured to close when the fluid pressure difference is greater on one side than on the other and to open when the pressure difference reverses (Figure 12-4). Not only are valves present in most hearts to prevent a back-flow of blood when the heart contracts, but valves are also

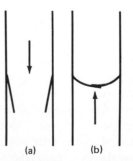

(a)   (b)

Figure 12-4 Schematic representation of valve action in the vascular system. When pressure is greatest in direction of arrow (a), valve opens; if back pressure is greater, (b) valve closes.

found in the venous and lymphatic systems—low pressure regions in the vascular circuit. The force available in the venous system is usually not sufficient to overcome the force of gravity acting on the lower extremities of the body and the presence of valves is required to prevent a back-flow of blood in the veins. Fluid movement in veins is aided by the contractions of somatic muscles surrounding them —an action that squeezes blood toward the heart. In some less active animals this type of driving force is the only one used by the vascular system. A similar mechanism is found in the vertebrate lymphatic system.

Another requirement for the proper functioning of the heart is that the many muscle cells making up its structure be coordinated to produce a nearly simultaneous contraction so that blood is forcefully ejected into the arterial system. Also the heartbeat must be rhythmic. The synchronization of cardiac muscle cell contractions due to spontaneous generation of action potentials and rapid conduction over a specialized conducting system (in the mammalian heart) was discussed in Chapter 9.

Leading from the heart are the large vessels designed to carry the blood rapidly to various parts of the body. These vessels, which include the aorta in vertebrates and the major arteries of all animals, must not only be large in order to reduce frictional effects of fluid passing through them but are also required to be distensible and possess elastic walls. The latter characteristic aids in producing a smooth flow of blood even when the heart action is pulsatile (see Section 12-13).

Arteries ramify into smaller vessels, the arterioles, which are supplied with smooth muscles for controlling lumen diameter. Arterioles function in the regulation of blood flow by directing blood to organs and tissues that are active and shunting blood away from resting or less active tissues. Such a mechanism is necessary since the volume of blood available is much less than the total capacity of the animal's circulatory system. Another function of arterioles is to aid in the regulation of local blood pressures.

Arterioles branch into numerous smaller vessels, the capillaries. Although capillaries are the smallest vessels of the closed circulatory system, their enormous number means that the total volume of all the capillary beds is immense. The small size of capillaries is a requirement for exchange of materials between the blood and interstitial fluid.

In the closed system the capillaries are the major functional components as far as exchange of materials between blood and interstitial fluid is concerned, and the entire circulatory system is designed to provide optimal conditions for material exchanges at the capillary level.

Capillaries fuse into collecting vessels, the venules, which in turn fuse into larger vessels, the veins. The venous side of the circulation returns blood to the heart for recirculation and reoxygenation. Veins must be large to reduce the forces needed to propel blood through them. Much of the cardiac pumping force has been dissipated by the time blood reaches the venous circulation, and venous blood pressures are much lower than arterial blood pressures. Veins are thin-walled and distensible and serve, when needed, as blood reservoirs in the animal.

At some time during the circulation cycle, blood usually passes through a respiratory organ, where the blood oxygen is replenished and gaseous waste products are eliminated. Also at some time during the cycle there is an opportunity to replenish nutrients as well as to eliminate nongaseous waste products of metabolism. The respiratory capillary beds have a high resistance to blood flow, and often accessory pumping organs are needed to propel blood through this region of the circulatory system. The higher vertebrates have solved this problem by the evolution of a chambered heart, which provides two pumps in one: the systemic (or general body) system and the pulmonary system.

The hearts, arteries, arterioles, capillaries, venules, and veins make up the closed circulatory system. Since each component has specific functions, each has specialized structural features. These structures and their functions will be discussed in various sections of this and the following chapter.

The open circulatory generally lacks capillaries, although in some cases capillaries are present to supply a given organ with blood. Normally blood empties from arteries into tissue spaces and after bathing the body cells drains into sinuses of the hemocoel. From the hemocoel the fluid passes into the heart for recirculation. In some cases veins are present to collect the blood before it reaches the heart.

The principles underlying circulatory system functioning will be discussed following a consideration of the physical principles governing fluid flows in tubular systems.

Hemodynamics

12-5. Fluid Flows. Since circulatory systems usually consist of a pump that forces fluid through a system of distensible tubes (blood vessels), an understanding of how such systems operate requires some knowledge of the laws governing fluid flows and the energies involved. The French physician, physicist, and physiologist Poiseuille (1799–1869) became interested in these aspects of circulatory activity and began investigating model systems in which water flowed through rigid cylindrical tubes. From these studies he derived a set of principles that are still valid for such systems.

However, the application of Poiseuille's results to circulatory system functioning meets some complications. Blood vessels are not rigid tubes. Not only are they distensible, but in addition they are capable of active dilation or constriction because of the presence of smooth muscle cells in their walls.

Further, water is a **Newtonian fluid**—one that obeys the laws of viscosity, that is, its viscosity does not change with flow rate. But blood is a multiphase system and acts as a **non-Newtonian fluid** in blood vessels smaller than about 0.5 mm in diameter. Also blood flow is pulsatile rather than smooth in most circulatory systems because of the nature of the contractile pump. Pulsatile flow results in changes in the kinetic energy of the fluid that are not taken into account in Poiseuille's laws. In spite of

these differences these laws provide a starting point for the understanding of fluid flows.

A **fluid** is a substance that cannot permanently withstand even slight shearing forces—forces that tend to change the shape of a substance and to cause a sliding of adjacent layers of the substance. Gases and liquids are both fluids, but gases are compressible and liquids are not.

12-6. Viscosity. Several factors affect the flow of blood, including the following: frictional forces between the layers of flowing blood, the inertia of the mass of blood that is to be moved and accelerated by the pulsatile action of the heart, and the force of gravity that affects the blood pressure in different parts of an animal.

Viscosity may be thought of as an internal friction between layers of moving fluid. It is defined as the ratio of stress to the velocity gradient. Stress is the force applied to the fluid per unit area to produce fluid motion, whereas the velocity gradient is the change in velocity from one layer to another. Fluid moving through a tube is modeled as a series of thin concentric layers slipping past one another—this is **laminar flow**.

Blood flow is laminar but cohesive forces between the blood and the blood vessel wall prevent the movement of a thin layer of blood in contact with the wall. The forces needed to produce blood flow are required to overcome the internal friction of the blood, not friction between the vessel wall and the blood.

When blood flows because of pressure gradients established by the contraction of the cardiac muscle, there is a gradient of velocity established across the width of the vessel lumen with successive cylindrical lamellae of blood moving with increasing velocities as the axis of the tube is reached. (Figure 12-5).

As shown in Figure 12-5, the velocity profile is a parabola, described by

$$v_r = v_m\left(1 - \frac{r_1^2}{r_0^2}\right) \qquad (12.1)$$

v_r is the velocity of flow at any vessel radius, r_1, and v_m is the maximal velocity at the radius of the vessel, r_0. The equation indicates that at

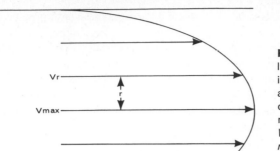

Figure 12-5 Illustrating the nature of laminar flow in a cylindrical tube. Velocities of the lamellae are distributed in a parabolic manner across the diameter of the blood vessel according to the relation $V_r = V_{max} (1 - [r^2/R^2])$, where V_r is the velocity of flow at any radius, r^2, V_{max} is the maximum velocity of flow at the center of the tube and R is the total radius of the tube.

$r_1 = r_0$, the velocity of flow of the outermost lamella is zero.

The maximal velocity of flow is related to the pressure gradient, ΔP—the pressure drop per unit length of vessel; and to the viscosity of the fluid, η, by

$$v_m = \frac{\Delta P r_1}{4\eta} \qquad (12.2)$$

The viscosity of the blood is an important factor in determining the flow rate. The viscosity of a fluid, as already stated, represents the resistance to shearing forces of adjacent layers of the fluid. Newton described the coefficient of viscosity, η, by

$$F = A\eta \left(\frac{\Delta v}{\Delta d}\right) \qquad (12.3)$$

where F is the tangential drag force (in dynes) between two layers of fluid in contact over an area A. The velocity gradient between two layers of fluid is Δv, and Δd is the distance between the centers of the two layers.

In summary, resistance to blood flow is the result of viscosity effects between adjacent layers of the flowing blood. Because blood is stationary in a thin layer next to the vessel wall, there is no resistance to be overcome between the blood and the vessel wall. The viscosity of the blood is an important factor in determining the rate of blood flow. The diameter of the vessel lumen is also an important factor.

The study of the properties of a system that determine its type of flow is **rheology**. Bayliss (1962), Copley and Stainsby (1960), and Wayland (1967) treat of these properties. The factors that affect blood viscosity will be

discussed in the section of this chapter devoted to blood.

12-7. Hydrostatic Pressure. Pascal (1623–1662) realized that three basic laws govern fluid pressure (force per unit area, usually with the units of dynes/cm²):

1. Fluid pressure is equal in all directions throughout a volume of fluid, from a given point in the fluid.
2. Fluid pressure is equal at all points lying in the same horizontal plane of a fluid.
3. The pressure increases with increasing depth under the free surface of the fluid. At the surface the pressure is atmospheric.

In fluids at rest, under gravity, pressure increases uniformly with depth, according to

$$P = \rho g h \qquad (12.4)$$

where P is the hydrostatic pressure, ρ is the density of the fluid in g/cm³, g is the acceleration of gravity (980 cm/sec²), and h is the depth in centimeters.

Pressures are often expressed in terms of mm of Hg or cm of H_2O. The absolute pressure of a column of mercury (density 13.6) 1 mm deep, from Equation 12.4, is 1330 dynes/cm². The absolute pressure of a column of water 1 cm deep is 980 dynes/cm² (the density of water is 1). Thus 1 mm Hg is equal to a column of water 1.36 cm deep. Pressures are measured either by U-tube manometers or by electromanometric transducers (Figure 12-6).

The hydrostatic factor, $\rho g h$, applies to the circulatory system when points in the system

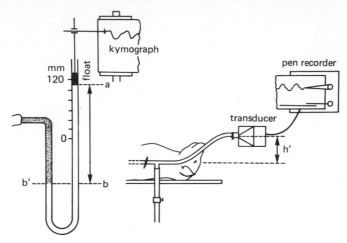

Figure 12-6 Pressure (h) may be measured using mercury-filled U-tube manometers (left) where h equals difference in mercury levels in two arms (b'-b and a); or by transducers that convert pressure changes into electrical signals (right). All manometric measurements of blood pressure require that the recorded pressure be corrected by the factor $\rho gh'$ unless the transducer or manometer is connected at the level of the cannula to the blood vessel. [After A. C. Burton (1965).]

lie above or below the level of the heart, which is taken as the reference point. Gravity can exert a considerable influence over the pressures found in different parts of the body. When the human body is horizontal, the mean arterial pressures in the brain and feet are about equal. But when the body is erect, the hydrostatic pressure reduces brain arterial pressure and increases absolute pressures in the lower extremities. Arterial pressure differences between head and feet may differ by 100 to 200 mm Hg, depending on whether a human is reclining or standing (Gauer and Thron, 1965).

Since veins are more distensible than arteries, blood tends to collect in them when they are below the level of the heart and when a gravitational pressure gradient is acting on them. The valves in the veins prevent any backflow of blood, and added propulsive force for blood flow is supplied by the contraction of the skeletal muscles surrounding the veins (Figure 12-7).

Note that gravitational forces do not stop blood flow; rather they cause blood to collect in the distensible veins. Once a vein is fully distended and filled with blood, the flow of blood continues because of the heart-produced forces and the siphoning effects in closed circulatory systems.

Humans who have stood still for long periods of time often faint because of the pooling of blood in the veins of the lower extremities and torso. Since there is no movement, muscle contractions are not present to aid blood flow against the hydrostatic pressure gradient. The pooling of blood in the legs and torso results in a diminished blood supply to the head and brain, hence the fainting. The fact that there is not enough blood in the circulatory system to fill the entire vascular network plays its part in this phenomenon.

Giraffes have an unusual problem because their heads are often 20 feet above the ground and 12 feet or more above heart level. Hydrostatic pressure from head to heart can be 120 mm Hg or more. In a quiet standing giraffe, mean pressure at the cephalic end of the carotid artery is about 90 mm Hg, and the mean pressure in the aorta is about 210 mm Hg. To withstand these pressures, which are higher than those normally found in mammalian circulatory systems, the major arteries in the neck of the giraffe are extremely thick and contain much elastic tissue. There is also a

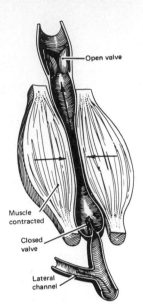

Figure 12-7 Diagram illustrating how contractions of skeletal muscles can cause blood flow in a vein. Blood flows upward because back pressure closes the lower valve, and the pressure opens the upper valve. [Redrawn from S. Grollman (1964) *The Human Body*. By permission Macmillan Company, New York.]

hypertrophy of the left ventricle, the heart chamber responsible for pumping blood into the peripheral system, so the heart can produce stronger contractions required to develop the pressures needed to supply the head with blood. For details of the methods used to study the circulation of the giraffe under natural conditions and the suggested mechanisms by which the giraffe's circulatory system compensates for extreme changes in hydrostatic pressure as the animal bends its neck, see Patterson et al. (1965); Van Citters et al. (1966), and Goetz et al. (1960).

Hydrostatic pressure due to gravitational force is a static pressure in the circulatory system and depends on the shape and position of the animal and the vertical relations of blood vessels to the heart. It is of lesser importance in determining blood flows than the pressure gradients and energy supplied by the contracting cardiac muscle.

12-8. Fluid Energies. The total energy of a fluid system is given by

$$E_t = P + \rho gh + \tfrac{1}{2}\rho v^2 \qquad (12.5)$$

where E_t is the total energy of the system; P is the pressure in dynes/cm^2; v is the velocity of fluid flow at the point h (the height above or below some arbitrary reference point) in cm/sec. The units of all these terms may be converted to mm Hg.

The pressure is the potential energy of the flowing fluid. The gravitational potential energy has already been discussed. Since it represents only a small factor in most circulatory systems, it will be generally ignored in the following discussion. The term $\tfrac{1}{2}\rho v^2$ is the kinetic energy factor of the fluid. In the

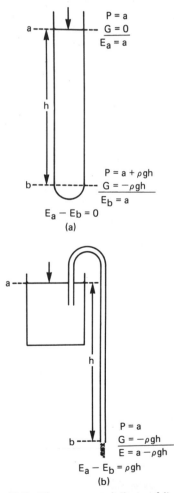

Figure 12-8 The energy relations of liquids in (a) a tube and (b) in a siphon. It is the total energy of the fluid that determines whether or not flow occurs.

absence of flow this term is zero, and all of the energy of the system is pressure energy and is the same at all points in a body of fluid (at some given horizontal plane).

If the total energy E_a at some point A in a fluid system is greater than the total energy E_b at some other point B, flow occurs from A to B, and the rate of flow depends on the energy difference between E_a and E_b. The flow of fluid is not governed by pressure differences alone. As shown in Figure 12-8, in a tube filled with water there is a pressure gradient between the top and bottom of the tube, but there is no fluid flow because the increasing pressure toward the bottom is exactly counterbalanced by a decreasing gravitational force. The total energy is the same throughout the tube. Figure 12-8a shows the appropriate relations of fluid energies for the top and bottom of the tube as derived from Equation 12.5. Figure 12-8b gives these relations for a siphon system

in which flow occurs. Again, it is not the differences in fluid levels alone that determine the direction of flow. If this were true, it would be difficult for blood to run uphill from the feet to the heart. It is the overall energy of the fluid in the circulatory (or any fluid) system that produces the observed amount of movement. Blood is always moving down an energy gradient.

The kinetic energy is the energy of the flowing blood. It is the energy that accelerates the mass of blood from the heart. The importance of the kinetic energy factor changes in different regions of the circulatory system as shown in Table 12-2. Ordinarily, the kinetic energy is of lesser importance in the arteries, capillaries, and small veins. But during exercise or exertion, the kinetic energy factor becomes important in large vessels such as the aorta or venae cavae.

As with other energy forms, the three energy

Table 12-2 Amount and Relative Importance of Kinetic Energy in Different Parts of the Circulation*†

VESSEL	RESTING CARDIAC OUTPUT				CARDIAC OUTPUT INCREASED 3 TIMES		
	VELOCITY (cm/sec)	KINETIC ENERGY (mm Hg)	PRESSURE (mm Hg)	KINETIC ENERGY (% OF TOTAL)	KINETIC ENERGY (mm Hg)	PRESSURE (mm Hg)	KINETIC ENERGY (% OF TOTAL)
Aorta, systolic	100	4	120	3%	36	180	17%
mean	30	0.4	100	0.4%	3.8	140	2.6%
Arteries, systolic	30	0.35	110	0.3%	3.8	120	3%
mean	10	0.04	95	Neg.		100	Neg.
Capillaries	0.1	0.000004	25	Neg.	Neg.	25	Neg.
Venae cavae and atria	30	0.35	2	12%	3.2	3	52%
Pulmonary artery, systolic	90	3	20	13%	27	25	52%
mean	25	0.23	12	2%	2.1	14	13%

* From A. C. Burton (1965). *Physiology and Biophysics of the Circulation.* Year Book Medical Publishers, Chicago, Ill. Reprinted by permission.
† The cases where kinetic energy should not be neglected—that is, where it is more than 5% of the total fluid energy—are indicated by italic figures. When an artery is narrowed by disease processes, the kinetic energy becomes very important. Neg. = negligible.

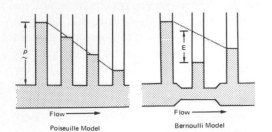

Poiseuille Model   Bernoulli Model

Figure 12-9 According to Poiseuille's model, when fluid flow occurs in a tube to which several vertical tubes are connected, the pressure drop in each vertical tube falls as indicated. According to Bernoulli's principle, when a tube narrows, flow rate increases and is accompanied by a corresponding drop in pressure as indicated by the middle vertical tube. Flow occurs down a gradient of total fluid pressure not down a pressure gradient.

factors of fluids are interconvertible. All of the energy ultimately is degraded into heat. During the flow of blood in the circulatory system, kinetic energy is transformed into pressure energy (or the reverse occurs). Bernoulli (1700–1782) showed that there is an interconversion of energies when fluid flows through a series of tubes of variable cross-section, and this is the situation found in circulatory systems.

As shown in Figure 12-9, if the cross-sectional area of a tube decreases, the velocity of flow must increase in the narrow-bore tube, since the same volume of fluid passing through the large tube in unit time, must also pass through the smaller tube. As the velocity of flow increases, the pressure decreases. Since the total energy of the fluid remains approximately constant, the pressure decrease is counterbalanced by a corresponding increase in kinetic energy (the hydrostatic pressure because of gravity is zero in a horizontal tube). Similarly, as the bore of the tube again widens, the velocity of flow decreases and the pressure increases as the kinetic energy also decreases. Changes of this type can occur in the circulatory system as blood moves from arteries to smaller arterioles to still smaller capillaries. On the venous side of the circulation capillaries merge into larger venules that in turn merge into larger veins and corresponding changes in

pressure and kinetic energies and flow rate can take place.

12-9. Blood Pressures. The contractile activity of cardiac muscle is responsible for generating the energies of blood flow, and these energies, as indicated above, take the forms of kinetic as well as pressure energies. Pressure gradients are established throughout the circulatory system.

Strictly speaking a pressure gradient is the rate of change of pressure along the longitudinal axis of a blood vessel. The term is used in the study of circulatory systems to refer to the head of pressure, or pressure difference, established between two points in the vascular system. The phrase " blood pressure " causes some confusion unless it is realized that the pressure measured at some point in the circulatory system will depend entirely upon the method used to record it.

There are three ways of measuring pressure in a blood vessel. If the cannula or catheter is inserted into a blood vessel facing upstream to the direction of flow, the pressure measured is an **end pressure**. Insertion of a cannula obstructs the blood flow and the kinetic energy of the moving blood is converted into a pressure energy against the cannula and measuring device. The end pressure recorded is too high by a factor of $\frac{1}{2}\rho v^2$ over the true blood pressure at that point.

If a cannula is inserted into a vessel pointing in the direction of flow, the pressure measured is a **downstream pressure** and is lower than the true blood pressure by some fraction of $\frac{1}{2}\rho v^2$. How much lower will depend on the shape of the cannula and its influence on the flow stream.

If a cannula is inserted perpendicularly to the direction of flow, the resulting pressure will be a true recording of the blood pressure at that point. This **side pressure** is not easy to measure, since the introduction of cannulas or measuring transducers usually obstructs the flow to some degree. Detailed methods and an excellent discussion of these methods for measuring circulatory system variables is found in Rushmer (1966).

The different pressures just described do not exist as such in a circulatory system; they are artifacts depending on the nature of the measuring method. There is only one absolute pressure in a blood vessel at a given point and this pressure is equal in all directions from that point.

Two other pressure terms are important when describing the movement of blood through a circulatory system. One is the **driving pressure** (or **pressure gradient**), which is the difference in pressure between two points in the system. The driving pressure can be defined as the fall in pressure per unit length: $(P_1 - P_2)/L$. P_1 is the pressure at the upstream point, and L is the distance between the two points. The driving pressure determines the rate of blood flow between these two points.

The other important pressure is the **transmural pressure**, P_t, which is a function of the intravascular blood pressure, P_i, and the tissue pressure, P_e, external to the vessel. The transmural pressure tends to stretch and expand the blood vessel wall and must be opposed by tensions exerted by elastic elements composing part of the vessel structure. It has been found that blood vessels resist stretch the more strongly they are being stretched, and this property is caused by the presence of both collagen and elastin fibers in the wall of the vessel. Increases in the transmural pressure that, otherwise, would tend to blow out the blood vessel wall are counterbalanced by increases in the tension opposing this pressure. Conversely, decreases in transmural pressure that would tend to cause closure of the blood vessel are counterbalanced by decreases tension of the elastic elements.

By combining the results of Poiseuille with the terms of Equation 12.4, we can see that

$$\dot{V} = \Delta P \frac{\pi}{8} \frac{1}{\eta} \frac{r^4}{L} \qquad (12.6)$$

This is the Poiseuille-Hagen equation, which related blood flow to four factors. The volume flow per unit time is $\dot{V}$. [A dot over a symbol is used to indicate flow per time; this follows the practice established for the standardization of symbols used in respiratory physiology,

Pappenheimer (1950). Often the symbol Q is used, but here this symbol will be reserved for quantities of materials, not volumes.] The term $\pi/8$ is a numerical factor resulting from the fact that blood vessels are cylinders and including also a factor arising in the course of the integration leading to Equation 12.6.

The viscosity of the blood is accounted for by the factor $1/\eta$. This indicates that the higher the viscosity, the less the flow rate, that is, the greater is the resistance to flow.

The last term of Equation 12.6 is a geometrical factor including the length of the vessel and its radius. Increasing lengths of vessels decrease the flow rate. It is important to note that the flow rate depends on the fourth power of the radius of the vessel. Thus relatively small changes in vessel radius can greatly influence the flow. For example, if the radius of a blood vessel is decreased by only 16 per cent, the flow is halved. Local flow in the circulatory system is controlled by arterioles that contain smooth muscle cells in their walls and whose contraction determines the size of the vessel lumen.

In the peripheral circulation the major means for controlling flow is through changes in the radius of blood vessels or alterations in blood pressure. These are localized controls found in arterioles, capillaries, and venules. Large arteries and veins do not affect flows as much as the smaller vessels.

12-10. Resistance to Blood Flow. The resistance to flow in the peripheral circulation is defined by

$$R_f = \frac{\Delta P}{\dot{V}} \qquad (12.7)$$

That is, peripheral resistance, R_f, is the ratio of the pressure drop between two points along a vessel to the total flow between those two points. The peripheral resistance to flow is also equal to $8\eta L/\pi r^4$. A measure of the difficulty of driving blood through a given section of a peripheral vascular bed is indicated as R_f.

Considering the circulatory system as a whole, the arterial-venous pressure difference is generally constant, maintained by the heart's

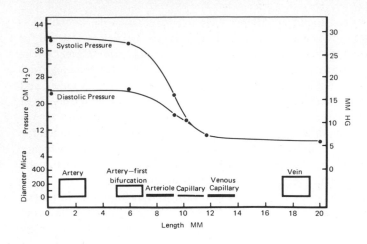

Figure 12-10(a) Pressure gradient in the mesenteric blood vessels of the frog. Systolic pressure is the highest pressure in the circulatory system and occurs during ventricular contraction; diastolic pressure occurs during the relaxation of ventricular muscle. The lower part of the figure shows the relative dimensions of various blood vessels. Note that the greatest pressure drop occurs in the arterioles, although there is also a significant pressure drop in the capillaries. [Redrawn and modified from Landis (1962).]

contractile force and the control systems to be described in later sections (Sections 13-17 and 13-18). Nor under normal conditions does the viscosity of the blood change greatly. The resistance of the peripheral circulation is brought about by pressure and flow changes in local peripheral beds through the mechanisms of arteriolar constriction and dilation, which alter the geometric factor of the Poiseuille-Hagen equation. And, as previously stated, blood pressure changes will occur when blood flow is from a vessel of one cross-sectional area to a vessel of a different cross-sectional area. Drops in pressure associated with the systemic

circulation are given in Figure 12-10a, b (see also Table 12-2). Figure 12-10b also includes estimates of the relative resistance of various parts of the vascular bed. It can be seen that the greatest resistance to flow is in the smaller vessels, especially the arterioles, and it is in these vessels that the greatest drop of blood pressure is found.

The resistance across a given vascular bed will depend on the pressure gradient because a change in this factor alters the transmural pressure, which, in turn, alters the geometry of the blood vessel. If, for example, one increases the arterial blood pressure experimentally,

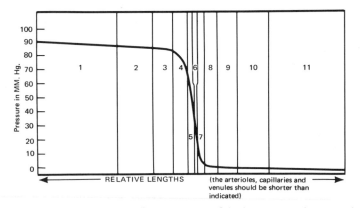

Figure 12-10(b) The pressures in different vessels of the human circulatory system related to their length. Numbers in brackets are estimates of the percentage of resistance of these vessels in the dog. [Data of Burton (1965) and Green (1950).]

1. Aorta	5. Arterioles	9. Main venous branches
2. Large arteries	6. Capillaries	10. Large veins
3. Main arterial branches	7. Venules	11. Vena cavae
4. Terminal arteries	8. Terminal veins	

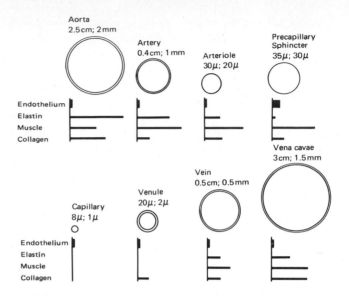

Figure 12-11 Schematic representation of the average sizes and composition of the walls of four types of blood vessels. (After Burton (1944).]

while maintaining venous pressure constant, the transmural pressure increases and the geometry of the blood vessel alters—the distensible vessel wall is pushed out. If one lowers the venous pressure while holding the arterial pressure constant, the transmural pressure decreases. In both cases the driving pressure increases, but the effects on the transmural pressure are different. There is a family of relations between blood flow and blood pressure that depend upon the particular changes that the transmural pressure undergoes (see Burton, 1962, 1965).

In this part of the chapter some of the factors that can be used to control (and change) flows and pressures in the peripheral circulation have been considered. In the following sections the affects of these factors on the circulation will be examined in relation to the particular structural features of various vessels in the circulatory system. Basically, changes in the diameter of blood vessels are used to alter blood flow and blood pressure as required by the particular conditions of the animal. It should be noted that these are local changes in the peripheral circulation. The heart beat and its control (see

Table 12-3 Some Physical Properties of Collagen, Elastin, and Smooth Muscle*

Tissue	Maximal Tensile Strength (kg/cm^2)	Young's Modulus (dynes/cm^2)	Maximal Extension (%)	Irreversible Elongation (% total elongation)	Hysteresis under Stretch Curve (%)
Collagen fibers (tendon)	660	1×10^9	50	67	57
Elastin fibers (ligamentum nuchae)	25	3×10^6	150	19	60
Smooth muscle					
contracted	—	1×10^5	300	—	—
relaxed	—	6×10^4	300	—	—

* Data from Burton (1962) and Wöhlisch et al. (1927).

Chapter 13) are responsible for maintaining the overall pressure and flow in the circulatory system.

Blood Vessels

12-11. Tissues of the Vascular Wall. Four basic types of tissues make up the structure of blood vessels. The amount of each present in a given vessel determines the properties of that vessel. The relative proportions of these layers as well as the average sizes of various blood vessels are diagrammed in Figure 12-11.

In all vessels there is an inner layer of endothelial cells. The specific functions of this layer and its detailed structural makeup will be considered in the section on capillaries. Its presence in arteries, including the aorta, provides a leakproof lining that retains blood within the vessel.

Next is found an elastic layer composed principally of the protein elastin, a fibrous connective tissue protein whose exact chemical nature is unknown. X-ray diffraction analysis reveals no organized structure in elastin fibers, and it is thought that elastin molecules are arranged in a rather random fashion in the fiber. This type of structure could account for the high extensibility of the fiber. A tetracarboxylic tetraamino acid has been found in elastin hydrolysates, and this unusual amino acid might be able to allow cross-bridge formation between four peptide chains in the fiber (Partridge et al., 1964). Elastin has a low tensile strength, but can be extended to twice its normal length without damage (see Table 12-3).

Next are found layers of smooth muscle fibers. Two types are found in blood vessels. Tension muscles (spannmuskeln) are connected to elastic fibers and cell membranes. They have the ability to raise the tension on the elastic tissues by their contractions. This activity affects the blood pressure within the vessel. Tension muscles are arranged longitudinally with the fiber axis.

Ring muscles are connected to each other, perhaps to elastic fibers, also by means of slack attachments. These muscles form helical rings around arterioles and some arteries. They are also found in the precapillary sphincters (Benninghof, 1930; Fischer, 1951).

In many cases the smooth muscle of the vascular wall has the ability for spontaneous activity, but smooth muscle is also greatly influenced by hormonal and other chemical stimuli. Such a system provides for localized control of blood flow without the continuous intervention of the central nervous system. The nature of the innervation of vascular smooth muscle is not understood. Although fibers of the sympathetic division of the autonomic nervous system are known to act as vasoconstrictors, not all arteries or arterioles respond similarly to excitation of these nerves. In mammals, for example, skin arteries and arterioles are constricted when the sympathetic nerves leading to them are stimulated. But these arteries do not respond to such external factors as pH or pCO_2 (the partial pressure of carbon dioxide). In contrast, arterioles and arteries in the brain are extremely responsive to changes in pH or pCO_2 but are little influenced by nervous activity.

Although nerve axon terminals are known to make connections with smooth muscle cells in some arteries, in general the distances separating axon terminals from vascular muscle cells is on the order of 1,000 to 4,000 Å (Verity and Bevan, 1967). Certainly not all smooth muscle cells in a given vascular wall receive innervation; therefore, the conduction of action potentials (when they do occur) is likely from muscle cell to muscle cell. Noradrenalin released by the nerve endings may diffuse and activate certain smooth muscle cells in a vessel; these cells may then activate the remainder of the cells (Roddie, 1967). That the situation is complex and not well understood may be seen by examination of the contents of a symposium in the *Journal of General Physiology* (1962) and one in *Bibliotheca Anatomica* **8** (1967).

Although in some cases contraction of vascular smooth muscle is accompanied by membrane depolarization, for example, in turtle vena cavae and aorta, rat mesentery arteries, or sheep carotid sinus, in other vessels microelectrode studies reveal that contraction occurs without any membrane depolarization, for example, in the rabbit pulmonary artery (see the review by Sonnenschein and White, 1968). Suggestions have been made that in the rabbit arteries, noradrenalin causes the release of Ca^{2+} from the smooth muscle cell membrane and that the Ca^{2+} release triggers the excitation of the contractile elements (Cuthbert, 1967). Smooth muscle cells generally have a poorly developed sarcoplasmic reticulum and transverse tubular system and may depend on the sarcolemma for Ca^{2+} to trigger contraction.

The fourth and outer layer of blood vessels is a collagenous connective tissue that is relatively inextensible. Collagen fibers are about twenty-five times as strong as elastin fibers, but fifteen times less extensible.

The description of these four layers is not meant to imply that they exist as separate, neatly arranged layers around the vessel. The constituents of different layers extend into one another, and it is usually difficult to separate them by dissection. The anatomy of the vascular wall has been reviewed by Comél and Laszt (1967).

12-12. Structural Properties of Vascular Walls. The properties of elasticity, viscosity, viscoelasticity, and plasticity are important for proper functioning of blood vessels. According to Landowne and Stacy (1957), **elasticity** is the ability of a substance to regain its original form after being deformed by an applied force—a **stress**. The deformation is a **strain**. If a material is completely or perfectly elastic, all energy applied to it by an external force is recoverable as mechanical energy. The length-tension diagram of a perfectly elastic material is shown in Figure 12-12. **Distensibility** is a measure of the stiffness of a material—its ability to resist stresses.

As previously defined, viscosity is a measure of the resistance (or lack of it) to flow of a liquid when a shearing force is applied to it. Because the walls of blood vessels exhibit some of the characteristics of both solids and liquids (they contain about 70 per cent water), both

viscosity and elasticity play a role in the functional characteristics.

Although a perfectly elastic substance has a relation between stress and deformation that is independent of time, a viscous or viscoelastic system when stretched develops a tension that is dependent not only on the degree of stretch but also on the rate of stretch. The faster such a system is stretched, the greater is the tension developed—the stretch-release curve of a viscoelastic system follows a hysteresis loop (Figure 12-12b).

Plasticity is a measure of the tendency of a material to retain a new shape after deformation. All of the properties just described are present to differing degrees in each type of blood vessel depending on the proportions of

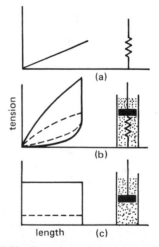

Figure 12-12 Length-tension curves of different materials. (a) Elastic materials exemplified by the stretching of a spring. Tension is linear with degree of stretch. (b) Viscous-elastic system exemplified by a spring to which is attached a damping or braking device in a fluid. Extension and release curves inscribe a hysteresis loop, the size of which depends on the velocity of extension and release. (c) Viscous device moving in a liquid; the material keeps every length to which it was brought by an external force that depends on the velocity of the extension. Solid curve, fast stretch; dotted curve, slow stretch. [After H. Bader (1963). "The anatomy and physiology of the vascular wall." In: Handbook of Physiology Section 2, Vol. 2 (W. F. Hamilton, ed), pp. 885-889. By permission American Physiological Society, Washington, D.C.]

collagen, elastin, and smooth muscle present in their walls.

In biological systems, the properties of a tissue may change with activity in the system. For example, smooth muscle when passively stretched exhibits plastic behavior. But upon contraction smooth muscle returns to its former length, and the properties of elasticity and viscoelasticity become dominant (see Reichel, 1960). Collagen fibers exhibit little plasticity under normal loads, but when they are overloaded they become plastic.

The circumference of a blood vessel determines the volume flow through the vessel and also the blood and transmural pressures. Those vessels with relatively large amounts of ring type smooth muscle have their lumens reduced upon muscle contraction, reducing the blood flow while increasing the blood pressure. Other vessels, such as arteries, have their elastic or viscoelastic properties altered upon contraction of tension muscles. In these vessels the contained blood volume may be altered as well as blood pressure.

Young's modulus, E, is a measure of the relation between applied stresses and resultant stretch

$$E = \frac{\frac{F}{A}}{\Delta\left(\frac{1}{L}\right)} \qquad (12.8)$$

where F is the applied force per unit area, A, and $\Delta(1/L)$ is the change in the reciprocal of the length. Young's modulus is equivalent to the dynes/cm² needed to extend the material by 100 per cent. Applied to a cylindrical tube, the force of Equation 12.8 is the circumferential tension over unit length of the tube.

The relation between pressure and wall tension, T, in an elastic cylinder is given by

$$T = P_t r \qquad (12.9)$$

where P_t is the transmural pressure and r is the radius of the tube. It is the pressure or force acting radially on each unit area of the vessel wall that is the transmural pressure, and this pressure depends on the elasticity of the blood vessel wall. The viscoelastic properties of the vessel wall are demonstrated by the fact that

the transmural pressure required to maintain a constant radius of a blood vessel decreases with time after the application of a transverse stretch.

12-13. Arteries. The aorta and arteries serve two major functions. They are the major conduits serving to direct blood to various parts of the organism from the heart. They are therefore relatively large blood vessels that offer little resistance to blood flow.

They also serve as buffers against changes in blood supply and pressure. During **systole**, the contraction of the ventricles (the atria are thin-walled chambers of the heart, and the contraction of their relatively smaller amount of cardiac muscle does not greatly effect blood pressure), a volume of blood is suddenly ejected into the aorta and major arteries (at this time the atria are shut off from the ventricles

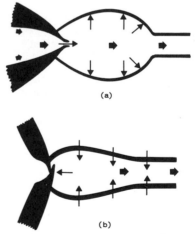

(a)

(b)

Figure 12-13 Schematic diagram of the maintenance of circulatory flow and pressure by the elastic walls of the aorta. (a) During ventricular systole blood flows into the aorta (heavy arrows); pressure differential (light arrows) cause valves between ventricle and aorta to open. The pressure causes aortic walls to distend. (b) At diastole, the pressure differential between ventricle and aorta is such that valves are closed. The elastic walls of the aorta have stored energy during systole and then release it during diastole driving blood into the peripheral circulation. Thus, even during ventricular relaxation blood continues to flow through the peripheral circulation. (See also Chapter 13.)

by valves that close during ventricular contraction). This sudden influx of blood would greatly increase the blood pressure and blood volume moving through the arterial system were it not for the distensibility of the aorta and arteries. The major arteries possess a thick layer of elastic tissue that allows them to expand when blood is ejected into them (Figure 12-13).

The aorta and arteries serve as a central arterial reservoir during systole. At this time they hold the blood ejected by the heart so that it is not all forced to enter the smaller arteries.

During **diastole** (the relaxation of the ventricles) the ejection of blood into the aorta slows and then stops while the ventricles refill. At this time the elastic recoil of the expanded arterial wall adds to the pressure gradient in the circulatory system, and therefore, the blood pressure is maintained relatively constant even while the heart is momentarily relaxing. The elastic recoil of the arterial wall ensures a continuous flow of blood. This ability of the major arteries to reduce the pressure fluctuations which would otherwise result from the nature of the contractile activity of cardiac muscle and to maintain a continuous blood flow is the Windkessel effect. The pressures in the circulatory system during systole and diastole are shown in Figure 13-21 on page 538.

A vessel with only an elastic layer could blow out at the higher pressures found during systole. The major arteries have a heavy coat of collagenous connective tissue that is relatively inextensible. This layer of stronger collagen fibers bears the stresses at times of high pressure and relieves stresses on the weaker elastic layer. Figure 12-14 diagrams the nature of the arterial wall and gives the names of the various layers. The thickness of each layer will vary depending on the particular artery.

The aorta, pulmonary artery, common carotid artery, and a few other larger arteries are elastic arteries with only a small amount of smooth muscle. That smooth muscle present is primarily tension muscle. Almost imperceptibly these arteries change into muscular arteries that contain increasing amount of smooth muscle, primarily of the ring type. The arrangement of muscle, elastic tissue, and collagen fibers is complex. Stretch imposed on the arterial wall produces different structural arrangements of the various fibers thus altering the elastic and viscoelastic properties of these walls to fit changing needs.

Although contraction of arterial smooth muscle could act as a mechanism for controlling pressure in the vessel by dilation or constriction, the small amount of smooth muscle present in larger arteries indicates that this is not a major function of these vessels. Because of the small resistance to flow in large arteries, there is only a slight pressure drop in these vessels.

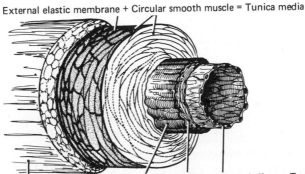

External elastic membrane + Circular smooth muscle = Tunica media

Tunica externa   Internal elastic membrane + Areolar + Endothelium = Tunica interna
connective tissue

Figure 12-14 Structure of the arterial wall [From Grollman. (1964) *The Human Body*. By permission of the Macmillan Company, New York.]

Table 12-4 Blood Volumes of Some Mammals*

SPECIES	BLOOD VOLUME (ml)	BLOOD VOLUME ml/kg (BODY WEIGHT)
Rat	12.3	54.3
Guinea pig	31.0	72.0
Rabbit	124	56.4
Sheep	2,480	58.0
Dog	2,840	92.5
Human		
male	5,420	77.7
female	3,960	66.1
Cow	24,100	57.4
Horse		
racing	42,750	109.6
working	48,400	71.7

* Data from Sjöstrand (1962).

12-14. Veins. Veins are variable in their wall structure. As indicated in Figure 12-11, veins contain less elastic tissue in their walls than arteries, and generally the venous wall is thinner than the wall of a corresponding artery. Because of their thinner walls, veins are more distensible than arteries. Normally the large veins are almost closed, and as pressure increases in them, they become more circular in cross-section. Upon becoming circular, the distensibility of the veins is reduced because the venous wall contains a high proportion of unstretchable collagen fibers.

The venous system acts as a distensible reservoir for blood. Table 12-4 gives the blood volumes of some mammals. Table 12-5 shows the estimated distribution of blood in various regions of the dog's circulatory system. Table 12-6 presents data on the geometry of a particular vascular bed of the dog. Data of this type are available on very few animals, but it is assumed that distributions of blood volumes and vessel capacities shown in the tables are similar to those of mammalian circulatory systems generally.

Veins have varying amounts of longitudinal

and circular muscle, although tension muscles attached to elastic fibers are usually lacking. Circular muscles are found mainly in the veins of the extremities. The proportion of circular to longitudinal smooth muscle parallels the amount of pressure normally encountered in a given vein. Wall tension in the transverse direction in a cylindrical tube is double that in the longitudinal direction. Thus, those veins subject to high hydrostatic pressures because of gravity will possess a higher proportion of circular muscle which supports the pressure. Table 12-7 compares the pressures, tensions, and dimensions typical of different vessels of the mammalian circulatory system.

The valves of veins are folds of the intima. (The tunica intima consists of the inner endothelial layer and the lamina propria, which is the connective tissue. The tunica media is the next structural layer of blood vessels and consists of smooth muscle cells intermingled with elastic fibers. The tunica adventitia is the outermost layer and consists of a mixture of collagenous and elastic fibers.) The valves consist of collagen and elastin fibers, and usually there is a thickened band of collagen around the vein at the site of origin of the valve. In most cases two valves face each

Table 12-5 Estimated Distribution of Blood in a 12 kg Dog

REGION AND VESSEL DIAMETER (mm)	VOLUME (ml)
Heart	140
Systemic arteries (> 0.3)	109
Pulmonary artery (> 0.3)	40
Systemic veins (> 0.3)	345
Pulmonary vein (> 0.3)	114
Systemic arteries (0.1–0.3)	10
Pulmonary arteries (0.1–0.3)	28
Systemic veins (0.1–0.3)	64
Systemic vessels (< 0.1)	112
Pulmonary vessels (< 0.1)	11
Total	973

* Data from Lawson (1962).

Table 12-6 Geometry of the Mesenteric Vascular Bed of the Dog*

VESSEL	DIAMETER (mm)	NUMBER	TOTAL CROSS-SECTIONAL AREA (cm)	LENGTH (cm)	TOTAL VOLUME (cm^3)
Aorta	10	1	0.8	40	30
Large arteries	3	40	3.0	20	60
Main arterial branches	1	600	5.0	10	50
Terminal arterial branches	0.6	1,800	5.0	1	25
Arterioles	0.02	40,000,000	125	0.2	25
Capillaries	0.008	1,200,000,000	600	0.1	60
Venules	0.03	80,000,000	570	0.2	110
Terminal veins	1.5	1,800	30	1	30
Main venous branches	2.4	600	27	10	270
Large veins	6.0	40	11	20	220
Vena cava	12.5	1	1.2	40	50
Total					930

* From A. C. Burton (1965). *Physiology and Biophysics of the Circulation.* Year Book Medical Publishers, Chicago, Ill. Reprinted by permission.

other (Figure 12-7). Not all veins have valves, for example, the vena cava and smaller veins lack these structures.

Veins are under venomotor tone due to the action of sympathetic nerves supplying the smooth muscles of these vessels. Veins dilate when the sympathetic supply is cut—one indication that there is a tonic discharge to them (Folklow, 1955; Landis and Hortenstine, 1950).

Table 12-7 Pressure, Tension, and Sizes of Vessels in the Circulatory System (Human)*

TYPE OF VESSEL	MEAN PRESSURE (mm Hg)	INTERNAL PRESSURE (dynes/cm^2)	RADIUS	TENSION IN WALL (dynes/cm^2)	AMOUNT OF ELASTIC TISSUE
Aorta and large arteries	100	1.3×10^5	≤ 1.4 cm	1.7×10^5	Thick, two coats
Small arteries	90	1.2×10^5	0.5 cm	6.0×10^4	Very elastic and also muscular
Arterioles	60	8.0×10^4	0.15 mm TO 62 μ	0.5–1.2×10^3	Thin elastic intima
Capillaries	30	4.0×10^4	4 μ	1.6×10^1	None
Venules	20	2.6×10^4	10 μ	2.6×10^1	Mostly none
Veins	15	2.0×10^4	200 μ	4.0×10^2	Slight
Vena cava	10	1.3×10^4	1.6 cm	2.1×10^4	Very elastic

* From A. C. Burton (1965). *Physiology and Biophysics of the Circulation.* Year Book Medical Publishers, Chicago, Ill. Reprinted by permission.

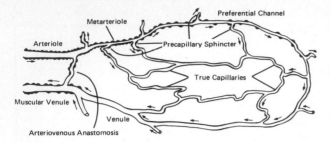

Figure 12-15 The microcirculation. [Adapted from various sources.]

12-15. The Microcirculation. Between the arteries and veins of the closed circulatory system lie the smaller vessels of the circulatory system—the peripheral circulatory or capillary beds—consisting of arterioles, capillaries, and venules. These vessels are the sites of local controls over the circulation and also the sites of material exchange between the blood and body fluids and cells. There are a variety of pathways from the arterial (high pressure) side of the circulation to the venous (low pressure) side of the circulation. These pathways are generally in parallel so that the flow through any one of them is only slightly affected by flow through the others. Figure 12-15 illustrates some of these pathways.

The **terminal arteriole** possesses a single layer of smooth muscle surrounding its endothelial lining. It is the final arterial ramification where capillaries begin to branch off. Terminal arterioles are 30 to 50 μ in diameter, and they blend imperceptibly into the capillaries (Zweifach and Metz, 1955).

Arterioles generally possess a higher proportion of smooth muscle than the arteries and are the small vessels of the peripheral circulation responsible for the distribution of blood through tissues and the local control of pressure.

Metarterioles is the term used to designate final segments of terminal arterioles from which capillaries are distributed (Chambers and Zweifach, 1944). They are generally of the same diameter as the capillaries and possess thin smooth muscle cells spaced at irregular intervals over the endothelial lining.

The **precapillary sphincter** is a muscular investment found at the branch point where a capillary leaves the arteriole (Figure 12-16). The smooth muscle cells often twine several times around the branch point, so that small contractions can narrow considerably the entrance to the capillary. This structure undergoes continual changes in vasomotor tone that alter the blood flow through the capillary independently of changes in the supply arteriole.

True capillaries are endothelial tubes with no smooth muscle and a minimal amount of connective tissue. The structure and functions of these vessels will be examined in some detail in the next section.

The capillary bed of a tissue is composed of numerous small vessels so that the breadth of the circulatory stream is greatly increased and there is also a great increase in the surface area available for material exchanges between the

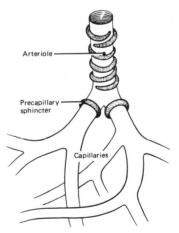

Figure 12-16 Capillaries formed by the branching of arterioles. The arteriole is shown with a smooth muscular spiral coating. The single smooth muscle cell at the junction forms a precapillary sphincter controlling blood flow through the capillary. [From S. Grollman (1964) *The Human Body*. By permission of the Macmillan Company, New York.]

blood and interstitial fluids (see Table 12-6). Although the number of capillaries is immense, the total volume of blood contained within them is only a small fraction of the total blood volume. This is because each capillary is extremely small in diameter and also not all capillaries are fully open at the same time.

Venules are often defined as the first post-capillary vessels where smooth muscle cells are found. The venules fuse into the larger valved veins. **Postcapillary vessels** are formed by the joining of capillaries and are 15 to 20 μ in diameter. Venules range from 30 to 50 μ in diameter. The microcirculation generally possesses little connective tissue, and the vessels are intimately embedded in the extracellular matrix so that there is a direct exposure of the vessels to the intercellular environment. Thus local influences can readily direct vasomotor responses.

The microcirculation has been studied in a variety of vertebrate systems including in particular thin mesenteries in many animals and other thin structures where the circulatory vessels are relatively easily illuminated and observed *in situ*. Structures such as the bat wing, hamster cheek pouch, rabbit ear, and the vertebrate eye have been studied. Capillary beds have also been studied in some skeletal muscles, intestinal walls, and lungs. The results of these various studies indicate that the arrangement of the microcirculatory vessels depends on the particular activities and requirements of a tissue although certain features are common to most. A major characteristic of many microcirculatory systems is that the concept of arterioles leading to capillaries leading to venules is not correct.

Zweifach (1937) first described what he called arteriovenous (a-v) bridges and which have since been named **preferential channels** or **thoroughfares**. These are direct connections between the arteriolar and venular sides of the circulation. The nature of these connections is illustrated in Figure 12-15. There is a preferential channel from the arteriole, and this channel loops back to the venule, which usually runs parallel to the arteriole. From the proximal portion of the terminal arteriole, the region of the metarteriole, true capillaries branch off at right angles. The capillaries form a network within the loop of the preferential channel.

The capillaries are not in the direct path between arteriole and venule. The main path is the preferential channel. The flow through the preferential channel can be regulated by the contraction or relaxation of the arteriolar smooth muscle cells. The flow through the capillary network in turn can be adjusted by the activity of the precapillary sphincters. Thus not only can the total blood flow through the entire loop be controlled (arterioles), but also the blood flow through individual capillaries or groups of capillaries (sphincters). Note that in this type of system the true capillaries connect back into the preferential channel, not into the venule. A preferential channel usually maintains a relatively constant diameter, very slight changes in radius serving to control blood flow. Generally speaking there is a constant pressure gradient between the arteriolar and venous ends of the channel.

Although the true capillaries are usually considered as the sites of exchanges between the blood and interstitial fluid, evidence is accumulating that an outward filtration of materials occurs in the preferential channel, whereas inward movement takes place at the capillary.

The paired arteriole-venule system described above is not always found. In some microcirculatory systems, for example, in many mesenteries, an arteriole emerges from its parent artery, descends into the mesentery, and then forms a loop joined by other vessels of the bed. Finally the arteriole empties into the vein accompanying the parent artery. In most beds, however, arterioles and venules are adjacent to one another until the final fusion of the capillary network.

The preferential channel is not a feature of all microcirculatory systems. They are not found in the urinary bladder or skin of the rat. There are indications that skeletal muscles, some mesenteries, and the serosal surface of the small intestine also lack this type of channel (see the review by Wiedeman, 1963).

The rabbit ear, bat wing, frog web, and frog

urinary bladder also lack preferential channels, and in these tissues blood takes alternate routes through the capillary network. Blood flow is characterized by constant changes in pathway through the capillaries. Local conditions perhaps influenced by the secretion or excretion of hormones, metabolites, and waste products control the precapillary sphincters and thus determine through which capillaries blood will flow from minute to minute.

Arteriovenous anastomoses (see Figure 12-15) are found in some tissues. These are direct connections between arteries and veins—channels through which the blood is carried without exchanges between the blood and interstitial fluid. Arteriovenous anastomoses (AVA) were first found in the rabbit ear (Grant, 1930) and later in human skin and the feet of birds (Grant and Bland, 1931). These workers considered them important in body temperature regulation. When a rabbit is cooled, for example, there is a constriction of the AVA in the ear, and heat is conserved by the animal. When the rabbit is warmed, the AVA dilate thus allowing a large volume flow through the ear and allowing heat to be lost to the surroundings. AVA are especially prominent in the skin where, again, their major function is thought to be in temperature regulation. Although most AVA arise from major arteries, many originate from small arterial branches. All seem to empty into larger veins. AVA are often coiled structures. On the arterial side they have very thick walls, and on the nonmuscular venous side, the wall is thinner and often funnel shaped. Typically AVA have diameters ranging from 10 to 70 μ.

AVA exhibit more contractile activity than arteries and have an independent action. They contract and dilate spontaneously and rhythmically, but with a rhythm independent of neighboring AVA or the artery from which they arise. AVA are capable of complete closure, unlike the typical arteriole. Shunts such as the AVA may be used when the constriction of small arteriolar vessels beyond the AVA increases resistance to flow. Under these conditions blood is diverted through the AVA, which is the pathway of least resistance.

From what has been said in this section, it is obvious that blood flow through a capillary bed is capable of continuous alteration depending on the needs of the tissue. Shifts in blood flow result from the activity of smooth muscle cells of arterioles, metarterioles, precapillary sphincters, and AVA. **Autoregulation** is the intrinsic ability of an organ or tissue to regulate its own blood supply without nervous system intervention—the ability to maintain a constant blood flow despite changes in arterial or venous pressure or changes in vascular resistance (Johnson, 1964). Not all tissues have this ability. For example, autoregulation is not found in the skin (Green and Rapela, 1964) and in the skin nervous control of the microcirculation predominates. The skin is well supplied with sensor receptors for heat, cold, pain, and so forth, and stimuli received by these sensors bear the primary responsibility for causing changes in blood flow. As previously indicated in Section 12-12, the brain relies primarily on local chemical stimulation to control microcirculatory blood flow. And various degrees of chemical and nervous control are found in other circulatory regions.

In some tissues the microcirculation takes on special structural arrangements to serve special functions. As we shall see in Chapter 14, such is the case with the glomerular circulation in the kidney as well as vasa recta renal circulation.

Another unusual circulatory arrangement is found in the hepatic system of vertebrates. In even the lowest vertebrates, the liver lies in the path of all circulatory vessels draining the splanchnic viscera—intestinal tract, spleen, and so forth (see Figure 12-17). The liver is a major organ affecting all cellular metabolism and homeostatic mechanisms, and it can function efficiently only while it can modify the blood passing through it. A copious blood flow is required for this purpose. About 20 per cent of the blood reaching the right ventricle of the mammalian heart comes from the liver.

The hepatic artery supplies oxygenated blood to the liver and has anastomotic connections with the hepatic portal vein bringing in blood from all the splanchnic viscera. The capillaries branching off from the interlobular arteries (which arise from the hepatic artery) enter the

Figure 12-17 Circulation of the vertebrate liver and splanchnic viscera. The liver receives both hepatic arterial inflow and hepatic portal vein inflow. The entire venous outflow of the abdominal gastrointestinal organs passes through the liver before reaching the hepatic veins. Sympathetic vasoconstrictor nerves innervate arterioles, sinusoids and intrahepatic veins, but the precise role of these nerves is unknown. Each segment of the system has its own resistance to flow (indicated by ——). All resistances are variable and effect the other resistances. For example, changes in intestinal blood flow resistance are reflected by secondary changes in hepatic portal flow. R_1 resistance of intestinal blood flow; R_2 resistance of splenic blood flow; R_3 resistance of portal vein; R_4 resistance of hepatic arteriole; R_5 resistance of postsinusoidal flow.

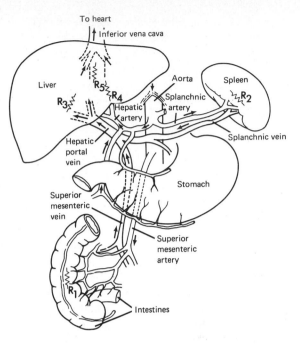

liver sinusoids. The terminal capillaries of the portal vein also drain into the sinusoids. From the sinusoids blood is collected in central veins of the liver lobules, which in turn combine as sublobular veins leading to the hepatic veins. This is an example of an open circulation in the vertebrate vascular system. Autoregulation is present in this system as well as what is termed reciprocity of flow (Hanson and Johnson, 1966). Generally there is a decrease in hepatic arterial or portal venous resistance to blood flow whenever there is a decline in flow through the reciprocal vessel. A decrease in hepatic artery blood pressure is accompanied by a fall in vascular resistance. All the resistance components of the splanchnic and hepatic circulation are variable, and changes in intestinal resistance, for example, produce corresponding changes in the hepatic portal flow.

Since the splanchnic circulation contains about 20 per cent of the total blood volume of the organism, the system acts as a reservoir from which blood may be obtained in emergencies. Sympathetic vasoconstriction of splanchnic arterioles contributes to the adjustment to flow resistance during these times. Auto-regulation is thought to arise from the hemodynamic properties of the vascular walls in the hepatic system, not to metabolite or

hormonal actions. Bradley (1963) reviews the hepatic and splanchnic circulation.

12-16. Capillary Structure. Capillaries possess no smooth muscle and are incapable of contraction. In the past, several hypotheses arose to allow for constriction and dilation of capillaries, but all have been disproven. Pericytes, the cells that intimately surround the capillaries, were thought capable of contraction and therefore able to change capillary diameters, but in mammals, at least, this is not the case. Endothelial cells themselves were once thought to swell, thus constricting the capillary lumen, but this also has been disproven (Illig, 1961). Changes in blood flow through capillaries must be considered to result from vasomotor action in arterioles, terminal arterioles, and precapillary sphincters.

According to Majno (1965) capillaries are vessels with diameters close to those of red blood cells, although the term is often used to refer to postcapillary vessels with diameters of up to 50 μ or more. However, the smallest veins seem to have quite different properties from the true capillaries, especially with regard to water permeability of their membranes.

Although capillaries are described as having a single layer of endothelial cells and as lacking smooth muscle, the electron microscope has shown that in fact there are a great variety of capillary types. Table 12-8 gives one classification scheme based on electron microscopic observations of the endothelial layer as well as on the type of basement membrane. A simplified scheme, together with some of the types of tissues possessing them, is given in the bottom part of the table.

Figure 12-18 shows diagrammatically the differences between continuous, fenestrated, and discontinuous capillaries. The latter are usually called sinusoids. Figure 12-19 illustrates the general characteristics of endothelial cells, the capillary basement membrane, and a pericyte. The endothelial layer may be composed of low endothelium such that the wall thickness of the capillary is 1 to 3 μ, or of high endothelium such that the capillary wall is from 2 to 4 μ thick. These are average ranges only; both thick and thin extremes are known.

The endothelial cells of many capillaries, as well as other blood vessels, are often about one-third filled with 600 to 700 Å in diameter vesicles. Some vesicles are in contact with the plasma membrane, and it has been suggested that these are pinocytotic vesicles responsible for transporting materials from the lumen of the capillary across the cell cytoplasm and out into the interstitial space. Measurements with radioactive-labeled compounds indicate that this is a very slow transport system, and its importance in capillary exchanges is not as yet clear.

Dense lines were observed with the light microscope at the intercellular junctions and were thought to represent an intercellular cement substance. And a major role in capillary transport was given to this material. But the electron microscope has shown that these areas are, in fact, regions of tight junctions between endothelial cells, and the role of a cement substance has been reduced accordingly. The spaces between endothelian cells making up the capillary wall may be simple channels or tortuous pathways depending on the particular capillary.

The basement membrane is a prominent structure external to the endothelial layer of

Table 12-8   Classification of Capillaries*

A. According to Bennet et al, 1959	
Type	**Description**
A	With a complete continuous basement membrane.
B	Without a complete continuous basement membrane.
1	Without fenestrations or pores.
2	With intracellular fenestrations or perforations.
3	With intercellular fenestrations or perforations.
α	Without a complete pericapillary cellular investment interposed between parenchymal cells and capillary.
β	With a complete pericapillary cellular investment interposed between parenchymal cells and capillary.

B. Simplified According to Majno, 1965	
Type	**Description**
I	Continuous capillaries with a continuous endothelial sheet (found in striated muscle, lung, myocardium, central nervous system, smooth muscle of digestive and reproductive systems, adipose tissues).
II	Fenestrated capillaries with intracellular openings (found in endocrine glands, renal glomerulus, ciliary body of eye, exocrine pancreas, salivary glands, swim bladder of fish, intestinal villi, rete mirabile of renal medulla, fish eye).
III	Discontinuous capillaries, with intercellular gaps—typical sinusoids (found in liver, spleen, and bone marrow).

* After Majno (1965). See also Figure 12-18.

the capillary. Recently it has been shown that this material is composed principally of collagen, not mucopolysaccharides as formerly believed. Collagenase treatment of the

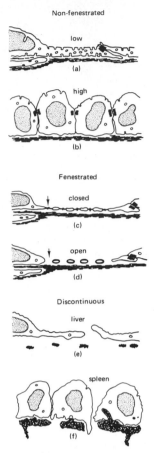

Figure 12-18 Classification of capillary vessels according to the continuity of the main filtration barrier (the endothelial sheet). (a) Continuous with no recognizable openings between cells. Low variety is found in striated muscle, cardiac muscle, central nervous system, smooth muscle of digestive and reproductive systems, and subcutaneous and adipose tissues. (b) Continuous, but high variety typical of postcapillary venules of lymph nodes and thymus gland. A similar endothelium is found in the large arteries when contracted. (c) Fenestrated with intracellular openings (arrow). Closed type found in endocrine glands, choroid plexus, and intestinal villi. (d) Fenestrated but open type found in renal glomerulus. (e) Discontinuous (sinusoidal) type with intercellular gaps. These are typical of liver and bone marrow. (f) Discontinuous type with different structural details. Typical of spleen sinusoids. [Redrawn from G. Majno (1965) "Ultrastructure of the vascular membrane" in *Handbook of Physiology*, Sec. 2, Vol. III. By permission of the American Physiological Society, Washington, D.C.]

basement membrane in the kidney glomerulus completely destroys this structure, although pepsin, trypsin, and other common proteolytic enzymes have no effect (Speidel and Lazarow, 1963). Similar findings were found for the lens capsule (Dische, 1964). The collagen is not laid down in typical fibers with a repeat period of 640 Å but has the form of amorphous lamellae and nonstriated fibrils. These observations may require reconsideration of the nature and functions of basement membrane. The generality of these findings is unknown.

Pericytes (also called Rouget cells) are found in intimate contact with small blood vessels. They are completely enveloped by the capillary vascular basement membrane that splits to surround them. There appears to be a wide variety of pericyte types, and little is known about their function except that many show phagocytic activity.

In continuous capillaries the tight junction region is probably a zone of filtration across which materials, excepting larger macromolecules, can rapidly pass. Fenestrated capillaries possess a continuous basement membrane, but the cells of the endothelium are often very thin (300 Å) and are pierced with fenestrae 0.1 μ or less in diameter. These openings are sometimes closed by a diaphragm of unknown material. The walls of fenestrated capillaries contain few vesicles and lack measurable ATPase activity. These are indications that pinocytosis and active transport processes are minimal. Fenestrated capillaries are typical of secreting tissues and of those tissues in which there is a rapid production or absorption of fluids. Luft (1963) believes that the diaphragms are the outer leaflets of the cell's unit membrane. He relates this same structure to the tight junction —the fenestrated wall permitting a more rapid exchange of materials.

In many fenestrated capillaries there are cells lying on the outside that extend pseudopods through the endothelial wall into the capillary lumen. These are colliculi or *Intrakapillarhoeckerchen* (Zimmermann, 1933). They are especially prominent in the renal glomerulus and their pseudopodal formation may be associated with phagocytic action. The

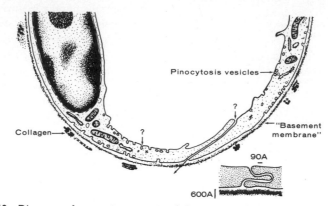

Figure 12-19 Diagram of current concepts of fine structure in a muscle capillary. The nucleus of a single endothelial cell is shown at left. The capillary may be formed by a single cell rolled into a tube or may be composed of several endothelial cells. The nature of the connection between the inside and outside at the junction of endothelial cells may be in the form of a straight slit or a slightly tortuous slit (see insert). [From D. W. Fawcett (1959) "The fine structure of capillaries, arterioles and small arteries" in *The Microcirculation. Symposium on Factors Influencing of Substances Across Capillary Wall.* By permission University of Illinois Press, Urbana, Illinois. pp. 1–27.]

size and number of fenestrae vary markedly in different capillaries; whether this variety reflects differences in permeability or function is not known.

The discontinuous capillaries or sinusoids lack, or possess only a broken, basement membrane. Intercellular gaps in the endothelium are prominent. They are found in those tissues in which whole cells and particulate matter must be added to or removed from the blood. Typically these activities are found in liver, spleen, and bone marrow.

Most of our knowledge of capillary structure and function has resulted from the study of vertebrate circulatory systems, but the capillaries of invertebrates are probably similar to those of the vertebrates.

12-17. Capillary Functioning. Classically the endothelial wall of capillaries has been considered the site of material exchanges between the blood and interstitial fluid, and although certain doubts have arisen over this concept, we shall begin our discussion by assuming this classical idea is correct.

Examination of the plasma and interstitial fluids of vertebrates reveals that their composition is essentially identical except for their pro-

tein contents. In humans, for example, plasma protein concentration is about 6.8 per cent, whereas interstitial fluid contains about 2.6 per cent protein. Ions, amino acids, sugars, and other solutes are present in equal concentrations in both fluids. The interstitial fluid is, therefore, essentially an ultrafiltrate of the blood. Any mechanism that is proposed to explain material exchanges in the microcirculation must account for the fact that about as much material as leaves the blood must be returned to it; otherwise, blood volumes would be rapidly depleted. Both absorption and filtration must occur in the system.

Starling in 1915 proposed that two driving forces acted on fluids and solutes in capillaries. One is the blood pressure, which tends to move water and solutes out of the capillaries. The other is the colloidal osmotic pressure (oncotic pressure) due to the presence of impermeable proteins in the plasma. This oncotic pressure tends to pull water and solutes into the capillary. The actual net movement of material depends on the differences between these two pressures. The capillary wall is assumed to be freely permeable to water and all solutes except macromolecules of molecular weight greater than about 65,000.

In general terms the driving force on water and solutes, the **filtration pressure**, is the algebraic sum of several terms

$$P_f = k(P_i - \pi_i - P_o + \pi_o) \quad (12.10)$$

P_i is the blood pressure (= hydrostatic pressure) in the capillary; P_o is the hydrostatic pressure of the interstitial fluid immediately outside the capillary; π_o is the oncotic pressure caused by proteins in the interstitial fluids; π_i is the oncotic pressure in the capillary caused by the presence of impermeable proteins, and k is a proportionality constant—the filtration coefficient—a measure of the permeability of the capillary wall to isotonic fluids. The filtration pressure is positive when materials move out of the capillaries (the process of filtration) and negative when materials move into the capillaries (the process of absorption).

Starling's hypothesis was that at the proximal, that is, the arterial end, of the capillary the blood pressure is greater than the colloid osmotic pressure and thus a net outward movement of water and solutes occurs (Figure 12-20). At the distal (or venous end) of the capillary, blood pressure has decreased as blood flowed along the capillary, and there has also been an increase in the osmotic pressure because the removal of water at the proximal end of the capillary has increased the concentration of impermeable proteins. Overall, at

the distal end of the capillary there is a net force tending to move water and solutes back into the capillary—the filtration pressure is negative.

Since the filtration pressure at the two ends of a capillary are not exactly matched, there is generally a small amount of fluid that does not get back into the blood vascular system at the level of the capillaries. This excess fluid with its solutes is picked up by the lymphatic system in vertebrates and is finally returned to the blood circulation. In this way blood volume as well as the interstitial fluid volume are maintained at constant levels under normal conditions.

Proof of this hypothesis depends on the ability to measure intracapillary blood pressure and osmotic pressure. One method of measuring capillary blood pressure directly is illustrated in Figures 12-21 and 12-22. A micropipet filled with saline solution containing heparin to prevent clotting is placed in a micromanipulator and connected to a manometer and syringe so that the pressures exerted on the tip of the pipet can be changed rapidly and accurately to balance the changing capillary pressure. As might be expected, the measurement of pressures in these minute vessels is technically difficult and many precautions must be taken to guard against artifacts.

Table 12-9 lists the pressure gradients and osmotic pressures of some tissues of several vertebrate species. From these results it would

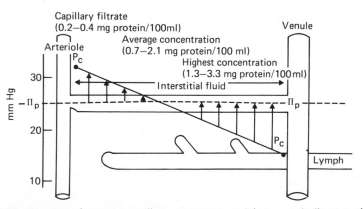

Figure 12-20 Diagram of average capillary pressures, protein concentrations, and osmotic pressures to illustrate the nature of filtration pressures at different regions of the capillary and the exchange of materials between capillaries and the interstitial fluids. [From E. M. Landis and J. R. Pappenheimer (1963) "Exchange of substances through capillary walls" in Handbook of Physiology, Section 2, Vol. 2 (W. F. Hamilton, ed), pp. 961-1034.]

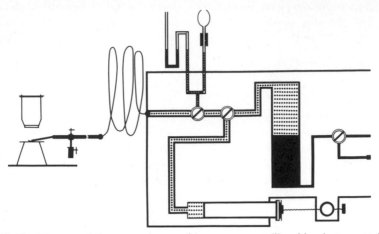

Figure 12-21 Diagram of the apparatus used to measure capillary blood pressure directly. The data of Figure 12–10(a) were obtained by this method. [After E. M. Landis (1962) "The capillary pressure in frog mesentery as determined by microinjection." *American Journal of Physiology* **75**: 548–570.]

seem that the Starling hypothesis does account for the outward and inward movements of water and solutes across the endothelial wall. This is, of course, based on the assumption that the capillary wall is freely permeable to water and all solutes except for some plasma

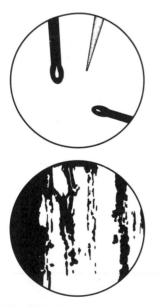

Figure 12-22 The micropipette is shown before introduction and after introduction into a capillary. [After E. M. Landis (1962) "The capillary pressure in frog mesentery as determined by microinjection." *American Journal of Physiology* **75**: 548–570.]

proteins. Presumably the passage of solutes accompanies the water movement in a bulk flow. Generally it is assumed that these materials move across the regions where tight junctions or fenestrae occur.

Although little work had been done on measurements of pressures in invertebrate systems, the indications are that the blood pressure is higher than the osmotic pressure even in those animals with open circulatory systems (see Table 12-9). This is always a prerequisite for ultrafiltration. From the data of Table 12-9, it may be noted that those animals with high protein concentrations (=high oncotic pressures) of the blood also have higher blood pressures. Thus, at least in vertebrates, the balance between capillary outflow and inflow can be maintained. The data given for the invertebrates is not greatly meaningful because these are average blood pressures and not necessarily those of the region where material exchanges occur. In addition, in those animals with open circulatory systems, the blood pressures at the site of exchange may be very low (invertebrate blood pressures are generally low in any case), and the hydrostatic pressure of the interstitial fluid becomes an important factor governing the direction of water and solute movement.

In vertebrates the relation between capillary

Table 12-9 Blood Pressures (P_i) and Oncotic Pressures (π_i) in Some Animals*

ANIMAL	P_i(mm Hg)†	π_i(mm Hg)†
MOLLUSCS		
Aplysia	1.8	0.02
Anodonta	4.4	2.06
Lymnea		
stagnalis	5.9	1.8
Octopus	38	3.2
CRUSTACEAN		
Homarus	8.5	1.2
VERTEBRATES		
Frog		
mesentery		
(capillaries)	10.6– 7.4	5–10
muscle		
(capillaries)	11.0– 7.0	5–10
skin		
(capillaries)	10.7– 7.4	5–10
Rat		
mesentery		
(capillaries)	31.3–12.5	16–21
Man		
skin		
(capillaries)	32.0–24.0	21–29

* Data selected from Landis and Pappenheimer (1963); Prosser and Brown (1961); Potts and Parry (1964).
† First number given is pressure at arterial end of capillary; second number is pressure at venous end of capillary.

blood pressure and the oncotic pressure of plasma proteins is quite labile. Vasomotor activity, as well as changes in hydrostatic pressure caused by gravity, can greatly alter the blood pressure of a given capillary bed. Overall, an equilibrium usually exists between blood and interstitial fluid volumes. During muscular activity, injury, high temperatures, and so forth, there is a general increased blood pressure with a consequent increase in filtration rate. Under these conditions a greater amount of fluid must be returned to the blood circulation through the lymphatic system.

Part of the Starling hypothesis states that

there is a free rapid mixing of materials in the interstitial fluid. The nutrients, oxygen, and such move out from the capillaries and mix rapidly with the interstitial fluid from which they move by diffusion into the cells. Similarly, cellular waste products, secretions, and the like move down their concentration gradient from the cell into the external environment and are carried with the interstitial fluid into the capillaries.

The use of newer instrumentation and techniques has brought into question some of the assumptions of the Starling hypothesis, although the basic features of filtration due to excess hydrostatic pressure in the capillaries and absorption due to excess osmotic pressure at the venous end of the capillaries are still considered valid. Wiederhielm (1966) using a combination of microscope and television camera could measure differences in light intensities in various parts of a capillary bed when a water-soluble dye was injected into arterioles or terminal arterioles. The camera of the TV system translates differences in light intensity in the microscopic field into corresponding changes in the video signal. In some cases a laser beam of coherent light was used which provided high light intensities at about the maximum absorption wavelength of the dyes used, thus increasing resolution. To eliminate diffraction effects caused by dust and other impurities in the laser beam path, a rotating ground glass disc was used between the laser and the microscope condenser. The diffusion of dye into the extravascular spaces, as well as the movement of dye through the capillary network, could be measured accurately.

With this technique differences in permeability were found in different regions of the capillary bed of the frog mesentery. For example, venules had the greatest permeability to water and also had a greater total cross-sectional area than the associated capillaries. From this it was inferred that the venules are the sites of highest water absorption in the microcirculation. Generally it had been assumed previously that the filtration coefficient was similar for all vessels of a given bed, but this is not the case in frog mesentery.

The diffusion of water and solutes through the extracellular medium was found to be very slow. This finding is difficult to reconcile with the concept of the interstitial space as a free fluid compartment. Since water movement is slow, the bulk movement of water and solutes postulated in the Starling hypothesis cannot be a dominant factor in the frog mesentery. According to the Starling concept the extra-capillary flow has to take place between the arteriolar and venous ends of the extracapillary environment.

Intaglietta and Zweifach (1966) using the measurement of red blood cell movements in occluded capillaries came to essentially the same conclusions regarding the sites of highest permeability in the microcirculation. They also found that outward filtration occurs in the vascular bed during vasodilation, whereas reabsorption takes place during vasoconstriction.

These results do not invalidate the Starling hypothesis that inward and outward capillary flow is governed by blood pressure and oncotic pressure differences. But they do bring into question the actual sites involved in water and solute movement and necessitates, perhaps, a separation of the two.

That interstitial hydrostatic and osmotic pressures play a role in overall water movements, as indicated in Equation 12.10, is true. But in most vertebrate tissues these forces are much smaller than their capillary equivalents. However, in muscle, for example, they may become predominant when the muscle contracts because during muscular contraction the hydrostatic pressure of the extracellular fluid can greatly increase.

There is a seemingly endless variety to be found in the structure and functions of the microcirculation, and this variety adds to the difficulty of studying these minute vessels and extravessel spaces. Sobin and Tremer (1966) point out that even in closely related animals, living in similar habitats, unexpected differences are found in the microcirculation of given organs.

12-18. The Lymphatic System.   The lymphatic system is a drainage pathway that became needed as high pressure circulatory systems evolved. In the previous section it was indicated that of the volume of material leaving the capillary, not all returns to the capillary from the interstitial fluid. As high pressure circulatory systems evolved, a partial answer to the restoration of fluid to the blood vascular system was an increase in plasma protein concentration—thus increasing the osmotic pressure tending to pull material into the venous side of the microcirculatory system. The lymphatic system was the remaining system needed to provide a control over the volumes of blood and interstitial fluids. Secondarily the lymphatic system has taken on a transport function in moving materials from the small intestine and liver to the blood vascular system. For example, most of the absorbed lipids are carried from the small intestine by the lymphatic system.

The lymphatic system consists of a branching series of closed vessels and a collection of lymphatic organs. The smallest lymph vessels, the lymph capillaries, consist of a single endothelial layer and are about the size and are as numerous as blood capillaries in tissues (Drinker and Field, 1933). Endothelial cells of the lymphatic system are flatter than those of blood capillaries, and lymph capillaries are usually flattened in shape, unlike blood capillaries, which are generally circular in cross-section. Medium-size lymph vessels are about 100 to 200 μ in diameter and possess a scattering of smooth muscle cells over their endothelial wall. Larger lymph vessels are composed of an endothelial layer covered with a connective tissue sheath in which are found elastic and smooth muscle fibers. Valves for one-way flow are found in larger lymphatics. These are paired flaps of the intima with their free ends pointing in the direction of lymph flow. However, they cannot withstand very much back pressure. Lymphatic vessels unite with other similar vessels, becoming larger and larger until finally all the lymphatics come together forming two main trunks—the right lymphatic duct and the thoracic duct. The former usually drains into the right innominate vein. The thoracic duct carries lymph from all parts of the body, excepting the upper right portion of the body, which is drained by the right lymphatic duct, and empties into the junction of the left internal jugular and sub-clavian veins (this is the general picture in mammals).

Lymph is not identical with interstitial fluid because the lymph capillaries are blind ended tubes and the lymph is formed from water and solutes of the interstitial fluid that first pass through an endothelial barrier. Lymph pressures are relatively low. In the mouse and rabbit ear lymph pressures average about 1.4 cm of H_2O (McMaster, 1946). In larger vessels pressures as low as 0.58 cm of H_2O have been recorded. These are end pressures (see Section 12-9) and are only reflections of the absolute lymph pressure. These pressures may be compared with the interstitial hydro-static pressure that amounts to about 1.9 cm of H_2O.

The flow rate of lymph depends on a variety of factors. Flow is aided by the contraction of skeletal muscles. Such flow is made unidirec-tional by the presence of valves in larger lymph vessels. In some cases, however, lymph vessels are clogged by cells, and the lymph becomes stagnant for relatively long periods of time. In amphibians and some teleosts, lymph flow is aided by the presence of lymph hearts—specialized regions of contractility that pump the lymph toward the heart. Generally speak-ing the flow of lymph back to the blood vascu-lar system is a slow process.

Conditions that inhibit the flow of lymph or which create a larger than normal filtration rate from the capillaries lead to edema—an increased volume of interstitial fluid, which can swell the tissues. Edema can result if overall blood pressure (established by the heart) is too high, or if the synthesis of plasma proteins is decreased thus lowering the blood osmotic pressure. The overall regulation of blood pressure and cardiac output is of importance because the activity of the heart is responsible for establishing the arterial-venous pressure differences that determine the relationship between capillary blood pressure and osmotic pressure.

The various lymphatic organs are located along the lengths of lymphatic vessels, and a major function of these organs is the produc-tion of lymphocytes, which are added to the lymph passing through the vessels. Lymphatic tissue is a loose-structured material consisting of a spongelike stroma and free cells in the meshes of the stroma. The lymphatic tissue in birds and mammals often form lymph nodes, which are the major lymphatic organs in these animals. Lymph nodes in mammals are found in the loose connective tissue of the axilla and groin, in mesenteries, and throughout the pro-vertebral region. Larger lymph vessels reach the nodes, where they form a marginal sinus. The lymph flows into the sinuses of the node and is finally collected by an efferent lymphatic vessel.

As already mentioned, the lymphatic organs, including the nodes, function in the production of lymphocytes. Lymphatic tissue is also an active agent in defense against foreign particles and microorganisms (see Section 3-13) and is part of the reticuloendothelial system. Phago-cytic cells in the sinuses serve as filters that scavenge particles from the lymph and destroy them. Such particles include red blood cells, pathogenic bacteria, as well as larger dust particles brought in by the respiratory tract and collected by macrophage cells of the bronchial nodes.

Blood

12-19. Constituents of Blood.   The discussion of blood in this chapter centers primarily upon the characteristics essential for proper circula-tion. Blood clotting, which is essentially bio-chemical in nature and which is covered in detail in most standard biochemistry textbooks, will not be discussed in this text; nor will the subject of immunology. Some aspects of the nature of blood or its constituents have already been described, including the general nature of amoeboid cells and their functions and the nature of the vertebrate erythrocyte. Other functions of the blood will be considered in the chapters on pH regulation, gas transport, and water and solute balance.

Blood contains cells, inorganic ions, organic ions and molecules, and proteins. In a given species these components are homeostatically maintained at relatively constant levels. In many organisms the relative concentrations of inorganic ions in the blood superficially resemble those of sea water, although generally Mg^{2+} and SO_4^{2-} are in lower concentration than in sea water (see Table 14-2). An exception to this generality is found in the bloods of many herbivorous insects that are poor in Na^+ but unusually rich in K^+ and Mg^{2+}.

Vertebrate blood may be separated by centrifugation into two fractions: the cellular fraction and the **plasma**. **Serum** is the fluid formed when a volume of blood clots. When the fibrin of the clot contracts, a straw-colored fluid is expressed that is similar in composition to plasma except that fibrinogen and some platelets are absent.

Blood proteins serve a variety of functions. They act in carbon dioxide and oxygen transport, serve as pH buffers, bind and hold in reserve inorganic cations, bind and transport hormones, function in blood clotting, act as antibodies, bind and transport nutrients and other water-insoluble materials, and may also serve as nutrient sources themselves. Blood proteins, especially the albumins, give rise to the blood colloid osmotic pressure essential for capillary functioning.

Most animals appear to possess a variety of proteins in their blood. In vertebrates these include hemoglobin and fibrinogen, a variety of albumins, and a variety of globulins (many of which act as antibodies in immunological reactions). Some animals, however, may possess only one or two blood proteins. In many invertebrates the osmotic pressure of the blood is maintained by the presence of free amino acids (see Chapter 14).

The color of bloods is due primarily to the presence of proteins or conjugated proteins that function in oxygen transport. These protein blood pigments include hemoglobin, hemerythrin, chlorocruorin, and hemocyanin. Hemoglobin is one of the most widely distributed proteins. It is found in representatives of all animal phyla. In vertebrates it is confined within erythrocytes in the blood, but in invertebrates it is found free in the blood as well as in other tissues. Of the other respiratory pigments only hemerythrin is found in cells; the others are always free in the blood. The functions and distributions of these pigments is considered in Chapter 17.

Human blood has a red cell count of about 6 million cells per mm^3. Normal white cell count is from 5,000 to 8,000 per mm^3. Plasma is about 90 per cent water by weight with a protein content of 7 per cent and an inorganic content of about 1 per cent. Ionic distribution in human blood and erythrocytes is listed in Table 6-9.

12-20. The Hematocrit. Blood is a thick suspension, and as described in Section 12-6, the viscosity of blood plays a role in determining the flow relationships in the cardiovascular system. The viscosity of blood in vertebrates is, to a major extent, determined by the concentration of erythrocytes and their condition.

The specific gravity of red cells is about 1.10, and that of plasma is about 1.03. The small difference in specific gravity means that, upon standing, the red blood cells of a sample of blood will slowly settle out of suspension at a rate called the **sedimentation rate**. The sedimentation rate depends on the size of the sedimenting particle and is, therefore, an index of the size and condition of the settling cell. Sedimentation rate in humans varies normally from 4 to 10 mm per hour depending on sex, age, health, and so forth. Clinically, sedimentation rate is used to provide an indication of inflammation and other pathological conditions. Increases in sedimentation rate are indicative of surface changes of the erythrocytes— changes that promote aggregation in the form of clumping or rouleaux formation. The normal low sedimentation rate shows that erythrocytes generally do not clump together.

The percentage of the total volume of blood occupied by erythrocytes is the **hematocrit**, and, in humans, is normally 40 to 50 per cent. The hematocrit is measured by centrifuging a sample of blood at standard conditions and determining the volume of packed cells. The

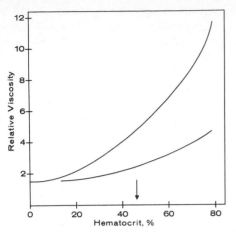

Figure 12-23 Relation of the relative viscosity of blood to the hematocrit. The upper curve shows the results when a viscosimeter was used; the lower curve the results when the vascular bed of the hind limb of a dog was used. Arrow points to the normal values of plasma and limb. [Data from Whittaker and Winton (1933).]

hematocrit depends on the rate of centrifugation and the time of centrifugation. It is normally measured in a tube of 5 mm bore and with centrifugation for 15 minutes at $1,500 \times$ g.

The viscosity of blood increases with increasing hematocrit (Figure 12-23). Hematocrits above 60 per cent indicate that distortion of erythrocyte shape has occurred, for otherwise the close packing needed for such a hematocrit value could not be obtained. The resultant high viscosity will mean disturbances in blood flow. The altered erythrocyte shape may also cause the cells to clog up small capillaries. In anemic conditions, where erythrocyte count is low, the effect on blood viscosity is such that blood velocity of flow is increased and blood pressure is lowered (see Equation 12.6).

12-21. Blood Volumes. An accurate knowledge of blood volume is necessary in some phases of hemodynamic study. Total blood volume (V_t) may be calculated from a knowledge of plasma volume, V_p, and the hematocrit, H, according to

$$V_t = \frac{V_p}{1 - H} \qquad (12.11)$$

But the blood volume determined in this manner is subject to sampling errors. The method

of course is not applicable to those animals lacking blood cells.

Dilution techniques are used in determining more accurate circulating blood volumes. Dyes such as Evans blue (T-1824) or tagged compounds such as ^{131}I-labeled serum albumin are injected into the circulation. Tagged cells are also used. For example, ^{51}Cr rapidly attaches to red cells and forms a stable complex. [59]Fe and ^{32}P tagged cells are also used.

The volume of blood may be determined from

$$V_t = \frac{Q}{S_p} \qquad (12.12)$$

where Q is the amount of material added (in mg) and the plasma concentration of the substance, S_p (in mg/ml), is measured by withdrawing blood samples and analyzing for the substance. Variations of these methods and the difficulties of blood volume measurements are discussed in Lawson (1962) and Sjöstrand (1962).

Blood volume variation occurs as conditions of the animal change. For example, at high altitudes, there is an increase in blood volume in mammals because of an increase in red blood cells. At high altitudes the oxygen content of the air is low, and more red blood cells are needed to attain sufficient oxygen. When blood volume is decreased, for example due to hemhorrage, volume receptors in the mammalian left atrium promote secretion of antidiuretic hormone (Chapter 14), and blood volume is made up from the interstitial fluid.

Most of the material of this chapter has centered upon the vertebrate peripheral circulation. In Chapter 13 I shall discuss the hearts and circulation systems of various animal groups and the major control systems that determine overall pressures and flows in circulatory systems. Again, most of the information will be from studies of vertebrates about whose circulatory systems most is known. A major point of emphasis is that in the closed system the capillary is the functional unit, and the structure and design of the system and its controls are for the purposes of capillary functioning and maintenance of blood and interstitial volumes.

References and Readings

Further references and readings on the circulatory system are found at the end of Chapter 13.

Bader, H. (1963). "The anatomy and physiology of the vascular wall." In: **Handbook of Physiology,** Section 2: Circulation. (W. F. Hamilton, ed.), Vol. 2, pp. 865–890. Washington, D.C.: American Physiological Society.

Bayliss, L. E. (1962). "The rheology of blood." In: **Handbook of Physiology,** Section 2: Circulation. (W. F. Hamilton, ed.), Vol. 1, pp. 137–150. Washington, D.C.: American Physiological Society.

Bennett, H. S., J. H. Luft, and J. C. Hampton (1959). "Morphological classification of vertebrate blood capillaries." *Am. J. Physiol.* **196:** 381–390.

Benninghoff, A. (1930). Blutgefasse und Herz. In: **Handbuch der Mikroskopische Anatomie der Menschen.** Vol. 4, pp. 1–225. Berlin: Springer-Verlag.

Bradley, S. E. (1963). "The hepatic circulation." In: **Handbook of Physiology,** Section 2: Circulation. (W. F. Hamilton, ed.), Vol. 2, pp. 1387–1438. Washington, D.C.: American Physiological Society.

Brecher, G. A. and P. M. Galletti (1963). "Functional anatomy of cardiac pumping." In: **Handbook of Physiology,** Section 2: Circulation. (W. F. Hamilton, ed.), Vol. 2, pp. 759–798. Washington, D.C.: American Physiological Society.

Burton, A. C. (1944). "Relation of structure to function of the tissues of the wall of blood vessels." *Physiol. Rev.* **34:** 619–642.

Burton, A. C. (1962). "Physical principles of circulatory phenomena: the physical equilibria of the heart and blood vessels." In: **Handbook of Physiology,** Section 2: Circulation. (W. F. Hamilton, ed.), Vol. 2, pp. 85–106. Washington, D.C.: American Physiological Society.

Burton, A. C. (1965). **Physiology and Biophysics of the Circulation.** Chicago, Ill.: Year Book Medical Pubs., Inc. 217 pp.

Chambers, R. and B. W. Zweifach (1944). "Topography and function of the mesenteric capillary circulation." *Am. J. Anat.* **75:** 173–205.

Comél, M. and L. Laszt, eds. (1967). "Morphology and histochemistry of the vascular wall." *Angiologica* (Basel) **2:** 225–434.

Copley, A. L. and G. Stainsby, eds. (1960). **Flow Properties of Blood.** Long Island City, N.Y.: Pergamon Press, Inc. 446 pp.

Cuthbert, D. W. (1967). "Electrical activity in mammalian veins." *Bibliotheca Anat.* **8:** 11–15.

Davson, H. (1964). **A Textbook of General Physiology,** 3rd ed. Boston: Little, Brown and Company. 1166 pp.

Dische, Z. (1964). "Glycans of the lens capsule—A model of basement membranes." In: **Small Vessel Involvement in Diabetes Mellitus.** (M. D. Siperstein; A. R. Colwell, and K. Meyer, eds.). Washington, D.C.: American Institute of Biological Sciences.

Drinker, C. K. and M. E. Field (1933). **Lymphatics, Lymph, and Tissue Fluid.** Baltimore: The Williams & Wilkins Company.

Fawcett, D. W. (1959). "The fine structure of capillaries, arterioles and small arteries." In: **The Microcirculation. Symposium on Factors Influencing Exchange of Substances Across Capillary Wall.** pp. 1–27. Urbana, Ill.: University of Illinois Press.

Fischer, H. (1951). "Über die funktionelle Bedeutung des Spiralverlaufes der Muskulatur in der Arterienwand." *Morph. Jahrb.* **91:** 394–446.

Folklow, B. (1955). "Nervous control of blood vessels." *Physiol. Rev.* **35:** 629.

Gauer, O. H. and H. L. Thron (1965). "Postural changes in the circulation." In: **Handbook of Physiology,** Section 2: Circulation. (W. F. Hamilton, ed.), Vol. 3, pp. 2409–2440. Washington, D.C.: American Physiological Society.

Goetz, R. H. et al. (1960). "Circulation of the giraffe." *Circulation Res.* **8:** 1049–1058.

Grant, R. T. (1930). "Observations on direct communications between arteries and veins in rabbit's ears." *Heart* **15:** 281–301.

Grant, R. T. and E. F. Bland (1931). "Observations on arteriovenous anastomoses in human skin and in the bird's foot." *Heart* **15**: 385–407.

Grassé, P. (1948–). **Traite de Zoologie.** 17 volumes, not completed. Paris: Masson et Cie. See especially Vol. 5.

Green, H. D. (1950). "Circulatory System: Physical Principles." In: **Medical Physics.** (O. Glasser, ed.), Vol. 2, pp. 228–251. Chicago: Year Book Medical Pubs., Inc.

Green, H. D. and C. E. Rapela (1964). "Blood flow in passive vascular beds." *Circulation Res.* **15** (Suppl.): 11–16.

Greene, C. W. (1900). "Contributions to the physiology of the California hagfish, *Polistrotrema stouti.* 1. The anatomy and physiology of the caudal heart." *Am. J. Physiol.* **3**: 366–382.

Greenfield, L. J. and A. G. Morrow (1961). "Cardiovascular hemodynamics of crocodilians." *J. Surg. Res.* **1**: 97–103.

Grégoire, C. (1962). "Blood coagulation." In: **Comparative Biochemistry.** (M. Florkin and H. S. Mason, eds.), Vol. 4, pp. 435–482. New York: Academic Press, Inc.

Grollman, S. (1964). **The Human Body.** New York: The Macmillan Company. 611 pp.

Hamilton, W. F. (1955). "Role of Starling concept in regulation of normal circulation." *Physiol. Rev.* **35**: 150–168.

Hanson, K. M. and P. C. Johnson (1966). "Local control of hepatic arterial and portal venous flow in the dog." *Am. J. Physiol.* **211**: 712–720.

Houston, A. H. (1959). "Osmoregulatory adaptation of steelhead trout (*Salmo gairdneri* Richardson)." *Can. J. Zool.* **37**: 729–748.

Hyman, L. H. (1940). **The Invertebrates: Protozoa through Ctenophora.** New York: The McGraw-Hill Book Co., Inc. 426 pp.

Illig, L. (1961). **Die terminale Strombahn.** Berlin: Springer-Verlag. 458 pp.

Intaglietta, M. and B. W. Zweifach (1966). Indirect method for measurement of pressure in blood capillaries. *Circ. Res.* **19**: 199–205.

Johnson, P. C. (1964). "Review of previous studies and current theories of autoregulation." *Circulation Res.* **15** (suppl.): 2–10.

Krogh, A. (1959). **The Anatomy and Physiology of Capillaries.** New York: Hafner Publishing Co., Inc. 422 pp.

Landis, E. M. (1926). "The capillary pressure in frog mesentery as determined by microinjection." *Am. J. Physiol.* **75**: 548–570.

Landis, E. M. and J. C. Hortenstine (1950). "Functional significance of venous blood pressure." *Physiol. Rev.* **30**: 1–32.

Landis, E. M. and J. R. Pappenheimer (1963). "Exchange of substances through capillary walls." In: **Handbook of Physiology,** Section 2: Circulation. (W. F. Hamilton, ed.), Vol. 2, pp. 961–1034. Washington, D.C.: American Physiological Society.

Landowne, M. and R. W. Stacy (1957). "Glossary of terms." In: **Tissue Elasticity.** (J. W. Remington, ed.), pp. 191–201. Washington, D.C.: American Physiological Society.

Lawson, H. C. (1962). "The volume of blood—a critical examination of methods for its measurement." In: **Handbook of Physiology,** Section 2: Circulation. (W. F. Hamilton, ed.), Vol. 1, pp. 23–49. Washington, D.C.: American Physiological Society.

Luft, J. H. (1963). "Fine structure of the diaphragm across capillary 'pores' in mouse intestine." *Anat. Rec.* **148**: 307–308.

Luisada, A. A., ed. (1961). **Development and Structure of the Cardiovascular System.** New York: The McGraw-Hill Book Company, Inc. 225 pp.

Majno, G. (1965). "Ultrastructure of the vascular membrane." In: **Handbook of Physiology,** Section 2: Circulation. (W. F. Hamilton, ed.), Vol. 3, pp. 2293–2375. Washington, D.C.: American Physiological Society.

Martin, A. W., F. M. Harrison, M. J. Huston, and D. M. Steward (1958). "The blood volumes of some representative molluscs." *J. Exp. Biol.* **35**: 260–279.

Martin, A. W. and K. Johansen (1965). "Adaptations of the circulation in invertebrate animals." In: **Handbook of Physiology,** Section 2: Circulation. (W. F. Hamilton, ed.), Vol. 3, pp. 2545–2581. Washington, D.C.: American Physiological Society.

Maynard, D. M. (1960). "Circulation and heart function." In: **The Physiology of Crustacea.** (T. H. Waterman, ed.), Vol. 1, pp. 161–226. New York: Academic Press, Inc.

McMaster, P. D. (1946). "Conditions in skin influencing interstitial fluid movement, lymph formation, and lymph flow." *Ann. N.Y. Acad. Sci.* **46:** 743–787.

Palade, G. E. (1960). "Transportation quanta across the endothelium of blood capillaries." *Anat. Rec.* **136:** 254.

Palade, G. E. (1961). "Blood capillaries of the heart and other organs." *Circulation Res.* **9:** 368–384.

Pappenheimer, J. R. (chairman) (1950). "Standardization of definitions and symbols in respiratory physiology." *Fed. Proc.* **9:** 602–605.

Partridge, S. M., D. F. Elsden, J. Thomas, A. Dorfman, A. Telser, and H. O. Pei-Lee (1964). "Biosynthesis of the desmosine and isodesmosine cross-bridges in elastin." *Biochem. J.* **93:** 30c–33c.

Patterson, J. L., et al. (1965). "Cardio-respiratory dynamics in the ox and giraffe with comparative observations on man and other mammals." *Ann. N.Y. Acad. Sci.* **127:** 393–413.

Potts, W. T. W. and G. Parry (1964). **Osmotic and Ionic Regulation in Animals.** Long Island City, N.Y.: Pergamon Press, Inc. 423 pp.

Prosser, C. L., ed. (1950). **Comparative Animal Physiology.** Philadelphia: W. B. Saunders Company. 888 pp.

Prosser, C. L. and F. A. Brown (1961). **Comparative Animal Physiology,** 2nd ed. Philadelphia: W. B. Saunders Company. 688 pp.

Reichel, H. (1960). **Muskelphysiologie.** Berlin: Springer-Verlag. 276 pp.

Roddie, I. C. (1967). "Electrical and mechanical activity in turtle arteries and veins." In: **Symposium on Electrical Activity and Innervation of Blood Vessels.** *Bibliotheca Anat.* **8:** 1–4.

Rushmer, R. F., ed. (1966). **Methods in Medical Research,** Vol. 11. Chicago: Yearbook Medical Publishers, Inc. 311 pp.

Smith, H. W. (1956). **Principles of Renal Physiology.** New York: Oxford University Press. 237 pp.

Sobin, S. S. and H. M. Tremer (1966). "Functional geometry of the microcirculation." *Fed. Proc.* **25:** 1744–1752.

Sjöstrand, T. (1962). "Blood volume." In: **Handbook of Physiology,** Section 2: Circulation. (W. F. Hamilton, ed.), Vol. 1, pp. 51–62. Washington, D.C.: American Physiological Society.

Sonnenschein, R. R. and F. N. White (1968). "Systemic circulation: local control." *Ann. Rev. Physiol.* **30:** 147–170.

Speidel, E. and A. Lazarow (1963). "Chemical composition of glomerular basement membrane material in diabetes." *Diabetes* **12:** 355.

Thorson, T. B. (1958). "Measurement of the fluid compartment of four species of marine chondrichthyes." *Physiol. Zool.* **31:** 16–23.

Thorson, T. B. (1961). "The partitioning of body water in Osteichthyes: phylogenetic and ecological implications in aquatic vertebrates." *Biol. Bull.* **120:** 238–254.

Van Citters, R. L., W. D. Kemper, and D. L. Franklin (1966). "Circulation in the giraffe." *Science* **152:** 384–386.

Verity, M. A. and J. A. Bevan (1967). "A morphopharmologic study of vascular smooth muscle innervation." *Bibliotheca Anat.* **8:** 60–65.

Wayland, H. (1967). "Rheology and the microcirculation." *Gastroenterology* **52:** 342–355.

Whittaker, S. R. F. and F. R. Winton (1933). "The apparent viscosity of blood flowing in the isolated hindlimb of the dog, and its variation with corpuscular concentration." *J. Physiol.* (London) **78:** 339–369.

Wiedeman, M. P. (1963). "Patterns of the arteriovenous pathways." In: **Handbook of Physiology,** Section 2: Circulation. (W. F. Hamilton, ed.), Vol. 2, pp. 891–934. Washington, D.C.: American Physiological Society.

Wiederhielm, C. A. (1966). "Transcapillary and interstitial transport phenomena in the mesentery." *Fed. Proc.* **25:** 1789–1798.

Wöhlisch, E., R. du Mesnil de Rochemont, and H. Gerschler (1927). "Untersuchungen über die elastischen Eigenschaften tierischer Gewebe." *Z. Biol.* **85**: 325–341.

Zimmermann, K. W. (1933). "Ueber den Bau des Glomerulus der Sauegerniere." *Z. Mikroskop-Anat. Forsch.* **32**: 176–278.

Zweifach, B. W. (1937). "The structure and reactions of the small blood vessels in Amphibia." *Am. J. Anat.* **60**: 473–514.

Zweifach, B. W. and M. Intaglietta (1966). "Fluid exchange across the blood capillary interface." *Fed. Proc.* **25**: 1784–1788.

Zweifach, B. W. and D. B. Metz (1955). "Selective distribution of blood through the terminal vascular bed of mesenteric structures and skeletal muscle." *Angiology* **6**: 282–289.

Pumping Organs: Types and Functions

13-1. Introduction. Although in this part of the chapter I shall be primarily concerned with the nature and activities of circulatory pumping organs, it will also be appropriate to discuss briefly the general nature of circulatory systems of various animal groups, some of the specialized functions of vascular or coelomic fluid systems, and some of the factors that led to the evolution of the four-chambered, double circulation hearts of birds and especially mammals. Adequate understanding of circulatory system functioning depends, in part, on a knowledge of the activities and habitats of the animals that possess them. Although some animals with vascular systems depend on the activity of cilia or body musculature contractions to move fluid through them, a majority of animals with blood vascular systems have a muscular pumping organ for this purpose. Such muscular systems are of several types, and any or all may be possessed by a given organism.

Pulsating vessels are simply blood vessels with a relatively heavy muscular layer that contracts in peristaltic waves, thus pushing the blood through the system. Such vessels are found in a variety of animals including members of the Annelida, Mollusca, Arthropoda, and some Vertebra. In many cases pulsating vessels are found in addition to a main pumping organ.

Tube hearts are found in most arthropods and also in the tunicates. They are more highly developed than the pulsating vessel, and often there is a thin atrium (receiving chamber) surrounding part of the heart, or the heart may lie free in a pericardial sinus. In the arthropods valved ostia are usually present through which the blood enters the heart from an atrium or pericardial sinus. As the heart contracts, usually in a peristaltic wave, blood can flow only into the arteries since the ostial valves close and prevent back flow.

Ampullar accessory hearts are booster pumps that provide sufficient driving force to pump blood through some peripheral regions of the circulation of some animals. Accessory hearts are common in insects and found at the

Chapter 13

Circulatory Systems—Types, Hearts, and Controls

bases of antennae, in the legs, and at the thoracic articulation of the wings. Branchial hearts of cephalopod molluscs aid the movement of blood through the gills. Fishes, amphibians, and reptiles possess lymph hearts—contractile lymph vessels which propel lymph through the system. In these organisms lymph enters into the venous system at many points, unlike the situation described for birds and mammals in Section 12-18.

Chambered hearts are found in many molluscs and in the vertebrates. They are compact muscular structures and are usually composed of cardiac (striated) muscle. One or more chambers receive venous blood, and one or more chambers pump blood out into the peripheral circulation. Birds and mammals evolved a double circulation such that one side of the heart provides oxygenated blood at relatively high pressures to all body cells (the somatic circulation) while the other side of the heart sends deoxygenated blood to the respiratory organs for reoxygenation (the pulmonary circulation). Other animals achieve a separation of oxygenated and deoxygenated bloods by different mechanisms (Section 13-8).

The following sections will describe in more detail the nature of hearts and circulatory arrangements found in major animal groups. First, however, the use of hydraulic pressures by invertebrate organisms will be briefly considered.

13-2. Hydraulic Systems. Although most invertebrate animals possess open circulatory systems in which pressures are much lower than those typical of closed systems, many of the invertebrates have mechanisms for developing high hydrostatic pressures of vascular or coelomic fluids. These pressures may be used for highly specialized activities.

In many soft-bodied animals the blood vascular or coelomic fluids serve as a hydraulic skeleton, functioning in lieu of a solid skeletal system in activities such as burrowing and locomotion. Extremely high pressures can be generated by the contraction of body musculature. For example, the nematode *Ascaris lumbricoides* in the relaxed condition has an internal body fluid pressure of about 16 mm Hg. This pressure rises to as high as 225 mm Hg during activity when body muscles are contracting (Harris and Crofton, 1957).

Members of the Acanthocephala possess an eversible proboscis and a heavy layer of circular muscle in the body wall. The rapid and lengthy extrusion of the proboscis is accomplished by muscular contractions producing a hydraulic force that moves the organ.

A hydraulic skeleton is important in the burrowing activities of earthworms and other annelids. It has been shown that the loss of coelomic fluid causes a decrease in burrowing ability in oligochaetes and polychaetes (Chapman and Newell, 1947). The hardening of the body needed for burrowing results not only from the contraction of body musculature but also from the transmission of hydraulic pressure generated in the coelomic fluid (Manton, 1961). The pressures generated in the marine worm *Arenicola* are 14 cm H_2O at rest and 27 cm H_2O during burrowing.

In sedentary marine annelids feeding and respiration are aided by pumping water through the burrow. Periodic muscular waves of contraction with accompanying changes in hydraulic pressures of body fluids move forward over the body of the animal and decrease the space found between the dorsal surface of the body and the burrow wall. This action drives water forward over the gills in a manner analogous to a rotary force pump (Figure 12-3). A constant supply of oxygenated water is provided from which the gills may extract oxygen. Food particles carried in the water are ingested.

Development of high internal fluid pressures is also found in some arthropods (Manton, 1958). In spiders, for example, hydraulic systems provide for the movement of certain leg joints that, for lack of space, cannot be supplied with extensor muscles (Ellis, 1944). Through as yet unknown mechanisms pressures as high as 45 mm of H_2O are developed in milliseconds and cause the legs to extend (Parry and Brown, 1959a). Hydraulic forces are also responsible for certain spine and palp movements used in defense (von Homann,

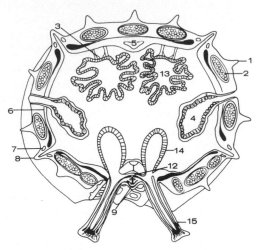

Figure 13-1 Section through an asteroid ray. (See Figure 13-2 for explanation of the numbers.)

1935). Jumping spiders that can cover distances of 20 cm or more use hydraulic pressure to extend the fourth pair of legs (Parry and Brown, 1959b). According to Ward (1969) with the evolution of a rigid exoskeleton the hydraulic system lost importance as a means of leg extension and support. Hydraulic systems would be expected wherever large areas of membrane are present that detract from the stiffness of the integument or wherever extensor muscles are lacking at a leg joint. However, even under these conditions mechanisms for appendage movement are present that are not hydraulic.

Burrowing by many molluscs is also enabled by the development of hydraulic pressures. For example, the razor clam *Ensis directus* protrudes its foot by forcing blood into it by the contraction of mantle muscles. The shape of the foot is regulated by the pattern of contractions and relaxations of its circular muscles. During burrowing the foot takes the form of a narrow cylinder as the circular muscles contract. When the foot is fully extended, the tip swells as the circular muscles relax. When the foot muscles contract, drawing the foot and its contained blood back into the shell, water is displaced as a jet directed through the space between foot and shell. This water jet clears a space for the advancing shell, protects the soft

tissue against erosion by the sand, and keeps sand out of the mantle cavity (Drew, 1907). Thus, a combination of hydraulic and muscular mechanisms allows the clam to dig into the sand. *Ensis* can also swim by slowly thrusting out the foot and then rapidly withdrawing it, with a simultaneous closure of the valves, so that water is expelled from the mantle cavity in a jet that jerks the clam backward about one-and-a-half times the length of the shell. Burrowing, swimming, and leaping in many molluscs are accomplished by similar hydraulic actions (see Morton, 1964).

13-3. Echinoderm Hemal and Water Vascular Systems. Members of the phylum Echinodermata have a body plan different from that of any other animal group and also possess a unique water-vascular system that deserves some comment here. Echinoderms have a radial symmetry impressed upon a primitive bilateral symmetry. They are predominantly pentamerous, as indicated by the typical five arms of starfishes or the five petals on the surface of a sand dollar. Echinoderms have an endoskeleton of calcareous ossicles covered by a ciliated epidermis (see Figure 13-1). The body of a starfish, for example, can undergo a considerable amount of bending and twisting although it is provided with a meshwork of calcareous plates. Meglitsch (1967) includes an account of the phylum Echinodermata.

Echinoderms have a large coelom, which is complexly divided and which gives rise to both a hemal and a water vascular system (=ambulacral system). The latter is a unique hydraulic system equipped with tube feet used for movement, burrowing, sensory reception, and respiration (Figure 13-2).

The hemal system is the circulatory system of echinoderms and is composed of a complex of hemal sinuses and an axial gland. Hemal tubes are found in association with the esophagus and other portions of the digestive tract. The hemal tissue extends out into each arm of a starfish and is always closely associated with the digestive tubes in the arms. The major function of the hemal system appears to be in the distribution of food. Coelomocyte cells

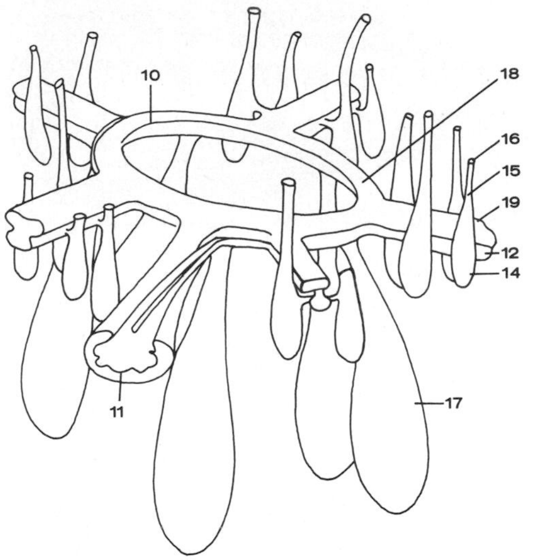

Figure 13-2 The water-vascular system of an asteroid starfish.

1. Spine	12. Radial water canal
2. Ossicle	13. Digestive gland
3. Absorptive hemal	(axial gland)
lacuna	14. Ampulla
4. Gonad	15. Podium (tube foot)
5. Apical nerve	16. Sucker
6. Intradermal	17. Polian vessel
sinuses	18. Oral coelomic ring
7. Ring sinus	sinus
8. Papula	19. Radial hyponeural
9. Radial nerve	sinus containing
10. Ring water canal	radial hemal canal
11. Stone canal	

are found in the hemal and coelomic fluids and probably serve to transport food materials from the digestive system to other body tissues. These cells are often seen to contain many particles of digested food materials. In holothurians the hemal system contains oxygen transport cells—hemocytes—and thus the system in this group serves in oxygen distribution. Although in hemal systems generally only a poor circulation is found, recently a heart was found in the Echinoid *Strongylcentrotus purpuratus* (a sea urchin). The **axial gland** which at various times has been considered a kidney, a brown gland, and a heart, has been shown to serve as a myogenic pump for the water vascular and hemal systems (Boolootian, 1964). In most cases there is no need for the hemal system to be highly developed, in part because the perivisceral coelomic fluid is well circulated by ciliary action and contraction of muscles. The walls of the hemal system are incomplete and all coelomic spaces communicate with one another to some extent, thus fluid circulation is found between all of them.

Water enters the water vascular system through a madreporite (=sieve plate) on the aboral (upper) surface of starfish (the following discussion is based primarily on structures and functions of starfish, subclass Asteroidea). Water is drawn through minute openings in the madreporite and flows down a calcareous-ringed stone canal to a ring canal. Flow is maintained by the propulsive action of cilia lining the inner walls of these canals. From the ring canal arise five radial canals, one to each arm. Many pairs of **tube feet** (=**podia**) are connected by short lateral canals to each radial canal. Tube feet are hollow, thin-walled tubes composed of connective tissue lined internally with longitudinal muscles. Excepting in brittle stars and crinoids, tube feet are connected to a rounded muscular sac, the **ampulla**. The radial canals and their lateral canals are tubes composed of a hyaline membrane and an internal layer of ciliated epithelium. Between the two layers are found circular muscles. The ampullae lie within the body, but the tube feet extend outside the calcareous ossicles in the center of the underside of each arm. They lie in the ambulacral groove and when necessary can be enclosed by movable spines lying on either side of the groove. Polian vesicles extend from the ring canal and serve as expansion sacs when the fluid in the system is put under pressure.

Contractions of circular muscles in the radial canals force water into the tube feet and extend them. A valve situated at the proximal end of each lateral canal prevents backflow of water into the canal when the feet are retracted by muscular action. In some species these valves are operated by pairs of muscles.

The operation of the system has been studied in two primitive Asteroidea—*Luidia ciliaris* and *Astropecten irregularis*—and is probably similar in most starfish (Heddle, 1967). In these starfish the tube feet can serve either for walking or burrowing in the sand. During walking, the water-vascular system extends the tube feet, they all point in one direction, and each arm assumes a posture in which the ambulacral groove is narrowed and the aboral surface widened. The extension and position of the tube feet are caused by the hydraulic pressures developed in them aided by contraction of various canal muscles. The positioning of the arms is accomplished by three sets of paired antagonistic muscles. Contractions of specific longitudinal muscles in the tube feet cause them to move in coordination carrying the animal across the surface. Although even in the extended condition a tube foot is a weak structure, when the hundreds of tube feet operate simultaneously, they can easily support the weight of the animal across a horizontal surface. Not a great deal is known about neuromuscular control systems in echinoderms. However the tube feet possess a variety of sensory receptor endings that presumably provide the information necessary for coordinated movements of the feet.

Digging requires lateral movements of the tube feet and a different posture of the arms. The arms become thinner and the tube feet by their lateral movements push sand from beneath the animal allowing it to sink into the substratum. The pushed out sand piles about the arms and finally when the mounds are high enough falls over the animal helping to cover it. Again, the build-up of hydraulic pressures in the water vascular system expands and strengthens the tube feet, and longitudinal muscles provide the lateral movements.

In addition to locomotion and burrowing, the thin-walled tube feet aid in respiration (Farmanfarmaian, 1963). Some echinoderms are observed to have regular cycles of retraction and extension of the tube feet. These are considered to serve a respiratory purpose. In some echinoderms the tube feet function in feeding. Their sensory endings detect food, and the feet collect the food and transport it along the ambulacral groove to the mouth. The epidermis contains papillae with mucous

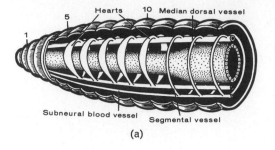

(a)

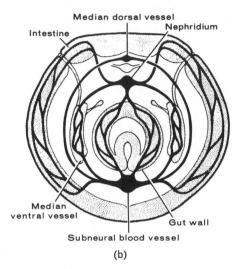

(b)

Figure 13-3 (a) Arrangement of main circulatory vessels in the earthworm. The hearts are pulsating vessels joining the median dorsal blood vessel to the ventral vessel. Numbers indicate segments. (b) Section through the earthworm showing circulatory arrangement.

glands and suspension feeding is common. The mucous secreted by the glands entraps food particles that are then gathered and transported by the feet. In the brittle stars locomotion is usually accomplished by the long flexible arms, and the tube feet are reduced in size and serve primarily food gathering, respiratory, and sensory functions. The tube feet of some echinoderms possess suckers that are used for attachment to the substratum. They may also be used to open the shells of clams and other molluscs that serve as food for the starfish. The starfish attaches suckers to each valve of the clam and then uses its arms to exert a steady strong pressure on the valves. This continuous pressure forces open the shells and the body of the clam is exposed to the starfish, which everts its stomach and secretes digestive juices over the clam.

Tube feet are often supplied with sensory receptors, and such tube feet lack suckers. The operation of the sucker, which is a pad of thickened epidermal cells, is produced by hydraulic mechanisms expanding the tube feet while longitudinal muscles cause a slight retraction of the feet. The result is a formation of a suction cup at the end of the foot. Echinoderm structure, physiology, and evolution are discussed in Boolootian, 1966; Meglitsch, 1967.

13-4. Annelids. The annelids typically have a closed circulatory system. There is a large dorsal blood vessel connected to a ventral blood vessel and several lateral vessels by transverse segmental vessels (Figure 13-3). Capillary networks ramify out from the dorsal vessel and rejoin again to form the other vessels.

The dorsal vessel pulsates rhythmically, its peristaltic action moving blood anteriorly in the animal. In higher annelids, one or more transverse segmental vessels (typically six in earthworms) are enlarged and invested with a thick muscular coat. They act as pulsating hearts, moving blood from the dorsal to ventral vessels. They possess valves for unidirectional blood flow.

Peristaltic waves in the dorsal vessel of the earthworm *Lumbricus variegatus* travel at speeds of 0.5 to 0.9 mm per second. The pattern of blood flow is usually anterior in the dorsal vessel and posterior in the ventral vessels. Depending on the species, other vessels may have contractile activity and aid in blood movement. In parallel with the blood vascular system is the coelomic fluid system in which cilia provide propulsive power for coelomic fluid circulation.

Very little is known about the hemodynamics of the annelid circulatory system, and many variations of circulatory arrangements are found within the phylum. Although it has been suggested that in oligochaetes and poly-

chaetes the vessel contractility is neurogenic in origin (see Section 9-3), primitive annelids appear to have myogenic hearts (Prosser and Zimmerman, 1943).

13-5. Molluscs. Most molluscan circulatory systems are open, the major exceptions being those of cephalopod molluscs. Detailed descriptions of the anatomy of molluscan circulatory systems are found in Grassé (1960); von Brücke (1925); von Buddenbrock (1965). Hill and Welsh (1966) review the physiology of circulatory systems in molluscs.

Typically the molluscan circulatory system has a single compact heart with two or more chambers, although accessory hearts are found in some species. There is a muscular ventricle and one or more atria (Figure 13-4 and Figure 13-5). Blood passes from the gills through veins into the atria and is then moved into the ventricle from where it is pumped through an aorta and its branches out into the peripheral circulation. The atrial-ventricular opening is guarded by valves to prevent back flow.

The aorta branches in a pattern dependent on the class of molluscs. In amphineurans and gastropod molluscs the finer branches of the arteries end in tissue sinuses. There is no continuation of the vascular endothelium in these sinuses, and thus blood directly bathes the body cells. In the pelecypods sinuses are

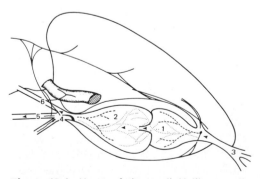

Figure 13-4 Heart of the snail *Heilix pomatia*. 1, Atrium; 2, ventricle; 3, pulmonary vein; 4, aorta; 5, visceral artery; 6, cephalic artery; 7, visceral mass; 8, intestine. [After Ripplinger (1957); broken lines indicate nerve distribution after Hill and Welsh (1966).]

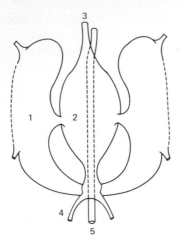

Figure 13-5 Heart of *Laevicardium crassum*. 1, Atrium; 2, ventricle; 3, aorta; 4, palial artery; 5, rectum. [After White (1942).]

confined to the foot region, and the remainder of the circulatory system is vascular with capillaries. In the cephalopods only a small region around the intestinal tract is open, the remainder of the system is closed. The pedal sinuses of amphineurans and gastropods are part of the hydraulic system used in swimming and burrowing (Section 13-2).

Isolated molluscan hearts beat better if they are perfused with a physiological solution or mechanically stretched. In order for the heart to beat, there must be some internal pressure tending to stretch the cardiac muscle fibers. The amplitude and the frequency of the heart beat are affected differently by a given pressure, and each has an optimum pressure for best performance. In the gastropod *Dolabella auricula* the **chronotropic response** (the change in beat frequency) to stretch of the cardiac muscle is mediated through the pacemaker region in the aorta. The **inotropic response** (change in the amplitude of the contraction) is mediated by all parts of the heart (Matsui, 1961). Stretching isolated bundles of cardiac muscle fibers results in both positive chronotropic and positive inotropic responses (positive is used here to indicate an increase in beat frequency or amplitude) (Nomura, 1963).

The nature of the filling of a heart is related to whether a circulatory system is open or closed, to the amount of cardiac musculature,

and to the general body plan and shape of the heart. In those molluscs enclosed in a shell and compressed by a muscular foot or in those molluscs encased in a muscular body wall, changes in activity will generate a changing hydraulic pressure internally. Ventricular systole raises the arterial blood pressure above the general body pressure, and blood can flow through the system. However, in an open circulatory system all the ventricular work is absorbed in raising the general internal pressure. During diastole the back arterial pressure becomes equal to the general internal pressure and valves are required to prevent the backflow of blood. Since the venous pressure also equals the general body pressure, during diastole there is a lack of pressure to fill the atrium. It has been suggested that atrial filling is accomplished by the contraction of the ventricle, which in a closed pericardial cavity will exert a suction on the atrial wall. Therefore, the atrium will fill as it expands and exerts a suction on venous blood. This idea is hypothetical but would explain the filling of atria in a closed pericardial space (see Figure 13-6).

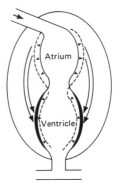

Figure 13-6 Schematic representation of a suggested mechanism for filling some molluscan hearts. As the ventricle contracts and is reduced in volume (indicated by dashed lines inside heavy ventricular wall) a suction is exerted on the atrial wall, and the atrium expands to greater volume (dashed line outside atrial wall). The atrium fills with blood that enters from the veins because of the suction in the expanding chamber. The reduction of ventricular volume acts on the atrial wall as the force is transmitted through the fluid filling the closed pericardial chamber.

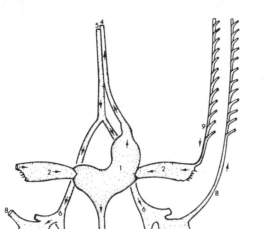

Figure 13-7 Hearts and major circulatory vessels of the cuttlefish *Sepia officinalis*. 1, Ventricle; 2, auricles; 3, posterior aorta; 4, cephalic artery; 5, cephalic vein; 6, vena cavae; 7, branchial hearts; 8, branchial arteries; 9, branchial veins. Arrows indicate directions of blood flow. [After Tompsett (1939).] Systolic/diastolic pressures measured in *Octopus* were: 30-50/15-35 in the aorta; 20-40/10 in the branchial hearts; 10-20/5-10 in the efferent branchial vessels; and 5-10/10-15 in the vena cava. [Johansen and Martin (1962).]

The veins of molluscs are sometimes contractile and aid in blood movement. Contractile vessels are said to occur throughout the systems of several cephalopods (Mislin and Kauffman, 1948) although this is disputed. For example, Johansen and Martin (1962) found that rhythmic contractile waves were present in the systemic ventricle and the branchial hearts but found no contractility of blood vessels. Smith (1962) reported peristaltic waves in the arm veins of *Octopus dofleini*. Accessory hearts are found as, for example, in the bivalve lamellibranch *Crassostrea gigas*, which uses accessory organs to pump blood through the high resistance system of the gills. From the gills blood passes into the arteries of the mantle, where its circulation is aided by the contractions of mantle muscles (Hopkins, 1936).

The cephalopod molluscs have an advanced type of circulatory system befitting these highly active animals (Figure 13-7). The cephalopod circulatory system has a pair of branchial hearts that accept low pressure venous blood and raise the blood pressure so that a rapid blood flow through the gill capillaries is achieved. With the exceptions of cephalopod circulatory systems, very few measurements have been made of the hemodynamic characteristics of molluscan systems. In most low pressures are found ranging from 1 to 10 mm Hg. But these pressures are variable and can change by a factor of ten during active body movements. Suggestions have been made that the heart of many molluscs serves mainly to provide a sluggish flow during rest and inactivity and to act as valves for the prevention of backflow. Especially in the more sedentary molluscs, such as scaphopods, the contraction of body muscles plays a dominant role in producing blood flows. Such animals usually have poorly developed hearts.

Johansen and Martin (1962) implanted cannulas in the anterior vena cava, the afferent branchial vessels, the efferent branchial vessels, and the anterior aorta of the octopus and measured the blood pressures in these vessels (Figure 13-8). Pressures are given as the ratio of systolic to diastolic pressure, the usual manner of expressing the pressures found in pulsatile circulatory systems. The difference between the systolic and diastolic pressure is the **pulse pressure**. In the octopus the mean aortic pulse pressure is about 15 mm Hg. The systolic pressure is high compared with that of most invertebrates. As shown in Figure 13-8 the venous pressure in the great veins is about 5 to 10 mm Hg, and this pressure is raised to 20 to 40 mm Hg by the branchial hearts.

Generally the heartbeat of molluscs is considered to be myogenic. The innervation that controls the beat established by the pacemaker of the molluscan heart is complex. The heart of the cuttle fish *Sepia officinalis* is innervated by about 1,600 nerve fibers from the cardiac nerve (Alexandrowicz, 1960). The heart of the clam *Mercenaria* and some other molluscs is accelerated by the addition of 5-hydroxytryptamine. This substance is normally present in high concentrations in the

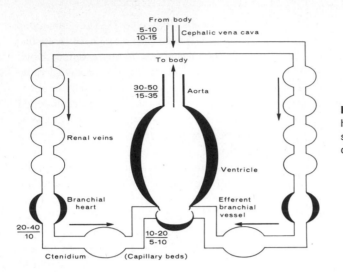

From body

$\frac{5-10}{10-15}$ Cephalic vena cava

To body

$\frac{30-50}{15-35}$ Aorta

Renal veins

Ventricle

Branchial heart

Efferent branchial vessel

$\frac{20-40}{10}$

$\frac{10-20}{5-10}$

Ctenidium   (Capillary beds)

Figure 13-8 Major vessels and the hearts of *Octopus*. Numbers show systolic/diastolic pressures. [From data of Johansen and Martin (1962).]

various ganglia of bivalves and gastropods. Molluscan hearts appear to receive both excitatory and inhibitory nerve fibers. In *Dolabella* the posterior portion of the visceral ganglion (the ganglion that supplies the fibers innervating the molluscan heart) sends inhibitory fibers to the heart, whereas the anterior region sends accelerator fibers to the heart. The visceral nerves of cephalopods inhibit heart rate.

13-6. Arthropods. The typical arthropod has an open circulatory system whose major pumping organ is a tube heart. The insects have a highly developed tracheal system for distributing oxygen to body cells, and in these animals the circulatory system is not required for this function. This has meant apparently that the circulatory system of insects was not required to become as elaborate as those of organisms which use the blood vascular system to supply oxygen and remove carbon dioxide from body cells. A generalized insect circulatory system is diagrammed in Figure 13-9. Blood passes through ostia into the heart and is pumped forward through short arteries to the brain region. Blood then drains back through various sinuses until it enters the hemocoel and again enters the heart.

Since the tube heart at diastole is in a collapsed condition, special arrangements are needed to fill the heart with blood. The tube heart has only a thin layer of muscle in comparison with other hearts and, as in other open circulatory systems, the venous or body pressures are not great enough to force blood into the heart. The tube heart of insects is suspended in a major blood sinus, the pericardium, by alary muscles attached also to the body wall. Usually each segment of the body has a set of alary muscles, and the sequential contraction of these muscles open the heart for filling (see Wigglesworth, 1954). The opening of the heart by these muscles creates a suction

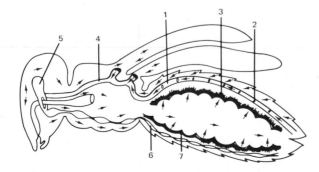

Figure 13-9 A generalized insect circulatory system. 1. Heart; 2. ostia; 3. pericardium; 4. anterior aorta; 5. brain; 6. nerve cord; 7. ventral septum. [After A. W. Martin and K. Johansen (1965).]

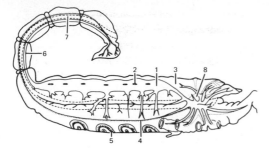

Figure 13-10 Circulatory system in the scorpion *Buthus*. This serves as an example of a representative arachnid circulatory system. 1, Heart; 2, ostium; 3, aorta; 4, ventral septum; 5, lung book; 6, posterior aorta; 7, digestive system; 8, brain. [After Newport (1843).]

so that blood can enter the heart from the pericardium. Insect hearts are neurogenic as are most arthropod hearts. Both insects and arachnids have contractile vessels that aid in driving blood through high resistance structures such as the wings or legs. The crustaceans lack such accessory pumps.

The scorpions and spiders among the arachnids have effective circulatory systems. Tube hearts are present (Figure 13-10). In

scorpions the blood is carried from the heart through aortae that distribute it to the various organ systems, and there are lateral arteries which carry blood to segmental structures and the viscera. The blood finally enters a ventral sinus and is pumped into the organs of respiration—lung books. Special muscles attach the ventral sinus to the pericardium and their contractions force blood through the lung books and then back into the pericardium.

Much more is known about the hearts and their control in the crustaceans and in the chelicerate *Limulus polyphemus* (the horseshoe crab) than about those of other arthropods. The tube heart of *Limulus* has been intensively studied and will be discussed in Section 13-14. The tube heart of a lobster is diagrammed in Figure 13-11 and a generalized lobster circulatory system in Figure 13-12. As in insects, short arteries usually lead blood into the head region of crustaceans so that the brain is well supplied with blood. The flow of blood is then directed posteriorly through sinuses until the blood is returned to the pericardial cavity. Blood enters the heart through valved ostia.

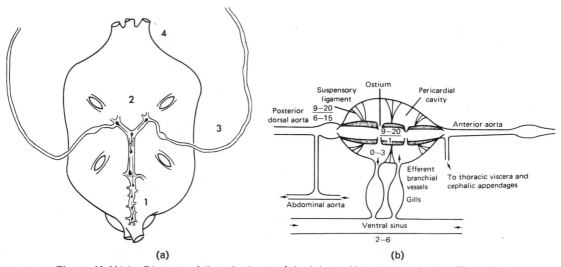

(a)　　　　　　　　　　　　　　　　　(b)

Figure 13-11(a) Diagram of the tube heart of the lobster *Homarus americanus*. The ostia through which blood enters the heart are shown (2) as well as the cardiac ganglion (1). (3) The dorsal nerve that controls activity of the cardiac ganglion through the central nervous system. (4) Anterior aortas. [Redrawn from Maynard (1961).] (b) Diagram of the central circulation of a decapod crustacean. The numbers represent the systolic/diastolic pressures recorded for the lobster *Homarus americanus*. [From B. T. Scheer (1963) *Animal Physiology*. By permission John Wiley and Sons, Inc., New York.]

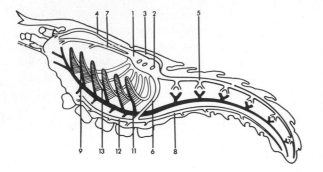

Figure 13-12 General scheme of circulation in a lobster. Main venous channels are shown in black. 1, Heart; 2, ostium; 3, pericardial sinus; 4, anterior aorta; 5, posterior aorta; 6, descending artery; 7, lateral cephalic artery; 8, abdominal artery; 9, afferent branchial vessels; 10, efferent branchial vessels; 11, ventral sinus; 12, thoracic artery; 13, gill.

The filling mechanism in crustaceans and most arachnids consists of elastic ligaments rather than contractile muscles. The heart during systole stretches the ligaments that attach it to the body wall. During diastole the ligaments pull upon the heart stretching it open and creating a suction that pulls blood into the heart. The beat of some hearts is such that the whole tube contracts almost at once; in other cases contraction may occur as a peristaltic wave passing anteriorly over the heart. Maynard (1960) reviews arthropod circulatory systems with emphasis on the crustaceans. The role of the cardiac ganglia in the beat of the crustacean neurogenic heart will be discussed in Section 13-14.

The importance of respiratory functions in the development of circulatory systems can readily be seen in the arthropods. In insects with a separate system for distributing oxygen to body cells, the circulatory system remains rather primitive or degenerate. In crustaceans, where the circulatory system must function in the transport of oxygen as well as in carrying nutrients and other materials, the circulatory system is more highly developed. Especially in active animals, which normally have a higher metabolic rate and greater oxygen need than more sedentary organisms, the circulatory system must produce higher blood pressures, or accessory organs must be present to move blood through the capillary beds of the respiratory organs. Many smaller crustaceans whose size or sedentary nature allow them to obtain oxygen readily from their environment have circulatory systems lacking hearts or with only poorly developed hearts. In sedentary or sessile animals throughout the invertebrate phyla, the

contraction of body wall muscles is a sufficient propelling force for blood circulation. In most animals of this type a heart, when present, is myogenic rather than neurogenic (this does not imply any correlation between activity and myogenicity or neurogenicity of hearts; the most active hearts known, those of the vertebrates, are myogenic).

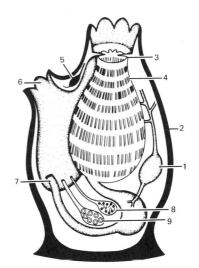

Figure 13-13 Schematic diagram of structure in an adult tunicate. 1, Heart; 2, tunic, a tough cellulose-containing membrane; 3, mouth (incurrent siphon); 4, pharynx with pharyngeal gill slits (branchial sac); 5, brain; 6, excurrent siphon of the atrium (an extensive body cavity); 7, anus; 8, gonad; 9, gonad (ovary). Blood passes from the heart through tubular cavities. Water enters the gill slits into the atrium and leaves the body through the excurrent siphon. The incurrent siphon leads to an enlarged branchial sac specialized for food gathering and aeration of blood. The branchial sac connects to digestive tract. The anus of the latter empties into the atrium.

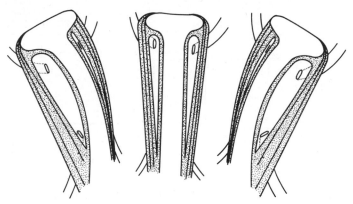

Figure 13-14 Diagram of the caudal heart of the Pacific hagfish. The median caudal heart cartilage, two caudal heart chambers, extrinsic muscles, and valves guarding the entrance and exit of each chamber are shown. (Left) Position during contraction of left extrinsic muscles. Left chamber fills while right chamber empties. (Middle) Rest position. (Right) Position during contraction of right extrinsic muscles. Left chamber empties while right chamber fills. [After Green (1900).]

13-7. Tunicates. The tunicates possess tube hearts and an unusual circulatory arrangement. The heart periodically undergoes a reversal of beat direction. The heart pumps blood for a certain time interval in one direction and then reverses and pumps blood in the opposite direction. The main blood vessels must function alternately as arteries and then as veins. The stimulus for beat reversal is an increase in pressure that affects the pacemakers located at either end of the heart. The blood pressure generated by the heart is not sufficient to move all the blood through the peripheral resistance. Thus blood tends to pool on the arterial side of the circulation. The increasing pressure of the accumulating blood stimulates the pacemakers to reverse activity. Pressure increases as small as 0.1 mm Hg are able to cause beat reversal (Kriebel, 1963). Reversal of beat has also been found in a few tube hearts of insects (Gerould, 1930). The general body plan and circulatory system of tunicates is diagrammed in Figure 13-13.

Perhaps the most obvious conclusion to be drawn from the discussions of the last few sections is that a great variety of circulatory arrangements exist even within small invertebrate groups. Another generalization is that much more work needs to be done on circulatory functioning in invertebrates. Only very recently have detailed studies of circulatory and water vascular systems been performed on groups such as the echinoderms. Hemodynamic information is lacking for most invertebrate animals.

13-8. Vertebrates—Fishes. In the vertebrates there has been an evolutionary trend toward the development of closed circulatory systems with high pressures and toward a separation of arterial oxygenated and venous deoxygenated bloods. If efficiency of a circulatory system is measured in terms of the ability of a group of animals to exploit a wide variety of environments, to achieve the capabilities of rapid movement and their associated requirement for a high metabolism, and to be capable of a high degree of adaptability, then the most efficient circulatory systems are those of birds and mammals. As was the case with the invertebrate groups, a variety of circulatory arrangements are found among the vertebrate organisms; and these reflect especially the variety of respiratory mechanisms used by these animals and the amount of oxygen available in a given habitat.

The most primitive living vertebrates, hagfishes of the order Myxinoidei, have open

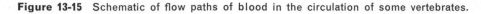

Figure 13-15 Schematic of flow paths of blood in the circulation of some vertebrates.

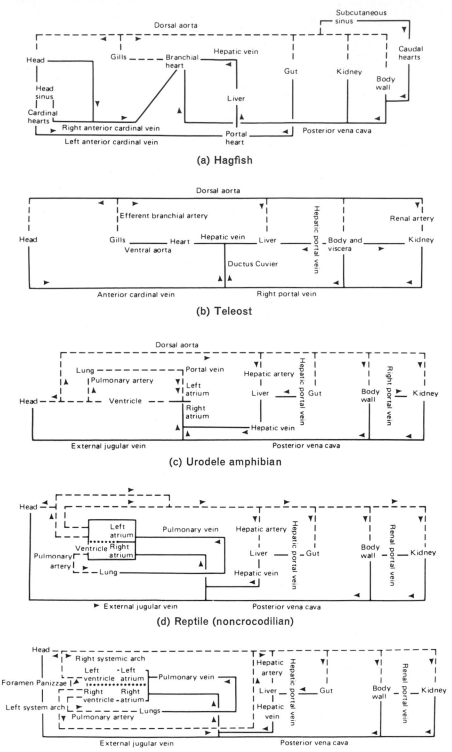

(a) Hagfish

(b) Teleost

(c) Urodele amphibian

(d) Reptile (noncrocodilian)

(e) Reptile (crocodilian)

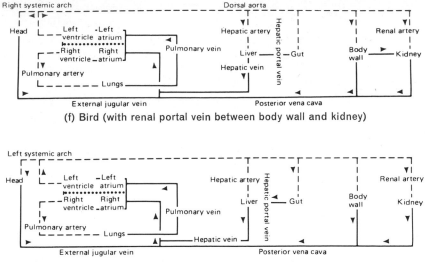

(f) Bird (with renal portal vein between body wall and kidney)

(g) Mammal (no renal portal vein)

circulatory systems with relatively low blood pressures. The hearts of these animals are aneural in contrast to those of all other vertebrates. (Randall, 1966; Ripplinger, 1950.) Lampreys and all other fish have a parasympathetic innervation of the heart (Couteaux and Laurent, 1958; Laurent, 1962). All other vertebrates have both parasympathetic and sympathetic heart innervation.

The cyclostomes generally (hagfishes and lampreys) are characterized by a circulatory system containing a series of accessory hearts. In addition to these decentralized pumps, blood is also moved with the aid of peristaltic contractions of certain blood vessels and contractions of the body musculature.

The caudal hearts of myxinoids are unique among accessory pumps. As diagrammed in Figure 13-14, they consist of a central flexible cartilagenous rod separating two caudal heart chambers and a paired set of muscles whose contractions flex this rod alternately to the left and then to the right. This pumping action allows one chamber to fill while the contralateral chamber is emptied. Each chamber of the caudal heart is connected to the caudal vein by a short vessel extending from the anterior margin of the organ. On the ventral anterior side of each chamber are openings communicating with the blood sinuses. Both

the entrance and exit pathways are guarded by valves.

The myxinoids also have cardinal hearts between the sinuses of the head and the portal and branchial hearts (Figure 13-15). They are nonmuscular chambers and operate on the basis of the contractions of surrounding specialized muscles. These hearts are guarded by valves located at the anterior end of the anterior cardinal vein (Cole, 1926). The portal heart of myxinoids has an inherent rhythmic beat and pumps blood through the common portal vein supplying the liver lobes.

There is, at present, little information concerning the mechanisms controlling and coordinating the activities of these various hearts. Chapman et al. (1963) measured intracardiac and intravascular pressures in the California hagfish *Eptatretus stoutii* and found systolic pressures ranging from 0.7 to 5.9 mm Hg. Injection of sea water into the cardinal vein caused an increased ventricular pressure—an indication that heart action and blood flow can be increased when necessary.

The hearts of teleost and elasmobranch fish are four-chambered (Figure 13-16) and are composed of typical vertebrate cardiac muscle fibers. Randall (1968) reviews the functional morphology of these hearts. The blood flow pattern of piscine circulation avoids the problem

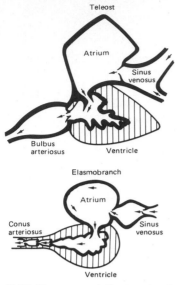

Figure 13-16 Diagrams of the hearts of a teleost fish, a trout (top), and of an elasmobranch, shark (bottom). [After D. J. Randall (1968) "Functional morphology of the heart in fishes" *American Zoologist* **8**(2): 179–189. By permission American Society of Zoologists.]

of separating oxygenated from deoxygenated blood. Venous blood from the anterior and posterior cardinal veins empties into the duct of Cuvier and is mixed with blood from the hepatic vein in the sinus venosus. Blood then enters in succession the atrium, ventricle, and bulbous arteriosus (teleosts) or conus arteriosus (elasmobranchs). From the conus or bulbous blood is pumped into the ventral aorta. As diagrammed in Figure 13-15 blood is sent through the gill capillaries for oxygenation before it is finally passed to the peripheral capillary beds via the dorsal aorta and the various cephalic arteries. The respiratory organ circulation is placed in series with the general circulatory pattern, and accessory hearts are often used to aid the movement of blood through the gills.

Because blood enters the gills after leaving the ventricle, a situation different from that seen in molluscs or arthropods, the heart itself contains unoxygenated blood, and an external blood supply for the cardiac cells themselves is now required. The coronary arteries, derived either from the branchial

arteries or the dorsal aorta (depending on the species), perform this function.

All heart chambers, except the bulbous, are contractile, although the sinus venosus is only weakly so. Valves are located at the sinoatrial and atrioventricular junctions and at the junction between the ventricle and the conus or bulbous. The conus contains several pairs of valves, and contractions of the conus appear to serve primarily as mechanisms for opening and closing the valves rather than for moving the blood (Stachell and Jones, 1967).

The pacemaker region lies in the sinus venosus as revealed by cooling specific regions of the heart and noticing the effect on the rhythmic beat (see Section 9-4). Typical of all vertebrates are the presence of other potential pacemaker regions in the heart. In teleosts these lie in the region of the atrioventricular junction and in the bulbus. These regions have lower rates of spontaneous activity than the pacemaker of the sinus venosus and are not part of the physiological heart beat.

As indicated in the diagrams of Figure 13-15, vertebrates have portal system circulations. The hepatic portal system sends all blood through the liver before it is returned to the general circulation. This allows the liver to remove materials absorbed from the digestive tract and to provide nutrients and other materials to the blood for distribution to body cells generally. The renal portal system allows a rapid exchange of waste products between the blood and the excretory organ.

Extensive study of pressures and cardiac outputs of teleost circulatory systems has been made only for the codfish. Pressures measured in the ventral aorta of fishes range from 15 to 70 mm Hg. In the codfish pressures in the ventricles ranged from close to 0 mm Hg at diastole to 45 mm Hg at systole. The stroke volume (the amount of blood ejected by the heart per beat, see Section 13-11) is about 0.9 ml per beat, and the cardiac output is about 10 ml blood per kg body weight per minute. Simultaneous pressure recordings in the ventricle and bulbus reveal that the bulbus smooths out the pulsatile pressure, and bulbus pressure and blood flow are prolonged far into ventricular diastole. The smoothing of the pressure is caused by the elastic walls of the bulbus—the same type of activity that was previously described for the aorta of mammals and other higher vertebrates.

In vertebrate groups above the teleosts and elasmobranchs, the development of lungs as respiratory organs greatly influences the nature of the circulatory system. The separation of oxygenated and deoxygenated blood (or of pulmonary and systemic circulations) is begun in the Dipnoi (lungfish) and amphibians. The lungfish have not been studied to any great extent, and more is known about circulatory functioning in the amphibians. Even in the latter group there is a diversity of circulatory arrangements because some amphibians depend on gills, others on lungs, and some on cutaneous, branchial, or esophageal respiratory surfaces for procuring oxygen (see Section 13-9).

The circulatory pattern of lungfish is different from that of teleosts especially in that there occurs a beginning of a separation of the ventricle into chambers so that an isolated pulmonary circuit begins to develop. In the lungfish the degree of separation of the chambers depends on the degree to which gills or lungs are used to obtain oxygen. This, in turn, depends on whether a species lives in oxygen-rich or oxygen-poor waters, on the degree to which gills have degenerated and become inefficient oxygen collectors, and on the period of time spent out of water in estivation.

The African lungfish *Protopterus aethiopicus* is an obligate air-breather and has an almost complete atrial septum dividing the receiving chamber into two atria. The ventricle has also become extensively divided. The bulbus is partially divided by endocardial rings that serve as a mechanism to provide separate channels for ventricular outflow to the pulmonary and the systemic circuits (Johansen and Lenfant, 1967).

13-9. Vertebrates—Amphibians and Reptiles.
Although amphibian circulatory systems have been studied in greatest detail in frogs, amphibians generally are characterized as

having a divided atrium although the degree of atrial separation does depend on the species. For example, some urodeles (salamanders) have an incomplete atrial septum or one that is highly perforate. This is true of those species that lack lungs or spend most of their time in water. The single ventricle of amphibians is trabeculate and spongy in structure. The sinus venosus is a conspicuous structure that receives blood from the great veins of the systemic circulation. The right atrium receives blood from the sinus venosus, the left atrium from the pulmonary veins when lungs are present. Atrioventricular valves are present. The bulbous cordis contains the spiral valve (Figure 13-17), whose function is to maintain a separation of blood flowing to the pulmonary and systemic circulations.

The degree of separation of blood flows is still a matter for debate. As stated above, a variety of circulatory arrangements are found in amphibians, and no single generalization can be made about blood flow in this group. The type of heart structure probably represents a

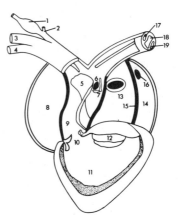

Figure 13-17 Diagrammatic ventral view of the internal structures of a frog heart. 1, Carotid sinus; 2, carotid artery; 3, right subclavian artery; 4, right pulmocutaneous artery; 5, spiral (longitudinal) valve; 6, left pulmocutaneous artery; 7, valves at exit to left pulmocutaneous artery; 8, right atrium; 9, conus arteriosus; 10, valves at exit to conus; 11, ventricle; 12, atrioventricular orifice; 13, sinus venosus; 14, left atrium; 15, interatrial septum; 16, pulmonary vein; 17, left carotid artery; 18, left subclavian artery; 19, left pulmocutaneous artery. [After J. S. Robb (1965).]

specialized condition associated with the mode of oxygen-collection and degree of terrestrial existence rather than a primitive one on the line of evolution leading to the avian and mammalian hearts (Foxon, 1955, 1964).

The classical theory of the separation of oxygen-rich and oxygen-poor bloods depicts blood flow as follows. Oxygen-rich blood from the lungs enters the left atrium through the pulmonary veins and passes into the left side of the ventricle. Oxygen-poor blood returning through the sinus venosus to the right atrium passes into the right side of the ventricle. The trabeculate structure of the ventricle tends to keep the two types of blood unmixed. Upon ventricular contraction the oxygen-poor blood in the right portion of the ventricle leaves the ventricle first because the opening of the bulbus cordis is closer to this side of the heart. The bulbus cordis is partially divided by the spiral valve. Because of the action of this valve, the oxygen-poor blood moves toward the pulmonary artery. Direction of flow is also aided by the lower pressure in the pulmonary vessels. For example, at this time in the contraction cycle the systolic pressure is not high enough to move blood into the carotid arteries. As ventricular contraction proceeds, the pressure increases and the spiral valve alters position, shutting off the flow of blood to the pulmonary artery and channeling blood into the systemic arches. Toward the end of ventricular systole, when pressure is reaching a peak, oxygen-rich blood is shunted toward the carotid arteries supplying the cranial region. The pressure is now great enough to move blood into this system of high resistance vessels. Thus both the structure of the heart and the different pressures in the system aid in achieving a separation of blood flows.

That such a selective distribution of blood does occur in some amphibians has been shown by various experimental methods. In some cases a dye such as Evans blue or a fluorescent dye is injected into the circulation and its movements followed visually. DeGraaf (1957) combined the use of the dye fluorescein with visual and cinematographic tracing and found that a selective distribution of oxygen-rich and oxygen-poor bloods occurred in the clawed frog *Xenopus laevis*. The flow patterns in *Xenopus* and the European frog *Rana temporaria* were found to be different. In *Rana* a selective flow occurs but is not due to sequential flow through the two sides of a spiral valve nor to pressure differences. Rather blood passes simultaneously on both sides of the spiral valve, and its distribution seems to depend upon asymmetries in the anatomy of the distributing arteries. The relative sizes of the atria vary in the two species, another factor in promoting differences in the flow pattern. Such differences may be correlated with the fact that *Xenopus* depends more on its lungs for obtaining oxygen than does *R. temporaria*. The latter depends greatly upon cutaneous intake of oxygen, which then passes into many vessels of the circulation.

The average blood pressure in the arterial arches of *R. temporaria* is 15/8. In *Xenopus* pressures in the carotid and systemic arches average 26/21, and diastolic pressure in the pulmocutaneous arch is much lower, about 13 mm Hg. Arterial pressure in the toad *Bufo bufo* is about 26/19. High pressures are maintained in anurans generally. Again, pressure differences in anuran species perhaps are correlated with the degree to which the animal depends on a pulmonary circuit and lungs for supplying oxygen.

Another method for analyzing selective distribution is to inject a radiopaque substance into the blood stream and follow its movement by radiographic techniques. Such studies have been performed by Johansen and his colleagues on several species of amphibians (Johansen and Hansen, 1968). The urodele amphibian, *Amphiuma tridactylum*, was shown to maintain an efficient double circulation (Johansen, 1964). During ventricular systole the systemic venous return is distributed to the pulmonary arteries, and blood from the pulmonary vein is sent mainly into the aortic arches from the left ventricle.

The status of a double circulation in amphibians requires more study. The blood flow is not simply by chance, and yet the classical hypothesis cannot entirely explain the flow.

More work must also be done on relating the nature and efficiency of a circulatory system to the physiological state of the animal as well as the conditions of its natural environment. Finally, it may be noted that in both anurans and urodeles the heart obtains its nutrients and oxygen from the blood passing through it. These are the only vertebrate groups in which coronary arteries are missing.

Two morphological patterns are found in the hearts of reptiles. In crocodilian species there is a complete ventricular septum (White, 1968). The crocodilian heart is unusual in that the right aortic arch arises from the left ventricle, whereas the left aortic arch and the pulmonary artery arise from the right ventricle. The foramen Panizza connects the left and right aortic arches at their bases (crocodilian and noncrocodilian circulatory systems are schematically compared in Figure 13-15).

The ventricle of noncrocodilians is divided into three subchambers in continuity with one another (Figure 13-18): the cavum ventrale bounded by a muscular ridge and from which the pulmonary artery arises; the cavum venosum into which the right atrium empties and from which the left and right aortic arches arise; and the cavum arteriosum into which the left atrium empties. Classically it was

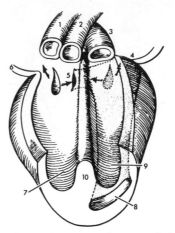

Figure 13-18 Schematic diagram of the squamate reptilian heart. 1, Right aorta; 2, left aorta; 3, pulmonary artery; 4, left atria; 5, interventricular canal; 6, right atria; 7, cavum venosum; 8, cavum arteriosum; 9, cavum pulmonare; 10, muscular ridge. [After White (1959).]

thought that mixing of blood occurred in the reptilian heart because of the presence of the left aortic arch in the crocodilian right ventricle and the continuity of the ventricular chambers in the noncrocodilian heart. But oxygen analysis of the blood found in the various heart chambers and in the great vessels indicates that mixing of bloods is minimal and the reptiles

Table 13-1   Oxygen Content of the Blood in the Heart and Vessels of Some Reptiles

Species*	Oxygen Capacity†	Right Aortic Arch	Left Aortic Arch	Pulmonary Artery	Right Atrium	Left Atrium
Snake[1]						
Coluber constrictor	7.37	7.18 [97.4]	7.22 [97.9]	1.72 [23.3]	1.45 [19.7]	6.90 [93.6]
Lizard[1]						
Iguana iguana	5.40	3.71 [68.7]	3.72 [68.8]	0.22 [4.1]	0.15 [0.27]	3.77 [69.8]
Alligator[2]						
Caiman sclerops		5.89	6.00	1.08	1.04	5.64
Turtle[3]						
Chelydra serpentina	6.01	3.50 [58.2]		2.54 [39.6]	1.78 [26.8]	4.02 [65.8]

* (1) White (1959); (2) White (1956); (3) Steggerda and Essex (1957).
† Oxygen content given as volume %. Numbers in brackets are % saturation of blood with oxygen based on the total possible oxygen capacity.

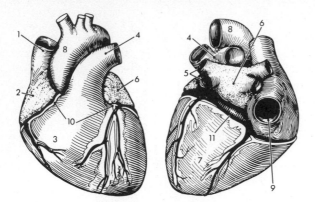

Figure 13-19 Exterior appearance of the human heart. Anterior surface on left, posterior surface on right. 1, Superior vena cava; 2, right atrium; 3, right ventricle; 4, pulmonary artery; 5, left pulmonary veins; 6, left atrium; 7, left ventricle; 8, aorta; 9, inferior vena cava; 10, coronary arteries; 11, coronary sinus. [After Grollman (1964).]

possess an efficient double circulation (see Table 13-1).

The maintenance of a double circulation has also been shown by dye tracing and flow analysis using electromagnetic flowmeter techniques. Some shunting of blood is found in turtles—a factor perhaps correlated with an aqueous environment in which some oxygen is obtained through tracheal-esophageal surfaces. In most reptiles the use of lungs as the major respiratory system has required an efficient separation of oxygen-rich and oxygen-poor bloods.

13-10. Vertebrates—Birds and Mammals. In the birds and mammals, animals that depend almost entirely on lungs for obtaining oxygen, there is a complete double circulation. The heart is a four-chambered organ with right and left halves acting as two separate pumps. The right atrium receives blood from the systemic venous circulation and passes it to the right ventricle from where it is pumped to the lungs for oxygenation. Oxygenated blood from the lungs flows to the left atrium, into the left ventricle, and then is pumped into the aorta, whence it is distributed through the systemic circulation. Figure 13-15 diagrams the pathways of flow in birds and mammals, as well as other vertebrate groups.

The atria play only a small role in pumping blood, although they may aid in the final filling of the ventricles. The muscular layer of the atria is very thin as compared with the thick muscular walls of the ventricles that must supply the power for moving blood through the circulatory system. Further there are no valves between the atrium and the pulmonary vein, and this also means that no significant pumping action could exist. Such valves are found in the hearts of teleosts, where the atrium plays a more important pumping function.

Although each side of the heart is required to pump an equal volume of blood per beat in order to achieve the conservation of blood volume, the resistance to flow in the pulmonary circuit is less than that of the systemic side, and less force is required to move blood through the pulmonary system. This is reflected in the heavier musculature of the left ventricle and the higher pressures found in the aorta and main arteries as compared with the pulmonary artery. Figure 13-19 illustrates the external appearance of a human heart (see also Figure 9-4). Figure 13-20 shows some of the major pathways of circulation in mammals.

The two sides of the heart act independently as far as mechanical activity is concerned and cardiac efficiency does not depend on their synchrony, at least in theory. But the contractile events on the two sides are nearly simultaneous because they share a common pacemaker and conduction system for activating the cardiac musculature (see Section 9-3).

The series of events of the cardiac cycle can be described in some detail for the mammalian heart as a result of detailed studies on the dog and on humans. Less is known about the avian heart contraction cycle, but it is assumed that its action is similar to that of the mammalian heart because only minor anatomical differences exist in the two groups as far as the heart and great vessels are concerned.

Historically the cardiac cycle was divided into the two major phases of systole and diastole—terms that refer to ventricular contraction and relaxation since these chambers of the heart have the most conspicuous pumping action. With the introduction of more reliable and precise techniques for measuring pressures and volumes within the ventricles and other chambers of the heart and for measuring pressures in the great vessels, the cardiac cycle could be further subdivided (Wiggers, 1921, 1952). Figure 13-21 shows the correlations of muscular activity; ventricular, atrial, and aortic pressure changes; ventricular volume; heart sounds; and electrocardiogram. Some of the subdivisions of the cardiac cycle shown in the figure are no longer used or are in disrepute.

The activity of the left ventricle (presumed similar to that of the right ventricle) during the cardiac cycle can be divided into four major phases based on alterations of pressure, the state of the cardiac valves, and changes in ventricular volume. The cardiac cycle cannot be discussed in terms of quantitative changes in blood flow because this parameter is still difficult to analyze in all chambers of the heart and in the great vessels.

The first major subdivision is that of ventricular filling. Following ventricular systole, the

ventricular muscle begins a rapid relaxation aided by elastic forces produced during contraction. During this early phase of diastole (formerly called isometric relaxation) the ventricular pressure still exceeds the atrial pressure, and no blood can flow into the ventricle. As relaxation proceeds, the fall in ventricular pressure continues until at some point pressure in the ventricle falls below the pressure in the atrium. At this point, the **atrioventricular (mitral) valves** open, and blood flows into the ventricle. For a short period of time ventricular relaxation continues and blood flows rapidly into the ventricle. Following the phase of rapid ventricular filling, during which 50 per cent or more of the inflow occurs, there is a period of slower filling (formerly called the period of diastasis) as the pressure in the atrium declines. At the end of this period of slow filling, a small amount of blood may be pumped into the ventricle due to the atrial contraction, but as already stated the volume so moved is probably insignificant. During the entire filling period, the **aortic** and **pulmonary valves** are closed because ventricle pressure is exceeded by those in the aorta and pulmonary artery.

The time of filling depends on the heart rate. As heart rate increases, the duration of diastole

Figure 13-20 Generalized scheme of the human circulatory system showing the major arteries and veins, as well as the major capillary beds. 1, Aorta; 2, pulmonary artery; 3, left atrium; 4, left ventricle; 5, right ventricle; 6, right atrium; 7, vena cava; 8, inferior vena cava; 9, hepatic vein; 10, liver sinusoids; 11, portal vein; 12, splanchnic artery; 13, digestive tract; 14, kidneys; 15, renal vein; 16, renal artery; 17, descending aorta; 18, lung arterioles; 19, lung capillaries; 20, lung venules; 21, pulmonary vein; 22, systemic artery; 23, capillaries; 24, systemic vein. [From S. Grollman (1964) *The Human Body*. By permission The Macmillan Company, New York.]

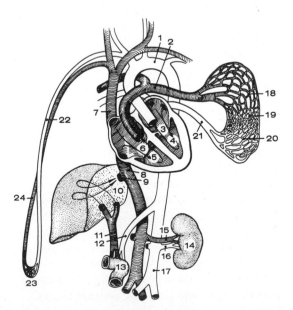

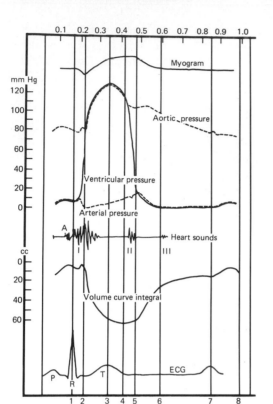

Figure 13-21 The cardiac cycle of human heart.

follows the increasing ventricular pressure as the ventricular muscle continues to contract. Aortic pressure must increase because the volume of blood pumped out by the ventricle cannot pass immediately into the systemic circulation because of the higher vascular resistance of the smaller arteries. It is at this time that some energy of the contracting ventricular muscle creates kinetic energy within the elastic walls of the aorta.

When the contraction of the ventricle stops, a rapid relaxation follows aided by the action of elastic elements within the cardiac musculature. These elastic elements have been stretched because of the differing orientations of muscle layers in the cardiac wall. The ventricular pressure falls at a slower rate than the aortic pressure (the aortic pressure falls due to flow of blood into the peripheral resistance vessels), and a period of reduced ejection of blood occurs. As ventricular relaxation continues, the ventricular pressure falls below the aortic pressure and finally the aortic valve closes. The entire ejection phase lasts about 0.2 seconds. The end of ejection is marked by the **dicrotic notch** or **incisura** on the aortic pressure curve. There is an aortic backflow as the aortic valve closes, and the dicrotic notch represents a pressure wave bouncing off the aortic valve.

At this time the ventricle is again a closed chamber because both inlet and outlet valves are closed, and during this period of isovolumetric relaxation the pressure falls rapidly as ventricular muscle tension decreases. When pressure falls to a level below that in the atrium, the atrioventricular valve opens and another cycle begins.

Pressure changes in the atria are difficult to measure without artifact because these pressures are lower pressures and change rapidly. Atrial volumes are also more difficult to determine because the atria, unlike the ventricles, are always open on the venous side. The factors involved in filling the atria are still debated. It is sometimes stated that atrial filling is accomplished solely by the forces exerted on the arterial side of the circulation, which are imparted to venous return, but this appears to be an oversimplified view. The

is more reduced than the duration of systole, and at extremely high rates, the time available for ventricular filling becomes so short that cardiac output is reduced because the ventricles do not have time to fill completely. At normal heart rates, the filling period occupies a little more than half of the cardiac cycle.

Ventricular filling stops abruptly when the ventricular muscle begins to contract. The initiation of contraction raises the pressure by a fraction of a millimeter of Hg, which is enough to close the atrioventricular valve but not enough to open the aortic valve. With both valves closed, the volume of the ventricle cannot change, and this phase of systole is called the period of isovolumetric contraction. When the pressure generated by the muscular contraction exceeds that in the aorta, the aortic valves (**semilunar valves**) are forced open and the ejection period of systole begins.

The blood in the ventricle is ejected rapidly into the aorta, and the aortic pressure closely filling of the atrium during ventricular systole depends not only upon the pressure of blood in the venous reservoir but also on the vigor with which the atrioventricular junction is moved. When the atrioventricular valves open during ventricular diastole, the decrease in atrial pressure can result in an acceleration of venous inflow to the atrium. The faster the valves open, the faster the pressure drops and the greater is the acceleration of ventricular filling. The anatomy of the heart indicates that ventricular contraction must cause some enlargement of the atria. This atrial expansion creates a suction that tends to draw blood into the atria from the venous side of the circulation.

The diaphragm and thoracic cavity also effect venous return. Intrathoracic pressure is negative, and the veins in the thorax tend to distend because of their positive pressure. This distension increases blood volume in the great veins because blood will flow into them from the lesser veins outside the thorax. During inspiration, intrathoracic pressure is about -6 mm Hg, and venous return to the heart is increased compared with the period of expiration when thoracic pressure is -4 mm Hg. Thus breathing has its effect on the filling of the atria as well as on arterial pressures. Any condition tending to increase blood volume in the venous system tends to increase the rate of atrial filling. Venoconstriction induced by adrenalin, for example, increases venous inflow to the atria by increasing venous blood pressure.

Because of its mechanical activity the heart wall vibrates over a wide range of frequencies. Some of these vibrations are in the range of human hearing and result in the heart sounds. By using a stethoscope or placing the ear on the body surface, at least two heart sounds will be heard in normal humans. The first sound (see Figure 13-21) is caused by the closure of the atrivoentricular valves. The second heart sound results from the closure of the aortic and pulmonary valves. The closure of these valves and the simultaneous occurrence of aortic back flow produces a sudden change in aortic pressure seen as the dicrotic notch on pressure recordings. In some cases a third sound is heard and is thought to result from the rushing of blood into the ventricle from the atrium— setting up a vibration of the ventricular wall. A fourth sound may be produced by the contraction of the atria.

Another category of cardiac vibrations are the heart murmurs, distinguished from heart sounds in that they have a gradual beginning and ending, a longer duration, and a higher pitch. Streamline flow is silent. When turbulent blood flow occurs, a murmur will be heard. Turbulent flow is usually caused in the heart by leaky cardiac valves allowing a backflow of blood. Heart sounds and murmurs are carried along the walls of the great vessels not in the blood stream itself (Faber and Purvis, 1963).

13-11. Cardiac Output. A proper understanding of circulatory functioning and the controls exercised over the circulatory system requires a knowledge of the amount of blood moved by the heart. The **cardiac output** is usually expressed as the **minute volume**—the volume of blood ejected by either ventricle in one minute. Often cardiac output is expressed in units of ml of blood ejected per minute per unit of body weight because this will allow a better comparison of the cardiac outputs of different animals. Dividing the minute volume by the heart beats per minute yields the **stroke volume**—the ml of blood ejected per beat of the heart.

It is important to note that the cardiac output refers to the quantity of blood ejected by either the right or the left ventricle, not both. This is based on the idea stated previously that the volume of blood moved per unit time in the pulmonary circuit must equal that moved by the systemic circuit and that there is no interconnection and shunting of blood between these circuits. In humans, at least, this assumption is for all practical purposes a correct one.

As we shall see in the final part of this chapter, the cardiac output and the heart rate are both susceptible to control and both play a role in determining overall circulatory performance.

Cardiac output is measured by either direct or indirect physical or chemical analysis of the blood (Hamilton, 1962, discusses the various methods used and their difficulties). The most widely known methods are based on the Fick principle set forth by Adolph Fick in 1870 but for which techniques were not available until about 1896. The Fick principle is one variant of a class of dilution methods based on the fact that if the amount of a substance entering or leaving a flow system is known, together with the concentration difference resulting from such exchange, then the volume of flow can be calculated.

The basic requirements for analysis by the Fick principle are as follows:

1. The system must carry an indicator whose concentration can be measured. In the case of the circulatory system this may be a substance normally carried by the blood, for example, oxygen or carbon dioxide, or one that can safely be injected into the blood stream, for example, gases such as acetylene; colored dyes; or radioactive compounds.
2. A *representative* sample of the blood flowing into or out of the system must be obtainable. Alternately some method for measuring the concentration of the indicator while it is in the blood in the intact animal must be available, for example, oximeters, based on photoelectric principles, can be used to measure the oxygen content of blood passing through surface regions such as the rabbit or human ear through which a beam of light can pass.
3. The total exchange or dilution of the indicator material in the system must be measurable.

The Fick principle can be expressed generally by the relation:

Blood flow (liters/minute)

$$= \frac{\text{Total exchange (ml or mg indicator per minute)}}{\substack{\text{Concentration of} \\ \text{indicator entering}} - \substack{\text{Concentration of} \\ \text{indicator leaving}}}$$

$$(13.1)$$

Analysis is often made using oxygen consumption and oxygen concentration changes because the oxygen used by an animal is readily measured by any of a variety of methods, and

the oxygen content of blood is also readily determinable. The appropriate relation for calculating cardiac output is as follows:

Cardiac output (liters/min)

$$= \frac{\text{Oxygen consumed (ml/min)}}{\substack{\text{Systemic artery } O_2 \\ (\text{ml } O_2/\text{ml blood})} - \substack{\text{Pulmonary artery } O_2 \\ (\text{ml } O_2/\text{ml blood})}}$$

$$(13.2)$$

For example, if a human consumes 250 ml O_2 per minute and arterial blood contains 19 ml O_2 per 100 ml of blood while venous blood contains 14 ml O_2 per 100 ml of blood, then the arteriovenous oxygen concentration difference is 5 ml O_2 per 100 ml blood (note that concentrations are usually expressed on the basis of 100 ml of blood). Dividing 5 into 250 and multiplying by 100 yields the result of 5 liters of blood pumped through the ventricle per minute (another way of looking at the result is to say that 50 hundred-milliliter volumes of blood must move through the heart in order to supply the 250 ml of oxygen consumed per minute, that is, every hundred milliliters of blood is providing 5 ml of oxygen).

Perhaps the most difficult part of this type of analysis has been the obtaining of a representative sample of venous blood. Different tissues have different metabolisms and therefore use different amounts of oxygen. The veins coming from different tissues will contain different oxygen concentrations. A well-mixed sample of venous blood is required for accuracy of the Fick method. This is now obtainable by inserting a small catheter (made of nonwettable, and therefore not clot-producing, plastic) into a peripheral vein such as the jugular and pushing it into the right ventricle or into the pulmonary artery from which well-mixed samples of venous blood can be obtained. The pulmonary artery is the best site for such sampling because laminar flows of blood exist even within the right ventricle and a mixed sample may not be obtained.

Indicator-dilution methods are widely used today for measuring cardiac output or blood flows through other regions of the circulatory system. The continuous-injection method

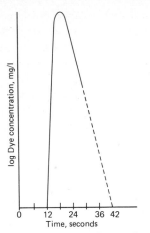

Figure 13-22 The nature of the dye dilution curve. Changes in dye concentration after injection into a vein. [After Hamilton (1953).] The curve exhibits a sudden deviation to the right, indicating the moment of recirculation of the indicator.

requires that an indicator substance (usually a colored dye or a radioactive material) be continuously injected into the venous system, preferably into the right ventricle. The material is then measured in an artery either by serial sampling or by continuously monitoring the concentration by some transducer device. The units of indicator injected per minute divided by the concentration of indicator in the arterial sample yields the cardiac output.

In rapid-injection indicator-dilution methods (which differ in principle from Fick methods), a single sample of indicator is injected into the circulation as close to the right heart as possible and its concentration is measured in an artery immediately following the heart either by serial sampling or by continuous monitoring techniques. A graph of the log indicator concentration against time is plotted. The concentration of the indicator at the sampling site first increases and then declines. The descent should be a straight line that suddenly deviates to the right at the moment when recirculation of indicator occurs (Figure 13-22). Cardiac output or flow through the system is calculated from

$$\text{Flow (l/min)} = \frac{60C}{ct} \qquad (13.3)$$

where C is the amount of indicator injected

into the system, c is the average concentration of indicator during the first circulation, and t is the time needed for complete passage of this quantity of dye through the system. In all dilution methods the determination of the moment at which recirculation of the indicator begins is a complicating factor requiring some manipulation of the data.

A variety of transducer methods are now used to determine flow rates (see Kramer et al. (1963). The electromagnetic flowmeter is based on the principle that a conductor moving at right angles to the lines of force of a magnetic field induces an electrical potential (the Faraday effect). An electromagnetic flowmeter contains a small electromagnet as a probe that can be placed around an artery or other vessel. If desired, the probe can be surgically implanted and blood flow measured in a normal freely moving animal by telemetry. The flowing blood (the conductor) induces a potential that is proportional to the velocity of flow and whose polarity is determined by the direction of flow in relation to the magnet. The potential is picked up by

Table 13-2 Heart Rates and Cardiac Output of Some Vertebrates*

Animal	Cardiac Output (ml/kg body wt/min)	Heart Rate (beats/ min)
Codfish (18°C)	9–10	30
Amphiuma	30	
Iguana (20°C)	40	20
Turtle (22°C)	60	40
Hummingbird		615
Ostrich		65
Duck	500	240
White rat	200	350
Dog	150	100
Man (resting)	85	70
Man (heavy exercise)	510	180
Elephant		30

* From M. S. Gordon (1968). *Animal Function: Principles and Adaptation.* New York: The Macmillan Company.

suitably placed electrodes and after amplification is recorded on an oscilloscope or penwriter. The method has the advantages of requiring neither opening of the arteries nor obstruction of blood flow. However, the construction of small electromagnets and the ability to record potentials without artifacts are difficulties of the technique. Ultrasonic probes, thermoelectric devices, and other transducers are also being introduced for measuring circulatory system flows.

Various measurements of cardiac output have shown that generally the cardiac output of mammals and birds is higher than that of lower vertebrates or of invertebrates when cardiac output is given on an equal weight basis (Table 13-2). Birds have very high heart rates and high cardiac outputs, and the smaller the bird the higher the heart rate. The latter is also generally true of mammals.

Electrical Activity of the Heart

13-12. Pacemakers and Conduction Systems.

Pacemakers and cardiac excitatory systems were described in Chapter 9, where the pacemaker cell was used as an example of a system that can produce spontaneous electrical activity. The various methods used to either locate or identify the type of pacemaker were also described in Chapter 9. Here I shall only briefly summarize what is known concerning the types of pacemakers found in various animal groups.

The hearts of vertebrates, tunicates, and molluscs are considered to be myogenic. There is still some debate on whether or not nerve cells occur in the hearts of some molluscans, but on the basis of electrocardiogram recordings (Section 13-13), all appear to be myogenic. In many molluscan hearts the pacemaker zone lies in the aortic region, and conduction of the impulse may be opposite in direction to the blood flow (Ripplinger, 1952). In many snails the pacemaker is diffuse, and the beat may originate from any point of the heart. The pacemaker of bivalve molluscs lies in the auricular region (Jullien and Morin, 1931).

The hearts of decapod crustaceans and of *Limulus* are neurogenic although the concept of myogenic and neurogenic hearts are not mutually exclusive. During embryonic development a myogenic heart beat is initiated in *Limulus* on the twenty-second day. Nerves do not appear until the twenty-eighth day, and only after this does the heart become neurogenic. The adult heart is accelerated by ACh, but the embryonic heart is unaffected by this substance.

Insect hearts are probably neurogenic and are regulated by extrinsic nerves and hormones. The hearts of honeybees, crickets, grasshoppers, and some cockroaches are accelerated by ACh. Some larval hearts appear to be unaffected by ACh, adrenalin, or other common cardioaccelerator or inhibitor substances. Insect hearts of some species probably contain several pacemaker zones because reversal of beat is found to occur, for example in silkworms (Gerould, 1930).

Nerve cells have been observed in the hearts of the annelids *Lumbricus* and *Arenicola* but not *Nereis*. The hearts of the first two worms are accelerated by ACh typical of neurogenic hearts. In both the annelid and the insect heart, distension of the heart by blood (which causes a stretching of the muscle fibers) is a necessary factor for an efficient contraction.

Whereas the hearts of the blood vascular systems of all vertebrates are myogenic, the lymph hearts of amphibians and fishes are usually excited directly by nerve fibers from the central nervous system. In man, as in other vertebrates with myogenic hearts, the embryonic heart begins to beat long before the differentiation of any nerve cells (His, 1893). The myxinoid heart remains nerve-free in the adult condition, and neuronal cells are found in the cardiac tissue of lampreys—probably the first vertebrate hearts to have extrinsic nervous control of the myogenic pacemaker.

The pacemaker of lower vertebrates is in the sinus venosus, which phylogenetically is the forerunner of the avian and mammalian sino-auricular node of the right atrium. Embryologically the SA node is derived from the primordial sinus venosus. The cells of embryonic heart muscle in tissue culture develop a rhythmic contraction. In the normal chick embryo coordinated heart muscle contractions begin before any nervous connections are made. The beat originates in the ventricle; as development proceeds, the point of origin moves toward the sinus venosus, and there is an increase in heart rate. In the chick heart several tissues have been shown by intracellular electrode recordings to be capable of spontaneous electrical activity, including the sinus venosus, the musculature of the sinoatrial valve, and the atrioventricular ring (Lieberman and Paes de Carvalho, 1963). In teleosts the sinus venosus, SA node, atrial floor, and the atrioventricular junction all contain potential pacemaking cells. If the sinus venosus is removed from an excised frog heart or turtle heart, the heart stops beating although after a time it may resume at a much lower rate. All of these observations point out that other regions of the heart beside the adult pacemaker may possess the ability to generate spontaneous potentials. The pacemaker of the adult heart guides the heart rate because its activity has the highest rate. It initiates a depolarization that spreads as an action potential over the cardiac muscle mass. The duration of the depolarization phase of the action potential of cardiac muscle is much shorter than that of repolarization, and that cell or group of cells with the fastest rate of spontaneous depolarization can influence all the other heart cells. It has been shown that in the embryonic rat heart a gradient of rate exists from the ventricle to the SA node, with the latter having the highest rate. It appears that all cardiac muscle cells in invertebrates are capable of spontaneous generation of potentials (see Krijgsman and Divaris, 1955).

The nature of the events underlying the development of pacemaker potentials was described in Chapter 9. The characteristic feature of the cardiac action potential is the long duration of the repolarization phase—the plateau (Figure 9-5). The plateau is especially prominent in cells of the ventricle and may be absent from atrial cells. The time course of the cardiac muscle action potential is about that of the contraction cycle. Since cardiac muscle cells have a long refractory period when they are inexcitable, a cardiac muscle cell cannot be easily restimulated during systole. This is a mechanism for ensuring that all cardiac cells contract at the same time and that the full force of contraction is available for pumping blood from the ventricles. If a stimulus should arrive just at the end of the refractory period, an extra beat (generally of the ventricle) may occur. This is the extrasystole. After an extrasystole (which sometimes occurs under normal conditions) the ventricle is in the refractory period and cannot respond to the next normal impulse arriving from the atrium. There is a compensatory pause in the ventricular beat until the next regular impulse arrives at the ventricle. The next contraction of the ventricle is more forceful than normal since the ventricle has filled with a larger than normal amount of blood, thus putting the ventricular muscle under a degree of stretch that allows a greater contraction (see Section 13-17). Because of the long duration of the repolarization phase and the consequent long refractory period, cardiac muscle, unlike striated skeletal muscle, cannot be tetanized. Stimuli are effective only during a short period in diastole. The conduction system of mammals, which allows a rapid spread of excitation over the entire heart, was also discussed in Chapter 9.

13-13. The Electrocardiogram. The electrical events occurring during the initiation and spread of the cardiac action potentials can be studied without exposing the heart. The technique of electrocardiography utilizes surface electrodes to pick up the electrical waves that pass over the heart during activity. The record of such electrical waves is the **electrocardiogram** (**ECG**; the abbreviation **EKG**, from the German, is sometimes found, especially in the older literature).

The study of electrical events associated with cardiac activity began with the work of Kolliker and Mueller in 1885 when they recorded what was called the negative deflection of the beating frog heart. In 1887 Waller made the first recording of a complete ECG. But electrocardiography received its main impetus from the work of Einthoven, who in 1903 developed the string galvanometer, an instrument sensitive enough to record the minute potentials of short duration associated with cardiac electrical activity.

Electrocardiography is based upon some extremely complicated theoretical topics in physics and biology. According to Schaefer and Haas (1962), electrocardiography can lead at best to the statement that the ECG may be adequately interpreted in light of the laws governing the behavior of electrical fields and the electrical activities of single cells. From the ECG one can gain some information about the spread of excitation over the heart, the nature of individual action potentials, and the like; and the ECG is an important clinical tool for diagnosing some pathological cardiac conditions. However, the ECG is not necessarily an indicator of heart functioning. The appearance of a normal looking ECG is no indication that cardiac muscle contractions are normal, and, conversely, impaired cardiac muscle functioning is not always evidenced by any changes in electrical activity. To diagnose pathological conditions by electrocardiography requires an extensive empirical background and experience with many ECG's.

The sequence of waves recorded from mammalian hearts includes the P wave, QRS complex, and T wave. The P wave represents the depolarization of the atria; the QRS complex represents basically the spread of excitation over the ventricles but includes also the repolarization of the atria; and the T wave represents the repolarization of the ventricles.

Figure 13-23 compares the ECG's of several vertebrate and invertebrate animals. Although the ECG is similar for most vertebrates, a V wave, representing depolarization of the sinus venosus, is found in those species in which this chamber is well developed. In fish and amphibians a small B wave is seen, preceding the T wave and indicating the depolarization of the conus arteriosus. The electrocardiogram gives an indication of whether a heart is neurogenic or myogenic. It is oscillatory, with bursts of

spikes, in the neurogenic heart. In myogenic hearts it is made up of slow waves.

In electrocardiography the connections (electrodes and wires) between the animal and the recording instrument are called **leads**. In human electrocardiography three **standard leads** are widely used and are designated as Leads I, II, and III. These are dipolar leads. Electrodes are placed on the right arm, left arm, and left leg (the actual position on the limb is unimportant since the limb can be considered simply as a wire connection—the calf or wrist areas are usually chosen for convenience when measuring the human ECG), and usually a ground lead is placed on the right leg to reduce electrical interference. The

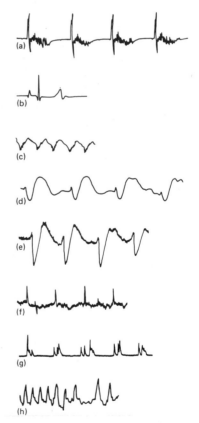

Figure 13-23 Electrocardiograms from various animals. (a) *Limulus*. (b) Eel. (c) Grasshopper. (d) Fresh water mussel. (e) Octopus. (f) Frog lymph heart. (g) Crayfish. (h) Ascidian. [From C. L. Prosser and F. A. Brown (1961) *Comparative Animal Physiology*, 2nd ed. By permission W. B. Saunders Company, Philadelphia.]

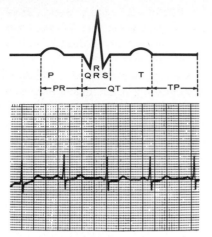

Figure 13-24 (Upper) Schematic of the human ECG showing the P, QRS, and T waves and the various important intervals. (Lower) Actual recording of a Lead I electrocardiogram from a human.

instantaneous differences in potential between the three possible pairs of leads are recorded:

Lead I   = RL (right arm, R, to left arm, L)

Lead II = RF (right arm to left leg, F)

Lead III = LF (left arm to left leg)

A human electrocardiogram recorded for Lead I is shown in Figure 13-24.

Other sets of leads are used in clinical work. F. N. Wilson in 1944 devised a set of unipolar leads in which an electrode on any of six precordial chest positions is connected to a central terminal, for example, a standard limb electrode connected into a network of electrical resistors such that its potential is unchanging and can serve as a reference for the active chest electrode. Schaefer and Haas (1962) or any standard text on electrocardiography discuss these leads in detail.

The theory underlying electrocardiographic recording and analysis cannot be described here because of lack of space. I shall only indicate that the potentials recorded by the surface electrodes represent the electrical fields produced by the moving waves of depolarization and repolarization passing over the cardiac tissue. The potentials that a pair of electrodes see depend upon the position of the electrodes as well as upon the direction of propagation of the potentials over the heart, the three-dimensional geometry of the cardiac tissue and the orientation of the heart in the thoracic cavity.

In simplest terms the heart can be considered a large dipole situated in the midst of an inhomogeneous conducting medium. Movement of the dipole causes out-spreading currents through the conducting medium, and it is these changing potential fields that are picked up by the surface electrodes.

Table 13-3 gives the various waves of interest

Table 13-3   Average Normal Pattern of a Human Lead I ECG

Wave or Interval	Amplitude (mV)	Duration (msec)	Underlying Activity
P wave	0.1	8	Atrial depolarization
P-Q interval	0.0	150–200	A-V delay time
Q wave	0.1	40–80	Ventricular depolarization
R wave	1.0	40–80	Ventricular depolarization
S wave	0.1		
S-T interval	0.0	100–250	(Period of ventricular ejection)
T wave	0.1	100	(Ventricular repolarization
T-P interval	0.0	300	(Time of heart diastole or rest)
Q-T interval	0.0	390	(Period of ventricular electrical and mechanical activity)

Total duration of ECG waves = 0.97 sec = 62 beats/min

and the intervals of the mammalian ECG. The P wave represents atrial depolarization. The P-Q interval represents the A-V delay time, the time it takes for the action potentials to pass from the AV node to the ventricles. This delay is probably caused by the time required for conduction of the impulse to the apex of the ventricles over the Purkinje conduction system before it spreads over the mass of the ventricular tissue. The final ramifications of the conducting fibers are of small diameter and therefore conduct impulses more slowly than the larger fibers of the bundles of the conducting system or the larger fibers of the cardiac muscle cells.

The Q and R waves, indications of ventricular depolarization, occur at a time when the atria are contracting. During the S-T period ventricular ejection of blood is taking place. The S deflection represents the late depolarization of the cardiac cell masses in the base of the ventricles. The T wave is due to ventricular repolarization. Again, it should be understood that the ECG represents electrical events only; correlation with mechanical activities must come from other types of studies using pressure, volume, or force transducers placed within the heart chambers.

During mechanical diastole a small potential difference (0.05 mV maximal) is sometimes seen, especially in Lead II recordings. This is the U wave, which may last, in the case of tachycardia, until the onset of the P wave. It may result from positive after-potentials of the Purkinje fibers. Such after-potentials are lacking in the main ventricular mass. Negative after-potentials may also play a role in its presence. These are known to occur in ventricular cells and can also occur as the result of stretching cardiac muscle fibers.

The ECG may be used to detect abnormalities in the cardiac rhythm and in the mammalian conduction system. Arrhythmias are disruptions of the normal heart rate, the rhythm, and the sequence of chamber excitation. The normal rhythm established by the SA node is the sinus rhythm. When the heart rate is below normal, the condition is bradycardia; when the heart rate is faster than normal, the condition is that of tachycardia. Arrhythmias are caused either by upsets in the normal sites of pacemaker activity or by disturbances in the conduction system.

Sinus arrhythmia is found in children and young adults and is a nonpathological condition in which the heart rate increases during inspiration and decreases during expiration. Sinus bradycardia (heart rate between 40 and 60 beats per minute) is due to a decrease in the rate of activity of the SA node. Sinus tachycardia (heart rate above 100 beats per minute) is due to the SA node producing impulses at a faster than normal rate. In all of these conditions the waves of the ECG have a normal appearance except for the rate.

If the SA node is damaged or when both the SA node and AV node are malfunctioning, therefore permitting either the AV node or the ventricles to assume its own slower pacemaker activity, slower nodal or ventricular rhythms may occur.

In atrial flutter a regular succession of P waves is seen in the ECG, occurring at a rate faster than the normal sinus rhythm, but only every second, third, or fourth of these P waves is followed by the normal ventricular response. The path of depolarization may be following an unusual pattern and returning to excite the SA node again before the depolarization reaches the ventricles.

If conduction pathways are damaged or blocked by drugs, various blocks to cardiac conduction are found. Conduction block can occur any place between the SA node and the ventricles but the AV node and the bundles are the likeliest sites of such blocks. In first-degree AV block the ECG shows a lengthening of the P-R interval. The AV node is particularly susceptible to anoxia and other fatigue-producing factors. In second-degree AV block atrial excitation does not lead each time to ventricular excitation and the ECG shows that all P waves are not followed by the QRS complex. The reasons why the cells between the atria and the AV node stop functioning are not known. Third-degree AV block occurs when the AV node is incapable of conducting impulses. In this case a pacemaker region in the node or in the ventricles controls the beat of the latter at a lower rate than normal.

Bundle branch block occurs when impulses pass the AV node in normal fashion but travel down only one of the two main branches of the Purkinje system. Excitation of the blocked ventricle takes place but only by a spread of current from the normal ventricle. In bundle branch block the ECG shows a greatly prolonged QRS interval (from the normal of 0.06 to 0.10 seconds to more than 0.12 seconds).

Blockages and other malfunctions of cardiac tissues can result from ischemia and infarction. Ischemia is a condition resulting from an insufficient oxygen supply and is reflected by an alteration in the T wave, presumably because cells deprived of oxygen cannot repolarize normally (among other factors the active transport systems will be functionally impaired). An infarct is any region of damaged cardiac tissue. If cardiac cells are damaged severely by oxygen lack, drugs, or other deleterious agents, scar tissue containing a high proportion of connective tissue is laid down. This process introduces electrically inexcitable material into the cardiac mass, and if such damage is extensive, the ECG pattern may show alterations. The conduction system itself may be affected if damage is widespread.

These are only a few of the abnormalities to be found in the ECG which represent impairment of the cardiac conduction of impulses. They are included here only as an indication of the types of phenomena the ECG may reveal when used as a clinical tool. It can be seen that their analysis depends on a knowledge of the normal durations of each of the ECG intervals and of the main ECG waves so that alterations in these can be determined. The amplitude of the ECG wave forms is not of such great importance because amplitude will depend upon many factors including the condition and contact of the recording electrodes. However, the direction of inflection does give some indication of cardiac electrical functioning. For detailed discussions of the clinical application of electrocardiography see Burch and Winsor (1960); Phibbs (1961); Riseman (1968); or the references in Scher (1962) or Schaefer and Haas (1962).

Other forms of electrocardiography are finding increasing use. For example, vector electrocardiography utilizes the information obtained from two standard leads displayed simultaneously on an oscilloscope or fed into a computer. If Lead I is connected to the horizontal amplifier input of an oscilloscope and if Lead III is connected to the vertical amplifier, the oscilloscope beam will trace a series of loops, one each for the P, QRS, and T waves. This type of display permits a better analysis of the ECG and shows more clearly the presence of abnormalities in the conduction system.

The electrocardiography of lower vertebrates or of the invertebrates has not reached the significance of that of mammals. For a discussion of the patterns of the ECG's of some of these animals see Zuckerman (1957).

13-14. The Cardiac Ganglion. The small number of nerve cells in the cardiac ganglia of the neurogenic hearts of crustaceans or *Limulus* constitute small integrating rhythmic systems. Cardiac ganglia have been likened to miniature central nervous systems although they differ in being capable of only a small number of functions and significant output patterns (see Maynard, 1960). They are useful preparations for studying the interactions of a few neurons arranged in a small working system. From them some useful ideas about the functioning and mechanisms of more complex nervous systems may be obtained.

The cardiac ganglion lies on the heart and contains the pacemaker cells. The number of cells depends on the species. The cardiac ganglion of the lobster *Homarus americanus* contains nine neurons as does that of a spiny lobster *Palinurus*. Other decapod crustaceans have fewer or greater numbers of neurons in the cardiac ganglion: crayfish (*Astacus*), 15; mantis shrimp (*Squilla*), 14; isopod (*Ligia*), 6; true crabs, Brachyura, 9. In all of these organisms the removal of the cardiac ganglion stops the heart.

In *Palinurus* the nine cells are divided into

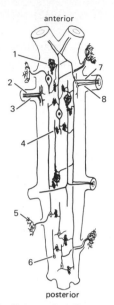

Figure 13-25 Schematic diagram of the heart and cardiac ganglion of *Panulirus*. 1, Large neuron cell body; 2, inhibitor nerve fiber; 3, accelerator nerve fiber; 4, neuropile in cardiac ganglion; 5, dendritic arborizations on which inhibitor fibers terminate; 6, small neuron cell body; 7, inhibitory nerve fiber; 8, accelerator nerve fiber. There are five large anterior and four smaller posterior cells. Normally in decapod crustaceans the four smaller cells are pacemakers, while the larger neurons are followers or motor neurons. [After Maynard (1954).]

er cells often show spontaneous activity although not in bursts. The pacemaker (or driver) cells have a slow pacemaker potential that spreads over the cell body and that gives rise to spikes in the axon. The pacemaker potential arises in either the dendritic or somal region of the neuron.

Follower cells exhibit several types of potentials including slow maintained depolarizations on which are superimposed small synaptic potentials caused by impulses arriving from the pacemaker cells. Follower cells also show spikes.

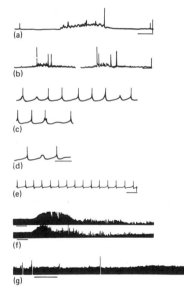

Figure 13-26 Potentials recorded from cardiac ganglion cells. (a) Slow depolarizations and (b) small synaptic potentials and varying sized spikes from follower cells of crab cardiac ganglion. (c) and (d) Continuous records showing pacemaker potentials in different relations to spike and not necessarily giving rise to spikes from spontaneously active pacemaker cells of lobster cardiac ganglion. (e) Same but with different time base. (f) Two records of slow waves and spikes from a multifiber preparation of an isolated cardiac ganglion from *Limulus*. (g) Single fiber spikes discharging at declining frequency from a *Limulus* cardiac ganglion. [Records from C. L. Prosser and F. A. Brown (1961). *Comparative Animal Physiology*, 2nd ed. By permission W. B. Saunders Company, Philadelphia. Original data on crab and lobster from Bullock and Terzuolo (1957). Original data on *Limulus* from Prosser (1943).]

two groups (Figure 13-25). The five anterior cells are larger than the four posterior ones. All are large enough to be implanted with microelectrodes and their potentials have been recorded (see Bullock, 1961). The neurons fire in a coordinated burst at the beginning of each systole and then are quiescent for the remainder of that cardiac cycle.

The pacemaker is located in the posterior group of smaller cells and may be a single cell. The five larger cells are the major motoneurons to the cardiac muscle and are called **follower cells**. They may be interconnected in any of several ways. Each primary pacemaker discharges many impulses (20 to 90) in each cardiac burst (Figure 13-26), and there are also present slow waves on which spikes are superimposed. Interburst impulses are also recorded. When separated from primary cells, the follow-

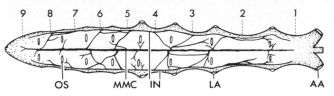

Figure 13-27 The tube heart of *Limulus polyphemus*. Segments are indicated by numbers. AA, Anterior arteries; IN, lateral nerves; LA, lateral arteries; MMC, medial nerve cord; OS, ostia. [After Carlson (1904).]

Many types of patterns of discharge have been recorded from the follower cells of various cardiac ganglia. Some possess interburst spontaneous impulses, others contain only bursts of spikes without synaptic potentials, some lack sustained depolarizations. It has been shown that a large follower neuron can affect another follower electrotonically. Two impulses can exist simultaneously in different parts of the same follower neuron. Follower cells cannot influence driver cells by spikes but may affect them electrotonically.

The crustacean cardiac ganglion is innervated by both accelerator and inhibitor nerve fibers from the central nervous system. Inhibition may affect driver and follower cells equally, or it may affect one cell type more than the other (Maynard, 1966). Stretching of the cardiac muscle increases the beat frequency possibly by mechanical stimulation of some neurons in the ganglion. Studies of the type discussed here for *Palinurus* have also been made for *Homarus*.

The *Limulus* heart (Figure 13-27) has eight pairs of ostia dividing it into nine segments. From the anterior half run five pairs of arteries and a single anteromedian artery. In addition to a dorsal cardiac ganglion with small multipolar neurons scattered through it and with large unipolar neurons located in segments 4 and 5, the heart has lateral nerves running along each side connected by thinner nerve fibers to a medial nerve. Conduction of excitation is from the pacemaker cells of the dorsal ganglion to the median and lateral nerves innervating the cardiac muscle cells.

Local warming applied to the fourth and fifth segments of the ganglion accelerates the heart rate, indicating that the pacemaker cells are in this region—probably the large unipolar

neurons. Removal of the ganglion stops the heart beat, but if the heart is then stretched or inflated with perfusion fluid, local and peristaltic contractions occur. This illustrates the capabilities of the cardiac cells themselves for spontaneous activity.

The blood entering the heart of *Limulus* is freshly oxygenated blood that has passed from the book gills into the pericardial cavity and then through the valved ostia into the heart.

Inhibition of the cardiac ganglia of crustacea occurs when the cardioinhibitory fibers are stimulated at frequencies above 5 to 10 seconds. Cardioaccelerator fibers usually require a faster frequency of stimulation to produce any effect on the ganglion. Inhibition usually has both negative chronotropic and inotropic effects. Gamma-amino butyric acid mimics the action of the inhibitor and may be the physiological inhibitor substance.

In addition to control by inhibitor and accelerator nerve fibers, there are indications that hormonal control is also present in crustaceans. Accelerator substances have been found in extracts of brain, eyestalks, and pericardial organs—all sites of neuroendocrine activity. However, the hormones themselves, the site of release, and the triggering agents for their release are uncertain. Just before and just after molting in some prawns, the heart rate increases. This is another indication that the heart rate may be controlled by hormones, for this period is one of intense hormonal activity in crustaceans.

The normal pathways of control of the cardiac ganglia are complex, and much more remains to be discovered concerning the physiological control of heart rate and amplitude in the neurogenic heart.

13-15. The Effect of Ions on the Heart. Sidney Ringer (1880–1882) in a series of classical studies showed that an excised heart continues to beat only if the perfusion medium contains Na^+, K^+, and Ca^{2+} in proper proportions and concentrations. The anions in the medium appear to have little influence unless they are toxic; it is the cation content which is most important. Although the three ions listed above are sufficient for most hearts, those of marine organisms often require Mg^{2+} as well (physiological perfusion solutions are given in Chapter 14).

Ion effects may be on the pacemaker, the conduction system, the contractile machinery, or all three. In some cases it is difficult to precisely determine the site of action of a particular combination of ions or of a particular concentration of ion. The role and requirement for ions in potential development and contractile activity have already been described in previous chapters. Here it is worthwhile to point out that alterations of the ionic environment, especially that of pacemaker cells, offers a good mechanism for controlling cardiac rate and, perhaps, tension development—an aspect of cardiac functioning to be considered in the last part of this chapter.

Table 13-4 lists the effects of various ions in higher or lower than normal concentrations on the hearts of various animals. It is seen that although generalizations can be made about the effects of high and low concentrations of Na^+, K^+, and C^{2+} on hearts, differences do exist especially between neurogenic and myogenic hearts with regard to responses to ionic concentrations and specific ions. Generally, high Na^+ stimulates the rate of the heart (by increasing pacemaker activity) and also increases the amplitude of contraction (by acting on the contractile machinery). In very high Na^+ concentrations the heart stops in systole.

High K^+ generally leads to an increased heart rate in vertebrates, but this is followed by a period of decreased conduction rate and decreased contraction so that the heart finally stops in diastole. Molluscan hearts are not very sensitive to changes in K^+ but are accelerated by 6-fold changes in K^+ concentration.

Low Ca^{2+} results in an increase of spontaneous activity of pacemaker cells. Increases in Ca^{2+} increase the threshold required to stimulate cardiac muscle cells (Weidmann, 1955). High Ca^{2+} also increases cardiac muscle tension development, whereas low Ca^{2+} reduces it. Generally Mg^{2+} has little effect unless the Ca^{2+} concentration is lowered. Under these conditions prolongation of the action potential occurs. The effects of Ca^{2+} and Mg^{2+} are difficult to interpret because each appears to have stabilizing influences on membrane structure as well as being involved in transport and other membrane functions.

The effects of any of these ions on the heart must be correlated with the actions of other ions, as well as with such factors as frequency of stimulation (if any), temperature, degree of stretch of muscle fibers, and so forth. For example, following a period of rest, the heart shows a steplike increase in successive contractions—the staircase effect (or treppe) first demonstrated by Bowditch (1871). A high tension without treppe is also produced by reducing the K^+ or increasing the Ca^{2+} concentration. The rate of rise of the treppe is facilitated by increasing Ca^{2+} or reducing K^+. Such results are obtained with no effect on the action potential amplitude, indicating that these effects are probably directly on the contractile machinery (including the excitation-contraction coupling system).

The depolarization of cardiac cells produced by lowering K^+ is reversed by simultaneously lowering the Ca^{2+}. Thus the actions of these two ions appear to be closely linked.

An excised heart may be kept beating only as long as the ionic environment is controlled with respect to both the particular cations present as well as their relative proportions. Single ions, even in isosmotic solution, are always toxic to an excised heart. It is the balanced activity of ions on pacemaker and contractile activity that keeps the heart beating normally.

13-16. Drugs and the Heart. The original experiments of Loewi (see Chapter 7) demonstrated that the secretion of acetylcholine by the vagus nerve was responsible for slowing the frog heart beat. Later work showed that heart

Table 13-4 Typical Effects of Ions in High (Supraoptimal) and Reduced (Suboptimal) Concentrations on Hearts with Respect to Rate, Amplitude, Tone, and State when Arrested*

ANIMAL	RATE†	AMPLITUDE	TONE	ARREST
HIGH SODIUM				
Frog (*Rana*)	+	Slight +	+	Tends to systole
Oyster (*Ostrea*)	+	+		Systole
Crayfish (*Cambarus*)	+	+	−	Systole (pure NaCl)
Limulus	+	−		
Mosquito larva (*Anopheles*)	+			
LOW SODIUM				
Frog	−	+ (conduction impaired)		Systole
Crayfish	−	−		Diastole
HIGH POTASSIUM				
Frog	+, then −	−	0, slight −	Diastole
Oyster	+		+	6X diastole
Clam (*Venus*)	Irregular		−	Systole
Spider crab (*Maja*)	+	+	+	Systole
Limulus	+	Fast weak beat		Systole, then relaxes
Mosquito larva	+	Fast weak beat		
LOW POTASSIUM				
Frog	Slight −	0, slight −	−	Systole
Oyster	Slight +			Systole
Clam	0, slight +	−		
Lobster (*Homarus*)	+			Diastole
Limulus	+	−		Diastole
HIGH CALCIUM				
Frog	Slight +	+	+	Systole
Oyster	−	+	+	Diastole
Clam	−	+, then −		6X diastole
Snail (*Helix*)	Slight −	−	−	Diastole
Crayfish	−			Diastole
Mosquito larva	+			
LOW CALCIUM				
Frog	Slight +, − in zero	−	−	Diastole
Oyster	+	−	+	Diastole
Clam	+	Slight −		Semisystole
Snail	0		Slight +	
Crayfish	+			Systole in zero Ca²⁺
Limulus	+			Systole

* From C. L. Prosser, and F. A. Brown (1961). **Comparative Animal Physiology.** 2nd ed. By permission from W. B. Saunders Company, Philadelphia.

† +, increase; −, decrease in activity.

rate was increased by the application of adrenalin or of noradrenalin. The antagonistic actions of the parasympathetic and sympathetic nervous systems provides a basic control mechanism for heart rate and cardiac output in the vertebrates.

The chemical transmitters mentioned above act directly on the pacemaker cells of the vertebrate heart. ACh reduces the slope of the pacemaker potential, inhibiting the rising pre-potential as well as the action potential. This is a result of the increased membrane permeability to K^+ brought about by ACh. The outward flux of K^+ is increased and depolarization is inhibited and, in fact, the membrane is hyper-polarized.

Catecholamines, such as adrenalin and nor-adrenalin, increase the rate of development of pacemaker potentials, thus producing a faster rate of firing of action potentials in pacemaker cells. The amplitude (or overshoot) of the action potential is also raised. These effects are brought about by an increased influx of Na^+, increasing the rate at which depolarization occurs. Adrenalin, secreted into the blood stream from the adrenal glands, is more effective than noradrenaline released by nerve fibers, in increasing the vertebrate heart rate.

The effects of these drugs on hearts other than those of vertebrates are not necessarily the same. In neurogenic hearts, for example, ACh causes an increased rate of pacemaker firing while adrenalin has little or no effect.

In some molluscs 5-hydroxytryptamine appears to be the excitatory (cardioaccelerator) transmitter. The application of 5-HT prevents hydrolysis of ACh by acetylcholinesterase and there is a resultant potentiation of the inhibitory effect of ACh in vertebrates, snails, and bivalves. Potentiation of ACh acceleration is found in crustaceans, insects, annelids, and *Limulus*. Acetylcholinesterase has been found in all the above hearts.

Several types of drugs are used experimentally or clinically on the heart. The cardiac glycosides (including the familiar digitalis, originally isolated from the foxglove, *Digitalis purpurea*) contain one or more molecules of monosaccharide sugar attached to a cyclopen-tanoperhydrophenanthrene steroid nucleus (Figure 2-23). These compounds directly augment the contractile force produced by the myocardium. They may also influence cardiac activity by acting on the vagal slowing rate, depression of the speed of impulse conduction, changes in ventricular excitability, or by altering peripheral resistance and venous return. Generally cardiac glycosides are noted for their positive inotropic effect. In low concentrations they increase the respiration of cardiac cells, an activity seen only on whole cells, not homogenates (see Hadju and Leonard, 1959).

Ouabain (= G-strophantin) is another cardiac glycoside whose actions on active transport were discussed in Chapter 6. It influences the force developed by cardiac muscle cells by influencing the rate at which tension can be developed (Wallace et al., 1963; Siegel and Sonnenblick, 1963). Goodman and Gilman (1965) discuss these substances in some detail. Generally cardiac glycoside action is related to their influences on ATP and to the transfer of energy to the contractile proteins associated with ionic transport mechanisms at the cell membrane and importantly at intracellular membranes.

The veratrine alkaloids are another group of plant derivatives with a generally positive inotropic action. Secondarily they alter the electrical properties of pacemaker cells and cause a bradycardia. Large doses result in extrasystoles and fibrillation. Veratrine reduces the conduction velocity along Purkinje fibers and causes a partial AV block.

Quinidine, an optical isomer of quinine, is a drug used to reduce atrial fibrillation. It lengthens the refractory period of atrial cells and thus reduces the maximal frequency at which atrial cells can produce action potentials. Quinidine also reduces the twitch tension of isolated cardiac muscle fibers, an indication that it may also perform this function in the intact animal.

These various drugs, as well as many others, work by either altering the permeability properties of pacemaker or cardiac muscle cell membranes or in some cases may directly act on the actomyosin system or the excitation-contraction coupling system.

Control of the Heart and Central Circulation

13-17. Starling's Law of the Heart. Nervous, hormonal, and physical agents are all involved in the variety of mechanisms that regulate heart rate and cardiac output. In this part of the chapter, we shall be interested primarily in those systems used to control cardiac output and cardiac activity as opposed to local controls that take care of local requirements in the peripheral circulation. Note that if the flow to one organ is increased, either the overall cardiac output must increase or the resistance of other organs must increase so that arterial pressure—vital to capillary functioning—is prevented from large fluctuations. It is by altering the activity of the heart that the mean arterial blood pressure in mammals is kept relatively constant despite the many fluctuations in local pressures, flow rates, and volumes that occur. Because of the many varied demands made upon the circulatory system, including especially those involved with respiration, temperature regulation, and excretory organ functioning, the controls exercised over the circulatory system are very complex. I shall discuss here the mammalian system because most is known about it, but even in the mammalian circulatory system much remains to be learned about the coordinating and integrating mechanisms that provide the regulation.

The first mechanism for controlling the cardiac output to be discussed here is based on properties of muscle cells already discussed in Chapter 10 and mentioned in this chapter several times. The Law of the Heart originated by E. H. Starling (1918) states that the energy of contraction of ventricular muscle is a function of the length of the muscle fibers at the start of shortening. If the ventricles are filled to a greater extent than usual, the subsequent systolic contraction is greater, and a greater stroke volume results. In this way the heart automatically controls the output according to the degree of input (or filling of the ventricles). Assuming that under normal conditions a similar volume of blood enters the ventricles before each contraction, if for any reason a residual volume of blood is left behind at one beat, the ventricles at the next beat will contain a larger than normal volume that will stretch the cardiac muscle fibers and cause them to respond with a greater contraction.

This regulating mechanism is thus based upon the fact that a muscle responds with a greater contraction if its fibers are stretched at the time contraction is initiated (the effect seen in preloading a muscle). There are, of course, limits within which this law can operate and excessive stretching, for example, results in less work being done by the heart.

Since the time of Starling, this law has been variously repudiated and reinstated. Starling himself said that the law as stated applied only to the isolated heart preparation. In the intact animal, hormonal and nervous controls are also operating and thus modifying the Starling mechanism. If these statements are kept in mind, then there is no difficulty in assessing the importance of the mechanism. There is no doubt that in the isolated mammalian heart the ventricular end diastolic volume is the determining factor controlling the contractile forces and the output volumes of the next systole. Starling's law operates in the intact animal but so do several other mechanisms.

Nervous and hormonal controls are responsible for adjusting the overall cardiac output under different conditions in the intact animal (Hamilton 1955). A major function of the Starling mechanism in the intact animal is to ensure that the volumes of blood ejected by the right and left ventricles over a given period of time are maintained equal. If, for example, right ventricular flow falls behind left ventricular flow, excess volumes in the right ventricle cause a greater contraction and a greater cardiac output in the next systole. This condition is maintained until the situation is corrected. In this way equal blood volumes are removed into the pulmonary and systemic circuits.

13-18. Innervation of the Mammalian Heart. The major elements regulating the arterial blood pressure and the cardiac rate are feedback loops involving the central nervous

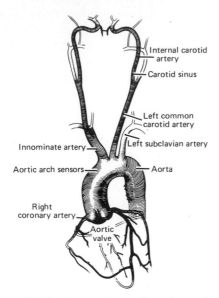

Figure 13-28 The aorta and major arteries supplying the head region in humans. The aortic wall and carotid sinus are major sites of sensory neurons (baroreceptors and chemoreceptors) supplying information to control centers for cardiac rate and vasomotor control in the medulla.

system, especially the parasympathetic and sympathetic divisions (see Chapter 11). The main controlling elements of the cardiovascular system are nerve centers found in the medulla. Endocrine secretions also aid in regulating both cardiac and blood vessel activities. The controlled elements include both the heart and the blood vessels, but in this section I shall consider only the heart. Blood vessel regulation is considered in Section 13-19. Feedback sensors exist in various parts of the circulatory system as well as in other regions of the body. Sensory elements in the aorta and in the carotid arteries are primarily responsible for overall cardiac and circulatory performance (Figure 13-28).

Figure 13-29 diagrams schematically the major nervous pathways and the location of the major sensory receptors concerned with cardiac control. As previously stated, sympathetic nerve fibers form cardioaccelerator nerves with endings on the atrial musculature. These neurons release noradrenalin and cause the heart rate to increase. Parasympathetic nerve fibers travel to the heart via the vagus

nerve and act as cardioinhibitory fibers by their release of ACh, which slows down pacemaker activity and thus slows the heart rate. The firing rate of these two groups of motor fibers is controlled by the antagonistic centers located in the medulla: the cardioaccelerator and cardioinhibitory centers.

The purpose of this control system is to increase heart rate whenever blood volume or blood pressure falls in the main arterial system and to decrease heart rate whenever blood volume or pressure increases above a normal level. It may be noted that an increase in heart rate serves to increase the minute volume only up to a point. At very high heart rates, the stroke volume begins to decrease, as a shortened diastolic period does not permit the ventricle to fill to its normal volume.

Pressoreceptors (or baroreceptors) are sensory endings that respond to changes in pressure. Many pressoreceptor endings are located in the walls of the aortic arch and in the region of the carotid sinus. Increases in arterial pressure cause a distension of the blood vessel walls and excite the pressoreceptor endings, so that their frequency of firing is increased. These receptor endings, as well as many others, fire

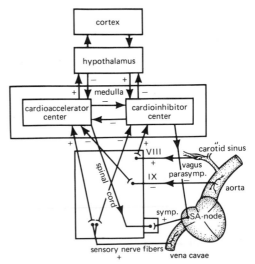

Figure 13-29 Schematic of pathways for controlling cardioacceleration and cardioinhibition. Activation activity is indicated by +, inhibitory activity is indicated by —.

continuously. It is the rate of firing that determines the particular responses made in the coordinating and integrating centers of the central nervous system. At present the factors or mechanisms that determine the normal level of firing and response are not known. Carotid and aortic pressoreceptors in the dog are inactive below 60 mm Hg blood pressure, and their firing rate reaches a peak in the range of 160 to 200 mm Hg. Pressures below 60 mm Hg in the aorta or carotid arteries result in serious derangements of brain blood flow and usually death.

Carotid receptors transmit information to the central nervous system via the ninth cranial nerve (glossopharyngeal); aortic receptors transmit information via sensory fibers of the tenth cranial nerve (vagus). If the pressure in the aorta or in the carotid sinus goes above normal, there is an increased firing rate of the sensory neurons to the cardioinhibitory center. Nerve impulses are sent out through the vagus that slow down the heart rate and thus decrease arterial pressure. Simultaneously, inhibitory impulses are sent from the cardioinhibitory center to the cardioaccelerator center, and the stream of impulses through the sympathetic system is reduced. The reverse activities occur if the blood pressure drops below normal. Thus a fine control over the rate of the heart is achieved by the two antagonistic centers and by the sympathetic and parasympathetic outputs from the central nervous system.

Chemoreceptor endings are found in the aortic body and in the carotid arteries. These are primarily concerned with controlling gas (oxygen and carbon dioxide) levels in the blood by their actions on the respiratory system. But under severe stress conditions their stimulation will also alter cardiac rates. As noted earlier, respiratory activities do play a role in affecting the cardiac rate and the volume of ventricle filling.

The carotid sinus reflex and the aortic reflex are the dominant systems for the regulation of blood pressure in the arteries. Regulation of cardiac output is achieved by Starling's law in so far as maintaining an equal output of the two sides of the heart. Cardiac output, per se,

appears to have no particular homeostatic regulation except indirectly by regulation of blood pressure. However, the activity of sympathetic neurons does affect stroke volume to some slight degree. Adrenalin and other catecholamines not only increase heart rate through their effects on the pacemaker but also have a positive inotropic effect. They increase the contractile effort of the cardiac musculature.

Although various other reflexes have been described by various workers as having some part in cardiac control, most are not understood or are difficult to experimentally verify. Only one—**the Bainbridge reflex**—will be discussed here. In 1915 Bainbridge discovered that intravenous injections of blood or saline produced a tachycardia in dogs. The tachycardia was not produced when the vagus nerves were transected. It was suggested that receptors in the great veins or in the left atrium responded to venous distension and caused an increase in heart rate which quickly removed the excess volume on the venous side. However, the expected tachycardia did not always result upon venous distension, and only in the past few years has any light been shed on the activity of this reflex system. Venous distension may increase or decrease the heart rate depending on the initial level of the heart rate (Jones, 1962). When the heart rate of dogs is below 140 beats per minute, intravenous injections usually result in cardiac acceleration. At more rapid initial rates, injections into the venous system slow the heart. Thus the reflex seems to be a mechanism for keeping the heart rate within a given range. At present the nervous pathways of this complex reflex are not known.

As indicated in Figure 13-30, there are connections between the cardioaccelerator and cardioinhibitory centers of the medulla and also connections between these centers and other regions of the brain. The heart rate can be altered by activity in higher centers. It is a common human experience that various emotional states can accelerate or slow down the heart rate. Emotional centers in the cortex and centers in the hypothalamus provide inputs into the medullary centers. Scientific evidence is now available that heart rate and other visceral

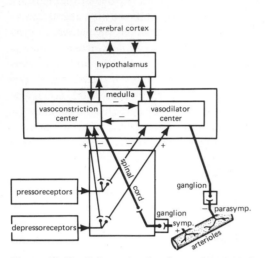

Figure 13-30 Schematic of pathways for control of vasomotor activity. Activation activity is indicated by +; inhibitory activity is indicated by −.

responses can be learned and controlled (Miller, 1969).

Endocrine glands play an indirect role in the control of heart rate and stroke volume. The release of adrenaline by the adrenal medulla is under the partial control of sympathetic nerves influenced by the cardioaccelerator center in the medulla. Under proper conditions, for example, in the flight or fight reflex of mammals, adrenalin is released into the blood stream and among other actions increases the heart rate and also the contractile force of the cardiac musculature. The adrenal medulla and other endocrine glands also aid in maintaining the proper metabolic and ionic environment for correct heart activity.

The cardiac centers are closely integrated with the vasomotor centers to be described in the next section. The regulation of cardiovascular activity is maintained by the coordinated actions of both groups of centers.

13-19. Vasomotor Control. In sections of Chapters 12 and 13 some factors responsible for local control of the peripheral circulation have been mentioned. Here we shall be concerned with the central nervous system regulation of vasomotor tone, although this subject cannot be properly separated from that of local regulation.

Control over the tone of arteriolar smooth muscle is maintained by two sets of nerves: vasoconstrictor fibers, which cause a contraction of the vascular smooth muscle, and vasodilator fibers, which bring about relaxation of these muscles. Although the activity of these neurons may be modified by metabolites released by a tissue, by adrenalin released by the adrenal medulla, or by histamine or ATP in some arterioles and arteries, their activity is also under the control of vasomotor centers in the medulla: the vasoconstrictor and vasodilator centers (Figure 13-30).

All vasoconstrictor fibers are part of the sympathetic system. Most vasodilator fibers are parasympathetic in origin, but one group is sympathetic and originates in the thoracolumbar region of the spinal cord. In addition to the pressoreceptors in the aortic arch and the carotid sinus, many other sensory neurons also affect vasomotor tone in various regions of the body. In fact almost every sensory nerve contains some pressor and depressor fibers. Any sensory neuron that promotes vasoconstriction is a **pressor nerve** since an increase in vascular tone causes an increase in blood pressure in that vessel. Sensory neurons causing vasodilation and a resulting fall in blood pressure are **depressor nerves**.

Stimulation of the pressoreceptors in the aortic arch and carotid sinus by higher than normal pressures leads not only to a slowing down of the heart rate but also a vasodilation of the major blood vessels. Both activities lead to a lowering of the blood pressure generally.

Although vasoconstrictors have a general distribution, vasodilators have a more limited distribution and their action is more localized. They do not control blood pressure generally nor do they affect the overall distribution of blood over large areas. Dilators are especially common in sweat glands and the walls of the digestive tract—sites where during temperature regulation, absorption of nutrients, or secretion of digestive enzymes, large amounts of blood may be required to flow.

In addition to their action on arterioles,

vasomotor dilators and constrictors also inner-vate some veins. Under increasing pressure in the aorta, for example, not only does the heart slow down because of an increased parasympathetic input to the pacemaker, but peripheral arterioles dilate either because of vasodilator activity or reduced sympathetic vasoconstrictor output. There is also a decrease in venomotor tone which reduces central venous pressure, that is, there is a shift of blood from the arterial to the venous side due to increased venous distensibility. Under hypotensive conditions, the reverse effects are seen.

It should be noted that stimulation of a vasoconstrictor nerve to a local region produces an increase in the peripheral resistance in that region, a local increase in blood pressure, a decreased amount of blood flow through the region, and a fall in venous pressure. Such changes will not influence overall circulatory blood pressure or blood flows in the cardiovascular system if the region affected is small. Because local strong stimulation, for example, cold or heat applied to a finger, will cause responses primarily only in that region, it is thought that accessory vasocontrol centers may exist in other parts of the central nervous system, which control such localized responses without making demands on the main vaso-motor centres in the medulla. It is perhaps well to emphasize that almost any strong local stimulus will produce vasoconstriction in the region to which the stimulus is applied, indicating the widespread occurrence of pressor nerves. But it should also be remembered that in some cases the stimuli are acting directly on the muscles of the vascular wall.

As was the case with cardiac rate, the degree of vasomotor activity is also influenced by higher brain centers. The emotional response of blushing is a familiar example of such higher control over vasomotor activity and represents a dilation of vascular muscles in the skin and a consequent increased blood flow through the smaller vessels.

Vasomotor tone is influenced by a bewildering variety of chemicals at the local level. The vasomotor actions of adrenalin and nor-adrenalin are very different, for example.

Adrenalin is a constrictor in skin and kidney blood vessels but a dilator in low concentration in muscle, liver, and coronary vessels. Nor-adrenalin is also a vasoconstrictor, or has no effect. ACh when perfused into most tissues causes vasodilation. Pituitary hormones such as vasopressin and antidiuretic hormone cause vasoconstriction and increased blood pressure. Bradykinin, another polypeptide hormone, is released during the activity of sweat glands and is a potent vasodilator. Angiotensin, an octa-peptide in the active form (see Chapter 14), a potent depressor substance found in the kidney, and bradykinin not only act directly on blood vessels but also seem to stimulate the secretion of other hormones by the adrenal medulla (Rovick and Randall, 1967, review the activities of these various substances).

Obviously then, the control of vasomotor activity is a complex one. This is not surprising in light of the many different requirements of various tissues and the different conditions under which animals may be required to function.

13-20. Integration of Circulatory Controls. The nature of the controls over cardiac activity and vasomotor tone have been briefly reviewed in the preceding sections. Little can be said about the nature of these controls in other than mammals, and even here much more information is needed. It should be stressed that this chapter (and the preceding one) have viewed the circulatory system in isolation from the other organ and homeostatic systems of the animal. In the following chapters the story of the circulatory system will be completed as ion and solute balance, temperature regulation, and respiration are discussed. Each of these homeostatic systems makes further demands on the circulatory system and increases the complexity of controls required for circulatory functioning. This is especially true of the birds and mammals—organisms that regulate more activities and with a finer degree of control than other animals do.

From what has been already said it should be apparent that vasomotor and cardiac control mechanisms are not isolated from one another.

The coordination and integration of these activities is a basic function of the central nervous system operating in conjunction with the endocrine system. Circulatory system regulation can be understood only when it is clear that both central and local control mechanisms exist. But how the circulatory system meets the often conflicting demands of other homeostatic operations is not known in any detail. Again, these various complexities and demands made on the circulatory system will become clearer when other organ systems are discussed in the following chapters.

At present the complexity of the overall controls and regulatory mechanisms is such that not much can be said here about these activities as they must take place in the whole animal. Systems analysis, while solving a few of the problems of circulatory control, has not yet reached any great stage of advancement because many of the factors involved have not been quantitated. Some of the problems of circulatory integration and control are discussed by Folkow et al. (1965) and Warner (1965).

References and Readings

Alexandrowicz, J. S. (1960). "Innervation of the hearts of *Sepia officinalis.*" *Acta Zool.* (Stockholm) **41**: 65–100.

Alexandrowicz, J. S. (1962). "An accessory organ of the circulatory system in *Sepia* and *Loligo.*" *J. Marine Biol. Assoc.* (U.K.) **42**: 405–418.

Berne, R. M. and M. B. Levy (1967). **Cardiovascular Physiology.** St. Louis, Mo.: The C. V. Mosby Company. 254 pp.

Boolootian, R. A. (1964). "A primitive heart in the Echinoid *Strongylocentrotus purpuratus.*" *Science* **145**: 173–175.

Boolootian, R. A. (1966). **Physiology of Echinodermata.** New York: Academic Press, Inc. 840 pp.

Bowditch, H. P. (1871). "Über die Eigenthümlichkeiten der Reizbarkeit, welche die Muskelfastern des Herzens Zeigen." *Ber. Sachs. ges. (Akad.) Wiss.* **23**: 652–689.

von Brücke, E. T. (1925). "Die Bewegung der Körpersäfte." *Winterstein's Handb. vergl. Physiol.* **1**: 826–1110.

Buchsbaum, R. (1948). **Animals Without Backbones,** 2nd ed. Chicago: University of Chicago Press. 405 pp.

von Buddenbrock, W. (1965). "Blut und Herz." **Vergleichende Physiologie,** Vol. 6. Basel: Birkhauser Verlag.

Bullock, T. H. (1961). "The origins of patterned nervous discharge." *Behavior* **17**: 48–59.

Bullock, T. H. and C. A. Terzuolo (1957). "Diverse forms of activity in the somata of spontaneous and integrating ganglion cells." *J. Physiol.* (London) **138**: 341–364.

Burch, G. E. and T. Winsor (1966). **A Primer of Electrocardiography.** Philadelphia: Lea & Febiger. 304 pp.

Burton, A. C. (1965). **Physiology and Biophysics of the Circulation.** Chicago: Yearbook Medical Publishers, Inc. 217 pp.

Carlson, A. J. (1904). "The nervous origin of heart-beat in *Limulus* and the nervous nature of co-ordination or conduction in the heart." *Am. J. Physiol.* **12**: 67–74.

Carlson, A. J. (1905). "Comparative physiology of the invertebrate heart." *Biol. Bull.* **8**: 123–168.

Chacalos, E. H. (1967). "Variations in small and large vessel volumes caused by cations, adrenaline, and histamine." *J. Physiol.* (London) **212**: 141–158.

Chapman, C. B., D. Jensen, and K. Wildenthal (1963). "On circulatory control mechanisms in the Pacific hagfish." *Circulation Res.* **12**: 427–440.

Chapman, C. B. and G. E. Newell (1947). "The role of the body fluid in relation to movement in soft-bodied invertebrates. The burrowing of *Arenicola.*" *Proc. Roy. Soc.* (London) **B134**: 431–455.

Clark, A. J. (1927). **Comparative Physiology of the Heart.** New York: Cambridge University Press. 157 pp.

Cole, F. J. (1926). "A monograph on the general morphology of the myxinoid fishes based on a study of *Myxine.* VI. The morphology of the vascular system." *Trans. Roy. Soc.* (Edinburgh) **54**: 309–342.

Couteaux, R. and P. Laurent (1958). "Observations au microscope éléctronique sur l'innervation cardiques des téléosteens." *Bull. Assoc. Anat.* **98**: 230.

DeGraaf, A. R. (1957). "Investigations into the distribution of blood in the heart and aortic arches of *Xenopus laevis.*" *J. Exp. Biol.* **34**: 143–172.

Drew, G. A. (1907). "The habits and movements of the razor shell clam *Ensis directus.*" *Biol. Bull.* **12**: 127–138.

Einthoven, W. (1903). "Die galvanometrische Registrierung des menschlichen EKG, zugleich eine Beurteilung der Anwendung des Capillar-Elektrometers in der Physiologie." *Pflüg. Arch. ges. Physiol.* **99**: 472.

Ellis, C. H. (1944). "The mechanism of extension of the legs of spiders." *Biol. Bull.* **86**: 41–50.

Faber, J. J. and J. H. Purvis (1963). "Conduction of cardiovascular sound along arteries." *Circulation Res.* **12**: 308–316.

Farmanfarmaian, A. (1963). "Respiration in echinoderms." *Int. Congr. Zool.* **16**: 3.

Fischer, H. (1951). "Uber die funktionelle Bedeutung des Spiralverlaufes der Muskulatur in der Arterienwald." *Morph. Jahrb.* **91**: 394–446.

Folkow, B. (1955). "Nervous control of blood vessels." *Physiol. Rev.* **35**: 629.

Folkow, B., C. Heymans, and E. Neil (1965). "Integrated aspects of cardiovascular regulation." In: **Handbook of Physiology,** Section 3: Circulation. (W. F. Hamilton, ed.), Vol. 3, pp. 1787–1824. Washington, D.C.: American Physiological Society.

Foxon, G. H. (1955). "Problems of the double circulation in vertebrates." *Biol. Rev. Cambridge Philos. Soc.* **30**: 196–228.

Foxon, G. H. (1964). "Blood and respiration." In: **Physiology of the Amphibia.** (J. A. Moore, ed.), pp. 151–209. New York: Academic Press, Inc.

Foxon, G. H., H. J. Griffith, and M. Price (1956). "The mode of action of the heart of the green lizard *Lecerta viridis.*" *Proc. Zool. Soc.* (London) **126**: 145–157.

Gerould, J. H. (1930). "History of the discovery of the heart beat in insects." *Science* **71**: 264–265.

Goodman, L. S. and A. Gilman, eds. (1965). **The Pharmacological Basis of Therapeutics,** 5th ed. New York: The Macmillan Company.

Gordon, M. S. (1968). **Animal Function: Principles and Adaptations.** New York: The Macmillan Company. 560 pp.

Grassé, P. (1948–). **Traite de Zoologie.** 17 volumes, not complete. Paris: Masson et Cie. (see vol. 5).

Greene, C. W. (1900). "Contributions to the physiology of the California hagfish, *Polistrotrema stouti.*" I. The anatomy and physiology of the caudal heart. *Am. J. Physiol.* **3**: 366–382.

Greenfield, L. J. and A. G. Morrow (1961). "Cardiovascular hemodynamics of crocodilians." *J. Surg. Res.* **1**: 97–103.

Grollman, S. (1964). **The Human Body.** New York: The Macmillan Company. 611 pp.

Hadju, S. and E. Leonard (1959). "The cellular basis of cardiac glycoside action." *Pharmacol. Rev.* **11**: 173.

Hamilton, W. F. (1953). "The physiology of the cardiac output (the Lewis A. Conner Memorial lecture)." *Circulation* **8**: 527.

Hamilton, W. F. (1955). "Role of Starling concept in regulation of the normal circulation." *Physiol. Rev.* **35**: 160–168.

Hamilton, W. F. (1962). "Measurement of the cardiac output." In: **Handbook of Physiology,** Section 2: Circulation. (W. F. Hamilton, ed.), Vol. 1, pp. 551–584. Washington, D.C.: American Physiological Society.

Harris, J. E. and H. D. Crofton (1957). "Structure and function in the nematodes: internal pressure and cuticular structure in *Ascaris.*" *J. Exp. Biol.* **34**: 116–130.

Heddle, D. (1967). "Versatility of movement and the origin of the asteroids." In: **Echinoderm Biology.** (N. Millott, ed.), pp. 125–140. *Symp. Soc. Zool.* (London), vol. 20. New York: Academic Press, Inc.

Hill, R. B. and J. H. Welsh (1966). "Heart, circulation, and blood cells." In: **Physiology of Mollusca.** K. M. Wilbur and C. M. Yonge, eds.), Vol. 2, pp.125–174. New York: Academic Press, Inc.

His, W. (1893). "Die Entwicklung des Herznervensystems bei Wirbeltieren." *Abh.*

Saechs. ges. Akad. Wiss. (Leipzig), Math-Phys. K1: **34**: 1–64.

von Homann, H. (1935). "Die Funktion des männlichen. Spinnentasters im Versuch. *Zool. Anzeig.* **15**: 73–75.

Hopkins, A. E. (1936). "Pulsation of blood vessels in oysters, *Ostrea lurida* and *O. gigas.*" *Biol. Bull.* **70**: 413–425.

Hutter, O. F. (1961). "Ion movements during vagus inhibition of the heart." In: **Nervous Inhibition** (E. Florey, ed.), pp. 114–123. Long Island City, N.Y.: Pergamon Press, Inc.

Hyman, L. H. (1940). **The Invertebrates: Protozoa through Ctenophora.** New York: McGraw-Hill Book Company, Inc. 726 pp.

Illig, L. (1961). **Die terminale Strombahn.** Berlin: Springer-Verlag. 458 pp.

Johansen, K. (1962a). "Cardiac output and pulsatile aortic flow in the teleost, *Gadus morhua.*" *Comp. Biochem. Physiol.* **7**: 169–174.

Johansen, K. (1962b). "Double circulation in the amphibian *Amphiuma tridactylium.*" *Nature* **194**: 991–992.

Johansen, K. (1964). "Cardiovascular hemodynamics in the amphibian *Amphiuma tridactylum* Cuvier." *Acta Physiol. Scand.* (Suppl.) **217**: 1–82.

Johansen, K. and D. Hansen (1968). "Functional anatomy of the hearts of lungfishes and amphibians." *Am. Zool.* **8**: 191–210.

Johansen, K. and C. Lenfant (1967). "Respiratory function in the South American lungfish, *Lepidosiren paradoxa.*" *J. Exp. Biol.* **46**: 206–218.

Johansen, K. and A. W. Martin (1962). "Circulation in the cephalopod, *Octopus dofleini.*" *Comp. Biochem. Physiol.* **5**: 161–176.

Jones, J. J. (1962). "The Bainbridge reflex." *J. Physiol.* (London) **160**: 298–305.

Jullien, A. and G. Morin (1931). "Observations sur l'automatisme du coeur isolé et des lambeaux cardiaques chez l'huitre." *Comp. Rend. Soc. Biol.* **108**: 1242.

Kramer, K., W. Lochner, and E. Wetterer (1963). "Methods of measuring blood flow." In: **Handbook of Physiology,** Section 2: Circulation. (W. F. Hamilton, ed.), Vol. 2, pp. 1277–1324. Washington, D.C.: American Physiological Society.

Kriebel, M. E. (1963). "Effect of blood pressure on the isolated tunicate heart." *Biol. Bull.* **125**: 358.

Krijgsman, B. J. and G. A. Divaris (1955). "Contractile and pacemaker mechanisms of the heart of molluscs." *Biol. Rev. Cambridge Phil. Soc.* **30**: 1–39.

Laurent, P. (1962). "Contribution à étude morphologique et physiologique de L'innervation du coeur des téléosteens." *Arch. Anat. Microscop. Morphol. Exp.* **51**: 337–458.

Lawson, H. C. (1962). "The volume of blood—a critical examination of methods for its measurement." In: **Handbook of Physiology,** Section 2: Circulation. (W. F. Hamilton, ed.), Vol. 1 pp. 23–50. Washington, D.C.: American Physiological Society.

Lieberman, R. and A. Paes de Carvalho (1963). "The electrophysiological organization of the embryonic chick heart." *J. Gen. Physiol.* **49**: 351–363.

Luisada, A. A., ed. (1961). **Development and Structure of the Cardiovascular System.** New York: McGraw-Hill Book Company, Inc.

Manton, S. M. (1958). "Hydrostatic pressure and leg extension in arthropods, with special reference to Arachnids." *Ann. Mag. Hist. Series 13,* **1**: 161–182.

Manton, S. M. (1961). "Experimental zoology and problems of arthropod evolution." In: **The Cell and the Organism.** (J. A. Ramsay and V. B. Wigglesworth, eds.), pp. 234–255. New York: Cambridge University Press.

Martin, A. W. and K. Johansen (1965). "Adaptations of the circulation in invertebrate animals." In: **Handbook of Physiology,** Section 2: Circulation. (W. F. Hamilton, ed.), Vol. 3, pp. 2545–2581. Washington, D.C.: American Physiological Society.

Martin, A. W., F. M. Harrison, M. J. Huston, and D. M. Stewart (1958). "The blood volumes of some representative molluscs." *J. Exp. Biol.* **35**: 260–279.

Matsui, K. (1961). "Effects of stretching on the beat of the isolated ventricle in the mollusc,

Dobella auricula." *Annot. Zool. Japan*, **34:** 51–96.

Maynard, D. M. (1954). "Direct inhibition in the lobster cardiac ganglion." Ph.D. dissertation. University of California, Los Angeles.

Maynard, D. M. (1960). "Circulation and heart function." In: **The Physiology of Crustacea.** (T. H. Waterman, ed.), Vol. 1, pp. 161–226. New York: Academic Press, Inc.

Maynard, D. M. (1961). "Cardiac inhibition in decapod crustaceans." In: **Nervous Inhibition.** (E. Florey, ed.), pp. 144–178. Long Island City: Pergamon Press, Inc.

Maynard, D. M. (1966). "Integration in crustacean ganglia." *Symp. Soc. Exp. Biol.* **20:** 111–149.

Meglitsch, P. A. (1967). **Invertebrate Zoology.** New York: Oxford University Press. 961 pp.

Miller, N. E. (1969). "Learning of visceral and glandular responses." *Science* **163:** 434–445.

Mislin, H. and M. Kauffmann (1948). "Der aktive Gefasspuls in der Arm-Schirmhaur der Cephalopoden." *Rev. Suisse Zool.* **55:** 267–271.

Morton, J. E. (1964). "Locomotion." In: **Physiology of Mollusca.** (K. M. Wilbur and C. M. Yonge, eds.), Vol. 1, pp. 383–423. New York: Academic Press, Inc.

Newport, G. (1843). "On the structure, relations and development of the nervous and circulatory systems, and on the existence of a complete circulation of the blood in vessels in Myriapoda and macrorous Arachnida." *Phil. Trans. Roy. Soc.* (London) Pt. 2, 243–302.

Nomura, H. (1963). "The effect of stretching on the intracellular action potential from the cardiac muscle fibre of the marine mollusc, *Dobella auricula.*" *Sci. Repts. Tokyo Kyoiku Daigaku* **B11:** 153–165.

Parry, D. A. and R. H. J. Brown (1959a). "The hydraulic mechanism of the spider leg." *J. Exp. Biol.* **36:** 423–433.

Parry, D. A. and R. H. J. Brown (1959b). "The jumping mechanism of salticid spiders." *J. Exp. Biol.* **36:** 654–665.

Phibbs, B. (1961). **The Cardiac Arrhythmias.** St. Louis, Mo.: The C. V. Mosby Company.

Prosser, C. L., ed. (1950). **Comparative Animal Physiology.** Philadelphia: W. B. Saunders Company. 888 pp.

Prosser, C. L. (1943). "Single unit analysis of the heart ganglion discharge in *Limulus polyphemus.*" *J. Cell. Comp. Physiol.* **21:** 295–305.

Prosser, C. L. and F. A. Brown (1961). **Comparative Animal Physiology,** 2nd ed. Philadelphia: W. B. Saunders Company. 688 pp.

Prosser, C. L. and G. L. Zimmerman (1943). "Effects of drugs on the hearts of *Arenicola* and *Lumbricus.*" *Physiol. Zool.* **16:** 77–83.

Randall, D. J. (1966). "The nervous control of cardiac activity in the tench (*Tinca tinca*) and the goldfish (*Carassius auratus*)." *Physiol. Zool.* **39:** 185–192.

Randall, D. J. (1968). "Functional morphology of the heart in fishes." *Am. Zool.* **8:** 179–189.

Ringer, S. (1880–1882). "Concerning the influence exerted by each of the constituents of the blood on the contraction of the ventricle." *J. Physiol.* (London) **126:** 380–393.

Ripplinger, J. (1950). "Le coeur des poissons. Son innervation extrinséque. Ses centres automatiques." *Ann. Sci. Univ. Besançon, Zool. Physiol.* **5:** 45–57.

Ripplinger, J. (1952). "De l'existence d'un centre d'initiation des contractions rhythmiques et d'un systéme de conduction de l'onde d'excitation au travers du myocarde, au niveau du ventricle d'*Helix pomatia.*" *Comp. Rend. Soc. Biol.* **147:** 333–336.

Ripplinger, J. (1957). "Contribution à étude de la physiologie du coeur et de son innervation extrinséque chez l'Escargot (*Helix pomatia*)." *Ann. Sci. Univ. Besançon, Zool. et Physiol.* **8:** 3–179.

Riseman, J. E. F. (1968). **P-Q-R-S-T: A Guide to Electrocardiogram Interpretation.** New York: The Macmillan Company. 320 pp.

Robb, J. S. (1965). **Comparative Basic Cardiology.** New York: Grune & Stratton, Inc.

Rovick, A. A. and W. C. Randall (1967).

"Systemic circulation." *Ann. Rev. Physiol.* **29:** 225–258.

Rushmer, R. F. (1962). "Effects of nerve stimulation and hormones on the heart; the role of the heart in general circulatory regulation." In: **Handbook of Physiology,** Section 2: Circulation. (W. F. Hamilton, ed.), Vol. 1, pp. 533–550. Washington, D.C.: American Physiological Society.

Rushmer, R. F., ed. (1966). **Methods in Medical Research.** Vol. 11. Chicago, Ill.: Yearbook Medical Publishers, Inc.

Satchell, G. H. and M. P. Jones (1967). "The function of the conus arteriosus in the Port Jackson shark, *Heterodontus portusjacksoni.*" *J. Exp. Biol.* **46:** 373–382.

Schaefer, H. and H. G. Haas (1962). "Electrocardiograph." In: **Handbook of Physiology,** Section 2: Circulation. (W. F. Hamilton, ed.), Vol. 1, pp. 323–416. Washington, D.C.: American Physiological Society.

Scheer, B. T. (1963). **Animal Physiology.** New York: John Wiley & Sons. 409 pp.

Scher, A. M. (1962). "Excitation of the heart." In: **Handbook of Physiology,** Section 2: Circulation. (W. F. Hamilton, ed.), Vol. 1, pp. 287–322. Washington, D.C.: American Physiological Society.

Siegel, J. H. and E. H. Sonnenblick (1963). "Isometric time tension relationships as an index of myocardial contractility." *Circulation Res.* **12:** 597–610.

Simons, J. R. (1957). "The blood pressure and the pressure pulses in the arterial arches of the frog *Rana temporatia* and the toad *Bufo bufo.*" *J. Physiol.* (London) **137:** 12–21.

Simons, J. R. (1959). "Distribution of the blood in the heart of some amphibia." *Proc. Zool. Soc.* (London) **132:** 51–64.

Smith, J. E. (1947). "The activities of the tube feet of *Asterias rubens* L. I. The mechanics of movement and posture." *Quart. J. Microscop. Sci.* **88:** 1–14.

Smith, L. S. (1962). "The role of venous peristalsis in the arm circulation of *Octopus dofleini.*" *Comp. Biochem. Physiol.* **7:** 269–276.

Starling, E. H. (1918). **The Law of the Heart.** Linacre Lecture (1915). New York: Longmans, Green & Company.

Steggerda, F. R. and H. E. Essex (1957). "Circulation and blood pressure in the great vessels and the heart of the turtle (*Chelydra serpentina*)." *Am. J. Physiol.* **198:** 320–326.

Thorson, T. B. (1958). "Measurement of the fluid compartment of four species of marine chondrichthyes." *Physiol. Zool.* **31:** 16–23.

Tompsett, D. H. (1939). "*Sepia.*" *L.M.B.C. Mem.* (Liverpool) **32:** 1–184.

Trautwein, W. and K. Uchizone (1963). "Electron microscopic and electrophysiologic study of the pacemaker in the sinoatrial node of the rabbit heart." *Z. Zellforsch.* **61:** 96-109.

Tucker, B. A. (1966). "Oxygen transport by the circulatory system of the iguana (*Iguana iguana*) at different body temperatures." *J. Exp. Biol.* **44:** 77–92.

Wallace, A. G., J. H. Mitchell, N. S. Skinner, and S. J. Sarnoff (1963). "Duration of the phases of left ventricular systole." *Circulation Res.* **12:** 611–619.

Ward, D. V. (1969). "Leg extension in *Limulus.*" *Biol. Bull.* **136:** 288–300.

Warner, H. R. (1965). "Control of the circulation as studied with analog computer techniques." In: **Handbook of Physiology,** Section 2: Circulation. (W. F. Hamilton, ed.), Vol. 3, pp. 1825–1842. Washington, D.C.: American Physiological Society.

Weidmann, S. (1956). "Resting and action potentials of cardiac muscles." *Ann. N.Y. Acad. Sci.* **65:** 663–678.

White, F. N. (1942). "The pericardial cavity and the pericardial gland of the Lamellibranchiata." *Proc. Malacol. Soc.* (London) **25:** 37–88.

White, F. N. (1956). "Circulation in the reptilian heart (*Caiman sclerops*)." *Anat. Rec.* **125:** 417–431.

White, F. N. (1959). "Circulation in the reptilian heart (Squamata)." *Anat. Rec.* **135:** 129–134.

White, F. N. (1968). "Functional anatomy of the heart of reptiles." *Am. Zool.* **8:** 211–219.

Wiggers, C. J. (1921). **The Pulse Pressure in the Cardiovascular System.** New York: Longmans, Green & Company.

Wiggers, C. J. (1952). **Circulatory Dynamics.** New York: Grune & Stratton, Inc.

Wigglesworth, V. B. (1954). **Principles of Insect Physiology.** New York: Cambridge University Press.

Woodley, J. D. (1967). "Problems in the Ophiuroid Water-Vascular system." *Symp. Soc. Zool.* (London) **20:** 75–103.

Zuckerman, R. (1957). **Grundriss und Atlas der Elektrokardiographie.** Leipzig: George Thieme Verlag.

General Concepts of Osmoregulation

14-1. Introduction. All organisms face osmotic problems even in isosmotic media. A variety of regulatory mechanisms are used to maintain proper internal osmotic concentrations and to prevent the development of destructive osmotic pressures. **Osmoregulation,** a term coined by Höber in 1902, refers to the collective activities of the variety of mechanisms used by organisms to control water movement and water volumes. As used by Höber, osmoregulation implied the maintenance of an internal osmotic concentration different from that of the external medium.

It is not enough, however, to control only water distribution because the ionic composition and concentrations of various compartments must also be regulated. As we have already seen, differences in the distribution of ions are found between the external and internal environments of organisms and also between various compartments within the organism. These ionic differences, that are needed for proper functioning of tissues and cells, are controlled by a variety of mechanisms whose activities fall under the study of **ionic regulation**. Since water and ionic regulation are inseparable activities in organisms, by extension the term osmoregulation is sometimes used to include both activities.

The field of osmoregulatory studies is a large and complex one. It includes studies of the overall mechanisms used to regulate internal water and solute content; the organs used for excretion, which are, in most cases, more important as ionic or water regulatory systems; the cellular activities, which are basic to these regulatory mechanisms; and the molecular basis for these mechanisms. Osmoregulatory studies are also concerned with the adaptive significance of these regulatory processes as they relate to the type of environment in which the animal lives and the mechanisms which some organisms use to adapt to changes in this environment.

Osmoregulation by most organisms must also be correlated with other homeostatic functions such as temperature regulation and pH regulation—activities which often

Chapter 14

Water and Solute Regulation

involve the use of body water or ions.

Historically the mechanisms of osmoregulation have been most intensively studied from the viewpoint of the functioning of the vertebrate renal system—the frog kidney has been analyzed in some detail (Richards, 1935). In a recent review Kirschner (1967) points out that until 1940 studies on renal processes and the mechanisms underlying osmoregulation in invertebrates were neglected except for a handful of research papers. Not until the 1950s had techniques and interest developed to the point where analyses of the mechanisms of urine formation and the control of osmoregulation in invertebrates become significant.

Even now the adaptive roles of renal and other osmoregulatory systems are stressed, and much remains to be discovered about specific mechanisms of osmoregulation at the cellular level. Over the past 30 years several important monographs and reviews have appeared covering various phases of osmoregulation. These contain much useful summarized data and concepts and include: Beadle (1957); von Buddenbrock (1956); Farrell and Taylor (1962); Krogh (1939); Martin (1958); Potts and Parry (1964); Prosser and Brown (1961); Ramsay (1954); Robertson (1960); Shaw (1964); and Shaw and Stobgart (1963). In addition, the *Handbook of Physiology*, Section 4, Vol. 1 (American Physiological Society, Washington, D.C.), contains several relevant chapters. The textbook edited by Mountcastle (1968) contains descriptions of the mammalian renal system.

In dealing with osmoregulation, we are concerned for the first time in this book with the homeostatic maintenance of the levels of a particular set of internal environmental variables: the water content (= water volume) and the solute content and distribution. As is true of any homeostatic activity, the input must equal the output if a variable is to be held at a constant level. Thus, if an organism is maintaining a constant internal water content, there must be an equality between the amount of water entering the body and the amount of water leaving the body, that is, water in = water out, if body water content is to be constant.

Similar statements can be made regarding the homeostatic maintenance of any internal environmental variable. Part of the discussion of this chapter will be concerned with the mechanisms that control the entrance of water into the animal and with those which control the exit of water from the animal. Both, in turn, may depend on mechanisms that control the movements of inorganic ions.

Water may enter an animal's body as the result of drinking, of food intake, of metabolic reactions that yield water as one of the products, and of osmosis caused by concentrations gradients across the exposed semipermeable membranes of the animal. Water may leave the organism in the urine of an excretory system, through the respiratory system, through sweat or other glands, by osmosis through the skin, and by exocytosis.

Osmoregulation is not the result of a passive chemical or physical equilibrium between internal and external water or solutes. Nor is it the result of a simple steady state between the animal and its environment. Rather, osmoregulation is the result of the active operation of negative feedback systems that control water and solute movements.

14-2. Some Terms Used in Osmoregulatory Studies. The basic concepts needed to understand osmoregulatory mechanisms have already been discussed in those chapters concerned with osmosis, diffusion, and active transport (Chapter 6); with the importance and role of water in biological systems (Chapter 2); and with compartmentation, adaptation, and regulation (Chapters 1 and 12).

Since osmotic pressure is often difficult to measure directly, other colligative properties of solutions, especially the freezing point depression and the vapor pressure lowering are used in the measurement of osmotic effects. For this reason the results of many osmoregulatory studies used the freezing point depression, Δ_f, to express osmotic concentrations. This may be converted to units of osmotic pressure, but more often it is converted to actual concentration terms by defining a freezing point

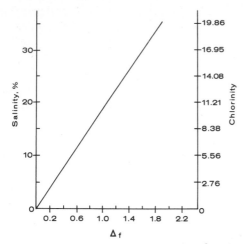

Figure 14-1 Relations between the freezing point depression and salinity and chlorinity.

depression of $-1.86°C$ as equal to an osmotic concentration of 1 Osmole. In biological studies molarity can generally be substituted for molality with little error, and the typical units of osmotic concentration are Osmoles per liter (Osmolar solutions).

A variety of units have been used to express concentrations of the external environment. The total solid content (in mg/ml) is often used for fresh water. Dissolved solutes in parts per million (ppm) is also used. Fresh water ranges from about 15 to 500 parts per million in solute concentrations.

Salinity, expressed as parts per thousand (S‰) is sometimes used to express the ionic concentration of sea water. Percentage of sea water is also used, where 100 per cent sea water is equal to a salinity of 33‰. Sverdrup et al. (1942) defined salinity as the total amount of solid material in grams dissolved in one kilogram of sea water when all the carbonate is converted to oxide, the organic matter is completely oxidized, and the bromine and iodine are measured as chlorine.

Since about 55 per cent of the constituents of sea water are in the form of chlorides, and because chloride is easily determined, the concentration of sea water is often expressed as the chlorinity—defined as the amount of dissolved chlorine, bromine, and iodine, assuming that the bromine and iodine have been replaced by

chlorine, given as grams of chlorine per kilogram of sea water (C‰). The chlorosity of sea water is defined as the chlorinity in grams per liter at 20°C and is obtained by multiplying the chlorinity by the density of sea water at 20°C. Salinity is related to chlorinity by

$$S‰ = [1.805 × C‰] + 0.03 \quad (14.1)$$

Figure 14-1 gives the relation between salinity, chlorinity, and the freezing point depression of aqueous solutions. Figure 14-2 gives the relation between the freezing point depression and the molarity and percentage concentrations of NaCl solutions.

14-3. Osmotic Environments and Animals. Most animal groups are marine, a smaller but significant number live in fresh water, and relatively few groups (insects, reptiles, birds and mammals chiefly) have achieved a terrestrial existence. A fourth environment with which we shall be concerned here is the brackish water habitat.

Each of these environments presents particular osmotic problems that must be solved by the animals living in them. It should be noted that I am using these terms in a very general sense, for example, the marine environment is not a homogeneous one but consists of many subenvironments. Table 14-1 gives the osmotic concentrations of some bodies of water. Since animal species of one group or

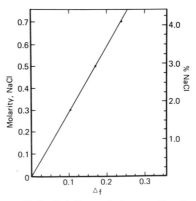

Figure 14-2 Relations between the freezing point depression and the NaCl molarity and percentage.

Table 14-1 Ionic Concentrations of Some Bodies of Water (in mmoles per liter)*

SOLUTE	AVERAGE OCEAN[1]	AVERAGE OCEAN[2]	AVERAGE RIVER[3]	LITTLE MANITOU LAKE, CANADA[3]	GREAT SALT LAKE, UTAH[3]	LAKE KIVU, CONGO[4]	LAKE ALBERT, CONGO[4]	LAKE EDWARD, CONGO[4]
Na^+	468.0	459.0	~0.08	780	3,000	5.65	4.21	4.86
K^+	9.89	9.72	~0.01	28	90	2.56	1.69	2.02
Ca^{2+}	10.2	10.0	~0.3	14	9	0.81	0.23	0.24
Mg^{2+}	53.4	52.0	~0.09	500	230	4.16	1.31	1.85
Sr^{2+}	0.159	0.151	—	—	—	—	—	—
Cl^-	553.0	535.0	~0.05	660	3,100	1.0	0.91	0.77
SO_4^{2-}	28.1	27.5	~0.08	540	150	0.31	0.26	0.34
Br^-	0.075	0.088	—	—	—	—	—	—
F^-	0.053	0.068	—	—	—	—	—	—
CO_2	0.016	—	—	—	—	—	—	—
HCO_3^-	1.9	2.28	—	—	—	15.0	7.54	9.5
CO_3^{2-}	0.20	—	—	—	—	1.5	0.77	0.95
Salinity	35.16	34.31	—	~70	~210	1.0	0.58	0.72
pH	8.17	—	—	—	—	9.1	9.2	—

* References: (1) Sverdrup et al. (1942); (2) Hutchinson (1957); (3) Rubey (1951); (4) Verbeke (1957).

another are found in all of these environments, it is obvious that animals generally speaking, can cope with a relatively wide variety of osmotic environments, although different species may use different methods for surviving in a given habitat. Such differences are one factor adding to the complexity of osmoregulatory studies.

Clarke (1924) summarized the information on analyses of waters from all over the world, and Hutchinson (1957) contains information on the composition of fresh waters. In addition to the environments just named (which, again, have many subdivisions according to actual salinity, depth, temperature, pH, and so forth), high salinity environments are also occupied by some animals. These include the salt lakes of which there are two types. One is formed from salts leached from sedimentary rocks or ancient oceans beds. These have a chemical composition generally similar to that of marine waters although their salinities are several times higher. The Great Salt Lake in Utah is an example of this type of salt lake. The other

type is formed from salts leached from volcanic rocks and generally has a composition differing from that of the oceans and is much more alkaline. The Lahontan Basin in Nevada is an example of this type. Both are formed in basins that have no outlet for their waters.

Table 14-2 presents the ionic composition of some body fluids and tissues of selected animals and compares them with the composition of standard sea water and soft and hard waters. Osmoregulation is needed by many animals because the range of conditions compatible with the survival of their cells is limited. The underlying causes of this limited range are presumably related to the evolutionary history of organisms and the nature of the macromolecules that make up such an important part of their structural and functional organization.

Macallum (1926) proposed that the inorganic composition of the intercellular fluids of animals resembled that of the primitive oceans of the geologically early period in which animals evolved. According to this hypothesis,

Table 14-2 Concentration of Some Common Ions in Animals, Sea Water, and Fresh Water (concentrations given as mM/kg water)*

Animal and Tissue	Na$^+$	K$^+$	Ca^{2+}	Mg^{2+}	Cl$^-$	SO$_4^{2-}$	Other
Standard Sea Water[1]	478.3	10.13	10.48	54.5	558.4	28.77	
Fresh water (soft)[2]	0.24	0.005	0.067	0.043	0.226	0.045	
Fresh water (hard)[3]	2.22	1.46	3.98	1.67	2.54	3.95	HCO$_3^{2-}$:2.02
Crab nerve (*Carcinus*)[4]	41	422	—	—	27	—	Amino acids: 444
Lobster (*Homarus*) q blood[5]	530.9	8.71	15.82	7.63	558.4	8.92	
Crab (*Maia*) blood[5]	487.90	11.32	13.61	44.14	552.4	14.38	
Squid (*Loligo*)[6]							
blood	440	20.0	10	54	560	—	
nerve	50	400	0.4	10	40	—	Isethionate: 270
Mussel (*Mytilus*)[7]							
adductor muscle	79	152	7.3	34	94	8.8	Amino acids: 295
Frog (*Rana exculenta*)[8] blood	109	2.6	2.1	1.3	78	—	HCO$_3^{2-}$: 26.6
Crayfish (*astacus fluviatilis*)[9]							
blood (mM/l blood)	212	4.1	15.8	1.5	199	—	HCO$_3^{2-}$:15
Mussel (*Anodonta cygnaea*)[10]							
blood	15.6	0.5	6	0.2	11.7	—	HCO$_3^{2-}$:12
Moth (*Bombyx mori*)[11]							
larva blood	3.4	41.8	12.3	40.4	14	—	
Rat (*Rattus rattus*)[12] blood	140	6.4	3.4	1.6	119	—	HCO$_3^{2-}$: 24.3

* References: (1) Potts and Parry (1964); (2) A. H. Coombes, as reported in Potts and Parry (1964); (3) Macan and Worthington (1951); (4) Lewis (1952); (5) Robertson (1949, 1953); (6) Koechlin (1955) and Hodgkin (1958); (7) Potts (1958); (8) Boyle and Conway (1941); (9) Huf (1934); (10) Potts (1954); (11) Duchâteau et al. (1953); (12) Conway and Hingerty (1946).

animals are dependent on ionic concentrations similar to those of the early oceans—which were thought to be much different from the oceans of today in ionic composition. The evolution of osmoregulatory mechanisms, therefore, would have been in the direction of maintaining this necessary internal composition.

This simple and attractive hypothesis fell into difficulty on several points. Geophysicists and geochemists now think that the oceans have remained basically the same for more than 2 billion years (see Rubey, 1951). Since fossils of recognizable metazoans are known from no longer than about 800,000,000 years ago, it appears that oceans have been of stable composition for a period of time longer than that during which metazoans have been evolving. Furthermore, as indicated by the data of Table 14-2, the ionic compositions of animal body fluids are not as similar as was thought at the time of Macallum. Measurements, using new methods of analysis including radioactive isotopes, have shown that there is actually a wide diversity in the composition and concentrations of ions in body fluids.

There is, at present, no good single answer to the question of why animals and cells are

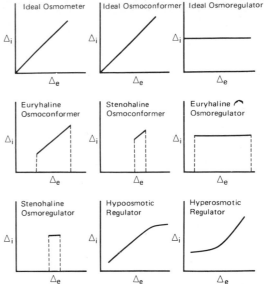

Figure 14-3 Graphs showing the various types of relationships between osmoregulatory abilities of animals and various osmotic environments. An osmometer is any device that changes volume, and thus concentration, in response to osmotic changes.

often limited in the range of ionic concentrations and osmotic concentrations they can withstand. Nor is it known why some cells can withstand a much wider range of osmotic concentrations than others. It has been argued that the development of active transport systems, which are basic to many osmoregulatory mechanisms, were a primary need before cells could develop from their primitive fore-runners (Brown and Stein, 1960). Cellular active transport systems are needed to supply metabolites as well as to regulate cellular ionic distributions.

Aquatic animals can be placed into categories based on their abilities to survive in different osmotic environments. **Stenohaline** organisms have only a limited tolerance to changes in the osmotic concentrations of the external environment. Most animals fall into this category. **Euryhaline** animals can tolerate a wider range of osmotic concentrations although the degree of tolerance depends on the length of exposure, age, environmental temperature, and similar factors. There is no sharp division between the two classes.

Animals, whether stenohaline or euryhaline, are also classed according to their ability to osmoregulate in different osmotic environments. **Osmoconformers** have an internal concentration that varies in parallel with changes in the external environment. They are not

capable of osmoregulation. **Osmoregulators** maintain their internal osmotic concentration at a constant level (or nearly so) as the external environment changes. As shown in Figure 14-3 euryhaline animals may regulate over part of their range and conform over other parts of the range.

Some animals change in volume (due to alterations of water content) as the external osmotic concentration changes. These are **volume conformers**. Others are **volume regulators** and maintain a constant volume in the face of external osmotic change. In addition to regulating water volume, animals can regulate the concentrations of inorganic ions and other solutes in their body fluids; they are **ionic regulators**. Animals with little ability to regulate internal ionic concentrations are **ionic conformers**, but no animal is completely lacking in this ability.

Organisms that live in the deep marine environment generally do not osmoregulate to any great degree since they depend on the constancy of deep ocean waters to provide a stable environment. This is not to say that ionic or volume regulation is not used by these animals to maintain a proper balance of ions in their body fluids and cells. Table 14-3 lists the types of animals (in categories based on osmoregulatory ability or lack of it) found in various environments, and the chief organ

Table 14-3 Excretory Organs and Their Role in Adaptation of Animals to Osmotic Environments*

ORGANISM	MAIN EXCRETORY ORGAN [ROLE]	OTHER ORGANS [ROLE]	URINE/BLOOD (Osm)
OSMOCONFORMERS (MARINE OR BRACKISH WATERS)			
Invertebrates			
Protozoa	Contractile vacuole [ion + volume regulation]	Body surface [excretion nitrogenous wastes]	Isotonic?
Nematoda	Renette cell [ion + volume regulation]	Body surface [as above]	Isotonic?
Annelida	Short undifferentiated tubule [ion + volume regulation]	Body surface [as above]	Isotonic?
Crustacea	Green gland with no nephridial canal [ion + volume regulation]	Gills [as above]	Isotonic
Mollusca	Bojanus organ [ion + volume reg.]	Gills [as above]	Isotonic
Rotifera	None	Body surface [ion + volume regulation; excretion nitrogenous wastes]	—
Gastrotricha	None	Body surface [as above]	—
Turbellaria	None	Body surface [as above]	—
Echinodermata	None	Body surface [as above]	—
Vertebrates			
Cyclostomata	Glomerulus + proximal tubule [ion + volume regulation]	Gills [excretion nitrogenous wastes]	Isotonic?
Elasmobranchii	Glomerulus + proximal and distal tubules [water excretion; ion + volume regulation; urea conservation]	Rectal gland [NaCl excr.]	0.75–1.0
Amphibia	Glomerulus + proximal + distal tubules [water excretion; ion + volume regulation; urea conservation]	Skin [?]	0.1–1.0
HYPOOSMOREGULATORS (MARINE OR HIGHER SALINITY WATERS)			
Invertebrates			
Crustacea	Green gland with no nephridial canal [ion + volume reg.; weak osmoreg.]	Gills [osmoregulation; NaCl excr.; excr. nitrogenous wastes]	1.0–1.6
Insecta	Malpighian tubules + hindgut [ion + volume regulation; osmoregulation; excretion nitrogenous wastes]	—	0.5–1.0
Vertebrates			
Teleostei	Glomerular or aglomerular + proximal tubule [ion + volume regulation]	Gills [osmoregulation; NaCl excr; excretion nitrogenous wastes]	0.85–1.0
Reptilia	Glomerulus + proximal and distal tubules [ion + volume regulation; excretion nitrogenous wastes]	Salt gland [osmoreg.; NaCl excretion]	0.1–1.0

Table 14-3   continued

Organism	Main Excretory Organ [Role]	Other Organs [Role]	Urine/Blood (Osm)
Mammalia	Glomerulus + proximal, distal and thin tubules, loop of Henle [ion + volume regulation; osmoregulation; excretion nitrogenous wastes]	—	0.1–1.6
Hyperosmoregulators (fresh water)			
Invertebrates			
Coelenterates	None	Body surface [ion + volume regulation; osmoregulation]	—
Nematoda	Tubule + renette gland, cuticle-lined duct [ion + volume regulation; osmoregulation]	Body surface [?]	Hypotonic
Annelida	Long differentiated tubule [ion + volume reg.; osmoregulation]	Body surface [?]	0.05–1.0
Mollusca	Bojanus organ [ion + volume reg. osmoregulation]	Gills [uptake NaCl; osmoregulation]	0.05
Insecta	Malpighian tubule + hindgut + rectum [ion + volume reg.; osmoreg.]	Anal papilla [uptake NaCl; osmoregulation]	0.03
Crustacea	Green gland with nephridial canal [ion + volume reg.; osmoregulation]	Giols [uptake NaCl; osmoregulation]	0.05
Vertebrates			
Elasmobranchii	Glomerulus + proximal and distal tubules [ion + volume reg.; osmoregulation]	Gills [excretion nitrogenous wastes; osmoreg.]	0.10
Teleostei	Glomerulus + proximal and distal tubules [ion + volume reg.; osmoregulation]	Gills [excr. nitrogenous wastes; uptake NaCl; osmoregulation]	0.10
Amphibia	Glomerulus + proximal & distal tubls. [ion + volume reg.; osmoregulation]	Skin [NaCl uptake; osmoregulation]	0.1–1.0
Reptilia	Glomerulus + proximal, distal, and thin segment, loop of Henle [ion + volume reg.; osmoreg.]	—	0.1–1.0
Mammalia	Glomerulus + proximal, distal tubules, and thin segment, loop of Henle [ion + volume reg.; osmoregulation; excretion nitrogenous wastes]	—	0.15–2.0
Regulation to water shortage (terrestrial)			
Invertebrates			
Insecta	Malpighian tubule + hindgut [ion + volume reg., osmoregulation; excr. nitrogenous wastes]	—	0.1–2.0

Table 14-3   continued

ORGANISM	MAIN EXCRETORY ORGAN [ROLE]	OTHER ORGANS [ROLE]	URINE/BLOOD (OSM)
Crustacea	Labyrinth with no nephridial canal [ion + volume reg., weak osmoreg.]	Gills [uptake NaCl; osmoregulation]	1.0–1.6
Mollusca	Bojanus organ [ion + volume reg.; osmoregulation; excr. nitrog. wastes]	—	0.5–1.0
Vertebrates			
Amphibia	Glomerulus + proximal and distal tubules [ion + volume reg.; osmoreg.; excr. nitrogenous wastes]	Skin [uptake NaCl; osmoregulation]	0.1–1.0
Reptilia	Glomerulus + proximal and distal tubules [ion + volume reg.; osmoregulation; excr. nitrogenous wastes]	—	0.1–1.0
Aves	Glomerulus + proximal, distal, and thin segment, loop of Henle [ion + volume reg.; osmoreg.; excr. nitrog. wastes]	Salt glands in marine [NaCl excr.; osmoregulation]	0.1–4.5
Mammalia	Glomerulus + proximal, distal, and thin segment, loop of Henle [ion + volume reg.; osmoreg.; excr. nitrog. wastes]	—	0.1–2.0

* Adapted from B. Schmidt-Nielsen (1964).

systems responsible for osmoregulation. It can be seen that all major animal groups are represented by species living in marine waters and that these are often conformers. They are relatively isotonic with their environment unless they are secondarily adapted to the marine habitat.

During the course of animal evolution, assuming that life originally developed in the oceans, most major phyla had groups that evolved to the point where they could inhabit the brackish water and later the fresh water environment. Under these conditions the major osmotic problem involves maintaining a hyperosmotic state because the body fluids are more concentrated than the external medium. Such animals are **hyperosmoregulators**, and they maintain osmolarities of internal body fluids ranging from about 200 to 300 mOsm. There is a tendency for the osmotic inflow of water and the outward diffusion of salts (= inorganic ions). The latter is counterbalanced by the development of active transport systems designed to bring salts into the body through specialized regions of the gills, skin, rectum, or other regions of the gastrointestinal tract. To eliminate excess water, all fresh water organisms, except the coelenterates and sponges, have developed kidneys or other excretory organs capable of producing a copious urine, hypotonic to body fluids (see last column of Table 14-3); and with osmolarities as low as 20 to 30 mOsm. The renal systems of fresh water organisms usually contain cells that can remove salts by active transport from the urine and restore them to body fluids. Some crustaceans and teleost fish have adapted to the fresh water habitat secondarily without the ability to form a hypotonic urine. This adaptation is accomplished by an increased efficiency of the gills in reabsorbing salts from the environment and the development of a highly impermeable outer covering to prevent osmotic outflow of water (see, for example, Parry, 1957, on fresh water prawns).

In the brackish water environment, especially in tidal regions or where rivers enter the oceans (estuarine environments), changes in the osmotic environment are frequent, and animals may have to cope with changes of from nearly fresh to nearly ocean water. Some animals in this environment possess cells that can conform to relatively large changes in osmotic concentration.

The terrestrial habitat lacks both water and salts in the surrounding medium (the air), and terrestrial animals often face the problem of both water and salt losses. In contrast to aqueous organisms, excretion occurs almost exclusively through the renal system and in mammals, birds, reptiles, and insects the kidney is responsible for salt, water, and nitrogenous waste excretion (the term kidney is used to define the principal excretory organ of an animal). A few terrestrial crustaceans, marine birds, and marine reptiles do excrete salt through the gills or through specialized salt glands (K. Schmidt-Nielsen, 1960; K. Schmidt-Nielsen and Fänge, 1958). Some mammals possess sweat glands through which water, salts, and nitrogenous wastes are excreted also.

Because a major function of the terrestrial animal's kidney is to conserve water and salts, the urine produced is less copious than that of the fresh water animal and is hypertonic to the body fluids. A kidney can function in osmoregulation only if it can produce a hyperosmotic urine when necessary.

Obtaining water in the terrestrial environment is often a serious problem. In the extreme terrestrial habitat, the dry hot desert, some animals have adapted to a lack of drinking water by obtaining water entirely from metabolic reactions and the water contained in foods. It is of interest to note that when a land or fresh water organism returns to the marine environment, it faces the same type of osmotic problems as does the desert animal. There is a shortage of available pure water and a tendency to overdevelop internal salt concentrations.

Hypoosmoregulators are found in the oceans and in high salinity waters. They are hypoosmotic to their environment and are exposed to an osmotic loss of water and an influx of salts by diffusion. Animals in this group include those which have secondarily returned to the oceans after adapting to fresh water or land. They include present day marine teleosts, seals, whales, and other cetaceans. These animals are in danger of desiccation although they live in an aqueous medium.

The above are generalizations designed only to portray the general problems faced by animals in various osmotic environments. The problems and mechanisms used to solve them may differ even in species of the same genera. Such diversity is abetted by secondary or tertiary adaptations to new environments. At the cellular level osmoregulatory mechanisms depend on active transport functions that are under nervous and hormonal controls. In addition, morphological adaptations, for example, the development of highly impermeable outer coverings, also play an important role in an animal's capabilities for osmoregulation.

14-4. Some Methods in Osmoregulatory Studies. Originally estimates of renal functioning or osmoregulatory abilities were obtained either by blocking the excretory openings and measuring weight changes in animals placed in different osmotic environments or by collecting urine from animals under varying experimental conditions and analyzing it chemically. At best, however, such methods give only a crude approximation of the activities responsible for osmoregulation and urine formation. The functioning of other organ systems in osmoregulation or excretion are inadequately examined by such methods.

Because the movement of specific materials across membranes and cell layers is an integral part of water, ion, or waste product exchanges, the introduction of radioactive isotopes greatly improved the ability to analyze urine formation or to determine the particular ions or other solutes associated with osmoregulatory mechanisms.

The ability of an animal to osmoregulate is intimately related to the environment in which the animal normally lives, and the physiological study of osmoregulation is allied to the science of ecology, which stresses the relationships of organisms to their environment. The full description of osmoregulatory activity requires accurate field observations of the animal in its natural habitat.

Physiological studies often include placing an organism or cell in different salinities to determine the changes that occur within the animal and the survival times of the organism. Such experiments yield results that differ according to the time of exposure of a given animal. Short-term experiments, as indicated in Chapter 1, provide data for transient changes in the biological system. Long-term experiments provide data for steady state analyses. An animal may survive for an hour in a given salinity and appear to be adequately osmoregulating, but if the salinity is above the normal range encountered and above the tolerance of the animal, the animal may not be capable of surviving long-term exposure. It may not be able to afford the continuous energy output required for osmoregulation. Since active transport is an essential part of most osmoregulatory mechanisms, energy expenditure is required by the organism for continued osmoregulation. The measurement of energy expenditure (usually in terms of oxygen consumption) is one method used as a guide in

determining whether or not an organism is regulating under a given set of conditions.

Because survival times and regulatory abilities of animals in abnormal environments vary markedly in different species, the experimental design of osmoregulatory studies is important. Further, only when physiological data on osmoregulatory or excretory abilities can be viewed in the light of the animal's natural habitat can adaptation and evolution be adequately discussed.

Several methods are used to determine the osmotic pressure or its equivalent (Levitt, 1964). Although osmotic pressure can be determined directly in an osmometer, indirect methods are generally used for biological samples because of limited volumes of body fluids available. Determination of the freezing point depression (cryoscopy) is often used.

The freezing point of a sample may be measured directly using an accurately calibrated thermometer such as the Beckman or Heidenhain thermometers (these are calibrated in at least hundredths of a degree), but such thermometers require at least a milliliter of sample. Indirect determination of the freezing point is also used and can handle samples as small as 0.01 ml (Gross, 1954). In this method a series of standard NaCl solutions are placed in capillary tubes. The samples of unknown are also placed in capillary tubes, and after sealing all the tubes they are frozen. The frozen samples are allowed to warm slowly, and the time of melting of each tube is noted. By graphing the times of melting of the standards, the observed times of melting of the unknowns permits interpolation of their concentrations. If desired, these concentrations may be put

Table 14-4 Some Physiological Salines*

ANIMALS:	MAMMALS	TURTLES	FROGS	LOBSTER	CRAYFISH	EARTH-WORM	INSECTS
% NaCl (g/100 ml)	0.94	0.79	0.68	2.64	1.20	0.80	0.75
Molarity NaCl	0.16	0.13	0.12	0.45	0.20	0.14	0.13

* These solutions are isotonic with the bloods of the animals indicated.

Table 14-5 Some Invertebrate Physiological Solutions

THE FOLLOWING STOCK SOLUTIONS ARE ALL ISOTONIC WITH SEA WATER (34.6‰)

SOLUTION	GRAMS PER LITER DISTILLED WATER
(1) 0.54 M NaCl	31.56
(2) 0.54 M KCl	40.26
(3) 0.36 M CaCl$_2$·H$_2$O	52.93 (or 39.95 of the anhydrous salt)
(4) 0.36 M MgCl$_2$·6H$_2$O	73.20 (or 34.28 of the anhydrous salt)
(5) 0.44 M Na$_2$SO$_4$·10H$_2$O	141.78 (or 62.6 of the anhydrous salt)
(6) 0.90 M NgSO$_4$·7H$_2$O	221.84
(7) 0.54 M NaBr·2H$_2$O	75.03 (or 55.7 of the anhydrous salt)
(8) 0.54 M NaHCO$_3$	45.36
(9) 0.90 M nonelectrolytes (glucose, etc.)	

MARINE INVERTEBRATE SOLUTIONS (USE THE NUMBER OF ml INDICATED OF THE ABOVE STOCK SOLUTIONS)

ANIMAL: SOLUTION	SIPUNC- ULIDS	*Homarus vulgaris*	*Cancer pagurus*	*Carcinus maenus*	COMMENT
(1)	830	897	816	858	A buffer system should be used with
(2)	18	26	21	21	these solutions. A Tris buffer (tris-
(3)	28	40	37	35	hydroxymethyl-aminomethane) is
(4)	146	19	73	51	often recommended.
(5)	63	18	53	35	

FRESH WATER AND TERRESTRIAL INVERTEBRATES SOLUTIONS (USE THE INDICATED VOLUMES OF STOCK SOLUTIONS AND DILUTE TO 1 LITER WITH DISTILLED WATER)

ANIMAL: SOLUTION	EARTH- WORM	LEECHES	*Helix*	*Limnaea*	*Ano-donta*	MUSSELS	COCK- ROACHES	*Astacus*	*Camba-rus*
(1)	250	210	220	85	1.9	38	290	330	380
(2)	5	8	7.5	5	0.9	3.7	5	10	10
(3)	5	5	2.5	8	9.3	3	5	29	39
(4)	1	—	7	13	0.4	—	—	7	7.2
(5)	1	—	5.5	—	2.3	—	—	—	—
(6)	—	—	—	—	—	—	—	—	4.4
(8)	—	3	3	3	26.0	—	—	—	—
Buffer*	100	100	350	—	—	—	—	100	—
pH	7.4	7.4	8.4	—	7.5	7.8	7.2	7.5	7.5

* The buffer is made of 0.01N Na$_2$HPO$_4$ brought to the desired pH by the dropwise addition of concentrated HCl. The solution for *Helix* is useful for most fresh water snails.

Table 14-6 Artificial Sea Waters (grams to make 25 liters)

NaCl	587.00	
KCl	16.50	
$CaCl_2 \cdot 2H_2O$	36.80	(or 27.8 g anhydrous $CaCl_2$)
$MgCl_2 \cdot 6H_2O$	266.00	(or 126.0 g anhydrous $MgCl_2$)
$NaHCO_3$	4.80	
Na_2SO_4	98.00	Constituents marked '*' may be omitted
$MgSO_4$	91.50	if the sea water is to be used for purposes
*KBr	2.40	other than the maintenance of cultures.
H_3BO_3	0.65	The final pH should be 8.1–8.4, adjusted
*$SrCl_2$	0.60	with bicarbonate if necessary.
*NaF	0.075	
*$LiNO_3$	0.05	
*Al_2Cl_6	0.025	
*$Na_2Si_4O_9$	0.125	

SMALL QUANTITIES OF SEA WATER MAY BE MADE FROM THE ISOTONIC SOLUTIONS GIVEN IN TABLE 14-5.

SOLUTION	MILLILITERS
(1)	739.6
(2)	18.05
(3)	28.00
(4)	145.70
(5)	63.00
(7)	1.05
(8)	4.60

into units of freezing point depression from data such as that given in Figure 14-2. Some methods of cryoscopy now permit determinations to be made on nanoliter samples.

Because the vaporization of water causes a lowering of the surrounding temperature as heat is absorbed by the vaporization process, the lowering of the vapor point of a solution can be determined by evaporating samples from a thermocouple. The latter is a junction between two dissimilar metals, which develops an electrical potential dependent on temperature. Thermoelectric measurements are very accurate and can use extremely small samples.

14-5. Physiological Solutions. In experimental studies there is often a need for a bathing or perfusion solution that maintains a proper osmotic balance between the cells of the prepa-

ration and the external medium. Because of their importance in all types of physiological experimentation, some physiological solutions are given in Tables 14-4, 14-5, 14-6, 14-7 and 14-8. The data of these tables have been derived from various sources including Hale (1955); Lockwood (1961); Pantin (1946); Prosser and Brown (1961); Prosser (1950); van Harreveld (1936). These references may be consulted for further details and references to perfusion fluids and their uses.

The simplest physiological solutions are **physiological salines**. These are NaCl solutions isotonic with the body fluids of the experimental animal (Table 14-4).

As pointed out in Chapter 12, solutions consisting of a single salt are not suited for maintaining osmotic balance for more than a relatively short period of time. It is more usual to

Table 14-7   Some Vertebrate Perfusion Solutions (grams/liter of solution)

SOLUTION (AND ANIMAL)	NaCl	KCl	MgCl$_2$	CaCl$_2$·2H$_2$O	OTHER
Locke's mammalian, avian	9.00	0.42	—	0.24	NaHCO$_3$: 0.20 Glucose: 1.00 Dissolve in 1 liter of distilled water.
Tyrode's mammalian, avian	8.00	0.20	0.05	0.20	NaH$_2$PO$_4$: 0.04 Glucose: 1.00
Harris's amphibian	5.26	0.22	—	0.22	MgSO$_4$: 0.12 Na$_2$HPO$_4$: 0.33 NaH$_2$PO$_4$; 0.07 Glucose: 0.54
Ringer's amphibian					
frog	6.00	0.22	—	0.29	NaHCO$_3$: 0.2
turtle	6.80	0.29	—	0.29	or: use 15 ml of 0.1 M Na$_2$HPO$_4$ and 6 ml 0.1 M NaH$_2$PO$_4$ for each liter of Ringer's. Final pH 7.2
Tris-Ringer's for amphibians	6.84	0.19	—	0.26	Tris: 0.24
Fresh water teleosts	6.42	0.15	—	0.22	MgSO$_4$: 0.12 NaHCO$_3$: 0.084 NaH$_2$PO$_4$: 0.06
Marine teleosts	7.8	0.18	0.095	0.166	NaHCO$_3$: 0.084 NaH$_2$PO$_4$: 0.06
Elasmobranchs	16.38	0.89	—	1.11	NaHCO$_3$: 0.38 NaH$_2$PO$_4$: 0.06

use a **physiological solution** or **perfusion fluid**, which is an ionically balanced isotonic solution. The original Ringer's solutions, developed empirically for work with frog heart muscle, have been modified by other researchers for use with other tissues and other animals. Such solutions are often named by prefixing the name of the modifier to the name Ringers; or by using the name of the animal for which the solution was developed.

Invertebrate physiological solutions are shown in Table 14-5; an artificial sea water for maintaining animals or for working with animal tissues is given in Table 14-6. Vertebrate physiological solutions are given in Tables 14-7 and 14-8. As shown in the tables, a series of concentrated stock solutions is often prepared from which physiological solutions for different animals or for different experi-

mental purposes can be made. It will be noted that different workers have arrived at slightly different formulas for physiological solutions for the same animal or animal group. Physiological solutions are generally buffered in order to maintain the preparation at some desired pH. Often a nutrient such as glucose is added as an energy supply for the tissue.

Although with some types of experimental preparations (for example, some frog nerves or muscles) simply bathing the preparation in the proper solution serves to maintain it in an active state, in other cases the organ or tissue must be perfused. The methods of perfusion are varied but in general supply the living material with an isolated and controlled fluid through the normal vascular bed of the tissue or organ (see Renkin, 1962). Although whole blood or blood from a donor animal is

Table 14-8   Kreb's Solutions for Mammalian Tissues

STOCK SOLUTIONS

No.	CONSTITUENT	MOLARITY	GRAMS PER LITER
(1)	0.90% NaCl	0.154 M	9.00
(2)	1.15% KCl	0.154 M	11.50
(3)	1.22% $CaCl_2 \cdot 2H_2O$	0.110 M	16.17 (or 12.20 g anhydrous salt)
(4)	2.11% KH_2PO_4	0.154 M	21.10
(5)	3.82% $MgSO_4 \cdot 7H_2O$	0.154 M	38.20
(6)	1.30% $NaHCO_3$	0.154 M	13.00
(7)	2.12% $NaH_2PO_4 \cdot H_2O$	0.154 M	21.25
(8)	0.1 M phosphate buffer, pH 7.4 (17.8 g $Na_2HPO_4 \cdot 2H_2O$ + 20 ml 1 N HCl; diluted to 1 liter with distilled water.)		
(9)	0.1 M phosphate buffer, pH 7.4 (17.4 g K_2HPO_4 + 20 ml 1 N HCl; diluted to 1 liter with distilled water.)		

VARIOUS TYPES OF KREB'S SOLUTIONS (NUMBERS IN PARENTHESES REFER TO ABOVE STOCK SOLUTIONS)

ADD SOLUTIONS IN ORDER INDICATED:

KREB'S-RINGER'S	KREB'S-RINGER'S-PHOSPHATE	KREB'S-RINGER'S-BICARBONATE
100 parts (1)	100 parts (1)	100 parts (1)
4 parts (2)	4 parts (2)	4 parts (2)
1 part (4)	1 part (4)	1 part (4)
1 part (5)	1 part (5)	1 part (5)
	12 parts (8)	21 parts (6)
	3 parts (3)	then gas for 10 minutes with 5% $CO–95_2$% O_2 or with 5% $CO–95_2$% N_2

Na$^+$-KREB'S	K$^+$-KREB'S	Ca^{2+}-FREE KREB'S
104.0 parts (1)	104.0 parts (2)	4.0 parts (2)
1.5 parts (3)	1.5 parts (3)	1.0 parts (4)
1.0 parts (7)	1.0 parts (4)	1.0 parts (5)
12.0 parts (8)	12.0 parts (9)	
1.0 parts (5)	1.0 parts (5)	

PERFUSION FLUIDS BASED ON KREB'S MAMMALIAN SOLUTIONS

Normal Kreb's	20 parts Na$^+$ Kreb's + 1 part K$^+$-Kreb's
$\frac{1}{2}$-normal Kreb's	20.5 parts Na$^+$ Kreb's + 0.5 parts K$^+$ Kreb's
2×-normal Kreb's	19 parts Na$^+$ Kreb's + 2 parts K$^+$ Kreb's
3×-normal Kreb's	18 parts Na$^+$ Kreb's + 3 parts K$^+$ Kreb's
4×-normal Kreb's	17 parts Na$^+$ Kreb's + 4 parts K$^+$ Kreb's
$\frac{1}{2}$-normal Ca^{2+}	6 parts Ca^{2+}-free Kreb's + 100.8 parts (1) + 0.75 parts (3) + 12 parts (8)
2×-normal Ca^{2+}	6 parts Ca^{2+}-free Kreb's + 98.5 parts (1) + 3 parts (3) + 12 parts (8)

* pH 7.4 is close to the level at which calcium precipitates. If a white precipitate does form, check the pH and lower to pH 7.4 or less.

All solutions listed are isotonic with rat serum and mixing in any proportion will produce isotonic solutions.

sometimes used, in most cases a physiological solution is used whose variables can be precisely controlled. In this way hormones, particular ions, or other chemicals can be tested for their effects on the preparation. Vascular perfusion is required if the tissue is too thick for oxygen and other materials to penetrate through it (even when a tissue is simply placed in a container of solution, air is usually bubbled through both to provide a sufficient oxygen supply and also to aid in stirring when other materials are added); if metabolism, fluid, or electrolyte balance are not adequately maintained in the absence of a circulating fluid; or if a whole organ or tissue is to be studied *in situ* under controlled conditions.

As already mentioned formulas for physiological solutions are generally empirical. The concentration of a given ion in a physiological solution is not usually the same as in the normal body fluids or tissues. One reason for this lies in the fact that ions in body fluids are bound, in part, to proteins. For example, about one-half the total Ca^{2+} of body fluids is bound to protein. Physiological solutions contain no protein generally and are made with a calcium concentration equal to about half that of the animal's body fluid calcium concentration. It is the free Ca^{2+} ions that contribute to osmotic concentration, not protein-bound calcium.

The Mg^{2+}, SO_4^{2-}, and in fact all ions excepting K^+, Na^+, and Ca^{2+}, which are present in physiological solutions usually serve no known function. They are often essential for activity and the survival of experimental preparations but for unknown reasons.

Excretory Organs

14-6. Types and Functions. I have already indicated that the term excretory organ is somewhat of a misnomer because in many cases the so-called excretory organ is concerned only or primarily with osmoregulation or ion or water balance. Whatever the function of an excretory organ may be, such systems are lacking only in coelenterates and echinoderms.

On the basis of their functional mechanisms, excretory organs can be grouped into four categories: (1) contractile vacuoles found in fresh water protozoans and sponges, and in marine ciliated protozoans; (2) Malpighian tubules and the hindgut of insects; (3) excretory tubules with flame cells or solenocytes found in platyhelminthes, nemertines, rotifers, gastrotrichs, cephalochordates, and some annelids; and (4) excretory tubules that utilize ultrafiltration to form the urine and are found in crustaceans, molluscs, and vertebrates.

Excretory tubules will be called "nephridia" when they occur in invertebrates and lower chordates and "nephrons" when found in vertebrates because in the latter group excretory tubules have a different phylogenetic origin. Nephridia closed at the inner end are **protonephridia**. They possess a flame cell or a solenocyte at the blind end. A flame cell has a tuft of cilia that projects into the lumen of the tubule; a solenocyte bears a single flagellum. Very little is known about the functional mechanisms of protonephridia.

Metanephridia are excretory tubules that open into the coelom by a ciliated funnel (the nephridiostome or nephrostome). Both protonephridia and metanephridia open to the outside of the body through nephridiopores. Frequently they enlarge into a urinary bladder just before reaching the external opening.

These classifications and descriptions are general, and many modifications of nephridia are found in different species. Also in many cases definite proof that excretory tubules included in group 4 above function on the basis of ultrafiltration is lacking, although similarities of ultrastructure indicate that this is correct. Only ultrafiltration systems are well understood.

Excretory systems may function in the excretion of nitrogenous waste products of metabolism or in the maintenance of the pH of body fluids. The major end products of lipid and carbohydrate metabolism are CO_2 and water; and there are few problems in eliminating these substances. Water, if not used by the animal, can be excreted in the urine, from respiratory surfaces, or through the skin. CO_2

can be excreted from respiratory organs or by diffusion through the skin. The end products of protein, nucleotide, and nucleic acid metabolism include, in addition to CO_2 and water, various nitrogen-containing compounds whose elimination is more of a problem. Some of these, for example, are toxic; some require more water for their elimination than the animal can afford. Table 14-3 indicates that it is primarily vertebrates and insects that require the use of the excretory organ for the excretion of nitrogenous compounds; most aqueous animals can simply lose ammonia by its diffusion into the surrounding medium. I shall return to these problems later in this chapter.

14-7. Micropuncture Methods. Before discussing the various types of excretory organs, it is worth mentioning briefly the methods of study of renal tubules. Although most of the methods were devised for the vertebrate nephron, they are also generally applicable, with modification, to the analysis of invertebrate excretory organs.

The method of micropuncture (Richards and Walker, 1937) utilizes microcapillary tubes to puncture and then withdraw samples from selected small regions of renal tubules. The micropipets used have diameters of about 10 μ, and samples as small as 0.06 μl can be taken. The excretory tubule is observed through a microscope, and a micromanipulator is used to position the micropipet. Micropuncture samples are analyzed by microchemical techniques, and their chemical composition is compared with that of arterial blood, urine, or samples of other body fluids or of other regions of the renal tubule. The osmotic concentration of such samples may also be determined by some of the recent methods of cryoscopy.

14-8. Stop-Flow Analysis. Stop-flow analysis is a technique used to determine the specific location of activities along the length of a renal tubule (Malvin et al., 1958). This method is based on the concept that if specific transfer activities take place in specific regions of an excretory tubule, the fluid along the length of

the tubule should exhibit differences in concentration patterns from point to point. The concentration pattern will be accentuated if tubular flow is momentarily blocked. When the flow is allowed to commence again, small rapidly-taken serial samples should reflect the concentration pattern within the tubule. Chemical markers are used that are absorbed, secreted, or unacted upon by excretory tubule cells (see Section 14-9).

In another variation of this method a given volume of a solution of known composition and containing a test substance is placed into a segment of the tubule. The sample is not permitted to move along the tubule, and at intervals micropuncture withdrawal of samples is performed. Chemical analysis reveals whether or not the test substance is absorbed by the tubule cells.

Such studies may be performed on exposed kidneys within the experimental animal. Kidney functions in vertebrates are often studied using thin kidney slices perfused with the appropriate physiological solution (Forster, 1948). The use of dyes such as phenol red, combined with direct microscopic observation of the kidney slice or isolated renal tubules (Forster, 1958) can provide information about the movement and sites of movement of various materials across the different regions of the tubule.

14-9. Electrical Potential Measurements. Microelectrode studies have revealed that transmembrane potentials exist across the membrane of kidney tubule cells. Potential differences—the transtubular potentials—are also found between the lumen and the exterior of the tubule across the entire cell. The transmembrane potential (sometimes called the transcellular potential) of the inner face of the proximal tubule cells of *Necturus maculosus* was found to be about -53 mV; that across the exterior surface was about -73 mV. The transtubular potential is about 20 mV, the lumenal side negative to the exterior (Whittembury, 1960). These potentials are close to the K^+ equilibrium potentials calculated for the tubule cells.

Measurements of transmembrane or transtubular potentials aid in determining which ions are present and transported in various regions of the tubule. In the glomerular region of the vertebrate kidney, there are no transmembrane potentials, and this is a region assumed to be freely permeable to all ions as well as water.

14-10. Clearance Studies.

All of the newer instrumental methods are aided by the classical techniques of renal clearance studies. The formation of urine in the vertebrate tubule, as well as in the crustacean tubule, is regarded as the result of three processes: (1) ultrafiltration of blood; (2) tubule cell absorption (= reabsorption) of some materials which are transported back into the blood; and (3) tubule cell secretion—the addition of materials to the tubular fluid from the tubule cells. Ultrafiltration forms the primary urine, which is then modified by the addition or removal of substances by absorption or secretion. Some kidneys of invertebrates do not utilize ultrafiltration to form urine, only a process of secretion.

Quantitative studies of excretory tubule functioning include determinations of the rates at which particular substances are filtered, secreted, or absorbed. The maximum rate at which any substance is removed (cleared) from the blood is the **clearance factor** (C_m). The plasma clearance of a substance is defined as the volume of blood plasma that would be required to provide the amount of substance excreted by the renal tubule per minute. Clearance is, thus, defined by

$$C_m = UV/P \qquad (14.2)$$

where the clearance, C_m, has units of ml/minute; P is the plasma concentration of the substance under study; V is the rate of urine flow/minute; and U is the urine concentration of the substance in g/ml.

The rate at which a substance is cleared from the plasma is dependent on the glomerular filtration rate (GFR), the renal plasma flow (RPF), and the transport maximum (T_m). The latter is a measure of the rate at which tubule cells absorb or secrete a material.

14-11. Glomerular Filtration Rate (GFR).

The GFR can be determined by placing a substance into the plasma that has the following characteristics: it diffuses freely through the glomerular membrane into the excretory tubule; it does not complex with plasma proteins; it is physiologically and metabolically inert and nontoxic; its concentration is readily determinable; and it is not reabsorbed or secreted by tubule cells. Inulin, a polyfructoside of about 5,000 molecular weight, has been extensively used for measuring the GFR.

The GFR is the volume of blood filtered per minute and is defined by

$$GFR = UV/P \qquad (14.3)$$

where U, V, and P have the same meanings as for Equation 14.2. Although the clearance equation can be used for any substance, Equation 14.3 is used only for substances that have the properties just listed.

In the experimental determination of the GFR, inulin is injected into the blood of an animal until the plasma concentration is brought to some definite level. At time zero, the animal is voided and the urine discarded. At some later time (usually one hour) samples of blood and urine are collected and their inulin concentrations measured. These values and the rate at which the urine was formed are inserted into Equation 14.3 and the GFR calculated.

14-12. Renal Plasma Flow (RPF).

The rate of plasma flow through the kidney can be determined by using a chemical marker that is cleared from the blood during a single passage through the kidney. Such a marker is *p*-aminohippuric acid (PAH). It is both filtered and secreted by tubule cells and about 90 per cent is removed during a single passage of a volume of blood through the kidney. Its clearance is a measure of the RPF. It is not an estimate of the total renal blood supply in animals that have both an arterial and a venous supply to the kidney. Because the RPF represents only the plasma volume of blood, which is about half the total blood volume, doubling the RPF gives an estimate of total volume of blood flow through the kidney.

14-13. Transport Maximum (T_m). The U/P ratio of a substance is a measure of the concentrating or diluting ability of an animal's kidneys for that substance. When the clearance of a given substance is determined simultaneously with that of inulin, a clearance ratio of 1 indicates that the substance is only filtered. When the ratio is greater than 1, tubular secretion of the substance has occurred. When the ratio is less than 1, the substance has been absorbed to some extent by the tubule cells.

The transport maximum, T_m, is the maximum rate at which tubular cells secrete or absorb a given substance. The T_m is equal to the rate of filtration minus the rate of excretion when a substance is absorbed. The T_m for a substance that is secreted equals the rate of excretion minus the rate of filtration.

PAH is often used in the analysis of T_m and other renal parameters. The rate of secretion of PAH is calculated from

$$T_{PAH} = U_{PAH}V - P_{PAH}F \cdot GRF \quad (14.4)$$

F is the fraction of PAH bound to plasma proteins, for it is known that about 10 mg of PAH binds to the protein in 100 ml of plasma. This binding must be accounted for when studying renal functions using a chemical marker. The dye, phenol red, has also been widely used in studies of tubular secretion and it also binds to plasma proteins (about 80 mg of dye per 100 ml of blood).

Particular values of the GFR, T_m, and so forth, as well as the way in which these various terms are used to characterize particular

kidneys, will be given in the sections that follow.

14-14. The Contractile Vacuole. These cellular organelles are found in fresh water protozoa, marine ciliated protozoa, and fresh water sponges. They are small vacuoles that fill with a clear fluid until a certain volume is reached, at this time the vacuole empties its contents to the exterior. The filling and discharging is usually rhythmical. Fresh water protozoans and sponges live in a hypotonic environment, and the contractile vacuole pumps out excess water resulting from osmotic inflow, thus preventing cellular swelling and disruption. The contractile vacuole may have a fixed site within the cell as in *Paramecium*, or it may appear to form at random sites as in *Amoeba*.

That the contractile vacuole functions in relation to the osmotic environment was shown as long ago as 1914 by Stempell and confirmed by Müller (1936). Figure 14-4 illustrates the dependence of the rate of activity of the contractile vacuole on the osmotic concentration of the medium. When the external environment increases in osmotic concentration, the rate of vacuole formation decreases and may stop. In addition to removing excess water brought in by osmosis, the contractile vacuole also removes water produced in metabolic reactions.

The contractile vacuole could also function in the excretion of waste products, but in protozoans there is no difficulty in excreting CO_2, ammonia, and other metabolic by-products

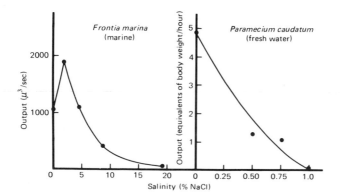

Figure 14-4 Showing the outputs of the contractile vacuoles of a marine and a fresh water protozoan when the organisms are placed in different salinities. [Data for *Frontia* from Müller (1936); for *Paramecium* from Herfs (1922).]

directly through the cell membrane by diffusion.

Although the mode of operation of the contractile vacuole is not known—how, for example, water enters the vacuole from the hypertonic cytoplasm—several recent findings have shown that Na^+ and K^+ ions are involved in ion and water balance in protozoans. Cells in a hypotonic medium have two problems: how to prevent the osmotic inflow of water (or to remove that water which does flow in) and how to prevent the outward diffusion of needed salts. These problems might be solved by the presence of an impermeable outer membrane or by the development of active transport processes to accumulate ions within the cell.

The former solution would not work because there is a need for cells to exchange materials such as oxygen and nutrients with the environment. Water movement, as discussed in Chapter 6, is generally linked with the active transport of solutes or perhaps with the contractile properties of membranes.

The fresh water ciliates *Spirostromum*, *Paramecium*, and *Tetrahymena*; the marine ciliate *Uronema*; and the amoebas *Chaos* and *Acanthamoeba* all have been shown to accumulate K^+ within the cell. *Chaos* and *Tetrahymena* actively transport Na^+ out of the cell, probably through the contractile vacuole. The cilates can also accumulate Na^+ when in a hypotonic medium. *Chaos* accumulates Cl^- above the environmental concentration by pinocytosis. The K^+ uptake and Na^+ output are not linked functions in protozoans. The halftime of Na^+ exchange in *Tetrahymena* is greatly increased when the activity of the contractile vacuole is slowed. The Na^+ concentration within the vacuole is up to 8 times greater than that of the cytoplasm.

On the basis of the latter observation, it has been suggested that the contractile vacuole actively transports Na^+ into the vacuole, thus raising its osmotic concentration above that of the cytoplasm and inducing an osmotic inflow of water. The mechanism by which the vacuole discharges its water content to the exterior is not known.

In *Paramecium* so-called nephridial canals

lead into the contractile vacuole, whereas in *Amoeba proteus* the vacuole seems to enlarge by the coalescing of many small vesicles that appear in the cytoplasm about the region of the vacuole. In both cases there is a concentration of mitochondria about the vacuole. This may represent the energy source for the active transport of an ion or might be a mitochondrial pump for collecting ions from the cytoplasm and feeding them to the vacuole. It is known that mitochondria can actively transport and accumulate ions. The energy of electron transport may be used directly for this purpose (Chapter 4).

Microelectrode studies reveal that the contractile vacuole in amoebas is 20 mV positive with respect to the cytoplasm, a fact that may be of significance in vacuole functioning.

In some fresh water protozoans and sponges, no signs of contractile vacuole formation have been observed, and the mechanisms by which these species maintain themselves osmotically is not known.

14-15. Coelenterates. Fresh water coelenterates present an interesting problem, for they have no recognized excretory organs or organelles and yet live in a hypotonic medium, possess a membrane highly permeable to water and salts, and retain cellular volumes at constant levels. Water enters at rates between 0.48 and 0.79 μ^3/μ^2 surface/atm/min (Lilly, 1955). An organism such as *Hydra* maintains an internal concentration equivalent to a 0.025 M NaCl solution. Although no observable water removal mechanisms have been found, they must obviously exist.

Coelenterates can excrete waste products by diffusion through their cell membranes without difficulty. Coelenterates also possess astrocytes, phagocytic cells that can engulf and remove foreign particles.

Another interesting facet of ionic regulation has been found in some marine coelenterates. The ionic composition of the mesoglea of pelagic medusae differs from sea water in that it has a lower concentration of SO_4^{2-} and Mg^{2+} ions, but a higher concentration of Na^+ ions. The ionic regulatory mechanisms of these

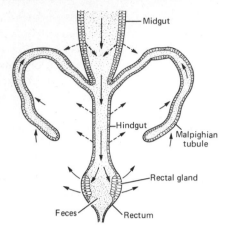

Figure 14-5 The insect excretory system. Directions of water movement indicated by arrows. [After V. B. Wigglesworth (1931). "Excretion in Rhodinus (Hemiptera)." *Journal of Experimental Biology*. By permission.]

animals are responsible also for achieving a proper buoyancy. For example, by reducing the normal SO_4^{2-} content by one-half, an increase in buoyancy of 1 mg/ml is achieved and the animal floats. In many aquatic organisms osmotic mechanisms are found to alter the densities of tissues in accord with needed buoyancies (Denton and Shaw, 1962).

Generally studies and observations of protozoans and coelenterates tend to place active transport of ions at the basis of osmoregulatory and other activities. The ability to use energy for the movement of ions and solutes appears to have evolved early in the history of animals.

14-16. Malpighian Tubules. The excretory system of insects (and other land arthropods such as centipedes and millipedes, as well as some arachnids) is composed of the malpighian tubules and hindgut (Figure 14-5). The malpighian tubules (which may be considered a form of protonephridia) are long slender blind tubules lying in the hemocoel with their upper ends bathed in blood. They open into the hindgut near its junction with the midgut. Although the malpighian tubules are modified in some insects for the production of silk or wax, two parts of the tubule are found in all insects and are concerned with osmoregulation and excretion. These are the upper region

lying in the hemocoel and the lower region opening into the hindgut. The number of malpighian tubules varies from 2 to more than 150 depending on the species.

The malpighian tubules produce a copious flow of urine, rich in K^+. For example, in *Carausius* (formerly *Dixippus*), the stick insect, the flow is from 4 to 6 mg/gram body tissue/hour. This is equivalent to a secretion of all the body water each day and all the body K^+ every three hours. K^+ and Na^+ are actively transported into the tubules from the blood, whereas Cl^-, sugars, and amino acids enter the tubules by passive diffusion. The primary urine is formed by secretion, not by ultrafiltration. In the hindgut most of the water and salts are reabsorbed, and uric acid (the insect by-product of protein metabolism) and any surplus salts are eliminated. Water is absorbed to such an extent that the uric acid is usually excreted in the form of dried crystals (Ramsay and Riegel, 1961).

The malpighian tubule cells possess a well-developed brush border—a feature associated with the secretion or absorption of materials as described in Chapters 6 and 7. The hindgut is lined with a thin, water-permeable cuticle, and the epithelial cells are often arranged in six longitudinal rows, sometimes forming the rectal glands.

The functions of the rectal glands are not known. It has been suggested that they are

Table 14-9 The Composition of the Serum and Urine of *Carausius morosus* (mM/l)*

Constituent	Serum	Plasma
Na^+	11	5
K^+	18	145
Ca^{2+}	3.6	1
Mg^{2+}	54	9
Cl^-	87	65
PO_4^{2-}	39	61
Uric acid	0.27	2.6
Total (mOsm/l)	320	317

* Data from Ramsay (1956).

involved either in salt or water absorption. Some workers feel that they are involved in salt secretion because the electrical polarity of the rectal gland cells is opposite to that of the cells of the vertebrate nephron that absorb salt.

Because of the wide variety of insects and their habitats, it is difficult to generalize about the operation of malpighian tubules or hindgut. The stick insect has been extensively studied by Ramsay and his colleagues.

As shown in Table 14-9 the total osmotic concentration of the urine formed in the malpighian tubules is nearly isotonic with the blood, although K^+ is much higher in concentration. When the upper portion of the malpighian tubule is removed and only the lower portion bathed in blood, a urine results that can be 40 mOsmoles hypertonic to the serum. Simultaneous measurements of the osmotic pressures of urine and serum show that the urine is always slightly more hypoosmotic than the serum—an indication that water is secreted into the tubules in the lower portion (Ramsay, 1952).

K^+ is secreted into the tubules against both electrical and concentration gradients, since the inside of the tubules is 10 to 20 mV positive with respect to the serum. The concentrations of Na^+ and K^+ in the rectal fluid are 19 and 320 mM/l respectively. This is another indication that water is removed from the urine and, perhaps, salt has been secreted by the rectal glands. The rate of water excretion is found to be proportional to the rate of K^+ secretion. Urine formation and K^+ secretion, in turn, depend upon the K^+ concentration of the blood, but are independent of blood Na^+ levels.

When the concentration of Na^+ or K^+ in the blood of Carausius is artificially raised by the injection of the appropriate salt solution, a long time is required for correction of the higher than normal levels. For several days Na^+ remains high, while K^+ remains high for at least 24 hours. The rates of Na^+ and K^+ secretion into the malpighian tubules are increased, but so also are the rates of reabsorption by the hindgut. But such an experimental procedure poses problems for Carausius that it never

faces normally. Its environment is a relatively stable one osmotically.

When similar experiments are performed on insects that inhabit more variable osmotic environments, for example, the blood-sucking bug, Rhodnius, or the mosquito Aedes, it is found that the rates of ion secretion and absorption are adjusted so that elimination of excess Na^+ and K^+ is effected almost immediately. Thus, the capabilities of the excretory system depend on the normal environment of the animal, and control mechanisms will vary in different species. Although there are indications that secretion and absorption of substances in insects are under hormonal control, much more remains to be discovered about the control systems.

As indicated in Chapter 9, insects are one of the few animal groups in which active transport of water has been shown to occur, although the mechanisms are not known. Insects face the problem of desiccation and active water uptake helps to alleviate this problem. Active water uptake has been found in several insect species and in a few ticks.

14-17. Protonephridia. Protonephridia are typical excretory organs in animals that lack a high pressure circulatory system and therefore lack the hydrostatic forces needed for ultrafiltration. However, little is known about the functioning of these organs. They are usually extremely small, and no methods of collecting their fluids have been devised.

Protonephridia are narrow ducts that end blindly in either flame cells or solenocytes. It has been suggested that the activity of the cilia or flagellum gives rise to negative pressures inside the lumen of the protonephridia. If this were the case, urine could be formed because of a higher external hydrostatic pressure driving water and solutes into the tubule. But it is difficult to imagine how such ciliary activity could give rise to the needed pressure differential.

Danielli and Pantin (1950) showed that alkaline phosphatase—an enzyme often found in high concentrations where active transport processes occur—is lacking at the blind end of the protonephridia, although it is present in lower reaches of the duct. Its absence at the blind end suggests that urine is not formed by active transport of materials. Its presence lower down in the duct suggests that there is a modification of the urine by reabsorption in this region. Such a modification of the urine is also suggested by the long and differentiated protonephridial ducts found in many invertebrates, for example, the rotifers.

Clearly, all such evidence is circumstantial and, in fact, there is no definite proof that protonephria function is osmoregulation. Suggestive evidence for the latter function is found in the rotifer, *Asplanchia*, where the rhythm of the flame bulb activity, of contractile bladder movements, and the volume of fluid flow, all can be altered by changing the osmotic gradient between the animal and its environment.

Kromhaut (1943) compared the protonephridial systems of marine, brackish, and fresh water forms of one turbellarian species, *Gyratrix hermaphorditus*, and found that differences in habitat were associated with major modifications in the nephridial system of this one species. In fresh water forms the protonephridial system is long and complex—an indication that a copious urine could be formed and modified so that salt is conserved and water removed. In several regions the protonephridia of the fresh water variety are enveloped by paranephrocytes—large cells, 50 to 60 μ in diameter, and of unknown function. The tubule runs into a contractile, pulsatile structure—the ampulla—and then the tubule enlarges into a bladder that opens to the outside through the nephridiopore.

In the brackish water form, the ampulla and paranephrocytes are absent, leaving only an undifferentiated tubule. The animal in this environment has less of an osmotic problem and presumably requires a less specialized osmoregulatory system.

In the marine form the entire system is missing. The organism is nearly isosmotic with sea water, and there is little demand for an osmoregulatory organ. Thus the development of the nephridial system appears to be correlated with the osmotic environment in which the animal lives.

14-18. Nematodes. The nematodes are discussed separately because they have an unusual excretory system (Chitwood and Chitwood, 1950). The system develops from the renette cell found in primitive marine nematodes and is not protonephridial in origin.

The excretory system of marine nematodes consists of a single glandlike cell that has a short duct opening to the exterior through an excretory pore. In fresh water forms the duct is lined with a thin impermeable cuticle. Fresh water nematodes also have a series of lateral tubules.

The system is considered to play a role in osmoregulation because the discharge rate increases with increasing hypotonicity of the external medium. Again, the nature of the renette cell and the mechanisms by which urine is formed are not known.

14-19. Annelids. Although primitive annelids have closed nephridia with numerous solenocytes, most annelids have paired open nephridia in each body segment. The nephridium opens

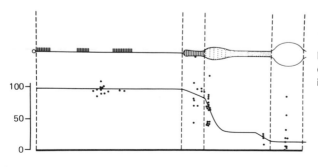

Figure 14-6 The osmotic pressure at different levels of the earthworm nephridium. [Redrawn after Ramsay (1949a).]

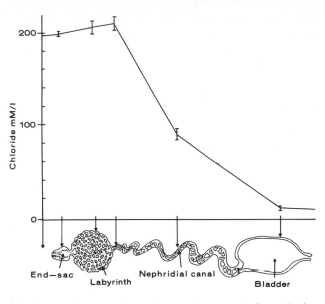

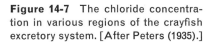

Figure 14-7 The chloride concentration in various regions of the crayfish excretory system. [After Peters (1935).]

into the coelomic cavity through a ciliated funnel, the nephridiostome. The coelomic fluid probably drains into the nephridium through the nephridiostome, aided by ciliary contraction. In the earthworm, *Lumbricus terrestris,* the coelomic fluid is always hypertonic to the blood. This concentration difference, produced by an unknown mechanism, may serve to withdraw water from the blood. The earthworm excretes a urine that is strongly hypotonic to body fluids except when placed in very concentrated media, in which case the urine becomes isotonic to the blood. This is a situation similar to that found in the vertebrate distal tubule. The parts of the nephridium and the corresponding tonicities of the urine are shown in Figure 14-6.

In terrestrial or fresh water annelids the nephridium is long and highly differentiated. In marine forms it is short and undifferentiated. This morphological difference is correlated with the nearly isosmotic condition of marine forms to sea water, which eliminates the need for a large urine output. In the long tubule of the earthworm, micropuncture studies have shown that from the end of the thin tubule to the muscular duct or bladder, the urine is increasingly hypotonic to the blood, an indication that absorption of salts takes place along most of the nephridial tubule. *Lumbricus* excretes both ammonia and urea

in approximately equal amounts through the nephridia.

14-20. Crustaceans. The crustaceans are an interesting group from the viewpoint of adaptive physiology because members of the class are found in marine, brackish, fresh, and high salinity waters, and in the terrestrial environment. It is possible to follow to some extent the adaptations that had to develop in order to permit this exploitation of various osmotic habitats. This facet of osmoregulation will be considered in later sections after the nature of the crustacean excretory system has been discussed.

Crustacean excretory organs consist of a pair of antennary glands (green glands) located in the head region and representing modifications of a primitive segmental metanephridial system. Generally, a gland consists of a coelomic sac (end sac), an excretory tubule, and an excretory duct sometimes preceded by a bladder. Depending on the particular environment of an animal, various modifications of these parts are found.

The coelomic sac leads into an involuted tubule, the labyrinth (Figure 14-7). Following the labyrinth in fresh water crustaceans is the nephridial canal, which is long in modern forms such as the crayfish. The excretory system of fresh water crustaceans forms a urine by ultrafiltration, followed by secretion and

587

reabsorption to modify the primary urine (Riegel and Kirschner, 1960). In crayfish, micropuncture studies show that the originally isotonic urine is modified by Na^+, K^+, and Cl^- reabsorption in all parts of the system including the bladder (Riegel, 1965).

The structural analogies between parts of the crustacean excretory system and those of the vertebrate nephron are striking. Electron microscope studies show that in the region of the coelomic sac podocyte-like cells are present in the crayfish. These cells are also present in the vertebrate glomerulus. In the crayfish labyrinth are found cells in a single layer which are similar in appearance to those of the proximal tubule of the vertebrate nephron. They possess a brush border that increases the effective surface area for the exchange of materials.

The crustacean excretory organs are little used for the excretion of nitrogenous wastes, rather these are eliminated by diffusion through the gills in the form of ammonia, although some urea and a little uric acid is also excreted. Uric acid is sometimes stored in nephrocytes or is utilized in white chromatophores (Mollitor, 1937). Uric acid is deposited in the integument of some terrestrial arthropods and lost with the molt (Dresel and Moyle, 1950).

Crustacean urine is generally isosmotic with the blood except in some fresh water species. *Artemia*, the brine shrimp, which lives in high salinity waters can produce a hypertonic urine but depends on other mechanisms as well for osmoregulation.

14-21. Molluscs. In lamellibranch molluscs the circulatory system is intimately related to the excretory system at the heart itself. Ultrafiltration of the blood occurs through the walls of the heart into the pericardium and then the filtrate (or urine) is passed through a pair of excretory ducts variously called kidneys, nephridia, or Bojanus organs.

Some species have a pair of such organs, others only a single one. The kidney consists of a glandular spongy portion and a thin-walled portion, the bladder. In *Anodonta cygnea* the blood filtrate passes through the kidney, where salt is reabsorbed while nitrogenous wastes are

secreted into the urine. A variety of molluscs including the marine *Octopus dofleini*, the abolone *Haliotis rufescens*, and the land snail *Achatina fulica* have been shown to excrete inulin with clearances of the same order of magnitude as those of vertebrates.

In the octopus urine is formed at a different location. A pericardial cavity surrounds an appendage of each branchial heart instead of the main heart. The site of formation of urine is not known for terrestrial gastropods because no fluid can be obtained from the pericardial cavity of any snail so far examined.

14-22. Structure of the Vertebrate Nephron. Much is inferred about the operation of invertebrate excretory tubules from knowledge of the vertebrate nephron—the excretory tubule about which most is known.

The mammalian kidney has the familiar bean shape (Figures 14-8 and 14-9) and contains about a million functional units, the **nephrons**. The kidney is a concentrically layered structure, centered about the renal papilla, which contains the openings of the collecting ducts that drain urine from the tubules. The relation of various parts of the nephron to the general kidney structure is shown in Figures 14-10 and 14-11. The medulla contains collecting ducts,

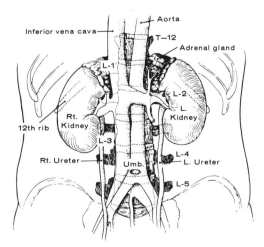

Figure 14-8 The location of the kidneys in the human. [From S. Grollman (1964) *The Human Body*. By permission from The Macmillan Company, New York.]

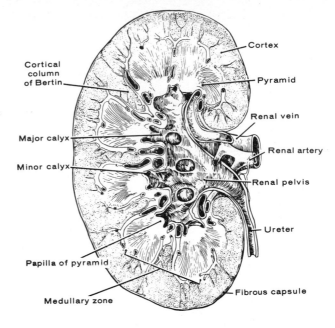

Figure 14-9 Longitudinal section of kidney. [From S. Grollman (1964) *The Human Body*. By permission from The Macmillan Company, New York.]

Labels on figure: Cortex, Cortical column of Bertin, Pyramid, Renal vein, Major calyx, Renal artery, Minor calyx, Renal pelvis, Ureter, Papilla of pyramid, Medullary zone, Fibrous capsule

loops of Henle, blood vessels, and supporting tissue. The overlying cortex contains glomeruli, proximal and distal convoluted tubules, blood vessels, supporting tissues, and nerves.

Such a layered arrangement is not typical of all vertebrate groups. The general shape of the kidney varies from being long and thin in fishes, highly lobular in birds, to compact in mammals. The nephrons in kidneys, other than those of birds and mammals, wander about seemingly at random, and there is no regularity of spatial arrangement. In different vertebrate groups the number of nephrons per kidney ranges from a few hundred to several thousand to a million in higher mammals.

The kidney has a rich blood supply with a specialized relationship of circulatory vessels to the nephron. At the hilus of the kidney, the renal artery divides into four or five large branches that run to the boundary between cortex and medulla. Here they turn and divide again, forming the arciform arteries. These give rise to smaller interlobullar arteries, which pass to the cortex of the kidney and divide into still smaller afferent arteries. The latter give rise to small capillary tufts containing about 50 capillary loops. Each tuft is a **glomerulus** and is surrounded by **Bowman's capsule** of the nephron. The combination of glomerulus and capsule is the **renal corpuscle**. It is at this site that primary urine is formed by ultrafiltration of the blood.

At the vascular pole of the capsule, the capillaries rejoin to form an efferent artery. Soon after leaving the region of the capsule, these arteries begin to branch forming a capillary network which surrounds the tubule. Each excretory tubule is well supplied with circulatory vessels.

The tubular blood supply differs in vertebrate groups. In most, excepting mammals, there is also a venous blood supply to the tubule. Venous blood from the lower extremities is carried through a renal portal vein to the kidneys. This blood vessel is absent in mammals. In aglomerular fish the entire blood supply is of venous origin. An arterial blood supply is found only when the nephron possesses a glomerulus.

The renal tubule is composed of several distinct regions that may be modified or absent in various vertebrates. From the renal capsule leads a long tubule, the first part of which is highly convoluted—the **proximal convoluted tubule**. This part of the nephron is found in all vertebrates and is formed of a cell layer distinguished by prominent brush borders. In more primitive fish such as the toadfish or

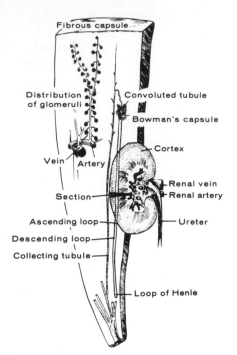

Fibrous capsule

Distribution of glomeruli

Convoluted tubule

Bowman's capsule

Cortex

Vein   Artery

Section

Renal vein
Renal artery

Ascending loop

Descending loop

Collecting tubule

Ureter

Loop of Henle

Figure 14-10 The relative position of the nephron in the kidney. [From S. Grollman (1964) *The Human Body*. By permission from The Macmillan Company, New York.]

goose fish, the nephron consists only of this segment.

Next comes the **straight segment** of the tubule, which at some point suddenly decreases in diameter from about 0.06 mm to 0.02 mm. The difference in the outside diameter of this thin segment is caused by the presence of a flatter pavement epithelium making up the tubule wall rather than the cuboidal or columnar epithelium found in other parts of the nephron. The straight segment is part of the **loop of Henle**. This loop makes a sharp U-turn in the medulla, returning again to the vicinity of the parent corpuscle. The thin segment is distinctive of the mammalian kidney and is found, in a poorly developed state, only in a few birds among other vertebrates.

Following the U-turn, the ascending straight segment runs into a more twisted portion of the nephron—the **distal convoluted tubule**. The cells of this ascending segment are similar to those found in the corresponding descending segment. They possess no brush border and

are cuboidal or columnar epithelial cells. The distal convoluted tubules lead into **collecting tubules**.

Collecting tubules combine to form a **collecting duct** that runs to the renal pelvis. Here the collecting ducts fuse to form the **ureter**, which leads to the bladder and then the excretory pore. The nephron of the human kidney when straightened is about 40 to 60 mm in length, the variation depending principally upon the length of the thin segment. As illustrated in Figure 14-11, two different types of nephrons may be found in a given kidney. The ultrastructure of the nephron is described in Dalton and Haguenau (1967).

The structure of the vertebrate nephron varies according to the evolutionary history and environment of each class. The cyclostomes have a metamerically segmented kidney and each segment has a glomerulus and tubule lacking a distal convoluted segment. This distal tubule, which is concerned with salt reabsorption and is an adaptation to the fresh water environment, is also secondarily absent in some marine teleosts. The absence of the distal tubule in the hagfish is a primitive characteristic.

The presence or absence of glomeruli in marine fish is not necessarily caused by adaptation to their environment but also represents their phylogenetic relationships. In marine teleosts, as stated above, the distal segment is often lacking. The glomerulus, which is the filtration system especially valuable to animals living in fresh water and needing to excrete a large volume of urine, may be present in marine fish because they evolved from fresh water forms, or it may be absent because of adaptive modifications when these fish returned to the marine environment. When marine teleosts do possess a glomerulus, it probably serves little function. Marine elasmobranchs avoid the problem of osmoregulation by conserving large amounts of urea in their blood and body fluids and tissues, and this makes them isosmotic or even hyperosmotic to the marine environment. Mammals have a well-developed thin segment of the loop of Henle (Figure 14-11), an adaptation that allows

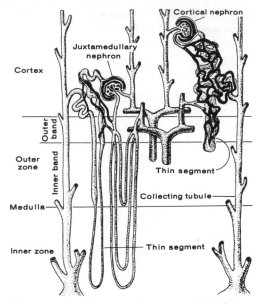

Figure 14-11 Diagram illustrating the relation of parts of the nephron to the layers of the kidney. As indicated, different types of nephrons are present. Some, the cortical nephrons, are located primarily in the cortical layer, whereas others, juxtamedullary nephrons, are located in the medullary layer. [Redrawn from Smith (1951).]

water reabsorption by the tubule and the ability to produce a hypertonic urine. Bird kidneys may possess tubular arrangements that are functionally equivalent to loops of Henle although of more complex organization. Countercurrent multipliers have been found in some avian kidneys.

14-23. Glomerular Functioning. In the vertebrate nephron primary urine is formed by ultrafiltration of blood in the glomerulus. The urine in the capsule is then modified during its passage down the tubule.

Five types of studies are used to determine definitely when an excretory organ operates on the basis of ultrafiltration-absorption-secretion. (1) Morphological studies are used to find a definite site for filtration, often using dyes to trace pathways of fluid movement; (2) micropuncture or stop-flow methods are used to analyze tubular fluids from various sites, and their composition is compared with that of blood or final urine; (3) the sensitivity to

pressure of tubular fluid formation is determined: (4) the amount of glucose and polymer excretion is determined; and (5) measurements of potential differences across the tubular membrane are made.

A filtration system, as described for capillary functioning in Chapter 12, operates on the basis of a sufficient pressure gradient to drive fluid and solutes across a membrane. In the case of the glomerular-capsule filtration process, the blood (hydrostatic) pressure must be great enough to overcome the colloid osmotic pressure of the plasma proteins. In addition, the pressure differences must be great enough to keep fluid moving in the tubule. The back pressure in the mammalian nephron is about 10 mm Hg, as determined by direct micropuncture studies. The colloidal osmotic pressure is about 25 to 30 mm Hg (Gottschalk and Mylle, 1956).

The net filtration pressure, under the simplest conditions, would equal the glomerular capillary blood pressure minus the oncotic pressure and the back pressure within the capsule. If the ureter is blocked and a pressure applied, thus raising the back pressure within the tubule, a point should be reached at which urine flow stops. This point would give an estimate of the glomerular capillary blood pressure.

Experiments along these lines have shown that the uretral pressure required to prevent urine flow varies from 10 to 60 mm Hg, with an average of about 40 mm Hg. If we add this to the colloidal osmotic pressure of about 30 mm Hg, it follows that the blood pressure in the glomerulus must be about 70 mm Hg. This is somewhat more than half of the mean arterial blood pressure of the mammal. Direct blood pressure measurements in the frog showed that the glomerular pressure amounted to about 50 per cent of the mean aortic pressure as expected from the calculations just given.

It is the lack of a high pressure circulatory system in some organisms that requires the excretory tubules to utilize secretion to form urine, rather than ultrafiltration. But filtration is always aided by the secretion of some materials by tubule cells. This, for example, is

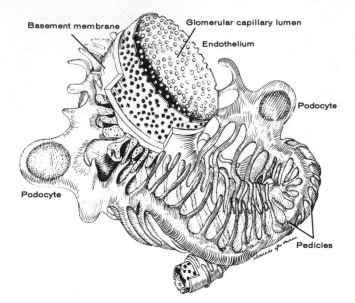

Basement membrane   Glomerular capillary lumen

Endothelium

Podocyte

Podocyte

Pedicles

Figure 14-12 Three-dimensional schematic representation of epithelial cells (podocytes) from the visceral layer of Bowman's capsule. [From J. A. Freeman (1964) *Cellular Fine Structure*. By permission McGraw-Hill Book Company, New York.]

required for materials formed faster than they can be filtered, which must be eliminated from the body. Secretion also aids in the differential excretion of substances.

Glomerular filtration is not, however, a requirement for efficient kidney function in vertebrates as evidenced by the aglomerular kidney of some groups. In aglomerular organisms, the presence of a renal portal system is needed to provide an adequate blood supply to the tubules so that waste products can be removed quickly.

The nature and rate of the filtration process depends, in part, on the nature of the membranes between the renal capillaries and the renal corpuscle. The glomerular membrane consists of three layers. The capillary wall itself

is a fenestrated endothelium with openings of about 600 Å in diameter covered with a thin diaphragm about 70 Å thick. There is a basement membrane (the lamina densa) of about 1,200 Å thickness. Finally there is an epithelial layer consisting of long-processed cells—the **podocytes**. The projections of these cells are called trabeculae and lead, in turn, to smaller interdigitating pedicles (Figure 14-12). The spaces between the pedicles are thought to function in the restriction of plasma protein movements. As shown in Table 14-10 only plasma proteins above a certain size are excluded from filtration. Both the anatomical and the biochemical properties of the glomerular membranes are responsible for this differentiation. The overall structure is such as to

Table 14-10 Sizes of Proteins and Their Ability to Penetrate the Glomerulus*

Proteins Excreted	Molecular Weight	Proteins Not Excreted	Molecular Weight
Gelatin	35,000	Hemoglobin	68,000
Egg albumin	34,500	Serum albumin	67,500
Hemoglobin	68,000	Serum globulin	103,800
		Edestin	208,000
		Hemocyanin	5,000,000

* Data from Bayliss et al. (1933).

Table 14-11 Urine Volumes Excreted by Some Animals from Various Environments*

ANIMAL†	URINE LOSS	OTHER AND COMMENTS
Protozoans		
Paramecium caudatum [FW]	115 equivalents of body volume/day	Output of contractile vacuole
Annelids		
Lumbricus terrestris [TM]	600 ml/kg/day	Body weight: 0.004 kg
Molluscs		
Anodonta cygnea [FW]	480 ml/kg/day	GFR—480 ml/kg/day; body weight: 0.05 kg
Sepia officinalis [SW]	42 ml/kg/day	GFR—42 ml/kg/day; body weight: 0.89 kg
Crustaceans		
Homarus vulgarus [SW]	48 ml/kg/day	GFR—48 ml/kg/day; body weight 0.50 kg
Carcinus maenas [SW]	32 ml/kg/day	GFR—32 ml/kg/day
Palaemonetes varians	0.42% of body weight per hour in sea water 0.15% of body weight per hour in 50% sea water 1.63% of body weight per hour in 5% sea water	
Eriochier sinensis [BW]	0.175% of body weight per hour	
Cambarus [FW]	0.217% of body weight per hour; very dilute urine	
Vertebrates—fish		
Myxine glutinosa [SW]	4.8 ml/kg/day	
Squalus acanthias	9.6 ml/kg/day	Body weight: 4 kg
gar pike [FW]	200–400 ml/kg/day	
sculpin [SW]	22 ml/kg/day	GFR—46 ml/kg/day; water swallowed: 116 ml/kg/day; water absorbed by gut: 72 ml/kg/day; extrarenal water loss: 42 ml/kg/day.
Vertebrates—reptiles		
Caiman sclerops [FW]	10–30 ml/kg/day	Cutaneous water loss: 33 mg/cm²/day Respiratory water loss: 4.9 mg/ml O_2
Iguana iguana		Cutaneous water loss: 4.8 mg/cm²/day Respiratory water loss: 0.9 mg/ml O_2
Sauromalus obesus [TA]		Cutaneous water loss: 1.3 mg/cm²/day Respiratory water loss: 0.5 mg/ml O_2
Vertebrates—amphibians		
Rana cancrivora [FW]	575 ml/kg/day	GFR—1400 ml/kg/day
[SW]	36 ml/kg/day	GFR—600 ml/kg/day
Rana esculentia [FW]	240 ml/kg/day	GFR—600 ml/kg/day

Table 14-11 continued

ANIMAL†	URINE LOSS	OTHER AND COMMENTS
Vertebrates—birds		
Larus glaucescens [TM]		GFR—3300; body weight: 0.7 kg
Vertebrates—mammals		
seal [SW]	24 ml/kg/day	GFR—3600 ml/cm²/day; body weight: 20 kg
man	1.5 liters per day	GFR—1,100 liters per day Man doing hard physical labor at 36°C can lose as much as 4.5 liters of water/ hour.

* Selected data from: Prosser and Brown (1961); Gordon (1968); K. Schmidt-Nielsen (1964). These references should be consulted for sources of data above.

† FW = freshwater; SW = seawater; BW = brackish water; TA = terrestrial arid; and TM = terrestrial moist environments.

permit the rapid passage of water and most solutes from the blood into the capsule lumen.

The movement of proteins and other large polymers has been studied in other types of excretory organs. For example, the crayfish can excrete dextrans with molecular weights up to only about 60,000. Crayfish excrete injected human serum albumin but not serum globulin nor their own hemocyanin (see Kirschner, 1967). Polymer excretion is used as a sign of filtration because secretion of such materials is not possible by transport through tubular epithelial cells unless pinocytosis is the mechanism of transport—an unlikely mechanism in the excretory tubule. In contrast with other vertebrate kidneys, the aglomerular kidney cannot excrete inulin (Forster, 1953).

Table 14-11 presents some data on the filtration rates and urine flows in a variety of animals. The filtration rates of most animals that have been examined range between 1 and 10 per cent of the body weight of fluid per hour. Sharp decreases in filtration rates are indicative of adaptations for hypotonic osmoregulation—as found in many marine invertebrates. The data for the crayfish point out that some animals can develop mechanisms other than filtration in order to survive in fresh water. The crayfish, as already stated, depends on an impermeable cuticle to cut down water

inflow and on the intake of salt by active transport through the gills in addition to its kidney (Riegel, 1961; Riegel and Kirschner, 1960).

The mechanisms used to control glomerular filtration rates will be considered after tubular functioning is described.

14-24. Tubular Functioning. The absorption of water from the primary urine that produces a final hypertonic urine in mammals is a result of the layered anatomical arrangement of the nephrons with their hairpin turns and the active transport of Na^+ in particular regions of the tubule. Water reabsorption occurs principally in the proximal tubule, and about one quarter of water reabsorption occurs in the collecting ducts.

The basic features of this system will be outlined here, but it should be noted that the details of the mechanisms are still not determined. Analysis of the system was accomplished primarily by micropuncture and cryoscopic studies that allowed the osmotic pressures and chemical compositions of the fluids in various intra- and extratubular regions to be determined (Hargitay et al., 1951; Wirz, 1955, 1961).

Tubular function with respect to water reabsorption depends upon a countercurrent

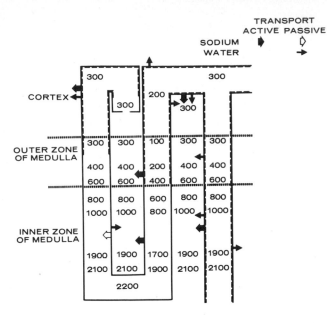

Figure 14-13 Countercurrent multiplier mechanism of the mammalian kidney operating in a long-looped nephron and the adjacent vasa recta. The numbers represent hypothetical osmolality values. Net movements are indicated by arrows. [After C. W. Gottschalk and M. Mylle (1959).]

multiplier system that sets up osmotic gradients between the tubular fluids, the peritubular space, and the peritubular blood vessels surrounding the tubule (B. Schmidt-Nielsen and O'Dell, 1961; B. Schmidt-Nielsen, 1961; Marsh et al., 1967; Morel and Guinnebault, 1961; Wirz, 1956). The glomerular filtrate that enters the capsule and the fluid in the proximal tubule are isosmotic with the blood. As shown in Figure 14-13, the filtrate becomes increasingly concentrated as it passes down the descending tubule toward the turn of the loop of Henle. As the fluid moves upward in the ascending limb, it becomes increasingly concentrated until at the level of the distal convoluted tubule the fluid may again be isotonic with the plasma. As fluid moves along the collecting duct, it again becomes hypertonic as water is absorbed by duct cells.

The underlying cause of these changing tonicities of the tubular fluid is the active transport of Na^+ by tubule cells of the ascending segment into the peritubular space. This segment appears to have a low permeability to water. The outward movement of Na^+ from the tubular fluid greatly increases the osmotic concentration of the peritubular fluid.

The increased peritubular osmotic pressure causes water to move from the descending tubule, down its osmotic gradient, into the

peritubular space. Thus, in the descending tubule there is an increasing concentration of solutes—the fluid becoming hypertonic. In the ascending limb, the outward movement of Na^+ causes increasing hypotonicity of the fluid.

Because of the morphological arrangement of the nephron and its U-turn, there is an upward movement of fluid in the ascending tubule and a downward movement of fluid in the descending tubule. This is a **countercurrent flow**. Because Na^+ is actively transported in larger amounts from the lower end of the nephron, a gradient of Na^+ concentration exists from the top to the bottom of the nephron. The countercurrent flow exaggerates this Na^+ concentration gradient, and the system is termed a countercurrent multiplier. There is also a gradient of concentration between the proximal and distal tubules with the proximal tubule tonicity being greater at each given level of the kidney.

In summary, the outward movement of Na^+ by active transport from the water-impermeable ascending tubule increases the osmotic concentration of the fluid outside the tubule and makes the tubular fluid hypotonic. The hypertonicity of the peritubular fluid causes the osmosis of water from the descending tubule, thus producing an increasing hypertonicity of the tubular fluid. Na^+ ions enter the descending tubule from the peritubular spaces. The result is a concentration of Na^+ ions especially in the region surrounding the U-turn of the loop of Henle. The increased Na^+ concentration in this region increases the rate at which Na^+ is actively transported out of the ascending tubule. This action reinforces the outward movement of water from the descending limb.

Overall, once the system has established a steady state, there is a relatively constant difference in osmotic pressure at each tubular level. The gradient requires the expenditure of energy, that used in the Na^+ active transport. Because of the higher concentrations of Na^+ and other solutes in the bend of the loop and in the renal spaces about this region, more material can diffuse passively into the blood vessels (the peritubular arterioles or **vasa recta** system). Since the blood becomes more concentrated in this region than in arterioles higher on the level of the nephron, it moves more slowly (see Chapter 12). Not only is this a way of returning materials to the blood, but it is a mechanism for preventing blood movements destroying the osmotic gradient established by the countercurrent multiplier system.

The arrangement of the blood vessels of the vasa recta also form a countercurrent system. But materials pass in or out of these vessels only by passive diffusion, not by active transport. The vessels operate as a **countercurrent exchange system**. Although material moves into the blood vessels from the peritubular spaces, the osmotic gradient is maintained because passive diffusion is too slow a process to counteract the effects of the countercurrent multiplier system of the nephron. The entire system operates in a manner so that the collection of needed materials by the circulatory system is highly efficient. Simultaneously waste products move out of the blood vessels and can diffuse into the tubule cells for secretion into the tubular fluids and finally excretion, but again the osmotic gradients needed for forming a hypertonic urine and the conservation of water are not disrupted.

Several as yet unproven assumptions are made in the model just described. It is assumed that the descending tubules are freely permeable to water and ions and that the cells of the ascending segment are impermeable to water.

The final concentration of urine occurs in the collecting ducts. Duct cells can actively transport Na^+ from the fluid as necessary. The concentration process again depends on the morphological arrangements of various parts of the nephron. The glomeruli, proximal and distal tubules are confined to the outer portion of the kidney, and these are the regions of relatively low osmotic concentrations. The loops of Henle run into the medulla—the region of increasing osmotic concentration. The collecting ducts also run into this area of high peritubular Na^+ concentration. Thus water can follow an osmotic gradient—flowing from the ducts into the renal space and then into the vessels of the vasa recta.

That nephron functioning in mammals depends on such morphological and physiological mechanisms is also indicated by the abilities of various mammals to form a hypertonic urine in comparison with the nature of their loops of Henle. In the beaver, for example, the loops are all short, and the urine reaches a maximum concentration of about 600 mOsm. In the rabbit there is a mixture of long and short loops and the maximum urine concentration approaches 1,500 mOsm. In the desert rodent, *Psammomys obesus*, only long loops are found, and the urine reaches concentrations as high as 6,000 mOsm. (B. Schmidt-Nielsen and O'Dell, 1961).

Several factors influence the osmotic gradients established at different levels of the nephron. The length of the loop of Henle and the concentration differences between the ascending and descending limbs are directly proportional to the maximal concentration gradient possible between urine and blood. The rate of flow through the nephron is inversely related to increasing gradient.

As might be expected, the final concentration and volume of the urine can be finely adjusted to meet the osmotic and solute requirements of the organism. In **water diuresis** (the formation of a dilute, generally copious urine) the fluid in the distal tubules becomes increasingly hypotonic to the blood plasma. Conversely, several conditions promote antidiuresis (production of a small volume of concentrated urine). As will be seen in later sections of this chapter, both hormonal and nervous controls are present for adjusting active transport rates and for maintaining constant blood flow and filtration rates in the animal.

14-25. Absorption and Secretion by Nephrons. In the preceding section, only the water and Na^+ movements required to produce a hypertonic urine were considered. Many solutes must be reabsorbed from the tubular fluid and passed back into the circulation. Other solutes, for example the waste products of metabolism, must be removed from the body, and if these are not filtered rapidly enough by the glomerulus, they must be secreted into the tubular fluids by the tubule cells.

Glucose is one material filtered by the glomerulus and also completely reabsorbed by tubule cells. The reabsorption is complete by the time the fluid has descended about half the length of the tubule. In mammals, under normal conditions, all glucose is actively transported out of the tubular fluid, and the urine is glucose free. The clearance of glucose is zero. From a knowledge of the plasma concentration of glucose and the filtration rate as determined by the use of inulin, the amount of glucose absorbed by the proximal tubule cells can be calculated. In humans the glucose T_m is about 350 mg glucose per minute.

If the glucose level of the blood plasma is raised experimentally, some concentration of glucose is reached at which glucose begins to appear in the final urine. If the plasma level is raised above this threshold concentration, the amount of glucose excreted increases until finally the glucose excretion becomes proportional to the plasma concentration. For humans this concentration is about 376 mg per 100 ml of blood. Such studies of the excretion of substances in relation to the plasma concentration of substances are known as renal titration studies.

The limits of the tubule cell's ability to actively transport a substance from the tubular fluid depends in part on the degree of loading of carrier molecules of which only a limited number exist. Once the carrier molecules are saturated with transported molecules, the substance cannot be completely removed from the tubular fluid and is excreted instead. Glucose transport in the kidney tubule depends on the intratubular Na^+ concentration (Khuri et al., 1966).

Phlorizin is a drug that inhibits glucose transport by both intestinal and renal tubule epithelia. By measuring the effects of various dosages of phlorizin on the glucose T_m, Diedrich (1966) attempted to determine the number of carrier sites available for glucose transport in the dog kidney. Assuming that one molecule of phlorizin inactivated one carrier site and that all phlorizin was bound to carrier sites when the glucose T_m was maximally depressed, it was calculated that there were 0.69 μmoles carrier moved from one side to another per minute. The movement of glucose across the tubule cell membrane was calculated to be 50,000 times slower than through the cytoplasm of the cell, thus membrane transport was the limiting factor in the movement of glucose from the tubular to the peritubular fluid.

Another organic solute whose movement is of importance in kidney functioning is urea, the mammalian major waste product of protein, purine and pyrimidine metabolism. Like inulin, the clearance of urea is independent of its plasma concentration but is dependent on the rate of urine flow. Although previously it was thought that urea moved passively into the tubular fluid, it is now considered that urea is actively transported as well. In rodents the site of active transport appears to be the collecting duct cells (Ullrich et al., 1967).

K^+ is an important ion, of which a certain amount must be conserved by the animal. The clearance of K^+ is normally about one-fifth its filtration rate, indicating that a large amount of K^+ is reabsorbed. When an animal is placed under conditions of K^+ loading or under conditions of dehydration, the amount of K^+ excreted becomes larger than the amount filtered. Thus K^+ can be both absorbed and secreted by tubule cells. It is generally thought that reabsorption takes place in the proximal tubule and that secretion occurs in the distal tubule. The proximal tubule accounts for about 75 per cent of the K^+ reabsorption, the site of further reabsorption is not yet known. Reabsorption takes place against an electrochemical gradient, and the tubular fluid K^+ concentration is less than that calculated from the measurement of transtubular potentials.

The excretion of Na^+, K^+, H^+, NH_4^+, and Cl^- and PO_4^- ions are interrelated processes in that the total ionic concentration is responsible for maintaining the pH of the blood and other body fluids. This topic will be considered at the end of this chapter.

Filtered amino acids are reabsorbed by the kidney tubule. The statements made in Chapter 6 concerning amino acid transport in the small intestine hold generally for amino acid transport by kidney tubule cells. Histidine and a few other amino acids are known to be reabsorbed in the proximal tubule, but the site of reabsorption of most amino acids is not yet known.

Proline, hydroxyproline, and glycine share a common carrier system as indicated by an analysis of the kinetics of their transport. The amino acids lysine, glycine, and alanine all depress glucose transport, but even large doses of glucose have no effect on the transport of these amino acids. This is evidence that the transport inhibition is not a simple competitive one for the same sites on a carrier.

Transport by cells of the kidney tubule is a complex activity because of the large number of substances that must be handled by the kidney. Probably each important metabolite, waste product, and inorganic ion has its own control mechanisms that regulate excretion or absorption.

14-26. Regulation of Nephron Functioning. The kidney is remarkable in that its blood flow is maintained at a constant level over a wide range of arterial blood pressures. The filtration pressure and the glomerular filtration rate are maintained relatively constant not only in the normal kidney but also in the denervated

kidney and in the isolated and perfused organ. This **autoregulation** seems to be due to activity of the preglomerular arterioles. Any nervous control over the renal vasculature is exerted by sympathetic vasoconstrictors acting on the smooth muscles of arteriolar walls.

It should not be surprising that the primary mechanisms used to regulate nephron functioning are hormonal in nature and are used to alter membrane permeability or to influence active transport mechanisms. Since under normal conditions the renal blood pressure and thus the glomerular filtration rate is constant, and since filtration is not a selective process in any case, any controls over the composition of the urine must be exerted at the tubule cell level.

Under extreme conditions, such as hemorrhage, the lowered blood pressure does effect the carotid pressure receptors, which, in turn, shunt blood from the kidneys to other organ systems. This lowers the GFR and urine formation rate.

One system that appears to be involved in the regulation of kidney blood supply is the **juxtaglomerular apparatus** (JGA). The JGA is a complex structure surrounded by both afferent and efferent renal blood vessels and therefore could play a role in the regulation of cortical blood flow. The JGA includes elements of the tubular epithelium at the U-turn of the loop of Henle, macula densa cells of the surrounding connective tissue, and granulated renin-containing cells of the afferent arterioles associated with the same nephron.

The ischemic kidney (one whose blood supply has been cut off) produces an enzyme renin which acts on a blood globulin angiotensinogen to produce a pressor substance angiotensin II (or hypertensin). Angiotensin is a **kinin**, which causes vasoconstriction in arterioles. Figure 14-14 outlines the steps involved in angiotensin formation in the blood.

In one hypothetical model for the operation of the JGA decreases in renal arterial blood pressure or flow rate are thought to act as a stimulus on the JGA to release renin (see Hatt, 1967; Tobian, 1967). It has been proposed, although no proof has been found, that baroreceptors are present in the renal

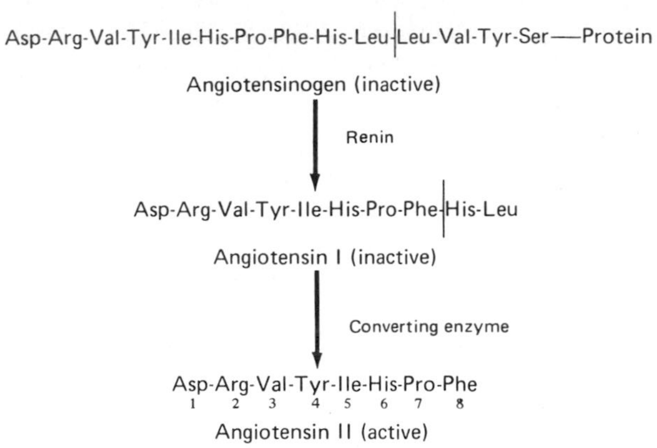

Asp-Arg-Val-Tyr-Ile-His-Pro-Phe-His-Leu-|Leu-Val-Tyr-Ser——Protein

Angiotensinogen (inactive)

↓ Renin

Asp-Arg-Val-Tyr-Ile-His-Pro-Phe-|His-Leu

Angiotensin I (inactive)

↓ Converting enzyme

Asp-Arg-Val-Tyr-Ile-His-Pro-Phe
1   2   3   4   5   6   7   8
Angiotensin II (active)

Figure 14-14 Reaction scheme for the formation of angiotensin.

vasculature which can respond to blood pressure drops.

Renin release leads to the formation of angiotensin, which by causing vasoconstriction raises the blood pressure in the renal arterioles, thus counteracting the pressure drop that stimulated renin release. The hypothesis has several weak points. No sensing system has been found as yet.

There is also supposed to be a stimulation of aldosterone release. Aldosterone, a steroid hormone (Figure 2-24) promotes Na^+ absorption by renal tubule cells and tends, therefore, to cause the removal of water from the urine by osmotic effects. But the aldosterone effect on Na^+ absorption is a slow one, not well suited for emergency situations. Nor has any relationship between angiotensin and ACTH, the adreocorticotropic hormone responsible for stimulating the growth and secretory activity of the adrenal cortex, been found. However, stimulation could be direct, not through ACTH. The threshold concentration for the angiotensin effect on aldosterone production appears to be lower than that for its vasoconstrictor activity, and this is why the former has been assumed to be an important action as far as renal regulation is concerned.

Unfortunately, no clear-cut picture of neurohormonal controls over water and solute regulation can be drawn. A variety of hormones can influence membrane permeabilities at sites throughout an organism, and very similar hormones may have quite different effects in different species.

Urine volume in vertebrates is controlled by antidiuretic hormones (ADH) produced by the hypothalamus and stored in the neurohypophysis. Osmoreceptors within the hypothalamus respond to increases of blood osmotic pressure that result from either water loss or salt gain. These receptors send impulses to the pituitary causing the release of ADH. ADH increases the permeability of tubule cells to water, and a smaller volume of urine is produced with a high osmolar concentration. Under these conditions when the osmolar content of the blood is lowered below normal, ADH release is inhibited and an excretion of copious amounts of a dilute urine occurs.

Neurosecretory hormones of the neurohypophysis of different species include vasopressin, oxytocin, arginine vasopressin, and lysine vasopressin (see Figure 11-32). These hormones generally decrease urine flow, alter blood pressure, and increase water permeability of amphibian skin and urinary bladder. But the effect in different species vary. For example, arginine vasotocin and oxytocin both stimulate water flow across bullfrog bladder, but the former is more than 300 times effective. Birds show a fall in blood pressure whenever any of these hormones is administered, but mammals show an increase.

Although the increased permeability to water was thought to be due to an increase in the pore radii through which water passed, Hays (1968) believes that no such change occurs. Rather he feels that water osmotic flow is limited by a thin dense barrier in series with a thick porous barrier that limits the diffusion of water. According to this hypothesis, vasopressin acts by markedly increasing the rate of diffusion across the outer barrier of a membrane. The molecular mechanisms by which vasopressin achieves this action are not known. Civan and Frazier (1968) using microelectrodes to analyze the electrical resistance changes following vasopressin administration to toad bladder found that about 98 per cent of the change occurred at a mucosal site on the outer surface of the membrane. Since the lateral interspaces between neighboring cells are implicated in the movement of water across epithelial membranes (Chapter 9) changes in their sizes induced by hormones might also be responsible for the observed increases in water permeability (Ganote et al., 1968).

Arginine vasotocin has been shown to increase the permeability to water of the skin, the distal convoluted tubule, and the urinary bladder of anurans. An animal injected with arginine vasopressin and immersed in water rapidly gains weight due to the increased flow of water across the skin and the flow of water from the urine into the blood from both the nephron and the urinary bladder. The various octapeptide hormones have other actions as well (Chapter 11).

Urine volume is also controlled by the hypothalamus and adrenal cortical aldosterone. Decreasing osmolarities of the blood stimulate osmoreceptors of the hypothalamus, and nerve impulses are sent to the adrenal cortex, which cause the release of aldosterone into the blood. Tubular reabsorption of Na^+ is increased by aldosterone, and K^+ reabsorption decreases. Since Na^+ is in much higher concentration than K^+ in tubular fluid, the result is an increase in the osmolarity of the blood and a decrease in that of the tubular fluids. There is an increase in urinary outflow also. All of these events tend to increase the tonicity of the blood. When normal levels are reached, the stimulation of the osmoreceptors in the hypothalamus is lessened, and aldosterone secretion is decreased. When fluid volumes are below a critical level due to losses from sweating, hemorrhage, vomiting, and so forth, or when excessive amounts of salt are ingested, the osmolarity of the blood plasma increases

and this signals the hypothalamus, via the osmoreceptors, to decrease the nervous output to the adrenal cortex thus inhibiting aldosterone secretion and causing more Na^+ to be excreted and more water to be conserved.

Although the general outlines of the neurohormonal controls over water and solute balance are known, the details are still in a confused state. As Potts (1968) points out, *in vitro* studies of hormonal effects on organs such as frog skin or bladder often yield results which are different from those observed in the intact animal.

Osmoregulation by Animals

14-27. Lower Invertebrates.   In this part of the chapter I shall briefly discuss the mechanisms by which animals are enabled to survive in various osmotic environment. I have chosen to discuss each important animal group as a unit, rather than considering each type of environment and the animals which live in that environment. This I believe aids in pointing out how different species within a given group of animals may exhibit profound differences in the mechanisms used to regulate osmotically even in the same environment. Unfortunately, in most cases the actual mechanisms used by animals to osmoregulate or even if a given animal can osmoregulate are not known. This is particularly true of smaller invertebrate animals.

It can be noted that water and solute balance depend basically on passive factors such as structural modifications of the skin permeability to water inflow or outflow, on active transport systems that either pump in or pump out some particular solute, on behavioral mechanisms such as water intake by drinking or choice among environments of different salinities in estuarine environments, on internal mechanisms that permit some substance to be conserved by the animal to raise its internal osmolarity without damage to body cells, or by Donnan-like systems.

As already stated, most marine invertebrates are isotonic with their medium and are osmotic conformers. As described in Chapter 6, cells and organisms are usually not true osmometers, that is, they do not exhibit a linear relationship between the tonicities of the external and internal media. Biological membranes are not strictly semipermeable, and there is also an osmotically inert fraction of the cellular material. Eggs of marine organisms are closest to being true osmometers. The sipunculid worm *Golfingia* is an example of an organism that closely approaches being a true osmometer. *Golfingia* like most sipunculid worms has a body wall that is impermeable to salts and acts as a semipermeable membrane (Adolph, 1936).

It may be noted that although marine invertebrates may be isotonic to their medium, different species possess widely different water contents, differ in the amount of water exchanged in a given time, and differ in the ionic composition of body fluids. In many cases osmotic conformers that have swelled when placed in a dilute medium do not recover normal body volumes when placed in a concentrated medium because they have lost some salts by diffusion and either cannot regain those particular salts or require an extremely long time to do so.

Marine protozoans are little understood as far as osmotic regulation is concerned. Both marine and endoparasitic protozoans are isotonic with their environments. Most are not capable of surviving for long changes in the external medium. The contractile vacuole found in a few marine protozoans is probably a mechanism for the selective excretion or absorption of ions. Fresh water protozoans exhibit variations in the extent to which they can withstand changes of the osmotic environment. *Paramecium woodruffi* and *P. calkinsi* can be adapted to live in sea water, but *P. caudatum* cannot. Although the internal contents of most protozoans appear to be dilute compared with that of the cells of metazoans, they are still hyperosmotic to the fresh water environment. Some fresh water protozoans appear capable of osmoregulation through the use of the contractile vacuole, but many appear to be stenohaline conformers.

The osmoregulatory abilities of coelenterates, sponges, echinoderms, turbellarians, rotifers, and nematodes are slight, and in most cases even the mode of ionic regulation is not known. Table 14-3 should be referred to for a summary of osmotic activity in animal phyla. From Table 14-3 it is evident that most animals are osmotic conformers dwelling in marine waters.

The flatworm *Procerodes ulvae* (formerly *Gunda*) is of interest as a brackish water organism. This flatworm lives in intertidal zones, where twice each day it is exposed to changes from hard river water to normal sea water. It cannot live in soft (calcium-free) water but swells and dies within about 48 hours. In dilute sea water or in fresh water containing Ca^{2+} swelling is prevented. In dilute media the water which enters the body of the animal osmotically moves into the parenchyma and collects in vacuoles in endodermal cells. In this fashion body volume is maintained relatively constant and other body cells avoid dilution. Upon exposure to fresh water about one-fourth of the body salts are lost in the first 50 minutes, and the final concentration of body fluids is about 6 to 10 per cent sea water (Pantin, 1931). When transferred to dilute sea water less salts are lost, and the rate of swelling is less than when transferred to fresh water. The worm cannot live indefinitely in hard fresh water and is unlike most brackish water organisms in that it is adapted to meet temporary stress not permanent osmotic stress (Potts and Parry, 1964). The role of Ca^{2+} is not known nor is the role of the excretory organs. On transference to dilute media the respiratory rate is increased (Beadle, 1931), and although this is sometimes taken to indicate some active process at work in osmoregulation, it has been pointed out that in some animals this is correlated not with increased active transport but with increased oxygen consumption by hydrated muscles and other organs (Schlieper, 1936; Flemister and Flemister, 1951).

Another group of organisms that are of interest but about which little is known are the endoparasites, especially the endoparasitic helminths. Intestinal parasites are subjected to variations in their environment and probably must have some form of osmoregulatory ability—at least short term regulation. *Ascaris lumbricoides*, for example, is normally hypoosmotic to intestinal fluids and probably secretes chloride actively. The role of its excretory organs is not known. In *Ascaris*, as in many organisms, it is difficult to determine the role, if any, of the gut lining in secretory activity.

The body fluid and tissue compositions of many animals are given in Prosser and Brown (1961) and in Potts and Parry (1964).

14-28. Osmoregulation in Annelids. Although most annelids are marine and osmoconformers, some species exhibit various levels of osmoregulation and so annelids are found in marine, brackish, and fresh waters, and also the terrestrial environment. Most polychaetes are stenohaline marine organisms, for example, *Nereis pelagica* and *Perinereis cultrifera*, while a few are euryhaline although still isosmotic with sea water, for example, *Arenicola marina*. All of these species swell when placed in dilute media and exhibit no volume regulation (see Jones, 1957; Jorgenson and Dales, 1957).

A few polychaetes such as *Nereis diversicolor* are capable of limited osmoregulation and volume regulation and can live in dilute brackish waters. This ability is due to a lessened permeability of the cuticle to both salts and water and the ability to absorb ions from a dilute medium. They can also form a dilute urine.

Nereis lighti can survive and reproduce in fresh water. Laboratory experiments on the survival capabilities of an organism in various media show only the ability of an individual animal to live; species survival will depend on appropriate changes in reproductive behavior under different osmotic conditions. *N. lighti* is viviparous, whereas most other polychaetes shed eggs and sperm into their environment. But most annelid eggs are not capable of survival in fresh water. In this medium they swell and burst. The eggs of *N. lighti* can survive in fresh water and can thus survive as a species in this medium.

In all euryhaline annelids isosmotic regulation at the cellular level is important. *Arenicola* can adapt to 50 per cent sea water by a decline in the concentration of amino acids in the body fluids from 427 to 180 mmole per liter, thus decreasing the osmotic gradient (Duchâteau et al., 1961). The muscles of this annelid also adapt to brackish water by losing amino acids. In many organisms osmotic concentrations are maintained in part by the presence of non-diffusing amino acids in the body fluids and the establishment of a Donnan-like system that aids in maintaining normal internal osmotic concentrations.

Earthworms are primarily adapted to a life in moist soil, an environment that is closer to that of fresh water than to a terrestrial one. Survival is aided by the presence of more efficient excretory organs that actively reabsorb Na^+. *Lumbricus terrestris* is a good hyperosmotic regulator and can survive in aerated fresh water or in moist air. Earthworms seem to live normally in a semidesiccated state and in dry air an earthworm can survive a loss of 50 per cent of its body water. *Lumbricus* is of some interest also because it has been found that its brain extracts influence water and solute regulation. Removal of the brain causes an increase in body water content and a decrease in Na^+. Implantation of another brain or injection of brain extracts reverses these changes. Earthworms are also aided in survival by behavioral mechanisms. *Lumbricus*, for example, moves toward moist environments and away from drier environments. Some earthworm species that cannot survive in water can sense and move away from fresh water.

The urine of earthworms is hypoosmotic to the blood at all concentrations of the medium. Salts lost in the urine are replaced from the food and also by active reabsorption probably by cells of the skin.

14-29. Molluscs. Marine molluscs are isosmotic with sea water and show both ionic and volume regulation to various degrees despite a permeability to both salts and water. Ionic regulation has been studied primarily in larger species such as cephalopods. These organisms utilize a differential excretion of salts, coupled with an active uptake of ions and water—the latter processes probably occurring in specialized cells of the gills. A majority of molluscs are osmotic conformers.

The euryhaline molluscs *Mytilus* and *Ostrea* remain isosmotic with sea water but can adapt their tissues to changing blood concentrations by alterations in the concentrations of free amino acids. The muscles of *Mytilus* and *Sepia* contain large concentrations of amino acids and trimethylamine oxide (a product of protein metabolism). These nondiffusible solutes aid in maintaining the osmotic concentration of the muscle cells. Those molluscs which inhabit brackish waters generally cannot maintain body fluids in a hyperosmotic condition and are generally osmotic conformers. Bivalves can resist changes in the environment temporarily by closing their shells.

Freshwater and terrestrial gastropods normally maintain very low blood concentrations of salts. This alleviates some of the osmotic differential usually found between bloods and the freshwater or terrestrial environments. Hyperosmotic regulation when present is achieved by a variety of mechanisms. *Helix aspersa* and *Otala lactata* have mechanisms for the rapid uptake of water from the environment. Desiccated snails can restore water balance in about an hour by crawling over wet paper in the laboratory. The nature of this water uptake is unknown. Water loss in terrestrial snails can be avoided by withdrawal into the shell. A reduced evaporation of water is found under these conditions, probably caused by the nature of the exposed mantle surface (collar), which is very impermeable to water compared with the rest of the mantle. Some land snails also store water in the mantle cavity. The excretory organs of fresh water gastropods excrete a dilute urine that aids in conserving salt, and there is an active uptake of Na^+ and Cl^- from the environment.

The transport of ions, excepting Ca^{2+}, has not been examined in fresh water and terrestrial molluscs. *Anodonta* and *Lymnaea* have body walls that are very permeable to Ca^{2+}, although there appears to be no active transport of this ion. Calcium is utilized in the for-

mation of the mollusc shell. This calcium may come either directly from the environment or from the blood, or as in one land snail *Euhadra nipponensis* may be derived from calcium taken in by active transport by epithelial cells of the foot (see review by Wilbur, 1964).

Ionic regulation is highly developed in pelagic molluscs and is an important mechanism for maintaining buoyancy in many of these organisms (Denton, 1964). In *Sepia* and *Nautilus* buoyancy is maintained by the removal of water from the shell chambers. This is brought about by the active transport of Na^+ from the chamber fluid until it is hypoosmotic with the blood. Water then osmotically flows into the blood against the blood's hydrostatic pressure.

Ocean squids of the family Cranchiidae move by means of water jets from the siphon, and the use of two small fins at the posterior end of the body. But these rapidly moving animals can also remain motionless hanging in the water. They possess an enormous coelomic cavity filled with fluid that amounts to about two thirds of the total volume of the animal. This fluid has a very low density (approximately 1.01). The fluid, which is almost isotonic with sea water, contains 480 mM ammonium and about 90 mM Na^+. The anion content is entirely Cl^-. The pH of the fluid is about 5, which helps to account for the retention of ammonium in contrast to molecular ammonia because the former does not pass readily through living tissues. The retention of the very low density ammonium chloride provides the required buoyancy.

14-30. Crustaceans. As already stated, crustaceans are found in a wide variety of osmotic environments. Some of the variety in osmoregulatory ability found in the crustaceans is indicated in Figure 14-15. Ionic regulation is a universal characteristic of crustaceans, but the mechanisms of ionic and osmotic regulation have been studied primarily in the larger decapod crustaceans.

Some pelagic crustaceans such as *Maia* and *Hyas* (both spider crabs) are isosmotic conformers, depending on the constancy of the deeper marine waters for their survival. Even

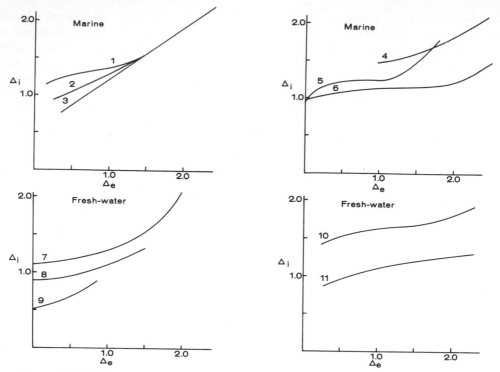

Figure 14-15 The osmoregulatory abilities of some crustaceans. Curve 1, *Carcinus;* Curve 2, *Hya;* Curve 3, *Maia;* Curve 4, *Cancer;* Curve 5, *Hemigrapsus;* Curve 6, *Artemia;* Curve 7, *Eriochier;* Curve 8, *Pachygrapsus;* Curve 9, *Astacus;* Curve 10, *Uca;* Curve 11, *Palae-monetes.*

these stenohaline organisms exhibit ionic regulation. *Maia* cannot withstand dilution of sea water by more than 20 per cent for more than a few hours. Most deep marine crustaceans show good volume regulation as well.

A number of poikilosmotic crabs do exhibit a limited hyperosmotic regulation in brackish waters. These are the shore crabs such as *Carcinus maenas* (curve 1, Figure 14-15) that live in waters from a few fathoms deep to tidal pools and estuaries whose concentrations may be about one-third that of sea water. *Cancer pagurus* has less hyperosmoregulatory ability but can withstand diluter waters.

A comparison of the permeabilities of the exoskeletons of crustaceans living in different environments shows that *Maia, Hyas,* and other conforming marine crustaceans are much more permeable to water and salts than *Carcinus, Cancer,* and other brackish water crustaceans. The least permeable exoskeletons

are those of fresh water crustaceans. Therefore, adaptations of the structure of the exoskeleton has played a role in allowing some species to advance into the brackish and then fresh water environments.

Differences are also found in the abilities to concentrate particular ions. A majority of marine crustaceans can concentrate K^+ and Ca^{2+}, but *Carcinus* can concentrate Na^+ and Cl^- as well. When *Maia* is placed in dilute sea water (20‰) it increases in weight by 3 per cent per hour; *Carcinus* under the same conditions maintains a constant weight. This difference reflects both differences in permeability and in the ability of the excretory system to eliminate water. When its excretory pores are blocked *Carcinus* in 50 per cent sea water gains weight at a rate of about 2 per cent per hour; *Hyas* gains weight by about 3 per cent per hour under the same conditions; while *Maia* increases in weight by 3.5 per cent per hour. It may be noted that the abilities of

Carcinus reflect its position as a highly evolved crab.

Some crabs, for example, *Eriocheir sinensis*, the Chinese mitten crab, and members of the genus *Gammarus*, can regulate in both fresh and marine waters. *Eriocheir* can hyperosmoregulate and lives in fresh water although it returns to the sea for breeding. Its permeability to salts and water is very low, and Na$^+$ is taken in by active transport from extremely dilute solutions. The urine is isosmotic or slightly hyperosmotic to the blood, and the volume of urine is low. The osmoregulatory ability of this crab arises from the enormous amount of active transport by gill cells and the lower permeability of the outer covering. In most brackish water crustaceans the excretory organs play little role in osmoregulation.

Hypoosmotic regulation is found in some shrimps, brine shrimps, and land crabs, for example in *Pachygrapsus crassipes*, which lives above the low tide region; in *Uca*, the fiddler crab, which lives for long periods in air on sand and mud flats, and in *Birgus*, the coconut crab. The prawns and grapsoid crabs are the only marine invertebrates known to be capable of hypoosmotic regulation. The mechanisms are mostly obscure although active transport by gill cells appears to be the chief mechanism for obtaining salt. *Birgus* is known to drink fresh water and places water in its gill chambers.

The brine shrimp *Artemia salina* lives in extremely concentrated salt solutions as well as in 10 per cent sea water. Below 25 per cent sea water its blood is hyperosmotic to the medium; above that it is hypoosmotic. Changes in the blood are due to ion exchanges not to gains or losses of water. *Artemia* continuously swallows the medium in which it lives; amd Na$^+$, Cl$^-$, and water are absorbed by the cells of the gut. This method of obtaining water in hyperosmotic media is similar to that used by marine teleosts.

In a hyperosmotic medium the branchiae of *Artemia* secrete Na$^+$ and Cl$^-$. Electron microscope studies of the branchia show that they contain organelles composed of stacks of disc-shaped mitochondria interlaced with flat-tened extensions of a canalicular system (Copeland, 1966). This would appear to be a mitochondrial pump for removing salts from the animal. Similar organelles have been found in the anal papillae of some insects. The gut is responsible for water balance in the brine shrimp; the gills for ion balance. In dilute media the gill cells can absorb Na$^+$ as water is lost through the outer covering.

Hyperosmoregulation by fresh water crustaceans is primarily dependent on the activity of the excretory organ. These can produce a copious dilute urine. Gill cells actively take up Na$^+$ from fresh water and the permeability of the outer surface is relatively low.

The terrestrial crab *Gecarcinus lateralis* has been the subject of recent investigation. This crab can live indefinitely on land and obtains water and salts from damp sand. Water is attracted by capillary action onto setae of the posteroventral surface of the body. It travels along body grooves onto the surface of the pericardial sac. The sac serves as a water storage organ (it swells prior to molting and probably serves as a source of hydrostatic pressure during ecdysis). Salt-absorbing cells are found in the respiratory lamellae of the gills. These cells are highly infolded, interdigitated and well supplied with mitochondria (Copeland, 1968). Salt is pumped into the animal and water probably follows an osmotic gradient. The intercellular spaces of this epithelial surface are suited for the Diamond model of water transport discussed in Section 6-24. It has also been shown that the foregut is permeable to water and salts in both directions and that the degree of permeability depends on neuroendocrine activity. The foregut of crabs without eyestalks is impermeable to water and salts (Mantel, 1968).

Many terrestrial crustaceans such as the isopods appear to survive because of behavioral mechanisms that lead them to moist or humid environments. In addition they have an impermeable cuticle and an excretory system that conserves water.

14-31. Insects. A majority of insects are terrestrial although many larvae mature in water. Terrestrial insects are faced primarily with the problem of conserving water, and osmoregulation is achieved principally by means of the excretory system, which is capable of producing an extremely concentrated urine, sometimes even a solid mass of uric acid crystals from which nearly all water has been reabsorbed.

The anal papillae of most aquatic larvae function in osmoregulation. These larvae do not normally swallow water. The anal papillae are highly permeable to water, and the malpighian tubules excrete any excess water that enters. The anal papillae of some mosquito and beetle larvae can absorb NaCl— an activity that in mosquitos is inhibited by anti-cholinesterases. Although the blood Na^+ concentration of the mosquito larvae is maintained by active absorption from the medium and reabsorption by the rectum, in some larvae salts are absorbed by the gut and the body surface is impermeable. Again, in the insects amino acids play an important role as osmotically active solutes. Water conservation in adult insects is aided not only by the absorption of water in the hindgut but also by the nature of the respiratory system, which is designed to reduce transpiration of water (see Chapter 16).

14-32. Vertebrates—Fishes. Marine teleosts live in a hypertonic environment and face the problem of osmotic water loss and the inward diffusion of salts. Basically four mechanisms are used to overcome these problems.

Marine bony fishes possess a relatively impermeable surface. The skin is made impermeable by a thickening of the dermous and the presence of impermeable scales. The inflow of water is also reduced because of the presence of a mucous covering of the skin. This material is produced by mucous glands, and although it is not impermeable to water or salts does slow down the diffusion of these materials (Van Ostend, 1957).

All hypoosmotic regulators appear capable of drinking sea water and absorbing water and monovalent ions from it. Eels and sculpins, for example, drink 50 to 200 ml/kg body weight per day and absorb about three fourths of the water and monovalent salts. Divalent ions taken into the gut by drinking sea water are not absorbed by the cells of the gut but are eliminated by the gut.

Marine teleosts produce a minimal volume of urine and so conserve water. Although some nitrogenous wastes are excreted in the urine, most are eliminated in the form of ammonia through the gills, thus conserving the amount of water that must be lost as urine. Any excess divalent ions that enter through the gut are also excreted in the urine.

Excess Na^+ or Cl^- brought in by diffusion or by drinking are eliminated through the gill epithelia. The excretory organs play only a slight role in ionic regulation because the urine volume is so small. Active transport of NaCl through gill cells is the major route for eliminating excess salt.

Some teleosts and cyclostomes are *anadromous*. They migrate from the sea into fresh water for breeding. *Catadromous* species migrate from fresh to salt water. Famous among the former are migratory species such as salmon and eels. It is of interest that the salmon stops swallowing water a few hours after it enters fresh water and also stops eating. In this way the osmotic inflow of water is reduced. Almost nothing is known about the osmoregulatory mechanisms of cyclostomes (Black, 1957), and no studies have been done on adult marine lampreys although the fresh water immature forms have been examined slightly.

The hagfishes are the only vertebrates that may be primitively marine. *Myxine* is isoosmotic with sea water and is unusual in that Mg^{2+} and SO_4^{2-} concentrations are much lower in the blood than in sea water (a situation also found in some crustaceans), whereas Ca^{2+} and K^+ are much lower in concentration and Na^+ is very high in concentration. It is not known whether these fish swallow sea water as part of the osmoregulatory mechanism.

Many of the euryhaline teleosts are excellent osmoregulators, and many can withstand transfers from sea water to fresh water or the reverse (many tropical fish of the aquarist are marine teleosts adapted to a fresh water environment). The mechanisms used for osmotic and ionic regulation in marine teleosts placed in hypoosmotic media are similar to those to be described for fresh water fish.

Marine elasmobranchs use another mechanism to osmoregulate in their sea water environment. While the salt concentrations of the body fluids of marine elasmobranchs are essentially similar to those of other marine fishes, they make themselves isoosmotic or even hyperosmotic to the environment by conserving large amounts of urea and trimethylamine oxide in their blood and tissues (Norris and Benoit, 1945). The osmotic concentration of the blood is often 10 to 50 mOsm/kg more than that of sea water, and therefore marine elasmobranchs can use mechanisms similar to those of fresh water fish for the excretion of water. There is a tendency for osmotic inflow and excess water is removed by the kidneys. However, there is also an inward diffusion of salt which must be eliminated. Also salt enters the body in organisms eaten by elasmobranchs (a problem of many marine animals).

Excess salts are excreted not by the gills but by specialized organs, the **rectal glands**. For example, the dogfish *Squalus acanthias* secretes about 2 ml/kg/hour of solution through its rectal glands; this is a volume about equal to the urine output of the animal. The rectal glands are responsible for eliminating excess monovalent ions, whereas the kidneys eliminate divalent ions. The gut plays little or no role in water or solute balance in elasmobranchs. Some urea which diffuses through the gut wall is eliminated in the feces.

A few elasmobranchs live in fresh water, and since these species also contain high urea concentrations in their blood and tissues, it is assumed that they are descended from marine ancestors. This urea complicates the problem of osmoregulation in these fresh water animals. The urine flow in fresh water elasmobranchs is about 150 to 500 ml/kg/day, and the urine is hypoosmotic to the blood. The tissues of elasmobranchs do not appear to be more impermeable to urea than those of other animals, but the kidney reabsorbs urea instead of excreting it. The cells of elasmobranchs have adapted in

some way to these high urea concentrations which would be toxic to other organisms.

Fresh water teleosts are more concentrated than their environment and face the danger of osmotic flooding and the loss of needed salts. Fresh water fish do not drink water, and cells of the gills are used to absorb Na^+ by active transport from the medium. The kidneys excrete a copious dilute urine. Some salts are also taken in with the food.

14-33. Vertebrates—Amphibians and Reptiles. The amphibians are not the only amphibious vertebrates. Some reptiles, most water snakes, and some birds and mammals also fall into this category. Such animals must be able to cope with problems of both the aquatic and the terrestrial environment.

Only a few species of fresh water frogs, toads, and a few salamanders have been studied with respect to the osmoregulatory mechanisms. In amphibians such as frogs the major routes for water movement are through the skin and outward through the urine. Solutes enter the animal through the skin and in the food and are eliminated by the skin and excretory organs (see Deyrup, 1964).

The excretory system of amphibians is modified from that of the fresh water fishes by the presence of a urinary bladder (Bentley, 1966) that stores urine produced by the kidneys and that may absorb both water and solutes from the urine. During dry periods aquatic amphibians do not void urine; they conserve water and solutes by increasing bladder absorption.

In adult amphibia the entire skin is much more permeable to water and solutes than that of fresh water teleosts, and the skin undertakes activities such as Na^+ active transport performed by the gills of teleosts. Both Na^+ and Cl^- active transport systems have been found in various amphibians.

No amphibian or reptile can produce a urine hyperosmotic to the blood. Fresh water amphibians and reptiles have blood compositions similar to those of the bony fishes. In reptiles the problem of osmotic flooding is reduced by the highly impermeable skin. Many fresh water reptiles appear to drink their medium, thus obtaining water as needed.

A few species of amphibians are euryhaline. One of these, the crab-eating frog *Rana cancrivora*, lives in a marine environment—the coastal mangrove swamps of southeast Asia. It can osmoregulate between fresh water and brackish water of about 28 per cent salinity in the adult form; the tadpoles can withstand a higher range of salinities. The blood of *R. cancrivora* is always hyperosmotic to the medium. In fresh water its blood contains about 40 mM/l urea, and in high concentrations of the external medium the blood can contain as much as 300 mM/l urea. The urine is hypoosmotic to the plasma with a lower urea content, and the electrolyte content is about one-tenth that of the plasma. The urea and electrolyte content of the urine account for only half the osmotic concentration, and the remainder is provided by as yet unidentified substances. Thus this frog utilizes urea conservation to maintain its body fluids hyperosmotic to the medium. The amount of salt lost through the kidneys is small, and active salt transport across the skin continues at high osmotic concentrations of the external medium; but the extrarenal mechanisms for salt loss are not known.

A few reptilian species are marine and represent four orders: turtles, snakes, lizards, and crocodiles. Sea turtles, marine iguanas, and sea snakes all have plasma osmotic and ionic concentrations similar to those of bony fishes. Their integuments are highly impermeable, and they also lack the exposed permeable surfaces of gills because they are air breathers. Their major problem is a continuing water loss because they must produce sufficient urine to eliminate metabolic wastes and they must lose some water by respiration. They are not known to drink water and the physiological mechanisms used to control water are not known. Urine is produced at a low rate, and the kidneys of these animals have a low GFR. Salt intake occurs, in part at least, through the food (see B. Schmidt-Nielsen and Davis, 1968).

Reptiles possess modified lachrymal glands (turtles) or orbital glands for the outward active transport of excess salt. Their kidneys cannot produce a hyperosmotic urine, and the salt glands are used as an extrarenal pathway for the elimination of monovalent ions. The green turtle *Chelonia mydas* can excrete a solution containing 650 meq NaCl per liter. The marine iguana *Amblyrhunchus cristatus* has an aggravated salt problem because it feeds on high salt sea weed, but it can excrete a solution from its nasal glands that contains as much as 850 mM Na^+ per liter (Schmidt Nielsen and Fänge, 1958).

Many marine turtles go on land only for egg-laying. The ability to osmoregulate of sea snakes is not known nor is that of crocodiles.

The fresh water soft-shelled turtle *Trinyx spinifer* has been found to possess an active Na^+ uptake mechanism in its pharyngeal membranes. Some species of turtles living in fresh water may also use the cloacal bursa or accessory bladder for Na^+ intake.

Even strictly terrestrial amphibians live near water because of their highly permeable skin, and most species depend on behavioral mechanisms for obtaining or conserving water. Amphibians cannot take up water as vapor from the air, and the only control they have over water loss in the terrestrial environment is that over urinary output. When out of water, amphibians produce a much more concentrated urine than when in water and the urine is low in NaCl. Desert species have tissues that can withstand a doubling of the internal osmotic concentration, and these animals may spend half the year burrowed deep in sand. New salt is probably obtained in the food.

Only a few of the high points of the problems associated with osmoregulation and ionic regulation in the amphibians and reptiles have been included in this section. Many problems still remain to be solved concerning these groups and their osmoregulatory abilities and mechanisms.

14-34. Vertebrates—Mammals and Birds. The birds and mammals are primarily terrestrial organisms whose problem is obtaining water and conserving salts. Although exposed permeable surfaces have been reduced to a minimum in these animals, water loss is continuous because of respiration and also because of temperature regulating mechanisms that depend in part on the evaporation of water from the body surface or from the respiratory surface. Some birds and mammals live in the marine environment (some birds must be considered as marine, and seals, whales, walruses, and others are aquatic marine mammals). Some are fresh water or at least amphibious, for example beavers, otters, and minks.

As in all tetrapods, the excretion of water and salts is under the control of hormones liberated by the pituitary and adrenal glands as previously indicated. Hormonal control can play an important part in the ability of some mammals to live in difficult environments. For example, the desert-dwelling kangaroo rat *Dipodomys merriami* always has an extremely high concentration of antidiuretic hormone in its blood and as a result produces a very small volume of urine per 24-hour period.

Birds generally compensate for water loss by drinking and also by obtaining water through their food. In birds (as in reptiles) the gut is an efficient absorber of water. The cloaca of some desert birds also appears to play a role in water conservation by absorbing water from the urine and feces. Those birds facing a salt problem can often excrete a urine that is about twice as concentrated as the blood and that is, in fact, a semisolid paste containing uric acid— the primary nitrogenous waste product of birds. In many respects birds are similar to reptiles in their osmo- and ionic regulatory abilities. However, the problems of birds are aggravated by their much higher metabolic rate and the correspondingly greater water loss through respiration and through temperature regulating mechanisms.

Many marine birds have nasal salt glands, and it appears that some desert birds also possess these organs. Most birds with salt glands can produce a hyperosmotic solution. Such birds include herring gulls, pelicans, albatrosses, and gannets (K. Schmidt-Nielsen,

1960). The domestic duck also has salt glands and can secrete solutions containing up to 640 mM Cl$^-$/l (Scothorne, 1959). Leach's petrel lives mainly on salt-containing crustacean plankton and comes to land only to breed. This bird can produce a solution containing up to 1,100 mM Na$^+$/l (K. Schmidt-Nielsen, 1960). Marine birds do not seem to drink water.

The nasal gland of the herring gull consists of many long tubular lobes, each with a central canal. A lobe contains many tubulous glands that drain into the central canal. The glands are supplied with capillaries with blood flowing in a direction opposite to that of the secreted fluid—a counter current flow system. Active transport of Na$^+$ into the glandular fluid from the blood occurs. Na$^+$, Ca^{2+}, Mg^{2+}, SO$_4^{2-}$, and HCO$_3^-$ are found in the secreted fluid.

Although both birds and mammals can produce a hypertonic urine, this ability is not greatly developed in many birds that have been studied, and therefore, extrarenal mechanisms are used by birds that face an excess of internal salt. An interesting exception is the North American Savannah sparrow, *Passerculus sandwichensis beldingi*, which can produce a urine containing as much as 969 mM Na$^+$/l (Poulson and Bartholomew, 1962). This bird lacks salt glands but does have loops of Henle, which function in an efficient countercurrent multiplier system. This sparrow drinks from saline waters in its arid environment. It can survive serum concentrations as high as 610 mOsm/l.

Generally birds rely on an efficient kidney, gut, and cloacal system to conserve water. When removal of excess salt is needed, an extrarenal system is most commonly used.

Marine mammals do not drink water to any great extent and rely on their food as the sole source of water. The water requirement of marine mammals is less than that of terrestrial mammals because no water is used for thermal regulation, and the water loss from the lungs is relatively smaller because more oxygen is extracted from the air taken in at each inspiration. Marine mammals have a slightly higher blood osmotic concentration than terrestrial mammals, and this also aids in osmoregulatory problems. Most marine mammals feed on teleosts rather than marine invertebrates. This is an advantage because teleosts have already performed the osmotic work of eliminating excess salts from their tissues. Whether marine mammals possess mechanisms for extrarenal salt loss is not known, but they can produce a hyperosmotic urine when stressed.

Terrestrial mammals usually obtain water by drinking, but some desert mammals obtain water almost entirely from their food and from metabolic reactions, for example, gerbils, *Gerbillus gerbillus*; sand rats, *Psammonomys obesus*. This type of mammal requires highly efficient kidneys that can reabsorb most of the water from the urine.

The desert environment poses the greatest problems for the terrestrial mammal, and a variety of mechanisms have been evolved to cope with this type of habitat. Gerbils and kangaroo rats can exist on air-dried foods and conserve water by producing small amounts of a highly concentrated urine. In their particular environments they do not face salt-loading problems. Sand rats obtain water from succulent plants, but because these plants contain high salt concentrations, their kidneys must be highly efficient in conserving water and eliminating salts. Since these rats live in the hot Sahara desert they lose large amounts of water by evaporation. All rodents lack sweat glands, and therefore, water losses are through the respiratory passages.

Kangaroo rats reduce respiratory evaporative losses by morphological changes of the nasal passages. These passages are very small, and the air passing through equilibrates thermally with the walls of the passages. The vapor pressure also equilibrates. The dry inhaled air warms to body temperature and water evaporates into it from the walls of the nasal passages causing a cooling of the walls. On exhalation this warm, water saturated air again comes into contact with the walls, cooling the air and causing a condensation of water onto the walls. This water is rapidly absorbed by osmosis. The air leaving the nasal passages contains much less water than it would if the nasal passages were wide and did not permit this exchange of heat and moisture (K. Schmidt-Nielsen, 1964, discusses the problems of desert animals).

The camel, in contrast to other mammals, can survive a loss of up to a third of its body water (K. Schmidt-Nielsen, 1960). The camel has a variety of mechanisms for surviving under arid conditions. Camels regulate body temperature by sweating if adequate water is available for drinking. But if water is unavailable, the camel's body temperature can rise to about 41°C and sweating stops. At night the body temperature can fall as low as 35°C and this low body temperature achieved during the night delays the beginning of sweating the following day. The camel can go for 17 days in summer without drinking, although it does not store water. The problems of the camel as well as those of most desert animals with regard to osmoregulation are intimately related to those of temperature regulation (see Chapter 15). It also appears that the camel can conserve some water because of the presence of microorganisms in the gut, which convert urea back to protein, thus making the water loss needed for urea excretion by the kidney much less than it would normally be.

Generally, then, mammals and birds obtain water by drinking or in the food. Water is conserved by an efficient kidney under neuroendocrine control. Water loss is primarily by respiratory evaporation or from sweat glands under nervous control. Salts are conserved by the kidney but are also eliminated by sweat or salt glands in some animals.

As was stated at the beginning of this part of the chapter, osmotic regulation is dependent on active transport mechanisms either by cells of the excretory organ or of skin, gills, gut, cloaca, or specialized glands. In addition, morphological adaptations such as the development of highly impermeable cuticles, specializations in nasal passages, or mucous glands are also of importance in allowing animals to live in the more difficult osmotic environments.

Nitrogen Excretion and Storage

14-35. Ammonia.   Reactions that lead to the production of useful cellular energy or the destruction of unneeded materials produce as products mainly water, CO_2, and nitrogen-containing compounds. The latter are often toxic or can yield no further useful cellular energy and so must be eliminated. The production and excretion of various nitrogen-containing substances is the subject of this part of the chapter.

Ammonia is the chief by-product of protein and amino acid metabolism. Since protein degradation results in the formation of amino acids, it is through reactions of the latter that ammonia is formed. Most ammonia is derived from amino acids, about 5 per cent results from purine metabolism. Ammonia is readily soluble in water and is diffusible and can thus be lost relatively readily through the skin and gills of aquatic organisms. Because it is toxic, it is usually present in low concentrations in the blood of animals. The maximal ammonia concentration in the blood of vertebrates is about 0.01 mg/100 ml (Florkin, 1949). In some invertebrates its concentration may be as high as 0.7 to 2.0 mg/100 ml blood, for example, in crayfish, lobsters, and snails. Organisms in which ammonia is the chief nitrogen-containing waste product are **ammonotelic**. Although most aquatic organisms are ammonotelic, some adaptations for the formation of other nitrogen-containing compounds to be used for osmoregulatory purposes were developed.

Ammonia is formed by deamination reactions of amino acids. Oxidative deamination transforms amino acids into keto acids that can be further oxidized in the TCA cycle with a further production of useful cellular energy. A family of enzymes, the amino acid oxidases, catalyzes these reactions. Although several steps are involved in the reaction, with flavins acting as intermediary hydrogen acceptors, the reaction can be written generally:

α-Amino acid $+ \frac{1}{2}O_2 \rightarrow \alpha$-keto acid $+ NH_3\uparrow$

or

α-Amino acid $+ H_2O \rightarrow \alpha$-keto acid $+ 2H$
$+ NH_3\uparrow$

The α-keto acid enters the TCA cycle (Figure 4-6) or the glycolytic pathway (Figure 4-5) or the β-oxidation pathway (Figure 4-7) and is broken down to CO_2 and water.

Nonoxidative deamination reactions also are known that are catalyzed by specific dehydrases. Generally these reactions lead to the formation of ammonia and either acetate or pyruvate. In mammals nonessential amino acids usually go to form pyruvate. Such amino acids are **glucogenic** because pyruvate can be used to synthesize carbohydrate in the form of glycogen. Essential amino acids generally form acetate upon deamination. These amino acids are **ketogenic** because the acetate, in the form of acetyl-CoA, is used in fatty acid synthesis.

Ammonia, in those animals in which it is not a major waste product, may be utilized in acid-base balance (Chapter 17). In mammals most of the ammonia eliminated by the kidneys is derived from blood glutamic acid. Free ammonia is liberated by glutaminase [E.C. 3.5.1.2.; L-glutamine amidohydrolase; L-glutamine $+$ $H_2O \rightleftharpoons$ L-glutamate $+ NH_3$]. Under conditions of acidosis, when blood H^+ ion concentrations are raised, ammonia formed in the kidney tubule cells diffuses into the tubule lumen and combines with hydrogen ions, forming HN_4^+. This reaction sequence is of importance, for Na^+ ions that have been filtered are exchanged for H^+ and recovered thus conserving the alkaline reserve of the organism, which is comprised primarily of Na^+. This method of regulating pH and conserving Na^+ has not been studied in those animals which excrete primarily ammonia.

Ammonia can be excreted only when there is an abundance of water for its elimination due to its toxicity in high concentrations. This is the case in marine invertebrates, marine teleosts, and all fresh water organisms. Although ammonia may be lost by diffusion through the surface of the animal, both the gills and to a lesser extent the excretory system play a role when the animal's integument is highly impermeable.

14-36. Urea and the Ornithine Cycle. As shown in Table 14-12, adult vertebrates above

Table 14-12   Nitrogen Excretion in Animals*

ANIMAL	AMMONIA†	UREA	URIC ACID	OTHER
Protozoa				
Paramecium	+			
Annelids				
Lumbricus	72	5	1.4	Allantoin
Aphrodite	80	0.2	0.8	
Echinoderms				
Asterias	39	11.7		
Molluscs				
Sepia	67	1.7	2.1	
Littorina (sea water)	40	12.6	0.8	
Limnaea (fresh water)	42	14	5	
Crustacea				
Carcinus	68	3	0.7	
Astacus	60	11	0.8	
Porcellio (terrestrial)	56	0	6	18 (unknown)
Insects				
Rhodnius	0		92	Creatine
Aedes aegypti	6.4	11.9	47	19 (unknown)
Vertebrates—fish				
Carassius	73	10		17 (unknown)
Torpedo	1.7	85.3		Trimethylamine
flounder	2.2	17.3	1.2	oxide; creatine
Vertebrates—amphibians				
Rana catesbiana	3.2	84		
Xenopus (adult)	75	25		
(larva)	78	27		
Bufo (adult)	15			
(larva)	80			
Vertebrates—reptiles				
Emys (semiaquatic)		47	2.5	
Testudo (semiarid)	4.1	22	52	
black snake (embryo)	20	60	20	
Vertebrates—birds				
hen	3	10	87	
Vertebrates—mammals				
man	3.5	85	2	
cat	6	78	0.1	Creatine, 10
dog	3	88	0.4	Allantoin, 4

* Data selected from Prosser and Brown (1961); Potts and Parry (1964); Scheer (1963).
† Data given as percentage of excreted nitrogen in different forms and does not include
  free amino acids or purine excretion.

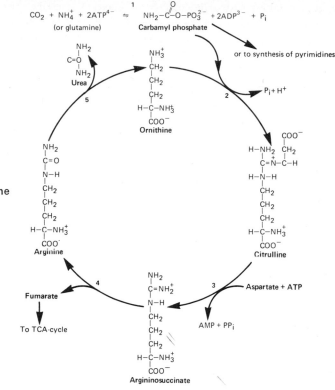

Figure 14-16 The Krebs ornithine cycle.

the fishes but including the elasmobranchs, excrete nitrogen primarily in the form of urea. Another exception is found in the birds and reptiles, which like the insects excrete large amounts of uric acid. Animals that excrete principally urea are **ureotelic**; those which excrete mainly uric acid are **uricotelic**. But, as Table 14-12 indicates, no animal excretes only one nitrogen-containing substance.

Urea is less toxic than ammonia and more soluble in water. Urea can be present in higher concentrations in the bloods of animals than ammonia without toxic effects, for example, in man 18 to 38 mg per 100 ml; in marine frogs, and elasmobranchs about 350 mg per 100 ml. Ureotelic animals include principally amphibians and mammals, although the former, unable to secrete a hyperosmotic urine, cannot exceed a urea urine concentration of about 250 mM/l and so must either excrete a large volume of urine or excrete other compounds.

Urea is formed in the mammalian liver through reactions of the Kreb's ornithine (or urea) cycle (Figure 14-16). The enzymes of this

cycle are also found in the mammalian kidney and in various tissues of other animals, but the formation of urea has been studied only in mammals. The enzyme arginase is present in the livers of ureotelic vertebrates but is absent in the uricotelic vertebrates.

The ornithine cycle provides a pathway for the formation of urea which ensures that molecules capable of providing cellular energy are not lost to the animal. The starting point of the reactions is the formation of carbamyl phosphate—a reaction which utilizes CO_2 and ammonia (derived chiefly from glutamine). The ornithine cycle is related to the TCA cycle, and one of the products of the ornithine cycle is fumarate, which can be further oxidized in the TCA cycle. It might also be noted that the formation of carbamyl phosphate is the initial step in the synthesis of pyrimidines. From Figure 14-16 it is evident that glutamic and aspartic acids play an important role in the cycle, and these two amino acids can serve as storage molecules for amino groups through reactions with ammonia to produce glutamine and asparagine. Aspartic acid is produced from the TCA cycle intermediate oxaloacetic acid, which in turn can be formed by the combination of fumaric and malic acids. As indicated above, in groups other than mammals enzymes for the entire ornithine cycle have not been found nor are other pathways for urea production known (see Cohen and Brown, 1960; Gilmour, 1961). However, they have not been carefully looked for in most cases.

14-37. Uric Acid and Purine Metabolism. Terrestrial reptiles, birds, most insects, and some snails are uricotelic and excrete uric acid. Uric acid has a low toxicity and is insoluble in water. It can thus be stored or excreted in crystalline form and, therefore, nitrogen excretion can be accomplished with little loss of water.

Uric acid is a purine (Chapter 2) and has the structure shown in Figure 14-17. The illustration also indicates the various components that furnish atoms and groups to the synthesis of uric acid. Purine biosynthesis appears to involve similar reaction sequences in all animals.

The degradation of nucleoproteins leads to additional nitrogenous waste products (Figure 14-17). Although some organisms directly excrete purines, usually enzymes are present that convert adenine or guanine to hypoxanthine or xanthine by deamination. Xanthine is converted to uric acid for excretion by some animal groups. Higher primates, including man, as well as the Dalmatian dog, lack the enzyme uricase and have higher concentrations of uric acid in their blood. The pathological condition of gout is associated with high levels of blood uric acid.

Further oxidation or uric acid leads to the formation of allantoin and allantoic acid. The former is found in the urine of mammals (except primates and Dalmatians), Diptera, and gastropod molluscs. Allantoic acid is further broken down to glyoxylic acid and urea. A few animals and many plants and bacteria possess urease, which degrades urea to ammonia and carbon dioxide. It will be noted from Figure 14-17 that the particular nitrogen-containing substance excreted by various animal groups depends upon the presence or absence of particular enzymes. This is one mechanism by which animals have been enabled to adapt to different osmotic environments. In many cases the immature form of an organism will possess a different metabolic nature than the adult form, and often these differences can be correlated with the different osmotic environments of the immature and adult animals. For example, the young of *Rana cancrivora* or of elasmobranchs cannot produce urea in large concentrations.

14-38. Other End Products of Nitrogen Metabolism. Various other nitrogenous waste products are excreted by animals. Trimethylamine oxide is found in marine fish and other organisms. The biosynthesis of this compound is not known (it may be produced by a nonbiological reaction). Although it is considered as a useful substance in osmoregulation, it may be of exogenous origin in fishes.

Both creatine and creatinine may be excreted by animals in small amounts (primarily in vertebrates). Creatine can be converted to creatinine and excreted in this form.

Detoxification processes are reactions in which some material harmful to the organism is transformed to a more innocuous substance. The reactions involving ammonia fall into this category. Benzoic acid is formed during fat metabolism and is toxic. In mammals it is detoxified by combination with glycine to form hippuric acid and excreted as such.

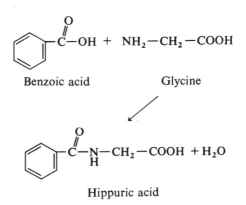

Benzoic acid   Glycine

Hippuric acid

In birds benzoic acid combines with ornithine to form ornithuric acid, which is excreted.

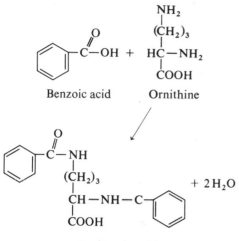

Benzoic acid   Ornithine

$+ 2 H_2O$

Ornithuric acid

Small quantities of free amino acids as well as purines and pyrimidines are also excreted in the urine. Because these are valuable materials to the animal, only minimal amounts are lost. As already stated, free amino acids play an important role in maintaining osmotic concentrations in some animals.

14-39. Some General Patterns of Nitrogen Excretion. The nature of the nitrogenous excretory products of an animal depends heavily on the mode of reproduction of the species and its osmotic habitat. The disposal of metabolic wastes is as great a problem (or greater) in the embryo as in the adult. Especially in the evolution of terrestrial life, the nature of nitrogen excretion was an important problem to be solved. These problems were considered by Needham (1942) and excellently summarized by Baldwin (1964).

The eggs of marine invertebrates are relatively permeable to water and solutes. Both food and oxygen can be supplied by diffusion from the environment, whereas waste products such as ammonia and CO_2 can diffuse into the external medium. Also most marine organisms hatch as immature larvae that float and can feed on plankton abundant in surface waters.

The eggs of fresh water organisms are much larger generally than those of marine animals, and fewer are laid per year. Larval forms of fresh water animals are rare, and the animal usually hatches from the egg in the form of a small adult that can swim after food. The fresh water organism must supply the egg with a larger amount of food and also a larger amount of salts, for unlike the marine organism the fresh water animal and its egg is hypertonic to the medium. It has been shown that marine eggs are provided with salts and nutrients from the environment, but a similarly permeable egg in fresh water would lose salts and other valuable substances. Many vertebrate eggs have a low permeability to water.

In the terrestrial environment the problem of water shortage during embryonic development arises. Animals have arrived at a terrestrial existence through the development of three basic reproductive mechanisms. **Viviparous** animals provide an internal aqueous environment for the developing young, and the proper environment is provided by the female's osmoregulatory systems until the embryo has reached a stage where its own regulatory mechanisms can support a separate existence.

Other animals undergo a semiaquatic existence in which the young are matured in an aqueous or at least a moist environment. Although the adults may be completely terrestrial, they must return to water for breeding and egg laying. This group includes, for example, amphibia and most turtles.

A third mechanism is the development of a **cleidoic egg**—an essentially impermeable box in which the embryo develops in complete isolation from the external environment, for example, in birds, most reptiles, insects. Amphibian eggs also have a low permeability. The egg is supplied with sufficient nutrients, salts, and water to support the embryo during its development. The water may be present in the form of large amounts of lipid that can be metabolized for energy and water production or in the form of water held in proteins such as egg albumin. The cleidoic egg presents the problem, however, of nitrogen excretion. The metabolizing cells of the embryo produce

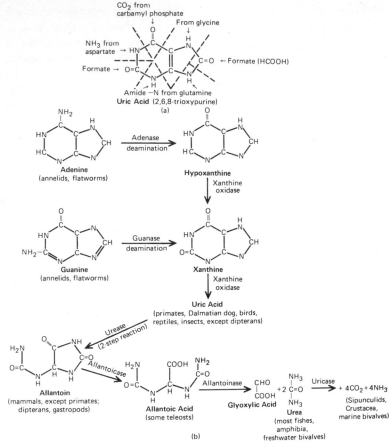

Figure 14-17   (a) The structure of uric acid showing the derivation of its constituent atoms. (b) Metabolic reactions for the degradation of purine and pyrimidine bases. The animal groups indicated excrete that product directly.

ammonia, which cannot pass through the impermeable shell. The animal that utilizes the cleidoic egg to provide water for the embryo must also be uricotelic. Uric acid can be formed and deposited in an insoluble form in the egg without being toxic. Urea would require too much water for solubilization, and hyperuremia is toxic to the tissues of most organisms. In addition to the groups listed above, cleidoic eggs are also typical of fresh water and terrestrial gastropods.

Many species inhabiting fresh water have not developed reproductive mechanisms for supplying salts to the embryos, and they must migrate to the sea for breeding. Such animals include the eel *Anguilla*, which migrates to the Sargasso Sea for spawning and the Jack-shrimp, *Leander*.

In marine gastropods uric acid production is very low, whereas terrestrial gastropods pro-

duce large amounts of uric acid. Thus, even within a single group of animals, excretory metabolism may differ according to the environments occupied by different members of the group.

The elasmobranchs have the problem of supplying the embryo with enough urea to maintain a high osmotic concentration of body fluids. In some species this is accomplished by laying urea-proof eggs in which metabolic ammonia is transformed into urea that cannot diffuse from the egg. In other species the viviparous habit is developed, and the mother supplies the embryo with urea.

Although adult amphibians are ureotelic, urea metabolism is established only in the mature adult at metamorphosis. The embryo and larva are ammonotelic because a sufficient supply of fresh water is available for ammonia excretion. A variety of habits is found in the reptiles depending on reproductive behavior and environment. Although most reptiles are uricotelic and produce cleidoic eggs, some turtles lay eggs in a moist environment in which enough water is present for urea production although not enough for ammonia excretion.

Note that the use of cleidoic eggs or viviparity requires other adaptations. For example, in both cases intrauterine fertilization is required. Also eggs can be laid away from water only if the young do not hatch in larval form. Although exceptions are found among the insects, in the vertebrates the larval stage is always part of the intraegg development. *Hylodes*, a tree frog, for example, lays terrestrial eggs, and the tadpole stage is passed through inside the egg, the young hatching in the form of a small adult. In other frogs the young hatch as tadpoles, which later metamorphosize into the adult form.

The type of nitrogenous waste excreted by an animal is related to the availability of water during both the embryonic and adult stages. Ammonia is always associated with an abundance of water. Uricotelism is associated with water shortage conditions and the need for water retention in insects, some gastropods, birds, and reptiles. These forms also produce cleidoic eggs. Ureotelism is associated with viviparousness as in mammals including monotremes and with elasmobranchs that depend on urea to maintain a hyperosmotic internal environment.

Often the pattern of nitrogen excretion changes when the embryo or larva reaches the adult stage. This is true of amphibians and some insects, for example, blowfly larvae produce ammonia; adult blowflies produce uric acid. Birds, snakes, and alligators produce urea before uric acid.

References and Readings

Adolph, E. F. (1936). "Differential permeability to water and osmotic changes in the marine worm *Phascolosoma*." *J. Cell Comp. Physiol.* **9**: 117–135.

Anderson, A. D. and R. L. Patton (1955). "Uric acid synthesis in insects." *J. Exp. Zool.* **128**: 443–451.

Bahl, K. N. (1947). "Excretion in the Oligochaetes." *Biol. Rev.* **22**: 109–147.

Baldwin, E. (1964). **An Introduction to Comparative Biochemistry,** 4th ed. New York: Cambridge University Press. 179 pp.

Barajas, L. (1966). "The development and ultrastructure of the juxtaglomerular cell granule." *J. Ultrastruct. Res.* **15**: 400–413.

Bayliss, L. E., P. N. P. Kerridge, and C. S. Russell (1933). "The excretion of protein by the mammalian kidney." *J. Physiol.* (London) **77**: 386.

Beadle, L. C. (1931). "The effect of salinity changes on the water content and respiration of marine invertebrates." *J. Exp. Biol.* **8**: 211–227.

Beadle, L. C. (1937). "Adaptation to changes in salinity in the polychaetes. Control of body volume and of body-fluid concentrations in *Nereis diversicolor*." *J. Exp. Biol.* **14**: 56–70.

Beadle, L. C. (1957). "Comparative physiology: osmotic and ionic regulation in aquatic animals." *Ann. Rev. Physiol.* **19**: 329–358.

Bentley, P. J. (1966). "The physiology of the urinary bladder of amphibia." *Biol. Rev.* **41**: 275–316.

Berglund, F. and R. P. Foster (1958). "Renal tubular transport of inorganic divalent ions by the aglomerular marine teleost, *Lophius americanus*." *J. Gen. Physiol.* **41**: 429–440.

Black, V. S. (1957). "Excretion and osmoregulation." In: **Physiology of Fishes.** (M. E. Brown, ed.), Vol. 1, pp. 163–205. New York: Academic Press, Inc.

Boyle, P. J. and E. J. Conway (1941). "Potassium accumulation in muscle and associated changes." *J. Physiol.* (London) **100**: 1–63.

Brown, F. and W. S. Stein (1960). "Balance of water, electrolytes, and nonelectrolytes." In: **Comparative Biochemistry.** (M. Florkin and H. S. Mason, eds.), Vol. 2, pp. 403–470. New York: Academic Press, Inc.

von Buddenbrock, W. (1956). "Ernährung, Wasserhaushalt und Mineralhaushalt der

Tiere." **Vergleichende Physiologie,** Bd. 3. Berlin: Birkhauser Verlag.

Chitwood, B. G. and M. B. Chitwood (1950). **An Introduction to Nematology.** Sect. 1, part 1. Baltimore: Monumental Printing Co. (B. G. Chitwood, Publisher). 213 pp.

Civan, M. M. and H. S. Frazier (1968). "The site of stimulatory action of vasopressin on sodium transport in toad bladder." *J. Gen. Physiol.* **51:** 589–605.

Clarke, F. W. (1924). "The data of geochemistry," 5th ed. *U.S. Geol. Survey Bull.* **770:** 1–841.

Cohen, P. P. and G. W. Brown (1960). "Ammonia metabolism and urea biosynthesis." In: **Comparative Biochemistry.** (M. Florkin and H. S. Mason, eds.), Vol. 2, pp. 161–244. New York: Academic Press, Inc.

Conway, E. J. and D. Hingerty (1946). "The influence of adrenalectomy on muscle constituents." *Biochem. J.* **40:** 561–568.

Copeland, D. E. (1966). "Salt transport organelle in *Artemia salina.*" *Science* **151:** 470–471.

Copeland, D. E. (1968). "Fine structure of salt and water uptake in the land crab, *Gecarcinus lateralis.*" *Am. Zool.* **8:** 417–432.

Cushnay, A. R. (1926). **The Secretion of Urine,** 2nd ed. New York: Longmans, Green & Co.

Dalton, A. J. and F. Haguenau, eds. (1967). **Ultrastructure of the Kidney.** New York: Academic Press, Inc. 240 pp.

Danielli, J. F. and C. F. A. Pantin (1950). "Alkaline phosphatase in protonephridia of terrestrial nemertines and planarians." *Quart. J. Microscop. Sci.* **91:** 209–214.

Denton, E. J. (1964). "The buoyancy of marine molluscs." In: **Physiology of Mollusca.** (K. M. Wilbur and C. M. Yonge, eds.), Vol. 1, pp. 425–434. New York: Academic Press, Inc.

Denton, E. J. and T. I. Shaw (1962). "The buoyancy of gelatinous animals." *J. Physiol.* (London) **161:** 14P–15P.

Deyrupp, I. J. (1964). "Water balance and kidney." In: **Physiology of the Amphibia.** (J. A. Moore, ed.), pp. 252–328. New York: Academic Press, Inc.

Diedrich, D. F. (1966). "Glucose transport carrier in the dog kidney: its concentration and turnover number." *Am. J. Physiol.* **211:** 581–587.

Dill, D. B., ed. (1964). "Adaptation to the Environment." **Handbook of Physiology,** Section 4, Vol. 1. Washington, D.C.: American Physiological Society. 1056 pp.

Dimtrup, A. B. J. (1928). "On the number, shapes, structures and surface areas of the glomerulus of the kidney of man and mammals." *Am. J. Anat.* **41:** 123.

Dresel, E. B. and V. Moyle (1950). "Nitrogenous excretion in amphipods and isopods." *J. Exp. Biol.* **27:** 210–225.

Duchâteau, G., M. Florkin, and J. Leclerqc (1953). "Concentrations des bases fixes et types de composition de la base totale de l'hemolymphe des insects." *Arch. Int. Physiol.* **61:** 518–549.

Duchâteau-Bosson, G., M. Florkin, and C. Jeuniaux (1961). "Rôle de la variation de la composante amino-acide intracellulaire das l'euryhalinité d'*Arenicola mariha.*" *Arch. Int. Physiol.* **69:** 97–116.

DuVigneaud, V. (1955). "Hormones of the posterior pituitary gland: oxytocin and vasopressin." *Harvey Lect.* **50:** 1–26.

Epstein, F. H., A. I. Katz, and G. E. Pickford (1967). "Sodium- and potassium-activated adenosine triphosphatase of gills: role in adaptation of teleosts to salt water." *Science* **156:** 1245–1247.

Farquhar, M. G., S. L. Wissig, and G. E. Palade (1964). "Glomerular permeability. I. Ferritin transfer across the normal glomerular capillary wall." *J. Exp. Med.* **113:** 47–66.

Farrell, G. and A. N. Taylor (1962). "Neuroendocrine aspects of blood volume regulation." *Ann. Rev. Physiol.* **24:** 471–490.

Fauré-Fremiet, E. and C. Rouiller (1959). "Cortex of contractile vacuole and its ultrastructure in the Ciliata." *J. Protozool.* **6:** 29–37.

Flemister, L. J. and S. C. Flemister (1951). "Chloride ion regulation and oxygen consumption in the crab, *Ocypode albicans* (Bosq)." *Biol. Bull.* **101:** 259–273.

Florkin, M. (1949). **Biochemical Evolution.** New York: Academic Press, Inc. 157 pp.

Forster, R. P. (1948). "Use of thin kidney slices and isolated renal tubules for direct study of cellular transport kinetics." *Science* **108:** 65–67.

Forster, R. P. (1953). "A comparative study of renal function in marine teleosts." *J. Cell Comp. Physiol.* **42:** 487–509.

Forster, R. P. (1954). "Active cellular transport of urea by frog renal tubules." *Am. J. Physiol.* **179:** 373–377.

Forster, R. P. (1958). "*In vitro* transport of dyes by isolated renal tubules of the flounder as disclosed by direct visualization, intracellular accumulation and transcellular movement." *J. Cell. Comp. Physiol.* **51:** 259–272.

Ganote, C. E., J. J. Grantham, H. L. Moses, M. B. Burg, and J. Orloff (1968). "Ultrastructural studies of vasopressin effect on isolated perfused renal collecting tubules of the rabbit." *J. Cell. Biol.* **36:** 355–367.

Gilmour, D. (1961). **The Biochemistry of Insects:** New York: Academic Press, Inc. 343 pp.

Goodrich, E. S. (1945). "The study of nephridia and genital ducts since 1895." *Quart. J. Microscop. Sci.* **86:** 113–392.

Gordon, M. S. (1968). **Animal Function— Principles and Adaptations.** New York: The Macmillan Company. 560 pp.

Gordon, M. S., B. H. Amdur, and P. F. Scholander (1959). "Further observations on supercooling and osmoregulation in arctic fishes." *1st Int. Congr. Ocean.* pp. 234–236.

Gordon, M. S., K. Schmidt-Nielsen, and H. M. Kelly (1961). "Osmotic regulation in the crab-eating frog, *Rana cancrivora.*" *J. Exp. Biol.* **38:** 659–678.

Gottschalk, C. W. and M. Mylle (1956). "Micropuncture studies of pressures in proximal tubules and peritubular capillaries of the rat kidney in relation to uretral and venous pressures." *Am. J. Physiol.* **185:** 430–441.

Grafflin, A. L. (1931). "Urine flow and diuresis in marine teleosts." *Am. J. Physiol.* **97:** 602–610.

Grafflin, A. L. (1936). "The problem of adapta-
tion to fresh and salt water in the teleosts, viewed from the standpoint of the structure of the renal tubules." *J. Cell. Comp. Physiol.* **9:** 469–475.

Gross, W. J. (1954). "Osmotic responses in the sipunculid *Dendrostomatum zostericolum.*" *J. Exp. Biol.* **31:** 402–423.

Hale, L. J. (1955). **Biological Laboratory Data.** London: Methuen & Co. Ltd. and Science Paperbacks.

Hargitay, B., W. Kuhn, and H. Wirz (1951). "Ein Modellversuch zum Problem der Harnkonzentrierung." *Helv. Physiol. Acta* **9:** 26–27.

Hatt, P. (1967). "The juxtaglomerular apparatus." In: **Ultrastructure of the Kidney.** (A. J. Dalton and F. Haguenau, eds.), pp. 101–141. New York: Academic Press, Inc.

Hays, M. (1968). "A new proposal for the action of vasopressin based on studies of a complex synthetic membrane." *J. Gen. Physiol.* **51:** 385–398.

Herfs, A. (1922). "Die pulsierende Vakuole der Protozoen, ein Schutzorgan gegen Aussüssung. Studien über Anpassung der Organismen as das Leben im Süsswater." *Arch. Protist.* **44:** 227–260.

Hodgkin, A. L. (1958). "Ionic movements and electrical activity in giant nerve fibers." *Proc. Roy. Soc.* (London) **B148:** 1.

House, C. R. (1963). "Osmotic regulation in the brackish water teleost, *Blennuis pholis.*" *J. Exp. Biol.* **40:** 87–104.

Hutchinson, G. E. (1957). **A Treatise on Limnology.** New York: John Wiley & Sons, Inc. 1015 pp.

Jamison, R. L., C. M. Bennett, and R. W. Berliner (1967). "Countercurrent multiplication by the thin loops of Henle." *Am. J. Physiol.* **212:** 357–366.

Jeuniaux, C., G. Duchâteau-Bosson, and M. Florkin (1961). "Variation of component amino acids of the tissues and euryhalinity of *Perinereis cultifera* GR and *Nereis diversicolor.*" *J. Biochem.* (Tokyo) **49:** 427–531.

Jones, M. L. (1957). "On the morphology of the nephridium of *Nereis* (Gruben)." *Biol. Bull.* **113:** 407–413.

Jorgenson, C. B. and R. P. Dales (1957). "The regulation of volume and osmoregulation in some nereid polychaetes." *Physiol. Comp. Oecol.* **4**: 357–374.

Khuri, R. N., W. J. Flanigan, D. E. Oken, and A. K. Solomon (1966). "Influence of electrolytes on glucose absorption in *Necturus* kidney proximal tubules." *Fed. Proc.* **25**: 899–902.

Kirshner, L. B. (1967). "Comparative physiology of invertebrate excretory organs." *Ann. Rev. Physiol.* **29**: 169–196.

Kirsten, E., R. Kirsten, A. Leaf, and G. W. Sharp (1968). "Increased activity of enzymes of the tricarboxylic acid cycle in response to aldosterone in the toad bladder." *Pflüg. Arch. ges. Physiol.* **300**: 213–225.

Kitching, J. A. (1954). "Osmoregulation and ionic regulation in animals without kidneys." *Symp. Soc. Exp. Biol.* **8**: 63–65.

Koechlin, B. A. (1955). "On the chemical composition of the axoplasm of squid giant nerve fibers with particular reference to its ion pattern." *J. Biophys. Biochem. Cytol.* **1**: 511–539.

Krogh, A. (1939). **Osmotic Regulation in Aquatic Animals.** New York: Cambridge University Press. 242 pp.

Kromhout, G. A. (1943). "A comparison of the protonephridia of fresh-water, brackish-water, and marine specimens of *Gyratrix hermaphroditus.*" *J. Morphol.* **72**: 167–181.

Laverack, M. S. (1963). **The Physiology of Earthworms.** Long Island City, N.Y.: Pergamon Press, Inc. 206 pp.

Levitt, J. (1964). "Osmotic pressure measuring devices." In: **Instrumental Methods of Experimental Biology.** (D. W. Newman, ed.), pp. 405–427. New York: The Macmillan Company.

Lewis, P. R. (1952). "The free amino acids of invertebrate nerve." *Biochem. J.* **52**: 330–338.

Lilly, S. J. (1955). "Osmoregulation and ionic regulation in *Hydra.*" *J. Exp. Biol.* **32**: 423–439.

Lockwood, A. P. M. (1961). "Ringer solutions and some notes on the physiological basis of their ionic composition." *Comp. Biochem. Physiol.* **2**: 241–289.

Lockwood, A. P. M. (1966). **Animal Body Fluids and their Regulation.** Cambridge, Mass.: Harvard University Press.

Ludwig, D. (1954). "Changes in the distribution of nitrogen in the blood of the Japanese beetle." *Physiol. Zool.* **27**: 325–334.

Macallum, A. B. (1926). "The paleochemistry of body fluids and tissues." *Physiol. Rev.* **6**: 316–355.

Macan, T. T. and E. B. Worthington (1951). **Life in Lakes and Rivers.** New York: William Collins Sons & Co., Ltd. 272 pp.

Malvin, R. L., W. S. Wild, and L. P. Sullivan (1958). "Localization of nephron transport by stop-flow analysis." *Am. J. Physiol.* **194**: 135.

Mantel, L. H. (1968). "The foregut of *Gecarcinus lateralis* as an organ of salt and water balance." *Am. Zool.* **8**: 433–442.

Marsh, D. J. (1966). "Hypo-osmotic reabsorption due to active salt transport in perfused collecting ducts of the rat renal medulla." *Nature* **210**: 1179–1180.

Marsh, D. J., R. B. Kelman, and H. C. Howard (1967). "The theory of urine formation in water diuresis with implications for antidiuresis." *Bull. Math. Biophys.* **29**: 67–89.

Martin, A. W. (1958). "Comparative physiology: excretion." *Ann. Rev. Physiol.* **20**: 225–242.

Mollitor, A. (1937). "Beitrage zur Untersuchung des Exkretsstoffwechsels und der Exkretion von *Eriocheir sinensis.*" *Zool. Jb.* **57**: 323–354.

Morel, F. and M. Guinnebault (1961). "Les mécanismes de concentration et de dilution de l'urine." *J. Physiol.* (Paris) **53**: 75–130.

Mountcastle, V. B., ed. (1968). **Medical Physiology,** 12th ed. 2 volumes. St. Louis, Mo.: The C. V. Mosby Company.

Müller, R. (1936). "Die osmoregulatorische Bedeutung der kontraktilen Vakuolen von *Amoeba proteus, Zoothamnium hiketes* und *Frontonia marina.*" *Arch. Protist.* **87**: 345–382.

Needham, J. (1942). **Biochemistry and Morphogenesis.** New York: Cambridge University Press. 785 pp.

Norris, E. R. and G. J. Benoit (1945). "Studies

on trimethylamine oxide. I. Occurrence of trimethylamine oxide in marine organisms." *J. Biol. Chem.* **158**: 433–448.

Orloff, J. and J. S. Handler (1961). "Vasopressin-like effects of adenosine-3',5'-phosphate (cyclic AMP) and theophylline in the toad bladder." *Biochem. Biophys. Res. Comm.* **5**: 63–66.

Osvaldo, L. and H. Latta (1966). "The thin limbs of the loop of Henle." *J. Ultrastruct. Res.* **15**: 144–168.

Padmanbhanaidu, B. and R. Ramanurthy (1961). "The influence of sex and size on the osmotic pressure, the chloride, and the free amino acids of the blood of the fresh water crab *Paratelphusa sp.* and the fresh water mussel *Lanellidans marginalis.*" *J. Exp. Biol.* **38**: 35–41.

Pantin, C. F. A. (1931). "The adaptation of *Gunda ulva* to salinity. III. The electrolyte exchange." *J. Exp. Biol.* **8**: 82–94.

Pantin, C. F. A. (1946). **Notes on Microscopical Techniques for Zoologists.** New York: Cambridge University Press.

Parry, G. (1957). "Osmoregulation in some freshwater prawns." *J. Exp. Biol.* **34**: 417–423.

Parry, G. (1966). "Osmotic adaptation in fishes." *Biol. Rev.* **41**: 392–444.

Peters, H. (1935). "Uber den Einfluss des alzegehaltes im Aussenmedium auf den Bau und die Funktion der Exkretionsorgane dekapoder Crustaceen." *Z. Morph. Oecol. Tiere.* **30**: 355–381.

Pitts, R. F. (1963). **Physiology of the Kidney and Body Fluids.** Chicago: Year Book Medical Publishers.

Potts, W. T. W. (1954). "The inorganic composition of the blood of *Mytilus edulis* and *Anodonta cygnea.*" *J. Exp. Biol.* **31**: 376–385.

Potts, W. T. W. (1958). "The inorganic and amino acid composition of some lamellibranch molluscs." *J. Exp. Biol.* **35**: 749–764.

Potts, W. T. W. (1968). "Osmotic and ionic regulation." *Ann. Rev. Physiol.* **30**: 73–104.

Potts, W. T. W. and G. Parry (1964). **Osmotic and Ionic Regulation in Animals.** Long Island City, N.Y.: Pergamon Press, Inc. 423 pp.

Poulsen, T. L. and G. A. Bartholomew (1962).

"Salt balance in the Savannah sparrow." *Physiol. Zool.* **35**: 109–119.

Prosser, C. L. and F. A. Brown (1961). **Comparative Animal Physiology,** 2nd ed. Philadelphia: W. B. Saunders Company. 688 pp.

Ramsay, J. A. (1949a). "The osmotic relations of the earthworm." *J. Exp. Biol.* **26**: 46–56.

Ramsay, J. A. (1949b). "The site of formation of hypotonic urine in the nephridium of the earthworm, *Lumbricus.*" *J. Exp. Biol.* **26**: 65–75.

Ramsay, J. A. (1950). "Osmotic regulation in mosquito larvae." *J. Exp. Biol.* **27**: 145–157.

Ramsay, J. A. (1951). "Osmotic regulation in mosquito larvae: the role of the Malpighian tubules." *J. Exp. Biol.* **28**: 62–73.

Ramsay, J. A. (1952). "The excretion of sodium and potassium by the malpighian tubules of *Rhodnius.*" *J. Exp. Biol.* **29**: 110–126.

Ramsay, J. A. (1954). "Movements of water and electrolytes in invertebrates." *Symp. Soc. Exp. Biol.* **8**: 1–15.

Ramsay, J. A. (1955). "The excretion of sodium, potassium, and water in the malpighian tubules of the stick insect *Dixippus morosus* (Orthoptera, phasmidae)." *J. Exp. Biol.* **32**: 200–216.

Ramsay, J. A. (1956). "Excretion by malpighian tubules of the stick insect *Dixippus morosus* (Orthoptera, phasmidae): calcium, magnesium, chloride, phosphate and hydrogen ions." *J. Exp. Biol.* **33**: 697–708.

Ramsay, J. A. and J. A. Riegel (1961). "Excretion of inulin by malpighian tubules." *Nature* **191**: 1115.

Renkin, E. M. (1962). "Techniques of vascular perfusion." In: **Physical Techniques in Biological Research.** (W. L. Nastuk, ed.), Vol. 4, pp. 107–136. New York: Academic Press, Inc.

Richards, A. N. (1935). "Urine formation in the amphibian kidney." *Harvey Lect.* **29**: 93–118.

Richards, A. N. and A. M. Walker (1937). "Methods of collecting fluid from known regions of the renal tubules in Amphibia and of perfusing the lumen of a single tubule." *Am. J. Physiol.* **118**: 111–120.

Riegel, J. A. (1961). "The influence of water loading on certain functional aspects of the crayfish antennal gland." *J. Exp. Biol.* **38:** 291–299.

Riegel, J. A. and L. B. Kirschner (1960). "The excretion of inulin and glucose by the crayfish antennal gland." *Biol. Bull.* **118:** 296–307.

Robertson, J. D. (1949). "Ionic regulation in some marine invertebrates." *J. Exp. Biol.* **26:** 182–200.

Robertson, J. D. (1953). "Further studies on ionic regulation in marine invertebrates." *J. Exp. Biol.* **30:** 277–296.

Robertson, J. D. (1960). "Osmotic and ionic regulation." In: **Physiology of Crustacea.** (T. H. Waterman, ed.), Vol. 1, pp. 317–339. New York: Academic Press, Inc.

Robertson, J. D. (1964). "Osmotic and ionic regulation." In: **Physiology of Mollusca.** (K. M. Wilbur and C. M. Yonge, eds.), Vol. 1, pp. 283–311. New York: Academic Press, Inc.

Rubey, W. W. (1951). "Geologic history of sea water. An attempt to state a problem." *Geol. Soc. Am. Bull. Paleoecol.* **62:** 1111–1148.

Scheer, B. T. (1963). **Animal Physiology.** New York: John Wiley & Sons, Inc.

Schlieper, C. (1936). "Die Abhängigkeit der Atmunsintensität der Organismen vom Wassergehalt und dem kolloidalen Zustand des Protoplasmas." *Biol. Zentr.* **56:** 87–94.

Schmidt-Nielsen, B. (1961). "Concentrating mechanisms of the kidney from a comparative viewpoint." *Am. Heart J.* **62:** 579–586.

Schmidt-Nielsen, B. (1964). "Organ systems in adaptation: the excretory system." In: **Handbook of Physiology.** (D. B. Dill, ed.), Section 4, Vol. 1, pp. 215–257. Washington, D.C.: American Physiological Society.

Schmidt-Nielsen, B. and L. E. Davis (1968). "Fluid transport and tubular intercellular spaces in reptilian kidneys." *Science* **159:** 1105–1108.

Schmidt-Nielsen, K. (1959). "The physiology of the camel." *Sci. Am.* **201**(6): 140–151.

Schmidt-Nielsen, K. (1960). "The salt-secreting glands of marine birds." *Circulation* **21:** 955–967.

Schmidt-Nielsen, K. (1964). **Desert Animals: Physiological Problems of Heat and Water.** New York: Oxford University Press.

Schmidt-Nielsen, K. and R. Fänge (1958). "Salt glands in marine reptiles." *Nature* **182:** 783–785.

Scothorne, R. J. (1959). "The nasal glands of birds. A histological and histochemical study of the inactive gland of the domestic duck." *J. Anat.* **93:** 246–256.

Scriver, C. R. and H. Goldman (1966). "Renal tubular transport of proline, hydroxyproline, and glycine." *J. Clin. Invest.* **45:** 1357–1363.

Shaw, J. (1964). "The control of salt balance in the Crustacea." *Symp. Soc. Exp. Biol.* **18:** 237–254.

Shaw, J. and R. H. Strobbart (1963). "Osmotic and ionic regulation in insects." *Adv. Insect Physiol.* **1:** 315–399.

Smith, H. W. (1936). "The retention and physiological role of urea in the Elasmobranchii." *Biol. Rev.* **11:** 49–82.

Smith, H. W. (1951). **The Kidney.** New York: Oxford University Press.

Smith, H. W. (1956). **Principles of Renal Physiology.** New York: Oxford University Press. 237 pp.

Smith, R. I. (1958). "A note on the tolerance of low salinities by nereid polychaetes and its relation to temperature and reproductive habit." *Union Int. Sci. Zool.* **B24:** 93–107.

Stempell, W. (1914). "Über die Funktion der pulsieren Vakuole und einen Apparat zur demonstrationen derselben." *Zool. Jb.* **34:** 437–478.

Strickland, J. D. M. and T. R. Parsons (1965). "A manual of sea water analysis." 2nd ed. *Bull. Fish. Res. Bd. Canada* **125:** 1–203.

Sverdrup, H. U., M. W. Johnson, and R. H. Fleming (1942). **The Oceans.** Englewood Cliffs, N. J.: Prentice-Hall, Inc. 1087 pp.

Tobian, L. (1967). "Renin release and its role in renal function and control of salt balance and arterial pressure." *Fed. Proc.* **26:** 48–54.

Ullrich, K. J., G. Rumrich, and B. Schmidt-

Nielsen (1967). "Urea transport in the collecting duct of rats on normal and low protein diet." *Pflüg Arch. ges. Physiol.* **295**: 147–156.

Vander, A. J. (1967). "Control of rennin release." *Physiol. Rev.* **47**: 359–382.

van Harreveld, A. (1936). "A physiological solution for fresh water crustaceans." *Proc. Soc. Exp. Biol. Med.* **34**: 428–432.

Van Ostend, J. (1957). "The skin and scales." In: **The Physiology of Fishes.** (M. E. Brown, ed.), Vol. 1, pp. 207–244. New York: Academic Press, Inc.

Verbeke, J. (1957). "Exploration hydrologique des Lacs Kivu, Edouard et Labert: Recherches ecologiques sur la faune des grands lacs de l'est du Congo Belge." *Inst. Roy. Sci. Nat. Belg.*, Vol. III, fasc. 1. 177 pp.

Weinstein, P. P. (1960). "Excretory mechanisms and excretory products of nematodes: an appraisal." In: **Host Influence on Parasite Physiology.** (L. E. Stauber, ed.), pp. 65–92. New Brunswick, N. J.: Rutgers University Press.

Whittembury, G. (1960). "Ion and water transport in the proximal tubules of the kidney of *Necturus maculosus*." *J. Gen. Physiol.* **43**: 43–56.

Wigglesworth, V. B. (1931). "Excretion in *Rhodinus* (Hemiptera)." *J. Exp. Biol.* **8**: 411–451.

Wigglesworth, V. B. (1932). "On the function of the so-called rectal glands of insects." *Quart. J. Microscop. Soc.* **75**: 131–150.

Wilbur, K. M. (1964). "Shell formation and regeneration." In: **Physiology of Mollusca.** (K. M. Wilbur and C. M. Yonge, eds.), Vol. 1, pp. 243–282. New York: Academic Press, Inc.

Wirz, H. (1956). "Der osmotische Druck in den corticalen Tubuli der Ratteniere." *Helv. Physiol. Pharmacol. Acta* **14**: 353–362.

Wirz, H. (1961). "Newer concepts of renal mechanism in relation to water and electrolyte excretion." In: **Water and Electrolyte Metabolism.** (C. P. Steward and Th. Stengers, eds.), pp. 100–108. New York: American Elsevier Publishing Co.

Wirz, H., B. Hargitay, and W. Kuhn (1951). "Lokalisation des Konzentrierungsprozesses in der Niere durch direkte Kryoskopie." *Helv. Physiol. Pharmacol. Acta* **9**: 196–207.

Yamamoto, G. (1959). "Behaviour and mucous secretion of Japanese march clam, *Corbicula japonica* Prime." *Bull Mar. Biol. Sta. Asamushi Tohoku Univ.* **9**: 141–144.

15-1. Introduction. In Chapter 4 it was pointed out that biochemical reactions as well as more complex activities of organisms are extremely sensitive to temperature, and therefore, the body temperature of an organism is an important factor in the life and survival of the organism. The study of body temperature and its regulation is an important aspect of physiology and has extensions in many directions.

Although the range of temperatures in the universe extends from near absolute zero in empty outer space to millions of degrees in the cores of the hottest stars; the temperature range over which life exists on earth is very limited. The lower temperature limit is at about the freezing point of water, 0°C, and the upper limit is about 50°C, the temperature at which most proteins begin to denature. Only a few algae live at temperatures up to about 70°C (Brock, 1967).

Animals in the past were often characterized as cold-blooded or warm-blooded. This inaccurate description of animals arose because the human body has a relatively high temperature even in the cooler extremities, and therefore many animals feel cold to the touch—thus their designation as cold-blooded. Some animals (especially birds and mammals) have body temperatures similar to that of humans, and since they feel warm to the touch were designated as warm-blooded.

However, the temperature of a so-called cold-blooded animal may approach that of a typical mammal and often is above the environmental temperature. The designations of cold-blooded and warm-blooded are not only inaccurate but also unscientific. Animals are better designated as poikilothermic or homeothermic. A poikilothermic animal is one whose body temperature varies with the environmental temperature, and a homeothermic animal maintains its body temperature at some relatively constant level (Figure 1-4). The birds and mammals are best able to regulate body temperature, but lower organisms are also capable of temperature regulation at least during certain periods of their life—often by using behavioral instead of strictly physiological mechanisms.

As previously stated, the regulation of any

Chapter 15

Nutrition and Body Temperature Regulation

internal variable involves the ability to maintain loss equal to gain, so that the variable
remains constant. In the case of temperature
regulation, heat loss must be equal to heat
gain. Organisms gain heat from two major
sources: (1) heat from the sun, either directly
or from the environmental surroundings and
(2) heat from metabolic reactions and muscular activity. The energy of metabolic reactions,
as well as other physiological activities, is
finally degraded into heat energy, and so all
animal cells are continuous heat generators.
In most animals this heat is rapidly lost to the
environment (as long as the environment is
cooler than the animal), and body temperature
is to a large degree dependent only on the
temperature of the environment; these are
ectothermic animals. A few animal groups have
the ability to regulate metabolism so that
metabolic heat production is a dominant factor
in determining body temperature; these are
endothermic animals. This group includes
principally the birds and mammals. However,
other animals possess this ability at certain
periods of their life, for example the larger
reptiles and fast-swimming teleosts, and insects
such as honeybees and many lepidopterans.
The term **heterothermy** is used to designate
animals that are capable of endothermic
temperature regulation although body temperature is not maintained at some constant
level.

Since the heat production by cells is important in temperature regulation and is a by-
product of metabolic oxidation and depends
on the type of nutrients utilized, I shall begin
this chapter with a brief discussion of animal
nutrition, feeding mechanisms, and calorimetry. I stress that space permits only a brief
consideration of these topics, and the interested
reader should refer to the references for further
details.

Nutrition

15-2. Nutritional Requirements. Animal nutrition has been defined as the series of processes
by which an animal takes in and assimilates

the various foods that are needed to promote
growth and replace worn tissues. As such the
science of animal nutrition is an inter-
disciplinary field including elements of biochemistry, physiology, thermodynamics, mi-
crobiology, animal behavior, and ecology.
Classic texts and references to animal nutrition
include: Beaton and McHenry (1964–1966);
Brody (1945); Consolazio et al. (1963);
Kleiber (1961); and Schoenheimer (1946).

All life is based on the ability of plants to
synthesize organic constituents from the
inorganic materials of the soil and atmosphere.
Organisms that can synthesize all essential
organic compounds from inorganic sources are
autotrophs and include the chlorophyll containing green plants (**phototrophs**) and the
chemosynthetic bacteria (**chemotrophs**). Most
animals are **heterotrophs** and require organic
materials as food. There are varying degrees
between the strict autotroph and the strict
heterotroph. **Mesotrophs** can synthesize most
of the organic materials they require, but they
do need certain organic vitamins in the diet. A
few animals are **saprozoic** and are primarily
parasites that can absorb large organic molecules through the body surface.

As previously stated (Chapter 2), some of the
20 naturally occurring amino acids found in
proteins are essential and must be taken in in
the diet. In man essential amino acids include
valine, leucine, isoleucone, lysine, methionine,
threonine, phenylalanine, and tryptophan. The
rat, in addition, also requires a source of histidine (Rose, 1949). Similar requirements are
found in a variety of organisms including the
ciliate protozoan *Tetrahymena* and the insect
Tribolium confusium. Some fatty acids are also
essential, and the rat, for example, requires
linoleic, linolenic, and arachidonic acids.
Similar requirements have been found in
several mammals that have been studied and
in some birds and insects. Although steroids
can be synthesized by mammals, especially the
basic steroid building block, cholesterol, other
animal groups, for example the insects, require
cholesterol or related sterols in the diet.

The inability to synthesize a particular substance represents a lack of particular enzymes.

Table 15-1   Vitamins

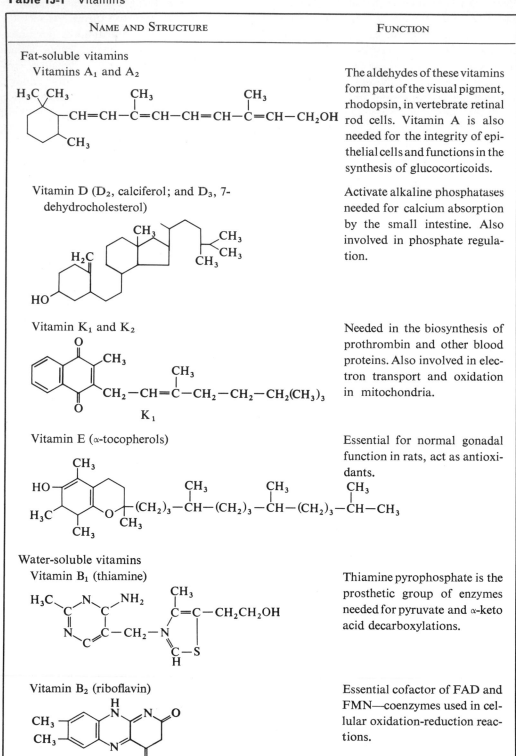

NAME AND STRUCTURE	FUNCTION
Fat-soluble vitamins Vitamins A_1 and A_2	The aldehydes of these vitamins form part of the visual pigment, rhodopsin, in vertebrate retinal rod cells. Vitamin A is also needed for the integrity of epithelial cells and functions in the synthesis of glucocorticoids.
Vitamin D (D_2, calciferol; and D_3, 7-dehydrocholesterol)	Activate alkaline phosphatases needed for calcium absorption by the small intestine. Also involved in phosphate regulation.
Vitamin K_1 and K_2	Needed in the biosynthesis of prothrombin and other blood proteins. Also involved in electron transport and oxidation in mitochondria.
Vitamin E (α-tocopherols)	Essential for normal gonadal function in rats, act as antioxidants.
Water-soluble vitamins Vitamin B_1 (thiamine)	Thiamine pyrophosphate is the prosthetic group of enzymes needed for pyruvate and α-keto acid decarboxylations.
Vitamin B_2 (riboflavin)	Essential cofactor of FAD and FMN—coenzymes used in cellular oxidation-reduction reactions.

Table 15-1 continued

Name and Structure	Function
Nicotinic acid (part of vitamin B complex)	Nicotinamide is a component of NAD and NADP (see Chapter 2 and Chapter 4).
Pyridoxine (vitamin B$_6$) 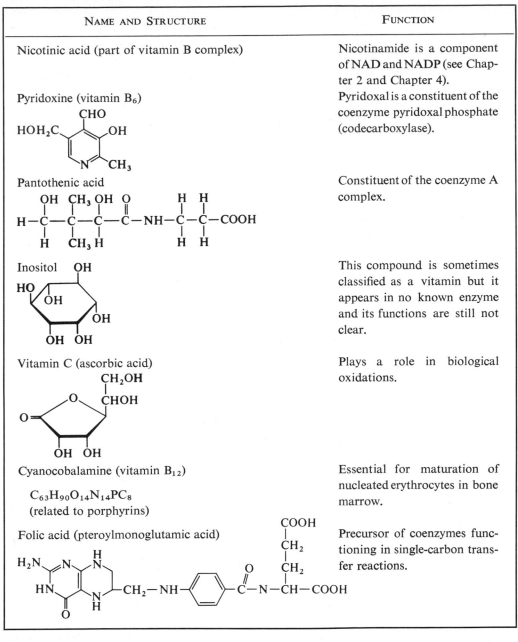	Pyridoxal is a constituent of the coenzyme pyridoxal phosphate (codecarboxylase).
Pantothenic acid	Constituent of the coenzyme A complex.
Inositol	This compound is sometimes classified as a vitamin but it appears in no known enzyme and its functions are still not clear.
Vitamin C (ascorbic acid)	Plays a role in biological oxidations.
Cyanocobalamine (vitamin B$_{12}$) $C_{63}H_{90}O_{14}N_{14}PC_8$ (related to porphyrins)	Essential for maturation of nucleated erythrocytes in bone marrow.
Folic acid (pteroylmonoglutamic acid)	Precursor of coenzymes functioning in single-carbon transfer reactions.

Essential amino acids such as arginine require six or seven enzymes for their synthesis (Davis, 1961). Complex essential amino acids often require more than a dozen enzymes for their synthesis. Many nonessential amino acids need only one or two enzymes for their synthesis. It appears that in some stage of animal evolution it became more efficient for animals to depend upon their dietary intake to supply certain materials rather than using the energy necessary to elaborate the enzymes required for their synthesis. The common sugar glucose and the common amino acid glycine can serve as starting points for the synthesis of many materials needed by animals.

In addition to basic nutrients such as

protein, lipid, and carbohydrate, animals also need certain organic molecules in trace amounts. These are the vitamins, which in most cases appear to be required as coenzymes in cells (Chapter 4). A listing of important vitamin groups and their general functions is given in Table 15-1. Vitamin needs appear to be similar in most animal groups.

Animals also require inorganic materials in their diets. Some are needed in relatively large amounts, for example phosphate, chloride, sodium, potassium, calcium, and magnesium. Iron is also needed for the synthesis of cytochromes and often of oxygen transport pigments such as hemoglobin. In addition animals require trace elements (or micronutrients) including cobalt, copper, fluoride, iodide, manganese, molybdenum, silicon, selenium, strontium, zinc, and vanadium. Barium and chromium are needed by some organisms. Since these elements are needed in such small quantities, it would appear that they play a role as enzyme cofactors but in only a few cases is the particular enzyme activity associated with a trace element known. Comparative aspects of nutrition are reviewed by Hutner and Provasoli (1965); House (1962) reviews insect nutrition, an animal group that has been extensively studied.

15-3. Feeding Mechanisms. Different animals eat many different types of food and use many diverse mechanisms to take in food. It is difficult to classify feeding mechanisms adequately, but a system devised by Yonge [1928; see also Nicol (1960)] for invertebrates is often used and can be extended to fit vertebrate feeding mechanisms.

Yonge based his classification on the nature of foods eaten. There are three major classes of feeders: (1) microphages, animals that eat small food particles; (2) macrophages, animals that eat large food particles or masses; and (3) fluid feeders, a small group of animals that feed on the fluids or tissues of animals. Subdivisions of each major type listed above are made on the basis of the actual feeding mechanism used by the animal.

Microphages include animals that use pseu-

dopods to take in food (radiolarians, foraminiferans); those which use cilia (ciliated protozoans, sponges, many worms, bivalve molluscs, anuran tadpoles); those which make use of mucous especially in the form of filtering sheets (gastropods, tunicates, ammocoetes); and those which use setae or similar filtering devices (copepods and other crustaceans, some teleosts, basing sharks, whalebone whales).

Many aquatic organisms known as filter feeders feed on suspended food particles and are often supplied with filtering devices. They rely on cilia, setae, or other devices to produce a flow of water from which food particles may be removed or trapped on feeding surfaces. Such a surface may be a moving cord of mucus that is propelled by cilia and that carries food particles to the digestive tract. Tentacles, often with poisonous spines or similar devices, or with sticky coverings, are used by some organisms to entrap small organisms or food particles that are then carried to the mouth. The poisonous nematocyts of hydra and other coelenterates are discharged by tactile and chemical stimuli and are used to stun prey (Lenhoff, 1961).

Although filter feeding is characteristic of many sessile organisms, it is also a method used by some active organisms. In the copepods and in *Daphnia*, filter feeding mechanisms are based on swimming movements and specialized appendages. A swimming current is produced by the rapid movements of the second antennae. This motion not only provides a propulsive force for swimming but also creates eddy currents on both sides of the body. These currents are directed through a filter chamber enclosed between the ventral body wall and the second maxillae. The latter carry long, featherlike setae. As water passes through the filter chamber, particles of food are trapped by the setae. These particles are then scraped off by long processes of the first maxillae and carried to the mouth.

Jørgensen (1966) discusses the different mechanisms and their efficiency in filter feeding. Materials the size of protein molecules or smaller are inefficiently retained by filter devices either of the mucus or setous types. But such mechanisms are used by some large organisms for taking in plankton (Morton, 1960). Filter feeding mechanisms are nonselective in that the type of food taken by the organism is not controlled. Food intake control consists only of stopping or starting the filtering action. Such nonselective feeders are usually omnivorous, taking in whatever types of food particles come their way. Filter feeders must also live in a nutrient-rich medium.

Macrophages include animals that have mechanisms for swallowing the surrounding medium (including burrowing and digging forms such as earthworms); or that have mechanisms for seizing prey for example, coelenterates, many polychaetes, most non-mammalian vertebrates, some mammals; or that have mechanisms for seizing, biting, rasping, grazing, and masticating food, for example, many gastropods, cephalopods, crustaceans, insects, cyclostomes, some birds, and most mammals.

Although filter feeders are restricted to an aqueous environment, macrophage feeders are not, and their feeding mechanisms permit a more selective choice of food. Most aquatic macrophages are carnivorous, whereas a majority of terrestrial macrophages are herbivores. Microphages differ from macrophages also in that the latter feed discontinuously—a situation which is also reflected in differences of the digestive systems of the two types of feeders.

Fluid feeders have mechanisms for sucking fluids (trematodes, nematodes, leeches, some insects, and the young of mammals) or for absorbing dissolved foods through their body surfaces (many parasites, some aquatic invertebrates). The food of fluid feeders is generally of small dimensions and in the dissolved state, and no mechanism is usually present for separating food from the medium.

15-4. Digestion—Some Mechanical Aspects. Digestion is the series of processes by which complex food particles and molecules are broken down into simpler substances that can be absorbed or utilized by cells. Digestion may

be either intracellular, extracellular, or both, even in animals that possess a digestive tract. Intracellular digestion is considered to be the primitive method, and its presence is usually taken as an indication of the primitiveness of a species. Intracellular digestion is found in all protozoans and sponges and is prevalent in the coelenterates, platyhelminthes, annelids, molluscs, and minor phyla (see Barrington, 1962; Beaton and McHenry, 1964–1966; Denison et al., 1961; Meglitsch, 1967; Yonge, 1937; Hyman, 1940).

In all animal groups excepting the protozoans and sponges, species are found that are partially or wholly extracellular digesters. Microphagous feeders are generally organisms with intracellular digestion. But because an animal is a macrophage is no indication that digestion is extracellular. It may be noted that extracellular digestion permits a differentiation of the digestive tract so that enzyme secretion, foot uptake, food and nutrient storage and transport, chemical digestion, absorption, and the formation of feces can each take place in specialized regions.

Digestion includes both mechanical and chemical activities. Mechanical treatment of foods is especially needed in herbivorous animals that depend on the utilization of cellulose and other plant materials, and in animals which prey on other animals with hard exoskeletons. Cellulose walls, for example, must be crushed before enzymes can reach the plant macromolecules.

Major cellulose users include the amphineuran and gastropod molluscs, which possess radulae—organs with chitinized teeth—that are able to scrape or file off small particles from plants. The radula has a to-and-fro motion controlled by specialized muscles. Herbivorous and many omnivorous mammals possess hard grinding teeth for crushing the cellulose walls of plants. Some insects have cutting and grinding mandibles for disintegrating cellulose and wood. In addition a variety of other mechanisms are found scattered throughout the animal kingdom for destroying plant cellulose walls. Aristotle's lantern of sea urchins is a specialized device for crushing algae and seaweed.

Many animals possess mechanical devices for crushing or mixing food masses. The gastroliths of the crayfish stomach (see also Chapter 11) can be used to grind food; earthworms, some birds, and reptiles have gizzards in which ingested sand grains or even pebbles are used to grind foods; and the gastrointestinal tracts of some animals are equipped with hardened walls in certain regions for food grinding, for example, the chitinized gastric mill of crayfish and similar structures in some molluscs.

In addition, peristaltic action of gastrointestinal wall musculature is used by many animals to grind and mix food materials inside the body of the animal. All of the methods listed above are used in the pretreatment of foods—preparing them for breakdown by enzymatic action—the fundamental step of all digestive processes whether intracellular or extracellular.

15-5. Digestion—Chemical Aspects. The final steps in the degradation of foodstuffs is accomplished by chains of enzymes—nearly all hydrolytic in nature: they include proteinases that break down proteins and peptides; lipases and esterases that act on lipid materials; and carbohydrases or glycosidases that break down poly- and disaccharides.

Many aspects of enzyme action have already been discussed in previous chapters, for example, Chapters 4, 6, and 10. In animals that are discontinuous feeders, hormonal mechanisms usually serve to produce a regular, ordered secretion of appropriate enzymes at the proper time and in the proper amounts within the digestive tract. Most of the material of this section will be based on mammalian studies because other animal groups have barely been touched with respect to specific enzyme digestive processes.

Chemical digestion is initiated in mammals by the saliva secreted by glands of the oral cavity. Three major pairs of glands, under nervous control, are involved in saliva secretion. These are the parotids, sublinguals, and submaxillary glands. Saliva contains α-amylase, which begins the digestion of starches

in some mammals, but the major component of saliva is a mucus secretion that serves to lubricate the passage of food masses through the esophagous during swallowing. Both olfactory and gustatory stimuli act to initiate the secretion of saliva. The sensory fibers involved are stimulated by the intake (and sometimes taste, smell, or sight) of food and initiate action in both sympathetic and parasympathetic fibers of the autonomic nervous system to cause glandular secretion. It may be noted that in many animals actions in the anterior portion of the gastrointestinal tract are initiated by nervous action, whereas hormonal controls dominate in other regions of the tract.

The same sensory fibers that initiate action in the salivary gland system also appear to stimulate activity in cholinergic fibers that innervate the gastric mucosa, resulting in the release of pepsin by the long tubular cells of the fundus of the stomach. Pepsin is an endopeptidase that breaks peptide bonds inside polypeptide chains and that requires an acid pH for optimum activity (about pH 1.8). The proper environment for pepsin activity is achieved through the secretion of HCl by parietal cells of the gastric mucosa. HCl secretion is initiated by the release of the hormone gastrin by the pyloric wall of the stomach. Gastrin is liberated into the circulation and reaches other stomach cells. Gastrin is a mixture of two heptapeptides (gastrin I and II). Gastrin secretion is initiated by mechanical or chemical stimulation of the pyloric wall.

Although pepsin begins the degradation of proteins and polypeptides in the stomach and although some lipase action also occurs there, the major phase of chemical digestion takes place in the small intestine. As far as proteins are concerned, both endopeptidases and exopeptidases act on these molecules. Endopeptidases cleave specific, centrally located peptide bonds within polypeptides and include pepsin, trypsin, and chymotrypsin. Exopeptidases catalyze the removal of terminal amino acid residues from polypeptides and peptides; they include amino peptidases, carboxypeptidases, tripeptidases, and dipeptidases. These are all generic names for families of enzymes. Each family contains a number of different enzymes with differing specificities for the amino acid residues involved in the bond to be hydrolyzed. The endopeptidases are secreted in the inactive zymogen form and must be activated in order to form the active peptidase (see Chapter 4).

Lipids are hydrolyzed by lipases and esterases in the small intestine to yield fatty acids and glycerol. However, fats are emulsified in order to present a large surface area for enzymatic action, and much fat appears to be directly absorbed in the form of fine droplets (less than about 0.5 μ in diameter and with a negative charge). Such droplets pass directly through the intestinal wall and into the circulation. Emulsification is caused by bile salts released from the gall bladder. Bile salts are released due to the action of the hormone cholecystokinin, which is secreted when chyme is present in the duodenum. The presence of fats in the intestine also triggers the release of enterogastrone, a hormone that is released into the blood and that inhibits the gastric secretion of HCl and pepsin.

A variety of enzymes that break down carbohydrates are released by the pancreas and intestinal mucosa. The glycosidases are highly specific enzymes that hydrolyze polysaccharides depending on the nature of the glycosidic bond, the size of the polysaccharide, and the type of ring structure present (furanose or pyranose). As indicated in Chapter 9, there appear to be trisaccharides and disaccharides, as well as some dipeptidases, located within the brush border of the intestal epithelium, and the final degradation of carbohydrate and peptides may be intracellular events combined with the transport systems for glucose and other simple sugars and the amino acids.

Many of the digestive enzymes of the small intestine are secreted in the pancreatic juice, which also contains large amounts of bicarbonate to neutralize the acid chyme entering from the stomach. Intestinal enzymes have optimal pH's at 7 or above and, therefore, require a pH environment different from that of the stomach.

Pancreatic secretion, as well as secretion by the intestinal wall, is under the control of hormones. Pancreozymin is released by the intestinal mucosa upon its stimulation by partially digested materials coming from the stomach. This hormone stimulates the release of enzymes by the pancreas. The hormone secretin is released by cells of the intestinal villa when acids are present in the intestine. Secretin initiates the flow of pancreatic fluid rich in bicarbonates that can neutralize the acid mixture of the stomach. Secretin initiated pancreatic flow is lacking in enzymes. Not until the acid is neutralized does the major release of enzymes begin. Secretin also activates reactions in the liver and the production of needed materials such as bile salts. Figure 15-1 outlines some of the hormonal controls found in the mammalian digestive system. It may be noted that invertebrate digestive systems appear to lack endocrine controls, instead materials in the food known as **secretagogues** appear to provide for the regulation of digestive events.

15-6. Invertebrate Digestive Enzymes. As already mentioned, the study of digestive enzymes and other events of the invertebrate

Figure 15-1 Diagrammatic scheme of hormonal controls over the digestive system.

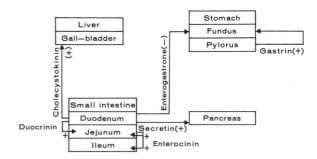

digestive system has lagged behind that of the vertebrate and especially the mammalian system. Enzymes similar to trypsin and chymotrypsin appear to be present in all invertebrates that have been examined; pepsin has been found only in the vertebrate stomach. However, it may be noted that nearly all cells examined contain a series of intracellular enzymes similar to pepsin, trypsin, and chymotrypsin. These are known collectively as cathepsins.

Insects are the only animal group known to possess proteolytic enzymes capable of degrading tough scleroproteins such as collagen, keratin, and fibroin. A familiar example is the clothes moth, which can digest wool because of the presence of a keratinase.

All animals that have been studied possess a wide array of carbohydrases—a situation to be expected in view of the abundance of carbohydrates in the living world. Some insects and molluscs, plus a few insect eating vertebrates have chitinases, which can digest chitin (Jeuniaux, 1961).

Since many animals are able to absorb fine droplets of emulsified lipids without the need for prior enzyme activity, lipases appear to be less abundant throughout the animal kingdom than are proteinases and carbohydrases. Phagocytosis may play a role in the transport of lipids into cells that can then digest these water-insoluble substances.

The lysosome system (Chapter 3) appears to be present in all cells, and intracellular digestion of all biological substances including lipids could occur by the activity of the hydrolytic enzymes of these organelles. Although the primary function of lysosomes may be the destruction of unneeded cellular materials, it is also associated with the digestion of materials brought into the cell by endocytosis.

The molluscs as a group possess many interesting evolutionary modifications of the digestive system. Most molluscs obtain their food by scraping surfaces to obtain algae and other detritus. The radula of the buccal cavity is an instrument well suited for this purpose. The radula is a toothed belt that passes over a strong supporting rod, the odontophore. The radula may be pushed out of the mouth by extrusion of the odontophore caused by the contraction of protractor muscles. When in place against a surface, the radula is moved back and forth over the odontophore by means of muscles. The teeth of the radula scrape away pieces of food from the surface. Worn teeth are constantly replaced by new ones formed at the back of the radula. The new teeth move forward as the front end of the radula wears away.

The radula may be modified in different ways depending on the eating habits of the particular species. Some molluscs bore through oyster or clam shells, and the radula can not only perform this boring operation but can suck away flesh from the prey. Herbivorous snails often have cutting jaws for biting off pieces of vegetation that are then fragmented as they pass over the radula. Some carnivorous snails possess the radula on the tip of an eversible proboscis that can be extruded with great speed, the radula teeth acting as weapons. Cone shells have hollow radula teeth filled with poison secreted by glands. In most molluscan filter feeders the radula is absent. For example, no radula is found in pelecypods even though shipworms and boring clams perform rasping operations. In this case the instrument is a modified shell valve.

The esophagus of molluscs often forms a crop, where food is stored and also where some digestion may occur. In the snail *Helix*, as well as in other gastropods the crop contains cellulase, which initiates the breakdown of plant materials. The esophagus leads into a stomach, which is usually associated with a large pair of digestive glands. These glands secrete enzymes into the stomach through ducts. Since some materials are absorbed by the ducts, intracellular digestion occurs in some species.

The primitive type of molluscan stomach has three regions: a sorting device, a style sac, and a grinding region. However, these regions are modified in various molluscs depending on their eating habits. The sorting region is found in microphagous species only, but the style sac and grinding region are widely distributed.

In what is considered a primitive molluscan stomach, that of the keyhole limpet *Diodora*, salivary glands secrete a mucus that forms a strand in which small particles of food are entrapped. Cilia move the strand into the stomach. In the sorting region, which consists of cilia and cuticular projections, the food is graded into small particles for digestion and large particles that are rejected or sent to the grinding mill. The grinding or crushing mill is a muscular region coated with chitin. In this region the larger particles are fragmented.

Mucus and rejected particles are carried in a deep groove of the stomach wall into the style sac. Cilia in this sac rotate the mucus, and it is compacted by muscular contractions. The material is then passed to the small intestine. Clams and many gastropods have a crystalline style that is a rod composed of a protein matrix onto which amylase is adsorbed. Cilia rotate this style and allow amylase to be mixed with the food materials. Such a style is found in species that have intracellular protein digestion; otherwise, the style would be digested. The crystalline style is typical of ciliary feeders and microphagous herbivores. Intestinal function in molluscs appears to be primarily concerned with condensation of feces. Further information on molluscan digestive systems may be found in Dean (1958); Wilbur and Yonge (1964); Meglitsch (1967).

15-7. Absorption. Food materials, especially in the form of amino acids, monosaccharides, and fatty acids and glycerol, are taken into intestinal cells by the transport processes described in earlier chapters. Although such processes have been best studied in the intestines of certain mammals, it is highly likely that they are similar in other animal groups.

In those animals with a digestive tract, there is usually a region specialized for the absorption of food molecules. In vertebrates this is the small intestine and in particular the brush border regions of intestinal epithelial cells (Chapter 9). In vertebrates water absorption is a function especially of the large intestine. This is also the site of feces formation.

15-8. Symbiosis. Before leaving the topic of digestion, the use of symbionts by various animals deserves mention. Enzymes for degrading cellulose, the most abundant organic material on earth, are not common in animal digestive systems. However, microorganisms usually possess this enzyme, and it appears to have become customary for animals to utilize intestinal flora and their cellulases to degrade this material.

In symbiosis both the symbiont and the host organism derive mutual benefit from the relationship. In mammalian ruminants microorganisms are used to break down plant materials that can then be completely digested and absorbed. Ruminants often possess specialized chambers of the digestive tract that serve as culture chambers for the microorganisms needed to provide cellulase and other digestive enzymes.

Most of the monosaccharides produced by microorganisms are used by themselves, but in the anaerobic environment of a cow's digestive tract, fermentation by microorganisms degrades monosaccharides to various fatty acids that are excreted by the microorganisms and used by the host. The microorganisms are provided a proper environment for growth and are furnished the amino acids they require because of the hydrolysis of protein by the host's proteinases. Microorganisms can also synthesize amino acids from ammonia and urea. The latter compound is released into the reticulorumen (the specialized chamber of the digestive tract where bacteria flourish) by the host instead of being excreted in the urine. Urea is now used in cattle feed because this waste product can be utilized by the microorganisms.

The host is provided with a supply of fatty acids and also with vitamins produced by the symbionts. The host does not need a full complement of glycosidases and is saved the energy of their synthesis. Nearly all animals depend upon their intestinal flora and fauna for a supply of at least certain vitamins.

Exact analysis of the nutritional requirements of an animal in terms of necessary vitamins, amino acids, or fatty acids demands that the contribution of microorganisms be known. Nutritional research, where possible, utilizes germ-free animals—animals completely cleansed of microorganisms and raised in a germ-free environment (Mickelsen, 1962). Studies with such animals reveal generally that there are many essential substances which have been overlooked in particular species because they are ordinarily supplied by microorganisms and are seemingly not needed in the diet.

Symbiosis has been extensively studied in several insect species. When cockroach nymphs from parents fed aureomycin or sulfathiozole are examined, these germ-free specimens are found to be incapable of growth on a natural diet—one adequate for normal nymphs (Brooks and Richards, 1955). In this case microorganisms are intracellular symbionts providing enzymes for the degrading of cellulose and other plant materials. The symbionts do not live free in the digestive tract but are in cells adjacent to the fat body next to the midgut. Intracellular symbionts make germ-free work difficult, because such organisms can be transmitted to the next generation in the eggs.

Intestinal symbionts of most insects appear to function, as in mammalian ruminants, in providing enzymes for the breakdown of cellulose. The crystalline style of some molluscs has been found to contain many spirochaetes. These microorganisms are thought to provide the mollusc with some digestive enzymes.

This discussion of digestion has been a brief one due to limitations of space. In addition to the various references given here, any standard biochemistry textbook may be consulted for further details on the chemical aspects of digestion.

Calorimetry and Metabolism

15-9. Calorimetric Methods. Digestion and animal metabolism are of interest in this chapter primarily from the viewpoint of the contribution of food materials to heat production and temperature regulation. The principles of energy exchanges were discussed in Chapter 4. The living animal was there

Table 15-2 Calorimetric Factors for the Basic Foodstuffs*

FACTORS AND UNITS	PROTEIN (1 gm)	FAT 1 (gm)	CARBOHYDRATE (1 gm)
Gas exchange†			
Oxygen (ml)	966	2,019	829
Carbon dioxide (ml)	782	1,427	829
Respiratory quotient, RQ	0.81	0.71	1.00
Energy			
Total (kcal)	4.4	9.5	4.2
Metabolizable (kcal)	4.1	9.3	4.1
Caloric equivalents:			
oxygen (1 liter)	4.60	4.69	5.05
carbon dioxide (1 liter)	5.68	6.63	5.05
Specific dynamic action	20	9	12

* Values are derived from studies on humans and are from Consolazio et al. (1963).
† Gas exchanges may also be expressed in terms of grams of oxygen or carbon dioxide by use of the following conversion factors:
    1 liter of oxygen = 1.4290 gm.
    1 liter of carbon dioxide = 1.9769 gm.
    1 gram of oxygen = 0.6998 liters.
    1 gram of carbon dioxide = 0.5158 liters.

stated to be an open system exchanging both matter and energy with the environment. By measuring the energy output and the energy input, and taking into account any storage of energy, it can be shown, as expected, that animals obey the laws of energy conservation and transformations that initially were defined for chemical and physical nonliving systems.

Various methods of calorimetry are used to gain an estimate of the energy content of food substances or the energy of metabolism in living systems. To a major extent it is the heats of combustion and oxidation of substances that are of importance because animals obtain their energy through oxidative metabolism. **Direct calorimetry** uses methods that directly measure the energy content of a system in units of caloric energy, that is, calories or kilocalories. **Indirect calorimetry** makes use of methods that determine the value of some factor related to and can be converted into caloric energy units. Such factors in living systems include the oxygen uptake and the carbon dioxide release by animals or cells.

The energy values of foods (as well as of waste products, secretions, and so forth) are often determined by combustion of the substance in a bomb calorimeter. In this direct method a measured quantity of the material is placed in the apparatus, which is then immersed in an insulated container holding a known volume of water. After the combustion of the substance, under conditions of constant volume so that the energy of combustion appears as heat only, the resulting temperature rise of the volume of water (measured by a precision thermometer or by a thermoelectric transducer) is multiplied by the specific heat of water to obtain the number of calories released during the combustion. This energy does not represent the total energy of the substance but only that energy available upon oxidation. The energy values of some food substances are given in Tables 15-2 and 15-3. The significance of the terms used in these tables will be explained in the next section.

Methods of direct calorimetry may be used to determine the energy metabolism of a whole animal, but these methods are difficult in practice, although relatively simple in concept. An animal may be enclosed in an insulated chamber, and the rise in temperature of the medium adjacent to the animal gives a measure of the animal's metabolism when multiplied by the specific heat of the medium.

Such methods give the heat loss by the animal per unit time. Direct calorimetry suffers from the major defect that the behavior and therefore metabolism of an animal enclosed in a chamber may change from the normal. The development of extremely sensitive thermoelectric transducers now makes it possible to measure the instantaneous heat loss from either whole organisms or their parts. In complete estimations of animal metabolism, the amount of food energy consumed (the energy intake) and the amount lost in urine, feces, and sweat must also be determined. Such complete analyses are difficult and tedious. Hardy (1963) discusses various calorimetric methods.

Table 15-3 Caloric Equivalents of RQ Values for Some Metabolites

Substance	Oxygen Needed to Oxidize 1 gm (ml)	Carbon Dioxide Produced (ml)	RQ	Heat (kcal)	RQ (ignoring protein)	Heat (kcal/mole O_2)
Cane sugar	785.5	785.5	1.00	3.96	0.71	106
Dextrose	746.2	746.2	1.00	3.74	0.75	107
Animal fat	2,013.2	1,431.1	0.71	9.50	0.80	109
Protein	956.9	773.8	0.81	4.40	0.85	110
Ethyl alcohol	1,459.5	972.9	0.67	7.08	0.90	111
					0.95	113
					1.00	114

Indirect methods are most often used in the physiology to gain an estimate of energy metabolism. Several relatively simple methods are available for measuring oxygen consumption. The rate of removal of oxygen from the environment by an aquatic animal was classically measured by the Winkler method (see Welsh and Smith, 1967); more frequently today polarographic techniques with oxygen electrodes are used (Davies, 1962; Otis, 1962); or gasometric analysis (see Umbreit et al., 1967).

For terrestrial animals the composition of the air in a closed chamber can be measured, and any changes in the oxygen or carbon dioxide content noted, by determining either volume or pressure changes.

15-10. The Respiratory Quotient. The respiratory quotient or RQ is defined as the ratio of the volume of carbon dioxide expired to the volume of oxygen consumed during the same time period by an animal. The amount of oxygen required and the amount of carbon dioxide produced during the oxidation of food depends on the chemical composition of the material. Although metabolic energy may be measured in terms of oxygen uptake or carbon dioxide production, in order to convert oxygen consumption to caloric units, the relative amounts of carbon and hydrogen oxidized must be known. The amount of oxidative water produced by an animal is extremely difficult to determine because such water, together with water of unknown origin, is released from the animal's body through a variety of different surfaces. But by determining oxygen consumption and carbon dioxide production simultaneously, the amount of water produced by oxidative metabolism can be calculated by difference.

When the RQ has been determined the relative amounts of carbohydrate and fat oxidized can be estimated and the caloric yield of oxygen can be calculated. The general formula of carbohydrates may be given as $(CH_2O)_n$, and during complete oxidation, oxygen is required only for the formation of carbon dioxide. The RQ of carbohydrate

oxidation is 1.00 as exemplified for the oxidation of glucose:

$$C_6H_{12}O_6 + 6O_2 \longrightarrow 6CO_2 + 6H_2O$$

$$RQ = 6 \text{ volumes } CO_2/6 \text{ volumes } O_2 = 1.00$$

The RQ for fats is less than unity because oxygen is needed for the oxidation of both carbon and hydrogen. The oxidation of tripalmitin, for example, gives

$$2C_{51}H_{98}O_6 + 145O_2 \longrightarrow 102CO_2 + 98H_2O$$

$$RQ = 102 \text{ volumes } CO_2/145 \text{ volumes } O_2 = 0.703$$

The RQ for protein is more difficult to determine because some of the oxygen and carbon of the constituent amino acids remain combined with nitrogen and are excreted as nitrogenous wastes in the urine and feces, that is, proteins are not completely oxidized in the body to carbon dioxide and water. By determining the amount of ingested protein and the amount of nitrogenous wastes excreted, it has been found that the amounts of carbon and hydrogen taking part in oxidative reactions need 138.2 grams of oxygen for the production of 152.2 grams of carbon dioxide. When these weights are converted to units of volume (see Table 15-3), the RQ of proteins is

$$\frac{77.52CO_2}{96.7O_2} = 0.802$$

The RQ does not give an exact analysis of the type of food material being oxidized by an animal, in part, because body cells are using various amounts of carbohydrate, fat, and protein simultaneously. Also animal cells can convert one food type into another before oxidation. The RQ is not a good index of the pathways of intermediary metabolism actually in use.

In many metabolic studies, when the experimental animal is in the resting or fasted condition (or both) protein utilization is minimal and RQ's are usually given only for fat and carbohydrate oxidation (Table 15-3). The oxidation of 1 gram of mixed carbohydrate gives about 4.0 kcal of energy; 1 gram of mixed fat gives about 9.5 kcal; and 1 gram of protein yields about 4.5 kcal. When calculating the heat production of a fasting aerobic animal from its oxygen consumption, it is usually assumed that each liter of oxygen consumption produces about 4.7 kcal of energy. After the ingestion of food, there is a marked increase in metabolism, and Rubner in 1885 found that each class of foodstuff when ingested caused a characteristic increase in heat production. This was termed the **specific dynamic action (SDA)** although Klieber (1963) suggested that a better term is **specific dynamic effect (SDE)**. Table 15-3 lists the specific dynamic effects of the three basic foodstuffs in the human. Protein gives the greatest effect. It is not that food acts as a stimulus to metabolism in the sense that hormones may stimulate activity but rather that some organs, especially the liver, must spend extra energy in preparing the products of digestion for entrance into metabolic pathways that lead to the extra heat production. For example, most of the extra energy liberation in mammals is needed for oxidative deamination of amino acids before they enter the TCA cycle.

15-11. Basal and Standard Metabolism. When the gross metabolism of an animal is measured, this is a measure of all of the varied activities taking place. The factors that influence metabolism are many and include muscular movements, recent muscular exertion, strong emotions, noises, discomforts and stresses, disease, extremes of temperature, recent ingestion of food, age, sex, weight, height, climate, quality of diet, estrus, pregnancy, time of day, and time of year (DuBois, 1963).

For any comparison to be made of the metabolic activities of either individuals of a species or of different species, a set of conditions must be established for the measurement of metabolism. These conditions are such that the animal is at ease physiologically, psychologically, and posturally and is in a quiet or resting state. Under these conditions metabolism reaches a minimum stable rate.

For mammals and birds this minimal metabolic state is called the **basal metabolic rate**

(**BMR**) and is determined with the animal in a resting condition and in a fasting state so that digestive processes are not going on which would require energy expenditure. In addition the animal should be under no thermal stress, that is, the metabolic rate is measured with the animal in a normal temperature environment so that energy is not being utilized in temperature regulation. When the animal is at these conditions, the energy metabolism is measured either continuously or periodically until a minimal stable level is reached. In humans the BMR is usually measured 12 to 14 hours after the last meal, with the subject in a reclining position at a comfortable temperature. The term basal is somewhat misleading, it refers not to the lowest possible energy metabolism of an organism but rather to a baseline to which other metabolic rates are referred. Sleep or drugs, for example, may result in metabolic rates much lower than the BMR.

Poikilothermic animals have metabolic rates that are temperature sensitive and therefore have no metabolic state corresponding with the mammalian or avian BMR. For organisms other than mammals and birds, the minimum fasting metabolism at a given temperature is the **standard metabolic rate** (**SMR**). For comparative purposes the SMR is usually measured at some biologically meaningful temperature.

In animals other than humans it is often difficult or impossible to achieve standard conditions for either BMR or SMR measurements. Both direct and indirect calorimetric methods require that the animal be enclosed or at least wear some type of mask so that oxygen consumption can be measured. Many organisms are psychologically upset by such treatment—a fact reflected in their restlessness and higher than normal metabolic rates. Many animals cannot achieve a resting state. For example, the elephant moves its ears, trunk, and tail continuously. In addition, large herbivorous animals such as the elephant must eat and digest food almost continuously because of the inefficiency of their digestive processes, thus a postabsorptive state is impossible to attain. The extremely high metabolism of small mammals also demands that they eat continuously, and here also postabsorptive conditions cannot be obtained. There is, therefore, a variety of factors which make SMR or BMR measurements somewhat difficult to use as a comparative index to metabolic activity.

15-12. Metabolic Rate, Body Weight, and Surface Area. Metabolic rates are expressed in a variety of ways. Typical units are ml O_2/ hour, liter O_2/day, kcal/hour, or kcal/day. For comparative purposes it is customary to express metabolic rate on a body weight basis: ml O_2/gm/hour, and so forth. Such expressions appear reasonable because the heat production of an animal is the result of heat production by all of its cells, and the weight of an animal is, to a first approximation, the sum of the weights of its cells. However, this does not take into account the amount of inert tissue present in an animal. The extracellular material, for example, does not metabolize oxidatively.

It is found that in any species, the larger the individual, the smaller its heat production per unit weight. In a single group such as mammals it was discovered early in the history of metabolic studies that although large mammals produce more heat per unit time than smaller ones, the rate of heat production per unit body weight per unit time is greater in a small animal than in a larger one. Heat production has been related to both body size and surface

area. The relation between heat production (=energy metabolism) and surface area was put into terms of the surface area law, which stated that heat production was correlated with the surface area of an animal.

Bartholomew (1968) suggests that such a relation was attractive because

1. Physical objects of similar geometry have surface areas that are proportional to the two thirds power of their volumes.
2. Oxygen consumption and heat production in mammals varies with approximately the 0.7 power of body weight, a number that is similar to the two thirds power.
3. Heat loss is directly proportional to surface area in mammals.
4. Surface area varies with the two thirds power of weight or volume and the relation between weight and volume of mammals is about 1:1.
5. Core temperatures of most mammals are similar and their heat loss should vary as the two thirds power of their weight.
6. Heat production in homeotherms is equal to heat loss, and therefore, metabolic rate is proportional to body surface because body surface area determines heat loss.

However, the surface law is only an empirical correlation, and energy metabolism has no causal relation to body surface area. Both poikilotherms and homeotherms show the

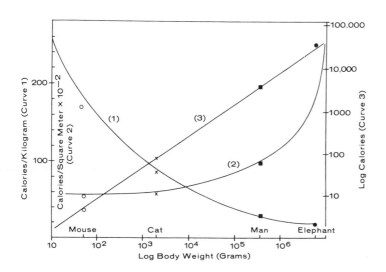

Figure 15-2 (Curve 1) Relation between heat production and log body weight in mammals. (Curve 2) Same data when heat production per square meter of surface area is plotted against log body weight. (Curve 3) Same data but on a log-log plot. [Data of Benedict (1938).]

same proportionality between metabolism and surface area, and if there were a causal relation between the two factors, the factors involved should be different for the two groups.

Figure 15-2 shows the relation between heat production and log body weight in mammals. Figure 15-2 also shows the same data when heat production/square meter of surface area is plotted against log body weight, and a log-log plot of heat production versus body weight. Such relations have also been found for other taxonomic groups such as lizards (Bartholomew and Tucker, 1964); fish (Kayser and Heusner, 1964); and for several invertebrate groups (see Zeuthen, 1953). The data of Figure 15-2 indicate that the metabolic rate is proportional to an exponential function of body weight

$$\log M = \log a + b \log W \qquad (15.1)$$

or

$$M = aW^b \qquad (15.2)$$

where M is the metabolic rate, W is the body weight, a is a proportionality constant, and b is the exponent. Surface area is about equal to $10 \times W^{2/3}$: Davson (1964) discusses these relationships and gives references to the work of Rubner and others which led to them; see also Klieber, 1963. The exponent b can be used to predict metabolic rates from body weight or surface area. The average value of b lies between 0.7 and 0.8 in most animal groups studied. But b is only an empirical factor with no theoretical significance.

I stress again that metabolic rates provide only one measure of an animal's activity and they depend heavily upon the conditions under which they are measured. Even normal metabolic rates vary. For example, metabolism in all living systems examined undergoes daily and seasonal cycles. Circadian rhythms (endogenous nearly 24-hour rhythms) are found for metabolic as well as other physiological activities (see Chapter 20).

Temperature Regulation

15-13. Heat Exchanges. As with any homeostatic regulation, temperature regulation im-

plies that heat loss must equal heat gain by an animal if the temperature is to remain relatively constant. Again, the adverb relatively must modify constant because the temperature of even a homeothermic animal fluctuates normally, for example, because of the circadian rhythms mentioned above.

Heat gain by organisms can arise either from the influx of energy from sunlight or from metabolic activity. Heat losses are occasioned by the physical processes of radiation, conduction, convection, and evaporation of water. Homeothermic animals regulate body temperature at low extremes of the temperature range by increasing metabolic heat production. At higher temperatures they increase heat loss particularly by the evaporation of water. In addition, muscular control over fur or feathers allows the thickness of these insulating layers to be altered according to the environmental temperature. Metabolic controls are generally called **chemical controls** because they involve control of chemical reactions in the organisms. Heat loss mechanisms generally are **physical controls** because they involve physical actions.

The exchange of heat energy between an animal and its environment depends on its nutrition, metabolism, and the physical mechanisms of heat exchange. The environment of animals is complex, the only exceptions being deep ocean waters and perhaps the subterranean habitat. In these environments energy exchanges are dominated by the ambient temperatures. The terrestrial environment is especially complex thermally, and there is no simple way of expressing components of energy fluxes. In perhaps its simplest terms the energy flux, T, can be related to the following:

$$T = R_s \pm R_t \pm C \pm C_a + M - LE \qquad (15.3)$$

where R_s is the solar radiation; R_t is thermal radiation from sources other than the sun; C is energy conduction; C_a is convection through the air; M is metabolic energy; L is the latent heat of evaporation of water; and E is the rate of evaporation of water. T is related to body

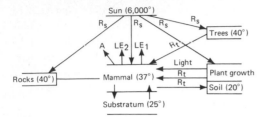

Figure 15-3 Diagrammatic representation of the thermal exchanges between an animal and its environment. R_s, solar radiation; R_t, thermal radiation; LE_1 evaporation from respiratory system; LE_2, evaporation from skin; A, thermal convection to air. Unmarked arrows represent direct conduction of heat.

temperature. Figure 15-3 diagrams these relationships for a terrestrial organism.

The heat content of an object is a measure of the motions of its constituent molecules and these motions determine the nature of physical methods of heat transfer. **Radiation** (electromagnetic) often in the frequency range of infrared may be emitted from the surface of a body at a higher temperature and absorbed by another body at a lower temperature. In the normal comfortable environment, mammalian skin temperature is about 32°C, and air temperature is about 25°C. The temperature differential is great enough so that a large part of the body heat is lost by radiation.

Conduction: When an object is in contact with another object, the molecular motions of the first object can be transferred to the other object by a process of simple bombardment, somewhat analogous to diffusional activity. Such transfer of molecular motions is thermal conduction. Air is a poor thermal conductor, whereas water is a relatively good thermal conductor. Because water also has a high heat capacity (Chapter 2) and requires large amounts of heat to be absorbed to warm it significantly, in hot weather humans often immerse their bodies in water as a means of cooling off.

Thermal convection is actually a special case of heat transfer by conduction. When the surrounding medium is a fluid (such as air or water), it will rise upon increases in temperature, and the layer of fluid next to a warm object when heated will rise and be replaced by another mass of cooler fluid. Heat loss by convection is difficult to measure because of the impossibility of accurately determining the rate at which air is warmed and replaced by cooler air. Such heat losses are usually lumped with conductive heat losses in physiological studies.

As explained in Chapter 2, the evaporation of water requires a large amount of energy, and this mechanism is therefore used to cool the bodies of many animals. Evaporative water losses occur from the skin after water has been secreted, for example, by sweat glands. Evaporative water losses also occur from respiratory surfaces and organs, including the skin. Respiratory water loss and sweating are two major processes used in temperature regulation and are under the control of the homeothermic animal. These mechanisms of cooling the body are available only to terrestrial animals.

The direction in which these various physical factors will transfer heat depends upon a variety of environmental factors. Conduction occurs only from regions of higher to regions of lower temperature. Evaporation of water takes place only if the air is not already saturated with water. Although radiation, convection, and conduction are the major routes for heat loss under normal conditions, when the ambient temperature is equal to the body temperature these methods are not operative. When the body temperature is exceeded by the ambient temperature, heat is transferred to the organism. It is under this condition that the terrestrial animal can still cool itself by water evaporation. The aquatic organism can do nothing to cool itself, except to use behavioral means to locate and move to a cooler environment, if possible.

It is important to note that the details of energy fluxes between an animal and its environment vary according to variations in a large number of factors including the nature of the species, the habitat, the time of day, the season of the year, the amount of cloud cover, and the humidity.

15-14. Chemical Methods of Heat Gain. Homeotherms, as already defined, are animals

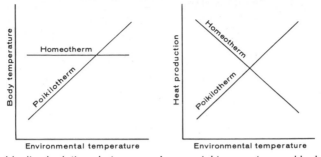

Figure 15-4 Idealized relations between environmental temperature and body temperature (left) and between environmental temperature and heat production (right). As indicated the homeotherm regulates body temperature while the poikilotherm does not. Heat production by a poikilotherm increases with increasing environmental temperature, similar to the manner in which a chemical reaction increases its rate with temperature. However, the homeotherm has the ability to regulate heat production so that with increasing environmental temperatures heat production falls.

that can regulate their body temperature over a relatively wide range of environmental temperatures (Figure 15-4). Figure 15-4 also illustrates that, whereas metabolic rate in poikilothermic animals increases with increasing ambient temperature and decreases with decreasing ambient temperature (similar to normal chemical reactions), the metabolic rate of homeotherms increases with decreasing temperatures and decreases with increasing ambient temperatures. It is this ability to control heat production that chiefly distinguishes true homeotherms from poikilotherms.

Normally changes in heat production are initiated only at lower extremes of the temperature range. At lower temperatures metabolic rate increases, and at higher temperatures metabolic rate decreases (Figure 15-4). Increased heat production in homeotherms arises from two sources. The most conspicuous mechanism by which a homeotherm increases heat production is by an increase in muscular activity. Shivering, for example, represents clonic contractions of skeletal muscle fibers. Muscle tissue is a good heat generator because the mechanical actions of muscular activity are converted into heat energy as are all the chemical reactions underlying all phases of contraction. At low temperatures impulses are sent to muscle fibers causing them to enter into asynchronous contractions. At higher temperatures the muscles are in their normal tonic state. Although actual locomotion by muscular contractions is also a method that can be used to generate heat under cold conditions, this mechanism appears to be used only by larger mammals. In small mammals exercise does not add heat, probably because the locomotory activity upsets the insulative properties of fur, thus permitting a greater heat loss. Shivering is not always a visible phenomenon, and intramuscular electrodes can be used to show that under cold conditions muscle tremors occur which produce heat but which are not visible to the human eye. Activation of muscles can be due to either central or peripheral nervous activity or both.

In mammals it has been found that muscular activity is not the only, or even the principal, method for increasing heat production. All tissues produce heat normally, and it has been found that in mammals the liver is hormonally stimulated to produce a large amount of heat under cold conditions. The liver is an especially active tissue metabolically and can produce a relatively large amount of heat from chemical reactions.

Another potent source of heat is the brown fat of rodents and other mammals. Brown adipose tissue was first found in rodent species and has since been demonstrated in five other mammalian orders including man and other primates. It is especially used in homeothermic animals exposed to cold and by hibernators.

Brown fat is distributed especially around the vital organs of the thorax, along the sympathetic ganglia of the central nervous system, and about the cervical and thoracic segments of the spinal cord. Evidence indicates that increased metabolic activity and thermogenesis by the cells of brown adipose tissue is stimulated by the sympathetic nervous system under cold conditions (Smith, 1964). It has also been shown that mitochondria from cells of brown adipose tissue of cold-acclimated rats (6°C) have about twice the normal oxidative rate as controls maintained at 26°C. Of particular interest is the fact that these mitochondria seem to lack the ability for oxidative-phosphorylation and the formation of ATP (Smith et al., 1966). The mitochondria carry out oxidation reactions, but the P/O ratio is unity or less, nor do coupling agents have any effect on such mitochondria. The electron transport system appears to be modified so that electron transfer and oxidation proceed only for the purpose of thermogenesis, such activities are not coupled to the incorporation of phosphate by ADP.

The location of brown adipose tissue is such that a ready exchange of heat to surrounding important tissues is possible. Brown adipose tissue is highly vascularized. The heat exchange to vital tissues is aided by a countercurrent exchange system. Arterioles and venules are so arranged that heat is carried to and warms neighboring tissues. Blood moving into the brown adipose tissue picks up the heat given off by metabolic reactions and transfers it, again through the blood, to neighboring tissues. Because of the distribution of brown fat, the system ensures that vital tissues, including the central nervous system, are warmed sufficiently for proper activity.

Although homeotherms are animals that regulate body temperature, this does not mean that all parts of the body are at the same temperature. The **core temperature** is that temperature which is regulated and is the temperature of the blood passing through the hypothalamus—the major center for temperature regulation. This is also the temperature

of the blood which passes through the deeper parts of the body, where vital organs are located. The blood is the major heat transfer system in the body and its temperature, in general, determines the temperatures of other body tissues. In many mammals the core temperature, at normal ambient temperatures, is about 37°C, and peripheral temperatures may be about 32°C. Appendages such as limbs, ears, or tails are always at a temperature lower than that of the core. This is also true of temperatures of skin and peripheral regions.

Homeotherms use peripheral cooling to lose excess heat, and the outer body surface is a source of heat loss because it is generally exposed to the environment. Homeotherms must not only supply blood to peripheral regions, even in cold environments, but they must also ensure that too much heat is not lost so that the core temperature falls. Such problems are solved by countercurrent thermal exchange systems that operate on principles similar to those described for kidney function (Chapter 14).

A countercurrent flow system is based on a particular arrangement of circulatory vessels such that veins are in contact with arteries and run parallel to them (Figure 15-5). In the peripheral regions of the body, for example, arterial blood at the higher core temperature flows to a region of lower temperature. Venous blood that has passed through the peripheral

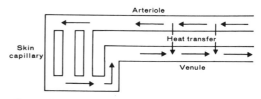

Figure 15-5 Diagrammatic representation of a countercurrent exchange system. Heat carried by arterial blood is transferred to parallel veins before reaching the cooler surfaces of the body. Through this mechanism heat is conserved by the animal. Such countercurrent flow systems have been discussed already for kidney function (Chapter 14) and will be considered again in Chapter 16 on respiration.

region is at a lower temperature than arterial blood because of heat loss to the environment. Because of the contact of vein with artery, the heat of the arterial blood is passed to the returning venous blood. Through this conduction of heat from artery to vein, the blood that reaches the periphery does not lose as much heat to the environment as would arterial blood that had not transferred some heat to the venous blood. Such a system provides for an exchange of heat to core-directed blood but still permits blood to carry essential nutrients and other materials to peripheral cells. The system also ensures that venous blood will not have a temperature low enough to act as a stimulus for the thermogenic machinery.

Thermal countercurrent exchange systems are found in many regions of the mammalian body. They are found, for example, in the circulation of the digestive tract and are needed there so that cold foods or liquids entering the digestive system do not remove too much heat from the lining of the tract. As already mentioned countercurrent systems also operate in the brown adipose tissue. In the flippers and flukes of porpoises, major arteries are completely surrounded by veins, allowing for a maximal heat exchange between arterial and venous bloods. This exchange prevents too much body heat from being lost from the broad surfaces of their flukes and flippers to the often cold marine waters in which these animals live. When it is necessary for heat to be lost,

blood is shunted to other venous pathways that are not in contact with arteries.

Although countercurrent thermal exchange systems are especially prominent in animals that live in colder climates and environments, such circulatory arrangements are found in animals of both the temporate and tropical environments as well.

Figure 15-6 illustrates some of the features of thermogenesis in homeotherms. The upper and lower critical temperatures define a **zone of homeothermy** in which the core temperature can be maintained at its normal level. In the **region of thermal neutrality** the environmental temperatures are such that neither physical nor chemical mechanisms for controlling heat production or heat loss need be employed. The only exception to this definition is that thermal conductance can be changed in this zone, but the energy expenditure for such change is so slight that it cannot be measured against the background of resting metabolism. Changes in the peripheral blood flow, fluffing of fur or feathers, and postural changes all affect thermal conductance but are negligible factors in energy metabolism.

At temperatures below those of the zone of thermal neutrality, chemical mechanisms are primarily the ones used to regulate body temperature. This is the **zone of chemical thermoregulation**. Lowered environmental temperatures in this zone result in increased thermogenesis. However, increased heat production can maintain body temperatures only

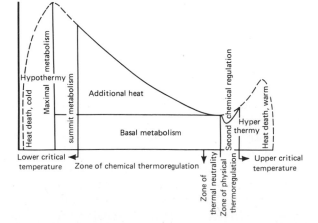

Figure 15-6 Representation of the heat production of a homeotherm in relation to environmental temperature.

within a given range of environmental tempera-ture. At the **lower critical temperature** heat loss becomes greater than can be made up by ther-mogenesis and the body temperature begins to fall and the animal enters the **zone of hypo-thermia**. If such environmental temperatures are maintained, a lower lethal temperature is found at which the animal dies.

At temperatures above the range of thermal neutrality, there is a narrow zone in which the animal successfully fights against overheating by panting or sweating. This is the **zone of physical thermoregulation**. In this zone there is sometimes found a transitory reduction in heat production—the second chemical thermoregu-lation. At the **upper critical temperature** heat production again begins to increase with increasing temperature of the environment, and the body temperature begins to rise as the heat loss mechanisms become unable to cope with the heat gain. This is part of the **zone of hyperthermia**. Finally, at some environmental temperature, the body temperature rises to such a level that death ensues. This is the **upper lethal temperature** (Gelineo, 1964). The upper and lower lethal temperatures depend on the particular animal, its time of exposure to high or low ambient temperatures, the effectiveness of its heat gain or loss mecha-nisms, and other factors.

The range of the various zones depends upon the particular animal studied. Rats, for example, have only a narrow range of thermal neutrality, about 1 to 2°C. Humans have a much broader zone of thermal neutrality, about 15°C [see the several chapters in the *Handbook of Physiology*, Section 4, Vol. 1, 1964 (American Physiological Society, Wash-ington, D.C.) which deal with temperature regulation and adaptation].

15-15. Heat Loss Mechanisms. Heat loss mechanisms are morphological or physiologi-cal devices that alter the conduction rate, con-vection rate, radiation rate, or evaporation rate from body surfaces. Heat loss mechanisms include insulating layers and adjustments in the thickness of such layers, sweat glands, vaso-motor responses that alter the amount of

blood carried to the surface areas, morpholo-gical adaptations of appendages such as ears, arrangements of circulatory vessels for counter-current heat exchanges, and behavioral mechanisms that alter the amount of body surface exposed to the environment.

Insulating layers in the form of fur, feathers, or hair, or an insulating layer of fats under the skin are found in homeotherms. Piloerector muscles, under control of the CNS, can cause fur, hair, or feathers to stand erect, and by thus increasing the depth of the insulating layer and its trapped air, the amount of heat loss is reduced under cold conditions. As pre-viously indicated air is a poor thermal con-ductor. Under warm conditions the relaxation of piloerector muscles allows the layer of insulation to lie flatter, thus decreasing the depth of air close to the skin and permitting a greater heat loss to the environment. In humans the hair has been lost, but the erector muscles are still present, and when the skin is exposed to cold stimulation, goose bumps form as the piloerector muscles contract.

Lipids are poor conductors of heat and a layer of fat under the skin serves as a good heat preserving material. Such insulation is especially prominent in animals that live in colder environments and is familiar as the blubber of arctic whales and similar ani-mals.

Behavioral mechanisms are used to change the amount of body surface exposed to the environment and, therefore, to change the amount of heat lost by conduction, convec-tion, or radiation. For example, in colder temperatures cats and many other mammals are seen to curl up. In this position a minimum body surface from which heat can be lost is presented to the environment. Under warmer conditions such animals may stretch out, thus providing a greater surface for heat loss. These postural mechanisms for controlling the amount of heat lost by the body surface are used by many so-called poikilothermic animals to give at least some degree of body tempera-ture regulation. Other behavioral mechanisms for controlling heat loss include the use of nesting materials, or the cuddling together of several animals. These are mechanisms used in cold conditions.

The evaporation of water, however, is a major route for the loss of heat in homeotherms. Some evaporation and loss of water occurs through **insensible perspiration**. About one third of the water lost by this pathway is from the respiratory surfaces, and the remainder is from the skin and has its origin in the interstitial fluid provided by the capillaries of the dermis. This water diffuses through the skin and is vaporized before it can wet the surface. When the environmental temperature rises, the cutaneous blood supply is increased thus increasing the supply of water for insensible perspiration.

When heat loss through conduction, radiation, convection or insensible perspiration can no longer prevent a rise in body temperature at higher environmental temperatures or during muscular exercise, then the sweat glands are innervated and water for evaporation is supplied by these structures.

Some mammals and all birds lack sweat glands. In these animals (which include, for example, dogs and cats) panting is initiated under warm conditions as a means of increasing evaporative losses from the respiratory tract. Sweating is an efficient mechanism for increasing heat loss, and in animals that possess sweat glands, there is usually no control system for regulating respiratory actions in response to temperature changes.

Sweat contains potassium in higher concentrations than those found in the blood plasma and also contains sodium ions. Some nitrogenous wastes such as urea are also secreted in the sweat. The volume of sweat on hot days or during exercise may be very high—under extreme conditions as much as 1 liter per day may be lost in humans. Normally a few hundred milliliters are lost per day. In the interests of water balance, the water lost through sweating must be recovered by the animal (this is also true of water lost by insensible perspiration or through the respiratory system). In addition, since the secretion of sweat involves the loss of sodium and potassium ions, there must also be salt intake to replace that lost. If, after loss of sweat, only water is taken in by the animal, a state of osmotic shock may result because the water intake further dilutes the salt concentrations of body fluids. To regain osmotic balance after sweating, there must also be salt intake. In animals that use panting as a means of evaporating water for heat loss, only water need be taken in to restore osmotic and water content balance (see also Chapter 14).

Sweat glands are innervated by cholinergic sympathetic neurons. The overall control of sweating is guided by the hypothalamus. This center is stimulated into activity by afferent impulses from heat receptors in the skin, and more importantly by direct information from the temperature of the blood passing through it. Sweating does not begin until some given level of body temperature is reached, and the initiation of sweating also depends on the humidity and temperature of the environment.

The primary control for sweating appears to be the result of measurement of core temperatures by the hypothalamus. However, in man, some sweat glands on the palm of the hand and sole of the foot appear to be controlled primarily by emotions that effect the cerebral cortex. These, however, represent only a few of the approximately 2.5 million sweat glands of the average human. References to sweating and other temperature regulating control systems are found in Benzinger (1964).

Vasomotor activity (vasoconstriction and vasodilation of arterioles) is used to shunt blood to various regions of the body. Vasomotor activity in skin arterioles determines the amount of blood passing through the skin and therefore determines the amount of heat that may be transferred from the blood to the environment. Increased vascular flow to the skin also results in a greater volume of fluid available for evaporation from the skin after diffusion or after secretion by the sweat glands. The regulation of vasomotor activity in blood vessels is under the control of the hypothalamus (see Section 15-16) and occurs by the pathways already described in Chapter 13.

At higher environmental temperatures or during periods of exercise, skin vessels dilate, and the flow of blood in the peripheral regions increases thus permitting a greater heat loss. During cold conditions skin blood vessels constrict and thus cut down the blood flow and heat loss from the skin. Stimuli for such vasomotor activity may occur either from localized warm or cold conditions with sensory impulses being generated by either cold or warm receptors. Or stimuli may be received in the hypothalamus directly because of the temperature of blood passing through it. In the latter case, the hypothalamus acts to regulate the temperature of the whole body, and vasomotor activity is generalized rather than localized.

Before concluding this discussion of mechanisms for temperature regulation, it is worth indicating that modern man can withstand a greater range of environmental temperatures than any other animal because of technological aids such as clothing or the various devices for heating or cooling the environment. It is also of some interest to consider the adaptations that were necessary for primitive man to inhabit the various thermal environments of the world. It appears that man first developed in a region of tropical savannah, where low temperatures were not encountered. Before entering climates in which whole body exposure to cold was encountered, he must have developed the necessary mechanisms for maintaining a high core temperature. To aid in outlining the evolutionary history of man, as well as to increase physiological knowledge, some physiologists have begun studies of the various primitive races to determine how they adapt to the more severe climates (see, for example, Scholander et al., 1958).

Hicks (1964) studied primitive Central Australian aborigines, tribes that live unclothed in a semiarid desert region whose normal maximal and minimal winter temperatures average 21°C and 4°C, respectively. The night environment of Central Australia imposes a severe thermal stress on unclothed humans. Although the natives do sometimes use windbreaks and small fires to decrease the effects of cold, these do not appear to be major factors in survival. Studies have shown that the aborigines, unlike white European or American subjects, do not increase heat production during the cold nights; rather they exhibit a much finer and more localized control over vasomotor activity, and their heat content decreases continuously during the cold night. The aborigines peripheral temperatures drop considerably. On cold nights the skin arterioles constrict at temperatures far above those at which white subjects would exhibit vasomotor action. If fires are used, the vasomotor control of the aborigines is such that arm arterioles close to the fire are dilated allowing heat to radiate into the blood, and the arm arterioles away from the fire may be completely closed. In this way maximum heat absorption and minimum heat loss is obtained.

African bushmen (see Hammel, 1964) now restricted to desert areas show thermal and metabolic responses during nights of moderate cold that are somewhat similar to those exhibited by the Australian natives. In five out of ten subjects, slight shivering and therefore increased heat production were found.

Alacaluf Indians of Tierra del Fuego live in a climate whose average winter temperatures are a maximum of 5.3 and a minimum of −0.3°C. Winds and almost continuous rain (rainfall averages about 275 inches per year) contribute to the uncomfortable climate. This group of Indians begin the night with a very high rate of metabolism, and this rate falls during the night until it reaches a level to which a white European subject's metabolism would have increased. The Alacaluf Indians thus differ from the Australian or African natives and depend upon a high metabolic rate for their survival in the cold. Indian subjects always had a higher metabolic rate than white subjects and also had lower skin temperatures (about 28° compared with 29.5° for white Europeans or Americans).

It may be noted that humans living in extremely cold environments such as the Arctic depend first on clothing and housing to protect them against cold. Generally speaking, for man to have spread over the various thermal environments of the earth required either adaptations in physical mechanisms of heat loss and the ability to withstand lower peripheral temperatures (Australian and African aborigines); in chemical mechanisms of heat production (Alacaluf Indians); or the development of sufficient technology to protect themselves (Esquimos).

15-16. Pathways of Temperature Control—The Hypothalamus.

In the preceding sections it has been mentioned several times that the nervous system and especially the hypothalamus act in controlling the mechanisms of temperature regulation. Although the hypothalamus accounts for less than 5 per cent of the brain's weight, it exercises control over an astounding number of homeostatic functions in mammals. These include temperature regulation, fluid and salt balance, and thirst and drinking mechanisms (see Cross, 1964).

Indications that the hypothalamus was the center involved in thermoregulation first came from brain surgery operations. It was found that cauterizing instruments (used to stop bleeding in smaller blood vessels) when brought near the hypothalamus caused the reactions normally associated with exposure to heat: sweating, cutaneous vasodilation, and a decrease in thermogenesis. By techniques involving the formation of brain lesions and observation of consequent physiological changes and by the use of microelectrodes to stimulate and record potentials in various regions of the brain, it was found that the anterior hypothalamus contained the neurons responsible for reactions to warm temperatures, and the posterior hypothalamus contained neurons responsible for reactions to cold. When lesions were made in the posterior hypothalamus, for example, the mammal failed to eat spontaneously, did not shiver, had no piloerection, and also assumed normal postures; thermogenesis was also inhibited. Thus, destruction of this region basically transformed a homeotherm into a poikilotherm.

Both central and peripheral mechanisms play a role in temperature regulation. The hypothalamus has two roles in thermoregulation. It integrates all of the sensory information available to the nervous system about temperature conditions both internal and external and also acts itself as a sensory mechanism for determining the core temperature. The hypothalamus also functions to integrate homeostatic functioning. Temperature control, for example, cannot lead to such losses of water by sweating or panting that osmoregulation is endangered. The hypothalamus exerts its effects in temperature regulation not only by causing the output of impulses along various motor neurons but also affects the thyroid and adrenal glands whose hormonal secretions can influence cellular metabolism in thermogenesis.

The peripheral mechanisms for temperature regulation include cutaneous and mucus membrane sensory receptors for heat and cold. Such receptors are activated usually in response to local environmental temperature changes, although in whole body exposure the stimulation may be general. Highly localized responses are exemplified by placing the hand in a container of cold water. Cold receptors in the hand send impulses to the CNS, and the hypothalamus effects a localized vasoconstriction in the affected area. Such stimulation does not normally induce changes in thermogenesis, sweating, or panting. The latter types of activity require a more general stimulation of cold receptors.

The integrating activity of the hypothalamus has already been mentioned. The complexity of such activity can be seen in such a simple act as performing exercise—an activity that tends to increase heat production and thus raise body temperature. In this case the hypothalamus must direct vasoconstriction and vasodilation so that the muscles receive an adequate blood supply for oxygen and nourishment, and other parts of the body must have their blood supply lowered because, as stated in Chapter 12, there is not sufficient blood to fill the entire volume of the circulatory vessels. Vasodilation of cutaneous vessels must occur to aid in eliminating excess heat; the rate of respiratory activity must be changed so that sufficient oxygen is supplied to the muscles and other tissues. Posture and balance must be maintained, and activity of the proper skeletal muscles must take place in a proper sequence to ensure this. As the core temperature rises, sweating must be initiated and thermogenesis decreased. The activities to ensure proper temperature regulation must not cause the levels of water or salt content to fall below dangerous levels.

Temperature regulation has been approached from the viewpoint of systems analysis and feedback controls (Hammel, 1968; Hardy, 1963; Milsum, 1966). Such analyses of course depend upon adequate information about the operation of the biological systems and the values of their variables.

Although the hypothalamus must contain some set-point mechanism—a thermostat that determines the temperature at which the body core is to be maintained—there is very little information concerning the nature of this device or its physiological or morphological basis.

It is of interest that the pathological condition of fever appears to result from some change in hypothalamic neurons that increase the temperature setting of the set-point mechanisms. Fever is basically a condition in which a higher than normal temperature is maintained by the animal's hypothalamus. The onset of fever is marked by all of the reactions normally seen when an animal is exposed to cold. There is shivering, piloerection, cutaneous vasoconstriction, and an increase in thermogenesis. The rate of heat loss is decreased, and the rate of heat production rises; thus the core temperature increases. Termination of fever is marked by those reactions normally seen upon exposure to high temperature as the body cools off.

The role of the hypothalamus in temperature regulation is complicated by its neuroendocrine activities (see also Chapter 11). The hypothalamus can stimulate the pituitary and therefore indirectly the glands (thyroid, adrenal cortex, pancreas) concerned with metabolic rate. The thermogenic activity of many mammals is controlled by hormonal actions mediated by the hypothalamus although direct nervous innervation of skeletal muscles and brown fat also play an important role. In response to nervous stimulation brown adi-

pose tissue increases its production of free fatty acids from lipid stores for use in oxidative metabolism (Correll, 1963).

Behavioral and Adaptive Temperature Control

15-17. Introduction. The preceding sections have presented the basic physical and chemical mechanisms used by homeotherms to control body temperatures. But other activities, especially behavioral mechanisms, are used by a variety of organisms including poikilotherms to at least periodically maintain a body temperature higher than that of the environment.

Homeothermic animals may not exhibit continuous endothermy, whereas members of the invertebrates and lower vertebrates, animals generally classed as poikilothermic ectotherms, may possess the ability for periodic endothermic activity. Since physiological, morphological, and behavioral adaptations have allowed both poikilotherms and homeotherms to exploit a variety of environmental niches that otherwise would be closed to them, the operational features of such adaptations will be considered in the following discussion. Behavioral adaptations are especially interesting because they extend the resources of the organism beyond the range of its normal physiological reactions (Precht et al., 1955).

15-18. Hibernation. Many smaller animals undergo periods of hypothermia and dormancy during the colder parts of the year. Some hibernators that have been studied in the laboratory include the European hedgehog *Erinaceus europaes* of the order Insectivora; the golden hamster *Mesocricetus auratus*, the European dormouse *Glis glis*, and the little pocket mouse *Perognathus longimembris*, all of the order Rodentia; dwarf lemurs *Microcebus* and fat-tailed lemurs *Cheirogaleus* among the primates; the American woodchuck *Marmota monax* and the European marmot *Marmota marmota*; a variety of ground squirrels including *Citellus beecheye, C. franklini, C. lateralis, C. parryi,* and *C. tridemlineatus*;

and some Chiroptera such as the little brown bat *Myotis lucifugus.*

Poikilotherms and hibernators both generally retreat into burrows during periods when the thermal environment is unfavorable. A hibernator is basically a homeotherm that acquires poikilothermic characteristics under cold conditions, although a hibernator never completely loses the ability to regulate body temperature. They simply regulate at a much lower temperature during hibernation (Hoffman, 1964; Kayser, 1957; Lyman, 1963).

The patterns of activity found in adaptive hypothermia are variable and complex. In fact, there is some difficulty in defining hibernation. Hibernation may be considered as a periodic regulated activity in which heart rate, metabolic rate, respiration rate, and so forth, are lowered while the core temperature is maintained at a new low level. Hibernation is also characterized by the ability for spontaneous or induced arousal to normal levels in a very short time (Hoffman, 1964). Some animals enter into states of torpor that are not necessarily induced by low temperatures and in which most physiological activity appears normal although body temperature may be several degrees below normal. This is the phenomenon of **estivation**—a summer activity of many mammals also observed in other groups (see Hudson and Bartholemew, 1964).

Hibernation can be induced in the laboratory by a large number of factors including gradual cooling of the animal, inadequate food, dehydration, lack of noise, and isolation. But such inducers are not successful in causing hibernation during the spring breeding season. In the late fall, however, many hibernators enter periods of dormancy and arousal even when laboratory conditions of temperature and photoperiod remain moderate and constant. Hibernation is not a period of prolonged torpor but is a period of alternating states of arousal and torpor.

Hibernation is often preceded by physiological and metabolic changes taking place gradually during the summer. Although this is true of some species, other species require a progressive lowering of the external tempera-

ture to induce hibernation. Dormice and pocket mice, for example, show marked signs of lowered body temperature just before hibernation. Hamsters on the other hand do not enter hibernation until physiological and biochemical preparations are almost complete. Many hibernating species including ground squirrels and marmots undergo a succession of preliminary torpor states before finally entering into hibernation. At each period of torpor the body temperature is lowered by a small amount.

During hibernation metabolic, respiratory, and cardiac rates may fall to anywhere from a tenth to a hundreth of their normal values depending on the species. In arousal the hibernator rapidly activates both heat-conserving and heat-producing mechanisms. The heart rate may quintuple in less than a minute. The stimulus responsible for arousal is not known. Initial arousal includes an increase in respiratory rate and a burst of muscle action potentials and contractions, followed by cardioacceleration. Shivering may become violent as the heart temperature approaches the normal level, but is not evident in the first stages of arousal.

Part of the arousal heat production is the result of muscular activity, but part comes from the stimulation of oxidation in brown adipose tissue. The countercurrent heat exchange system of brown fat blood vessels provides a route by which heat is rapidly passed to vital tissues such as the nervous system including brain and autonomic ganglia and the heart. These are the organs which warm up most rapidly. Once the circulatory and nervous system are warmed up sufficiently to operate normally, the remainder of the body begins to warm and to approach the core temperature normally maintained by the animal. Hibernation from this viewpoint appears to result from changes of the hypothalamic set-point temperature. Arousal is a highly coordinated process in which the central nervous system plays a major role. The endocrine system also plays some part in hibernation and in preparation for hibernation. That this is so is based partly on the fact that photoperiodism is an important factor in inducing hibernation and is also a variable whose cycles are often correlated with corresponding changes in endocrine activity. However, the basic mechanisms used in the nervous and endocrine control of hibernation still remain to be determined.

As indicated above, the process of hibernation and the factors that induce or inhibit it vary markedly from one species to another. Space does not permit a description of how various animals differ in their hibernation activities, but the references listed above will provide such details. Basically hibernation is a mechanism that permits an animal to survive during colder seasons when food is in short supply. At the same time the hibernator during the rest of the year is an active homeotherm and can be active on cooler days when many poikilotherms must be inactive.

15-19. Invertebrate Thermal Control and Adaptation. Invertebrates generally are poikilothermic ectothermic animals, and only a few show any ability to even periodically control their body temperature or their thermal environment. Among terrestrial animals only a few insects, some reptiles, and mammals and birds have been found to be endothermic. However, it should be noted that most studies of thermal regulatory ability are performed on animals under laboratory conditions which are usually far from those of the normal environment. It has been especially found that reptilian and amphibian behavior under normal conditions is quite different from that permitted by limited laboratory environments.

At the molecular level many organisms show adaptation to warm or cold environments, and those animals which normally inhabit warm environments have a greater ability to withstand higher temperatures than those inhabiting lower temperature environments. Poikilotherms living at high temperatures may have proteins that are less thermolabile (see in Prosser, 1967). This is, for example, considered to be the case for organisms that can inhabit hot springs although

undoubtedly other factors also play a role in such adaptation (Brock, 1967).

Some animals that live in environments with a variable temperature appear to possess cells capable of withstanding a wider range of temperatures. But as mentioned previously, why some cells can withstand wider ranges of environmental variables than other cells is not understood at present.

Many animals can enter into states of activity when conditions are adverse and survive until favorable conditions return. This is exemplified by estivation in snails. During warm temperatures or under conditions of water lack, a snail can withdraw into its shell and can secrete a thin film of mucus across the peristome. Such estivating snails may burrow into the ground and reach a microclimate of lower temperature than the air or may climb high on vegetation to benefit from wind cooling (Howes and Wells, 1934; Waterhouse, 1955). Snails may also hibernate by withdrawing into their shells and secreting a thick layer of calcareous material and mucous across the peristome. Many snails survive over winter in this condition. Diapause in insects (see Chapter 11) is a mechanism that anticipates adverse conditions and allows the insect to survive during bad environmental conditions. Slugs are capable of some thermal regulation because these molluscs have a highly permeable skin from which water evaporation during high temperatures can maintain the body temperature at low values.

Nearly all organisms possess sensory mechanisms and reflex behavior patterns that enable them to at least make an attempt to move away from an unfavorable thermal environment, often by burrowing in the ground. Such mechanisms are, of course, unsuccessful in sessile or slow-moving animals, especially when the thermal environment is poor for a great distance or lasts for a long period of time. However, it should be stressed that the various microenvironments, for example, the environment a few inches below the ground or a few inches above it, may be at a quite different temperature than general air temperatures, and many invertebrates seek out these favorable microclimates and thus survive.

Endothermy among invertebrates is perhaps best known by the activities of honey bees (Simpson, 1961). The individual bees of a colony can cluster together and maintain the center of a hive at 35°C during the summer (the periphery of the hive is at a temperature of about 30°C and is less constant). During the winter the whole nest is maintained several degrees above the vital minimum, which is about 10°C. Bees have very high metabolic rates; a resting bee consumes about 1 μl O_2 per minute, which on a body weight basis is comparable to the oxygen consumption of a human performing manual labor. The temperature of the hive is maintained by clustered bees whose combined heat output maintains the temperature at high levels. By fanning its wings, a bee not only produces about 100 times more heat than a resting bee, but also provides air currents that circulate the heat and smooth out temperature variations throughout the nest. A brood nest may have a temperature of 34 to 35°C maintained to about ±0.5°C.

The clustering of bees is a heat conservation mechanism, and bees reflexively cluster upon stimulations involving sight, sound, odors of abdominal scent glands, and temperature. The minimum number of bees that will cluster depends upon the temperature. At lower temperatures a smaller number of bees can be stimulated into clustering than at higher temperatures, where perhaps 50 bees are a minimum number that can be induced to cluster. This thermal control of the nest by bee colonies, which is needed for proper reproduction and for development of young bees, is based on both physiological heat production and behavioral mechanisms associated with clustering and wing fanning. Bees may also cool a hive during warm weather by standing at the hive entrance and fanning their wings to produce a current of air through the hive. Ants and other social insects exhibit similar behaviors in maintaining colonies at proper temperatures.

Winged insects are capable of increasing body temperature by beating their wings without flight. Such activity is found, for example, in locusts. Flight generally represents a high expenditure of metabolic energy, and insects in flight may have body temperatures in the region of the thorax 10 degrees higher than those of other parts of the body (see Church, 1960). Control of temperature in insects may also be achieved by postural reflexes, running reflexes, and similar mechanisms. For example the locust *Schistocerca* sits broadside to the sun at low temperatures and may lie on its side so that the lateral surface is perpendicular to the sun's rays, thus exposing a maximal surface to maximal heating effect. When the body temperature is high enough, the locust turns to face the sun, thus exposing a smaller surface to heating. At high temperatures locusts and other insects may raise their bodies off the ground by extending the legs, thus permitting a flow of air around the body and simultaneously avoiding the usually hotter ground (see, for example, Waloff, 1963; Chapman, 1965).

At temperatures below freezing many insects die because the tissues freeze. However, the temperature of tissue freezing is usually less than zero degrees because of the presence of salts and other solutes in the body fluids and tissues. Also supercooling occurs. Some insects have high concentrations of glycerol in their body fluids, and this prevents freezing at temperatures close to zero (Asahina, 1966).

15-20. Amphibians. This group of vertebrates is generally distinguished by a lack of tolerance for high body temperatures compared with other vertebrates. The ready movement of water across the amphibian skin has been mentioned previously, and terrestrial amphibians lose body water rapidly by evaporation. Although physiologically speaking amphibians are poorly designed to withstand terrestrial life, by the use of behavioral mechanisms and a capacity to acclimatize thermally, they have become an abundant group on land, especially in humid tropics.

Amphibians generally have low metabolic rates and can go for long periods of time without food. This enables them to estimate when temperature becomes too high or when water is in short supply. Some burrowing amphibia can remain in a state of dormancy underground for two years or more.

Amphibians have good capacities for thermal acclimation. In addition to being able to compensate for the effects of temperature on metabolic rate, their locomotor activity can also be adjusted to the temperature of the environment. The critical thermal maximum is the temperature at which locomotor capacity is reduced to the point where the animal cannot escape from adverse thermal conditions that lead to death. The critical thermal maximum differs in different species and also is dependent on the past thermal history of the individual. Acclimation is rapid in most amphibia so that such a mechanism is of advantage even when environmental temperatures change relatively rapidly (over the course of a few weeks, the adjustments considered here are relatively long term adjustments, not changes of an hour or so).

15-21. Fishes. Most aquatic organisms have body temperatures which are about the same as the water in which they live. Any heat produced by a fish is carried by the blood to the gills and rapidly lost to the water. However, several factors can modify this heat loss at least for some period of time. Countercurrent exchange systems function in some fish to aid in the conservation of body heat. Large fish when undergoing sustained activity raise their body temperatures by several degrees due to increased muscular heat production. However, most fish, like other aquatic poikilotherms, must depend upon good thermal sensory reception and escape reflexes to remove them from extremes of the thermal environment. Fish also, like amphibians and reptiles, can acclimate well to changes in temperature. Those fish living in cold arctic waters appear to have an antifreeze substance in their tissues that prevents freezing when temperatures fall below those at which their body fluids would normally freeze (see Fry, 1964).

15-22. Reptiles. Although reptiles were long considered as poikilothermic, ectothermic

animals, such a generality has been shown to be invalid. At least one reptile, the Indian female python *Python molurus bivittatus* regulates its body temperature during the brooding season by thermogenesis (Hutchison et al., 1966). During the period when its eggs are incubated (a period some 30 to 40 days in duration), the python coils about the eggs and can maintain its body temperature about 7°C above that of the environment. Above 33°C the metabolic rates of incubating and nonincubating pythons are the same, but at environmental temperatures below 33°C, the oxygen consumption and heat production of the incubating python increase, whereas those of the nonincubating python decrease. During the period of endothermic activity, the thermogenesis is accompanied by muscular contractions analogous to the shivering of birds and mammals.

In addition, many reptiles, although lacking thermogenic mechanisms for body temperature regulation, do use behavioral mechanisms to great advantage in maintaining body temperatures above those of the environment during cold conditions. Reptiles in the laboratory seem completely poikilothermic because this unnatural environment usually lacks the features that in the wild reptiles use for behavioral thermoregulation. Much work has now been done, especially with lizards, on behavioral thermoregulation (see Schmidt-Nielsen, 1964; Brattstrom, 1965; and various chapters in the *Handbook of Physiology*, Section 4, Vol. 1, American Physiological Society, Washington, D.C.).

Among lizards the Galapagos marine iguana *Amblyrhynchus cristatus* inhabits a unique thermal environment. It lives on barren rocky shores exposed to high temperatures during the day, but it feeds on marine algae in the cool waters of the Peruvian current offshore of the Galapagos Islands. While on land it maintains a body temperature of about 37°C, using behavioral mechanisms with respect to body orientation and posture. In the water it is in an environment 10 to 15°C cooler than its preferred body temperature. It has been shown that the rate of heat loss is only about half the rate at which heat may be gained from the environment, and this difference in rates is an advantage in maintaining a relatively high body temperature in the water (Bartholomew and Lasiewski, 1965).

A slower rate of heat loss means that the iguana can maintain its high body temperature for a longer period of time while in the water; and the higher rate of heat gain means that the iguana will rapidly warm up when it leaves the water and goes on land to be exposed to the sun. The differences in cooling and heating rates appear to depend on circulatory system arrangements and countercurrent heat exchange systems that tend to keep heat in the core of the body. The heart rate, for example, is less during heating than cooling. Thus during cooling less blood is moving to transport heat from the core to the periphery, while during heat gain, a higher heart rate transports blood (and heat) faster from the periphery to the core. Peripheral vasodilation and vasoconstriction might also aid in producing differential rates of heating and cooling under different environmental conditions (these have not yet been demonstrated).

Behavioral mechanisms by which body temperatures are controlled have been examined in a variety of lizards (see, for example, Hammel et al., 1967; McGinnis and Dickson, 1967). The horned lizard *Phrynosoma coronatum*, for example, when heat gain must be minimized, lies with the long axis of the body parallel to the sun's rays and appresses the ribs in order to present as small a surface area as possible to the sunlight. When the lizard must increase heat gain and raise its body temperature, it lies with the body oriented at right angles to the sunlight and spreads the ribs and flattens the dorsal surface so that a maximal amount of heat from the sun can be absorbed by its body. In reptiles generally it appears that the body temperature is proportional to the surface area exposed to direct sunlight.

Lizards and other reptiles burrow at night when desert or mountain temperatures are at their lowest. Some warmth from the day remains underground, and the reptile's body is prevented from freezing. At sunrise the lizard, which may have reached a body temperature as low as 5°C during the night, slowly emerges from its burrow and orients itself to the sunlight so that maximal heat is obtained. Lizards can attain body temperatures that are 30°C above that of the air by proper orientation. Upon emergence from their burrows some lizards orient themselves with the head raised and directed toward the sun so that the brain and nervous systems are quickly warmed. This orientation permits faster responses and activities. Some lizards burrow with the head upward so as to take advantage of any sunlight for warming this region of the body in preference to others.

On sunny days, when air temperatures are below those of the normal body temperature, a lizard will move into the sunlight and orient itself to obtain maximal heat gain. As soon as the body temperature reaches a normal level, the lizard moves into the shade. With proper body orientation the rate of heating can be as high as 1°C per minute.

The desert iguana *Dipsosaurus dorsalis* maintains body temperatures at high levels. Active individuals may have body temperatures exceeding 45°C. These animals can be active during the midday heat of the desert. The body cells and tissues are in some way adapted to very high temperature. Oxygen consumption, heart beat, and other physiological functions continue to temperatures as high as 48°C, the highest known tolerance to temperature found in the vertebrates. Such adaptation is found in the optimal temperatures of enzymes. For example, the optimal temperature for activity of myosin-ATPase varies with the species of lizard. Species that have adapted to high temperatures have higher optimal temperatures for ATPase activity (Licht, 1964).

The skin of reptiles is relatively impermeable to water, and water loss occurs primarily across the bucal mucosa and from the respiratory system. In reptiles the breathing rate usually increases with increases of the environmental temperature. Some large lizards hold their mouths open and breathe deeply at high temperatures. This mechanism for cooling the body is similar to the panting of dogs and other mammals. Some lizards use color changes via chromatophores to alter the amount of heat absorbed or reflected by the skin.

It is evident then that reptiles do have some ability to maintain body temperatures at high levels and that in at least one known case this temperature is much higher than any found in birds or mammals. Thus the term "cold-blooded" has little meaning. Reptiles that live in extreme environments such as the desert are useful animals to study with respect to the ability of poikilotherms to control body temperatures. Most poikilotherms must, however, enter periods of torpor or low activity when temperatures become low. By exploiting the regulation of thermogenesis, homeotherms can be active at temperatures where poikilotherms must be inactive.

15-23. Birds and Mammals. The mechanisms used by birds and mammals in temperature regulation have already been described in previous sections. It should be indicated, however, that homeotherms may often be poikilothermic at birth or hatching (see Figure 1-5). Only in young birds or mammals well insulated at birth by fur or feathers is good temperature regulation found. Most passerine birds are altricial: they are hatched blind, naked, and poikilothermic. Most nonpasserine birds are hatched at a more advanced stage of development. They are precocial and have the capability for temperature regulation. Often in young birds and mammals high body temperatures are maintained only by the protective presence of the parent.

In birds thermogenesis always appears to be accompanied by shivering; this is in contrast to some mammals in which thermogenesis is brought about only by increased metabolism of the liver or brown fat.

It is found that most small mammals, especially those in extreme climates such as the desert, are nocturnal. Perhaps one reason for this is that the noctural habit is of advantage to a small mammal, which has a relatively larger surface area to body weight ratio, that is, a high surface-volume ratio. Against a thermal gradient an animal can lose heat only by water evaporation, but the amount of water to be lost by a small mammal during the day, if body temperature is to be regulated, can amount to 15 per cent of its body weight. This is far too high a water loss for small animals to maintain. By being nocturnal an animal can escape the high daytime temperatures and therefore avoid the necessity for large water losses for cooling.

Small mammals are also generally burrowing animals. Burrowing and the nocturnal habit both aid in temperature control, although their primary significance probably is in protecting against predation. However, such behavior is useful in enabling small mammals to occupy niches in environments such as the desert, which otherwise would be hostile to survival. Large mammals are usually diurnal, and their size is a deterrent against burrowing. Although they must be active during the day, when temperatures are the highest, even in hotter environments their relatively smaller surface-volume ratio minimizes heat loss and gain through the body surface and especially minimizes the need to evaporate large volumes of water for cooling. Also based on its larger bulk and the thermal capacity of water (Chapter 2), a large animal can absorb more heat with less temperature increase. Further, large animals can cover more territory than smaller ones, and thus locomotion as an escape from adverse conditions becomes an important mechanism in temperature control.

Most birds are diurnal and are exposed to the higher temperatures of the daytime hours during periods of activity. Small birds and mammals have very high weight-metabolic rate ratios, and in flying animals especially only limited amounts of energy can be stored in the form of fats. Birds have body temperatures which average 4 to 5°C higher than those of mammals. Under many environmental conditions they experience no difficulty in losing heat. When heat must be lost by other than passive physical mechanisms such as radiation or conduction, birds use panting and evaporation of water. None possesses sweat glands, and insensible water loss is minimal because of the insulating cover of feathers. Panting in birds may, however, actually raise body temperature, because of the high metabolic rate that accompanies the muscular activity. Some birds in which the floor of the mouth and the anterior part of the esophagus are thin and highly vascularized have developed gular panting. These areas can be fluttered either by self-contained muscles or by other body muscles. In this way water evaporation is increased with little energy expenditure. Such a mechanism is found in owls, herons, cormorants, pelicans, and doves.

Because of the high surface area to weight ratio and the high metabolic rate to weight ratio, small birds and mammals are extremely vulnerable to starvation. As already mentioned, they can store little energy in the form of fat. Some hummingbirds during flight have metabolic rates as high as 43 ml O_2 per gram weight per hour, although during inactivity the rate can fall as low as 0.4 ml O_2 per gram weight per hour (Lasiewski, 1963; Morrison, et al., 1962). In many small birds and mammals, for example, in bats, there occurs a daily period of torpor in which energy is conserved and body temperatures are lowered. Such torpor is possible because the body cells of these animals can survive slightly lower temperatures than those normally associated with birds and mammals.

In addition to thicker layers of insulating materials, other morphological adaptations are found in animals that inhabit colder environments. For example, the ears of rabbits in the arctic are shorter than those of the same species in warmer regions. The shorter ear provides less surface area for heat loss to the environment and thus conserves body heat and maintains the body temperature of the arctic animal.

Camels that live in the hot desert have short hair along the flanks in the autumn; during the summer a coat of shorter smoother hair is developed. However, camels that live in cooler climates have coats of very long hair plus short fine body hair. This is one example of morphological adaptations to the thermal environment. Camels have adapted to the desert environment through a combination of many modified functional abilities (see also Chapter 14). Camels store heat during the day and can survive high body temperatures. When dehydrated, their metabolism is lowered.

Various forms of behavior play an important role in temperature regulation of all mammals, even those of temperate climates (see, for example, Baldwin and Ingram, 1967). As pointed out by Hensel and Hildebrandt (1964) even in cases where physiological or morphological adaptations were thought responsible for survival in extreme climates, it often turns out that such survival is possible mainly because of behavioral responses. For example, the survival of Eskimos consists mainly in avoiding the cold.

References and Readings

Asahina, E. (1966). "Freezing and frost resistance in insects." In: **Cryobiology** (H.T. Meryman, ed.) New York: Academic Press, Inc.

Baldwin, B. A. and D. L. Ingram (1967). "Behavioral thermoregulation in pigs." *Physiol. Behav.* **2:** 15–22.

Barrington, E. J. W. (1962). "Digestive enzymes." *Adv. Comp. Physiol. Biochem.* **1:** 1–65.

Bartholomew, G. A. (1968). "Energy metabolism." In: **Animal Function: Principles and Adaptations** (M. S. Gordon, ed.) Chap. 3, pp. 48–65; Chap. 8, pp. 290–354. New York: The Macmillan Company.

Bartholomew, G. A. and R. C. Lasiewski (1965). "Heating and cooling rates, heart rate and simulated diving in the Galapagos marine iguana." *Comp. Biochem. Physiol.* **16:** 573–582.

Bartholomew, G. A. and V. A. Tucker (1963). "Control of changes in body temperature, metabolism, and circulation by the agamid lizard, *Amphibolurus barbatus.*" *Physiol. Zool.* **36:** 199–218.

Beaton, G. H. and E. W. McHenry, eds. (1964–1966). **Nutrition: A Comprehensive**

Treatise. 3 volumes. New York: Academic Press, Inc.

Bělehrádek, J. (1930). "Temperature coefficients in biology." *Biol. Rev.* **5**: 30–58.

Benedict, F. G. (1938). "Vital energetics." *Carneg. Inst., Wash.,* Rept. 503. 215 pp.

Benzinger, T. H. (1964). "The thermal homeostasis of man." *Symp. Soc. Exp. Biol.* **18**: 49–80.

Brattstrom, B. H. (1965). "Body temperature of reptiles." *Am. Midland Naturalist* **73**: 376–422.

Brock, T. D. (1967). "Life at high temperatures." *Science* **158**: 1012–1019.

Brody, S. (1945). **Bioenergetics and Growth.** New York: Reinhold Publishing Corporation. 1023 pp.

Brooks, M. W. and A. G. Richards (1955). "Intracellular symbiosis and production of aposymbiotic cockroaches." *Biol. Bull.* **109**: 22–39.

Chapman, R. F. (1965). "The behavior of nymphs of *Schistocerca gregaria* (Forskål) (Orthoptera; Acridiae) in a temperature gradient with special reference to temperature preference." *Behavior* **24**: 283–317.

Chew, R. M. (1961). "Water metabolism of desert-inhabiting vertebrates." *Biol. Rev.* **36**: 1–31.

Church, N. S. (1960). "Heat loss and the body temperatures of flying insects." *J. Exp. Biol.* **37**: 171–185; 186–212.

Consolazio, C. F., R. Johnson, and L. Pecora (1963). **Physiological Measurements of Metabolic Functions in Man.** New York: McGraw-Hill Book Company. 505 pp.

Correll, J. W. (1963). "Adipose tissue: ability to respond to nerve stimulation in vitro." *Science* **140**: 387–388.

Crawford, E. D. and K. Schmidt-Nielsen (1967). "Temperature regulation and evaporative cooling in the ostrich." *Am. J. Physiol.* **212**: 347–353.

Cross, B. A. (1964). "The hypothalamus in mammalian homeostasis." *Symp. Soc. Exp. Biol.* **18**: 157–193.

Davies, P. W. (1962). "The oxygen cathode." In: **Physical Techniques in Biological Re**search (W. L. Nastuk, ed.) Vol. 4, pp. 137–179. New York: Academic Press, Inc.

Davis, D. D. (1961). "Origin of the mammalian feeding mechanism." *Am. Zool.* **1**: 229–234.

Davson, H. (1964). **A Textbook of General Physiology,** 3rd ed. Boston: Little, Brown and Company. 1166 pp.

Dawson, W. (1960). "Physiological responses to temperature in the lizard *Eumeces obsoletus.*" *Physiol. Zool.* **33**: 87–103.

Dean, D. (1958). "New property of the crystalline style of *Crassostrea virginica.*" *Science* **128**: 837.

Denison, R. H., S. Springer, B. Schaeffer, D. E. Rosen, E. C. Olson, C. Gans, and D. D. Davis (1961). "Evolution and dynamics of vertebrate feeding mechanisms." *Am. Zool.* **1**: 177–234.

DuBois, E. F. (1963). **Basal Metabolism in Health and Disease,** 3rd ed. Philadelphia: Lea & Febiger.

Edholme, O. G. and H. E. Lewis (1964). "Terrestrial animals in cold: man in polar regions." In: **Handbook of Physiology** (W. B. Dill, ed.) Section 4, Vol. 1, pp. 435–445. Washington, D.C.: American Physiological Society.

von Euler, C. (1961). "Physiology and pharmacology of temperature regulation." *Pharmacol. Rev.* **13**: 361–398.

Fry, F. E. J. (1964). "Animals in aquatic environments: Fishes." In: **Handbook of Physiology** (W. B. Dill, ed.) Section 4, Vol. 1, pp. 715–728. Washington, D.C.: American Physiological Society.

Gelineo, S. (1964). "Organ systems in adaptation: the temperature regulating system." In: **Handbook of Physiology** (W. B. Dill, ed.) Section 4, Vol. 1, pp. 259–282. Washington, D.C.: American Physiological Society.

Hammel, H. T. (1964). "Terrestrial animals in cold: Recent studies of primitive man." In: **Handbook of Physiology** (D. B. Dill, ed.) Section 4, Vol. 1, pp. 413–434. Washington, D.C.: American Physiological Society.

Hammel, H. T. (1968). "Regulation of internal body temperature." *Ann. Rev. Physiol.* **30**: 641–710.

Hammel, H. T., F. T. Caldwell, and R. M. Abrams (1967). "Regulation of body temperature in the blue-tongued lizard." *Science* **156**: 1260–1262.

Hardy, J. D., ed. (1963). **Temperature—Its Measurement and Control.** 3 volumes. New York: Reinhold Publishing Corporation.

Hemmingsen, A. M. (1960). "Energy metabolism as related to body size and respiratory surfaces, and its evolution." *Rep. Steno. Hosp., Copenhagen* **9**: 1–110.

Hensel, H. and G. Hildebrandt (1964). "Organ systems in adaptation: the nervous system." In: **Handbook of Physiology** (D. B. Dill, ed.) Section 4, Vol. 1, pp. 55–72. Washington, D.C.: American Physiological Society.

Hicks, C. S. (1964). "Terrestrial animals in cold: Exploratory studies of primitive men." In: **Handbook of Physiology** (D. B. Dill, ed.) Section 4, Vol. 1, pp. 405–412. Washington, D.C.: American Physiological Society.

Hoffman, R. A. (1964). "Terrestrial animals in cold: hibernators." In: **Handbook of Physiology** (D. B. Dill, ed.) Section 4, Vol. 1, pp. 379–403. Washington, D.C.: American Physiological Society.

House, H. L. (1962). "Insect nutrition." *Ann. Rev. Ent.* **6**: 13–26.

Howes, N. H. and G. P. Wells (1934). "The water relations of snails and slugs." *J. Exp. Biol.* **11**: 327–343; 344–351.

Hudson, J. W. and G. A. Bartholomew (1964). "Terrestrial animals in dry heat: estivators." In: **Handbook of Physiology** (D. B. Dill, ed.) Section 4, Vol. 1, pp. 541–550. Washington, D.C.: American Physiological Society.

Hutchison, V. H., H. G. Dowling, and A. Vinegar (1966). "Thermoregulation in a brooding female Indian python, *Python molurus bivittatus.*" *Science* **151**: 694–696.

Hutner, S. H. and L. Provasoli (1965). "Comparative physiology: Nutrition." *Ann. Rev. Physiol.* **27**: 19–50.

Hyman, L. (1940). **The Invertebrates,** Vol. 1. New York: McGraw-Hill Book Company, Inc.

Jeuniaux, C. (1961). "Chitinase: an addition to the list of hydrolases in the digestive tract of vertebrates." *Nature* **192**: 131–136.

Jørgensen, C. B. (1966). **Biology of Suspension Feeding.** Long Island City, N.Y.: Pergamon Press, Inc.

Kayser, C. (1957). "Le sommeil hivernal, problème de thermorégulation." *Rev. Can. Biol.* **16**: 303–389.

Kayser, C. and A. A. Heusner (1967). "Le rythme nychthéméral de la dépense d'énergie. Étude de physiologie comparée." *J. Physiol.* (Paris) **59**: 3–116.

Kleiber, M. (1961). **The Fire of Life.** New York: John Wiley & Sons, Inc. 454 pp.

Lasiewski, R. C. (1963). "Oxygen consumption of torpid, resting, active, and flying hummingbirds." *Physiol. Zool.* **36**: 122–140.

Lenhoff, H. M. (1961). "Activation of the feeding reflex in *Hydra littoralis.*" *J. Gen. Physiol.* **45**: 331–344.

Licht, P. (1964). "The temperature dependence of myosin adenosine triphosphatase and alkaline phosphatase in lizards." *Comp. Biochem. Physiol.* **12**: 331–340.

Licht, P. (1967). "Thermal adaptations in the enzymes of lizards." In: **Molecular Mechanisms of Temperature Adaptation** (C. L. Prosser, ed.) pp. 131–146. Washington, D.C.: American Association for the Advancement of Science.

Lyman, C. P. (1963). "Hibernation in birds and mammals." *Am. Sci.* **51**: 127–138.

McGinnis, S. M. and L. L. Dickson (1967). "Thermoregulation in the desert iguana *Dipsosaurus dorsalis.*" *Science* **156**: 1757–1759.

Meglitsch, P. A. (1967). **Invertebrate Zoology.** New York: Oxford University Press. 961 pp.

Mickelsen, O. (1962). "Nutrition—Germfree animal research." *Ann. Rev. Biochem.* **31**: 515–548.

Milsum, J. H. (1966). **Biological Control Systems Analysis.** New York: McGraw-Hill Book Company. 466 pp.

Morton, J. E. (1960). "The function of the gut in ciliary feeders." *Biol. Rev.* **35**: 92–140.

Morrison, P. (1962). "Modification of body temperature by activity in Brazilian hummingbirds." *Condor* **64**: 315–323.

Nicol, J. A. C. (1960). **The Biology of Marine**

Animals. London: Pitman Publishing Company, Ltd. 707 pp.

Otis, A. B. (1962). "Some physical techniques used in the study of external respiration." In: **Physical Techniques in Biological Research** (W. L. Nastuk, ed.) Vol. 4, pp. 181–214. New York: Academic Press, Inc.

Precht, H., J. Christophersen, and H. Hensel (1955). **Temperatur und Leben.** Berlin: Springer-Verlag. 514 pp.

Prosser, C. L., ed. (1967). **Molecular Mechanisms of Temperature Adaptation.** Washington, D.C.: American Association for the Advancement of Science. 390 pp.

Rose, W. C. (1949). "Amino acid requirements of man." *Fed. Proc.* **8:** 546–552.

Schmidt-Nielsen, K. (1964). "Terrestrial animals in dry heat: desert rodents." In: **Handbook of Physiology** (D. B. Dill, ed.) Section 4, Vol. 1, pp. 493–507. Washington, D.C.: American Physiological Society.

Schoenheimer, R. (1946). **The Dynamic State of Body Constituents.** Cambridge, Mass.: Harvard University Press.

Scholander, P. F., H. T. Hammel, K. L. Andersen, and Y. Loryning (1958). "Metabolic acclimation to cold in man." *J. Appl. Physiol.* **12:** 1–8.

Simpson, J. (1961). "Nest climate regulation in honey bee colonies." *Science* **133:** 1327–1333.

Smith, R. E. (1964). "Thermoregulatory and adaptive behavior of brown adipose tissue." *Science* **146:** 1686–1689.

Smith, R. E., J. C. Roberts, and K. J. Hittleman (1966). "Nonphosphorylating respiration of mitochondria from brown adipose tissue of rats." *Science* **154:** 653–654.

Umbreit, W. W., R. H. Burris, and J. F. Stauffer (1964). **Manometric Techniques,** 4th ed. Minneapolis: Burgess Publishing Company. 305 pp.

Ushakov, B. (1965). "Thermostability of cells and proteins of poikilotherms and its significance in speciation." *Physiol. Rev.* **44:** 518–560.

Waldbauer, G. P. (1968). "The consumption and utilization of food by insects." *Adv. Insect Physiol.* **5:** 229–298.

Waloff, Z. (1963). "Field studies on solitary and transient desert locusts in the Red Sea area." *Antilocust Bull.* **40:** 1–92.

Waterhouse, F. L. (1955). "Microclimatological profiles in grass cover in relation to biological problems." *Quart. J. Roy. Meteorol. Soc.* **81:** 63–71.

Welsh, J. H. and R. I. Smith (1967). **Laboratory Exercises in Invertebrate Physiology,** 2nd ed. Minneapolis: Burgess Publishing Company.

Wilbur, K. M. (1964). "Shell formation and regeneration." In: **Physiology of Mollusca** (K. M. Wilbur and C. M. Yonge, eds.) Vol. 1, pp. 243–282. New York: Academic Press, Inc.

Wilbur, K. M. and C. M. Yonge, eds. (1964). **Physiology of Mollusca,** 2 volumes. New York: Academic Press, Inc.

Yonge, C. M. (1928). "Feeding mechanisms in the invertebrates." *Biol. Rev.* **3:** 21–76.

Yonge, C. M. (1937). "Evolution and adaptation in the digestive system of the metazoa." *Biol. Rev.* **12:** 87–115.

Zeuthen, E. (1953). "Oxygen uptake as related to body size in organisms." *Quart. Rev. Biol.* **28:** 1–12.

Gases

16-1. Introduction. It is the need for oxygen in the final steps of cellular oxidation-reduction reactions of the cytochrome system that makes oxygen such an essential material for all animals. Carbon dioxide is a gaseous byproduct of the oxidation of protein, carbohydrate, and fats (see Chapter 4). Oxygen consumption and carbon dioxide production are nearly inseparable activities, and together they constitute animal respiration.

Animal respiration is conveniently divided into three phases: (1) **external respiration**—the mechanisms by which an animal obtains oxygen from the external environment and the mechanisms by which carbon dioxide is eliminated to the external environment; (2) **gas transport**—the mechanisms used to distribute oxygen to all of the body cells of an animal after it has been extracted from the external environment by the respiratory organs and also the mechanisms by which carbon dioxide is transported from body cells to sites of elimination; (3) **internal respiration**—the metabolic reactions of oxidation-reduction in which oxygen is consumed and carbon dioxide (and energy) are produced. In this chapter we are concerned only with the first two phases (internal respiration was dealt with in Chapter 4).

To understand animal respiration, we must consider not only the nature of respiratory organs but also the mechanisms used to control respiration and the nature of respiratory system adaptations to different environments. As with other homeostatic functions, respiration in the animal must be integrated with and coordinated to all of other regulatory activities. Gas transport mechanisms, in addition to providing a route by which oxygen and carbon dioxide may be transported, also in many animals serve as part of the pH regulating mechanism.

As is true of other homeostatic systems, the respiratory organs and their controls have received the most attention in the vertebrates and especially in mammals. Thus, much of the detail of this chapter will be based on respiration in these groups.

Chapter 16

Animal Respiration

16-2. Oxygen Diffusion and Solubility. Oxygen diffuses only very slowly through aqueous media, and diffusion alone is an unsatisfactory mechanism for removing oxygen from the external environment and supplying it to all body cells. Only if the organism is smaller than about 1 mm in diameter, is diffusion adequate to supply its oxygen requirements (see Chapter 6). This does not mean that diffusion of respiratory gases is not an important part of respiratory activity. Diffusion is the basic mechanism by which oxygen or carbon dioxide cross respiratory membranes or move from body fluids into cells; however, diffusion must be aided by other mechanisms that ensure a constant supply of oxygen for the animal and removal of carbon dioxide. In all larger organisms there is a need for specialized vascular surfaces for extracting oxygen from the environment and mechanisms for moving

Table 16-1   Oxygen Consumption of Some Animals*

Organism	Weight	Temp. (°C)	Oxygen Consumption (ml O_2/g wet weight/hour)
Protozoa			
Paramecium	0.001 mg		0.5
Tetrahymena			2.8
Nematodes			
Rotylenchus			0.66
Ascaris			0.50
Annelids			
Arenicola			0.03
Molluscs			
Mytilus	25 g		0.022
Helicella	170 g	23	0.186
Pecten		20	0.07
Crustaceans			
Astacus	32 g		0.047
Homarus		15	0.50
Insects			
Vanessa			0.4–0.7 (rest)
			100 (flying)
Tenebrio (larva)		12	0.182
Vertebrates (poikilothermic)			
Cyprinus (carp)	200 g		0.10
Esox (pike)	200 g		0.35
Rana	35 g	16	0.056
rattlesnake	2 kg	16	0.07
Vertebrates (homeothermic)			
mouse	20 g	37	2.5 (rest)
			20 (running)
man	70 kg	37	0.2 (rest)
			4.0 (max. work)

* Data from Prosser and Brown (1961) and Krogh (1959).

the medium so that the greatest possible oxygen supply is available.

The amount of oxygen required by an animal depends on its size (as indicated in Chapter 15, smaller animals have a higher metabolic rate per unit of body weight and therefore usually require more oxygen on a unit weight basis than do larger animals). However, the activity of an animal also determines its oxygen needs. Table 16-1 presents some data on oxygen consumption in different animals. In so far as possible the data of Table 16-1 are for animals in the basal or standard state.

Oxygen diffusion is relatively slow in water as compared with its diffusion in air. The diffusion coefficient at 20°C for oxygen in air is about 11; in water the diffusion coefficient is about 0.00003; in a tissue such as muscle the diffusion coefficient is about 0.00001.

The solubility of oxygen in water is much less than its concentration in the atmosphere. The atmosphere contains about twenty times as much oxygen as can be dissolved in a given volume of water. This means that, as compared with an air-breather, an aquatic animal must pass a much greater volume of the medium over its respiratory surfaces in order to obtain a given volume of oxygen. In addition, the density and viscosity of aqueous media are greater than those of air, and thus more work must be done to move the aqueous medium in order to obtain oxygen.

The carbon dioxide content of natural water is very low, often zero; and because carbon dioxide is very soluble in water and has a much higher rate of diffusion than oxygen, the concentration gradient of carbon dioxide between the animal and its environment is favorable for the diffusion of carbon dioxide from the

Table 16-2 Absorption Coefficients of Some Gases in Water*

| TEMP. (°C) | ABSORPTION COEFFICIENT† | | | TEMP. (°C) | ABSORPTION COEFFICIENT† | | |
	OXYGEN	CARBON DIOXIDE	NITROGEN		OXYGEN	CARBON DIOXIDE	NITROGEN
0	0.0489	1.713	0.0235	17	0.0328	0.956	0.0163
1	0.0476	1.646	0.0230	18	0.0322	0.928	0.0160
2	0.0463	1.584	0.0224	19	0.0316	0.902	0.0157
3	0.0451	1.527	0.0219	20	0.0310	0.878	0.0155
4	0.0440	1.473	0.0214	21	0.0304	0.854	0.0152
5	0.0429	1.424	0.0209	22	0.0299	0.829	0.0150
6	0.0418	1 377	0.0204	23	0.0293	0.804	0.0148
7	0.0408	1.331	0.0199	24	0.0288	0.718	0.0145
8	0.0398	1.282	0.0195	25	0.0283	0.759	0.0143
9	0.0389	1.237	0.0190	26	0.0278	0.738	0.0141
10	0.0380	1.194	0.0186	27	0.0274	0.718	0.0139
11	0.0372	1.154	0.0182	28	0.0269	0.699	0.0138
12	0.0364	1.117	0.0179	29	0.0265	0.682	0.0136
13	0.0356	1.083	0.0175	30	0.0261	0.655	0.0134
14	0.0349	1.050	0.0172	35	0.0244	0.592	0.0126
15	0.0342	1.019	0.0168	40	0.0231	0.530	0.0118
16	0.0335	0.985	0.0165	50	0.0209	0.436	0.0109

* Data from *Handbook of Chemistry and Physics*, 40th ed. Chemical Rubber Publishing Co. (1958–1959).
† The absorption coefficient is the volume of gas (when reduced to NTP) absorbed by one volume of water when the pressure of the gas itself is 760 mm Hg.

animal. Because the terrestrial atmosphere also contains only a very low carbon dioxide concentration, about 0.04 per cent, the elimination of carbon dioxide from the animal is generally not such a problem as the obtaining of oxygen. Carbon dioxide in water is converted almost immediately to bicarbonate, and this buffering action serves to maintain a higher pH of aqueous media compared with the pH that would result from the presence of the acidic carbon dioxide itself. The conversion of carbon dioxide to bicarbonate also serves to lower the carbon dioxide concentration of aqueous environments, thus maintaining a favorable concentration gradient for diffusion from the animal.

The oxygen content of water varies according to both temperature and salt concentration. A 2.9 per cent NaCl solution can contain maximally 40 ml O_2 per liter when equilibrated with oxygen at 0°C and at 1 atmosphere pressure; pure water under these same conditions can hold 50 ml O_2 per liter.

The higher the temperature, the less the amount of oxygen (or other gas) a given volume of water can contain. This means that at higher temperatures, the amount of oxygen available to aquatic animals decreases. Tables 16-2 and 16-3 illustrate the relations between gas concentrations and the temperature and salinity. Concentrations are expressed in terms of the **absorption coefficient**—the amount of gas which could dissolve in a given volume of water when the pressure of the gas is 1 atm. The volumes are given in terms of normal temperature (0°C) and pressure (1 atm = 760 mm Hg), although the gas goes into solution at temperatures other than 0°C. The volume of gas that can dissolve decreases in proportion to decreases in its pressure. This is true regardless of the presence of other gases.

Deep bodies of water may have low oxygen concentrations because oxygen is only slowly distributed by diffusion. Oxygen diffuses from the atmosphere into the surface waters and then can be distributed to deeper waters

Table 16-3   Solubilities of Gases in Various Salt Solutions*

SOLUTION	OXYGEN	CARBON DIOXIDE	NITROGEN
NaCl solutions			
0 g NaCl/kg solution	0.049^0†	1.713^0	0.0235^0
	0.0364^{12}	1.117^{12}	0.0179^{12}
	0.0288^{24}	0.718^{24}	0.0145^{24}
28.91 g NaCl/kg solution	0.0401^0	1.489^0	0.0152^0
	0.0306^{12}	0.980^{12}	0.0116^{12}
	0.0248^{24}	0.695^{24}	0.0093^{24}
36.11 g NaCl/kg solution	0.0380^0	1.439^0	0.0142^0
	0.0291^{12}	0.980^{12}	0.0110^{12}
	0.0236^{24}	0.677^{24}	0.0089^{24}
Ringer's solution			
	0.0480^0		
	0.0340^{10}		
	0.0310^{20}		
	0.0260^{30}		
Sea water (34.96 salinity)	6.89 ml O_2 per liter (= 9.8 mg per liter)		

* Data from: Umbreit et al. (1964); Prosser and Brown (1961); Sverdrup et al. (1942).
  Gas solubilities except for sea water are given as the absorption coefficient.
† Superscripts indicate temperature.

effectively only by circulation of the water. In swamps or below the thermocline of lakes, circulation is poor and oxygen concentrations are low. The situation is aggravated by the presence of any oxygen consuming bottom dwellers or by oxidative processes involving bottom detritus. Bodies of water with poor circulation, pollution, and the like usually become depleted of oxygen. Often algal growth appears. Algae can live anaerobically but can also utilize any oxygen present and thus further deplete the oxygen supply needed for animal life, Heavy algal growth is one sign of pollution in bodies of water.

Various phases of respiration and of the nature of gases and gaseous environments are discussed in the *Handbook of Physiology*, Section 3, "Respiration" and in Umbreit et al. (1964). Before proceeding to a consideration of respiratory organs and other aspects of animal respiration, it is convenient to briefly define some of the terms used in gas studies.

16-3. Gas Volumes and Pressures. Normal atmospheric pressure at sea level can support a column of mercury 760 mm in height (760 mm Hg pressure = 1 atm.) The atmosphere is composed of 78.09 per cent nitrogen, 20.95 per cent oxygen, 0.93 per cent argon, and 0.031 per cent carbon dioxide (percentages here are mole % = volume %). These figures are for dry air with a total dry pressure of 755 mm Hg. The atmosphere contains an average water vapor content with a pressure of 5 mm Hg. On the basis of air containing water vapor, the nitrogen content is 79.02 per cent, oxygen 20.94 per cent, and carbon dioxide 0.04 per cent. On any basis the atmosphere is composed almost entirely of nitrogen and oxygen with argon and carbon dioxide making up less than 1 per cent of the atmospheric composition.

Each gas in a mixture of gases contributes to the total pressure in direct proportion to its percentage of the composition (Dalton's law). The pressure exerted by nitrogen at sea level is: (0.7902) (760 mm Hg) = 600.55 mm Hg. Partial pressures are symbolized as P_{N_2}, where the subscript indicates the gas under discussion. The partial pressure of oxygen in

the atmosphere is 159.16 mm Hg, and the partial pressure of carbon dioxide is 0.30 mm Hg. When the total pressure of a gas mixture is 760 mm Hg, the partial pressure of any given gaseous component may be calculated from:

$$P_x = \frac{x}{100} P \qquad (16.1)$$

where P_x is the partial pressure of the gas, P is the total pressure of the gas mixture, and x is the per cent volume of the given gas.

The partial pressure of a gas is dependent on the amount of water vapor present in the gas mixture. The higher the temperature, the more water evaporates per unit time, and such water vapor takes up volume within the gas mixture, thus changing the proportion of gases present. Atmospheric gases are usually dried before measurements are made, and their contents are usually expressed in terms of dry air. To calculate partial pressures of respiratory gases, the

Table 16-4 Vapor Pressure of Water

TEMP. (°C)	P_{H_2O} (mm Hg)	TEMP. (°C)	P_{H_2O} (mm Hg)
0	4.579	20	17.535
1	4.926	21	18.650
2	5.294	22	19.827
3	5.685	23	21.068
4	6.101	24	22.377
5	6.543	25	23.756
6	7.013	26	25.209
7	7.513	27	26.739
8	8.045	28	28.349
9	8.609	29	30.043
10	9.209	30	31.824
11	9.844	31	33.695
12	10.518	32	35.668
13	11.231	33	37.729
14	11.987	34	39.898
15	12.788	35	42.175
16	13.634	36	44.563
17	14.530	37	47.067
18	15.477	38	49.692
19	16.477	39	52.442

water vapor pressure is first subtracted from the total atmospheric pressure. Table 16-4 gives water vapor pressures at some different temperatures.

For example, during inspiration in humans atmospheric air enters the lungs, which are at a temperature of about 37°C, and the atmospheric air becomes saturated with water vapor. To calculate the partial pressure of oxygen, the water vapor pressure at 37°C is subtracted from the atmospheric pressure: $760 - 47 = 713$ mm Hg. The P_{O_2} is then equal to $(713)(0.2095) = 149.4$ mm Hg. On a similar basis, the P_{CO_2} is zero, and P_{N_2} is 564 mm Hg.

Gas volumes, of course, depend on both temperature and pressure. In order to compare gas volumes, measured volumes are usually converted to normal temperature and pressure (NTP). Normal temperature is taken as 0°C, and normal pressure is 760 mm Hg. Gas volumes measured at any temperature and pressure may be converted to NTP conditions by the equation:

$$V = \frac{V_o P_o (273)}{(760)(273 + t)} \qquad (16.2)$$

where V is the gas volume corrected to NTP; V_o and P_o are the observed volume and pressure, respectively; and t is the temperature in °C.

When a gas is dissolved in a liquid, the term gas tension is used to indicate the content of gas within the liquid. Gas tensions are dependent on the partial pressure of the gas above the liquid in the atmosphere and are usually expressed in terms of the gas partial pressure.

Respiratory Organs and their Control

16-4. Lower Aquatic Invertebrates. Most lower phyla do not possess specialized respiratory surfaces or organs. Rather, they depend on the diffusion of oxygen from the medium across cells of the integument into the body. In protozoans, coelenterates, porifera, and in most platyhelminthes, nematodes, rotifers, and annelids oxygen obtainment depends on a favorable concentration gradient between the environment and the animal and the presence of a body surface permeable to oxygen. Various mechanisms are used to provide a constant circulation of water past or through the animal because oxygen diffusion itself is usually too slow to replenish that lost from the medium immediately adjacent to the animal.

In most animal groups (excepting the vertebrates and cephalopod molluscs), little is known about the mechanisms that regulate oxygen uptake or utilization. Passive diffusion itself depends on the oxygen concentration gradient, the surface across which oxygen must diffuse, and the temperature. Many animals exhibit **dependent respiration** in which oxygen uptake is directly related to the external oxygen tension. This type of respiratory control is found even in higher animals such as the lobster (Thomas, 1954).

The rate of oxygen uptake from the environment usually depends on the degree of oxygen utilization in cellular oxidative metabolism. If cellular energy metabolism increases, so also does oxygen uptake increase. The use of oxygen by cells creates a greater oxygen concentration gradient between cells and body fluids; thus oxygen diffuses faster into the cells. This movement of oxygen, in turn, creates a greater concentration gradient between body fluids and the external environment, and more oxygen moves into the animal. As previously stated, oxygen movements depend first on appropriate concentration gradients. Similar statements can be made about the outward movement of CO_2 from cells to the environment.

Circulatory mechanisms that provide for a movement of the external medium, whether it be aqueous or gaseous, may in general be called **ventilation mechanisms**. When oxygen is required or when carbon dioxide is in too high an internal concentration, ventilation rates are increased; but the direct stimuli for such activity are unknown for most animal groups. Low oxygen tensions or high carbon dioxide tensions are known to stimulate increased ventilation rates in vertebrates. The effects of these stimuli on lower organisms vary. For example, high CO_2 tensions stimulate respiratory activity in molluscs, some arthropods, and annelids. However, in crustaceans such as *Balanus* and *Carcinus* and in the annelid *Tubifex*, changing the CO_2 tensions has no effect on oxygen uptake.

Many organisms make use of surface cilia or flagella to provide currents of water past inner or outer surfaces. Although such currents may be used primarily for food gathering, they also serve to prevent the film of water next to the body from becoming oxygen depleted as oxygen diffuses across the body surface. Flagella are used by sponges to provide such flows of water, which may amount to as much as 31 liters of water circulated for each milliliter of oxygen consumed (Jørgenson, 1965).

Echinoderms in some cases use the tube feet as respiratory organs, and the contractions of these organs provides for a continuous oxygen supply (see Section 13-3). The water-vascular system and other current flows through the echinoderm body assist in providing oxygen to body cells and in regulating pH (Irving, 1924, 1926).

In annelids the circulatory system is well developed, and oxygen transport pigments are often used to convey oxygen to all parts of the body (see Section 16-15). Gill-like structures are found in some annelids. *Nereis* uses its parapodia for oxygen uptake; *Arenicola* possesses gills along its body; and Terebellidae have branchial tufts. Gills are highly vascularized, thin surfaces that greatly facilitate the diffusion of oxygen from the environment into the blood.

Burrowing worms such as the Echiuroid *Urechis* often pass streams of water over the body surface using contractile movements of the body to pass water through the burrow. *Arenicola* propels water over its body by peristaltic contractions, and its ventilation rate increases as the oxygen tension of the environment decreases (van Dam, 1938).

The respiratory organs of most invertebrates are external gills, and these present some problems because they are more easily damaged than respiratory surfaces placed internally.

External gills with their rich blood supply also present good sites for parasitic invasion.

16-5. Molluscs. Molluscs live in a variety of habitats including marine, fresh, and stagnant waters and the terrestrial environment; and the group exhibits a variety of respiratory mechanisms. Marine molluscs generally possess specialized respiratory organs—the gills or ctenidia. Respiratory currents are produced by the action of cilia aligned laterally on each side of ctenidial filaments. These filaments are highly vascularized. The water currents are so arranged that they flow in a direction opposite to that of the blood within each filament and thus a countercurrent system is established which leads to a more efficient removal of oxygen from the water. Ctenidia are found in all molluscan classes except the Scaphapoda, but in many species they are missing or greatly reduced, and in all molluscs other forms of oxygen exchange may be utilized.

In cephalopods the ventilation mechanism consists of rhythmic contractions of the mantle, inducing the inhalation and exhalation of water. Water with a fresh supply of oxygen is kept flowing continuously over the gills by the coordinated activity of the mantle musculature, the funnel, and its inlet valves. In *Sepia* at rest, the rate of respiration is about 55 inspirations per minute; in *Eledone* respiration is at a rate of 12 to 24 inspirations per minute. Small specimens ventilate more rapidly than larger ones.

Cephalopod ventilation movements are under the control of neurons running from the palliovisceral (posterior subesophageal) lobe of the brain. Although it has been shown that increased concentrations of CO_2 increase the frequency and, to some extent, the amplitude of respiratory contractions, the precise stimulus needed for respiratory regulation is not known. It could be either the CO_2 tension itself or the hydrogen ion concentration of the body fluids that is a function of CO_2 tension. The receptors are not yet recognized although they might be present in a respiratory center of the brain. Respiration increases markedly when an animal is stimulated or excited, and during locomotion very strong contractions of the mantle occur. The cephalopod molluscs include some of the most active invertebrates, and it is not surprising that their respiratory systems are highly developed.

Fresh water pulmonate snails lack gills and possess a modified mantle cavity that acts as a lung. The roof of the mantle cavity is highly vascularized, and the opening of the mantle cavity opens to the exterior through a narrow muscular opening. Most shore dwelling molluscs are also air breathers. However, all retain the ability to breathe under water, making use of water currents provided by ciliary tracts. Some shore dwelling molluscs possess neither ctenidia nor a large mantle cavity and depend on cutaneous respiration through unspecialized regions of the mantle and foot for their oxygen supply.

Gastropod molluscs living in tidal zones can use air trapped in the mantle to supply oxygen during periods when they are immersed in water. Ctenidia are of little use unless supplied with water currents. In molluscs exposed periodically or continuously to the atmosphere, ctenidia become detrimental because of water loss through their surfaces. Any development of respiratory organs must be balanced against the problem of desiccation. Molluscs that are likely to be exposed to the air in many cases have retained the operculum on the foot, which closes the shell aperture when the body is withdrawn into the shell and thus protects them from desiccation.

Some molluscs possess the blood respiratory pigment hemocyanin. In shore dwelling molluscs this at best increases the oxygen carrying capacity of the blood by about 3 per cent (Carter, 1931). Some molluscs have hemoglobin in some muscles, and this respiratory pigment appears to act as an oxygen store. Newell (1964) and Hunter (1964) review the relation of habitat to respiratory mode in molluscs. Ghirreti (1966) has reviewed molluscan respiration generally.

16-6. Arthropods—Chelicerates and Insects.
As indicated previously, the successful occupation of the terrestrial environment can be

accomplished only when respiration in air can be accomplished without extreme water loss. Successful land animals have developed an internal organ of respiration that permits the intake of sufficient oxygen without undue loss of water. There are exceptions to this generalization. For example, smaller animals have a high surface to volume ratio; and even though their body surface is covered in such a way as to minimize water loss, they may still obtain sufficient oxygen through the body surface. Larger animals may live in a moist terrestrial environment and survive with a body surface unprotected against water loss.

The arthropods as a group have successfully invaded the terrestrial environment. Their relatively impervious exoskeleton protects the terrestrial organism against water loss while favoring the adaptation of internal respiratory surfaces in the aquatic organism. Lower chelicerates such as *Limulus* possess book gills, and higher chelicerates such as arachnids may possess book lungs, although other respiratory organs have also developed.

Book gills represent evaginations of the body surface, and each is composed of about a hundred thin leaves. Ventilation of respiratory surfaces in arthropods depends on muscular activity because cilia are generally lacking. The book gills are opisthosomal appendages, and their rhythmic movements circulate water over the vascularized gill surfaces and also drive blood into the gill leaves during each

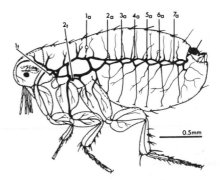

Figure 16-1(a) Tracheal system of the flea *Xenopsylla*. 1_a to 7_a, abdominal spiracles; 1_t to 2_t, thoracic spiracles. [Redrawn after Wigglesworth (1950).]

forward motion. This mechanism serves the function of booster hearts already discussed (Chapter 13).

Book lungs are invaginations of the body surface and are collections of flat hollow plates through which air can circulate. They are found in scorpions and other arachnids. Book lungs are located in an atrium or chamber with an external opening, the spiracle. In some species the spiracle can be opened or closed to control water loss, and in some arachnids muscular movements can be used to move the book lungs, thus producing ventilation. However, neither modification appears necessary to produce adequate respiration in most arachnids, which are basically small organisms. When the book lungs of scorpions are removed, respiration falls to zero, an indication that body surfaces play no role in oxygen uptake.

Many arachnids, as well as insects, possess a tracheal system for respiration. Tracheal systems arise as invaginations of ectoderm and generally are open externally through spiracles located behind the coxa of an appendage. Trachea are cylindrical, chitin-lined tubes, the chitinous lining preventing their collapse. Spiracles usually occur in pairs on each segment of the body and are often supplied with valves whose primary function is to prevent undue water loss. Internally the trachae ramify and penetrate through the body tissues finally ending in small tracheoles 1 to 2 μ in diameter. Tracheoles in insects end blindly and lack the chitinous lining; they are walled only by a thin membrane. Although the tracheolar ending is sometimes filled with fluid, the tracheal system generally is gas filled. The nature of the tracheal system of two insects is shown in Figure 16-1.

In most cases the tracheal system is both an organ for taking up oxygen from the air and a system for circulating oxygen to all body cells (however, in some cases the tracheal system is used only to bring in oxygen from the air, and this oxygen is then distributed to body tissues by the blood). The state of development of the tracheal system depends upon the evolutionary position of a given insect. In more primitive forms the tracheal system of each segment is unconnected with those of adjacent segments but in more highly evolved orders the trachea form an interconnected network (see Wigglesworth, 1954). The most primitive orders of insects lack a tracheal system and can survive by utilizing the general body surface for oxygen intake.

Air enters the trachea by diffusion through the spiracles. Although such diffusion is unaided by ventilation in lower insect orders, in higher orders oxygen diffusion can be controlled by opening or closing the spiracular valves. In fleas, for example, the valves on two pairs of spiracles are kept open during periods of rest, when all other spiracles are closed. Only under conditions of extreme activity are all spiracles open; at other times there is a rhythmic opening and closing of the valves.

Although in smaller insects simple diffusion of oxygen inward and carbon dioxide outward is sufficient for proper gas exchange, such a system is not adequate for larger or more active insects. A combination of rhythmic spiracular valve activity, coupled with muscular contractions of the body wall, aids in ventilation in the latter insects. These are coordinated activities which produce a flow of air through the tracheal system usually from anterior to posterior through interconnected tracheal tubes of all segments. The muscular activities that aid in air flow may be the result either of a peristaltic compression brought about by the contraction of body wall muscles; a telescoping

Figure 16-1(b) Tracheal system of a grasshopper, showing some of the main air tubes and air sacs. [From R. Buchsbaum (1948) *Animals Without Backbones*, 2nd rev. ed. The University of Chicago Press, Chicago.]

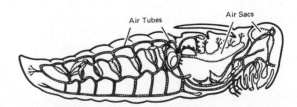

action; or a dorsoventral flattening of the body. In flying insects, the movement of the wings and the action of flight muscles aid in supplying oxygen through proper ventilation during periods of activity.

Three phases are recognized in respiratory movements in insects (McCutcheon, 1940): (1) an inspiratory phase lasting 250 msecs (during the last 25 to 50 msec of this period the thoracic spiracles are open); (2) a compensatory phase lasting about 1 second during which the abdominal spiracles are closed as are the thoracic spiracles; (3) an expiratory phase also about 1 second in duration (during this period the abdominal spiracles are open during the final 300 msec).

Air enters the tracheal system anteriorly during the inspiratory phase, is moved posteriorly during the compensatory phase, and is exhaled during the final phase from the posterior spiracles. These actions serve to renew the oxygen supply within the tracheal system and to force air into the smaller branches of the system during the compensatory phase when all spiracles are closed.

The opening and closing of the spiracles is under nervous system control, and there are respiratory centers in the nerve cord as well as outside the nerve cord. The duration of the open period of the spiracles is determined by the carbon dioxide tension of the blood and is also sensitive to the oxygen tension of the incoming air.

Oxygen diffuses from the tracheoles into the body tissues. Tracheoles are not rigid inert tubules. In fact, they have been observed to move toward areas of oxygen deficiency (Wigglesworth, 1959). Many problems remain to be solved concerning the nature of gas exchange at the tracheolar level. The tracheolar fluid is thought to play an important role in insect respiration. This fluid can move in the tracheoles and is presumably absorbed by osmosis or some similar mechanism at the end of the tracheole. Removal of the fluid would aid in drawing oxygen into the fine-diametered tubules and could also serve as a means of transporting oxygen from the tracheole into the tissue fluids. If the fluid does not move

through the tracheolar membrane, then oxygen would have to diffuse through this fluid into the body fluids, and as already stated, oxygen diffusion through liquids is relatively slow.

Other adaptations for oxygen uptake are found in various insects, especially in aquatic insects. Modifications of the spiracle or of the body wall adjacent to the spiracle result in structures known as **spiracular gills** (Hinton, 1968). These are found primarily in the pupal stages of certain flies and beetles. They allow respiration to occur in water. Spiracular gills possess **plastrons**, which are gas films of constant volume and an extensive air-water interface. Plastrons are held in position by various **hydrofuge** structures (= nonwetting surfaces), and they prevent the insect from getting wet or drowning. Oxygen can enter through water-air interfaces and diffuse through air channels into the spiracles. In some cases plastrons once charged with air need never be exposed to the atmosphere because they allow for an adequate exchange of gases dissolved in the surrounding water. Thus the organism can remain permanently submerged. Plastrons are found in the developing

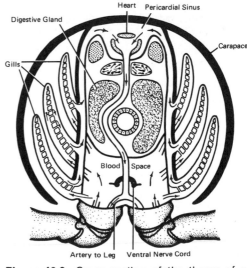

Figure 16-2 Cross-section of the thorax of a lobster to show relations of gill chambers to other organs and the path of blood through some of the main blood channels. [From R. Buchsbaum (1948) *Animals Without Backbones*, 2nd rev. ed. University of Chicago Press, Chicago.]

stages of many terrestrial insects and are of use since these are often exposed to rain or other moist conditions. Plastrons are composed of waxy secretions or of hydrophobic hairs.

The trachea is an extremely efficient respiratory system. Respiratory rates and oxygen consumption by insects often are very high (see Table 16-1); in fact oxygen consumption in some active insects reaches the highest levels known in the animal kingdom.

16-7. Arthropods—Crustaceans. Aquatic crustaceans are equipped with efficient gills and with mechanisms for providing a constant flow of water past them. Gills in crustaceans are external, vascularized, thin membranes that permit the rapid diffusion of oxygen from the medium into the blood and of carbon dioxide from the blood into the environment. Usually the gills lie in a branchial chamber and are protected by the overlying carapace (Figure 16-2). These statements are generalizations, and as in other animal groups the exact nature of the respiratory system of crustaceans depends on the nature of the animal and its habitat.

Various mechanisms are used to ventilate respiratory surfaces. Most Entomostraca (a term used to designate smaller crustaceans, excepting Malacostraca) have thin exoskeletons, and much of the respiratory exchange occurs directly across the body surface. However, most of these organisms also possess gills. In many cases these are part of the appendages, and ventilation is produced by normal swimming movements. In filter feeders, the currents used to bring in food may also be those used to ventilate gills.

Often the use of the body surface for respiratory activity has been accompanied by a reduction in number or size of gills. Ostracods, for example, have a relatively heavy outer covering richly vascularized, and the gills are poorly developed.

In many branchiopods all of the thoracic appendages are used to provide a water flow past the gills. In decapod crustaceans a specialized structure, the scaphognathite on the second maxilla, functions as a paddle to produce water currents. In isopods, amphipods,

and stomatopods the beating of abdominal pleopods produces the needed water currents.

Current flows are often complex. For example, in decapod crustaceans the currents often are initiated at the ventral hypobranchial portion of the gill chamber, flow first posteriorly, then turn dorsally between the gill lamellae, and finally flow anteriorly and out through the anterior exhalant respiratory openings. Such complex current flows permit a maximal amount of oxygen to be removed from the water. Respiration in crustaceans has been reviewed by Wolvekamp and Waterman (1960).

Gills are modified depending on the particular habitat. Generally a reduced mass of gill tissue is correlated with increasing ability to live on land. Whereas crabs living in the low tidal region were found to have 26 gills, other species living in the intertidal zone had only about 18 gills, and beach crabs had about 12. Amphibious decapods and amphipods tend to develop a highly vascularized branchial cavity (similar to the adaptations seen in the mantle cavity of terrestrial snails, Section 16-5) and reduce gill tissue. Again, reduction of gill surface is important to a terrestrial animal because gills are a site of large water loss.

Grapsoid land crabs circulate air through a vascularized branchial cavity; branchial tufts are membranous vascularized projections into the cavity that are used as the loci of gas exchange. However, most amphibious crabs fill the branchial cavity with water using an opercular flap to close off this chamber while on land. In all of these cases movements of the carapace and the scaphognathite are used to produce ventilation.

Isopods are terrestrial crustaceans that use part of their pleopods for respiration. The respiratory endopodite can be covered with a protective exopodite to cut down water loss. Ventilation is accomplished by movements of the appendages.

The rate of ventilation varies with the species and the conditions of the environment. In a crayfish, *Astacus astacus*, 0.2 to 0.8 liters of water per hour are moved past the gills. A 322 g lobster, *Homarus gammarus*, circulated 9.8 liters per hour past the gills. In the latter species, increased ventilation occurred under conditions of low external oxygen tension. As indicated previously high CO_2 tensions increase ventilation rates in some species and decrease it in others. As was the case for insects and other invertebrate groups, much remains to be discovered concerning the stimuli required to alter respiratory rates in crustaceans and about the pathways by which such information is received and coordinated.

Some crustaceans use respiratory pigments to increase the oxygen carrying capacity of their blood (see Section 16-15). However, generally crustacean blood has only a moderate oxygen carrying capacity. For example, lobster blood (with hemocyanin) can carry about 1.7 ml O_2/100 ml, whereas cephalopod molluscs such as *Octopus* can carry about 4.5 ml O_2/100 ml blood; and lower vertebrates such as the carp can carry 12 ml O_2/100 ml of blood.

This brief review of invertebrate respiratory mechanisms is sufficient to illustrate that adaptations of respiratory organs generally involve the appearance of specialized respiratory surfaces, a tendency for such surfaces to move internally, and the development of ventilation mechanisms to ensure a sufficient supply of oxygen. Internally, respiratory adaptations include principally improvements in mechanisms for the transport of respiratory gases and for picking up oxygen at respiratory surfaces. Such adaptations were needed, along with others, for animals to achieve the terrestrial habitat.

16-8. Vertebrates—Fishes. The major respiratory organs of fishes are gills, which consist of filamentous leaflets protected in an opercular chamber. However, some fish also use cutaneous respiration. As mentioned in Chapter 14, the gills of fish serve not only as respiratory organs but also function in the excretion of waste products of metabolism and in the secretion of salts.

Fish gills are supported on gill arches (Figure 16-3) from which project the gill filaments, each of which has a group of secondary lamellae on the dorsal and ventral sides. The secondary lamellae are the respiratory exchange surfaces. The flow of blood in the secondary almellae is oppositely directed to that of water flow over the gills—another example of a countercurrent exchange system, which, in this case, facilitates transfer of oxygen from the environment to the blood. Respiratory systems and their control in fish are reviewed by Hughes and Shelton (1962).

The secondary lamellae consist of two epithelial layers kept separated by pillar cells (Figure 16-3). In these cells the presence of fibrillar material which appears similar to the fibrillar material seen in smooth muscle in the electron microscope is, perhaps, an indication that these are contractile cells which can control the dimensions of the blood spaces in the lamellae and thus control blood flow.

Elasmobranchs and teleosts, in a majority of cases, use a double pump mechanism to maintain what amounts to a continuous flow of water over the gill surfaces. During quiet respiration water flows from the buccal cavity to the opercular cavity in teleosts (the latter cavity is similar to the parabranchial cavity of elasmobranchs) through the interdigitating

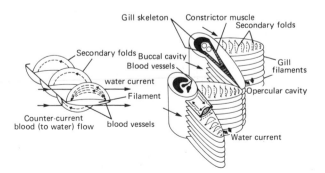

Figure 16-3 Structure of gill arches. The filaments of adjacent rows touch at their tips. On the left is shown part of a single filament with three secondary folds on each side. The countercurrent system in which blood flow is opposite to water flow is shown. [After G. M. Hughes (1961).]

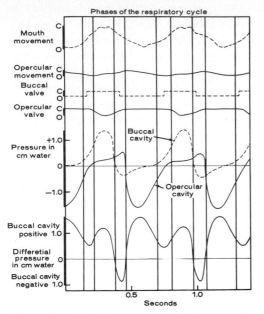

Figure 16-4 Breathing movements of the mouth and operculum of a 70 g trout. Also shown are associated changes in the pressures of the buccal and opercular cavities. O and C represent the opened and closed positions of the mouth, operculum, and their associated valves. [From G. M. Hughes and G. Shelton (1958) "The mechanism of gill ventilation in three freshwater teleosts" *Journal of Experimental Biology.* **35**: 807-823.]

tips of the lamellae (Figure 16-3). During activity the gill filaments are moved apart by small muscles, and the resistance to water flow between the two cavities is decreased. The buccal cavity acts as a positive pressure pump, and the opercular or parabranchial cavities act as suction or negative pressure pumps.

During ventilation, muscles can depress the buccal floor, and water flows into the oral cavity as pressure in the expanding cavity falls below that of the medium. The opercular flaps close at this time. As the opercular muscles relax, the opercular cavity expands creating a pressure on the back side of the gill filaments. Because this pressure is lower than the pressure in the oral cavity, water flows from the oral to the opercular cavity across the gill lamellae. This initial phase of respiration is followed by a closure of the mouth and an active elevation of the buccal floor thus creating a positive

pressure in the oral cavity. The result is additional water flow to the opercular cavity, which still has a negative pressure. As the pressure builds up in the anterior cavity, the pressure in the posterior gill chambers rises above that of the external medium, and water is forced outside as the gill flaps are forced open. Figure 16-4 shows the pressure changes occurring in different parts of the ventilation system of the trout (Hughes and Shelton, 1958).

A few fish such as mackerel and sharks maintain a continuous flow over the gills during swimming by keeping the mouth open and allowing water to flow directly over and through the gills. Good control over gas exchange is achieved by the degree to which the mouth is opened, and this system is inexpensive energetically because there is no need for the use of respiratory muscles while swimming.

Cyclostomes have gills in the form of pouches that are attached internally to the pharynx and that open to the exterior either through a single tube (*Myxine glutinosa*) or through separate gills slits (*Petromyzon*). A relatively complex pumping mechanism consisting of a velum and velar scrolls is used to scoop water from the environment and direct it through the gill pouches (Johnson, 1966). Velar pulsations vary in frequency between 11

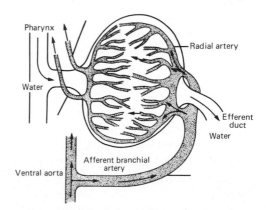

Figure 16-5 Countercurrent flow system of blood and water in the gill body of the hagfish. This mechanism facilitates gas exchange across the gill membranes.

and 100 per minute, and such measured variation probably depends on the metabolic state and the activity of the animal. Hagfish utilize a countercurrent system to facilitate oxygen exchange (Figure 16-5).

It may be noted that in all chordates ventilation and feeding mechanisms share the pharynx. In fishes only seldom is the ventilation current used as a filter feeding mechanism. Hagfishes possess nostrils through which water is drawn into the pharynx anterior to the gill pouches. In lampreys the anterior access to the gill pouches is via the mouth only. The presence of nostrils is not always a sign of a ventilation mechanism. In lungfish, for example, the nostrils are used only for chemoreception, and water enters the pharynx only through the mouth.

In addition to the ability to change the rate of ventilation movements and therefore the rate of oxygen exchange, teleosts can also modify the blood flow through the gill lamellae. It has been found that adrenalin favors blood flow through the lamellae and acetylcholine increases blood flow through a system of non-respiratory blood vessels. This is a shunting system which runs through the center of the gill filament.

Some fish are air breathers and a few like the mudskipper *Periophthalmus* can spend most of their time on land near the water. Eels are capable of overland migrations during which they rely mainly on cutaneous respiration. However, as in other animals, cutaneous respiration is a problem because of the simultaneous loss of water and salts. Many fish gulp air at the surface to take in a bubble from which various parts of the alimentary tract can extract oxygen. The buccal surface, the pharynx, or the stomach are modified in various species and become highly vascularized to serve as respiratory membranes.

Lungfish depend on the extraction of oxygen by ventral diverticula, which are structures homologous to vertebrate lungs. The arterial circulation is derived from the sixth aortic arch, and the venous drainage goes directly to the heart as in terrestrial vertebrates (see Chapter 13.) Lungfish such as *Lepidosiren*

suffocate if access to air is denied them because of the extremely poor development of their gill circulation. In lungfish the lungs are inflated as the fish rises to the surface and gulps a large air bubble that is forced into the lung. Lungfish such as *Lipidosiren* and *Protopterus* can withstand long periods of drought by entering into a state of estivation (see Section 15-18) in which metabolism and respiration are minimal. *Protopterus* during estivation secretes about itself a lipoprotein tube, a waterproof covering that prevents water loss. The tube has only one opening anteriorly to the surface.

Respiration is coordinated with cardiac activity; and the codfish *Gadnus*, for example, when removed from water and unable to breathe, reduces its heart rate—a situation also seen in diving mammals (Leivestad et al., 1964).

Swim bladders of present day fish are thought to be derived from the lungs of primitive ancestors. Swim bladders are not used in respiration but serve to maintain equilibrium. Gases in the swim bladder are obtained from air dissolved in the blood at atmospheric pressure, and secretory mechanisms are used to transfer the air from the blood to the swim bladder. A fish suspended at a depth of 1,000 meters has a pressure of 100 atmospheres within its swim bladder, a pressure the same as that at the surface (see Scholander, 1954).

16-9. Vertebrates—Amphibians. The skin, buccal cavities, and lungs are all utilized in varying degrees by different groups of amphibia, and again dependence on a given respiratory surface depends greatly on the animal's habitat. Amphibian respiration has been reviewed by Foxon (1964).

Gills, usually external, are found in larval amphibians and are maintained into adult life by a few aquatic salamanders. Salamanders of the order Plethodontidae are lungless and depend primarily on cutaneous respiration. Frogs and toads rely both on cutaneous respiration and pulmonary respiration. Generally with increasing terrestrial habit there is an increased dependence on pulmonary ventilation.

Some indication of an animal's dependence on cutaneous and pulmonary respiration can be obtained by determination of the location of respiratory capillaries. In the aquatic newt *Triton* the skin contains about 75 per cent of such capillaries. In the tree frog *Hyla* 75 per cent of the respiratory capillaries are in the lungs.

Frogs appear to excrete CO_2 primarily through the skin. In the more terrestrial frog *Rana temporaria* oxygen uptake through the lungs is about three times as great as that through the skin. But in the more aquatic frog *Rana esculenta* lungs and skin play about equal roles in oxygen exchange (Krogh, 1959). It is of interest that the skin of the back and thighs (regions more exposed to the air) contains more capillaries than skin of the underparts of the body. Thus cutaneous respiration is aided by the morphological distribution of capillaries. The skin of frogs and to a lesser extent that of toads must be kept moist for gaseous exchange to occur freely. This is true of all respiratory surfaces, for otherwise the permeability of the membrane is drastically reduced.

Lungs are internal respiratory surfaces, well protected from the environment. The lungs of vertebrates exhibit a wide variability in complexity from the simple saclike organs of lungfish to the complexly divided lungs of birds and mammals. Generally there has been an evolutionary trend for increasing subdivision of air pathways and increasing surface area for gaseous exchange as animals tended to the terrestrial environment.

The first airway leading to the lungs is the trachea. In higher vertebrates the trachea divides into **bronchi**, but in amphibians the trachea ends at the anterior pole of the lungs, and cartilagenous plates maintain a connection between the trachea and the lungs. In frogs the lungs are divided by incomplete septa between which are interspersed secondary septa bounding the alveoli or terminal air spaces where gaseous exchange occurs. The alveolar diameter of the frog lung is smaller than that of mammals, and this is correlated with the larger respiratory surface found in mammals. The respiratory surface of the frog

Rana is about 20 cm² for each cubic centimeter of air contained in the lungs; in man it is about 300 cm².

Air and blood come into close contact in the alveoli and are separated only by a barrier composed of thin epithelial cells that line the alveolus and of endothelial cells of the capillary wall. Between are interstitial elements including a basement membrane and connective tissue. This barrier is only about 0.5 μ thick, and thus oxygen need not diffuse over a large distance to get into the blood. Importantly for the operation of the lungs, a thin surface film covers the alveolar epithelium (see Section 16-10).

During ventilation in frogs several inspirations of air ventilate only the buccal surface for each inspiration that ventilates the lungs.

In lunged amphibia the sixth aortic arch provides a pulmonary arterial supply. In the anurans (frogs and toads) the sixth arch divides into pulmocutaneous arteries supplying the lung and some regions of the skin. The pulmonary vein returns blood from the lungs directly to the left atrium, but cutaneous veins return oxygenated blood from the skin to the systemic venous system. In Chapter 13 it was indicated that anatomically the amphibian heart is not separated into pulmonary and systemic circulations. Such a division would be inefficient because of the use made of cutaneous respiration and the fact that oxygenated blood from the skin is returned to the systemic venous system.

Although the functional properties of lungs in general will be discussed in the next section, the movements of ventilation in frogs is worth describing here. Inflation of the frog lung is accomplished by a positive-pressure buccopharyngeal pump. Inspiration is initiated by muscular contractions that lower the buccal floor. Simultaneously the nostril is opened. A negative pressure is created by the expansion of the buccal cavity, and air flows inward through the nostrils. The glottis, a flap protecting the opening of the respiratory tract (trachea), is closed at the beginning of inspiration. In the next step, the glottis opens, and the nostrils close. The buccal floor is elevated, and the pressure drives air through the trachea and into the lungs causing them to inflate. After inflation a period of buccopharyngeal pumping is observed, an activity concerned with olfaction rather than respiration. Expiration of the inspired air is brought about by the compression of the body wall musculature, smooth muscle contractions in the lung walls, and the elastic recoil of the lungs. This combination of forces expels air through the opened glottis and nostrils. Again, it requires a combination of muscular forces to move air into the lungs, where oxygen diffusion into the blood can occur; further muscular activity removes the previously inspired air from the lungs.

The Mammalian Respiratory System

16-10. Structure. Because of the relative simplicity of the methods of analysis and the amenability to quantitative analysis, the mammalian respiratory system is probably the best understood of any physiological system. The structure and function of the mammalian respiratory system will be described here principally in terms of the human system, which is well understood and which is also similar to mammalian respiratory systems generally (see *Handbook of Physiology*, Section 3, Respiration, American Physiological Society, Washington, D.C.).

The lungs of mammals serve other functions than that of gas exchange. As already noted they are involved in temperature regulation and water loss. In addition to providing a site for gaseous exchange, the lungs also serve to warm incoming air and to saturate it with water vapor.

Air enters the body through the mouth and nose; the latter possesses mucous membranes that filter foreign particles from the entering air. The air then passes through the pharynx, through the open glottis, through the larynx, and into the trachea—a large tube held open by rings of cartilage that encircle it transversely.

The trachea enters the thoracic cavity and branches into two major air passages, the bronchi, one of which leads to each lung. The bronchi ramify profusely, finally forming smaller tubes, the bronchioles. Except for the smallest terminal bronchioles, all of these tubes have cartilaginous rings. Bronchioles are also equipped with smooth muscle fibers. The terminal bronchioles lead into an expanded portion known as the atrium and from the atrium a number of alveoli open (Figure 16-6a).

The lungs are masses of spongy and elastic tissues and lie in the airtight thoracic cavity. The lungs are enclosed by the visceral pleura, a layer of connective tissue anatomically contiguous with the pericardium. The parietal pleura is another membranous layer lying next to the thoracic cage. Between the two pleura is a thin layer of fluid that lubricates the lungs and membranes during their movements (Figure 16-6b diagrams these structures).

Ribs form the side walls of the thoracic cage, and between the ribs are intercostal muscles that can cause movements of the ribs. The base of the thorax is formed from the diaphragm, a sheet of muscle. The diaphragm is dome shaped in the relaxed condition of the diaphragm muscle fibers.

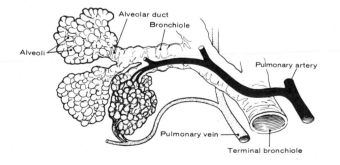

Alveolar duct
Bronchiole
Alveoli
Pulmonary artery
Pulmonary vein
Terminal bronchiole

Figure 16-6(a) Showing the smaller structures of the human pulmonary tree. The alveoli are the sites of gas exchanges between the air in the lungs and the fluids of the capillaries.

The intercostal muscles are innervated by intercostal nerves derived from the thoracic region of the spinal cord. The diaphragm is innervated by the phrenic nerves derived from a plexus in the cervical region. These muscles and nerves are the main respiratory apparatus. When breathing is heavy, as in exercise, accessory respiratory muscles of the abdominal wall and upper chest are called into play.

16-11. Lungs. The lungs are elastic bodies that can return to their normal shape after a deforming force is removed. The inflation of the lungs is accompanied by an increase in potential energy. The conversion of this potential energy into kinetic energy during deflation provides part of the force needed to expel gas. The lungs may be considered as passive elements in the ventilation process although their elasticity plays a major role in ventilation. It may be noted that the lungs of mammals are inflated by the development of negative pressures in contrast to the positive pressure systems of frogs and lungfish.

The elasticity of the lungs is often studied by filling them with air or saline solution and measuring the resulting pressure under static conditions. When volume is plotted against pressure, a straight line results whose slope is a measure of the stiffness (compliance)—the change in volume per unit change in pressure in units of liters per centimeter of water. It is found that the pressure necessary to enlarge the lungs to a given volume is less when the

lungs are filled with liquid than when they are filled with air. There is not as much elastic recoil in a liquid filled lung. Such differences depend on surface tension differences, which in turn are dependent on the nature of the interfaces present. In the liquid-liquid interface condition present when the lungs are filled with a liquid, the surface tension is greatly reduced and depends only on the elasticity of the lungs. When a gas-liquid interface is present, as in the air-filled lung, the compliance includes both the elastic properties of the lungs and the significant surface tension of the interface.

The surface tension is caused by a film of liquid that layers the alveolar surfaces of the lungs. At an interface the attractive forces between molecules are directed downward and sideways more than upward, and this surface force is the surface tension. Laplace showed that the surface tension, T, is related to the pressure, P, and the radius, r, in an object such as a soap bubble ($4T = Pr$). If two bubbles have different radii, the pressure in the larger will be less than that of the smaller. And when two such bubbles are connected, the small bubble will empty into the larger. Alveoli have different sizes, and with a uniform surface tension it would be expected that small alveoli would empty into larger ones, but this does not normally occur.

The stability of alveoli is produced by the presence of a surface coating, a **surfactant**, which causes a nonlinear change in surface

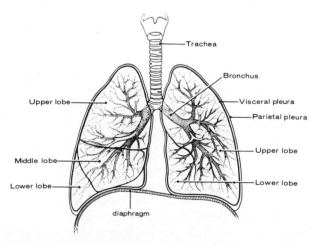

Figure 16-6(b) Diagrammatic representation of the lungs and their membranes.

Trachea

Bronchus

Upper lobe

Visceral pleura

Parietal pleura

Upper lobe

Middle lobe

Lower lobe

Lower lobe

diaphragm

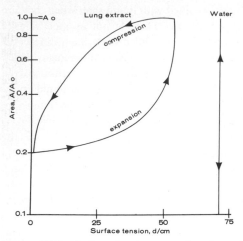

Figure 16-7 Surface tension as a function of surface area of films. The surface tension of water remains constant, whereas that of lung extracts from mammals show hysteresis. [After Clements and Tierney (1965).]

tension with surface area. Figure 16-7 compares the surface tension changes of water with those of lung extracts. As the lungs are filled with air, alveoli that are most inflated have higher surface tensions than do those that are underdistended. This serves to stabilize alveoli of different sizes.

The surface coating in mammalian alveoli is a complex of protein with dipalmityl lecithin. Whereas surfactants have been most intensively studied in mammals, such substances have been found in all birds, reptiles, and amphibians studied (Pattle, 1965).

16-12. Ventilation. Since the air space in the lungs directly communicates with the outside air, the pressure within the lungs (the intrapleural pressure) will be equal to the atmospheric pressure, unless some volume change occurs in the lungs.

Contraction of the inspiratory muscles (the diaphragm and external intercostal muscles) enlarges the thoracic cavity and causes a reduced pressure between the lungs and the thoracic wall (the intrathoracic pressure) (Figure 16-8). This reduction causes the lungs to expand and reduces the intrapleural pressure. The alveoli and bronchioles expand, and air at atmospheric pressure flows through the upper respiratory tract and into the alveoli and bronchioles, where the pressure has been reduced below atmospheric by the expansion.

The intrapulmonic pressure is the force causing movement of air into and out of the lungs and is the pressure gradient between the lung spaces and the atmosphere. When the diaphragm contracts, the sheet of muscle flattens lowering the floor of the thoracic cavity and thereby increasing its volume. Under these conditions intrapulmonic pressure is reduced, and air flows into the lungs.

The external intercostal muscles cause a rotation of the ribs upward and laterad and a movement of the sternum forward. These actions increase the circumference of the thoracic cavity and thus enlarge its volume also.

To expire air, the inspiratory muscles relax, and the thoracic cavity returns to its normal volume. The elastic recoil of the lungs aids in restoring them to their deflated volume. These forces increase the intrapulmonic pressure and cause air to move from the lungs, through the upper respiratory tract and into the atmosphere.

These are the ventilation movements respon-

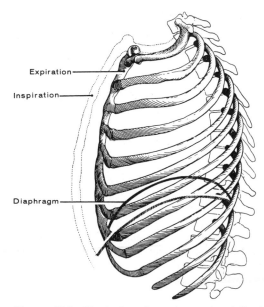

Figure 16-8 Illustrating the movements of the ribs and diaphragm that increase the volume of the thorax during inspiration and decrease the volume during expiration.

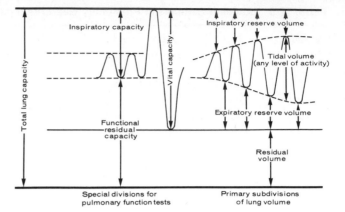

Figure 16-9 Lung volumes and capacities of humans as measured with a spirometer.

sible for bringing fresh air into the lungs and into contact with the alveolar surfaces and for removing the stale air during exhalation.

The volume of air that can be taken into the lungs can be measured by any of many forms of spirometers. The **vital capacity** is the volume of air expired by the most forceful expiration after a maximal inspiration. It is the total movable air in the lungs (Figure 16-9). The **residual volume** is the amount of air remaining in the lungs after the most forceful expiration and amounts to about 1.5 liters in humans. The **total lung volume** is the sum of the vital capacity and the residual volume and amounts to about 6 liters in humans. The **tidal volume** is the actual amount of air moved at each cycle of inspiration-expiration. It varies according to the needs of the organism and is about 500 ml in humans at rest. The **dead space** is a volume of about 150 ml, where air remains in those parts of the respiratory tract, such as the bronchi, where no gas exchange can occur.

All of these ventilation movements are designed to bring fresh air into the alveoli, where oxygen can diffuse down its concentration gradient into the oxygen-depleted venous blood and where carbon dioxide can diffuse from the blood into the air for elimination to the atmosphere.

It is worth noting that a standardized set of symbols has been developed for describing respiratory activities and gas exchanges and are used for describing circulatory actions as well (Otis, 1964; Pappenheimer, 1950). These symbols are given in Table 16-5.

16-13. Respiratory Control. Breathing consists of inspiratory-expiratory cycles and is a rhythmic oscillatory activity. This activity is affected by a variety of neurons from various regions of the brain including the cortex, pons, medullary reticular formation, and brain stem (for discussions of respiratory control see Comroe, 1965; Pitts, 1946; Wang and Ngai, 1964; Widdecombe, 1964). The regulation of respiration in mammals is complex, and many factors enter into such control. Knowledge of these regulatory mechanisms has been achieved by systematic dissection of the brain, the use of localized electrical stimulation and recording, the use of local injections of chemicals, and by localized ablations. Generally the results have indicated that there is not one discrete control center for respiratory activity.

The cerebral cortex can initiate changes in the respiratory rate or amplitude and is an important factor in activities such as talking, laughing, singing, sneezing, or coughing, whereas the removal of the cerebral hemispheres, cerebellum, and anterior brain stem produces no particular changes in the respiratory activity. Transections at the level of the pons and then the medulla produce increasingly greater alterations in respiratory rhythms, and it appears that in these portions of the CNS are the centers responsible for the automatic adjustment of respiratory rate and rhythm.

The medulla appears to be the site of control of respiratory rhythmic activity. When the medulla is completely isolated from any

Table 16-5 Standard Symbols in Pulmonary Gas Exchange

Symbol	Definition	Units and Examples	
Quantitative variables			
P	Gas pressures and tensions	P_{CO_2}	Partial pressure of CO_2, mm Hg
V	Gas volume	V_T	Volume of tidal air, ml
$\dot{V}$	Gas volume/unit time (gas flow)	$\dot{V}_E$	Flow of expired air, ml/minute
$\dot{Q}$	Volume flow of liquids	$\dot{Q}_a$	Arterial blood flow, ml/min
C	Concentration in blood phase	C_{CO_2}	Blood CO_2, ml/100 ml blood
F	Fractional concentration of gas in dry gas phase	F_{O_2}	Concentration of O_2 in dry air
f	Frequency of respiration		Breaths per minute
R	Respiratory exchange ration (RQ)	$\dot{V}_{CO_2}/\dot{V}_{O_2}$	
D	Diffusion capacity	$D_{L_{CO_2}}$	ml CO_2/min/mm Hg ΔP_{CO_2}
Subscript qualifying symbols for gases (capital letters)			
I	Inspired gas		
E	Expired gas		
A	Alveolar gas		
T	Tidal gas		
D	Dead space gas		
B	Barometric		
L	Lungs		
Subscript qualifying symbols for blood (small letters)			
a	Arterial		
v	Venous		
c	Capillaries		
b	Blood in general		
Other symbols and terms			
$\bar{X}$	Dash above symbol indicates a mean value		
$\dot{X}$	Dot above symbol indicates a time derivative		
STPD or NTP	Standard temperature and pressure, dry air		
BTPS	Body temperature and ambient pressure, gas saturated with H_2O		
ATPD	Ambient temperature and pressure, dry		
ATPS	Ambient temperature and pressure, saturated with H_2O		

neural input, the respiratory rhythm of inhalation and exhalation continues. Although the vagus nerves normally supply a neuronal input that modifies the medullary respiratory center, transection of the vagus nerves does not stop respiratory activity although such activity may be slowed. This is similar to the situation in the heart, where the pacemaker maintains its rhythm when the vagus fibers to the heart are transected.

The respiratory centers in the medulla consist of inspiratory and expiratory groups of neurons that reciprocally inhibit each other to produce an oscillatory action resulting in rhythmic breathing. However, the nature of this still somewhat hypothetical interaction between neurons is not known, nor do we know which neurons are involved.

In addition to the medullary centers, there are also centers in the pons which aid in the regulation of breathing. The apneustic center when freed from the inhibitory influence of the pneumotaxic center causes a sustained inspiration. The role of these neurons in the automatic cycle of breathing is not yet known.

The pneumotaxic center is also located in the pons and acts to inhibit sustained inspirations.

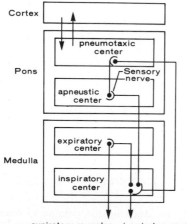

expiratory muscles   inspiratory muscles

Figure 16-10 Schematic diagram of the nervous pathways responsible for regulating respiratory acitivity. Sensory input (not detailed in diagram) may be from stretch receptors in lungs, from baroreceptors or chemoreceptors in carotid sinuses, or from cutaneous sensory fibers.

Both the pneumotaxic and apneustic centers are probably innervated by ascending neurons from the medulla. Figure 16-10 diagrams these respiratory centers and indicates some of the afferent signals used to modify respiratory rate or amplitude.

At one time it was thought that stretch-reflexes (the Hering-Breuer reflexes) were responsible for the rhythmic respiratory action. Stretch receptors in the lungs respond to the degree of inflation or stretch of the lungs and send impulses through vagus fibers to the respiratory centers of the medulla. These impulses inhibit the inspiratory center, and its output to the inspiratory muscles is stopped. There is a time delay in response to muscle stretch, and inspiration can reach completion before the inspiratory center is inhibited. This is a positive feedback control. It is not considered to create the rhythmicity of breathing because the receptors respond only to relatively extreme degrees of stretch, and also, as indicated above, transection of the vagus nerves does not inhibit this rhythmic action.

Other sensory inputs affect breathing rates. Especially important are chemoreceptors and baroreceptors located in the carotid sinus and aortic arch. Impulses from these receptors are carried by the vagus and glossopharyngeal nerves to the medullary centers. Chemoreceptors of the carotid sinus and aortic arch are sensitive to the P_{O_2} of the blood. They fire continuously at normal blood P_{O_2} levels, and their rate of firing greatly increases when the P_{O_2} is reduced to about 50 mm Hg (normal blood P_{O_2} in the arteries is about 100 mm Hg). Increase in the blood P_{CO_2} increases the sensitivity of the chemoreceptors to lowered oxygen levels. Impulses from the chemoreceptors excite the inspiratory center as well as the cardioexcitatory centers of the medulla. Baroreceptors are stretch receptors activated by changes of intravascular pressure. A rise in blood pressure increases the frequency of baroreceptor impulses and inhibits respiration rate. However, these receptors are probably more important to circulatory system control than to normal respiratory activity.

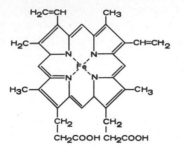

Figure 16-11 Heme portion of the hemoglobin molecule. Four pyrole rings are joined by methylene bridges to form the large porphyrin ring structure. The heme includes an atom of iron that acts as the site of the attachment of an oxygen molecule. This same basic structure is found in the cytochromes, although the various side groups attached to the pyrole rings differ. The chlorophyll molecule of green plants also has this type of structure, although the metal atom is magnesium and the side groups also are different.

The medulla has regions that are directly sensitive to changes in P_{CO_2} levels of the cerebrospinal fluid, which in turn are dependent on the P_{CO_2} of the blood. It also appears that the neurons capable of spontaneous discharge and responsible for the basic rhythmic activity of respiration are directly sensitive to the carbon dioxide levels of blood passing by them.

Respiratory control has been analyzed in terms of systems analysis (see, for example, Milsum, 1966). The respiratory system is, in many respects, part of the excretory system of the animal and respiratory control is designed to adequately eliminate CO_2 and also to maintain normal levels of blood CO_2, oxygen, and H^+.

Under conditions of stress, accessory muscles of the abdominal wall and upper thorax can be called into activity. Their contractions increase the depth of breathing and thus the amount of air moved into and out of the lungs at each cycle.

Transport of Respiratory Gases

16-14. Hemoglobin. Once oxygen has diffused from the atmosphere across the respiratory surface and into the blood, it is often transported by means of respiratory pigments. This is needed, at least in larger and active animals because of the relatively low solubility of oxygen in aqueous solutions. Vertebrate blood plasma can contain maximally about 0.3 ml of O_2 per 100 ml. However, by using transport pigments the concentration of oxygen carried by the blood may amount to 5 to 30 ml O_2 per ml depending on the species.

Oxygen transport pigments are conjugated proteins, that is, proteins complexed with another organic molecule or with one or more metal atoms. Because of the nature of the conjugated group, such transport molecules are colored and thus the term respiratory pigment.

Transport pigments contain metal atoms such as Cu^{2+} or Fe^{3+} to which oxygen can reversibly attach. Respiratory pigments are not oxidized by oxygen, rather they are oxygenated, that is, they combine reversibly with molecular oxygen. Respiratory pigments are of value not only because they allow the blood to carry a larger amount of oxygen than would otherwise be possible, but also because they quickly remove oxygen from solution at the

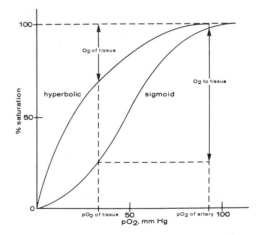

Figure 16-12 Showing the natures of oxygen saturation curves of respiratory pigments. The sigmoidal or hyperbolic nature of the curve depends on the properties of the respiratory pigment. It can be seen that a pigment with a sigmoid curve delivers more oxygen to tissues than does one with a hyperbolic curve at any given pO_2.

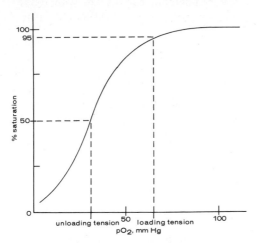

Figure 16-13 Oxygen dissociation curve of human hemoglobin. The loading tension is the pO_2 at which the respiratory pigment is 95 per cent saturated with oxygen. The unloading tension is the pO_2 at which the respiratory pigment has reached 50 per cent delivery of oxygen.

respiratory surface, thus maintaining a concentration gradient down which oxygen can diffuse. In addition, it is of value to carry molecular oxygen, O_2, rather than single oxygen atoms. Further the oxygenation process allows the pigment to pick up oxygen at sites of high oxygen tension and to unload the oxygen at sites of low oxygen tension (the latter being the body cells that require the oxygen).

In vertebrates the respiratory pigment is hemoglobin (see Roughton, 1964). Hemoglobin has a molecular weight of 68,000 and is composed of two pairs of polypeptide chains. Each chain carries an iron-containing heme group (Figure 16-11). The hemoglobin molecule is capable of transporting four oxygen molecules. When four oxygens are attached to hemoglobin the resulting complex is **oxyhemoglobin** and is said to be fully saturated with oxygen. The **oxygen capacity** of blood is defined as the total amount of oxygen that can be taken up by a unit volume of the blood and includes that oxygen transported by respiratory pigments as well as that in solution (the oxygen capacities of some animal bloods and body fluids are given in Table 16-6).

At a given pH the amount of oxygen that a given quantity of hemoglobin can pick up depends on the partial pressure of oxygen (Figure 16-12). The oxygen pressure is usually given in units of mm Hg, and the loading of the hemoglobin is given as the percentage of saturation with oxygen. Such plots are oxygen dissociation curves. The oxygen dissociation curve for human hemoglobin is given in Figure 16-13. It may be seen that at about 40 mm Hg oxygen tension a small fall in the P_{O_2} will allow a relatively large amount of oxygen to be released by the hemoglobin. Because 40 mm Hg is about the P_{O_2} of body fluids and tissues, hemoglobin is adapted to unload its oxygen at pressures close to those of the cells that need it. At higher P_{O_2} levels, which fall in the range of alveolar oxygen concentrations, hemoglobin becomes completely saturated with oxygen.

The term **half-saturation pressure** is given to the P_{O_2} at which hemoglobin (or any respiratory pigment) is only half-saturated with oxygen. A respiratory pigment with a lower half-saturation pressure has a higher affinity

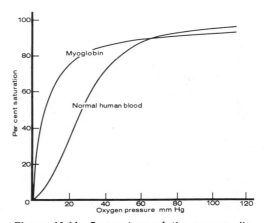

Figure 16-14 Comparison of the oxygen dissociation curves of myoglobin and hemoglobin. The sigmoid curve of hemoglobin is a measure of the ability of hemoglobin to release oxygen readily to tissues at relatively high values of the pO_2. The hyperbolic curve of myoglobin shows that this respiratory pigment will not release oxygen until pO_2 of tissues becomes relatively low. This is a feature expected of a molecule acting as an oxygen storage pigment. Myoglobin does not deliver oxygen to tissues until normal oxygen supply is insufficient to permit high activity.

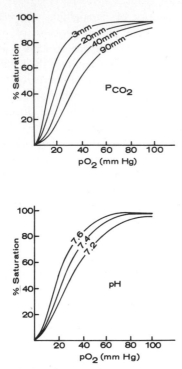

Figure 16-15 Oxygen dissociation curves for hemoglobin. The effects of changes in pH and P_{CO_2} are shown. This is the Bohr effect.

for oxygen when compared with a pigment having a higher half-saturation pressure. It is of interest to compare the muscle oxygen-storage pigment myoglobin with hemoglobin (Figure 16-14). Myoglobin has a half-satura-tion pressure of about 6 mm Hg, and that of human hemoglobin is about 24 mm Hg. Myoglobin remains complexed with its oxygen until the oxygen levels of the muscle are lowered considerably—a time at which the muscle requires oxygen.

It will be noted that the oxygen dissociation curve of myoglobin is hyperbolic, whereas that for hemoglobin is sigmoid. Myoglobin contains only one chain (Figure 2-14) and one heme group and can combine with only one oxygen molecule. The sigmoid oxygen dissocia-tion curve of hemoglobin results from the com-bination of hemoglobin with four oxygen molecules. As is desirable in an oxygen storage pigment, myoglobin hangs onto all of its oxygen at oxygen tensions where hemoglobin is 98 per cent dissociated.

The hemoglobin equilibrium with oxygen was mathematically described by Hill (1910):

$$\frac{y}{100} = \frac{KP^n}{1 + KP^n} \qquad (16.3)$$

where y is the per cent saturation with O_2; P is the partial pressure of oxygen; K is the equilibrium constant of the reaction; and n is a measure of the interaction between heme groups. After rearranging and taking the logarithms of both sides:

$$\log \left(\frac{y}{100 - y}\right) = \log K + n \log P \qquad (16.4)$$

A plot of $\log [y/(100 - y)]$ against $\log P$ yields a straight line whose slope is n. The intercept on the $\log [y/(100 - y)]$ axis gives the value of K. For myoglobin which contains only 1 heme group, $n = 1$. For hemoglobin between 20 and 98 per cent saturation, $n = 2.7$.

In hemoglobin the interaction of one heme group with an oxygen molecule influences the affinity of the other heme groups for oxygen (increases it). Since the three-dimensional structure of hemoglobin (Chapter 2) shows that the heme groups are relatively separated, it is thought that combination of oxygen with one heme group affects the total protein structure, thus making other heme groups more available for oxygenation.

Oxygen dissociation curves are also affected by the pH and by the blood P_{CO_2}. Low pH or high P_{CO_2} both shift the curve to the right (in most cases). This is the Bohr effect and is important in oxygen transport pigment func-tioning (see Figure 16-15). In the capillaries the P_{CO_2} about active tissues is elevated, and the blood is slightly more acid. Under these condi-tions the shift of the oxygen dissociation curve to the right under the influence of pH facili-tates oxygen unloading and therefore increases the amount of oxygen available to the active cells. The mechanisms by which P_{CO_2} and pH affect the dissociation curve appear to be different, although high P_{CO_2} does cause a low blood pH. Rises in temperature also shift the oxygen dissociation curve to the right.

Hemoglobin in different vertebrate groups may differ in structure and oxygen carrying ability (Figure 16-16). For example, lamprey

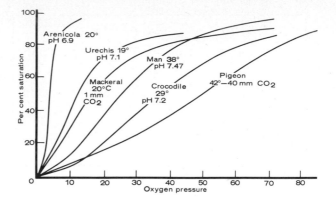

Figure 16-16 Oxygen dissociation curves of hemoglobin-containing bloods of various animals. [Data from various sources reported in Prosser and Brown (1961).]

hemoglobin contains only one heme group. Hagfish have hemoglobins that contain one and two heme units. Hemoglobin is commonly found in many invertebrates, but its presence is not indicative of an oxygen transport function. As already indicated, some snails possess hemoglobin in certain muscles, and here it presumably acts as an oxygen storage pigment.

Hemoglobin acts as a transport pigment in most annelids, nemerteans, phoronids, and echiuroids. Hemoglobin may be present in solution in the blood, but its efficiency as a respiratory pigment is increased when it is packed into cells as is the case in most vertebrates. The protein portion of hemoglobins has molecular weights ranging from 17,000 to over 3,000,000 as in some annelids. In the unoxygenated state hemoglobin is dark red, in the oxygenated state it is bright red.

16-15. Other Respiratory Pigments. Other oxygen transport pigments are found in the invertebrates. **Hemocyanin** is a copper-containing protein that functions in oxygen transport in gastropod and cephalopod molluscs, in crustaceans, arachnids, and in *Limulus*. Its molecular weight ranges from 1 million to 7 million. In the oxygenated state it is blue, and in the unoxygenated state it is colorless or white. Hemocyanin is never found contained within cells but always in suspension in the blood. One molecule of hemocyanin contains two copper atoms and can combine with one molecule of oxygen.

Hemerythrin is a nonheme protein respiratory pigment found in sipunculids, priapulids, and brachiopods. It is purple when oxygenated and brownish when unoxygenated. It is contained within coelomocytes that circulate in the coelomic fluid. The molecular weight of hemerythrin is about 100,000, and each molecule contains several iron atoms. One oxygen molecule combines with two or three iron atoms.

Chlorocruorin has a structure resembling that of hemoglobin except that in the heme group one vinyl group is replaced by a formyl group. The pigment is green in both the oxygenated and unoxygenated states. It is found in two families of marine polychaetes: the Serpulidae and Sabellidae. Chlorocuorin has a molecular weight of about 3 million, and as with hemoglobin, one oxygen molecule combines with each of its four heme groups. The pigment occurs in suspension in the blood.

Some worms may have both chlorocruorin and hemoglobin, whereas other species may have only one or the other. In some molluscs the blood contains hemocyanin, and muscles contain hemoglobin. Thus the presence of one respiratory pigment does not exclude the presence of others.

Figures 16-17 and 16-18 show the oxygen dissociation curves of some different respiratory pigments and also show the nature of the curves for different species. Although all of the curves appear basically similar, differences in the half-saturation tensions, in the degree of sigmoidness of the curves, and the effect of pH on the curves may differ. A given pigment may not exhibit the Bohr effect in a given animal,

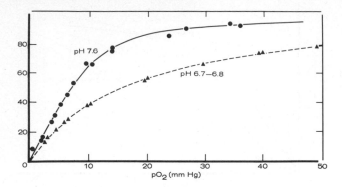

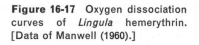

Figure 16-17 Oxygen dissociation curves of *Lingula* hemerythrin. [Data of Manwell (1960).]

although all of the respiratory pigments have been shown to exhibit such behavior in some species. In some cases, high CO_2 tensions enhance the uptake of oxygen by the pigment, an effect known as the reverse Bohr effect.

Generally oxygen transport pigments are adapted to the environment in which the animal lives. For example, the inverse Bohr effect facilitates oxygen uptake at low P_{O_2} and high P_{CO_2} in the external environment. Animals whose respiratory pigments exhibit this effect or in which the Bohr effect is absent live in stagnant waters or in mud where oxygen tensions are low.

The Bohr effect appears to be physiologically unimportant in frogs and decapod crustaceans because the difference between the P_{CO_2} in arteries and veins is not great. However, in cases where extreme muscular activity is used and where the output of CO_2 is thus great, the Bohr effect will be of value in obtaining oxygen unloading at the tissue cell level.

16-16. Carbon Dioxide Transport. Carbon dioxide produced by tissue cells is transported to the lungs or other respiratory surfaces for excretion. Only small amounts of CO_2 are in solution in the blood because of reactions that occur in the plasma and in the erythrocytes of vertebrates.

CO_2 dissolved in water forms carbonic acid, H_2CO_3, a reaction speeded by the enzyme carbonic anhydrase found in the blood of many animal species. In vertebrates carbonic anhydrase occurs primarily in the erythrocytes. Carbonic acid can dissociate into H^+ and HCO_3^- and these ions then can enter into

the acid-base regulating mechanisms to be discussed in the next section.

Some carbon dioxide (15 to 20 per cent) reacts with hemoglobin:

$$HbNH_2 + CO_2 \rightleftharpoons HbNHCOOH$$
$$\rightleftharpoons HbNHCOO^-$$

where the NH_2 represents amino groups of the amino acids of the hemoglobin. The complex is known as carbaminohemoglobin.

At the respiratory surface CO_2 diffuses from the blood to the atmosphere or aqueous

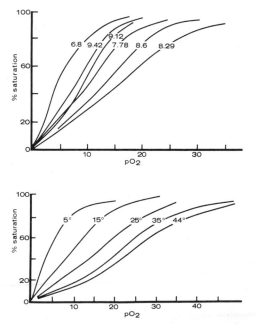

Figure 16-18 Oxygen dissociation curves for *Limulus* hemocyanin at different pH's and at different temperatures. This hemocyanin exhibits a reverse Bohr effect. [Data from Redfield and Ingalls (1933).]

Table 16-6 Oxygen Capacities of Various Bloods*

ANIMAL	ml O_2/ 100 ml BLOOD	TRANSPORT PIGMENT
Molluscs		
Helix pomatia	1.2–1.6	Hemocyanin
Loligo pealei	3.8–4.5	Hemocyanin
Octopus vulgaris	3.1–5.0	Hemocyanin
Busycon canaliculatum	2.1–3.4	Hemocyanin
Crustaceans		
Maja squinado	0.8–1.31	Hemocyanin
Callinectes sapidus	1.3	Hemocyanin
Carcinus maenus	1.1–1.2	Hemocyanin
Cancer pagarus	1.6	Hemocyanin
Homarus vulgarus	3.0–3.1	Hemocyanin
Astacus fluviatilis	2.4	Hemocyanin
Limulus polyphemus	0.7–2.1	Hemocyanin
Worms		
Arenicola	5.7–8.7	Hemoglobin
Sipunculus	1.6	Hemerythrin
Urechis	2.2–6.7	Hemoglobin
Spirographis	9.8–10.6	Chlorocruorin
Vertebrates		
Rana esculenta	9.8	Hemoglobin
Crocodilus acutus	9	Hemoglobin
Columba	20	Hemoglobin
Homo sapiens	20	Hemoglobin

* Data from Prosser and Brown (1961); Dhéré (1928).

medium. Carbonic anhydrase catalyzes the reverse reaction from that given above and aids in forming CO_2 that can be eliminated. The direction of the reaction depends on the P_{CO_2}. Where the CO_2 pressure is low, as in the region of the respiratory exchange surface, H_2CO_3 is split into H_2O and CO_2, and the latter moves down its concentration gradient to the exterior.

It may be noted that the interactions of P_{CO_2} and P_{O_2} levels at different sites in the animal are coordinated and intermeshed in such a way that oxygen diffusion to tissue cells is facilitated just where oxygen is most needed, while oxygen intake from the environment is also facilitated. Similarly, carbon dioxide removal from the tissues to the blood and then from the blood to the external medium is facilitated by the actions involved in oxygen transport. The two systems are interwoven to fill the requirements of the organism.

16-17. Acid-Base Balance. A full discussion of acid-base regulation is found in Roughton (1964) or in West et al. (1968). Here space permits only a discussion of the basic events that take place to maintain proper hydrogen ion levels in the blood and tissues.

When CO_2 diffuses into the blood and forms carbonic acid, the dissociation of the latter forms H^+ and HCO_3^-. The hydrogen ions, unless buffered, would cause dangerously low pH levels in the animal. The hydrogen ions are taken up by the proteins of the blood in exchange for metal ions such as K^+ and Na^+. $NaHCO_3$, $KHCO_3$, and phosphates are formed in the blood (the discussion here will be based on events in mammals). Thus plasma components act to buffer the blood pH and prevent it from decreasing. These reactions also ease the further formation of HCO_3^- from carbonic acid and keep CO_2 flowing into the system from the tissues (again it may be noted that this is based on the maintenance of adequate concentration gradients. When a given substance is converted to a new compound, the concentration of the latter does not influence the diffusion of the original substance).

Erythrocyte hemoglobin also aids in buffering the blood pH and allows more CO_2 to enter the blood from body tissues. Then CO_2 diffuses into the erythrocytes from the plasma and is converted to H_2CO_3 by erythrocyte carbonic anhydrase. Again, the carbonic acid dissociates to form H^+ and HCO_3^- within the cell.

At the tissue level, hemoglobin gives up its oxygen and may then combine with H^+: $Hb^- + H^+ \rightleftharpoons HbH$. This reaction is of extreme importance in maintaining the pH of the cell at a constant level. The structure of hemoglobin is such that when it gives up

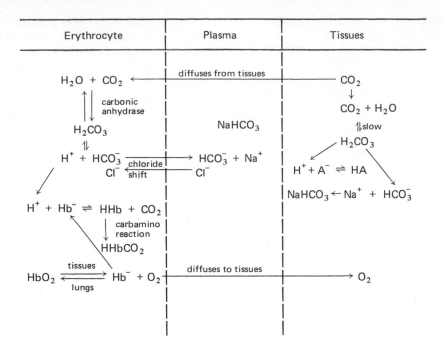

Figure 16-19 Important reactions used in the transport of carbon dioxide. These reactions serve to maintain the pH of the blood and body tissues.

oxygen it is converted at the right time and the right place to a substance capable of combining with the hydrogen ions formed as a result of CO_2 diffusion from the tissues.

The HCO_3^- ion concentration within the erythrocyte increases because of the reactions just described, and bicarbonate diffuses out to the plasma. As stated in Chapter 6, the erythrocyte membrane is not permeable to cations, so in order to preserve electrical neutrality, for every HCO_3^- ion that diffuses into the plasma, a Cl^- moves into the erythrocyte, where it associates with an alkali metal ion, usually Na^+ or K^+. This is known as the chloride or Hamburger shift.

At the respiratory surface all of these reactions reverse because CO_2 can diffuse into the external medium. When hemoglobin combines with oxygen, it releases hydrogen ions (the Haldane effect). The oxygenated hemoglobin associates with the alkali metal ions that were originally associated with the Cl^-. Chloride ions diffuse out of the cell, and HCO_3^- diffuses back into the cell to react with the H^+. Carbonic acid is formed and then

rapidly converted by carbonic anhydrase to CO_2 and water. The CO_2 follows its concentration gradient and diffuses out of the cell, through the plasma, into the external environment.

It is to be noted that the operation of this system depends upon the presence of proper levels of protein, alkali metal ions, Cl^-, HCO_3^-, and phosphate. The overall system is diagrammed in Figure 16-19. In Chapter 14 it was stated that one function of the kidney is to maintain proper levels of Na^+ and K^+ in the body fluids. An important need for relatively high levels of these ions arises from the requirement for these substances in the buffering system that maintains blood pH at its proper level even while the acid waste product CO_2 is being transported. The kidney tubules have enzyme systems and buffering mechanisms that trade waste products such as NH_4 and H^+ for ions such as Na^+ and K^+. There is also an exchange of HCO_3^- for Cl^-. The pH is maintained constant while simultaneously needed ions are retained.

Proteins may have many ionizable side

groups because of the nature of their constituent amino acids, and a molecule such as hemoglobin is capable of reacting with 20 to 50 positively charged ions. That is, the buffering capacity of proteins is relatively high. When blood proteins are low in concentration because of disease or metabolic upsets, H^+ begins to accumulate, lowering the blood pH and finally resulting in the condition of **acidosis**. Low blood pH will, in turn, create low pH's of the body fluids and cells. Unless such a condition is rectified, death will ensue because cells can withstand only relatively small changes in pH. In mammals, for example, changes in the blood pH greater than a few tenths of a pH unit result in death.

Respiratory-Circulatory Adaptations

16-18. Diving Animals. In both vertebrates and invertebrates there has been found a good correlation between adaptations of the respiratory and circulatory systems and the ecological distribution (see Gordon, 1968). In this and the following section, I will briefly discuss some of these adaptations that have permitted animals to exploit different environments or to survive environmental changes. The stress will be on vertebrates because, again, these animals have been most intensively studied. The important factors in the environment that necessitate such adaptations include oxygen tension of the medium, the temperature, and the pH. General references to vertebrate respiratory adaptations include Foxon (1964); Fry (1957); Hughes (1963); Krogh (1959) and Rahn (1967). References to vertebrate circulatory adaptations include Anderson (1966); Elsner et al. (1966); Johansen and Martin (1965) and Simmons (1960).

Interesting adaptations are found in animals that are air-breathing but also can dive under water and remain submerged for relatively long periods of time. Table 16-7 presents the durations and depths achieved by some diving mammals.

The major problems facing the air breather when under water include a lack of available oxygen, difficulty in eliminating carbon dioxide, and the proper distribution of available oxygen to proper regions of the body. In addition deep-diving animals often encounter low temperature zones (where heat conservation becomes important) and high pressures. Coming up from a dive also presents a problem because gases in the lung expand and

Table 16-7 Duration and Depths of Diving Mammals*

ANIMAL	DURATION (min)	DEPTH (m)
Platypus	10	—
Mink, *Mustela vison*	3	—
Harbor seal, *Phoca vitulina*	20	—
Walrus, *Odobenus rosmarus*	10	80
Gray seal, *Halichoerus grypus*	20	100
Sperm whale, *Physeter catodon*	75	900
Blue whale, *Sibbaldus musculus*	49	100
Harbor porpoise, *Phocaena phocaena*	12	20
Beaver, *Castor canadensis*	15	
Man (average)	1	
Skin divers (experienced)	2.5	

* Data from Irving (1964).

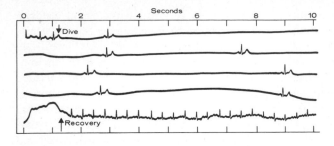

Figure 16-20 Sections of an ECG from an 8-minute dive of a seal (*Halichoerus*). Note how rapidly the diving bradycardia developed after dive started. [From data of Scholander (1940).]

dissolved blood gases of low solubility (especially nitrogen) form bubbles in the blood. The last phenomenon is familiar as diver's bends or caison disease. Danger of bubble formation is probably greater in human divers wearing diving suits (where there is a continuous inflow of air and thus a build-up of nitrogen) than in natural divers.

Several adaptations are found that allow animals to dive under water. In diving seals the lactic acid concentration of arterial blood does not increase during a dive, indicating that the muscles retain their lactic acid rather than releasing it into the blood. This retention aids in maintaining a normal level of blood pH. Similar retention has also been found in ducks and alligators (Anderson, 1961). Muscle blood flow is reduced during diving because of vasoconstriction, which persists even during long dives. Blood flow to the head region is always maintained.

Heart rate generally falls during diving, but arterial pressure is maintained because the peripheral resistance is high and cardiac output is decreased (Elsner et al., 1966). All diving mammals examined exhibit a highly elastic enlargement of the aorta that doubles the diameter of the ascending aorta. This device may provide the energy (through elastic recoil, see Section 12-13) necessary to maintain diastolic pressure. Some cardiovascular changes found in diving mammals are illustrated in Figure 16-20.

Diving mammals do not have larger lung volumes than nondivers. Large whales, in fact, have only about 50 per cent the lung volume per unit weight of other mammals. Scholander (1960) has suggested that the lungs of whales collapse during deep dives. This would cause all respiratory gases to be in the dead space regions, and there would be a decrease in the diffusion of nitrogen into the blood. In this manner caisson disease would be prevented because only a small amount of nitrogen would require disposal upon reemergence. In general, diving animals do not appear to take in oxygen reserves by increased inspiration before diving.

To some extent diving animals tend to have a larger blood volume than non divers and in many cases have a greater oxygen carrying capacity in the blood. Oxygen dissociation curves vary according to the structure of hemoglobin found in various species. As already indicated, a shift of the dissociation curve to the right indicates a respiratory pigment with a relatively higher oxygen tension loading point. An animal with such a pigment would have an oxygen-transport capability of limited use in environments of low oxygen tension. The relation between hemoglobin structure and oxygen-carrying capacity is a good example of how a biochemical characteristic can limit the distribution of animals. Not much is now known about the structural modifications of hemoglobin that are correlated with increases or decreases or oxygen capacity (see Scholander, 1960). In three species of porpoises it has been found that the oxygen carrying capacity of the blood is correlated with the oxygen tensions of the water inhabited by each genus (Ridgway and Johnston, 1966). Similar studies with seven species of squirrels have also shown correlations between environment and hemoglobin-oxygen affinity (Hall, 1965).

In alligators and crocodiles there is a more exaggerated Bohr effect found as compared with terrestrial lizards. Unloading of oxygen is facilitated by acidification of the blood, an action that would tend to occur under water when carbon dioxide cannot be eliminated.

Diving mammals generally have myoglobins that unload at lower oxygen tensions than those of nondivers. These oxygen reserves are utilized by the muscles which receive little blood flow during a dive.

In general then it appears that diving mammals are enabled to remain under water on the basis of an oxygen reserve (myoglobin in the muscles, and perhaps oxygen in venous blood reservoirs), a lowered metabolism, a decrease in cardiac output, a peripheral vasoconstriction while maintaining blood flow to the central nervous system, the presence of a larger volume of blood with a greater oxygen carrying capacity caused by adaptations of the hemoglobin molecule, and a decrease in sensitivity of the control systems for respiration and circulation to increasing carbon dioxide concentrations. At this time very little is known concerning the nature of central nervous system controls over these activities in the diving animal.

16-19. High Altitude Adaptations. The effects of high altitudes on humans has been of some interest in recent years, especially because of the Olympic contests held in Mexico and in Colorado. The major problem of high altitudes is caused by the drop in barometric pressure and a consequent decrease in P_{O_2} at progressively higher altitudes. This leads to a decrease in the $P_{O_{2a}}$ and to problems of hypoxia.

A major adaptation allowing animals to live at high altitudes is a greater oxygen affinity of hemoglobin. Animals such as the llama and vicuña have hemoglobins of much greater oxygen affinity than their low altitude relatives. High altitude mammals have hematocrits and red blood cell counts that are similar to those of sea-level relatives. When sea-level animals become acclimated to high altitudes, it is found that the red blood cell count and hematocrit are increased; however, the oxygen dissociation curve is not altered. Thus oxygen carrying capacity of the blood is increased by increasing the amount of hemoglobin available. It seems that hypoxia in mammals causes the release of a hormone erythropoietin. This hormone stimulates red blood cell production and release from the bone marrow. The kidney appears to be the site of production of this hormone.

When a sea-level animal is brought to high altitudes, the first signs of adjustment are seen as a sympathetic vasoconstriction in the skin and kidneys while blood flow to the brain, heart, and skeletal muscles is increased. After some time at a high altitude, tissue vascularization increases—an action that decreases the distance over which oxygen must diffuse to the tissue cells. It may be noted that tissues do not appear to change their oxygen requirements during acclimation.

Ventilation, driven by chemoreceptor controls, increases progressively up to about 19,000 feet. At higher altitudes pulmonary ventilation cannot supply oxygen needs. At about 23,000 feet the arterial oxygen saturations falls below 50 per cent, and at this point unconsciousness results. At about 12,000 feet mental functions become disrupted and hypoxia causes sleepiness, mental fatigue, and headache in humans. Hyperventilation cannot offset hypoxia above certain limits. Among other factors hyperventilation depresses blood P_{CO_2} and elevates the pH. The H^+ receptors in the medulla then act to inhibit respiration until pH can be lowered by renal mechanisms to the normal point. As blood pH is lowered, the medullary centers can again increase respiratory activity.

Many birds have been observed at altitudes of 23,000 to 27,000 feet. However, the mechanisms that allow them to adjust to high altitudes have not been studied. Many amphibians and reptiles have been observed at high altitudes. In these animals food and water supply appear to be a more limiting factor than hypoxia. Further details on high altitude adaptations may be found in the several volumes comprising Section 3 of the *Handbook of Physiology* (American Physiological Society, Washington, D.C.).

References and Readings

Anderson, H. T. (1961). "Physiological adjustments to prolonged diving in the American alligator *Alligator mississippiensis.*" *Acta Physiol. Scand.* **53:** 23–45.

Anderson, H. T. (1964). "Stresses imposed on diving vertebrates during prolonged underwater exposure." *Symp. Soc. Exp. Biol.* **18:** 109–127.

Anderson, H. T. (1966). "Physiological adaptations in diving vertebrates." *Physiol. Rev.* **46:** 212–243.

Anderson, H. T. and P. F. Scholander (1957). "Physiological response to air exposure in codfish." *Science* **126:** 505.

Antonini, E. (1965). "Interrelationship between structure and function in hemoglobin and myoglobin." *Physiol. Rev.* **45:** 123–170.

Briehl, R. W. (1963). "The relation between the oxygen equilibrium and aggregation of subunits of lamprey hemoglobin." *J. Biol. Chem.* **238:** 2361–2366.

Buck, J. (1962). "Insect respiration." *Ann. Rev. Entomol.* **7:** 27–56.

Carter, G. S. (1931). "Aquatic and aerial respiration in animals." *Biol. Rev.* **6:** 1–35.

Clements, J. A. and D. F. Tierney (1965). "Alveolar stability associated with altered surface tension." In: **Handbook of Physiology** (W. O. Fenn and H. Rahn, eds.), Section 3, Vol. 2, pp. 1565–1583. Washington, D.C.: American Physiological Society.

Comroe, J. H. (1965). **The Physiology of Respiration.** Chicago: Yearbook Medical Publishers.

deReuck, A. V. S. and M. O'Connor, eds. (1962). **Pulmonary Structure and Function.** Boston: Little, Brown and Company. 403 pp.

Dhéré, C. (1928). "Sur quelques pigments respiratoires des Invertebres." *Rev. Suisse Zool.* **35:** 277–289.

Elsner, R. W., D. L. Franklin, R. L. van Citters, and D. W. Kennedy (1966). "Cardiovascular defence against asphyxia." *Science* **153:** 941–949.

Elsner, R. W., W. F. Garey, and P. F. Scholander (1963). "Selective ischemia in diving man." *Am. Heart J.* **65:** 571–572.

Fange, R. (1966). "Physiology of the swim bladder." *Physiol. Rev.* **46:** 299–322.

Foxon, G. E. H. (1964). "Blood and respiration." In: **Physiology of the Amphibia** (J. A. Moore, ed.), pp. 151–209. New York: Academic Press, Inc.

Fry, F. E. J. (1957). "The aquatic respiration of fish." In: **The Physiology of Fishes** (M. E. Brown, ed.), Vol. 1, pp. 1–63. New York: Academic Press, Inc.

Ghirreti, F. (1966). "Respiration." In: **The Physiology of Mollusca** (K. M. Wilbur and C. M. Yonge, eds.), Vol. 2, pp. 175–207. New York: Academic Press, Inc.

Gordon, M. S. (1968). **Animal Function: Principles and Adaptations.** New York: The Macmillan Company. 560 pp.

Grollman, S. (1964). **The Human Body.** New York: The Macmillan Company. 611 pp.

Hall, F. G. (1965). "Hemoglobin and oxygen affinities in seven species of Sciuridae." *Science* **148:** 1350–1351.

Handbook of Physics and Chemistry, 40th ed. (1958–1959). Cleveland, Ohio: The Chemical Rubber Company.

Hill, A. V. (1910). "The possible effects of the aggregation of the molecules of hemoglobin on its dissociation curve." *J. Physiol.* (London) **40:** 4.

Hill, R. (1936). "The oxygen dissociation curve of muscle myoglobin." *Proc. Roy. Soc.* (London) **B120:** 472–483.

Hinton, H. E. (1968). "Spiracular gills." *Adv. Insect Physiol.* **5:** 65–162.

Hughes, G. M. and G. Shelton (1958). "The mechanism of gill ventilation in three freshwater teleosts." *J. Exp. Biol.* **35:** 807–823.

Hughes, G. M. and G. Shelton (1962). "Respiratory mechanisms and their nervous control in fish." *Comp. Physiol. Biochem.* **1:** 275–364.

Hunter, W. R. (1964). "Physiological aspects of ecology in nonmarine molluscs." In: **Physiology of Mollusca** (K. M. Wilbur and C. M. Yonge, eds.), Vol. 1, pp. 83–125. New York: Academic Press, Inc.

Irving, L. (1924). "Ciliary currents in the starfish." *J. Exp. Zool.* **41:** 115–124.

Irving, L. (1926). "Regulation of the hydrogen

ion concentration and its relation to metabolism and respiration in the starfish." *J. Gen. Physiol.* **10**: 345:–358.

Irving, L. (1939). "Respiration in diving mammals." *Physiol. Rev.* **19**: 112–134.

Irving, L. (1964). "Comparative anatomy and physiology of gas transport mechanisms." In: **Handbook of Physiology** (W. O. Fenn and H. Rahn, eds.), Section 3, Vol. 1, pp. 177–212. Washington D.C.: American Physiological Society.

Johansen, K. and A. W. Martin (1965). "Comparative aspects of cardiovascular function in vertebrates." In: **Handbook of Physiology** (W. F. Hamilton and P. Dow, eds.), Section 2, Vol. 3, pp. 2583 2614. Washington, D.C.: American Physiological Society.

Jørgensen, C. B. (1965). "Quantitative aspects of filter feeding in vertebrates." *Biol. Rev.* **30**: 391–454.

Krogh, A. (1959). **The Comparative Physiology of Respiratory Mechanisms.** Philadelphia: University of Pennsylvania Press. 142 pp.

Kuhn, W., A. Ramel, H. J. Kuhn, and E. Marti (1963). "The filling mechanism of the swim bladder, generation of high gas pressures through hair-pin countercurrent multiplication." *Experientia* **19**: 497–522.

Leivestad, H., H. Anderson, and P. F. Scholander (1964). "Physiological responses to air exposure in codfish." *Science* **126**: 505.

Manwell, C. (1960). "Oxygen equilibrium of brachiopod *Lingula* hemerythrin." *Science* **132**: 550–551.

McCutcheon, F. H. (1940). "The respiratory mechanism of the grasshopper." *Ann. Ent. Soc. America* **23**: 35–55.

Milsum, J. H. (1966). **Biological Control Systems Analysis.** New York: The McGraw-Hill Book Company, Inc. 466 pp.

Newell, G. E. (1964). "Physiological aspects of the ecology of intertidal molluscs." In: **Physiology of Mollusca** (K. M. Wilbur and C. M. Yonge, eds.), Vol. 1, pp. 59–81. New York: Academic Press, Inc.

Nicol, J. A. C. (1967). **The Biology of Marine Animals,** 2nd ed. New York: John Wiley & Sons, Inc. 699 pp.

Otis, A. B. (1964). "Quantitative relationships in steady-state gas exchange." In: **Handbook of Physiology** (W. O. Fenn and H. Rahn, eds.), Section 3, Vol. 1, pp. 681–697. Washington, D.C.: American Physiological Society.

Pappenheimer, J. R. (1950). "Standardization of definitions and symbols in respiratory physiology." *Fed. Proc.* **9**: 602–605.

Pattle, R. E. (1965). "Surface lining of lung alveoli." *Physiol. Rev.* **45**: 48–79.

Pitts, R. F. (1946). "Organization of the respiratory center." *Physiol. Rev.* **26**: 609–630.

Prosser, C. L. and F. A. Brown (1961). **Comparative Animal Physiology,** 2nd ed. Philadelphia: W. B. Saunders Company. 688 pp.

Radford, E. P. (1964). "The physics of gases." In: **Handbook of Physiology** (W. O. Fenn and H. Rahn, eds.), Section 3, Vol. 1, pp. 125–151. Washington, D.C.: American Physiological Society.

Rahn, H. (1967). "Aquatic gas exchange theory." In: **Respiration Physiology** (N. B. Slonin and J. R. Chapin, eds.), Vol. 1, pp. 1–12. St. Louis, Mo.: The C. V. Mosby Company.

Redfield, A. C. (1934). "The haemocyanins." *Biol. Rev.* **9**: 175–212.

Ridgway, S. H. and D. G. Johnston (1966). "Blood oxygen and ecology of porpoises of three genera." *Science* **151**: 456–458.

Riggs, A. (1965). "Functional properties of hemoglobins." *Physiol. Rev.* **45**: 619–673.

Roughton, F. J. W. (1964). "Transport of oxygen and carbon dioxide." In: **Handbook of Physiology** (W. O. Fenn and H. Rahn, eds.), Section 3, Vol. 1, pp. 767–825. Washington, D.C.: American Physiological Society.

Scholander, P. F. (1940). "Experimental investigations on the respiratory function in diving mammals and birds." *Hvalradets Skrifter, Norske Videnskaps*—Akad. Oslo **22**.

Scholander, P. F. (1954). "Secretion of gases against high pressures in the swim-bladder of deep sea fishes." II. Rete mirabile. *Biol. Bull.* **107**: 260–277.

Scholander, P. F. (1960). "Oxygen transport

through hemoglobin solutions." *Science* **131**: 585–590.

Scholander, P. F., H. T. Hammel, H. LeMessurier, E. Hemmingsen, and W. Garey (1962). "Circulatory adjustment in pearl divers." *J. Appl. Physiol.* **17**: 184–190.

Simmons, J. R. (1960). "The blood-vascular system." In: **Biology and Comparative Physiology of Birds** (A. J. Marshal, ed.), Vol. 1, pp. 345–362. New York: Academic Press, Inc.

Sverdrup, H. U., M. W. Johnson, and R. H. Fleming (1942). **The Oceans.** Englewood Cliffs, N.J.: Prentice-Hall, Inc. 1087 pp.

Thomas, H. J. (1954). "The oxygen uptake of the lobster (*Homarus vulgaris*)." *J. Exp. Biol.* **31**: 228–251.

Umbreit, W. W., R. H. Burris, and J. F. Stauffer (1964). **Manometric Techniques,** 4th ed. Minneapolis: Burgess Publishing Company. 305 pp.

van Dam, L. (1938). "On the utilization of oxygen and regulation of breathing in some aquatic animals." Doctoral dissertation. Groningen.

van Rossum, J. M. (1963). "The relation between chemical structure and biological activity." *J. Pharm. Pharmacol.* **15**: 285–316.

Wang, S. C. and S. H. Ngai (1964). "General organization of central respiratory mechanisms." In: **Handbook of Physiology** (W. O. Fenn and H. Rahn, eds.), Section 3, Vol. 1, pp. 487–505. Washington, D.C.: American Physiological Society.

West, E. S., W. R. Todd, H. S. Mason, and J. T. Bruggen (1966). **Textbook of Biochemistry,** 4th ed. New York: The Macmillan Company. 1595 pp.

Widdecombe, J. G. (1964). "Respiratory reflexes." In: **Handbook of Physiology** (W. O. Fenn and H. Rahn, eds.), Section 3, Vol. 1, pp. 585–630. Washington, D.C.: American Physiological Society.

Wigglesworth, V. B. (1954). **Principles of Insect Physiology.** London: Methuen & Co., Ltd.

Wigglesworth, V. B. (1959). "Migration of tracheoles." *J. Exp. Biol.* **36**: 632–640.

Wolvekamp, H. P. and T. H. Waterman (1960). "Respiration." In: **Physiology of Crustacea** (T. H. Waterman, ed.), Vol. 1, pp. 35–100. New York: Academic Press, Inc.

THIS final part of the book considers some aspects of sensory reception and some examples of animal behavior. Although sensory receptors have been classified and their potentials discussed in Chapter 8, many aspects of sensory physiology have not yet been considered. In preceding chapters, when receptors formed part of a physiological system, they were generally interoreceptors used to measure changes in the internal environment. In these last chapters exteroreceptors, which provide the animal with information about the external environment (both the physical and the biological environments) and whose excitation leads to external responses such as body orientation, locomotion, and animal interactions are considered.

In its broadest sense animal behavior is the totality of things an animal does. In addition to responses of the types listed above, other important aspects of sensory perception and behavior include the production of sensory sensations, the capacity for memory, learning, and consciousness, and the utilization of endogenous rhythmic activities. Behavior is a broad subject, and it is impossible to cover it adequately here. Animal behavior may be observed and quantitated under natural conditions. It may be studied by placing an animal under controlled laboratory conditions. Behavioral mechanisms can be studied in terms of sensory physiology, neurophysiology (for example, the basic reflexes and endogenous activities of the CNS discussed in Chapter 11), and endocrine responses. Animal behavior is intimately associated with animal ecology, the study of animals in relation to their environment. The adaptive aspects of sensory reception and behavior, together with studies of comparative behavior, are important when evolution and survival of animals is a consideration.

In addition to sensory reception, I have included a discussion of two special effectors in this part of the book. Chromatophore color changes and light production by organisms are often important adaptive mechanisms and play a role in animal behavior.

I wish to stress again that, in comparison with the other parts of this book, this part is more general with less specific information or detailed coverage. Space limitations simply preclude a full discussion of the topics mentioned here. However, I think that enough information is given so that the reader will see how all of the various systems discussed in previous parts of the book come into full play to produce the animal activities described here. Examples of animal behavior or information processing are selected primarily because they are ones of some interest to me. It is hoped that they illustrate the principles involved in sensory perception and animal responses.

The activities of the whole animal, that is, of its

Part IV

Some Aspects of Sensory Physiology and Information Processing

integrated and coordinated systems, are a logical culmination of any discussion of animal physiology. The basic physical and chemical mechanisms on which nerves, synapses, receptors, and contractile elements function were given in earlier chapters. Some basic actions of nervous and endocrine systems were also presented. Where possible in this part of the book, I have discussed mechanisms underlying receptor activities; but a major feature of sensory reception, sensory sensation, and behavior is the interconnected networks of elements that take part in the activities of the animal. Our understanding of these is extremely limited at the minute. Sensory sensations, memory, and consciousness are concepts that have very little basis in factual theories relative to other topics of physiology, and it was my choice to abbreviate these topics in order to maintain the length of the book at a reasonable level.

Mechanics of Light Perception

17-1. Some Characteristics of Light. A sea of electromagnetic radiation bathes the surface of the earth and includes x-rays, ultraviolet, visible, and infrared light, microwaves, and radio waves. Only a small range of wavelengths of the total radiant energy spectrum makes up what is termed visible light—the radiation that is directly perceived by many animals (Figure 17-1).

Electromagnetic radiation travels at the speed of light (186,000 miles/sec) in the form of small packets or quanta of energy. The energy of a given quantum of radiation depends on its wavelength; the smaller the wavelength, the greater the energy. The ability to respond to light (or to any other wavelength of radiation) is based on the ability of molecules to absorb quanta of energy, thereby altering their own energy levels (see McElroy and Glass, 1961). Wavelengths below about 300 mμ contain enough energy to break covalent bonds in molecules that absorb them; quanta with wavelengths above approximately 1,000 mμ are not energetic enough to create much change in the energy of a molecule that absorbs them.

The visible spectrum lies between about 300 to 800 mμ, although some animals can detect ultraviolet wavelengths down to about 210 mμ. However, intense ultraviolet light is damaging to cells and their molecules. Wavelengths within the visible spectrum have energies that can produce significant changes in the energy levels of the molecules that absorb them and yet not enough energy to destroy such molecules.

All life on earth is based upon photosynthesis, a process that traps the energy of sunlight and uses this energy to synthesize the organic materials upon which living systems are based. Photosynthesis utilizes chlorophylls to absorb radiant energy. The chlorophylls are similar in structure to the respiratory pigment hemoglobin except that the functional atom is magnesium instead of iron. In addition carotenoid pigment molecules often act as accessory light-trapping agents in photosynthesis. All animal photoreceptor visual pigments are also carotenoids,

Chapter 17

Light and the Animal

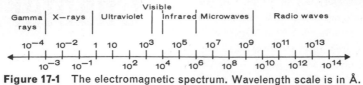

Figure 17-1 The electromagnetic spectrum. Wavelength scale is in Å.

and these molecules cannot be synthesized by animals but must be obtained in the diet, usually as lipid-soluble vitamins (see Chapter 15). It is also of some interest that visible light falls in the wavelength range that most readily penetrates through water—and life is thought to have originated in water (Brett, 1957).

Nearly all animal groups exhibit a photosensitivity based on the presence of certain cells in the surface epithelia that respond to the presence or absence of light. Such a **dermal light sense** is especially prominent in protozoans through annelids and also in fish and amphibians. Some neurons associated with the central nervous system can also sense light. For example, pigmented ganglion cells in the mollusc *Aplysia* and nerve cells in the sixth abdominal ganglia of crayfish are excited by illumination (Kennedy, 1963). The pineal organ of vertebrates is also light sensitive (Kelly, 1962). In most cases the function of such light sensitive cells is not known.

Although various forms of electromagnetic radiation exhibit a diversity of influences on living systems (see Giese, 1964), in this chapter I shall discuss only photoreception and specialized photoreceptors. There are a variety of photoreceptor organs found in the animal kingdom. The most primitive are those found in some protozoans, for example, the eyespot associated with the flagellum of *Euglena*. These concentrations of carotenoid pigments are capable of detecting only the presence or absence of light.

In metazoans the term eyespot is used to designate simple collections of photoreceptor cells. Eyes are more complex receptor organs capable of forming some type of image on the photoreceptive surface. In the inverte-

brates some eyes are similar to pinhole cameras. They consist of an opaque chamber pierced by a small hole that allows the passage of a narrow beam of light. An inverted image

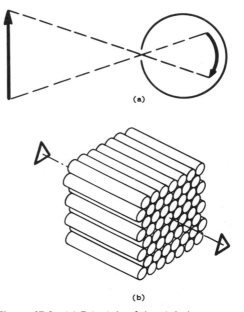

Figure 17-2 (a) Principle of the pinhole camera, used in many invertebrate eyes. Light passes into an opaque chamber through a small hole, and an inverted image of the object is formed on the back surface. The size of the image is inversely proportional to the distance of the object. Although both near and far objects can be focused, the amount of light entering through the pinhole is small and resolution is poor. (b) Invertebrate compound eyes are composed of a parallel array of tubular elements. Only light falling on a given element parallel to its axis can reach the photoreceptor surface and the image formed is the same size as the object and only those objects of the same size or smaller than the eye can be completely imaged unless the tubular elements are arranged around the surface of a sphere.

is formed on the opposite wall of the chamber (Figure 17-2a). This eye lacks efficiency because only a small amount of light from the object can reach the receptor surface. If the pinhole is enlarged to increase the amount of light entering the eye, resolution is lost. If the hole is narrowed, further diffraction effects ensue that also cause a loss in resolution. However, this type of eye does not require focusing mechanisms for near and distant objects, and the size of the image is inversely proportional to the distance of the object.

Many invertebrates possess compound eyes. This photoreceptor organ is composed of a number of tubular elements that possess light sensitive surfaces (Figure 17-2b). The cells are separated by opaque walls. The image formed is the same size as the object, and thus only those objects of the same size or smaller than the eye can be completely imaged. However, if the elements of the compound eye are arranged around the surface of a sphere with the axes pointing to the center, this disadvantage is overcome. Only when light falls on a given cellular element parallel to its axis, can it reach the photoreceptor surface.

The vertebrate eye and the eye of cephalopod molluscs are the most highly developed organs of vision in the animal kingdom. These eyes use a lens (refractive element) to focus light from an object and to form an inverted image on the retinal surface (Figure 17-3).

This eye will be described in the next section.

In nature light is usually polarized as a result of light scattering by particles in gaseous or liquid media or as a result of refraction and reflection at interfaces (the Fresnel effect). The compound eye of many animals, especially in the arthropod group, is capable of determining the plane of polarized light, and these animals can use such information for orientation or directed locomotion. The term direction eye is used to describe any eye capable of determining accurately the direction of a source of illumination.

Some general references to sensory physiology include Granit (1955); Case (1966); and various chapters in the *Handbook of Physiology*, Section 1, "Neurophysiology" (American Physiological Society, Washington, D.C.).

17-2. Structure of the Vertebrate Eye. I shall begin the discussion of photoreceptors with a description of the vertebrate eye—a visual organ that is one of the most highly developed receptors and one that has been well studied. The eye of the human can be used as an example of the vertebrate eye generally and serves to illustrate the principles upon which nearly all vertebrate eyes function. Details of the structure, functions, and adaptations of vertebrate eyes are found in Davson (1962) and Walls (1942).

The structure of the eye is shown in Figure 17-3. The retina serves as a photosensitive

Figure 17-3 Structure of the mammalian eye. A focusable lens and the transparent cornea are used to focus the image of an object on the light sensitive retina.

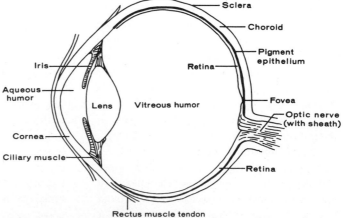

surface on which the cornea and lens form an inverted image. The amount of light admitted to the eye is controlled by the iris, a diaphragm-like device that opens under low light intensities to permit more light to strike the retina and that closes down under more intense illumination to protect the retina from damage. The amount of light is also controlled statically by the presence of a black lining that serves to absorb light quanta that pass through the retina without absorption. In some vertebrates, for example, the cat, vision in dim light is enhanced by the presence of a reflecting rather than a nonreflecting layer. Any light quanta that have passed through the retina without absorption are reflected off this layer back through the retinal photoreceptors for another change for absorption. In many submammalian species the photoreceptor cells (rods and cones) possess a contractile segment. When this region relaxes, the outer segment thrusts into the pigment epithelium, and the receptor pigment is partially masked. When this region contracts, the outer segment with its visual pigment is retracted out of the pigmented epithelium, and the amount of light reaching the visual pigment is increased.

In elasmobranchs, teleosts, amphibians, and reptiles (snakes), the lens of the eye can, like a camera lens, be moved back and forth for accommodation—the ability to focus images of objects at different distances from the lens. In birds, mammals, and some reptiles, focusing is accomplished by muscular contractions that alter the curvature of the lens. The disadvantage of the latter method is that with age the substances forming the lens loose elasticity. Children can normally focus on objects 2 to 3 inches from the eye, but adults can focus on objects no closer than 6 to 8 inches.

All lenses suffer from various types of aberration that distort the final image. Chromatic aberration occurs because shorter wavelengths of light are refracted more strongly than are longer wavelengths, and when both ranges of wavelengths pass through a lens, the shorter wavelengths come to a focus closer to the lens. In a camera this problem is solved by using two different types of glass with different refractive properties. The vertebrate lens is made of only a single protein material, and biologically the problem of chromatic aberration is solved by eliminating shorter wavelengths. The human lens, for example, is yellow because it absorbs ultraviolet and violet wavelengths. Only longer wavelengths pass through and need be focused. In addition, the central nervous system appears able to ignore any small amount of chromatic aberration still present. In primates there is also a yellow pigment, the macula lutea, dispersed over the fovea—a region of high concentration of receptor (cone) cells. This yellow pigment aids in the elimination of shorter wavelengths of light.

Spherical aberration is found in lenses because they usually focus light waves more sharply at their boundaries than at the center of the lens. The eye corrects for spherical aberration by reducing the curvature of the cornea at its margins and by increasing the density (and thus refractive index) of the material at the center of the lens. These two effects balance out peripheral and central focusing problems.

17-3. The Retina. Vision includes a series of events of increasing complexity. Once light has passed through the refractive cornea and lens and has been focused on the retina, light quanta must be absorbed by visual pigments in receptor cells, and the energy changes must be converted to nerve impulses. The many inputs from the retina to the central nervous system must be integrated and coordinated by the brain to yield visual sensations and to produce appropriate visual responses. The retina is the structural element of the eye responsible for light absorption and the initiation of nervous responses.

The position of receptor cells in the retina is such that light must pass through all of the other retinal layers before reaching the receptors. This retinal inversion of the vertebrate eye means that light must pass through nerve cells and their processes, connective tissue, and blood vessels before reaching the receptor cell visual pigment. This is not a great problem because the retina is very thin and mainly transparent. Nerve fibers are concentrated in only one small spot (the blind spot) about 1.5 mm in diameter in humans. At this point the fibers of ganglion cells collect to form the optic nerve. Only in this region is light unable to reach receptor cells. In addition, the fovea is not overlaid with blood vessels or nerve fibers, and since most of the cone cells are concentrated in this region, good vision becomes possible.

The organization of the retina is composed of nine layers with the innermost layer closely attached to a pigment epithelium, the choroid coat that absorbs extra light and prevents image blurring by internal reflected light. The layers are numbered beginning with the outermost layer and include: (1) an internal limiting membrane; (2) a layer of nerve fibers; (3) the ganglion layer; (4) the inner molecular layer; (5) the inner nuclear layer; (6) the outer molecular layer; (7) the outer nuclear layer; (8) the external limiting membrane; and (9) the rod and cone cells containing visual pigments (Dowling and Boycott, 1966; Polyak, 1941).

The first four layers comprise the neuroepithelial layer and are first order neurons. The fifth layer contains bipolar, amacrine, and horizontal cells. The sixth layer contains second order neurons. The seventh and eighth layers include third order neurons that proceed to the primary optic center in the brain. The rod and cone cells are arranged in a single-layered mosaic and are interconnected by a complex network of interconnecting neurons. A schematic of the types of interconnections found in the retina is given in Figure 17-4.

There are five basic cell types found in the complex structure of the retina. There are, in the human retina, about 250 million rod cells and about 6 million cone cells. The receptor cells converge in a complex synaptic network on bipolar cells. The bipolars, in turn, send impulses to about a million ganglion cells, whose fibers form the optic nerve.

Since the ganglion cells are much fewer in

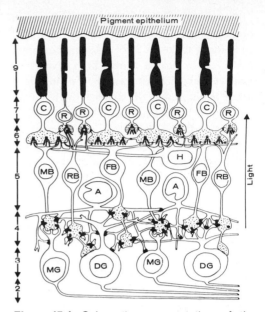

Figure 17-4 Schematic representation of the interconnections found in the vertebrate retina. C, cone cells; R, rod cells; H, horizontal cells; MB, midget bipolar cells; RB, rod bipolar cells; FB, flat bipolar cells; A, amacrine cells, MG, midget ganglion cells; DG, diffuse ganglion cells. The numbers correspond to the layers of the retina listed in the text. [Modified from Dowling and Boycott (1966).]

number than are the receptor cells, there must be a large degree of convergence within the retina. Convergence is maximal at the periphery of the retina, where many rods may converge on a single ganglion cell. Convergence is minimal in the fovea, where one cone cell may synapse with a single ganglion cell through a single bipolar.

The role of amacrine and horizontal cells is not yet understood (see Yamanaga and Ishikawa, 1965; Dowling and Boycott, 1965). Tight junctions have been found between horizontal cells of the retinas of carps and sharks—an indication that these cells could form a functional electrically transmitting syncytium. The horizontal cells of the human and tortoise retinas are not so connected but do have long fibrous processes that extend for large distances over the retinal surface. These findings suggest a role of lateral connectivity between receptor elements.

The retina is formed embryologically as an outpouching of the brain, and its neuronal complexity makes it a good example of brain tissue. As indicated above, both divergence and convergence of neuronal connections occur in the retina. Although retinal activity will be further considered in Section 17-7, it can be indicated here that a minimum of three cells are interposed between the initial visual sensory action and the conduction of impulses into the brain. This pathway includes the receptor cell, the bipolar cell, and the ganglion cell. However, most receptor cells do not possess an isolated impulse pathway to the ganglion cell. As stated above, most bipolar cells receive stimuli from a number of receptor cells, often including both rods and cones. A partial overlap exists between receptor areas and can affect the discharge of neighboring ganglion cells. This is one method for increasing visual acuity. In addition, the horizontal cells may provide lateral connections between receptor fields. Rod and cone axons have been shown to be interconnected in some cases even before they synapse with bipolar cells. Although rods and cones are considered as two separate visual systems, they possess a large degree of interconnectivity. It is important to realize that because of different types of interconnectivity between receptor cells and ganglion cells, different retinas may see quite differently.

17-4. Rod and Cone Cells. Rods and cones are differentiated into inner and outer segments (Figure 17-5). The inner segment is the site of normal cellular metabolism and also contains the photoreceptor synaptic endings. The outer segment is cylindrical and thin in rods; it is conical and shorter in cones. The outer segment contains the visual pigment, those molecules that absorb light and initiate the visual response. The visual pigment is distributed in or on numerous membranous lamellae that arise, at least in part, as invaginations of the outer limiting membrane of the outer segment. In the inner segment are found many long, thin mitochondria, often packed together in a structure known as the "elip-

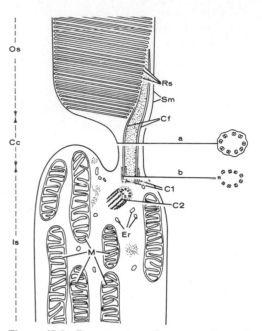

Figure 17-5 Fine structure of a mammalian rod cell. Os, outer segment; Cc, connecting cilium; Is, part of inner segment. The outer segment is filled with membranous lamellae, Rs, originating from the outer surface membrane, Sm. Ciliary filaments, Cf, are found in the connecting neck region. Note the typical ciliary structures, a, b, in this region and the presence of two centrioles, C1, C2. The inner segment contains many mitochondria, M, and endoplasmic reticulum, Er. [After E. D. P. deRobertis (1960) "Some observations on the ultrastructure and morphogenesis of photoreceptors." By permission from *Journal of General Physiology* **43**(suppl.): 1–13.]

soid." The neck or bridge that connects the inner and outer segments has the structure of a cilium, and visual receptor cells generally appear to be ciliary derivatives.

The different shapes of the outer segments of rods and cones may contribute to their differing functions and properties. The receptor cells also differ in the nature of their visual pigments. The **duplicity theory of vision** states that rods are for night vision under conditions of decreased light intensities and cones are for daylight and color vision.

Rods are responsible for **scotopic vision** or vision under dim light conditions. Although in the past it was thought that rods are more sensitive to light than cone cells, some evidence now indicates that the sensitivities (threshold to light stimuli) are similar in the two cells; the differences in response arise mainly because of the nature of the neuronal network into which each cell type delivers its response. Maximum rod density in the human retina is about 160,000 per mm², whereas cone density outside the fovea is about 5,000 per mm². Scotopic vision is aided not only by a relatively high concentration of rod cells throughout the retina but also by the extensive convergence in the rod neuronal system. A patch of even dim light falling on the retina has a chance to hit at least a few rod outer segments and initiate a visual response.

Cones are responsible for **photopic vision**, or vision in bright light, and for color vision. The fovea contains only cone cells, and these are present in high concentration—about 146,000 per mm². Because there is less convergence in the cone system than in the rod system, in bright light the stimulation of a single cone may result in activity in a ganglion cell.

Visual acuity is a measure of the resolving power of an eye. Acuity may be increased by increasing the number of sensing elements in a given volume of the retina or by decreasing the amount of neuronal convergence. Scotopic vision is made possible at the expense of visual acuity by increasing the concentration of receptors and the amount of convergence of the conduction pathways. Dim light has a chance of being absorbed by some rod cells, and the large convergence of pathways aids in producing some response. Thus sensitivity to light is increased (sensitivity is a measure of the threshold of stimulation needed to excite the photoreceptor or to provide a light sensation). In dim light far less quanta fall on the retina, but only a few quanta need fall on any of many rods to produce a response in a ganglion cell. In photopic vision, the amount of light falling on the cones must be high in order to produce a response because of the many one-to-one relations between cones and ganglion cells. The light intensity must be sufficient to ensure that the cone cell

absorbs a quantum of light. Thus sensitivity is decreased, but acuity is increased both by the lack of convergence and by the high concentration of cones in the fovea.

If a human subject is placed in a dark room, the visual threshold is at first high; that is, a strong light stimulus is needed to produce a sensation. But after about half an hour the threshold has fallen to a point where the subject is dark adapted, and the sensitivity to light is as much as a thousand times greater than initially. Under this condition vision is peripheral, that is, a test object is seen best when its image is formed outside of the foveal area (where only cones are present). Such an image is achromatic; that is, there is no sensation of colors, only of different light intensities. Different wavelengths are not seen as colors but as different intensities.

On raising the intensity of a colored light stimulus to a dark adapted subject, a point is reached at which a sensation of color is obtained. This chromatic threshold is the level at which the light intensities cause the stimulation of cones. It should be noted that stimuli of different wavelengths but of the same light intensity do not produce the same sensations of brightness.

17-5. Photochemistry. Differences in response to particular wavelengths by different retinas or by rod and cone cells depend to some extent on differences in the visual pigments that absorb light in the photoreceptor cells. The chemistry of visual pigments has been extensively studied, and the visual process is best understood at this level (Hubbard et al., 1965; McElroy and Glass, 1960; Morton and Pitt, 1969; Wald, 1968; see also the reviews by Alpern, 1968; Creutzfeldt and Sakmann, 1969).

An **absorption curve** is a plot of the number of light quanta absorbed by a molecule at various wavelengths of incident light. An **action spectrum** is obtained by plotting the number of quanta absorbed that at various wavelengths leads to a visual response by the animal. This is a measure of the spectral sensitivity of the eye or retina, that is, an

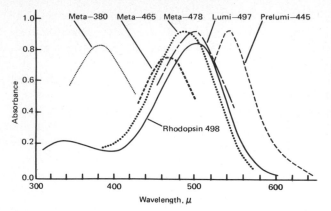

Figure 17-6 Absorption spectrum of rhodopsin and some intermediates obtained during bleaching. The action spectrum of the human retina falls on top of the curve shown for rhodopsin absorption. The numbers represent wavelength (in Å) of maximal absorption. [From data of Wald and Brown (1965).]

indication of the wavelengths optimally absorbed by the pigments of the eye. The strongest argument that a given molecule is acting as a visual pigment is provided when the action spectrum of the eye matches the absorption curve of the isolated and purified pigment molecule. Again, this is based on the fact that vision can result only following the absorption of light quanta by some molecule in the eye. The wavelength at which absorption by the pigment is most efficient should be the wavelength of light that the eye perceives best.

The absorption spectrum of human rhodopsin, the visual pigment of rod cells, is given in Figure 17-6. The human action spectrum falls on top of this absorption curve and the similarities of the two curves is evidence that scotopic vision is based on light absorption by rhodopsin. Human spectral sensitivity is best at about 500 mμ, the maximal rhodopsin absorption also occurs at this wavelength.

Kuhne in 1876 was the first to extract from rod cells a pigment that he called visual purple because of its purplish-red color. This pigment is now called rhodopsin. It is the visual pigment of the rod cells of all terrestrial vertebrates and most marine teleosts. Rhodopsin consists of a protein, **opsin**, and an aldehyde of vitamin A. The aldehyde of rhodopsin is **retinal$_1$** (formerly called retinene, retinene$_1$, or vitamin A aldehyde). The structure of vitamin A and the various isomers of retinal are shown in Figure 17-7.

Vitamin A is a derivative of plant carotenoid

pigments and is composed of a chromophoric (colored) system of alternating single and double bonds. The presence of these conjugated double bonds allows the possibility of various cis and trans isomers. Although the 11-*cis* isomer is the least probable because of the instability caused by steric hindrance (the —H of carbon 10 and the —CH$_3$ of carbon 13 interfere with one another and keep the molecule from being planar), this is the isomer that is found in rhodopsin.

Rhodopsin is a difficult protein to characterize because it is not soluble in water; it is extremely unstable with respect to temperature and pH and tends to denature with extraction procedures. It is extracted in digitonic solutions (digitonin is a form of detergent that solubilizes lipids), and the digitonin molecules form miceller complexes with the rhodopsin that make the molecular weight of the visual pigment difficult to determine. Cattle rhodopsin appears to have a molecular weight of about 32,000, whereas frog rhodopsin has a molecular weight of about 54,000 (see Wolken, 1966). It is likely that one retinene molecule is complexed with one opsin molecule to form rhodopsin, although this is not yet proven.

Visual pigments of vertebrates and invertebrates are found to consist of an opsin plus either retinal$_1$ or retinal$_2$. Retinal$_2$ has a second double bond in the 3,4 position of the ring structure (Figure 17-7). Retinal$_2$ is found in the retinas of fresh water fish. Opsin is a

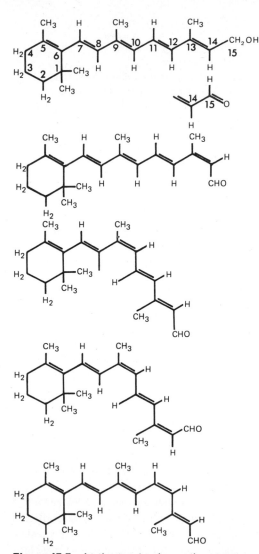

Figure 17-7 At the top is shown the structure of vitamin A_1 (retinol₁). The inset shows the aldehyde form (retinal₁). The configuration of vitamin A_1 shown is the all-*trans* form. Vitamin A_2 and retinal₂ have the same structure but with the addition of another double bond between carbons 3 and 4 of the ring structure. The remaining structures present some of the isomers of retinal₁. In descending order they are the 13-*cis*, the 9-*cis*, the 9,13-*dicis*, and the 11-*cis* isomers. It is the latter which is found in visual pigments although there is steric hindrance, and hence instability, because of the crowding of the carbon 10 hydrogen and the carbon 13 methyl group.

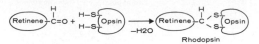

Figure 17-8 Schematic representation of the reaction between retinene and opsin to form rhodopsin.

class name, the protein varies in different species and even within different cone cells or rod cells of a given retina. The different absorption maxima found for different visual pigments appear to depend primarily on the nature of the protein, although the retinal moiety also contributes to determining the maxima. Among the other isomers of retinal, only the 9-*cis* form can combine with opsin to form a light-sensitive pigment. These **isopigments** have not yet been found to occur naturally in any retina. The amount of rhodopsin extractable from different retinas lends credence to the theory that it is the visual pigment of rod cells. It is obtained in large amounts from guinea pig retinas that have few if any cone cells; but rhodopsin cannot be extracted from chicken retinas that have only cone cells.

Figure 17-8 shows schematically how retinene is believed to combine with opsin to form rhodopsin. Rhodopsin (and other visual pigments) bleaches in the presence of light. This reaction transforms the 11-*cis*-retinal to the all-*trans*-retinal form, and the rhodopsin splits so that the protein is freed. The reaction scheme is diagrammed in Figure 17-9. This reaction initiates the visual response. The only known action of light is to cause the isomerization of the 11-*cis* form to the all-*trans* form of retinal. Even in the dark, rhodopsin will undergo the changes that lead to the separation of opsin and retinal.

The further events in the visual process which lead to the production of action potentials are not known. The change in the rhodopsin molecule initiated by the absorption of light obviously leads to energy changes in the system, but how this energy is transduced into membrane activities is not known.

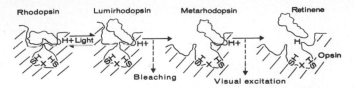

Figure 17-9 Schematic diagram showing the action of light on rhodopsin. The 11-*cis* isomer is converted to all-*trans*-lumirhodopsin. From this point chemical reactions proceed through a series of steps to produce all-*trans*-retinol. The transformation of retinal₁ causes changes in the conformation of opsin and finally the rhodopsin complex splits up. The various rearrangements may expose reactive groups that can trigger excitation in the rod outer segment. The overall change in rhodopsin is known as bleaching. [After Hubbard and Kropf (1959).] See also Figure 17-10.

As shown in Figures 17-9 and 17-10, a variety of intermediates can be found during the bleaching reaction, when experimental conditions provide control of temperature and other factors. Each of these intermediates has its own absorption maximum. Some occur in the presence of light and are the result of photoreactions, others occur in the dark and are thermal reactions. The significance of all of the changes and the natural role, if any, of these experimentally produced intermediates is not known. However, it is of interest that electrical responses can arise from certain of these reactions.

The electroretinogram (ERG) is measured by placing an active electrode on the corneal surface and an indifferent electrode elsewhere on the eye or body (Figure 17-13). The electrodes are attached to an amplifier whose output is read on an oscilloscope. When a dark-adapted eye is exposed to a flash of light, an initial silent period lasts about 1.5 msec in mammals. The period may be much longer at lower temperatures. Then a biphasic ERG wave is recorded. Initially there is an a wave, which is temperature sensitive and logarithmically related to light intensity. It may result from the formation of metarhodopsin. The a wave is followed by the b wave.

Brown and Murakami (1964, 1967) found another electrical response that occurred in the so-called latent period. This is now called the early receptor potential (ERP). It has no measurably latency and usually requires a flash of light about one million times as intense as would produce a moderate ERG.

The ERP is also biphasic and consists of a fast cornea-positive and a slow cornea-negative wave. At 5°C the latter wave disappears. The ERP has its source in the action of light on the visual pigment and is obtained even when retinas are cooled to $-30°C$ or heated to 48°C. To produce the ERP, the rhodopsin must have its normal orientation in the outer segments. If this orientation is destroyed by heat treatment, the ERP is lost. One flash of light produces the ERP, and a second flash of light acting on an intermediate stage of bleaching produces an ERP of reversed polarity. This action is probably on the photoregeneration reaction in which the all-*trans* form of retinal is isomerized to the 11-*cis* form. It is of interest that these results have been found both for the rat and the squid retinas.

There is no evidence that the ERP generated by rhodopsin is part of the visual excitation mechanism, but the ERP does present a valuable tool for studying the bleaching process *in situ*. It is still a mystery how intramolecular changes of the type responsible for the ERP can change the potential difference between the front and back of the eye.

Figure 17-10 illustrates the pathways of bleaching and regeneration of retinal and rhodopsin. If visual sensitivity is to be maintained, the visual pigment must be regenerated following bleaching. Part of the regeneration is caused by a photochemical isomerization of all-*trans*-retinal to 11-*cis*-retinal. Some steps of the recovery process can occur either in the light or in the dark, for example, the

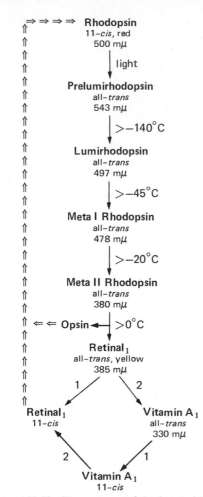

Figure 17-10 The pathway of rhodopsin bleaching and the reactions by which all-*trans*-retinal is restored to the 11-*cis* form. The temperatures shown are those that must be reached in order to obtain the indicated product (the bleaching reaction is run at cold temperatures). The mμ values are the wavelengths of maximal absorption of the various pigments. The enzyme retinal isomerase (1) converts the all-*trans* to the 11-*cis* isomer. Only 30 per cent or less of all-*trans*-retinal is directly converted to the 11-*cis* isomer. Most of the all-*trans*-retinal passes through the reactions utilizing the enzyme alcohol dehydrogenase (2) and the coenzyme NAD^+ or $NADP^+$, depending on the species.

reactions that convert all-*trans*-retinal to the 11-*cis* form directly or through vitamin A via enzymatic reactions. The enzymes of these reactions are alcohol dehydrogenases or, in some cases, retinol dehydrogenases specific

only for retinol. NAD^+ is required as a coenzyme in frogs and reptiles; $NADP^+$ is required in other animals.

The phenomenon of dark adaptation arises from the need for the light-adapted eye to produce visual pigment when placed in the dark, that is, the rhodopsin bleached by the light must be regenerated. After exposure to light and then placement in the dark, retinal cones require only about five minutes for a return to full sensitivity. The restoration of a full complement of rod rhodopsin requires 30 to 40 minutes in humans. The regeneration of rhodopsin follows exactly the return of sensitivity of the retina to light, further evidence that rhodopsin is the scotopic pigment of the retina.

The fully dark adapted eye is very sensitive to illumination. Only 5 to 15 photons are needed to produce a visual sensation during scotopic vision. Although one rod can be excited by one photon, the excitation of a single rod is not sufficient to produce a visual sensation. Both temporal and spacial summation are required in the neural networks of the retina in order for vision to occur and about 5 to 8 rods must be stimulated simultaneously in the human retina when dim brief flashes of light are used as stimuli. Such sensitivity to dim illumination is not found in the fovea, where only cones are present. The varying sensitivities of rod and cone cells are thought to be caused by the nature of the neural connections not by differences in visual pigment sensitivity.

17-6. Distribution of Visual Pigments.   All visual pigments are thought to be composed of an opsin molecule complexed with either retinene$_1$ or retinene$_2$. The names of various classes of visual pigments and their composition are given in Figure 17-7.

Although, as previously stated, there appears to be a functional one-to-one relationship between cone cells and bipolar cells, there seems to be some question about the presence of a one-to-one cellular contact (Willmer, 1965; Pedler, 1965). There are even questions concerning the distribution of retinal receptor cells into two groups, for example, in the fovea of *Sphenodon* only rods are found—bringing into question the proposed role of cones in visual acuity. A similar situation is found in owls, whose retina contains both rods and cones but with no foveal distribution of cones. In the retina of the nocturnal gecko, only rods are found, and there may be five or more bipolar cells per rod, a finding at odds with the concept that rods show great covergence, and cones show a one-to-one relation with bipolar cells. These points have been raised only to point out that variations in the nature of the rod and cone distribution may occur in different species and more information is needed about the detailed morphology of receptor cells. More work needs to be done especially on the identification of the nature of receptor cells on the basis of the type of visual pigment they contain, rather than on gross morphology that can be different even in the same cell type.

As indicated previously, a variety of visual pigments are now recognized based primarily on differences in the wavelength of maximal absorption. Such differences appear to depend primarily on the nature of the opsin present. An early generalization was that terrestrial and marine vertebrates possessed only $retinal_1$-based visual pigments, and that fresh water vertebrates possessed only $retinal_2$-based pigments. Euryhaline fishes and other species that divide their life cycle between fresh water and the marine or terrestrial environment were thought to have varying mixtures of rhodopsin and porphyropsin.

During the past few years an enormous number of species have been examined for the nature of their visual pigments, and the generalizations just made, although correct for a majority of species, do have their exceptions. Morton and Pitt (1969) present an excellent account of the visual pigments in animals.

Fresh water fish may have two or more visual pigments in the rods. For example, the chub *Luciscus cephalus* has pigments that absorb maximally at 510_1 and 543_2 mμ (the subscripts 1 and 2 will be used to refer to $retinal_1$- and $retinal_2$-based pigments, re-

spectively). However, over two dozen other species of fresh water fish were found to have but a single rod pigment with an absorption maximum ranging from 513 to 534 mμ. These were all rhodopsins.

Some marine fish also have two visual pigments in their rods. The mackerel *Scomber scombrus* has pigments with absorption maxima at 522_1 and 487_2 mμ. But again most marine teleosts have a single visual pigment based on $retinal_1$ and with a range of absorption maxima of 478 to 512 mμ.

The lamprey *Petromyzon marinus*, which lives in landlocked waters, and the lamprey *Entosphenus tridentatus*, which migrates between fresh and marine waters, both have a visual pigment with maximal absorption at 497_1 mμ. Deep marine elasmobranchs have pigments with a range of absorption maxima of 478 to 490 mμ, and a shallow water marine elasmobranch *Begaprion breverostris* has a maxima at 501_1 mμ. A few marine teleosts have been found to possess $retinal_2$-based pigments.

To some extent the visual pigments may be adapted to the environment of the animal. The spectral energy of sunlight has a broad absorption maxima near 500 mμ. Distilled water absorbs visible light maximally at about 475 mμ. Clear ocean water has a maximal transmission to wavelengths in the range of 470 to 475 mμ, and thus animals in clear ocean waters are exposed primarily to blue wavelengths. In murky waters transmission occurs optimally at higher wavelengths (600 to 750 mμ).

In the molluscan and arthropod eyes that have been examined, the visual pigments appear to be 11-*cis* isomers of $retinal_1$ (see review by Wolken, 1966). The eyespot of *Euglena* contains a pigment astaxanthin, which is a derivative of β-carotene. Astaxanthin is also found in the integument and eyes of crustaceans and has an absorption band that is maximal at 500 mμ. Carotenoid-derivatives are also implicated as visual pigments in coelenterates and platyhelminthes, and absorption maxima are similar to those of rhodopsin.

Although rhodopsin-like visual pigments have been isolated from some insect eyes, many questions still remain concerning the nature of insect visual pigments generally. Part of the difficulty in determining the nature of arthropod visual pigments is caused by the presence of other eye pigments that are nonreceptive in function.

Honeybees, blowflies, and many other insects, as well as some crustaceans such as *Daphnia*, are sensitive to ultraviolet. The sunlight that reaches the earth's surface includes ultraviolet radiation with wavelengths down to about 297 mμ. Although the ultraviolet sensitivity of the human eye is just below 400 mμ (this is visual sensitivity; human or other eyes can be burned by ultraviolet and thus damaged), the sensitivity of many insect eyes is to the whole natural range of ultraviolet wavelengths. One wonders how the world appears to an animal that sees in the ultraviolet as well as in the visible range of the spectrum.

17-7. Cones and Color Vision.

Primates and a few other mammalian species, birds, lizards, turtles, frogs, teleosts, and several invertebrates are capable of distinguishing between different colors, that is, they possess color vision.

Ideas of color vision center upon the Young-Helmholtz theory (see Crawford, 1965). Young in 1802 postulated that there were three basic receptor units each with some selective wavelength of maximal absorption. Although Young stated that only three different types of receptors were needed to produce color vision, later workers extended this concept to include three different absorbing pigments. Thus basic color vision is trichromatic; and by the use of three different primary colors, various mixtures may produce all of the colors that can be observed. Although color vision can be hypothetically related to three different visual pigments and three different classes of cones at the receptor level, the actions of the central nervous system which result in color sensations are unknown.

The existence of three different cone pigments has only recently been found (Wald, 1964; Wald and Brown, 1965). Such pigments were demonstrated in the human retina by measuring the absorption spectra of single rod and cone cells. The spectrum of the dark adapted eye and that of the wholly bleached retina provides an overall difference spectrum that represents the foveal absorption by its photopigments. Microspectrophotometry was first developed sufficiently to measure the difference spectrum of retinal cones by Hanaoka and Fujimoto (1957), who studied the retinas of carp. A portion of the retina may be viewed through a microscope, and the focused image of a single rod or cone is passed through a microspectrophotometer after the surrounding area is masked off. Beams of monochromatic light as little as 1 μ in width are used.

Such measurements are not easy because the presence of other pigments must be accounted for. For example, absorption caused by macula pigment (which absorbs maximally at 430, 455, and 484 mμ in humans) must be subtracted from the overall spectrum. Stray light must also be minimized, and narrow beams of light should be used (see, for example, Rushton, 1965). Each of the foveal pigments can be bleached selectively by altering the wavelength of light used.

Human cone visual pigments include ones with absorption maxima at 435, 540, and 565 mμ. However, it should be noted that the only cone pigment which has been extracted so far from cones is iodopsin, and the direct measurements of the absorption spectra of cones cannot as yet be related to the action spectrum of cones. Cone visual pigments are generally called iodopsins. Cones are divided into three classes sensitive to blue, red, and green, respectively. The normal fovea contains chlorolabe with a maximal absorption at 540 mμ. This green-absorbing pigment is missing in the eyes of deuteropes (green color blind subjects). Another pigment is erythrolabe with a maximal absorption at about 570 mμ. This red absorbing pigment is lacking in the eyes of protanopes (red color blind subjects). The presence of a third blue-absorbing pigment, cyanolabe is still debated.

It is not known whether each cone contains only one visual pigment, contains three visual pigments, or varying mixtures of pigments. Generally, it is believed that one cone cell contains only one pigment.

The cones of many birds, reptiles, and amphibians contain colored oil droplets through which light must pass before it reaches the visual pigment in the outer segment. Because the chicken cone contains only iodopsin, it has been considered that color vision in this animal results from selective absorption by the different colored oil droplets found in different cones. However, this was disputed by Walls (1942) who considered that the oil droplets were present in order to reduce chromatic and other aberrations in the eye. In many cases, for example in birds, only one color oil droplet appears to be present.

Land (1964, 1965) suggests that color vision depends primarily on the nature of the retinal and brain neural networks. He proposes that all receptors with a given wavelength of sensitivity are connected in a retinal-cerebral network—the **retinex**. Land considers that color vision sensations are the result of three sets of retinexes functioning to integrate and coordinate stimuli received by the retina, and that the retinexes use lightness scales not color directly. This does not rule out the idea that cones may utilize different pigments but does suggest that the sensitivity of the cones is to brightness and pattern, not color.

For example, two black and white photographic slides may be taken of the same scene. One is taken with, for example, a red filter over the lens (S_1), the other is taken with a green filter over the camera lens (S_2). These two slides are then projected on a screen through two projectors so arranged that the images are superimposed on the screen. If a red filter is placed over the lens of the projector with S_1 and a green filter is placed over the lens of the projector with S_2, a full color image is seen identical with the natural scene. In fact, any two filters may be used with the two projectors, as long as that used with S_1

has a longer wavelength than that used for S_2. Even when the two filters are both green, with a wavelength separation of only 10μ, the image still retains all of the color of the original, even though only green light is reaching the screen. Thus, in this case color vision appears to depend upon integration of information in the nervous system, specifically on the varying intensities of light reflected from the screen, not upon the absorption of different colored wavelengths by specific retinal pigments.

Space does not permit a full description of this and other theories concerning color vision. Needless to say many problems still remain in both the physiology and the psychology of color vision. The references given in this and preceding sections may be consulted for further details.

17-8. Processing of Visual Information. From the stimuli falling on the millions of retinal receptor cells, the retinal neurons and those of the central nervous system must be able to produce order so that the temporal and spatial events are translated into the correct visual sensations or the proper reflex actions.

Very little is known about potentials arising in bipolar cells, but recording from ganglion cells is possible by pushing microelectrodes through the front of the eye and inward to make contact with the retinal surface. The properties of the array of receptor cells surrounding a given ganglion cell can be determined by the use of photic stimulation of the area about the tip of the microelectrode. Such experiments have shown that receptive fields are present in the retina.

Ganglion cells are found to be continuously active and the receptive field about a given ganglion cell may be up to 8° in extent (= a 1 to 2 mm circle in the cat retina, for example). The illumination of a small patch in the center of such a receptive field produces an "on" response. Impulses are generated in the ganglion cell only when the light is turned on. When two outer zones are illuminated, an "off" response may occur, that is, there is a decrease in the number of impulses generated

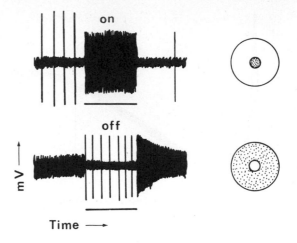

Figure 17-11 Schematic drawing of the nature of "on" and "off" responses that can be recorded from cat retinal ganglion cell. Bar beneath each figure shows time of stimulus application to a light adapted cell. To right are diagrammed receptor fields—shaded area indicates general region of stimulation. If both fields are stimulated simultaneously, the result is an "on" followed by an "off" response.

by the ganglion cell (Figure 17-11). Some fields may be represented as an inhibitory center surrounded by an excitatory off center. Although a variety of such fields may exist and represent interconnected neuronal cells,

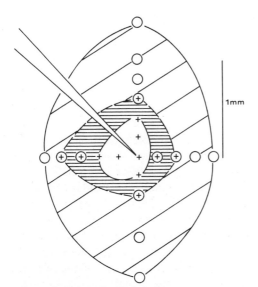

Figure 17-12 Schematic representation of the distribution of discharge patterns in the receptive field of a ganglion cell of the cat retina. The recording electrode is shown with its tip placed at nucleus of ganglion cell. The exploring stimulus spot was 0.2 mm in diameter. Crosses in central part of field were sites of only on discharges; in the diagonally hatched periphery only off discharges were found; in the intermediate zone, horizontally hatched, discharges were on-off. [After Kuffler (1953).]

the important generalization emerges that a given ganglion cell may be either excited or inhibited depending on the particular area of the retina stimulated and on the nature of the photic stimulus. Figure 17-12 illustrates a receptor field and its responses in the cat retina. The ERG of a cat is shown in Figure 17-13.

Ganglionic receptor fields may also function in color vision. In goldfish ganglion cells that produce on-off responses with white light may produce on impulses at one wavelength and off responses at another wavelength. This difference means that patches of cone cells with particular spectral sensitivities may induce both excitatory and inhibitory activities in ganglion cell layers in addition to any color responses.

Single cell activity has been recorded from the inner nuclear layer. The response to stimulation is in the form of a slow potential called an S potential after Svaetichin (1953), who first discovered them in goldfish. The first response to a light stimulus is a negative wave of potential, which upon termination of the stimulus decays and is followed by a brief positive response. Different intensities of stimulation produce only greater amplitudes of S potentials, the cells do not produce impulses. The responsible cells may be horizontal cells. In the cat retina some cells respond to different wavelengths by changing either the amplitude or the polarity of the response. One cell shows a maximum positive response

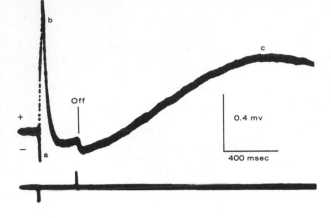

Figure 17-13 Electroretinogram (ERG) of cat, showing major deflections: a wave, b wave, and c wave. The eye was light adapted and retina was stimulated by a circular light spot which was large and intense. Onset and termination of stimulus are shown in lower record. [From K. T. Brown (1968) "The electroretinogram: its components and their origins" *Vision Research* **8**: 633–678. By permission.]

to wavelengths in the red, and the maximum negative response is to green wavelengths; this cell is called an R-G cell. Another cell type gives a maximum positive response to yellow and a maximal negative response to blue; this is called a Y-B cell. Such responses indicate that the S potential can be used in color discrimination by a mechanism first proposed by Hering. In a modernized general form this theory states that the retina contains some receptor fields which respond oppositely to red and green and other fields which respond oppositely to yellow and blue. At this level of retinal integration the sensation of yellow, which is as vivid as that of the other primary colors and yet for which there exists no separate visual pigment, may be accounted for. This opponent-response theory thus accounts for aspects of the visual response which are difficult to understand by the Young-Helmholtz theory alone.

Following strong excitation, a reduced level of firing of ganglion cells is found; after a period of inhibition an increase in spontaneous firing of ganglion cells occurs. In a uniformly illuminated area of the retina, the receptor cells maintain a given level of activity that is modified by inhibitory influences of surrounding receptor fields. However, cells lying in the light, but at the edge of the illuminated area, receive less inhibition and are more active because some nearby units that would normally inhibit them are lying in darkness. Under these conditions retinal

fields at the edge of an illuminated area may be more active than those lying fully in the illuminated region. These are factors which aid in increasing contrast in the formed image.

There are many other types of receptive fields in the retina, and a given receptor field may have a quite different response to a moving photic stimulation than to a stationary stimulus. Inhibition of activity at one site on the retina by illumination of another nearby site is typical of all vertebrate eyes.

It should be evident that the output of the retina is the result of a large amount of integration and coordination of information received by the receptor cells and depends greatly on the connections made at various retinal levels between receptor and bipolar cells and between bipolar and ganglion cells. Vertical and horizontal connections are introduced by the horizontal and amacrine cells to further complicate the neuronal network. In the last part of this chapter, these networks and receptor fields will be considered in terms of the final visual sensations recorded by the brain of the animal.

The optic nerves leave the retina and pass to the optic chiasma. At the chiasma decussation of the nerve occurs to an extent depending on the species and the vertebrate group. In all vertebrates except mammals and a few birds, all optic fibers cross over to the opposite side of the brain. In man those nerve fibers from the temporal half of the retina remain on the same side of the brain, while those fibers from the nasal half of the retina decussate. In primates generally about half the fibers from a given retina cross over. The degree of crossing over is a determinant in the degree of binocular vision possessed by the animal. Binocular vision and depth perception, in part at least, involve the fusion of similar receptor field impulses from similar regions of the two retinas. Such mixing occurs in the cerebral cortex.

From the optic chiasma, nerve fibers pass directly to the lateral geniculate body. Of the nerve fibers 80 per cent terminate in these nuclei and synapse with lateral geniculate neurons. Each of these neurons receives axon terminals of several optic nerve fibers, and each optic nerve fiber branches to innervate several lateral geniculate neurons. The latter travel to the visual cortex, where they synapse with about a hundred million cortical neurons (in humans). About 20 per cent of the optic nerve fibers pass through the lateral geniculate bodies to the midbrain region, where they function in reflex control of eye movements and pupil diameter.

Many different cell types are found in the visual cortex, but generally the result of the passage of nerve fibers from the retina to the cortex is to produce a crude topographical map of the retinal surface on the surface of the cortex. However, the fovea is represented by an amount of cortical surface equal to that used for all the rest of the retina—correlated probably with greater visual acuity associated with stimulation of the foveal region and perhaps also with the ability for color vision.

Complex receptive fields are found in the cortex. Activities of the primary visual cortex are relayed to the secondary visual cortex, to the motor cortex, and to association areas. Both inhibitory and excitatory fields are found in the visual cortex. At present there are not even hypothetical concepts available to explain the phenomena of conscious visual perception or color sensations. This is true of other sensory perceptions as well. Discussion and review of the activity in higher visual centers is found in Creutzfeldt and Sakman (1969); Kabrisky (1966); Broadbent (1965);

Young (1964a); and in the *Handbook of Physiology*, Section 1 (3 volumes), American Physiological Society, Washington, D.C.

17-9. The Arthropod Compound Eye. A variety of visual receptors are found in the invertebrates, but the discussion here will be limited to arthropod eyes, which have been most extensively studied. Arthropods have two main types of eye. The simple eye is a small unicorneal photoreceptor with a cup-shaped retina. When a lens is present, this cup-shaped eye is called an **ocellus**. The simple eye and the ocellus are partially surrounded by a pigment layer. Light coming through the open end of the cup can stimulate the receptor cells; light from other directions cannot. The angular aperture of the open end of the cup is usually less than 180° and determines the field from which stimuli can reach the sensory cells. The simple eye often functions in directed responses, for example, in orientation toward or away from a light source.

The **nauplius eye** is found in crustacean larvae and persists in the adult of most crustaceans. It is a median single eye usually consisting of three ocelli. Little is known about the functioning of the crustacean nauplius eye although in *Daphnia* it has been suggested that it is concerned with responses to pressure, temperature, pH, x-rays, and ultraviolet (Baylor and Smith, 1957). The nauplius eye lies close to a blood sinus, and its functioning may, in part, depend upon neuroendocrine-like activities.

Arachnids possess several pairs of simple eyes and lack compound eyes. Scorpions and spiders have a pair of median anterior eyes that are different from the other, or lateral, eyes. *Limulus* is unusual in that it has a pair of compound eyes and a pair of median dorsal ocelli. Insects have a pair of compound eyes and usually three dorsal ocelli. Crustaceans have a pair of compound eyes, sometimes mounted on movable stalks (in some Branchiopods and most groups of higher Malacostraca).

The compound eye is composed of from

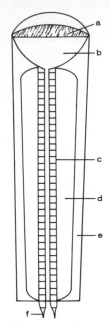

Figure 17-14 The parts of a generalized ommatidium. a, Cells just under the cornea; b, crystalline cone; c, rhabdome; d, visual (retinula) cells; e, retinal pigment cells; f, visual cell axon.

two dozen to over 10,000 optical units—the **ommatidia**. An ommatidium usually consists of 6 to 8 sensory or **retinula** cells with axons. The sensory cells are arranged in a ring about a central region the **rhabdome**. The latter consists of a region of close-fitting and interdigitating **rhabdomeres**, which are composed of retinular cell membranes elaborated as a system of tubes tightly packed at right angles to the surface of the cell and often also at right angles to the direction of incident light. The rhabdomere is considered to be the primary photoreceptor structure where visual pigments are located. In this respect it is analogous to the elaborate membrane systems of the outer segments of rod and cone cells.

The distal portion of the ommatidium is filled by a crystalline **cone** secreted by a ring of cells in the ommatidial wall. The distal end of the ommatidium is covered by a transparent cornea. The walls of the ommatidium also contain pigment cells. Distal pigment cells surround the cone and the space between the cone and the sense cells. Proximal pigment cells surround the sense cells. These structures

are typical of compound eyes in molluscs and other invertebrate groups as well as arthropods. Figure 17-14 shows the parts of a generalized ommatidium.

Ommatidia may be divided into two groups depending on their structure and functioning. In the **apposition eye** each ommatidium receives light from a restricted portion of the visual field as determined by the orientation of the ommatidial axis and the refractive properties of the cornea and crystalline cone (= lens). In apposition eyes the sensory cells and their rhabdomeres touch at the base of the cone (Figure 17-15). The cone and rhabdome act as light guides, and an image formed in a single ommatidium has no significance (Kuiper, 1962). The retinula cells of the apposition eye are surrounded by pigment cells that optically isolate each ommatidium from its neighbors. Only axial rays of light are carried into the rhabdomeres, off-axis rays are rejected and absorbed.

In **superposition eyes** the sensory cells and their rhabdomeres are separated from the cone although usually attached to it by crystalline

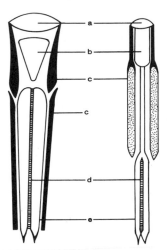

Figure 17-15 Structural differences of the ommatidia of an apposition (left) and a superposition (right) eye. a, Cornea; b, crystalline cone; c, accessory pigment cells; d, rhabdome; e, visual (retinula) cells. Note that in superposition eye the retinula cells are connected to the crystalline cone by crystalline threads that act as light guides. [After Wigglesworth (1954).]

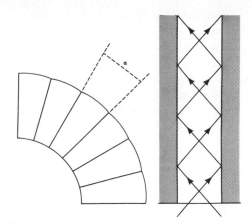

Figure 17-16 (Left) The visual angle, a. Light entering an ommatidium at a more oblique angle is only partially reflected in the rhabdome and becomes absorbed by the surrounding retinula cells. (Right) Illustrating how light rays entering in the visual angle can be internally reflected and finally produce a visual effect on the sensory cell.

threads that act as light guides (see Figure 17-15). The cells are only slightly pigmented and therefore the direction of light is confused by internal reflections in the eye, although in larger insects the separate retinula cells receive different amounts of light originating from different directions.

The crystalline threads act as light guides, and migration of pigment away from these threads allows a larger fraction of incident light to pass down them to the sensory cells. A light wave guide cannot function when pigment touches the outside of it because of internal reflections that diffuse the image. When the pigment is removed, more light passes through the guide. There appears to be no optical integration of the images received by separate ommatidia in the superposition eye. The only known exception is found in the eye of the firefly *Lampyris* in which a superposition image is formed by optical fusion from several ommatidia.

The arrangement of pigment granules is not constant. Pigment can move from one position to another and such movements are called retinomotor or photomechanical phenomena. Retinomotor activity regulates the photosensitivity of the eye and is especially

prominent in superposition eyes. Pigment migrates in a proximal direction under the action of light; in the dark it moves distally. In this way the amount of light reaching the visual cells is regulated. Pigment movements and their mechanisms are discussed in Chapter 18.

Visual acuity is determined by the angular distance between ommatidial axes if there is no overlap in the ommatidial fields (Figure 17-16). Such an eye can readily detect movements in the visual field but is not very effective in distinguishing form in stationary objects. Superposition eyes are commonly found in decapod crustaceans and in night-flying insects. Day-flying insects most commonly have apposition eyes. Figure 17-17 diagrams image formation in the superposition eye.

The complexity of neuronal postretinal connections is enormous; and, as in vertebrates, those invertebrates with compound eyes devote a large fraction of the central nervous system neurons to visual functions. Discussions of the compound eye of various invertebrate groups are found in Bullock and

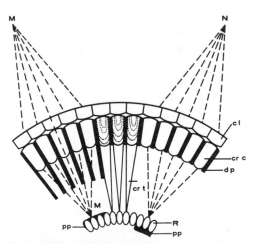

Figure 17-17 Path of light rays in a superposition eye. On the right, pigment is shown in a distal position (dp); on the left, pigment is shown after migration to a more proximal position. Note how such an effect can cut off more oblique light rays. cl, Cornea; cr c, crystalline cone; cr t, crystalline threads; R, rhabdome; pp, protective pigment.

Horridge (1965); Kuiper (1962); Waterman (1960); and Wiersma (1966).

The compound eye of *Limulus* has received much attention especially with respect to electrophysiological events. This eye differs in its structure from the compound eye of insects and crustaceans. Each eye contains about 700 ommatidia, each with a conical corneal lens and with various cell types including small pigment cells, 10 to 12 elongate pigmented retinula cells, and usually one bipolar **eccentric cell**. Eccentric or accessory cells are found in many compound eyes. Their function is not known, although in *Limulus* these cells produce action potentials. Both retinula and eccentric cells have axons with small branched collaterals converging on those from other ommatidia.

Potentials recorded from the *Limulus* eye include small slow potentials with small spikes. These are thought to come from damaged cells. Large slow potentials are found that may represent activity in the retinula cells. These potential waves lack spikes or, at best, have a few very small spikes. Slow potential changes with very large spikes are found and are thought to represent eccentric cell activity. There is some question as to whether or not retinula cell axons possess spikes (Borsellino et al., 1965).

The frequency of response of a given ommatidium is decreased when neighboring ommatidia are illuminated. This decrease is called "lateral inhibition." Because antidromic impulses in the optic nerve have an inhibitory effect, electrical not photochemical activity is thought to be responsible for this type of inhibition (Hartline et al., 1956).

The ERG of *Limulus* (and also of crustaceans such as *Cambarus* and *Eriocheir* and insects such as the cockroach and *Dixippus*) shows slow waves with the cornea negative. The wave is usually monophasic. The amplitude of the ERG varies with light intensity. The ERG is thought to originate in the receptors of the *Limulus* eye, but in other arthropods it may also include components of activity from optic ganglia.

Because only one train of impulses can be recorded from the bundle of fibers originating in a single ommatidium, either impulses are generated in only one of the retinal cells or all of the retinal cells fire synchronously. Evidence indicates that all of the retinula cells of an ommatidium are electrically interconnected and that the small spikes recorded from the retinula cells are always synchronous with a large spike in the eccentric cell (Smith et al., 1965). Light adaptation in the *Limulus* eye decreases the magnitude of a response to a given stimulus strength, but the speed of response is increased.

Some Behavioral Aspects of Vision

17-10. Visual Responses. Although visual perception can be tested relatively easily in human subjects capable of describing or otherwise detailing responses to visual stimuli, some difficulties are encountered in analyzing responses to visual stimuli in other animals. Several indirect methods are used to measure animal responses to photoreceptor activity. Although electrical recording methods are useful in the analysis of receptor cells and in tracing out pathways of impulse flow in the central nervous system or retina, the visual abilities of an animal are usually studied by other methods. Of these the **optimotor response** has been especially valuable in collecting quantitative data on visual reception.

Animals give an indication of visual reception of stimuli through a variety of responses including tensing or jerking of the body, movements of the head or eyes, and waving of the antennae in arthropods (Wallace, 1958). Any such movements or even the production of muscle action potentials can be used to provide clues about the nature of visual perception when a stimulus enters the visual field. In nearly all animals moving stimuli are the most effective in producing optomotor responses.

A stationary, walking, or flying animal can be placed at the center of a rotating drum with

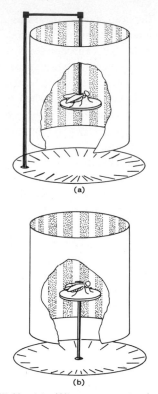

Figure 17-18 (a) When an animal is held fastened inside a rotating cylinder, its own turning movements cause a rotation of the disc beneath its feet. This is a measure of the open loop optomotor response. (b) A closed loop system allows the organism to move freely on the platform inside the rotating cylinder. In the optomotor response of a normal fly, the fly's movements result in a decrease in the apparent angular velocity of a cylinder rotating about it. When the fly is held fastened and its walking efforts rotate a turntable beneath it, there is no reduction in the relative angular velocity of the cylinder, and the feedback loop supplying information for the optomotor response is broken. [After Mittelstaedt (1964).]

a striped pattern (Figure 17-18). Any movement on the part of the animal in response to the moving pattern is usually in the same direction as that of the drum, but the animal's movement is not as great as the movement of the visual field. A number of uses can be made of such an experimental system. A good measure of visual acuity is obtained by determining the minimum effective angle of repetition in the pattern needed to elicit a

response. Half of this angle is called the **elementary visual angle**.

By using colored stripes alternated with shades of neutral gray it is possible to show the presence or absence of color vision. There is no color vision if each color that produces an optomotor response has a corresponding shade of gray that also produces a response. In using this technique, it is important that proper controls be used that eliminate sensitivity to polarized or ultraviolet light. Some animals with known color vision do not respond positively to optomotor testing, and this method cannot be used as the sole criterion for the presence or absence of color vision.

When the speed of the rotating drum is altered, a minimal rate of movement needed to elicit the optomotor response can be found —the **optomotor flicker fusion frequency.** One can also determine the drum rotation speed (for a given pattern and size of stripes) at which response is maximal. The black and white striped patterns can be altered in many ways to analyze the nature of optomotor responses. For example, velocity of rotation, degree of contrast between stripes, number and width of stripes, shape of visual contours, total illumination, and alterations in color patterning can all be used for testing an animal.

A variety of animals have been tested using this type of experimental apparatus. Wolf (1933) used a version of this system to measure visual responses in honey bees. The flicker fusion response was used to obtain information about the visual pigments and retinal functioning in crayfish (Crozier and Wolf, 1939). Kalmus (1949) studied *Drosophila* and other flies.

Hassenstein (1961) used a refinement of the optomotor system to analyze visual perception in the beetle *Chlorophanus viridis* (see Figure 17-19). The animal is held fixed while a Y-maze globe rotates beneath it. In the original apparatus the animal tended to turn with the movement of the drum so that displacement of the surroundings was minimized. The organism and moving pattern constitute a closed-loop feedback system. In the

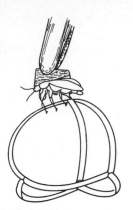

Figure 17-19 Optomotor responses in the beetle *Chlorophanus viridus* were measured as the direction the organism took at forks in a rotating Y maze placed beneath it. [After Hassenstein (1961).]

Hassenstein apparatus the feedback loop is opened and the animal is prevented from changing its position relative to the stimulus. The beetle "walks" along the spherical maze and continuously reaches Y-shaped branches that provide a choice of right or left turns. The particular choice made by the beetle provides a measure of its turning tendency as induced by movement. Right and left choices will be statistically equal if there is no turning tendency, but if there is some optokinetic turning reaction, the proportion of right to left turns will measure the intensity of the reaction.

From the use of this apparatus and of a refined system in which the insect's field of vision could be appropriately restricted, Hassenstein found that when successive light stimuli were presented to the beetle, a motor response was initiated only when the stimuli activated ommatidia no more than two ommatidia apart. Only two ommatidia had to be stimulated to evoke a response. When the time interval between stimuli was changed, it was found that maximum response occurred when stimuli were about a fourth of a second apart. However, some response was seen even when stimuli were 10 seconds apart, indicating that some physiological effect lasted for 10 seconds after the stimulation of the first ommatidium. The order of stimulus presentation determined the direction of movement; reversal of the order caused a reversal in the direction of movement (see Reichardt, 1961; Bullock and Horridge, 1965).

The Hawaiian swimming crab, *Podophthalmus*, has a long basal segment of the eye (Figure 17-20) and not only can eye stalk movements be observed as part of the optomotor response but also the optic ganglia and their connections can be studied with microelectrodes. Recordings can be made from various levels of the optical integrating system. This is one of the few invertebrates in which it has been possible to obtain some information about the coordination and

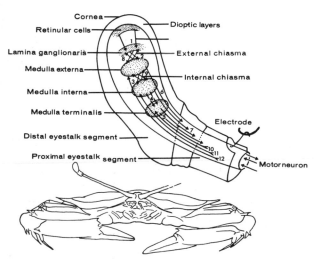

Figure 17-20 The Hawaiian swimming crab *Podophthalmus* is shown in frontal section. A schematic diagram of the optical ganglia and their connections are shown above. [After Waterman et al. (1964).]

integration of visual information by the central nervous system (see Wiersma, 1966).

Mathematical models of these various systems have been developed (Reichardt, 1961, 1965) and optokinetic models for crabs are given by Horridge (1966). It can be pointed out that in optomotor responses there is always a lag of the eyes behind the moving stimulus and feedback systems operate to control eye movements although always with some error. Activity in one eye induces movement and control of the other eye even when the latter is blinded or held in the dark. Eyes are continuously undergoing small movements that, in the case of humans, improve the visual performance.

17-11. Orientation Behavior.   Visual clues are among the most important stimuli for controlling the orientation and locomotion of animals. Some of the terminology of orientation and locomotion studies can be introduced suitably at this point. Orientation includes those mechanisms used to control the attitude of the animal in space (and time) and to guide its locomotion. Orientation may be induced by external or internal stimuli and may also be initiated by endogenous activity on the part of the nervous system.

The definitions and terms used here are primarily those of Fraenkel and Gunn (1931), although some modifications are necessary (see Jander, 1963; Markl, 1965). Orientation can be subdivided into two main categories. Primary orientation is the assumption of the basic body position in space of either a moving or a stationary animal. Examples would include the head up, two-footed stance of humans; the ventral surface down, horizontally-positioned body of fish in water; or the four-footed, head forward position of dogs. Secondary orientation is a result of an animal's positioning and moving itself in response to various environmental stimuli. Primary orientation is to a large extent determined by activities on the part of proprioceptive receptors and is basically a normal balancing of the body.

Orientation resulting from locomotor activity may be of several types, each with its subdivisions. **Kineses** are locomotor reactions undirected with respect to the source of stimulation. Subdivisions of kineses depend on the nature of the response and include orthokineses, in which there is a relationship between the change in velocity of locomotion or the frequency of locomotor activity and the intensity of stimulation; and klinokineses, which express a relationship between the frequency of directional changes during locomotion and the intensity of the stimulus.

Taxes are characterized as directed locomotory activities toward (a positive taxis) or away from (a negative taxis) the source of stimulation. The long axis of the body must take on a definite position relative to the stimulus source. Taxes are subdivided on the basis of the nature of the stimulating agent and include: phototaxes (responses to light); geotaxes (responses to gravitational stimuli); chemotaxes (responses to chemical stimuli); electrotaxes (responses to electrical fields). Each of these subdivisions depends on activity in a given class of receptor. When an organism makes simultaneous readings of a stimulus with separated receptors and its motion is relatively straight without body turnings, one speaks of a tropotaxis. When an organism makes successive readings of a stimulus and its motion exhibits turning from a straight path, the action is a klinotaxis. Tropotactic orientation implies the presence of paired symmetrical receptors.

There are also some transverse orientations in which the animal may move with the body at some fixed angle to the direction of the stimulus. The light-compass reaction in which the body is maintained at some angle to a source of light rays is an example of a transverse orientation. Also included in this category are dorsal light reactions in which the animal maintains posture by keeping the dorsal side always toward the light (usually sunlight from above). Such reactions are common in crustaceans, insects, fish, and reptiles. For example, some fish can be induced to swim on their side or with their ventral side up, if the gravity receptors are rendered inoperative and the direction of the light is varied (Tinbergen, 1951). Posture in most cases is a result of information received by both visual and gravitational sensory elements. Statocyts, organs of balance in some animals, are lacking in others, who probably maintain themselves in the proper orientation by using visual reception.

17-12. Role of Vision in Behavior. Because light waves travel in straight lines, visual stimuli can play an important role in guiding the locomotion of animals. Visual clues may be used for direction finding and for complicated navigational activities (see Chapter 19). In such basic animal activities as food selection, visual activities are important. For example, in chicks it is small rounded three-dimensional objects that stimulate the pecking reaction although color also plays some role (Hess, 1960; Fantz, 1957). Light also plays an important role in predator-prey relationships, and although often any moving object is captured by a predator, in most cases only specific shapes will elicit a food gathering response. This is, for example, the case in cuttlefish, which feed on small crabs and whose feeding reactions are elicited even when the crabs are placed behind a glass plate (Wells, 1962). Visual stimuli also are of importance in such intraspecific activities as sexual behavior.

Orientation toward light is found even in animals with primitive eyespots such as *Euglena. Euglena* exhibits a photoklinotaxis in which directed locomotion is toward a light source but in which the body turns to successively sample the light intensity on the two sides. This flagellate has good intensity discrimination, but its photoreceptor is not a good directional receptor. Similar photoklinotaxis is found in fly larvae. Phototaxis also occurs in species of animals that lack even eyespots. For example, *Hydra* show such a response, probably because of dermal light sensors. Phototropotaxis is found in planarians because these animals have paired visual receptors located on each side of the head and can make simultaneous comparisons of the light intensities on the two sides of the body. They move

in such a manner as to maintain light intensities equal on the two receptors and thus can move in a straight line toward the light source.

In both *Euglena* and planarians there is a positive phototaxis, but because of differences in the number, nature, and positioning of the receptor organs, two different methods are used to approach the light. It should also be added that *Euglena* responds positively only to weak light; strong illumination causes a negative phototaxis.

Most decapod crustaceans, some insects, and cephalopod molluscs are able to orient to the plane of polarized light. It has been shown that this ability depends on the fine structure of the rhabdomere, which consists of close packed arrays of microvilli protruding axially from the retinular cells (Figure 17-13). The microvilli of all the rhabdomeres of a retinula cell are oriented in only two directions perpendicular to each other. The light sensitivity of the ommatidium is localized only in these structures, and it is thought that the visual pigment molecules are aligned along the membranes of the microvilli with their major dichroic axis parallel to the long axis of the microvillus. Because all the microvilli of a given rhabdomere are closely parallel to one another, they form a dichroic analyzer that is maximally sensitive to photons vibrating in a direction parallel to the microvilli. The system of perpendicularly oriented microvilli forms a two-channel analyzer for polarized light.

Pairs of functional analyzer units in the crab *Cardiosoma* were found to have maximal sensitivity, as shown by measurement of the ERG upon light stimulation, to polarization in the same retinal directions as the rhabdomere microvilli observed in the electron microscope. In turn, these directions correspond with the horizontal and vertical axes of the animal's normal orientation. Two or three functional analyzer units are formed of the seven retinular cells found in an ommatidium.

These results were obtained by experimental procedures which space does not permit describing here. However, a description of the methodology together with a review of theories concerning sensitivity to polarized light is given in Waterman and Horch (1966). Such a mechanism has been found in both apposition and superposition eyes of crustaceans. It is of interest that this same type of mechanism is found in the camera eye of cephalopods (the cephalopod eye is described in the next section).

Although one ommatidium of the arthropod eye functions in image perception, it also contains subunits so that at the cellular and molecular levels the plane of polarized light can be detected. The action potentials produced by differing responses of the microvilli permit the animal to orient itself and its locomotion. Such locomotion, for example, includes vertical migration in which animals move up or down in the water depending on the time of day. In turn this behavior is influenced by the fact that the sun at different times of day will be in different positions thus altering the plane of polarized light. The use of polarized light in light compass reactions and direction finding has been examined in many species, especially in bees (see von Frisch, 1965).

17-13. Form Vision, Learning, and Memory in Cephalopods. Although nearly all animals react to a moving visual stimulus, it is more difficult to determine how animals see shapes and forms (if they do so at all). Crustaceans, for example, appear to have little ability to discriminate between different shapes. However, a large number of invertebrates will react to simple forms when they are presented as black shapes on a white background (Carthy, 1958).

Form vision has been extensively studied in the eye of the octopus (Young, 1961). Octopuses can be trained by reward and punishment techniques. When one shape is presented and associated with a reward (in the form of food) and another shape is presented and associated with a punishment (in the form of mild electrical shock), an octopus can learn to distinguish between the two forms and select the one that results in food. Using techniques of this type, researchers can determine whether or not a given form is ever

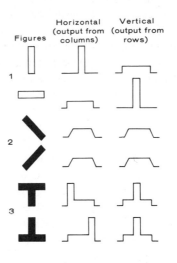

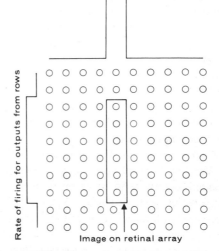

Figure 17-21 Shape discrimination in *Octopus*. (a) A hypothesis for derivation of horizontal and vertical projections of a figure on the retina [After Sutherland (1960).] (b) Some shapes and the ability of *Octopus* to perceive them. The visual analysis system of *Octopus* was considered to break down an image into two projections: horizontal and vertical with respect to the retinal array. The system is, however, more sensitive to differences in the horizontal plane because up/down mirror images are distinguished more readily than left/right mirror images. This hypothesis does not explain all the facts about visual perception in *Octopus* but is a beginning.

distinguishable by the animal and evaluate the relative effectiveness of different shapes as visual stimuli. Figure 17-21 shows some different shapes and indicates the degree to which an octopus can distinguish them.

Although some of the more primitive molluscs or those living in deep (and therefore dark) waters lack eyes, most members of the phylum do possess specialized photoreceptors. These range from simple eyespots and ocelli, sometimes on stalks, to the complex eyes of the cephalopods (Wells, 1966). The eye of cephalopod molluscs is a camera eye, similar in most respects to that of the vertebrates. There is a single lens, formed of two halves joined together, whose shape is controllable by ciliary muscles for accommodation (the ability to focus on near and far objects). The retina is not inverted as in the human eye, and thus the photoreceptor elements are directly exposed to incident light. Nerves and blood vessels lie behind the retinular cells. The retina is composed of rhabdomes analogous to those of arthropod eyes. Each rhabdome is made up of four radially arranged rhabdomeres of four retinal cells. There are about 7×10^6 rhabdomeres in the retina of *Octopus*, which is thus equivalent to the vertebrate retina in receptor density.

From a consideration of the types of shapes that an octopus can learn to distinguish, it appears that there are more horizontally oriented receptive fields in the retina than there are vertically oriented fields. Vertical differences are made easier to recognize because of illumination and gravity clues. It is found that the horizontal position of the retina plays an important role in form discrimination, and it is not unexpected to find that this type of visual activity is interwoven with sensory information from the statocyts, which provide gravitational and orientational clues to the animal, that is, information about the relative position of the retina aids in discrimination of shape (see Sutherland, 1960; Wells, 1963).

The ability of an octopus to recognize shapes thus depends, first, on the nature of neuronal connections between receptive fields of the retina. During normal behavior of the octopus

various mechanisms are used to restrict responses to particular shapes useful in feeding behavior (it should be noted that the experiments discussed here are all concerned basically with the elicitation of feeding responses). In its natural environment the octopus ignores many clues that during training become effective stimuli. This is part of the signature principle of Quastler (1965), who stated that at biological levels from the molecular to the ecosystem, animals ignore much of the incoming information and utilize only a small fraction of the total information. This small fraction is the signature.

Cephalopods are animals of often rapid movement and with a highly developed visual and tactile sense. Their brains are especially developed in those areas associated with integrating and coordinating visual information. Memory and learning have been studied in these animals because, again, they can be trained by reward and punishment. It is of some interest to briefly discuss here a few of the findings relating visual reception, tactile discrimination, and actions of the central nervous system.

By cutting or destroying various parts of the octopus brain (see Figure 17-22), researchers showed that the ability to learn different shapes was abolished by removing the vertical lobe or by transecting the superior frontal-vertical tract. Such operations also prevented any reestablishment of learning ability.

It was also shown that the octopus can learn to distinguish textural differences by the sense of touch (the receptors are suckers on the tentacles). Tactile discrimination is based on the degree of distortion that various objects produce in the suckers. Nerve networks associated with the inferior frontal and subfrontal lobes are exclusively concerned with touch learning.

When crabs (the normal food of the octopus) are excluded as a component of the learning situation, it was found that the octopus can be taught in the absence of a vertical lobe, and it is now considered that memory stores are located in the optic lobe. Young (1962)

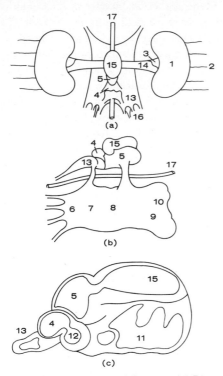

Figure 17-22 The brain of *Octopus*. (a) Diagram of brain seen from above after removal of surrounding cartilage. (b) The same from the side. (c) Diagram of a medial longitudinal section through the supraesophageal lobes. 1, Optic lobe; 2, optic nerves; 3, olfactory lobe; 4, inferior frontal lobe; 5, superior frontal lobe; 6, brachial lobe; 7, anterior chromatophore lobe; 8, pedal lobe; 9, pallioviscenal lobe; 10, posterior chromatophore lobe; 11, basal lobe; 12, subfrontal lobe; 13, buccal lobe; 14, optic commissure; 15, vertical lobe; 16, nerves to arms; 17, esophagus. [After Young (1964a).]

considers that the vertical and superior frontal lobes function as a pair, regulating the probability of an attack on objects seen. The visual analyzing system appears to exist within the optic lobes, and one function of the superior frontal and vertical lobes is to maintain activity in optic lobe nerve circuits until the arrival of sensory signals that indicate the results of action taken in response to visual inputs. The superior frontal lobe multiplies signals from the optic lobes so that all parts of the brain receive inputs that originated in specific retinal areas (Maldonados, 1964). This may be sum-

marized as follows: when the octopus sees an object that it has learned to distinguish as associated with food, it attacks and takes hold of the object. The object held by the suckers of the tentacles causes information to be sent to the brain, and this information is integrated with the information received from visual receptors to determine the further action on the part of the animal. Discrimination of shape or form depends on the retinal fields stimulated. The frontal and vertical lobes maintain a circulation of impulses in the optic lobes until action can be decided upon. Such activity might be through neuronal cascades and loops as described in Chapter 11.

The inferior frontal, subfrontal, and buccal lobes must all be intact for full tactile discriminatory learning. The sensory input from each arm enters the brain on that same side, and the effect of any changes in learning is at first limited to that side. After two or more hours the effects of experience registered on one side can spread across and modify activity on the other side of the brain. No such spread is seen, however, if the inferior frontal system is split by a longitudinal cut.

One model for tactile discrimination and learning is shown in Figure 17-23. This model takes into account several cell types found in the subfrontal and other lobes. So called classifying cells are critical to touch learning. They do not send processes outside the subfrontal lobe but synapse with other cells in this lobe. These cells, in turn, send processes to other large cells within the lobe or to cells

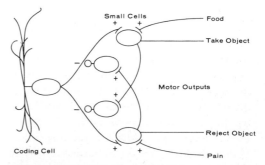

Figure 17-23 A model for learning in the Octopus. [After Young (1965).]

outside the lobe. It is thought that a classifying cell is preset to respond to a particular frequency of sensory input. This part of the learning system is inate. The two processes of the classifying cell are connected to either attack or nonattack cells with inhibitory cross-connections so that an animal does not attempt to carry out both actions at once. If a proper frequency of input stimulation reaches a given classifying cell, the octopus will attack what it feels, otherwise it will not. There are many small cells found in the subfrontal lobe, and these may be the inhibitory connections needed to safeguard the system and provide only one type of action. Such inhibitory activities on the part of this and other octopus brain lobes fall into the same pattern that has been found in the vertebrate brain. In central nervous systems generally it seems that inhibitory actions are of more importance in producing coordinated activities than are excitatory neurons.

This discussion raises many other questions concerning nervous system integration of information. The nature of the memory process and learning is not understood, because especially at the molecular and cellular levels these processes as yet have no good explanation. The discussion also points out that visual sensations result from extremely complex actions both in the retina and within the brain and that the nature of these interactions still remains to be discovered.

Most of the vertebrates studied show excellent form discrimination. It has been possible, for example, to analyze form vision in frogs by recording the electrical activity of ganglion cells of the retina in response to small spots of light illuminating the retina. A variety of different retinal receptive fields have been shown to exist, some of which respond to initiation (on-units) or cessation of the stimulus (off-units) or to both (on-off units). Off units often continue to react for several seconds after the illumination is stopped (Barlow, 1953a, b). Lateral inhibition is found in the frog retina, as described for *Limulus*. Electrical activity of stimulated off-units is reduced by simultaneous stimulation of adjacent units.

Maturana et al. (1960) showed that two other receptive field units are present. They are convex edge fields, which respond to a moving edge if it is convex rather than straight, and dark receptors, which are continuously active with a maximum impulse output in darkness and a minimum output in strong illumination. All of these units interact with one another and are likely involved in the different activities of the frog. For example, off units are concentrated at the rear of the retina and may aid a frog in orienting to a fly before striking at it. Frogs will strike only at moving objects (Maturana et al., 1960).

References and Readings

Abrahamson, E. W. and S. E. Ostroy (1967). "The photochemical and macromolecular aspects of vision." *Prog. Biophys.* **17:** 179–215.

Alpern, M. (1968). "Distal mechanisms of vertebrate color vision." *Ann. Rev. Physiol.* **30:** 279–318.

Bagnara, J. T. (1963). "The pineal body and the body lightening reaction of larval amphibians." *Gen. Comp. Endocrinol.* **3:** 86–100.

Barlow, H. B. (1953a). "Action potentials from the frog's retina." *J. Physiol.* (London) **119:** 58–68.

Barlow, H. B. (1953b). "Summation and inhibition of the frog's retina." *J. Physiol.* (London) **119:** 69–88.

Barr, L. and M. Alpern (1963). "Photosensitivity of the frog iris." *J. Gen. Physiol.* **46:** 1249–1265.

Baylor, E. R. and F. E. Smith (1957). "Diurnal migration of plankton crustaceans." **Recent Advances in Invertebrate Physiology,** pp. 21–35. University of Oregon, Eugene.

Baylor, E. R. and F. E. Smith (1958). "Animal perception of X-rays." *Rad. Res.* **8:** 466–474.

Blum, H. F. (1961). "Does the melanin pigment of human skin have adaptive value?" *Quart. Rev. Biol.* **36:** 50–63.

Borsellino, A., M. G. F. Fuortes, and T. G. Smith (1965). "Visual responses in *Limulus*."

Cold Spring Harbor Symp. Quant. Biol. **30:** 429–443.

Brett, J. R. (1957). "The eye." In: **The Physiology of Fishes.** (M. E. Brown, ed.), Vol. 2, pp. 121–154. New York: Academic Press, Inc.

Bridges, C. D. B. (1965). "Absorption properties, interconversions, and environmental adaptations of pigments from fish photoreceptors." *Cold Spring Harbor Symp. Quant. Biol.* **30:** 317–334.

Bringley, G. S. (1960). **Physiology of the Retina and the Visual Pathway.** London: Edward Arnold & Co.

Broadbent, D. E. (1965). "Information processing in the nervous system." *Science* **150:** 457–462.

Brown, K. T. (1968). "The electroretinogram: its components and their origins." *Vis. Res.* **8:** 633–678.

Brown, K. T. and M. Murakami (1964). "The biphasic form of the early receptor potential of the monkey retina." *Nature* **204:** 739.

Brown, K. T. and M. Murakami (1967). "Delayed decay of the late receptor potential of monkey cones as a function of stimulus intensity." *Vis. Res.* **7:** 179–189.

Brown, P. K. and G. Wald (1964). "Visual pigments in single rods and cones of the human retina." *Science* **144:** 45–52.

Bullock, T. H. and F. P. J. Diecke (1956). "Properties of an infra-red receptor." *J. Physiol.* (London) **134:** 47–87.

Bullock, T. H. and G. A. Horridge (1965). **Structure and Function in the Nervous System of Invertebrates,** 2 volumes. San Francisco: W. H. Freeman & Company, Publishers.

Burfers, A. C. J. (1952). "Optomotor reactions of *Xenopus laevis.*" *Physiol. Comp. Oecol.* **2:** 274–281.

Carthy, J. D. (1958). **An Introduction to the Behavior of Invertebrates.** London: George Allen & Unwin, Ltd.

Case, J. (1966). **Sensory Mechanisms.** New York: The Macmillan Company. 113 pp.

Crawford, B. H. (1965). "Theories of color vision." In: **Colour Vision** (A. V. S. de Reuch and J. Knight, eds.), pp. 152–173. Boston: Little, Brown and Company.

Creutzfeldt, O. and B. Sakmann (1969).

"Neurophysiology of vision." *Ann. Rev. Physiol.* **31:** 499–544.

Crozier, W. J. and E. Wolf (1939). "The flicker response contour for the crayfish." *J. Gen. Physiol.* **23:** 1–9.

Crozier, W. J. and E. Wolf (1939). "The flicker response contour for the crayfish. II. Retinal pigment and the theory of the assymetry of the curve." *Biol. Bull.* **77:** 126–134.

Davson, H., ed. (1962). **The Eye,** 4 volumes. New York: Academic Press, Inc.

deRobertis, E. D. P. (1960). "Some observations on the ultrastructure and morphogenesis of photoreceptors." *J. Gen. Physiol.* **43** (suppl.): 1–13.

Dowling, J. E. and B. B. Boycott (1966). "Organization of the primate retina: electron miscroscopy." *Proc. Roy. Soc.* (London) **B166:** 80–111.

Fantz, R. (1957). "Form preferences in newly hatched chicks." *J. Comp. Physiol. Psychol.* **50:** 422–430.

Fraenkel, G. S. and D. L. Gunn (1961). **The Orientation of Animals.** New York: Dover Publications, Inc.

von Frisch, K. (1956). **Bees: Their Vision, Chemical Senses, and Language.** Ithaca, N.Y.: Cornell University Press.

von Frisch, K. (1965). **Tanszprache und orientierung der Bienen.** Berlin: Springer-Verlag. 578 pp.

Fuortes, M. G. F. and G. F. Poggio (1963). "Transient responses to sudden illumination in cells of the eye of *Limulus.*" *J. Gen. Physiol.* **46:** 435–452.

Giese, A. C., ed. (1964). **Photophysiology,** 2 volumes. New York: Academic Press, Inc.

Glickstein, M. (1969). "Organization of the visual pathways." *Science* **164:** 917–925.

Granit, R. (1955). **Receptors and Sensory Perception.** New Haven, Conn.: Yale University Press.

Hanaoka, T. and K. Fujimoto (1957). "Absorption spectrum of a single cone in carp retina." *Japan. J. Physiol.* **7:** 276–285.

Hartline, H. K., H. G. Wagner, and F. Ratliff (1956). "Inhibition in the eye of *Limulus.*" *J. Gen. Physiol.* **39:** 651–673.

Hassenstein, B. (1961). "Wie sehen Insekten Bewegungen." *Naturwissenschaften* **48**: 207–214.

Hess, E. H. (1960). "Sensory processes." In: **An Introduction to Comparative Psychology.** (R. H. Walters, D. A. Rethlingshafer, and W. E. Caldwell, eds.), pp. 74–101. New York: McGraw-Hill Book Company, Inc.

Hinde, R. A. (1970). **Animal Behavior: A synthesis of ethology and comparative psychology.** New York: McGraw-Hill Book Company, Inc. 876 pp.

Horridge, G. A. (1966). "Study of a system, as illustrated by the optokinetic response." *Symp. Soc. Exp. Biol.* **20**: 179–198.

Hubbard, R., D. Bownds, and T. Yoshizawa (1965). "The chemistry of visual photoreception." *Cold Spring Harbor Symp. Quant. Biol.* **30**: 301–316.

Hubbard, R., and A. Kropf (1959). "Molecular aspects of visual excitation." *Ann. N.Y. Acad. Sci.* **81**: 388–398.

Jander, R. (1963). "Insect orientation." *Ann. Rev. Entomol.* **8**: 95–114.

Jander, R. (1965). "Die Phylogenie von Orientierungsmechanismen der Arthropoden." *Verh. Deutschen Zool. Gess.* (Jena): 266–306.

Kabrisky, M. (1966). **A Proposed Model for Visual Information Processing in the Human Brain.** Urbana, Ill.: University of Illinois Press. 88 pp.

Kalmus, H. (1949). "Optomotor responses in *Drosophila* and *Musca*." *Physiol. Comp. Oecol.* **1**: 127–147.

Kelly, D. E. (1962). "Pineal organs: photoreception, secretion, and development." *Am. Sci.* **50**: 597–625.

Kennedy, D. (1963). "Physiology of photoreceptor neurons in the abdominal nerve cord of the crayfish." *J. Gen. Physiol.* **46**: 551–572.

Krinsky, N. I. (1958). "The lipoprotein nature of rhodopsin." *Arch. Ophthalmol.* **60**: 231–239.

Kuffler, S. W. (1953). "Discharge patterns and functional organization of mammalian retina." *J. Neurophysiol.* **16**: 37–68.

Kuiper, J. W. (1962). "The optics of the compound eye." *Symp. Soc. Exp. Biol.* **16**: 58–71.

Land, E. H. (1964). "The retinex." *Am. Sci.* **52**: 247–264.

Land, E. H. (1965). "The retinex." In: **Colour Vision.** (A. V. S. deReuck and J. Knight, eds.), pp. 217–223. Boston: Little, Brown & Company.

Lettvin, J. Y., M. D. Maturana, W. S. McCulloch, and W. H. Pitts (1959). "What a frog's eye tells the frog's brain." *Proc. Radio Engrs.* (N.Y.) **47**: 1940–1951.

Maldonado, H. (1964). "The control of attack by *Octopus*." *Z. vergl. Physiol.* **47**: 656–674.

Markl, H. (1965). "Wie orientieren sich Ameisennach der Schwerkraft?" *Unschau*: 185–188.

Maturana, H. R., J. Y. Lettvin, W. S. McCulloch, and W. H. Pitts (1960). "Anatomy and physiology of vision in the frog *Rana pipiens*." *J. Gen. Physiol.* **43**: 129–175.

Mazokhin-Porshnyakov, G. A. (1969). **Insect Vision.** Translated by R. Masironi and L. Masironi. New York: Plenum Press. 306 pp.

McElroy, W. D. and B. Glass, eds. (1961). **Light and Life.** Baltimore, Md.: Johns Hopkins University Press. 924 pp.

Miller, W. H., G. D. Bernard, and J. L. Allen (1968). "The optics of insect compound eyes." *Science* **162**: 760–767.

Mittelstaedt, H. (1964). "Basic control patterns of orientational homeostasis." *Symp. Soc. Exp. Biol.* **18**: 365–386.

Morton, R. A. and G. A. J. Pitt (1969). "Aspects of visual pigment research." *Adv. Enzymol.* **32**: 97–171.

Nicol, J. A. C. (1962). "Animal luminescence." *Adv. Comp. Physiol.* **1**: 217–273.

Pedler, C. (1965). "Rods and cones—a fresh approach." In: **Colour Vision.** (A. V. S. deReuch and J. Knight, eds.), pp. 53–83. Boston: Little, Brown & Company.

Pedler, C. and H. Goodland (1965). "The compound eye and first optic ganglion of the fly. A light and electron microscopic study." *J. Roy. Micro. Soc.* (London) **84**: 161–179.

Polyak, S. (1941). **The Retina.** Chicago: University of Chicago Press. 607 pp.

Prosser, C. L. and F. A. Brown (1961). **Comparative Animal Physiology,** 2nd ed. Philadelphia: W. B. Saunders Co. 688 pp.

Quastler, H. (1965). "General principles of systems analysis." In: **Theoretical and Mathematical Biology.** (T. H. Waterman and H. J. Morowitz, eds.), pp. 313–333. Waltham, Mass.: Blaisdell Publishing Company.

Reichardt, W. (1961). "Autocorrelation, a principle for the evaluation of sensory information by the central nervous system." In: **Sensory Communication.** (W. A. Rosenblith, ed.), pp. 303–317. Cambridge, Mass.: Massachusetts Institute of Technology Press.

Reichardt, W. E. (1965). "Quantum sensitivity of light receptors in the compound eye of the fly *Musca*." *Cold Spring Harbor Symp. Quant. Biol.* **30:** 505–515.

Rushton, W. A. H. (1963). "A cone pigment in the protanope." *J. Physiol.* (London) **168:** 345–359.

Rushton, W. A. H. (1965). "Cone pigment kinetics in the deuteranope." *J. Physiol.* (London) **176:** 38–45.

Rushton, W. A. H. (1965). "Stray light and the measurement of mixed pigments in the retina." *J. Physiol.* (London) **176:** 46–55.

Sebeok, T. A. (1965). "Animal communication." *Science* **147:** 1006–1014.

Smith, T. G., F. Baumann, and M. G. F. Fuortes (1965). "Electrical connections between visual cells in the ommatidium of *Limulus*." *Science* **147:** 1446–1447.

Steven, D. M. (1963). "The dermal light sense." *Biol. Rev.* **38:** 204–240.

Sutherland, N. S. (1960). "Theories of shape discrimination in *Octopus*." *Nature* **186:** 840–844.

Sutherland, N. S. (1962). "Visual discrimination of shape by *Octopus*: squares and crosses." *J. Comp. Physiol. Psychol.* **55:** 939–943.

Sutherland, N. S. (1964). "The learning of discrimination by animals." *Endeavour* **23:** 140–152.

Svaetichin, G. (1953). "The cone action potential." *Acta Physiol. Scand.* **29** (Suppl. 106). 565.

Tinbergen, N. (1951). **The Study of Instinct.** New York: Oxford University Press.

Verveen, A. A. (1963). "Fields of touch receptors in frog skin." *Exp. Neurology.* **8:** 482–492.

Wald, G. (1964). "The receptors of human color vision." *Science* **145:** 1007–1016.

Wald, G. (1968). "Molecular basis of visual excitation." *Science* **162:** 230–239.

Wald, G. and P. K. Brown (1965). "Human color vision and color blindness." *Cold Spring Harbor Symp. Quant. Biol.* **30:** 345–361.

Walls, G. L. (1942). **The Vertebrate Eye and Its Adaptive Radiation.** Cranbrook Institute of Science Bulletin, **19.** Bloomfield Hills, Michigan: 785 pp.

Wallace, G. K. (1958). "Visual scanning in the desert locust *Schistocerca gregaria* Forskål." *J. Exp. Biol.* **36:** 512–525.

Waterman, T. H., ed. (1960). **The Physiology of Crustacea,** Volume 2. New York: Academic Press, Inc.

Waterman, T. H. and K. W. Horch (1966). "Mechanism of polarized light reception." *Science* **150:** 467–475.

Waterman, T. H., C. A. G. Wiersma, and B. M. H. Bush (1964). "Afferent visual responses in the optic nerve of the crab, *Podophthalmus*." *J. Cell. Comp. Physiol.* **63:** 135–155.

Weber, E. H. (1851). **Tastinn und Gemeingefuhl.** Braunschweig: Vieweg Verlag. 49 pp.

Wells, M. J. (1962). **Brain and Behavior in Cephalopods.** Stanford, Calif.: Stanford University Press. 171 pp.

Wells, M. J. (1963). "Tactile discrimination of shape by *Octopus*." *Quart. J. Exp. Biol. Psychol.* **16:** 156–162.

Wells, M. J. (1966). "Learning in the octopus." *Symp. Soc. Exp. Biol.* **20:** 477–507.

Wiersma, C. A. G. (1966). "Integration in the visual pathway of crustacea." *Symp. Soc. Exp. Biol.* **20:** 151–178.

Wigglesworth, V. B. (1954). **Principles of Insect Physiology.** London: Methuen & Co., Ltd.

Willmer, E. N. (1965). "Duality in the retina."

In: **Colour Vision** (A. V. S. deReuch and J. Knight, eds.), pp. 89–104. Boston: Little, Brown and Company.

Wolf, E. (1933). "Critical frequency of flicker as a function of intensity of illumination for the eye of the bee." *J. Gen. Physiol.* **17:** 7–19.

Wolken, J. J. (1960). "Photoreceptors: comparative studies." *Symp. Comp. Biol.* **1:** 145–167.

Wolken, J. J. (1966). **Vision: biophysics and biochemistry of the retinal photoreceptors.** Springfield, Ill.: Charles C. Thomas, Publisher. 193 pp.

Yamanaga, E. and T. Ishikawa (1965). "The fine structure of the horizontal cells in some vertebrate retinas." *Cold Spring Harbor Symp. Quant. Biol.* **30:** 383–392.

Young, J. Z. (1961). "Learning and discrimination in the octopus." *Biol. Rev.* **36:** 32–96.

Young, J. Z. (1962). "The optic lobes of *Octopus vulgaris.*" *Proc. Roy. Soc.* (London) **B245:** 19–58.

Young, J. Z. (1964a). **A Model of the Brain.** New York: Oxford University Press. 348 pp.

Young, J. Z. (1964b). "Paired centres for the control of attack by *Octopus.*" *Proc. Roy. Soc.* (London) **B159:** 565–588.

Young, J. Z. (1965). "The organization of a memory system." *Proc. Roy. Soc.* (London) **B163:** 285–320.

Chromatophores

Chapter 18

Chromatophores and Bioluminescence

18-1. Nature and Functions of Chromatophores. This chapter will describe two types of special effectors of animals: chromatophores, which are responsible for color changes or intensity of shading changes in animals; and bioluminescent cells which produce light. It seems appropriate to discuss them directly after the discussion of photoreception because they present another aspect of the relation between light and the animal.

Chromatophores are specialized effector cells that contain pigment. The position or dispersion of the pigment can be reversibly changed to alter the color of the animal or the intensity of coloration of the animal. Chromatophores are found in coelenterates, annelids, insects, crustaceans, echinoderms, fishes, reptiles, and amphibians, and in cephalopod molluscs (not all species of these groups possess such cells, however).

This definition excludes cells which contain nonmigrating pigments, for example, the melanin-containing **melanocytes** of vertebrates. A **melanophore** is a melanin-containing chromatophore. Since one definition of "melano" is black or dark, the term melanophore is also suitable for any dark chromatophore of an invertebrate animal (see Fingerman, 1970; Fitzpatrick et al., 1966; Prosser and Brown, 1961).

Chromatophores are usually located in epithelia of the skin although they are sometimes found in deeper tissues. The color change they can produce physiologically may occur in a few milliseconds, a few minutes, or over the course of an hour or more, depending on the animal group. Chromatophores can also intensify the color of an animal by an increase in chromatophore number or in the quantity of pigment they contain, but these are morphological rather than physiological activities and require much longer periods of time for accomplishment.

Chromatophores are usually classified on the basis of their color (see Bagnara, 1966): melanophores (black); xanthophores (yellow); erythrophores (red); and leucophores (white). Some cells contain iridescent reflecting pigment and are known as iridophores or iridocytes.

A single chromatophore cell contains only one type of pigment. But several chromatophores often cluster together forming an organ known as a **chromatosome** in which two or more differently colored pigments may be present. Monochromatic chromatosomes consist of two or more cells all containing the same-colored pigment. Polychromatic chromatosomes consist of two or more cells with several cell types present, each cell type having a different color.

Many chromatophore responses are made on the basis of the coloration of the background upon which the animal finds itself. Therefore, a major function of chromatophores appears to be in protective coloration, a mechanism that enables the animal to hide from predators. In some animals chromatophores act as protective mechanisms against overheating from sunlight. A light animal reflects more light and thus absorbs less heat than a dark animal. The pigment cells of arthropod eyes may be considered as chromatophores. In these cells the migration of pigment controls the amount of light reaching the receptor surface and also in some cases serves to limit the visual field of the ommatidia.

18-2. Cephalopod Chromatophores. Cephalopod chromatophores function on a basis different from that of all other animal chromatophores (except for those in a few pteropod molluscs). Each chromatophore organ of a cephalopod consists of a pigment

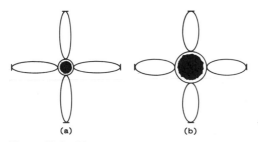

(a)   (b)

Figure 18-1 Diagrammatic representation of squid chromatophores in the pigment-dispersed state (a) and pigment-concentrated state (b).

cell and from 2 to 20 radial muscle fibers (Figure 18-1).

The ability of squids to change color extremely rapidly has long been recognized: and the black, yellow, red, and brown chromatophores in the skin of cephalopods can disperse and concentrate pigment very quickly, allowing rapid color changes, paling, and flushing of the surface of the animal. Such color changes are controlled by a nervous innervation, and they resemble muscular movements in that there can be colored twitches, colored tetani, or paling relaxations. Florey (1969) reviews concepts of cephalopod chromatophore structure and function and also provides significant new information concerning their ultrastructure and functioning.

When the radial, obliquely striated muscles attached to the central pigment cell contract, they stretch out the pigment cell, and its pigment granules become dispersed over a wider area, thus coloring that portion of the skin. When the radial muscles relax, the pigment cell retracts, and the pigment is concentrated into a small ball. Using electron microscope observations of the ultrastructure and microelectrodes to measure potentials in the various regions of the muscle cells and nerve, it was possible to obtain information regarding the mechanisms of operation of these chromatophores (Kriebel and Florey, 1968).

The pigment granules are contained within an elastic sacculus in the pigment cell, and the sacculus wall is composed of a very fine filamentous material (Figure 18-2). The sacculus is attached to the equator of the pigment cell by fine strands or **haptosomes**. The cell membrane of the pigment cell in the retracted condition is highly folded and is attached to the radial muscle fibers by a dense basal lamina. Although the radial muscles are separate fibers, at the borders close to the pigment cell membrane, the muscle membranes form tight junctions that permit electrical current flows from one cell to another. The basal lamina is missing in these regions, further reducing the electrical resistance between cells. The radial muscle fibers act as a functional electrical syncytium at

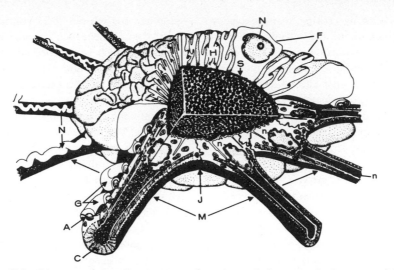

Figure 18-2 Diagram of the ultrastructure of a retracted chromatophoric organ of *Loligo opalescens*. A, Axon; C, contractile cortex of muscle fiber; F, folds of cell membrane of chromatophore; G, glia cell that covers the axon and its terminal structures; H, haptosomes attaching folds of the cell membrane to the elastic sacculus (S) that encloses the pigment granules; m, mitochondria in the core of the muscle fiber; N, nerve terminals; n, nucleus of muscle cell; M, muscle fibers; J, junction between adjacent muscle fibers. The sheath cells that cover the chromatophore and the muscle fibers are not shown. [After R. A. Cloney, and E. Florey (1968) "Ultrastructure of cephalopod chromatophore organs" *Z. Zellforsch* **89**: 250–280.]

their lateral basal edges. The specific membrane resistance of this region is 13 to 23 ohm-cm² as compared with a membrane resistance of the regular fiber surface of 1×10^3 ohm-cm².

The muscle fibers have a core densely packed with mitochondria. Sets of thick and thin filaments are found in the periphery, and each set is separated from its neighbors by obliquely oriented sarcoplasmic reticulum. Each chromatophore is innervated by several motor axons, and differently colored chromatophores are independently innervated. A motor axon runs the length of the contractile portion of each muscle fiber. The axon zigzags back and forth over the fiber in a groove, where intimate contact is made along the length of the cell. From one to four axons innervate each muscle cell.

Stimulation of a motor axon causes a local postsynaptic potential that can be measured anywhere along the length of the muscle, presumably because of the continuous contact of the axon with the muscle membrane

along its length. Chromatophores undergo phasic contractions as a result of action potentials passed from muscle cell to muscle cell at their basal junctions, and all fibers can contract synchronously.

Tonic contractions can also occur in these chromatophores. Sometimes during stimulation of the nerves it was observed that the muscle fibers relaxed, and this was taken as evidence that inhibitory nerve fibers were present. However, Florey found no such nerve fibers. The tonic contractions appear to result from miniature end plate potentials caused by the leakage of ACh from the motor axon terminal. These EPP's can become relatively great in amplitude, great enough to cause contraction of the muscle and dispersal of pigment.

The relaxation of the muscle fibers sometimes observed during nervous stimulation may be due to the presence of 5-hydroxytryptamine. The salivary glands of some cephalopods secrete 5-HT, and its normal role may be to assist in the control of chromatophores by causing their relaxation (see Bacq and Ghiretti, 1952). The nerve fibers innervating the chromatophore do not release 5-HT. It has been shown to relax the radial muscles, but it does not affect either nerve or muscle membrane potentials; and its effect may be exerted directly on the Ca^{2+} excitation-contraction coupling system.

The application of ACH causes tonic contractions of the muscle fibers. Tetrodotoxin abolishes responses to nerve stimulation but does not block the ACh action, an indication that ACh acts on the muscle not the nerve. However, ACh does not appear to be the normal transmitter in this system because cholinergic blocking agents do not alter neuromuscular transmission nor does ACh seem to alter the transmembrane potential or electrical resistance of the muscle fibers. ACh may act on the excitation-contraction coupling mechanism.

When the muscle fibers contract they pull out the pigment cell membrane, and the sacculus which is attached to the membrane is also stretched out. When the fibers relax, the elasticity of the sacculus is assumed to cause it to resume its smaller size, thus concentrating the pigment and causing the animal to pale. This system is extremely rapid because, as stated previously, neuromuscular systems generally are suited for rapid responses. External stimuli as well as emotional stimuli cause color changes in cephalopods.

18-3. Crustacean Chromatophores. The chromatophores of crustaceans, especially decapod crustaceans, have been the object of much study, although much still remains to be learned about the nature of pigment concentration and dispersal and the structure of chromatophore cells.

In all animals, except the cephalopods,

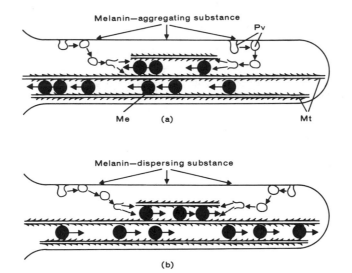

Figure 18-3 A model for the possible role of microtubules in either centripetal (a) or centrifugal (b) migration of melanin pigment granules in melanophores. Me, Melanosomes; Mt, microtubules; Pv, micropinocytotic vesicles. Because the microtubules themselves are not contractile, it is proposed that an arrangement of cross-bridges between the microtubules and pigment granules leads to a sliding mechanism similar to that proposed for muscular contraction (Chapter 10). Transmitter or hormonal substances are thought to get into the cell by micropinocytosis and to act either directly on the surface of the cellular organelles involved or through a system of secondary messengers to determine the direction of melanosomal sliding. [From R. Fujii, and R. R. Novales (1969) "Cellular aspects of the control of physiological color changes in fishes." By permission from *American Zoologist* **9**: 453–463.]

chromatophores are irregularly shaped cells containing pigment granules that can be concentrated in a small area of the cell (maximal concentration results in a punctate condition of the chromatophore) or dispersed over a wider area of the cytoplasm. Movement of pigment in crustacean chromatophores is under control only of hormones; there is no nervous system innervation of crustacean chromatophores. In other animals chromatophore control may be nervous, hormonal, or a combination of the two.

Chromatophore cells have a relatively fixed shape, and the mechanisms by which pigment granules move are still unknown. Electron microscope studies of a variety of chromatophores have not revealed any inner membraneous system in which pigment granules are contained (see, for example, Fujii, 1966). Microtubules have been found in some chromatophores, and these are often arranged parallel to the direction of pigment movement (Bikle et al., 1966; Novales and Novales, 1966).

Various mechanisms have been proposed to explain pigment migration. Marsland (1944) on the basis of high pressure experiments came to the conclusion that pigment migration depended on viscosity changes in the cytoplasm. High pressure causes a reversible breakdown of microtubules and also causes a dispersal of pigment (Marsland and Meisner, 1967). Colchicine, which causes a breakdown of microtubules, also slows down the aggregation of melanin granules in the melanophores of the fish *Fundulus heteroclitus* (Wikswo and Novales, 1969). Thus, microtubules are more and more becoming implicated in pigment migration.

Pigment migration might be accomplished by contractile events associated with microtubules (see Figure 18-3). Although microtubules themselves are not thought to be contractile, some observations reveal the presence of finer filaments associated with the cytoplasm or with pigment granules. These filaments might form a sliding mechanism with the microtubule to move pigment granules (see, for example, Rebhun, 1967).

Kinosita (1953) found that melanosomes (melanin pigment granules) are negatively charged and proposed that pigment migration occurred by electrophoretic mechanisms (Figure 18-4). Such mechanisms could be set into operation through membrane depolarization or by hormonal activities within the cytoplasm. Hormones are thought to enter chromatophores via micropinocytosis and to

Figure 18-4 According to the electrophoretic model of melanosomal migration the pigment migrates through the cytoplasm in a direction opposite to the flow of the intracellular current due to the potential gradient along the cellular processes. (a) Centripetal migration; (b) Centrifugal migration. Er, Smooth endoplasmic reticulum; Me, melanosomes. [From R. Fujii and R. R. Novales (1963) "Cellular aspects of the control of physiological color changes in fishes." By permission from *American Zoologist* **9**: 453–463.]

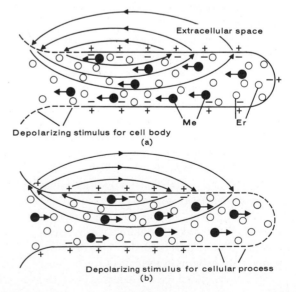

exert their effects directly on the pigment system. However, at present none of the theories are satisfactory in accounting for all aspects of pigment migration.

It is difficult to generalize about crustacean color changes because such a variety of responses are found in different groups. According to Prosser and Brown (1961) decapod crustaceans can be placed into either of three groups. Group 1 (*Palaemonetes, Leander, Orconectes,* and so on) have chromatophore systems that usually contain red, yellow, blue, and white pigments. On eyestalk removal, Group 1 animals darken rapidly as the red and yellow pigments disperse, and the animals remain in this condition permanently.

Group II includes only the genus *Crago,* which has eight differently responding chromatophore types so that these animals can show changes in color pattern as well as changes in shading and hue. Following eyestalk removal, there is an initial transitory darkening of the telson and uropods and a blanching of the rest of the body. After about one hour the telson and uropods blanch, and the remainder of the body darkens.

Group III includes the true crabs (*Uca, Eriochier, Callinectes,* and so on), and the chromatophores may have black, red, yellow, or white pigment. Eyestalk removal in *Uca* causes a rapid blanching with the black chromatophores punctate and white pigments dispersed.

In the nineteenth century it was found that removal of the eyestalks led to a darkening in *Crangon* and *Palaemonetes.* Later it was shown that when the blood of a light-colored *Crangon,* which had been adapted to a white background was injected into a dark dark-adapted specimen, the latter blanched. It was then shown that the blanching agent could be obtained from extracts of eyestalks. These various experimental findings indicated that color change was an endocrine controlled reaction. Parker (1948) has an excellent review of the older literature on chromatophores. Chassard-Bouchaud (1965) discusses pigmentary patterns in a variety of crustaceans.

The sinus gland (see Chapter 11) is the source of hormones that activate crustacean chromatophores. However, materials secreted by this organ can arise from the X organ, the brain, or ventral ganglia. The various chromatophorotropins of crustaceans have not been adequately characterized as yet. Many appear to be small peptides. For example, a red pigment concentrating substance from eyestalks of *Pandalus borealis* is an octapeptide containing aspartic, glutamic, glycine, leucine, proline, serine, tryptophan, and phenylalanine (Fernlund and Josefsson, 1968; Fingerman, 1965).

The erythrophores of *Palaemonetes vulgaris* are controlled by both a pigment-dispersing hormone and a pigment-concentrating hormone. The latter is dependent on Na^+ for full activity, and the former requires Ca^{2+}. Ouabain inhibits the response to the concentrating hormone, and tetrodotoxin enhances it. The membrane potential of the chromatophore is hyperpolarized by the concentrating hormone, and the amplitude of the hyperpolarization is directly related to the degree of pigment concentration. Adenosine 3′,5′-monophosphate (cyclic AMP) increases the dispersion of red pigment and is considered as a secondary messenger in this hormonal action as it is in many others (see Fingerman, 1969).

When a prawn is placed on a black background, a stimulus is supplied to the neurosecretory gland to release red-pigment-dispersing hormone (RPDH). The RPDH then causes an increased flux of Ca^{2+} into the chromatophores. This Ca^{2+} activates cyclic AMP, which then triggers pigment dispersal. On a white background there is a release of red-pigment-concentrating hormone (RPCH), which causes a concentration of erythrophore pigment and a consequent paling of the animal.

It is still debated whether or not similar hormones are responsible for concentrating pigments in all colors of chromatophores or whether there is a separate hormone for each type. It appears that the various responses listed for Group I, II, and III animals are caused by the specific natures of various chromatophores, not to differences in hormones. The eyestalk extract of any group will cause the normal reaction of any group into which it is injected. There are probably 3 to 6 hormonal factors in decapod crustaceans responsible for pigment dispersal and concentration. However, this is a question still to be answered.

Chromatophore responses are **primary responses** if they are evoked by nonvisual stimuli and **secondary responses** if they are initiated by the excitation of visual pathways. Visual responses are very important in color changes produced to match the background of the animal. However, factors such as temperature and humidity, acting on temperature or humidity receptors, may also cause chromatophore pigment changes.

In a few cases chromatophores appear capable of responding directly to environmental stimuli. Chromatophores in the frog *Xenopus*, for example, behave in this manner (Waring, 1963). In arthropods, the pigment cells of the compound eye can also react directly to light. The distal pigment cells have their pigment concentrated close to the retinula cells during bright illumination and dispersed toward the crystal cones in dim light. The retinula cells themselves contain melanin that migrates toward the photoreceptive area during bright illumination. However, hormonal controls are also exerted over these pigment movements. During light adaptation pigment migration is controlled by hormones produced in the eyestalk. The hormone for dark adaptation is thought to come from the postcommissural organ.

The proximal pigment cells contain guanine, a light-reflecting pigment. During light adaptation the guanine migrates below the basement membrane, and light can be absorbed by other pigments within the cell. During dark adaptation the reflecting pigment moves above the basement membrane, and the dark pigment moves below it. The guanine can now reflect any light that is not absorbed by the retinula cells and thus gives the latter a chance to absorb the light. This mechanism enhances sensitivity in dim light (see Welsh, 1930; Kleinholz, 1936).

That chromatophores can function in temperature regulation has been shown by Brown and Sandeen (1948) and Wilkens and Fingerman (1965). When crabs with maximally dispersed melanin are exposed to the rays of bright sunlight, their body temperatures increase much faster in comparison with control crabs with maximally concentrated melanin. Pale crabs reflect much more light than dark crabs, especially in the longer wavelengths, where light has a greater heating capacity.

18-4. Vertebrate Chromatophores. Knowledge of color changes in vertebrates is much more satisfactory than for invertebrates, and the identity of hormones and nervous transmitters is known in many cases. A complicating factor is that a mixture of hormonal and nervous mechanisms may be used in some cases. For example, elasmobranchs depend upon only hormonal controls, whereas teleosts generally use a mixture of hormonal and nervous mechanisms. Both parasympathetic and sympathetic fibers may be involved in the nervous pathways. The former produces pigment concentration, the latter pigment dispersion. Although there is direct proof that melanophores of teleosts are innervated by melanin-concentrating nerve fibers, the existence of melanin-dispersing axons is still indirect.

Adrenaline released by the adrenal glands; intermedin; adrenocorticotropic hormone (ACTH), and melanophore-stimulating hormone (MSH) from the pituitary; and thyroxine from the thyroid are all involved in chromatophore pigment migration.

Adrenaline and noradrenaline cause pigment concentration. Thyroxine activates melanophores of many vertebrates probably through secondary messengers. In tadpoles of *Xenopus* the injection of thyroxine causes blanching as the melanin of melanophores becomes concentrated. However, the response is due to the release of MSH by the pituitary, which only in this species concentrates melanin (Chang, 1957). Intermedin causes pigment dispersal in erythrophores of *Phoxinus*.

In the eel *Anguilla* chromatophores are

under a dual control. Melanophore pigment disperses in response to sympathetic nerve impulses and to the presence of melanophore-concentrating hormone (MCH). In the catfish *Ameirus* the system is similar except that MCH is absent. This type of system is diagrammed in Figure 18-5.

Reptilian chromatophores are controlled only by nerves (*Chamaeleon*); only by hormones (*Anolis*); or by both (*Phrynosoma*). The polychromatic chromatosomes of chameleons are innervated by both pigment dispersing and pigment concentrating nerve fibers. This provides for the relatively rapid and remarkable color changes in these animals.

As shown in Figure 18-5, a major factor in determining the disposition of chromatophore pigments is the nature of the visual background. The chromatophore response

depends on the nature of light reflected from the substratum as well as on the light received directly. The retinal elements are divided to produce different responses for each type of light source.

Space has permitted only a bare outline of chromatophore systems in different animals. In addition to references already given, the papers of Fingerman (1970); Novales and Davis (1969); Chavin (1969); and Quevedo (1969) may be consulted for further details.

Bioluminescence

18-5. Functions and Nature of Bioluminescence. Because bioluminescence is the enzymatically controlled production of light by organisms, it seems fitting to include it here as part of the discussion of light and the animal. When some molecules absorb energy, they reemit the energy in the form of light. This phenomenon has been known for a long time in chemical systems, and the production of so-called cold light by chemilumescence is similar in principle to the production of light by organisms except that in the latter an enzyme catalyst is involved in the reaction.

The biochemistry and physiology of light emission by organisms was extensively reviewed by Harvey (1953). Since that time many advances have been made in the analysis of the biochemistry of bioluminescence in various animal and plant groups (Cormier and Totter, 1964). In addition, several symposia volumes have appeared that cover both bioluminescence and the physical mechanisms underlying light production in general (Johnson and Haneda, 1966; McElroy and Glass, 1961).

Bioluminescence is of interest from several viewpoints. It is an excellent tool for the analysis of photochemical reactions and can give clues as to the nature of photosynthetic molecular mechanisms; it has aided in the study of the kinetics of biological processes (Johnson et al., 1954); and it was the first cellular reaction to which absolute reaction rate theory was applied (see Chapter 4). It is

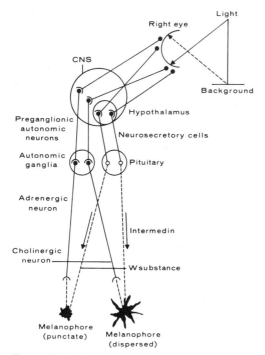

Figure 18-5 Schematic representation of chromatophore control in the eel *Anguilla*. Note that both nervous and hormonal controls are present. Note also the differences in response that occur depending on whether light is received directly from overhead by the retina or whether light is reflected off the background. [After Scharrer and Scharrer (1963).]

useful in analyzing the effects of drugs, narcotics, temperature, pressure, and pH on living systems. It is a handy tool for enzyme studies because the reaction can proceed in the cell and be measured without destroying or damaging the cell. This is possible since the light given off by the reaction can be measured externally to the system using photocell transducers. The physiology and biochemistry and the evolution and adaptation of light-emitting reactions are of considerable interest in their own right (McElroy and Seliger, 1962).

Bioluminescence is found in scattered groups of the living world. It is present in some bacteria, fungi, cytoflagellate protozoans, coelenterates, insects, crustaceans, annelids, and some fishes.

In some cases bioluminescence appears to have no functional significance. For example, no function can be ascribed to luminescence in bacteria that are too small to respond to light as a stimulus and that lack photoreceptor organs. Similar statements can be made for many marine protozoans that are bioluminescent. Light emission in these organisms is incidental, perhaps, to reactions in which metabolic waste products or by products are destroyed or altered to usable forms. The marine annelid *Chaetopterus* lives in a U-shaped burrow it builds in mud and sand in shallow water. Although it is one of the most luminescent of animals, it is difficult to imagine any functional significance of light to an animal that never leaves its closely fitting tube.

In some cases bioluminescence serves as a defensive mechanism. The deep-sea squid *Heteroteuthis* produces a luminescent material which is used in a manner similar to that of the use of ink by other squid. It emits a burst of luminescence that allows it to escape a dazzled predator. A fish *Malaeocephalus laevis* possesses a glandular organ whose luminescent secretion can be squeezed out by the contraction of muscles near the anus. The light serves to blind predators (Hickley, 1926).

Some species of angler fish use bioluminescence as a lure. Dipteran larvae (Bolito-philidae), which live in caves in Waitomo, New Zealand, spin long sticky threads that hang down 15 to 60 cm and that glisten with bioluminescent materials. These threads serve as lures and attract the prey on which the larvae feed (Harvey, 1952).

Bioluminescent systems play a role in the reproductive behavior of a variety of animals. The mating of fireflies depends in many cases on a very accurately timed signal system. Females of *Photinus pyralis* cannot fly. They crawl up on a blade of grass in the evening, and during darkness begin to emit flashes from their bioluminescent organs in response to flashes of males which fly within 3 to 4 meters. The female response occurs 2 seconds after the male's flash (at 25°C). When the female responds, the male turns and flashes again. The female responds again and after about six of these exchanges the male and female come together for mating. The male will not respond to a female unless her flash occurs 2 seconds after his own. A variety of signal systems are found in different firefly species. Some depend on flash interval, others depending on length of flash. Some species of fireflies are able to mimic responses of other species and draw these in as prey.

The swarming of the fireworm *Odontosyllis* (a marine polychaete) at the surface of the ocean is timed by lunar and circadian rhythms (see Chapter 20). However, the actual mating of male and female is guided by bioluminescent reactions of the female. The larger females surface and begin swimming at a particular time in the evening and become luminescent as they swim in small circles. They discharge eggs and a luminescent secretion that forms a halo of light about the eggs. The males, swimming upward from deeper water, are attracted to the circle of light and upon swimming into the circle discharge their sperm, which fertilize the eggs. Thus bioluminescence aids these small animals to find eggs in the large expanse of the ocean and so allows the species to survive.

Bioluminescence is highly developed in some deep-sea teleosts (although in many cases the luminescence is caused by bacteria cultured in specialized organs on the fish's body). There are sexual differences in the photophore patterns, and mating may depend on the recognition of these luminescent signals in waters so deep that sunlight does not penetrate.

Although nearly all major phyla have representatives possessing bioluminescence, these are either marine or terrestrial species. However, no terrestrial vertebrate has been found that is luminescent. In fresh waters only a few bacterial species and a limpet *Latia neritodes* (Bowden, 1950) have been found to have bioluminescent capabilities. The meaning of this in terms of biological evolution and adaptation is not known.

18-6. Bacterial Luminescence. The substrate of any bioluminescent reaction is given the generic name **luciferin**. The enzyme of any bioluminescent reaction is called **luciferase**. In bacteria luminescent reactions are pyridine nucleotide-linked reactions of the general nature:

$$NADH + H^+ + FMN \rightleftharpoons FMNH_2 + NAD^+$$

$$FMNH_2 + RCHO + O_2 \xrightarrow{Luciferase} FMN + RCOOH + LIGHT$$

An NADH oxidase catalyzes the first reaction, and luciferase catalyzes the second reaction, which is the light-producing step. RCHO represents a long chain aldehyde. Aldehydes with 7 to 14 carbons will enter into the light-producing reaction in various species. It can readily be seen that these are reactions involving normal metabolic substrates and coenzymes (Chapter 4) and may serve to produce usable fatty acids.

18-7. Firefly Bioluminescence. The general reaction for firefly bioluminescence is an adenine nucleotide-linked reaction:

$$LH_2 + ATP + O_2 \xrightarrow[Mg^{2+}]{Luciferase} LIGHT + PP + AMP + L(O)$$

LH_2 represents reduced luciferin, which has the structure:

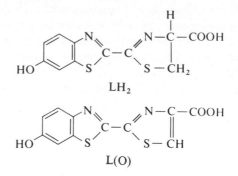

$L(O)$ is oxidized luciferin.

The actual sequence of reactions can be written (McElroy and Seliger, 1963):

$$E + ATP + LH_2 \xrightleftharpoons{Mg^{2+}} E—LH_2—AMP + PP$$

$$E + LH_2—AMP + O_2 \longrightarrow E—L(O)—AMP + H_2O + LIGHT$$

$$E + L(O)—AMP \rightleftharpoons E—ATP + L(O)$$

The first reaction involves the production of luciferyl adenylate, which contains AMP linked through its phosphate group to the luciferin in carboxyl group so that high energy is retained in the complex.

At pH 7.1 the reaction emits yellow-green light with a wavelength of maximum intensity at 562 mμ. At a pH of 5.5 or less the emission is brick red with a maximum intensity at about 616 mμ.

Fireflies possess light organs in which the bioluminescent reaction takes place. These lanterns are located in the abdomen (see Buck 1966). Firefly lanterns are stimulated by nerve impulses, and it is probably the release of ACh that triggers the light reaction. Although some workers think that nervous excitation triggers the release of a burst of air from nearby tracheoles and that this air with its oxygen initiates the light reactions, it is more likely that the trigger reacts directly on the system.

18-8. Other Invertebrate Luminescent Systems. As has been true of other physiological activities, the number of species that have now been studied with respect to bioluminescent reactions is becoming very large, and space limitations precludes a description of all such studies. Only some of the more significant systems are mentioned in the following.

Some bioluminescent systems operate through relatively simple enzyme-substrate reactions. One highly studied system is that of the ostracod *Cypridinia hilgendorfii*. The requirements for light emission are only oxygen, luciferase, and *Cypridinia* luciferin, which has been crystallized and has the structure shown:

Gonyaulax polyhedra is a marine dino-flagellate that shows a diurnal rhythm in its luminescence (see Chapter 20). The dino-flagellates are generally considered the source of luminescence seen in the oceans at night. Their bioluminescent systems are also simple although the exact structure of the luciferin is not known. Salt is required for light production, and the intensity of emitted light depends roughly on the NaCl concentration of the medium.

Cytoplasmic particles, **scintillons**, have been isolated from marine dinoflagellates. These are light emitting particles which are semi-

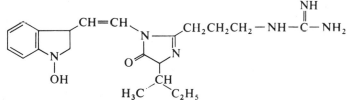

Bioluminescence in this case is an extra-cellular phenomenon in contrast to the previous examples which occurred intracellularly. *Cypridinia* has two types of highly granular cells in which it is thought that enzyme and substrate are separately synthesized. These are secreted into the water where the bioluminescent reaction takes place.

Of interest is the finding that certain fish of the families Apogonidae, for example, *Apogon ellioti*, and Pempheridae, for example, *Parapriacanthus ransonneti* and *Pempheris klunzingeri*, have a luciferin and luciferase that are cross-exchangeable with those of the crustacean *Cypridinia* (Haneda et al., 1966). The spectral properties of the emitted light is the same in all of these groups, although obviously the fish and the crustacean are not related (see also, Sie et al., 1961). If both groups synthesize the same luciferin-luciferase system, then this is a remarkable case of evolutionary development bringing about the production of the same proteins and substrates in two diverse groups of animals. Suggestions have been made that the fish chemicals are obtained by the fish eating the ostracods, but the distribution of the two groups is somewhat against this idea.

crystalline in nature (DeSa and Hastings, 1968; De Sa et al., 1963; Bode and Hastings, 1963). Guanine is a major component of scintillons, which are covered with a lipoprotein layer containing the enzyme and substrate (Hastings et al., 1966). Scintillons of the dinoflagellate *Noctiluca* are similar to those of *Gonyaulax*. Scintillons are of interest because they represent a mechanism by which a single cell can stop and start a chemical reaction and exhibit bioluminescent flashing. Eckert (1965) found that bioluminescence in *Noctiluca* was controlled by action potentials passing over the surface membrane of the cell.

The bioluminescence of the sea pansy *Renilla reniformis* is based on an adenine-containing nucleotide, oxygen, luciferase, and an oxidizable substrate. The nucleotide is 3′-5′-diphosphoadenosine (DPA), but the nature of the luciferin is not known. Calcium ions are needed for the reaction. Studies on other coelenterates have revealed the presence of various other luminescent materials: halistaurin from hydromedusan *Halistaura* (Shimomura et al., 1963); aequorin from the hydromedusan *Aequoriaea*.

A luminous clam (*Pholas dactylus*) and a luminous annelid (*Odontosyllis enopia*) appear to have light emitting systems similar to those of *Cypridinia* although further chemical characterization of the luciferins involved is needed.

18-9. Bioluminescence in Fishes. Bioluminescence in teleosts is usually intracellular although a few cases of extracellular luminescence are known (Nicol, 1962). The teleosts in some cases possess photophore organs that may possess a lens, reflector surface, and pigmented layers with a bioluminescent layer at the bottom. This organ, in a sense acts as an eye in reverse, that is, the system is designed to intensify the beam of light emitted by the luminescent system. Such photophores may also be equipped with lids for cutting off the light beam when necessary.

Some deep-sea teleosts, as well as some squids, depend for their bioluminescence on the presence of symbiotic bacteria that are cultured in specialized organs. Such organs may also be supplied with lenses, pigment layers, and lids to control light output. These organs receive a rich blood supply presumably to supply nutrients to the luminescent bacteria. Bassot (1966) gives a comparative morphology of luminescent organs.

References and Readings

Bacq, Z. M. and F. Ghiretti (1952). "La sécrétion externe et interne des glandes salivaires postérieures des céphalopodes octopodes." *Arch. Intern. Physiol. Biochim.* **60**: 165–171.

Bagnara, J. T. (1966). "Cytology and cytophysiology of non-melanophore pigment cells." *Intern. Rev. Cytol.* **20**: 173–205.

Bassot, J. (1966). "On the comparative morphology of some luminous organs." In: **Bioluminescence in Progress.** (F. H. Johnson and Y. Haneda, eds.), pp. 557–610. Princeton, N. J.: Princeton University Press.

Bikle, D., L. G. Tilney, and K. R. Porter (1966). "Microtubules and pigment migration in the melanophores of *Fundulus heteroclitus*." *Protoplasmia* **61**: 322–345.

Bode, V. C. and J. W. Hastings (1963). "The purification and properties of the bioluminescent system in *Gonyaulax polyedra*." *Arch Biochem. Biophys.* **103**: 488–499.

Bowden, B. J. (1950). "Some observations on a luminescent fresh water limpet from New Zealand." *Biol. Bull.* **99**: 373–380.

Brown, F. A. and M. I. Sandeen (1948). "Responses of the chromatophores of the fiddler crab, *Uca*, to light and temperature." *Physiol. Zool.* **21**: 361–371.

Buck, J. (1966). "Unit activity in the firefly lantern." In: **Bioluminescence in Progress.** (F. H. Johnson and Y. Haneda, eds.), pp. 459–474. Princeton, N. J.: Princeton University Press.

Buck, J. and E. Buck (1968). "Mechanism of rhythmic synchronous flashing of fireflies." *Science* **159**: 1319–1327.

Chang, C. Y. (1957). "Thyroxine effect on melanophora contraction in *Xenopus laevis*." *Science* **126**: 121–122.

Chavin, W. (1969). "Fundamental aspects of morphological melanin color changes in vertebrate skin." *Am. Zool.* **9**: 505–520.

Chassard-Bouchaud, C. (1965). "L'adaptation chromatique chez les Natantia (Crustaces, Decapodes)." *Cahiers Biol. Mar.* **6**: 469–576.

Cloney, R. A. and E. Flory (1968). "Ultrastructure of cephalopod chromatophore organs." *Z. Zellforsch.* **89**: 250–280.

Cormier, M. J. and K. Hori (1964). "Studies on the bioluminescence of *Renilla reniformis*. IV. Nonenzymatic activation of renilla luciferin." *Biochim. Biophys. Acta* **88**: 99–104.

Cormier, M. J. and J. R. Totter (1964). "Bioluminescence." *Ann. Rev. Biochem.* **33**: 431–458.

DeSa, R. and J. W. Hastings (1968). "The characterization of scintillons. Bioluminescent particles from the marine dinoflagellate, *Gonyaulax polyedra*." *J. Gen. Physiol.* **51**: 105–122.

DeSa, R., J. W. Hastings, and A. E. Vatter (1963). "Luminescent crystalline particles: an organized subcellular bioluminescent system." *Science* **141**: 1269–1270.

Eckert, R. (1965). "Bioelectric control of bioluminescence in the dinoflagellate *Noctiluca.*" *Science* **147**: 1140–1145.

Fernlund, P. and L. Josefsson (1968). "Chromactivating hormones of *Pandalus borealis.* Isolation and purification of the 'red-pigment concentrating hormone.'" *Biochim. Biophys. Acta* **158**: 262–273.

Fingerman, M. (1963). **The control of chromatophores.** Long Island City, N.Y.: Pergamon Press, Inc.

Fingerman, M. (1965). "Chromatophores." *Physiol. Rev.* **45**: 296–339.

Fingerman, M. (1970). "Comparative Physiology: Chromatophores." *Ann. Rev. Physiol.* **32**: 345–372.

Fingerman, M., K. R. Rao, and C. K. Bartell (1967). "A proposed uniform method of reporting response values for crustacean chromatophorotropins: the standard integrated response." *Experientia* **23**: 962.

Fitzpatrick, T. B., W. C. Quevedo, A. L. Levene, V. J. McGovern, Y. Mishima, and A. G. Oettle (1966). "Terminology of vertebrate melanin-containing cells." *Science* **152**: 88–89.

Florey, E. (1969). "Ultrastructure and function of cephalopod chromatophores." *Am. Zool.* **9**: 429–442.

Fujii, R. (1966). "A functional interpretation of the fine structure in the melanophore of the guppy *Lebistes reticulatus.*" *Annot. Zool. Jap.* **39**: 185–192.

Haneda, Y., F. H. Johnson, Y. Masuda, Y. Saiga, O. Shimomura, H. D. Sie, N. Sugiyama, and I. Takatsuki (1961). "Crystalline luciferin from live *Cypridina.*" *J. Cell. Comp. Physiol.* **57**: 55–62.

Harvey, E. N. (1952). **Bioluminescence.** New York: Academic Press, Inc. 649 pp.

Hastings, J. W., Q. H. Gibson, J. Friedland, and J. Spudich (1966). "Molecular mechanisms in bacterial luminescence: on energy storage intermediates and the role of aldehyde in the reaction." In: **Bioluminescence in Progress** (F. H. Johnson and Y. Haneda, eds.), pp. 151–186. Princeton, N. J.: Princeton University Press.

Hickley, C. F. (1926). "Bioluminescence in fishes." *J. Mar. Biol. Assn.* **14**: 495.

Johnson, F. H., H. Eyring, and M. J. Polissar (1954). **The Kinetic Basis of Molecular Biology.** New York: John Wiley & Sons, Inc. 874 pp.

Johnson, F. H. and Y. Haneda (1966). **Bioluminescence in Progress.** Princeton, N. J.: Princeton University Press. 650 pp.

Kinosita, H. (1953). "Studies on the mechanism of pigment migration within fish melanophores with special reference to their electric potentials." *Annot. Zool. Jap.* **26**: 115–127.

Kriebel, M. E. and E. Florey (1968). "Electrical and mechanical responses of obliquely striated muscle fibers of the squid to ACh, 5-hydroxytryptamine and nerve stimulation." *Fed. Proc.* **27**: 236.

McElroy, W. D. and B. Glass, eds. (1961). **Light and Life.** Baltimore: Johns Hopkins University Press. 924 pp.

McElroy, W. D. and H. H. Seliger (1962). "Origin and evolution of bioluminescence." In: **Horizons in Biochemistry.** (M. Kasha and B. Pullman, eds.), pp. 91–102. New York: Academic Press, Inc.

Marsland, D. (1944). "Mechanism of pigment displacement in unicellular chromatophores." *Biol. Bull.* **87**: 252–261.

Marsland, D. and D. Meisner (1967). "Effects of D_2O on the mechanism of pigment dispersal in the melanocytes of *Fundulus heteroclitus*: a pressure-temperature analysis." *J. Cell Physiol.* **70**: 209–216.

Nicol, J. A. C. (1960). "The regulation of light emission in animals." *Biol. Rev.* **35**: 1–42.

Novales, R. R. and W. J. Davis (1969). "Cellular aspects of the control of physiological color changes in amphibians." *Am. Zool.* **8**: 479–488.

Novales, R. R. and B. J. Novales (1966). "Electron microscopic studies of pigment movements in melanophores." *Am. Zool.* **6**: 576.

Novales, R. R., B. J. Novales, S. H. Sinner, and J. A. Stoner (1962). "The effect of sodium, chloride, and calcium concentrations on the response of melanophores to melanocyte-stimulating hormone (MSH)." *Gen. Comp. Endocrinol.* **2:** 286–295.

Parker, G. H. (1948). **Animal Colour Changes and their Neurohumors.** New York: Cambridge University Press. 377 pp.

Prosser, C. L. and F. A. Brown (1961). **Comparative Animal Physiology,** 2nd ed. Philadelphia: W. B. Saunders Company. 688 pp.

Quevedo, W. C. (1969). "The control of color in mammals." *Am. Zool.* **9:** 531–540.

Rebhun, L. I. (1967). "Structural aspects of saltatory particle movement." *J. Gen. Physiol.* **50** (Suppl.) 223–239.

Seliger, H. H. and W. D. McElroy (1962). "Chemiluminescence of firefly luciferin without enzymes." *Science* **151:** 683–685.

Seliger, H. H., J. B. Buck, W. G. Fastie, and W. D. McElroy (1964). "The spectral distribution of firefly light." *J. Gen. Physiol.* **48:** 95–104.

Shimomura, O., F. H. Johnson, and Y. Saiga (1963a). "Further data on the bioluminescent protein, Aequorin." *J. Cell. Comp. Physiol.* **62:** 1–8.

Shimomura, O., F. H. Johnson, and Y. Saiga (1963b). "Extraction and properties of Halistaurin, a bioluminescent protein from the hydromedusan *Halistaura.*" *J. Cell. Comp. Physiol.* **62:** 9–16.

Sie, E. H., -C., W. D. McElroy, F. H. Johnson, and Y. Haneda (1961). "Spectroscopy of the *Apogon* luminescent system and of its cross reaction with the *Cypridina* system. *Arch. Biochem. Biophys.* **93:** 286–291.

Terpstra, W. (1963). "Investigations on the identity of the light-emitting molecule in *Photobacterium phosphoreum.*" *Biochim. Biophys. Acta* **75:** 355–364.

Terpstra, W. and C. L. Steebberge (1964). "Influence of some inhibiting and activating substances on the light reaction in vitro of *Photobacterium phosphoreum.*" *Biochim. Biophys. Acta* **88:** 267–277.

Waring, H. (1963). **Color Change Mechanisms of Cold-Blooded Vertebrates.** New York: Academic Press, Inc. 266 pp.

Welsh, J. H. (1930). "The mechanics of migration of the distal pigment cells in the eyes of *Palaemonetes.*" *J. Exp. Zool.* **56:** 459–487.

Wikswo, M. A. and R. R. Novales (1969). "The effect of colchicine on migration of pigment granules in the melanophores of *Fundulus heteroclitus.*" *Biol. Bull.* **137:** 228–237.

Wilkens, J. L. and M. Fingerman (1965). "Heat tolerance and temperature relationships of the fiddler crab, *Uca pugilator,* with reference to body coloration." *Biol. Bull.* **128:** 133–141.

Mechanoreceptors

19-1. Types of Mechanoreceptors. Mechano-receptors respond to mechanical forces such as stretch, compression, or applied torque. These forces are produced by factors including movements of body parts relative to one another, gravitational field changes resulting from alterations of the animal's orientation in space, stretches resulting from the contraction of muscles, or vibrations transmitted through either the internal or external medium. It is somewhat difficult to make clear distinctions between some modalities of mechanoreceptors. Simpler mechanoreceptors include stretch receptors, tendon organs, touch, pressure, and pain receptors. Equilibrium or position receptors are designed to provide information about the animal's position with respect to gravity. Hearing organs are used to detect vibrations.

The activities of some mechanoreceptors have already been discussed. In Chapter 11 the role of stretch receptors in the control of muscle was described. Stretch receptor activities were also mentioned in Chapter 16 on respiration. The Pacinian corpuscle—a pressure receptor of mammals—was considered at the cellular level in Chapter 8 (sensory receptors were defined generally in Chapter 8 also). Baro- or pressoreceptors were given as part of the control system regulating circulatory and respiratory activities. In this chapter the discussion will be limited to certain mechanoreceptors that respond to changes in the external environment.

Most mechanoreceptors are primary sense cells that respond directly to mechanical forces. In fact, most cells are able to respond directly to mechanical deformation or stress. For example, smooth muscle cells contract in response to stretch and cardiac muscle cells show a positive inotropic response to stretch. However, gravitional and vibrational forces are not capable of directly stimulating neurons. Therefore, receptors designed to detect these external stimuli have secondary sense cells (often hair cells) that can transduce gravitional or vibrational forces into mechanical deformation. Such deformation may lead

Chapter 19

Mechano-reception

to potential changes that in turn excite a neuron, or the deformation may be transmitted as such to a closely positioned neuron that responds with impulses when its membrane is deformed.

The discussion here will be limited to vertebrates, especially mammals, and to arthropods especially insects, because these are the animal groups in which mechanoreceptors have lent themselves to analysis most readily.

19-2. Pain, Touch, and Temperature Receptors.

Many touch receptors are bare nerve endings, but some specialized structures are also found, for example, the Pacinian and Meissner's corpuscles. Many touch receptors are associated with hairs that have the ability to amplify a stimulus upon mechanical manipulation.

In the human about 700,000 pressure or touch receptors are found in the skin; most of these are concentrated on the fingers or about the face, especially on the tip of the tongue and on the lips. Since the tips of the extremities and the more anterior portion of the body of mammals have become important in either manipulative skills or in the exploration of the environment, it is not surprising that these areas are richly supplied with sensory receptors (Rose and Mountcastle, 1959).

Touch receptors not only convey information about the presence of tactile stimuli, they may also possess discriminatory abilities for both the intensity of stimulus and for the spatial direction or arrangement of the stimulus. The greatest ability to discriminate between intensities of stimulation or to determine the extent of spatial separation of separate stimuli occurs in areas of greatest concentration of sensory receptors. In mammals touch receptors include a wide variety of morphological types. Many have the form of bulbs or corpuscles. Meissner's corpuscle, for example, is a touch receptor located in the outer layers of the skin. The Pacinian corpuscle is a deep touch or pressure receptor located in deep layers of skin, in the connective tissue about muscles, tendons, and joints, and in the mesenteries supporting the visceral organs. Somesthesia in humans is discussed by Mountcastle and Darian-Smith (1969).

Pain is a sensory experience initiated by injurious or threatening stimuli. There are both painful sensations and reflex actions in response to painful stimuli. Intensive stimulation of almost any sensory neuron appears capable of producing a painful sensation, and only recently has it been shown that specialized receptors for pain exist.

Generally the sensation of pain is evoked by either of two sets of nerve fibers. Some C fibers when sufficiently stimulated result in burning pain; small Δ fibers function in signaling prickling pain. The latter is usually a short term effect, while the former may continue for long periods of time—as long as the stimulus remains. The lack of adaptation shown by the nerve fibers is expected in a sensory system that signals the presence of danger that should not be ignored.

It is not known whether pain receptors respond directly to the noxious stimulation or whether such stimulation, by causing tissue damage, indirectly stimulates the receptors because of the release of chemicals by the damaged tissue. Since histamine is found in relatively large quantities in tissues to which harmful stimuli have been applied, it has been suggested that this substance is responsible for stimulating pain receptors. However, it now seems more likely that tissue damage releases proteolytic enzymes into the extracellular fluid and that these enzymes react with gamma globulins to produce polypeptides which excite sensory nerves and which also act as vasodilators (Lewis, 1960). Neurokinin is the name given to only one polypeptide that has been isolated from damaged tissue and is also released during the stimulation of the distal end of a transected dorsal root (Chapman et al., 1961). Bradykinin may also be involved in stimulating nocioceptive neurons. Since pain is a human sensation, nothing is known about this type of sensory experience in other animals.

Temperature receptors will be discussed briefly, although in the strictest sense they are not mechanoreceptors. There are two sets of sensory fibers involved in temperature reception in mammals. One is concerned with measuring the degree of warmth, and the other measures the degree of cold of the environment. In humans cold spots outnumber warm spots by from 4 to 10 to 1. The distribution of temperature receptors over the surface of the body is not uniform, and such receptors are more concentrated on the face and hands than on other parts of the body. Different regions of these areas, in turn, may show marked differences in receptor distribution. For example, the forehead contains very few warm receptors but many cold receptors.

Temperature receptors are bare nerve endings, the terminals of delta fibers. These fibers proceed over pathways to the thalamic region, where their information is integrated and coordinated to produce responses described in Chapter 15. Temperature receptors, if stimulated by the threshold stimuli just discussed, can also give rise to pain sensations.

19-3.   Equilibrium Receptors—Crustaceans. The equilibrium body position of any animal is usually the result of a combination of visual, proprioceptive, tactile, and gravitational stimuli sensed by appropriate sensory receptors. Those receptors responding to gravitational influences are often termed equilibrium receptors. Many animals respond to gravity and exhibit geotaxic responses. Even single cells have the capabilities for responding to gravity. For example *Paramecium* exhibits a negative geotaxis although the mechanism for such activity is unknown.

The gravity receptors of crustaceans, vertebrates, and molluscs are **statocysts** and may respond either to static forces of gravity or to acceleration forces. They are generally round or cylindrical spaces filled with fluid and lined with sensory hairs. In crustaceans these hairs are chitinous structures innervated at their bases by primary sense cells. The term sensory hair in other animal groups refers to cilialike projections from either a nerve or an epithelial cell. Most statocysts contain a **statolith** consisting either of sand grains picked up from

the environment or calcareous concretions produced by the animal. The statolith moves about in the fluid medium of the statocyst and exerts mechanical distortions on the sensory hairs.

Some statocysts are diagrammed in Figure 19-1. The statocysts of crustaceans have received much attention, and those of the lobster have been analyzed with respect to responses of single sensory cells. Originally it was thought that the crustacean statocyst was an organ of hearing (it may also serve this purpose but only for low frequency sound waves and only in some animals). In 1893 Kreidl substituted iron filings for the normal statoliths of shrimp (crustaceans lose the statoliths at each molt, and they are replaced with new sand grains. If iron filings are substituted for sand in the animal's environment, it will use these as the statoliths). By using a magnet to move the iron filings, it was shown that the organs were used to control body orientation, depending on the forces exerted by the statoliths on the sensory hairs.

Not all crustaceans possess statoliths, and many planktonic species depend upon the direction of sunlight and its plane of polarization. Statocysts in crustaceans are located in the base of the first pair of antennae (Malacostraca); in the protocerebrum (copepods and amphipods); or in the last body segment (some isopods). In those cases where both light and gravity play a role in body orientation, the dominant stimulus varies according to the species. Some crustaceans are photoventral and swim back down, for example, *Artemia* and *Lysmata*; others are photodorsal and swim with the dorsal side to the light, for example, most Cladocerans and marine Malacostraca. In addition to light, proprioceptors on the legs also provide clues for orientation.

Statocyst activity may be examined either by analyzing behavioral responses to stimulation or by making electrophysiological recordings from the sensory cells. The first type of experimentation has dominated because of the small size of most sensory neurons. The eyestalks and limbs of crustaceans may make compensatory movements in a direction

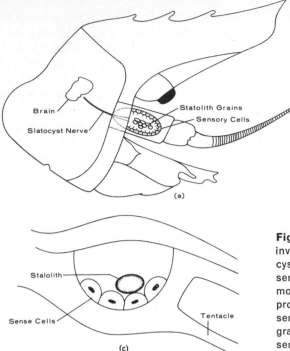

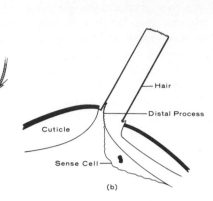

Figure 19-1 Schematic representation of some invertebrate mechanoreceptors. (a) Type of statocyst typically found in crustaceans. (b) Insect sensory hair. (c) Statocyst of cephalopod molluscs. In statocysts pressure of statolith produces nerve impulses in sensory axon. In sensory hair cell movement of hair due to gravity, pressure, etc. produces impulses in sensory axon.

opposite to that of any body rotation, and by following such movements an indication of the statocyst operation can be obtained.

If a blinded specimen of *Palaemonetes* is rotated about its longitudinal axis, the maximum eyestalk deflection occurs at 90° right or left. When the animal is turned upside down, the eyestalks return to their normal resting position. If one statocyst is removed, the maximum eyestalk deflection is found at an angle of 60° when rotation is toward the side from which the statocyst was removed and at 120° when rotation is toward the opposite side. The statocyst floors are slanted at a 30° angle from the horizontal, and this plays a part in the horizontal turning response. Normally the outputs of the statocysts are equal and opposite (in their inhibitory and excitatory actions). If the animal is rotated about the longitudinal axis, one statocyst provides a greater stimulus than the other and a reflex recovery occurs (Schöne, 1954).

Not all crustaceans exhibit eyestalk reflexes if the movement of the legs relative to the thorax is prevented (this eliminates proprioceptive responses from effectors on the leg).

Under the conditions just described *Astacus*, *Carcinus*, *Maia*, and *Paleamon* still exhibit the reflex; *Uca*, *Palinurus*, and *Pagurus* do not.

It may be noted that if a statocyst is removed from one side, the interpretation of responses which can be compared with the normal is made difficult because the central nervous system no longer receives a continuous background discharge from both statocysts, and normally the nervous system functions on the basis of background information from both statocysts as well as on changes in impulse frequencies due to rotational movements. Electrophysiological experiments with the lobster *Homarus americanus* demonstrated that, while in the normal resting position, each statocyst maintained a continuous flow of impulses from its sensory neurons. When the lobster is rotated, each hair organ exhibits a bell-shaped curve of discharge frequency with a maximal rate of discharge at 90° of rotation. If the rotation is initiated from an upside down position, a similar curve is obtained.

Because each lobster statocyst is provided with about 400 hairs, a large number of inputs flow into the central nervous system. In addition each position of the lobster's body displaces a different group of hairs in each statocyst. Therefore, the inflow of information into the central nervous system is complex. In addition, in the lobster some receptors (Type I) respond only to absolute position, and others (Type II) respond only to rate and direction of rotation. Integrative activity in the crustacean nervous system is discussed in several articles in Volume 20 of the *Symp. Soc. Exp. Biol.*

19-4. Mechanoreceptors—Insects. A wide variety of mechanoreceptors are known in insects. The gravity receptors make up a diverse group of mechanoreceptors and differ from the statocyst organs of most other animals. Some aquatic bugs, for example, trap an air bubble between the hair and antennae and use this bubble as a statolith. The bubble tends to rise because it is less dense than water and presses against sensory hairs (Rabe, 1953) These insects also use visual clues in their orientation.

Sensory receptors are scattered over all parts of the insect cuticle, and similar appearing receptors may have different functions when found in different locations. Sensilla trichodea are tactile sensory organs that are placed in hollow extensions of the exocuticle, the hard outer covering that prevents much direct interaction between body tissues and the external environment. These sensilla (= sensory hairs) are especially abundant at joints and regions between body segments. They consist of a sensory cell in a socket. The shaft of the hair is rigid, and any force applied to it is transmitted to and amplified by the membrane of the sensory neuron, resulting in the production of a nerve impulse (Pringle, 1938). Some of these organs are innervated by only one neuron, others may be innervated by several neurons, indicating a variety of sensory functions including that of chemoreception.

Sensilla chaetae (sensory spines) are also distributed over all parts of the cuticle and are mechanoreceptors that function in proprioception as well as other mechanoreceptor activi-

ties. Sensilla campaniformia (sensory pores) are mechanoreceptors that function in gravity reception and proprioception.

Chordotonal organs (= scolophorous organs) are mechanoreceptors and proprioceptors distributed over the insect body (Hubbard, 1959). They lie below the hypodermis and consist of from one to 400 sensilla, each with one nerve cell and 2 to 3 characteristic cells. The cap cell (distal cell) is attached to an organ or part of the body wall, whereas a ligament is usually attached to some other part of the body. The sensory cell is thus attached to two different parts of the body, and any movements of the body cause impulses to arise in the neuron. A group of scolopidia make up one chordotonal organ. The functions of this receptor depend upon its precise location. In some mosquito larvae they are located on the antennae and act as ears. Some are located close to the trachea, to muscles involved in respiratory movements, to blood vessels, to body muscles, and to joints. The impulses of these differently located receptors are thought to be used in reflexes involving hearing, body position and orientation, blood pressure control, tracheal air pressures and flows, and muscular movements

Although the morphology of many insect receptors has been described, little is known concerning specific functions of many of these, and the pathways by which information flows in the central nervous system are also unknown. The complexity of interactions and inputs is especially great in insects that fly. Some reflexes involved in flight and locomotion, which utilize these mechanoreceptors, will be described in a later part of this chapter.

19-5. Equilibrium Receptors—Vertebrates. In vertebrates the organ of equilibrium is the labyrinth, which is basically a statocyst containing the equivalent of several statoliths, each of which is responsible for detecting particular movements and directions of movement by the animal. Labyrinths, as is true of statocysts generally, occur in pairs. The structure of the human statocyst is shown in Figure 19-2. It consists of a pars superior—including the semicircular canals and utriculus—and a pars inferior—including the sacculus and lagena.

This complex of chambers and semicircular canals is filled with endolymphatic fluid and is located within the body part of the head. The utriculus and sacculus are bony chambers lined with sensory cilia and are analogous to the invertebrate statocyst. The sacculus contains two otolith organs, whose functions are not clear. In fish they seem to be involved in hearing. In crocodilian reptiles the lagena (a patch of sensory hair cells) appears as an outgrowth of the sacculus and in higher vertebrates becomes associated with hearing.

The utriculus contains three patches of sensory cells each bearing an otolith. Otoliths are calcareous concretions secreted by the animal and are analogous to the statoliths of invertebrates. The utriculus senses changes in body position or in gravity.

The semicircular canals are oriented perpendicular to each other. At one end of each canal is an ampulla containing a crista consisting of rows of hair cells whose cilia are embedded in a gelatinous sheet. Any rotational movement causes the bone and gelatinous sheet to move while the fluid in the canal remains motionless because of inertia.

The gelatinous sheet (= cupola) is a sort of swinging door extending across the ampulla, and it is bent whenever endolymph movement and canal movement are out of phase. The anatomical arrangements are such that the ampullar receptor neurons are excited only when there is an accelerative force directed in the plane of the canal. Thus the three semicircular canals each respond to movement in only one plane (Figure 19-2). All hair cells in an ampullary organ have their cilia oriented in the same direction. Three semicircular canals function well in providing the nervous system with information respecting body position; however, lampreys have only two canals, and hagfish have only one.

Movements of the cupola during rotation and at the termination of rotation of the head are associated with the condition of nystagmus, a reflex movement of the eyes. At the start of rotation the eyes move in the direction of the movement to fixate on some point in the visual field that is followed until it moves out of the visual field. The eyes then flick ahead to a new fixation point until it also passes from view. This sequence of movements allows the animal to maintain visual orientation; and most vertebrates also rely on visual clues for orientation information. If body rotation continues steadily, nystagmus ceases as the cupula returns to its rest position. Nystagmus begins again at the termination of rotation, but the direction of the eye movement is opposite to what it was originally. Once cupula and fluid have come to equilibrium, nystagmus ceases.

The functions of different regions of the labyrinth were first studied by cutting the nerves to various parts or by destroying particular chambers of the organ, and noting the

Figure 19-2 Structure of the human labyrinth.

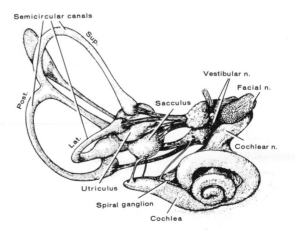

results of these operations on the orientational behavior of the animal. The postural adjustments of most fish eyes and fins are not altered when a sacculus or lagena is cut (Lowenstein, 1957), but they are lost when both utriculi are destroyed or eliminated from the efferent nervous pathway. The otolith receptors of elasmobranchs show a background discharge in all positions. Impulses from various receptors are recorded against this background and show maximal activity in particular spatial orientations of the animal's body (Lowenstein and Sand, 1940). Still other receptor neurons respond to position changes regardless of the direction of this change.

Some species of fish have a resting position in which the head is maintained much lower than the tail (headstanders) or the tail is much lower than the head (tailstanders). In a series of ingenious experiments using a centrifuge that held experimental equipment, experimental animals, and the experimenter, it was shown that increases in gravity (represented by increases in the centripetal field) did not change the posture of the animal, and this suggests that shearing forces on the utricular statolith do not change with increased gravity (Braemer and Braemer, 1958). This is the case only if the statolith is horizontal in the normal tailstanding posture and was shown correct by morphological analysis of the penguin fish. In another tailstander, the pencil fish, the angle of the body relative to the horizontal was found to decrease as the fish was rotated more rapidly in the centrifuge. This could mean only that the statolith is not horizontal in the normal resting posture, and this also was found to be correct upon morphological examination.

In order to determine whether shearing forces or pressure forces were responsible for otolith activity, a centrifuge was used to increase the mass of the otolith, and it was found that shearing forces were the agent responsible for exciting the hair cells. Shearing forces and pressures have different increments during centrifugation, and it is possible to determine which is being compensated for by the animal's labyrinth (von Holst, 1950).

Impulses from the equilibrium organs are conducted via the eighth nerve to the brain, but not much is known concerning central nervous system mechanisms by which information from the labyrinthine systems are coordinated and integrated.

Hearing

19-6. Insects. Sound reception is a large subject area, and space permits only some generalizations to be made here. The back and forth motion of a particle about some equilibrium position is a vibration, and in any continuous medium vibrating particles impart displacement to neighboring particles by elastic forces. These disturbances take the form of periodic compressional waves, and sound receptors are those excited by such waves in gases, liquids, or solids. The term hearing is often restricted to the case of air-borne vibrations (von Buddenbrock, 1952) or to cases where a sound source is located by the animal (Pumphrey, 1950).

Vibration receptors in insects have been studied in some detail in certain species because of their known role in behavior and because of the accessibility of some insect sound receptor organs and neurons to direct analysis. Sounds are used as a means of communication in several insect orders, for example, Orthoptera, Hymenoptera, and Cicadidae; and some insects possess sound producing organs such as the tymbal organs of cicadas (see Chapter 10).

Many of the insect sensilla mentioned in Section 19-4 may possess sensory cells capable of serving as vibration detectors, an action based on the response of sensory hairs to mechanical vibrations. Either the hairs are moved directly by the sound waves, or the sound waves may transmit vibrations to other regions of the body that in turn stimulate the hairs (Autrum, 1963). Hair cells generally are sensitive to vibration frequencies in the range of 0.5 to 10 kc/sec. Some chordotonal organs can respond to air or water-borne vibrations with frequencies from about 0.1 to 1.0 kc/sec.

747

Johnston's organ, in addition to responding to other types of mechanical stimuli, also responds to air-borne vibrations with frequencies from 0.05 to 0.5 kc/sec. This organ is found on the antennae of all insects and is similar in structure to the chordotonal organs except that cap cells are not present. It contains not only a variety of sensory cells but also a complex layer of neurons. Subgenual organs are another subclass of chorodotonal organs that respond to air-borne vibrations with frequencies up to 10 kc/sec. These are found in Orthoptera, Lepidoptera, Hymenoptera, and Hemiptera.

Tympanal organs are specialized receptors for sound with frequencies from 0.1 to 200 kc/sec (see Figure 19-3). They are modified tracheal structures with a thin membrane separating the external environment from a chamber containing sensory hairs. They are located on the antennae (Diptera); the legs (Orthoptera); or on the thorax or abdomen (Lepidoptera, Hemiptera). The number of innervating neurons ranges from 2 to 70.

The tympanal organ of noctuid moths has been especially studied (Roeder, 1963; Roeder and Payne, 1966). Vibrations striking upon the tympanal membrane are transmitted into the air-filled tympanic cavity. A fine strand of tissue, the acoustic sensillum is suspended across this cavity and bears two sensory neurons. These are A cells or acoustic sensory cells. There is also a B cell present, which extends fine processes into the surrounding membrane; but its function is unknown. It might be a proprioceptor responding to stresses placed on the tympanal cavity during flight and allowing central nervous system correction for such alterations in the sound chamber. The vibrations of the air in the tympanic cavity serve to excite the sensory neurons that respond with nerve impulses.

Sensitivity to intensity and frequency of stimulation are important characteristics of any sound receptor. Insects generally have good sensitivity to varying intensities of sound. In noctuid moths, although only two sensory nerve cells are present, the tymbal organs can respond to a wide range of frequencies. However the pattern of spike frequencies is not greatly altered by changes in frequency, an indication that frequency discrimination is not good. When a pure tone (a sound with a single frequency) is presented to the moth, the action potentials occur with greater frequency and are longer lasting the more intense the sound.

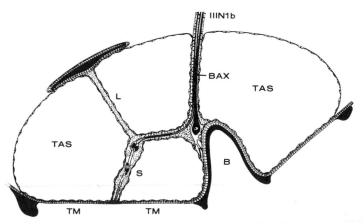

Figure 19-3 Tympanic organ of noctuid moths. Sensory cells (S) are attached to a tympanic membrane, exposed at the surface of the moth's thorax. A third and larger cell, BAX, sends its axon through the tympanic nerve, III N1b. Its function is not known. Tas, Tympanic air sacs; Cu, cuticular skeletal elements. [From A. E. Treat and K. D. Roeder (1959) *Journal of Insect Physiology* **3**: 262–270.]

The louder the sound the greater is the response latency, and there thus appears to be a temporal relation between sound stimulus intensity and the time and duration of the nervous response. The two neurons have different thresholds, and therefore, different intensities will result in different response patterns (Roeder, 1964).

The membrane of the moth tympanal organ is displaced the most when sound waves strike it perpendicularly. This mechanism allows discrimination of the sound source. In addition, the presence of paired receptors on opposite sides of the body also allows source location, that is, the moth possesses binaural sound location. For example, when a sound is presented to a moth from one side, there will be a difference in the spike generation times in the two receptors, and the degree of difference can serve as a clue to the direction of the sound. Binaural organs will permit a measure of the difference in sound intensity reaching the two organs when the source is to one side because the sound will strike each tympanal membrane at a different angle. Thus the sound intensities will differ, resulting in different frequencies of impulses in the two organs, a difference that the central nervous system can interpret in terms of source. The ears of noctuid moths are capable of detecting the high-pitched cries of predator bats and are used in reflex escape movements (see Roeder, 1963).

19-7. The Lateral Line of Fishes. Hearing in fishes is a poorly developed sensory modality, and in this section the lateral line organ is discussed primarily because it is the major sensory apparatus of both elasmobranch and teleost fish and possesses rudimentary sound receptor cells.

The lateral line organs consist of rows of hair cells in the walls of canals that extend the length of the body and over the head. The canals may be either closed to serve as a protection for the sensory cells of fish which live in rough waters or may be in the form of open grooves. The hair cells are often grouped into neuromasts, and the cilia of the sensory cells are often embedded in a gelatinous cupula. Movements of the cupula are initiated by water movements in the canals and cause shearing forces to be applied to the hair cells. The resultant distortional forces cause depolarization of the hair cell membrane, thus stimulating synapsing neurons.

Electrophysiological recording from the lateral line nerves shows that there is a continuous spontaneous firing of the neurons and that water movements cause superimposed spikes on the background discharge. Water flow in a given direction stimulates some groups of receptor cells and inhibits others.

The lateral line organs may have some role in the detection of the rate of movement through the water. Hair cells can respond to vibrations with a frequency up to 200 cps and may play a subsidiary role in low frequency hearing.

More importantly, the lateral line organ is involved in the detection and localization of objects in the water, and in some species certain cells are modified to respond to electrical fields (see Chapter 8 for a discussion of this subject and the references). It has been proposed that the specialized ampullae of Lorenzini are stimulated by changes in water pressure, weak electrical fields, and the salt concentration of the water. The evolution of the lateral line organ and its relation to other vertebrate sense organs is discussed by Denison (1966), and its functional significance is discussed by Dijkgraaf (1963).

Fish also possess an inner ear that contains both equilibrium receptors (the labyrinth) and hearing receptors. Since the tissues of fish have about the same density as water, any sound impinging on the surface of the head can pass directly through the tissues to the inner ear. Therefore, no external structures are required, and fish lack the external and middle ear structures found in higher vertebrates (see Section 9-8).

19-8. Hearing in Mammals. The structure of the mammalian ear is diagrammed in Figure 19-4. Most mammals (the exceptions include marine mammals such as whales, seals, and

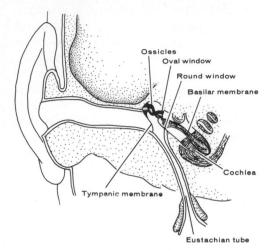

Figure 19-4 Structures of the outer ear of humans.

porpoises) have an external ear consisting of a pinna and an ear canal. The pinna is used to select sound waves from certain frequencies and concentrate them in the ear canal. Although the pinna may serve as a direction detecting device in some animals, it is not essential for this purpose (see Webster, 1966). For example, Payne (1961) showed that the barn owl, which lacks a pinna, has an extremely highly developed ability to locate sound sources, although feathers aid in this activity.

The middle ear consists of the bony ossicles and the tympanic membrane. The sensory hair cells used for hearing are bathed in a liquid and air-borne sounds must be converted and amplified into vibrations of a liquid. The viscosity and compressibility of liquids is much higher than that of air. To transduce air-borne vibrations into liquid-borne vibrations of similar amplitudes requires a much greater force. The components of the middle ear serve as an impedance matching system for this conversion.

In mammals the three ossicles (malleus, incus, and stapes) act as a lever system performing an amplification function. The malleus is attached to the tympanic membrane (= eardrum) over a relatively large area (50 to 90 mm² in humans), and the other end of the lever system is attached to the oval window of the cochlea over a smaller area (3.2 mm²). The energy absorbed at the large tympanic membrane is transferred with little amplitude change to the smaller area of the oval window. The ratio of the two areas is the transformation coefficient and a measure of the amplification. This system is found only in mammals. Birds, for example, have only one ossicle (the columella).

The three ossicles are part of a mechanism that also damps out intense sounds, thus avoiding damage to the delicate sensory structures of the inner ear. The ossicles are associated with two auditory muscles. The tensor tympani inserts on the malleus and is innervated by the trigeminal nerve. The stapedius muscle inserts on the stapes and is innervated by the facial nerve. These are synergistic muscles whose contractions, triggered by loud sounds, prevent low frequency sound waves from causing great movements of the ossicles. They dampen out sound waves with frequencies below about 1,000 cps. Low frequencies have greater amplitudes as compared with higher frequencies of sound waves, and the amplitude is a measure of the intensity or force of the sound. The auditory muscles contract reflexively during swallowing and coughing, as well as at times of loud noises. Such damping reduces sound levels by as much as 40 db (the decibel, db, is a measure of sound intensity. A decibel $= 10 \log E/E_r$, where E is the intensity of a signal and E_r is the intensity of some reference).

In summary the middle ear may be considered as a mechanical transducer whose function is to convert low-stiffness vibrations picked up by the tympanic membrane from the air of the external auditory canal into stiffer and more energetic vibrations suitable for transmission through the fluids of the inner ear.

The inner ear begins at the membranous oval window, where sound energy enters the cochlea as compressional waves in the perilymph. Sound waves are transmitted through the scala vestibuli and, after a delay down a return channel, the scala tympani (see Figure

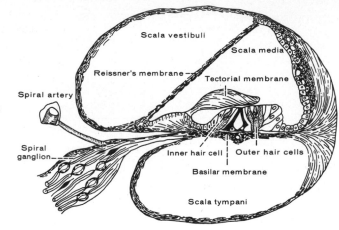

Figure 19-5 Important structures of the inner ear.

19-5). These two channels are filled with perilymph. They are separated by another membranous channel, the endolyph-filled scala media, except at the end where the latter terminates and the two perilymph-filled chambers are connected by the helicotrema. The traveling compression waves escape through the membranous round window into the middle ear.

The perilymph is not compressible to any great degree, and so any inward deflection of the oval window causes an outward movement of the round window. If the inward movement is slow, that is, caused by lower frequency waves, then perilymph in the scala vestibuli can move through the helicotrema into the scala tympani and then to the round window. Higher frequency waves take a shorter route and pass across the membrane of the scala media to displace two membranous partitions: the basilar membrane and Reissner's membrane.

The basilar membrane contains the sensory hair cells used to detect vibrations. This membrane is supported on a body shelf running the length of the cochlea, which is the major organ of hearing. It has four rows of hair cells whose cilia are embedded in the tectorial membrane. The hair cells of the organ of corti lack kinocilia, although the basal bodies are retained; they do retain their stereocilia. In all of the sensory cells, the orientation of cells is maintained as evidenced by the positions of the basal bodies. Figure 19-6 compares the structure of a general hair cell with one from the basilar membrane. The illustration also presents a proposed mechanism for the production of potentials by these cells in response to cilia distortions. Distortion of the cilia is presumed to alter the membrane permeability and those effect membrane potential changes.

A displacement of fluid in the scala vestibuli causes a displacement of the scala media toward the scala tympani, and the basilar membrane rotates around its point of attachment at the inner margin. The tectorial membrane is pivoted at a different point so that movement of the cochlear partition causes a shearing force to be exerted on the stereocilia of the sensory cells embedded in their gelatinous base.

The mechanics of the basilar membrane is not understood completely because this membane is complex in structure (the discussion here is based on the work of von Békésy (1965; his researches from 1928 to 1958 were collected and published in 1960). The basilar membrane is composed of about 30,000 fine cross-strands joined by connective tissue. It increases in width by about four times as it passes from the base of the cochlea to the apex. The **resonance theory of hearing** proposes that each strand resonates at a different frequency with high frequency responses at the base and low frequency responses at the apex, response to

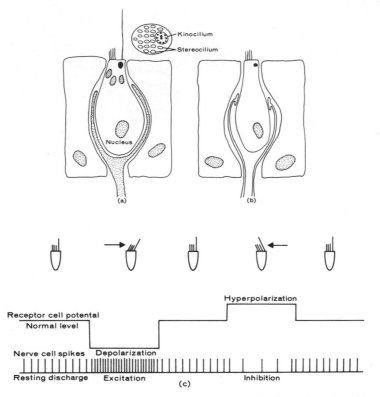

Figure 19-6 (a) Hair cell with stereocilum and kinocilium. (b) Hair cell without kinocilium, found in the organ of corti. (c) Diagram showing membrane potential changes that occur when kinocilium is bent in directions indicated.

each frequency being limited to only a small part of the membrane (see Figure 19-7).

Since all the strands are interconnected, resonance at one point must initiate traveling waves moving along the membrane. At low frequencies the membrane moves as a unit in synchrony with each sound cycle; at higher frequencies the displacement peaks are situated closer to the basal end of the membrane.

Various membranes, depending on their structure, will vibrate in different patterns when a force is applied at one point. The various possible modes of vibration are illustrated in Figure 19-7. Traveling waves exhibit a maximum displacement in a thin membrane

according to the frequency of the stimulus. Although the resonance theory modified to include the presence of traveling waves accounts for many properties of the auditory apparatus, much still remains to be discovered.

In animals with smaller cochleas the response to higher frequencies should improve because with the known elasticity of the basilar membrane the relation between distance along the membrane and the most effective stimulus frequency is a logarithmic one. As dimensions decrease, the response to higher frequencies is increased. This theory is supported by the fact that smaller mammals, in general, can hear higher frequencies than larger ones. For ex-

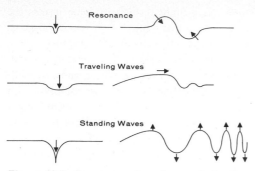

Figure 19-7 Resonance, traveling, and standing wave models.

ample, the bat can hear frequencies up to about 200 kc per second. Frequency response then is thought to be determined by the particular area of the basilar membrane that responds to a stimulus and causes deformation in sensory hairs. Pitch discrimination is probably dependent upon which nerve fibers are excited.

The primary receptor cells in the human cochlear number about 17,000, and these cells make complex synaptic contacts with neurons of the spiral ganglion which runs along the central mass of the cochlear spiral. From here sensory fibers run with the eighth nerve to the brain. In some manner the complex vibrations imparted to the basilar membrane are translated into action potentials by the sensory hair cells, and this information is sent to the brain for decoding. As was the case for visual sensation, it is at the point where many nerve fibers are carrying action potentials, that our understanding of auditory sensations decreases. The auditory cortex shows the same type of overlapping connections that was described for the visual cortex.

Control of Insect Flight

19-9. Initiation and Maintenance of Flight. I have chosen insect flight and some associated activities to serve as example of how mechanoreceptors, including those for hearing, can be used to control a relatively complex process. Any animal that flies has a great problem in spatial orientation, and such problems are aggravated by the mechanical stimuli produced as a result of their own motion. It is of interest that the CNS of flying animals (birds and insects) has much of its structure devoted to controlling flight and the orientation of the animal, lessening the amount of nervous tissue that can be used for learning. In these animals we find behavior that is largely innate when compared with animals such as mammals in which the nervous system has developed so that learning, memory, and sensations are the dominant actions (see, for example, the discussion in Wiener, 1961).

The flight muscles of insects and their basic properties were described in Chapter 10. The stimulation of the insect brain directly can cause the initiation of flight, but normally flight occurs only when the thoracic ganglion is in an appropriate state. The most important reflex for initiating flight in insects generally is the tarsal reflex, which occurs when contact is lost with the ground (von Uexküll, 1908). Flight is initiated by beginning a discharge of impulses to the indirect flight muscles. The tarsal reflex is found in all insects except the Coleoptera.

Some insects also require the stimulus of wind on the head, antennae, or wings to initiate flight or to maintain it (Hollick, 1940; Weis-Fogh, 1956a, b). A few insects can maintain flight in still air, for example, *Drosophila*. Other insects need a moving visual field to maintain flight, and this sensory input is also a good initiator of flight. Insects that are predators and must carry prey during flight can initiate flight while their legs are on the ground. The subesophageal ganglion is the CNS structure needed in all insects to relay impulses that initiate flight. When the brain of the locust is destroyed, flight initiation may still occur, but removal of the subesophageal ganglion prevents flight initiation.

In *Schistocerca* the motor discharge to the flight muscles is synchronous with the frequency of beat starting with the first cycle of wing activity (Wilson, 1961). In flies there is a high-frequency burst of impulses to the indirect flight muscles at the initiation of flight, but the frequency then falls to lower values during steady activity of the wings. The central nervous system mechanism by which various stimulating agents maintain flight muscle excitation is unknown.

19-10. Dipteran Halteres. The Diptera are the most agile of insect fliers and have developed a unique equilibrium organ, the haltere. Diptera have a single functional pair of wings; the primitive second pair takes the form of small club-shaped receptor organs. This haltere retains the large number of sensory receptors found on the fully developed wing and is innervated by some 400 sensory nerve fibers.

The haltere oscillates as rapidly as the flight wings and behaves as an oscillating gyroscope that resists displacement forces. Its clublike shape prevents influences on it by aerodynamic forces. The resistance of the haltere to displacement forces sets up stresses in its cuticle and activates its mechanoreceptors (hair cells). These signals are used by the CNS to correct movements of the wings by acting on the indirect flight muscles, as well as on muscles that position the wing, thus providing for stable flight.

Removal of one haltere does not impair flight. Only when a fly is also blinded does haltere removal upset flight (Faust, 1952). This is an indication that visual clues are also important in the maintenance of flight equilibrium.

Other balancing mechanisms have developed in some insect groups. In dragonflies, for example, movements of the head relative to the thorax causes responses in cervical hair plates. Impulses from these guide activity in the flight control muscles. The head of the dragonfly is heavy and connected to the remainder of the body only by a thin neck. It acts through inertia to activate the sensory receptors because during a roll, for example, it tends to get left behind. Different combinations of sensory hairs are stimulated by acceleration in different directions. The CNS of the dragonfly coordinates all this information and provides impulses to the proper flight control muscles so

that stable flight results. In some insects the forewings are modified as balancing organs, again using hair cells as the receptors.

Night flying insects use antennae, head, abdomen, or limbs as gravity organs. In addition, the antennae of flies are equipped with acceleration receptors that measure flight speed. Flies without antennae crash because they tend to land to quickly. The sense organs appear to be Johnston's organ already discussed.

19-11. Analysis of Locust Flight. The flight of locusts has been studied in some detail by Weis-Fogh (1964). Recent reviews by Pringle (1968) and Wilson (1968) describe several aspects of insect flight. When considering insect flight, it must be remembered that one group of indirect flight muscles provides power for wing movement; another group of muscles control wing angle and other control mechanisms.

In the locust *Schistocerca* the wings beat at a frequency of about 17 cps in the tilted stroke plane (Figure 19-8). Frequency varies with power although the range of frequency variation is small. Wing movements have been studied by suspending locusts from an aerodynamic balance in front of an open-jet wind tunnel. The two pairs of wings are out of phase during flight but have a constant phase relationship (Figure 19-8). In locusts the basic up and down movements of the wings are confined mainly to one plane. Wing movements are neurogenic; each movement is initiated by a nerve impulse to the flight muscles (this is not the typical situation in insects, see Chapter 10). During the downstroke of the wing, the anterior side of each wing is pronated (twisted downward), and during the upstroke the wings are supinated (the anterior side is twisted upward). The latter is not under muscular control, but pronation is effected by a group of controller-depressor muscles.

Y-shaped strands of connective tissue stretched between the thoracic cuticle and the base of the wing contain sensory receptor elements. One branch of the Y carries scolo-

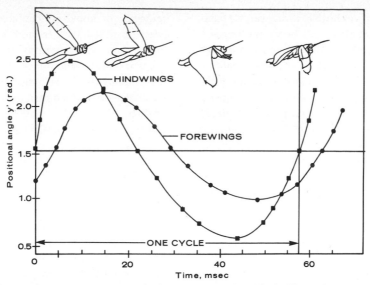

Figure 19-8 The wing movements of a desert locust in level flight. The ordinate is the angle of the long axis of the wing, as measured in the stroke plane, and the abscissa is the time. The two pairs of wings are out of phase, but the phase relationship between them is constant. [From T. Weis-Fogh (1956a) "Biology and physics of locust flight. II. Flight performance of the desert locust (*Schistocerca gregaria*)" *Philosophical Transactions of the Royal Society* (London) **B239**: 459–501.]

poforous sensilla that discharge during the downstroke, but these appear to have no direct influence upon flight. Rather they are homologous to the tympanic receptors of noctuid moths (Section 19-6). The other branch of the Y contains stretch receptors, each of which generates one or two spikes during a normal upstroke. In addition, campaniform sensilla on the underside of the wings are sensitive to wind and acceleration forces; these fire during the downstroke (Wilson, 1961). When the Y is destroyed, all control of flight is lost.

Three thoracic ganglia generate what has been called the **central concert** of motor impulses for activating wing musculature. The latter consist of an elevator group, a depressor group, and the controller-depressor group. The sensory receptors mentioned above provide a **peripheral concert** of sensory impulses that signals the position of the wings and the forces acting on them.

It turns out, however, that control of locust flight is not accomplished by a closed feedback loop. The central concert is the result of endogenous activity on the part of the CNS,

and although requiring some input stimuli to initiate activity, during flight the system continues to produce motor impulses generated by some type of preset inate central command system.

Coupling between the central concert and the peripheral concert is very loose, and the latter is completely ignored when, for example, the speed of flight is such that no time is available for reflex adjustment of flight. Although this type of system cannot speedily or accurately adjust flight movements, in the normal range of operation it serves perfectly well. In this type of system an input signal will be used only if it occurs during a part of the normal cycle in which some adjustment is possible; otherwise the sensory input is ignored. Thus, much of the sensory information is lost by the CNS or is used to excite the central concert only in a tonic way. In this system the movements of the wings continue, even under adverse conditions, as long as no specific stop signal is given.

Such a system is difficult to analyze because the highly developed methods of systems analysis are not applicable. Moreover, we have little understanding of how endogenous rhythmic activity is produced and utilized by the CNS. Further analysis of locust flight is needed to gain understanding of the mechanisms by which antagonistic and synergistic muscle groups are coupled during flight activity. There may be a system of mutually inhibiting sets of muscles with superimposed excitatory couplings between some groups.

19-12. Echolocation in Moths and Bats. The behavioral interactions of moths and bats are included here because of the excellent work of Roeder (1963) in analyzing the system, both at the neurophysiological and at the behavioral level, where moth and bat interact. Although much work still must be done, the system does illustrate how various levels of physiological and morphological phenomena may be studied and how such levels interact to produce whole animal behavior patterns. In Section 19-6 the tympanal organ of noctuid moths was described. Acoustic orientation has been discussed by Roeder and Payne (1966).

Night-flying moths react with evasive maneuvers to a wide variety of stimuli including the high-pitched sounds emitted by echolocating predator bats. The tympanal organ responds to sounds with frequencies between 10 and 200 kc/second; but they are most sensitive to frequencies in the range of 40 to 80 kc/second, the range that also corresponds to the calls of many bat species. Both orientation and avoidance behavior may be initiated in the moth by a bat cry.

Recordings from the tympanic nerves of moths exposed in a field to flying bats have given an indication of the nature of the moth's activity. Moths can hear bats when they approach within about 120 feet. Bats can detect moths when about 15 to 20 feet distant. Under binaural conditions that tympanal organ closest to a bat approaching from one side responds with spikes from the A-fibers. The other ear of the moth does not hear the bat until a later time, when its fibers also initiate spike generation. The tympanal organ closest to the approaching bat generates a higher

frequency of impulses than that on the side away from the bat. In addition there is a difference in the response times of the two tympanal organs determined by the differences in sound intensities reaching each. This, again, is a dual system which permits sound location.

Observations of free moths show that, upon hearing a bat cry, several patterns of behavior can result. In some cases the flight movements of moths become erratic and rapid; moths twist, turn, dive to the ground, and so forth. Some moths become motionless on the ground; others initiate flight from the ground. Whatever reaction may appear, there is no doubt that the tympanal organ of the moth detects the cry of the bat from distances of more than 100 feet and that impulses established by sound reception lead to evasive or hiding actions on the part of the moth. Before considering further the purpose of these different maneuvers, it is worth describing echolocation mechanisms.

Echolocation is a mechanism for orientation in which an energy form emitted by an animal interacts with features of the environment and is returned to the animal where any changes in the energy can be detected. In most cases the energy is in the form of high-pitched sounds.

In the eighteenth century it was known that a blinded bat could fly about a room, avoiding obstacles in its path. Later it was shown that the little brown bat *Myotis lucifugus* could avoid wires with diameters as small as 1.2 mm, spaced a foot apart, as long as its ears and mouth were in a functional condition (Griffin and Galambos, 1941). Bats, while flying, emit ultrasonic sounds, that is, sound frequencies too high for human ears to detect, although audible to most small mammals. Humans can hear frequencies only up to about 20 kc/second whereas bat cries are in the range of 40 to 100 kc/second. The little brown bat emits cries lasting only a few milliseconds and in bursts that are modulated with peak intensities near the middle of each burst and a drop of 40 kc/second during the course of the burst. The big brown bat *Eptesicus fiscus* when hunting emits longer pulses at a rate of about 10 per second. Upon detecting prey the pulse rate increases while the pulse duration decreases.

The bat has a uniquely developed laryngeal apparatus in which the cricothyroid muscles are greatly developed and the arytenoid cartileges are ossified and fused. Some bats (the vespertilionid bats) fly with their mouths continuously open, while others (rhinolophids) fly with closed mouths and emit cries through the nose. In many bat species the ears are very large, presumably to serve as better directional devices. Some bats have a second or tragus ear whose function is not yet known. The cochlear nucleus and inferior nucleus are greatly enlarged areas of the auditory nervous pathway (Griffin et al., 1963). Bat species differ greatly in the nature of their ultrasonic emissions, mechanisms for emitting and mechanisms for receiving echoes.

When compared with the intensity of emitted pulses, the echoes returning from the environment are very weak. Sound energy falls with the square of the distance traveled; thus the returning energy levels must be only a fraction of that emitted. In the ear of the bat, as well as of the moth, the time differences of pulses reaching the two organs, as well as differences arising from pulse generation time by the sensory receptor cells because of different intensities of the same sound reaching the two ears must permit directional detection of objects from which the sound waves reflect. In addition it has been shown that the nature of the target from which the waves bounce can also be determined; for example, a moth can distinguish a rubber disc from a mealworm (Webster, 1963).

The mechanism by which echolocation works is not yet determined. It has been modeled as a beat frequency system (Pye, 1963), based on the fact than an echo has a slightly higher frequency than the emitted pulse because of a Doppler shift. Interaction between the emitted and returning sound waves will produce beat notes of lower frequency when the waves are in phase. The frequency of these beat notes is proportional to the relative velocities of the bat and the target, and such a system would provide a mechanism for homing in on a target. However, several objections to this model exist. For example, jamming of a bat's echolocation system is best accomplished with high frequency sounds, whereas according to the beat note model, this should best be done with low frequency sounds (Griffin et al., 1963).

Target detection and prey capture by bats has several phases. In the initial phase of hunting, a bat will emit pulses of sound that are frequency modulated and sweep from 100 to 40 kc per second during every pulse. An approach phase is initiated when the bat turns toward detected prey; here the pulse interval and the pulse duration both shorten, whereas the frequencies stay the same. A terminal phase occurs during which the frequency of the emitted cries drops to about 25 kc per second, pulse duration to about 0.5 msec, and pulse interval to 5 msec. This cry is an audible buzz and is used by bats when prey is captured and also when landing after flight.

Some marine animals have also developed echolocation systems. Such orientation and detection systems are of use when light conditions are poor. In the oceans light intensities fall rapidly as depth increases, and in addition many ocean waters are murky because of the presence of suspended particles. A familiar example of such systems is that of porpoises and dolphins (see Kellogg, 1961; Poulter 1963).

We have seen that moths take on a variety of evasive maneuvers when an approaching bat is detected. When a bat is at a distance, any type of evasive flying action would be wasteful unless the moth turns and flys in a direction away from the bat. Moths do turn and fly in an opposite direction when bat cries are detected and located at relatively large distances, from 30 to 100 feet distance, depending on the moth species. But at closer distances, approximately 15 to 20 feet, moths go into a variety of evasive actions designed to complex the problem of the bat in detecting the moth and its flight direction. A moth may react to a bat with an abrupt dive in which the wings are folded. The dive may a be a power dive, or in some cases the wings flutter only occasionally.

The dive may begin as an abrupt deviation from a horizontal flight path or it may be preceded by a short turn, climb, or loop. A moth may make a series of tight turns that carry it slowly to the ground. After landing, some moths remain motionless for half a minute or more, and others resume level flight just as they touch the ground.

All of these actions make it more difficult for the bat to catch the moth. Roeder estimates that for every 100 moths that escape the bat by using such tactics, 60 moths that have failed to use erratic behavior are caught. The bat in flight has a ballistics problem in which it must compute where to dive in order to intercept the moth in its flight; erratic behavior of the moth compounds the calculation problem of the bat.

Some moths produce ultrasonic sounds themselves, and it has been shown that playback or recorded moth cries causes bats to turn away from the moth it is pursuing (Dunning and Roeder, 1965). It is doubtful that moths can jam the echo locating system of the bat because this is extremely difficult to do even under laboratory conditions. Many moths that produce sounds are also producers of chemicals that bats dislike or have morphological structures such as spurs on the wing, making it difficult for bats to capture and eat them (Blest et al., 1963). It may be that some moths emit cries simply to warn the bat of their presence so that the bat can avoid them.

References and Readings

Autrum, H. (1959). "Nonphotic receptors in lower forms." In: **Handbook of Physiology** (H. W. Magoun, ed.), Section 1, Vol. 1, pp. 369–385. Washington, D. C.: American Physiological Society.

Autrum, H. (1963). "Anatomy and physiology of sound receptors in invertebrates." In: **Acoustic Behavior of Animals** (R. G. Busnel, ed.), pp. 412–433. New York: American Elsevier Publishing Company.

Batschelet, E. (1965). **Statistical Methods for the Analysis of Problems in Animal Orientation and Certain Biological Rhythms.** Washington, D. C.: American Institutes of Biological Science. pp. 298.

Beidler, L. M. (1962). "Taste receptor stimulation." *Prog. Biophys.* **12**: 107–151.

von Békésy, G. (1960). **Experiments in Hearing.** New York: McGraw-Hill Book Company, Inc. 745 pp.

von Békésy, G. (1962). "The gap between the hearing of external and internal sounds." *Symp. Soc. Exp. Biol.* **16**: 267–288.

von Békésy, G. (1965). "Cochlear mechanics." In: **Theoretical and Mathematical Biology** (T. H. Waterman and H. Morowitz, eds.), pp. 172–197. Waltham, Mass.: Blaisdell Publishing Company.

Blest, A. D., T. S. Collett, and J. D. Pye (1963). "The generation of ultrasonic signals by a new world arctiid moth." *Proc. Roy. Soc.* (London) **B158**: 196–207.

Braemer, W. and H. Braemer (1958). "Orientation of fish to gravity." *Limnol. Oceanogr.* **3**: 363–372.

von Buddenbrock, W. (1952). **Vergleichende Physiologie,** Vol. 1, "Sinnesphysiologie." Basel: Birkhäuser Verlag. 504 pp.

Chapman, R. F. (1969). **The Insects,** Vol. 1. New York: American Elsevier Publishing Company. 819 pp.

Chapman, L. F., A. O. Ramos, H. Goodell, and H. G. Wolff (1961). "Neurohumoral features of afferent fibers in man. Their role in vasodilation, inflammation, and pain." *Arch. Neurol.* **4**: 617.

Denison, R. H. (1966). "The origin of the lateral-line sensory system." *Am. Zool.* **3**: 369–370.

Dethier, V. G. (1963). **The Physiology of Insect Senses.** London: Methuen & Co., Ltd. 266 pp.

Dijkgraaf, S. (1963). "The functioning and significance of the lateral line organs." *Biol. Rev.* **38**: 51–106.

Dunning, D. C. and K. D. Roeder (1965). "Moth sounds and the insect catching behavior of bats." *Science* **147**: 173–174.

Faust, R. (1952). "Untersuchungen zum

Halterenproblem." *Zool. Jb. All. Zool. Physiol.* **63**: 325–366.

Gould, E., N. C. Negus, and A. Novick (1964). "Evidence for echolocation in shrews." *J. Exp. Zool.* **156**: 19–38.

Griffin, D. R. (1958). **Listening in the Dark.** New Haven, Conn.: Yale University Press.

Griffin, D. R. and R. Galambos (1941). "The sensory basis of obstacle avoidance by flying bats." *J. Exp. Zool.* **86**: 481–506.

Griffin, D. R., J. J. G. McCue, and A. D. Grinnell (1963). "The resistance of bats to jamming." *J. Exp. Zool.* **152**: 229–259.

Hinde, R. A. (1966). **Animal Behavior.** New York: McGraw Hill Book Company. 2nd ed. 876 pp.

Hollick, F. S. J. (1940). "The flight of the dipterous fly *Muscina stabulans* Fallén." *Phil. Trans. Roy. Soc.* (London) **B230**: 357–390.

von Holst, E. (1950). "Quantitative Messung von Stimmungen im Verhalten der Fische." *Symp. Soc. Exp. Biol.* **4**: 143–172.

Hubbard, S. J. (1959). "Femoral mechanoreceptors in the locust." *J. Physiol.* (London) **147**: 8P–10P.

Katsuki, Y. (1965). "Comparative Neurophysiology of hearing." *Physiol. Rev.* **45**: 380–423.

Kellog, W. N. (1961). **Porpoises and Sonar.** Chicago: University of Chicago Press.

Lewis, G. P. (1960). "Active polypeptides derived from plasma proteins." *Physiol. Rev.* **40**: 647.

Lim, R. K. S. (1970). "Pain." *Ann. Rev. Physiol.* **32**: 269–288.

Littler, T. S. (1965). **The Physics of the Ear.** "*Int. Ser. Mono. on Phys.*," Vol. 3. Long Island City, N. Y.: Pergamon Press, Inc.

Lowenstein, O. (1957). "The acoustico-lateralis system." In: **The Physiology of Fishes** (M. E. Brown, ed.), Vol. 2, pp. 155–186. New York: Academic Press, Inc.

Lowenstein, O. and A. Sand (1940). "The individual and integrated activity of the semicular canals of the elasmobranch labyrinth." *J. Physiol.* (London) **99**: 89–101.

Lowenstein, O. and A. Sand (1940). "The

mechanism of the semicircular canals. A study of the responses of single-fibre preparations to angular accelerations and to rotation at constant speed." *Proc. Roy. Soc.* (London) **B129**: 256–275.

Mountcastle, V. and I. Darian-Smith (1968). "Neural mechanisms in somesthesia." In: **Medical Physiology** (V. Mountcastle, ed.), Vol. 2, pp. 1372–1423. St. Louis, Mo.: The C. V. Mosby Company.

Neuhaus, W. (1956). "Die Unterscheidungsfähigkeit des Hundes für Duftgemische." *Z. vergl. Physiol.* **39**: 25–43.

Payne, R. S. (1961). "The acoustical localization of prey by the barn owl." *Am. Zool.* **1**: 379.

Poulter, T. C. (1963). "Sonar signals of the sea lion." *Science* **139**: 753–754.

Pringle, J. W. S. (1938). "Mechanoreceptors on the palps and campaniform sensilla on the legs of cockroaches." *J. Exp. Biol.* **15**: 101–138.

Pringle, J. W. S. (1957). **Insect Flight.** New York: Cambridge University Press. 132 pp.

Pringle, J. W. S. (1968). "Comparative physiology of the flight motor." *Adv. Insect Physiol.* **5**: 163–227.

Prosser, C. L. and F. A. Brown (1961). **Comparative Animal Physiology,** 2nd ed. Philadelphia: W. B. Saunders Company. 688 pp.

Pumphrey, R. J. (1950). "Hearing." *Symp. Soc. Exp. Biol.* **4**: 3–18.

Pye, J. D. (1963). "Mechanisms of echolocation." *Ergeb. Biol.* **26**: 12–20.

Rabe, W. (1953). "Beitrage zum Orientierungsproblem der Wasserwanzen." *Z. vergl. Physiol.* **35**: 300–325.

Roeder, K. D. (1963). **Nerve Cells and Insect Behavior.** Cambridge, Mass.: Harvard University Press.

Roeder, K. D. (1964). "Aspects of the noctuid tympanic organ having significance in the avoidance of bats." *J. Insect. Physiol.* **10**: 529–546.

Roeder, K. D. and R. S. Payne (1966). "Acoustic orientation of a moth in flight by means of two sense cells." *Symp. Soc. Exp. Biol.* **20**: 251–272.

Rose, J. and V. Mountcastle, (1959). "Touch and kinesthetics." In: **Handbook of Physiology** (H. W. Magoun, ed.), Section 1, Vol. 1, pp. 387–430. Washington, D. C.: American Physiological Society.

Schneider, D. (1964a). "Insect antennae." *Ann. Rev. Entomol.* **9**: 103–122.

Schneider, D. (1964b). "Vergleichende Rezeptorphysiologie am Beispeil der Riechorgane von Insekten." *Jahruch* 1963 *der Max Planck Gesellschaft.* 150–177.

Schöne, H. (1954). "Statozystenfunktion und statische Lageorientierung bei dekapoden Krebsen." *Z. vergl. Physiol.* **36**: 241–260.

Teichmann, H. (1959). "Uber die Leistung des Geruchssinnes beim Aal [*Anguilla anguilla* (L.)]." *Z. vergl. Physiol.* **42**: 206–254.

Treat, A. E. and K. D. Roeder (1959). "A nervous element of unknown function in the tympanic organ of moths." *J. Insect Physiol.* **3**: 262–270.

von Uexküll, J. (1908). "Studien über Tonus. V. Die Libellen," *Z. Biol.* **50**: 168–202.

Webster, F. A. (1963). "Active energy radiating systems: the bat and ultrasonic principles. II. acoustical control of airborne interceptions by bats." In: *Proc. Inter. Cong. Technology and Blindness*, Vol. 1, pp. 49–135 New York: American Foundation for the Blind.

Webster, D. B. (1966). "Ear structure and function in modern mammals." *Am. Zool.* **3**: 451–466.

Weis-Fogh, T. (1956a). "Biology and physics of locust flight. II. Flight performance of the desert locust (*Schistocerca gregaria*)." *Phil. Trans. Roy. Soc.* (London) **B239**: 459–510.

Weis-Fogh, T. (1956b). "Biology and physics of locust flight. IV. Notes on sensory mechanisms in locust flight. *Phil. Trans. Roy. Soc.* (London) **B239**: 553–584.

Weis-Fogh, T. (1964). "Control of basic movements in flying insects." *Symp. Soc. Exp. Biol.* **18**: 343–361.

Wever, E. G. (1966). "Electrical potentials of the cochlea." *Physiol. Rev.* **46**: 102–127.

Wiener, N. (1961). **Cybernetics.** Cambridge, Mass.: The Massachussetts Institute of Technology Press. 2nd ed. 212 pp.

Wilson, D. M. (1961). "The central nervous control of flight in a locust." *J. Exp. Biol.* **38**: 471–490.

Wilson, D. M. (1968). "The nervous control of insect flight and related behavior." *Adv. Insect Physiol.* **5**: 289–338.

Zotterman, Y. (1959). "Thermal sensations." In: **Handbook of Physiology** (H. W. Magoun, ed.), Section 1, Vol. 1, pp. 431–458. Washington, D. C.: American Physiological Society.

Chronobiology

20-1. Physiological Rhythms. In microorganisms, plants, and animals, a wide variety of biochemical, physiological, and behavioral activities have been shown to occur with a reproducible regularity such that peaks of activity occur at regular intervals. Halberg (1969) uses the term **chronobiology** for the temporal aspects of all types of biological phenomenon.

Many physiological changes occur with a reproducible waveform. For convenience, these can be divided into three major groups. There are high frequency rhythms where the period τ (the reciprocal of frequency) is less than about 30 minutes. Examples of such high frequency rhythms are respiratory rates, heart rates, and waves of the EEG. There are also low frequency rhythms with periods ranging from about 6 days to a year or more. For example, menstruation in human females is a biological rhythm with a period of about 28 days (Chapter 11).

Of greatest concern here are medial frequency rhythms whose period lies between thirty minutes and about 6 days. Of special interest are **circadian rhythms**, patterns of activity with a period of about 24 hours (20 to 28 hours being the usual range). Although initially many rhythms were thought to have a period of exactly 24 hours, to coincide with the 24 hour day night cycle of the terrestrial day, it was found that few periods of biological rhythms are of 24 hour duration and the term circadian, meaning about a day, was coined to describe these periodic activities (Halberg, 1959). Circadian rhythms are exhibited in such diverse activities as cell metabolism, behavioral activities, color changes, or whole-animal activity in metabolism or locomotion.

20-2. Endogenous Circadian Rhythms. Although it was originally thought that circadian rhythms were imposed by stimuli resulting from the day-night cycle, it has now been shown that such periodic activities are endogenous, that is, they exist because of internal mechanisms in the animal or plant. They do not require external stimulation for their continuance.

Chapter 20

Chronobiology, Biological Clocks, and Animal Communication

For example, the cockroach *Blaberus* exhibits, as do many other animals, a circadian rhythm of peak running activity. When the cockroach is placed in a controlled environment (in this case constant temperature and constant illumination, preferably constant darkness), the circadian rhythm of peak running activity occurs unabated. A peak of running activity occurs every 24 hours, 34 minutes. The absolute magnitude of the activity may change, but the time at which each peak arises does not change (see Harker, 1964). Such rhythm, maintained under constant conditions, is known as a free running rhythm.

This is not to say, however, that under maintained abnormal conditions the period of the rhythm will not change. When the cockroach is kept in continuous light, for example, the period of the rhythm will change after several days and become 24 hours, 42 minutes. This new period is retained during the duration of continuous light. This is not a loss of rhythm, only a change in period. In these experiments, the rhythmic activity itself cannot be caused by either temperature or illumination because these are both constant factors incapable of acting as stimuli. Aschoff (1958) concluded that constant light causes a decrease in the normal period of a rhythm in diurnal animals and an increase in the normal period of the rhythms of nocturnal animals. The intensity of a background factor may also have some influence on the periodicity of a rhythm. For example, in many cases the decrease in the period of a rhythm of a diurnal animal is smaller as increasing intensities of light are used.

Although these experiments point out that changes in light or temperature are not the stimuli that produce a circadian rhythm, there are many other factors in the environment which might do so. If no environmental factors are found to cause the rhythm, then the rhythm is endogenous and caused by some internal mechanism with a built-in periodicity. Such mechanisms are referred to generally as **biological clocks**. A biological clock not only permits an animal to determine the time of

day, it also permits the animal to make actual time measurements. This statement will be amplified in the following sections.

Brown (1960, 1969) believes that rhythms are maintained by some external factors in the environment. In his work he used the fiddler crab *Uca*, which exhibits color changes due to chromatophore activity. This color change is basically a circadian rhythm, although it is influenced by other periodicities as well. Generally these crabs pale in the early evening and darken at about daybreak, remaining in the darkened condition during the day. When *Uca* is placed in the dark at constant temperature, the rhythmic variation in shading persists for as long as two months, although no clues from either light or temperature changes are available to it. Nor does the rhythm depend on changes in barometric pressure or humidity (these undergo daily alterations, as do most natural factors in the environment). When crabs are maintained under conditions of constant light, constant temperature, constant barometric pressure, and constant humidity, the circadian rhythm of color change persists. Brown thought that changes in cosmic radiation intensity might be responsible for the rhythm; but when animals are placed in deep salt mines, where the cosmic radiation can be considered constant, the rhythms are still maintained. For example, honey bees visit flowers or a feeding station at a given time of day, and this circadian rhythm can be conditioned by training. A colony of bees placed in a salt mine under constant light and temperature showed no alteration in their time of feeding and visited the feeders (which were kept empty) at the same time they were accustomed to at the surface (Renner, 1957). It appears that Brown's original idea that some external factor was responsible for maintaining the rhythm is not correct (at least in those cases examined thoroughly). However, see Brown et al., 1970.

When bees reared in Paris were transported to New York, the bees continued to visit empty feeders at the hour they were accustomed to do so in Paris. Local conditions imposed no change on this circadian rhythm although the timing of environmental factors is quite different in New York because of the change in latitude and longitude.

Biological clocks are not temperature-dependent, that is, within the physiological temperature range increases or decreases in temperature do not increase or decrease the period of a rhythm. This is to be expected, if poikilothermic animals, for example, depend for survival on an accurate timing mechanism. Pigment changes in fiddler crabs continue with a rhythm of normal periodicity between temperatures of about 3°C and 36°C.

Circadian rhythms are not completely temperature insensitive. Most are stopped when very low temperatures are reached. For example, when fiddler crabs are placed in sea water at about 2°C and left there for 6 hours and then rewarmed to room temperature, it is found that the rhythm of color change, although continuing with the same period, has been set back by six hours. It is as though the biological clock had been stopped by the low temperature and, when restarted by warming, was able to keep the same time but was six hours slow. One of the difficulties of analyzing the mechanism of biological clocks is to find a biological system that is not sensitive to temperature until low temperatures are reached. The temperature coefficients of biological systems are usually above 1, but that of the biological clock is 1 or less. It has been suggested that biological clocks depend on an alteration of processes with different temperature coefficients (Bünning, 1964).

The presence of circadian rhythms means that homeostasis cannot imply that some internal variable is maintained at a constant level. Rather, a variable is held within a given range of values with peaks and troughs occurring at particular times of day. For example, the body temperature of mammals undergoes a normal circadian rhythm under controlled (as well as natural) conditions. It may also be noted that isolated tissues or organs can maintain their circadian rhythms. For example, isolated segments of hamster intestine undergo circadian rhythms of peak contraction, a rhythm which is also independent of temperature in a certain physiological temperature range (Bünning, 1964).

20-3. Entrainment, Synchronization, and Zeitgebers. All circadian rhythms are considered to be endogenous rhythms, but this does not mean that under certain conditions their periods or amplitudes of peak activity cannot be changed by environmental factors. In fact, such changes are necessary since a circadian rhythm being less than or greater than 24-hours will soon get out of step with the light-dark cycle of the earth's day. For example, a nocturnal animal whose peak activity occurs during the night, simply by following a circadian rhythm would find itself active during the day. In nature, therefore, an animal that is drifting out of synchronization with its environment must become resynchronized. The circadian rhythm must be **entrained** to the 24-hour day. Entrainment is the process by which a periodic repetition of light and dark, or a periodic temperature cycle, causes a circadian rhythm to remain synchronized with the same period as the entraining factor cycle (Bruce, 1960).

Light and temperature cycles are the dominant factors in such entrainment, although other environmental factors may also play a role in some animals. For example, as a result of periodic mechanical stimulation by waves on the shore, a beach isopod *Excirolana chiltoni* becomes entrained in its activity cycles with the tides.

Most circadian rhythms so far studied cannot be entrained to artificial light-dark cycles shorter than about 16 hours. In most cases the duration of the light-dark cycle must be longer than this. Activity periods in mice, for example, can be entrained only when the light-dark cycle has a duration of 21 to 27 hours. Bees cannot be trained to come to food when the duration of the light-dark cycle is other than 24 hours, although the exact time of day can be determined by training.

That circadian rhythms are both endogenous and inherited has been clearly shown in the case of lizards (Hoffman, 1957, 1959).

Lizards hatched from eggs kept under constant conditions of light and temperature (so that these factors are not influencing the developing embryo) show a good circadian rhythm of activity. Lizard eggs kept on an 18 hour artificial day (9 hours light, 9 hours dark) upon transferal to constant conditions of light and temperature produced lizards with the same circadian rhythm as lizards from eggs kept on a 36 hour artificial day (18 hours light, 18 hours dark). That is, differences in the treatment of eggs made no differences in the subsequent behavioral activity of the lizards. One of the best indications that circadian rhythms are endogenous arises from the observation that in a population of lizards, the period of the rhythm varies slightly from individual to individual. This would not be the case if the period were established by a cycling of external factors. It also indicates that endogenous rhythms are based on the particular biological clock of an individual, in accordance with the principle that internal variables within a species have a range of values depending on the precise genetic make-up of each individual, as well as its past history, present state, and so forth.

Any factor that acts as a stimulus for synchronizing an endogenous rhythm with the external environment is a **zeitgeber** (= cue or synchronizer). The chief zeitgebers are temperature and light. For example, in the fruit fly *Drosophila* it is advantageous for eclosion (emergence from the pupae) to occur just before sunrise, when the newly emerged insects will not be exposed to the sunlight immediately. This timing prevents their desiccation because their cuticles are not hardened and waterproofed upon emergence. When fruit fly cultures are maintained for a long period under conditions of constant darkness, it is found that eclosion occurs asynchronously in the population, that is, flies emerge from the pupae at random times of day. However, one exposure of the pupae to light (a flash as brief as 1/1200 second can be used) acts as a zeitgeber and causes a synchronization of eclosion in the population. Eclosion is so synchronized that emergence

occurs at some multiple of 24 hours after the light stimulus. The light, in essence, is analogous to a sunrise and emergence of pupae now will occur 24, 48, 72, and so on, hours after the zeitgeber at what would be the next sunrise (see Pittendrigh and Bruce, 1957). Examples of many circadian rhythms as well as detailed discussion of synchronization and phasing of rhythms are discussed in Bünning (1964); Harker (1964); Sollberger (1965); Richter (1965); Aschoff (1965).

20-4. Nature of Some Circadian Rhythms. The analysis of experimental data to detect the presence of circadian and other rhythms is not an easy task. In an interesting paper on this topic Cole (1957) was able to generate a circadian rhythm for the unicorn in numbers selected from a table of random numbers. In addition to the normal difficulties of devising proper experimental and control situations, the analysis of frequency data requires good statistical methods and the proper frequency analysis (Batschelet, 1965; Halberg, 1969).

Periodic rhythms other than circadian may be present, and their effects augment or hide a circadian rhythm. Marine organisms living in tidal zones often have periods of activity that are the result of a combination of both a circadian and a tidal rhythm (tidal rhythms have a period of 12.4 hours and occur 50 minutes later each day). This is true, for example, of the color changes in fiddler crabs which occur 50 minutes later each day. The color change is greatest in amplitude when the peaks of both circadian and tidal rhythms coincide every 15 days.

The small pelagic fish *Leuesthes tenuis* (grunion fish) of the North American Pacific coast makes use of the spring tides that occur in the months of April through June in its reproductive behavior. At the times of these highest tides, the grunion ride the waves onto the beach and deposit eggs and sperm in the sand. During the next 15 days, the embryos develop on the beach at a level where no waves from normal tides reach. At the end of this period the next spring tide occurs, and the young fish which have now developed sufficiently to hatch are washed out to sea by the waves which now reach their place of development (Clark, 1925). Here is a case where the development time is such that it matches the period between highest tides and thus permits development in a suitable environment.

It is now recognized that although the duration of the terrestrial year has not changed during past ages, there have been changes in the duration of the day, week, and month. Very ancient (now fossil) animals must have experienced circadian rhythms of shorter or longer duration than those of present animals. Measurements of fossil growth rates, for example, that of coral reefs, indicate that circadian rhythms were different (Lamar and Merifield, 1967; Pannella and MacClintock, 1967; Runcorn, 1964; Scrutton, 1964).

The nature of biological clocks is not known. They have some of the properties of physical oscillators, and several models of biological clocks have been developed based on the properties of such oscillators. These are of two types: harmonic oscillators (pendulums) have frequencies which are relatively insensitive to the influence of external factors, although their amplitudes are changed easily; relaxation oscillators have amplitudes which are insensitive to external influences, although their frequencies are readily changed. Although the harmonic oscillator is characterized by a sinusoidal wave, that of relaxation oscillators is more angular and can be synchronized more readily and over a wider range of frequencies. Biological clocks appear to fall somewhere in between these two types of physical oscillators, and evidence can be found for either model. There is a danger in describing endogenous rhythms and their mechanisms in terms of relatively simple physical devices, and such models have not solved the problem of what processes are at work in cells, tissues, organs, and whole animals to produce endogenous rhythms.

Single cells usually show several endogenous rhythms. *Gonyaulax* exhibits circadian rhythms in its bioluminescence, metabolism,

and reproductive behavior (Hasting, 1964). At one point it was hypothesized that DNA or RNA might be molecules responsible for endogenous rhythms because bursts of ultraviolet light affect the nucleic acids of the cells and can also alter rhythms in single-celled organisms. But visible light which is a zeitgeber of many rhythms has no direct effect on nucleic acids. It is probably a mistake to ascribe to any single molecule the activities that result in such complex actions as biological clocks possess.

Communication and Navigation in Bees

20-5. Navigation and Biological Clocks. Many animals make use of their biological clocks for the purpose of navigation. In this discussion I shall concentrate on the work done with bees because these insects exemplify the use of many sensory systems and communications systems to produce complex behavior. Kalmus (1964) reviews animal navigation generally. The information given here is taken primarily from the monograph by von Frisch (1967).

Navigation is used almost synonymously in many cases with animal orientation, especially with respect to sun navigation or sun orientation. Sun compass orientation resides in the ability of many animals to determine direction based on the position of the sun and the ability to use a biological clock and an internal computing system to determine the position the sun should have and the changes in the sun's position during the day. Navigation usually refers to the determination of an animal's latitude and longitude by celestial navigation—by the position of sun, moon, or stars. All navigational mechanisms are of value in migration to a better environment or in activities such as homing or traveling between a food supply and home territory.

Bees are useful organisms for studies on navigation or communication. They are social animals that move out from the hive or colony on regular foraging expeditions. When food is found, the worker returns to the hive with loads of nectar or pollen and communicates to other workers the necessary information to allow them to find the food source. Such information includes distance and direction to the food and its quantity and quality. Because workers, especially scouts, move so regularly between hive and food, it becomes possible to study readily the features of this behavior. In addition, individual bees may be marked, for example, by coloring, so that their behavior can easily be followed.

Bees are readily trained to come to a rich source of food by putting out containers of sugar water. It is found that bees will come to such a food source at a given time of day. Bees have a good time sense. Their biological clocks permit them to determine the time of day and are also used in their navigation. Figure 20-2 illustrates generally the nature of sun compass reactions and points out that an animal orients its movements because of its ability to determine the angle it must maintain between the sun and the food source or hive in order to arrive at the proper location. This assumption implies an ability to compute where the sun should be at any given time of day. Most animals use the azimuth of a celestial body for its navigation (the azimuth is the angle between the vertical plane through a celestial body and the meridian; the altitude of the sun or other body is not usually part of the information used by an animal.)

Bees trained on Long Island to go to food pots located in a particular direction from the hive (at a particular time of day), when transferred to Davis, California, were found to emerge from the hive 24 hours after the training time, showing that they were able to keep track of time. The direction of search for food, however, shifted from that used on Long Island, and the amount of the shift in direction was the difference between the azimuth of the sun at Davis and that at Long Island at the time of food searching. The bees had no way of knowing that they had been moved to a locale where the azimuth of the sun at a given time of day was different from that of Long Island; they behaved correctly

except for using a wrong local time. Azimuth was the same at the same local time, but not the same bee time.

Bees do not have to see the sun to be able to navigate. They can do so on completely overcast days. Part of this ability is based on their capabilities in determining the plane of polarized light that, in turn, depends on the sun's position in the sky. Bees can detect differences of about $2.5°$ in the direction of polarized light, and it is interesting that this is the angle of acceptance of the ommatidia of the bee's compound eye (see Chapter 17). Bees, under natural conditions, depend heavily, as do most navigating animals, on visual observation of landmarks. Bees on their way to a food source, for example, will often fly out of the direct flight path in order to pass over some feature of the terrain that has become familiar to them.

Sun compass orientation has been found in a variety of arthropods Pardi and Papi, 1952). Kramer (1949, 1952) showed, in some classical experiments, that starlings also were capable of sun navigation, and this ability has now been recognized in many other birds.

20-6. Bee Dances. von Frisch found that scout bees (the members of a hive that go foraging for new food supplies), after finding a good food source, returned to the hive and could communicate information about the food source to the other workers. This communication takes the form of dances upon the hive. In these dances bees make use of their biological clocks, their distance and direction determining mechanisms, their sense of gravity, and their sense of sound.

When a scout finds food within a distance of about 10 meters of the colony, she returns to the hive and may initiate a round dance in which she runs in a circle of small diameter on the vertical face of the hive comb. In this dance there are sudden reversals of direction and then turnings back to the original direction (Figure 20-1). The dance may last only a second or may continue for several minutes. The dance occurs only in the midst of a cluster of bees, never on an empty or sparsely

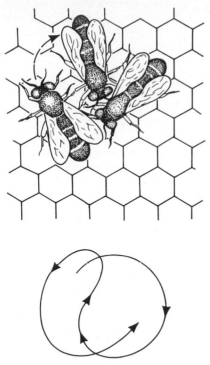

Figure 20-1 The round dance of the worker honeybee is performed on a vertical face of the hive comb. This dance is performed when food is found at short distances from the hive. This dance signals distances, not directions, of food sources.

occupied comb. The dancer is followed by a train of 2 to 8 other bees that extend their antennae and attempt to hold them in contact with the dancer's adomen. After the dance is ended, these workers turn away and prepare to fly out from the hive.

Such a round dance indicates to other workers that a good food supply is present at a relatively short distance from the hive. It is basically an indication that food at an already known source is in good supply. When other bees do not know the exact location of the food, they fly out in all directions searching for it.

In a hive where bees are feeding only on natural flowers, each group of bees has its own preferred flower and, in fact, bees which have fed on one flower, may remain in the hive when that particular flower is not available.

The round dancer attracts only the bees which are feeding on the type of food that the dancer has found. The dancer has picked up a smell of a given food, and that smell is the attractant for her group bees. Only these group bees go out after the food. The bees may not know where the food is, but they go out searching because they know that what they want is close by.

When food is found further away—about 100 meters or more from the hive—the returning scout begins a **tail-waggling dance**. This is also performed on the vertical face of combs inside the hive. In the waggle dance the bee runs straight ahead for a given distance, returns in a semicircle to the starting point, again runs through the straight part, describes a semicircle in the opposite direction, and so on. The straight part of the dance is accompanied by a wagging of the abdomen at a frequency of 13 to 15 waggles per second.

The angle of the straight segment of the dance from the vertical gives the angle between the sun and the food supply (See Figure 20-2). This angle changes during the duration of the dance as the dancer compensates for the movement of the sun across the sky (the dance may last for 30 minutes). The dancer is accompanied by a group of followers who, as in the case of the round dance, extend their antennae and attempt to make contact with the dancer. These followers must translate the angle of the straight segment of the dance with the vertical into the angle between sun and food supply. This is the angle they must follow to find the food. To dance at a given angle from the vertical requires that the dancer make use of gravity receptors and a computer that converts the sun compass angle into a vertical angle. Furthermore, the nervous system must make the necessary changes in this angle as time passes and the angle between sun and food is changing.

In addition to direction, the waggle dance also indicates the distance of the food from the hive. This information is carried in the tempo of waggles during the straight segment, although the time of each circling movement is also correlated with distance. In addition,

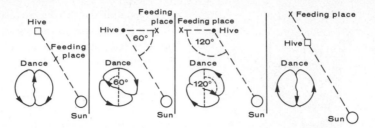

Figure 20-2 The waggle dance of the honeybee worker is also performed on the vertical face of a hive comb (inside the dark hive). The direction of the waggle run across the diameter of the circle of the dance provides information about the direction of the discovered food source from the hive. Note that the following bee must transpose the angle of the dance to the vertical to an angle relative to the sun when it sets out to find the food. These dances are persistent, and the angle of the waggle run changes as the sun travels across the sky. Usually persistent dances are used to communicate the finding of a suitable site for a new hive. [After von Frisch (1953).]

during the waggle run the dancer makes a series of buzzing sounds at about 2.5 times the rate of waggles (Esch and Esch, 1965; Wenner, 1964). The frequency of the sounds is about 300 to 400 cps. The sounds are produced from the thorax, where the flight muscles are located and might possibly represent an intent to fly without actually flying, thus acting as a stimulatory agent on the other workers.

The distance of food from the hive is determined only by the outward path to the food and is based on energy expended, not on actual distance. If the dancer was forced to fly against the wind or to fly up a hill, the resultant dance is given in terms of the flight energy used (Wenner, 1962; Bisetzky, 1957). If a bee is forced to walk to food several feet away, upon returning to the hive its waggle dance indicates that food is a long distance away because the energy a bee uses to walk is much greater than that needed for flying.

If the waggle dance or the round dance is of long duration, it is interrupted one or more times. During these pauses the dancer distributes the contents of its honey stomach to the followers. The honey stomach is a pouch into which a worker deposits some honey (food) before each foraging flight. The amount of honey placed in this stomach is directly proportional to the distance from hive to food (Istomina-Tsvetkova, 1960). It can serve as an energy supply for long flights. Pauses in the dance are initiated by sounds produced by

the followers. This squeaking is regarded by von Frisch as a demand for the delivery of a food sample. When a tape recording of such squeaking is played at high intensity through a hive, all the workers become motionless. It is probable that under natural conditions the sound is effective only when followers are in physical contact with the dancer. The pause perhaps allows followers to smell the food particles brought back by the dancer. The antennae contain the sensory receptors for hearing and for olfaction.

When food is not abundant at a source, the dancer performs a silent dance with no sound production during the waggle run. Under these conditions the follower bees do not go out to seek the food.

Thus a series of movements and sounds are used to communicate the presence and source of food to other workers. Scouts also communicate the location of possible sites for a new hive when bees are swarming. Such dances often last several days, and except for duration are similar to the food waggle dances. During the course of these very long dances it has been shown that the vertical angle of the straight segment alters day and night to keep pace with the movements of the sun (Lindauer, 1961).

20-7. Homing and Migration in Other Animals. Homing and migration have been extensively studied in birds because many are noted either for homing or long distance migration. These activities are directed toward some goal. In many cases the goal itself is out of sensory contact with the animal. Although visual clues and celestial navigation are important orientational mechanisms, a variety of other mechanisms must also be used. As indicated several times already, animals have a large number of sensory modalities, and the more of these an animal can use in orientation, the greater are its chances of selecting the proper behavioral activity.

Homing pigeons have received wide attention, although much of the work has been concerned with proving (or disproving) that they utilize celestial navigation exclusively in their homing (see Matthews, 1955). One difficulty in experimental work with free flying organisms has been to follow their flight paths successfully. Recently the use of airplanes, helicopters, miniature radio transmitters, and other telemetric devices has aided in overcoming this difficulty.

It has been found that pigeons use compass orientation, bicoordinate navigation, and landmark orientation to reach their home (Michener and Walcott, 1966). Strong winds do not deter birds from their true course; nor does atmospheric visibility have any great effect on orientation; the time of day does not greatly affect the path taken; and landmarks more than 5 miles from the flight path are generally ignored. Pigeons appear to initiate their flights by using sun compass orientation. If such a course proves incorrect, the birds stop or make abrupt turns. Only within about 5 miles of home do landmarks appear to play any role in the orientation.

Many birds migrate during the night. Although Sauer (1957, 1960) by using an artificial sky projected by a star projector in a planetarium obtained some evidence that warblers orient by star navigation, his results are not accepted by other workers (see, Schmidt-Koenig, 1964). As yet there is no satisfactory explanation for bird migration over long distances at night or over oceans, where visual clues are minimal.

It has sometimes been suggested that animals can orient to the earth's magnetic field. But at present the only conclusive evidence for such orientation has been found in the activity of the snail *Nassarius*, which appears to orient to weak magnetic fields (Brown et al., 1960). The phase of the moon and time of day could be correlated with variations in this response, but the role of such orientation under natural conditions is questionable, and the receptors for such weak magnetic fields are not known.

Chemical Communication and Pheromones

20-8. Chemoreception. Chemoreception is the ability to detect chemicals (ions or molecules) in the environment. Detection of chemicals in a gas phase is **olfaction** (smell), and the detection of chemicals in a liquid phase is **gustation** (taste). Olfaction is of important adaptive significance because this mode of chemical detection can permit molecules from relatively great distances (borne on wind or water currents) to be sensed. The division of chemoreception into taste and smell is appropriate in vertebrates because the receptors for the two activities differ morphologically and send impulses to different parts of the brain. This division is not always justified for chemoreceptors of invertebrates.

All chemoreceptors of invertebrates and most of those in vertebrates are primary sense cells—usually bipolar neurons. The taste buds of vertebrates are secondary sense cells. Chemoreception is almost a universal sensory modality among animals. Even the bacterium *Escherichia coli* exhibits chemotactic behavior (Adler, 1966 a, b; Baracchini and Sherris, 1959). By their metabolism bacteria create gradients of nutrients or oxygen and then respond by moving (using their motile flagellae) toward regions of higher oxygen or nutrient concentration. These bacteria can move in straight lines over distances many times their body length and can also reverse direction.

Chemoreceptors in invertebrates are usually separate single cells, often scattered through the surface epithelium. Sensory organs are common only in higher invertebrates and vertebrates. Discussions of chemoreception in various animal groups are found in Milne and Milne (1962); Moncrieff (1951); Prosser and Brown (1961).

Chemoreception is the basis for many behavioral activities of animals, including communication. Although fundamental uses of chemoreception include the seeking of food and avoidance of noxious environments, it may also be used to detect the location of adequate humidity environments or suitable drinking water; and in many animals secreted chemicals serve as sexual attractants for the opposite sex. Chemicals are used to lure prey or to drive away predators. Chemoreception has been extensively studied in insects because of the economic importance of discovering insect attractants or repellants and because insect chemoreceptor systems are more amenable to physiological investigation than those of most other animals.

Very little is known about the mechanism of action at chemoreceptive sites. Puzzling problems remain concerning the specificity (or lack of it) found in chemoreceptors, the molecular nature of chemoreception, and the nature of the coordinating and integrating mechanisms that can make chemoreception such a selective sensory modality.

Flies such as *Phormia* are useful experimental animals for both behavioral and electrophysiological analysis of contact chemoreception (taste). When the chemoreceptors of the tarsi contact a solution containing an acceptable substance, the mouthparts (proboscis) are immediately extended. This is the initial feeding action. Large numbers of flies can be tested rapidly, and therefore good quantitative data on taste can be obtained (flies are mounted on small glass rods by fixing them in place with warm wax, and then fine brushes with the test solutions are brought into contact with the tarsi and the proboscis response noted). Flies are always first tested with water to ensure that they are not simply thirsty. It is possible to determine which substances are acceptable as well as which rejected, and

the threshold concentrations required to elicit a response can be determined.

The lowest concentration of a solute that produces proboscis extension is the **behavioral threshold** of that substance. This is not necessarily identical with the **receptor threshold**, the lowest concentration of a solute which causes the production of a receptor potential. A variety of factors determine whether or not a given molecule or molecular class can stimulate a chemoreceptor, for example, although the properties of sugar molecules are basically similar, flies reject triose and tetrose sugars but accept hexoses and disaccharides. Heptoses are also rejected. In a given class of sugars there are found different thresholds of acceptance. Among the hexoses D-fructose has a behavioral threshold of 0.0058 M; glucose 0.132 M; and mannose 7.59 M. Disaccharide behavioral thresholds range from 0.0098 for sucrose to 5.01 M for cellobiose. There is a difference in the acceptability of stereo isomers. For example, α-D-methyl glucose has a behavioral threshold of 0.069 M while β-D-methyl glucose is not acceptable at any concentration.

The oil-solubility of molecules is another factor involved in the stimulation of receptors. In a given family of molecules, those with longer chains (lower water solubility) show higher thresholds. This correlation may be related to the lipoprotein nature of cell membranes.

Behavioral experiments suffer the defect of measuring only responses initiated by a population of sensory cells. They cannot answer questions concerning the distribution of sensory cell classes in a given population nor can they determine the response range of single receptors. Electrophysiological recording methods are suited for determining responses of single receptors.

Of the several neurons present in certain sensory hair cells of *Phormia* (and other flies as well), one is found to be specific in its response in that only carbohydrates can produce electrical activity in this neuron. One neuron responds only to salts. Impulses from this neuron are the largest and most readily identifiable of all chemoreceptor neurons. The salt cell responds to both anions and cations, although Ca^{2+} inhibits it. It is also stimulated by procaine and other anesthetics, although these agents block dendritic conduction (Wolbarsht and Hanson, 1965). Another neuron is a water receptor, and the effective stimulus is distilled water. The neuron is inhibited by sugars and salts in concentrations as low as 0.01 M (Evans and Mellon, 1962).

Although there are four neurons present in these chemoreceptors in flies, only 3 taste modalities have been discovered. The function of the fourth neuron is not known.

Olfactory receptors in insects have received attention, and the measurement of cell potential changes has shown that a substance may produce excitation (a positive potential), may have no effect on cell potential, or may inhibit it (making the cell potential more negative). In some cases three neighboring receptors may each show one of these responses. Some receptors of olfaction in insects are highly specific. Olfactory cells on the long antennal hair sensillum of the silkmoth respond only to sexual attractants (see Section 20-9). Measurements of the sensitivity of these receptors in *Bombyx* showed that about 90 molecules had to strike the antennal sensory organ per second to elicit an impulse in one cell. On the basis of the dosages used only about 40 cells out of the 40,000 total were hit by one molecule per second. It appears likely that a cell is struck only once, and therefore, a single molecule striking a receptor cell is sufficient to change its potential. To elicit a behavioral response about 1,200 molecular impacts were needed (Boeckj et al., 1966). The dendritic regions of chemoreceptor cells are usually exposed to the atmosphere through minute pores in the sensillum in order that molecules can impact on these areas.

It is difficult to analyze taste and smell experimentally even in humans (Lettvin and Gesteland, 1966). In mammals and most other vertebrates, taste buds are specialized organs for responding to chemicals in solution. They are generally located on the dorsal surface of the tongue, although in fish they are distributed over the body surface. A taste bud is composed of goblet-shaped clusters of 30 to 40 columnar epithelial cells (secondary sense cells). Epithelial cells about 200 μ below the surface continually undergo mitotic division, and the daughter cells move toward the surface. As these differentiating cells move upward, small cytoplasmic granules (1,000 to 1,500 Å in diameter) appear and move toward the cell periphery and then discharge their contents into the intercellular spaces (Matoltsky and Parckkal, 1965). This material forms a protective coating over the surface epithelium and prevents substances from reaching the developing cells and nerve endings beneath the surface. An experimental preparation of mammalian taste buds is made by treating the tongue with collagenase, after which the surface layer including taste buds can be stripped off and a bag of sensory epithelium formed. Different solutes can be placed on one side and their rate of penetration through the epithelium determined. The cells in human taste buds normally have a life of about 10 days. They are worn away due to mechanical disturbances and replaced by new cells from below.

The apical ends of the sense cells project microvilli into tiny taste pores and serve as connections to the fluid on the tongue surface. The bottom of the taste pore is sealed with a dense material. There are about 12,000 taste buds in man. The sensory cells are innervated by nerve fibers that lose their myelin sheaths as they pass through the basement membrane. Large fibers end on two or more receptor cells, and the endings of small fibers invaginate the receptor cell membrane. Both types of fibers have terminals filled with synaptic vesicles and mitochondria.

The distribution of taste buds is such that there is a region of high density of sensory endings with a high sensitivity to chemoreception; other regions of the tongue are insensitive to most chemicals. How different tastes arise is not known. It is often assumed that the character of each taste cell is determined during its differentiation by the particular nerve fiber that innervates it. This is based on the hypothesis that a given axon can provide information only about one taste sensation

771

and that all cells innervated by a given axon respond to only one type of chemical. These are unproven concepts at present.

Humans have four basic taste sensations: sweet, sour, bitter, and salt. The tip of the tongue is most sensitive to sweet, the sides to sour, and the back to bitter substances. Salt sensitivity is distributed over most of the receptor surfaces. Electrophysiological recording has shown that single receptors can respond to all or some of these types of substances. Several vertebrates, including primates other than man, can also detect distilled water. Dogs can taste sugars but not saccharine, whereas pigeons respond to saccharine but not sugars. Cats and chickens show no response to either sugars or saccharine. Thus variations in sensitivity to various classes of molecules are found in the vertebrates.

Olfaction in vertebrates is more complicated a phenomenon than taste. Olfactory endings are located at the back of the nose, covered by a sheet of mucous. In humans there are up to 20 million olfactory receptors, each terminates in about 20 cilialike filaments. These are primary sense cells and send axons directly to the brain. The nasal epithelium also contains bare nerve endings from fibers of the trigeminal nerve. These endings are responsive to chemicals, often to ones different from those which excite the olfactory endings. The number of modalities of olfaction is immense; as many as 10,000 different smells can be detected by humans. Although it is thought that the terminal cilia are receptor sites, the nature of olfactory reception is still unknown. One problem is that molecules quite different in size or structure may smell the same, whereas quite similar molecules may smell differently. Another problem is that olfactory cells are very small, and it has been difficult to obtain electrophysiological recordings from single cells. However such recordings have now been made from frogs (Tucker, 1963; Shibuya, 1964; Moulton, 1963; Lettvin and Gesteland, 1965). Single unit responses consist of spikes from single cells superimposed on a slow potential wave called the electroolfactogram (EOG). However no relationship has yet been found between the electrical responses and the various categories in olfactory responses.

Many odors can be detected by fish and mammals even although some of the test substances are never found normally in the environment. Animals such as the dog respond not only to pure odors but can also detect and distinguish between mixtures of odors (Neuhaus, 1956). Chemoreception is important to fish, and activities such as homing or migration are, in part at least, guided by recognition of home waters according to their chemical characteristics.

The civet *Viverra zibetha* secretes a pheromone (see Section 20-9) from an para-anal glandular pouch, and this substance is used for defense and also as a territory marker (Wilson and Bossert, 1963). The pheromone is civetone. The musk deer *Moschus moschiferus* produces a pheromone, muskone, which functions as a sexual attractant.

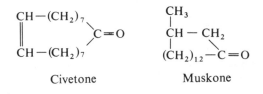

Civetone   Muskone

20-9. Pheromones and Chemical Communication in Insects. Chemical signals exchanged between individuals of the same species are **pheromones** and may be considered as hormones secreted outside the animal, which cause a specific reaction either in the form of a behavioral response or in a particular developmental process (Karlson, 1960). Although pheromones are usually considered as species-specific molecules, some chemicals are now known which are secreted by one species and are effective in stimulating other species.

With respect to communication, pheromones cause a variety of actions on the part of individuals. They may cause the dispersal or aggregation of a population. When populations of the flour beetle *Tribolium confusum* become dense, quinones released from the abdominal glands cause the individuals to disperse. This is essentially a negative chemotactic reaction to the released substance and serves to spread the population over a wider area with a better chance of obtaining food (see Naylor, 1959). Insect aggregation, through the action of pheromones, is exemplified by the behavior of honey bees and other social insects (Renner, 1960; von Frisch, 1967). When worker honeybees find a good source of food, they release pheromones from an abdominal scent gland to aid other workers in finding the food. Similar activity is found when a new hive is started. One component of the pheromone secretion is geraniol, but at least four other compounds are present (Bock and Schearer, 1962). Many insects including ants and bees lay trails for other members of their species or colony to follow by secreting and depositing substances as they travel (Cavill and Robertson, 1965; Lindauer, 1961).

Pheromones are important as sexual attractants. Although the honeybee queen (*Apis mellifera*) lacks the worker scent gland, she possesses other groups of glandular cells on the second, third, and fourth abdominal segments. These produce chemicals that act as sexual attractants. The queen bee also has mandibular glands that secrete 9-oxydecenoic acid, which attracts workers. The mandibular glands also produce the queen substance,

$$CH_3—CO—(CH_3)_5—CH=CH—COOH$$

If this substance is ingested, only sterile female workers are produced, but when the queen bee dies or is lost, the metabolism of the female workers is changed through endocrine activity, and new queens are produced (Butler et al., 1961). Similar actions are found in termite colonies (Lüscher, 1960).

Female silkworm moths (*Bombyx mori*) secrete a sexual attractant, bombykol:

$$CH_3—(CH_2)_3—CH=CH—CH=CH$$
$$—(CH_2)_8—CH_2OH$$

Only the antennal chemoreceptors of the male are excited by this substance, those of the female are insensitive. When sensed by the male, a behavior pattern is initiated such that the male flies to the female. Many studies have been made of the effectiveness of sexual attractants in the gypsy moth *Porthetria dispar*.

Females secrete the pheromone glyplure

$$CH_3—(CH_2)_5—CH—CH_2—CH=CH$$

with branches:

$$O \qquad (CH_2)_5$$
$$CO—CH_3 \qquad CH_2OH$$

Depending on wind speeds, gypsy moth females can attract males from up to 4,500 meters away.

The nature and requirements of pheromones is being studied. For different functions, there should be corresponding differences in the molecules. For example, a sexual attractant should be stable for relatively long periods because it is often used for communication over long distances. A molecule used as an alarm substance should have a shorter life. Compounds smaller than about 5-carbon atoms are usually not used as chemical communicants, presumably because small molecules cannot contain the information of larger ones, nor do sensory receptors possess the ability to respond specifically to such small molecules. The ant *Iridomyrmex pruinosus* uses 2-heptanone as an alarm pheromone. Researchers investigated 49 ketones and 35 nonketones for their alarm activities and found that the relationship between such activity and molecular shape was such that ketones could have only a very limited variation if the substance were to excite the receptor. However, a wider degree of molecular shape is permissible among nonketones.

These have been but a few examples of how chemicals are used to induce behavioral responses on the part of animals. Although insects were used as examples here, pheromone activity is found in many animal groups (Sebeok, 1965).

20-10. Chemicals and Behavior in Coelenterates.

Coelenterates have long been known to be very sensitive to the presence of food particles in the water. Recent work with *Hydra* and other coelenterates has been of interest in pointing out the use of chemoreception in behavioral activities such as feeding.

Loomis (1955) found that glutathione, a tripeptide found in all organisms, controls the specific feeding reactions of *Hydra*.

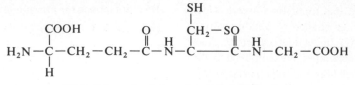

Glutathione (γ-glutamyl-L-cysteinylglycine)

Before feeding the mouth is closed, and the tentacles are outstretched and relatively motionless. Upon sensing food, the tentacles are withdrawn in sweeping movements toward the central vertical axis of the animal. Then the tentacles bend to the mouth, which now opens. Food is deposited in the mouth by the tentacles.

This sequence of reactions is specifically initiated by concentrations of glutathione as low as 10^{-5} molar (Lenhoff, 1961), but only reduced glutathione will serve as the stimulus. Glutathione is a naturally occurring substance and is released when the body wall of prey is punctured by the nematocysts of the tentacles.

Glutathione serves only to initiate the reaction sequence of feeding. For the complete feeding behavior to occur, a solid contact stimulus is necessary, that is, in addition to glutathione being present, the tentacles must also feel a material if ingestion is to occur. If the latter contact is not present, there is only a waving of the tentacles and an opening of the mouth.

That glutathione can initiate feeding behavior in *Hydra* is an indication of the fact that food as such is not sensed by these animals. It is generally true that a given pattern of behavior in any animal is triggered by only a small number of different external stimuli. The animal generally does not respond to general phenomena such as food but rather to some specific feature of the environment that is associated with the more general phenomenon. These environmental stimulating agents were called "representative stimuli" by Jennings (1906). In this sense the male gypsy moth is not responding to a female but only to the presence of a particular chemical in the air.

Not all coelenterates respond to reduced glutathione. In *Cordylophora* the trigger substance for feeding is the imino acid proline

(Fulton, 1963); in *Corymorpha* both glutathione and glycine can trigger the reaction (Wyman, 1965). The Portuguese man-of-war *Physalia physalia* is triggered into the feeding reaction by glutathione (Lenhoff and Schneiderman, 1959).

Other animals have now been shown to initiate feeding behavior in the presence of specific chemical agents. For example, feeding in the mosquito *Aedes aegypti* is triggered by adenosine triphosphate (Galun et al., 1963), although the search for suitable food is initiated and carried out by other stimulating agents. In no organism has the receptor cell responsible for responding to a chemical for the initiation of feeding reactions been identified. It has been suggested that unspecialized nerve cells in coelenterates may function as chemoreceptors. This is not an unlikely situation, especially in coelenterates which exhibit little neuronal differentiation at a detectable level. Also nerve cells generally are responsive to chemical stimuli, in coelenterates all that is required are some neurons with specific receptor sites for glutathione or other feeding triggers.

Behavioral patterns in coelenterates are now of some interest to many physiologists and have been the subject of a recent symposium published in *Am. Zool.* **5** (1965).

References and Readings

Adkisson, P. L. (1966). "Internal clocks and insect diapause." *Science* **154**: 234–241.

Adler, J. (1966a). "Chemotaxis in bacteria." *Science* **153**: 708–716.

Adler, J. (1966b). "Chemotaxis in *Escherichia coli*." *Cold Spring Harbor Symp. Quant. Biol.* **30**: 289–292.

Aschoff, J. (1958). "Tierische Periodik unter dem Einfluss von Zeitgebern." *Z. Tierpsychol.* **15**: 1–30.

Aschoff, J. (1960). "Exogenous and endogenous components in circadian rhythms." *Cold Spring Harbor Symp. Quant. Biol.* **25**: 11–28.

Aschoff, J., ed. (1965a). **Circadian Clocks.** Amsterdam: North Holland Publishing Co.

Aschoff, J. (1965b). "Circadian rhythms in man." *Science* **148**: 1427–1432.

Baggerman, B. (1957). "An experimental study on the timing of breeding and migration in the three-spined stickleback *Gasterosteus aculeatus* L." *Arch. Neerl. Zool.* **12**: 105–317.

Baracchine, O. and J. C. Sherris (1959). "The chemotactic effect of oxygen on bacteria." *J. Path. Bacteriol.* **77**: 565–574.

Barber, S. B. (1961). "Chemoreception and thermoreception." In: **Physiology of Crustacea** (T. H. Waterman, ed.), Vol. 2, pp. 109–131. New York: Academic Press, Inc.

Batschelet, E. (1965). **Statistical methods for the Analysis of Problems in Animal Orientation and Certain Biological Rhythms.** Washington, D.C.: American Institute of Biological Sciences. 298 pp.

Bisetzky, A. R. (1957). "Die Tänze der Bienen nach einem Fussweg zum Futterplatz." *Z. vergl. Physiol.* **40**: 264–288.

Bock, R. and D. A. Shearer (1962). "Identification of geraniol as the active component in the pheromone of the honeybee." *Nature* **194**: 704–706.

Boeckj, J., K. E. Kaissling, and D. Scheider (1966). "Insect olfactory receptors." *Cold Spring Harbor Symp. Quant. Biol.* **30**: 263–286.

Brahmachary, R. L. (1967). "Physiological clocks." *Inter. Rev. Cytol.* **31**: 65–89.

Brown, F. A. (1959). "Living clocks." *Science* **130**: 1535–1544.

Brown, F. A. (1960). "Response to pervasive geophysical factors and the biological clock problem." *Cold Spring Harbor Symp. Quant. Biol.* **25**: 57–71.

Brown, F. A. (1969). "A hypothesis for timing of circadian rhythms." *Can. J. Bot.* **47**: 287–298.

Brown, F. A., J. W. Hastings, and J. D. Palmer (1970). **The Biological Clock: Two Views.** New York: Academic Press, Inc. 94 pp.

Brown, F. A. and Y. H. Park (1967). "Association-formation between photic and subtle geophysical stimulus patterns—a new biological concept." *Biol. Bull.* **132**: 311–319.

Browne, L. B. and E. S. Hodgson (1962). "Electrophysiological studies of arthropod chemoreception. IV. Latency, independence, and specificity of labellar chemoreceptors of the blowfly, *Lucilia.*" *J. Cell. Comp. Physiol.* **59**: 187–202.

Bruce, V. G. (1960). "Environmental entrainment of circadian rhythms." *Cold Spring Harbor Symp. Quant. Biol.* **25**: 29–48.

von Buddenbrock, W. (1952). **Vergleichende Physiologie.** Vol. 1: "Sinnesphysiologie." Basel: Birkhäuser.

Bünning, E. (1964). **The Physiological Clock.** Berlin: Springer-Verlag. 143 pp.

Butler, C. G. (1967). "Insect pheromones." *Biol. Rev.* **42**: 42–87.

Butler, C. G., R. K. Callow, F. R. S. Johnston, and N. C. Johnston (1961). "The isolation and synthesis of queen substance, 9-oxodectrans-2-enoic acid. A honeybee pheromone." *Proc. Roy. Soc.* (London) **B155**: 417–432.

Byrne, W. L., et al. (1966). "Memory transfer." *Science* **153**: 658–659.

Cavill, G. W. K. and P. L. Robertson (1965). "Ant venoms, attractants, and repellants." *Science* **149**: 1337–1345.

Clark, F. N. (1925). "The life history of *Leuresthes tenuis*, an atherine fish with tide controlled spawning habits." *Calif. Fish and Game Comm. Fish. Bull.* **10**.

Clark, R. B. (1966). "The integrative action of a worm's brain." *Symp. Soc. Exp. Biol.* **20**: 345–380.

Cliffe, E. E. and S. G. Waley (1958). "Effect of analogues of glutathione on the feeding reaction of hydra." *Nature* **182**: 804–805.

Cole, L. C. (1957). "Biological clock in the Unicorn." *Science* **125**: 874–876.

Dingman, W. and M. B. Sprom (1964).

"Molecular theories of memory." *Science* **144**: 26–29.

Esch, H. and I. Esch (1965). "Sound: an element common to communication of stingless bees and to dances of the honeybee." *Science* **149**: 320–321.

Evans, D. R. and D. Mellon (1962). "Electrophysiological studies of a water receptor associated with the taste sensilla of the blowfly." *J. Gen. Physiol.* **45**: 487–500.

Everson, R. (1960). "Daily rhythmic variation of blood coagulation times in four species of rodents." *Physiol. Zool.* **32**: 281–287.

von Frisch, K. (1953). **The Dancing Bees.** London: Methuen & Co., Ltd.

von Frisch, K. (1967). **The Dance, Language, and Orientation of Bees.** (translated by L. E. Chadwick). Cambridge, Mass.: The Belknap Press of the Harvard University Press.

Fulton, C. (1962). "Environmental factors influencing the growth of *Cordylophora*." *J. Exp. Zool.* **151**: 61–78.

Fulton, C. (1963). "Proline control of the feeding reaction of Cordylophora." *J. Gen. Physiol.* **46**: 823–838.

Galun, R., Y. Avi-dor, and M. Bar-Zeev (1963). "Feeding response in *Aedes aegypti*: stimulation by adenosine triphosphate." *Science* **42**: 1674–1675.

Halberg, F. (1959). "Physiologic 24-hour periodicity: General and procedural considerations with reference to the adrenal cycle." *Z. Vitamin—Hormon—Ferment-forsch.* **10**: 225–296.

Halberg, F. (1969). "Chronobiology." *Ann. Rev. Physiol.* **31**: 675–725.

Harker, J. E. (1964). **The Physiology of Diurnal Rhythms.** New York: Cambridge University Press.

Hastings, J. W. (1964). "The role of light in persistent daily rhythms." In: **Photophysiology** (A. Giese, ed.), pp. 333–361. New York: Academic Press, Inc.

Hendricks, S. B. (1963). "Metabolic control of timing." *Science* **141**: 21–27.

Hoffmann, K. (1957). "Über den Einfluss der Temperatur auf die Tagesperiodik bei einem Poikilothermen." *Naturwissenschaften* **44**: 358.

Hoffman, K. (1959). "Die Aktivitatsperiodik von im 18- und 36-Studen-tag erbruteten Eideschsen." *Z. Verg. Physiol.* **42**: 422–432.

Istomina-Tsvetkova, R. (1960). "Contribution to the study of trophic relations in adult worker bees." *Inter. Beekeeping Congress XVII.* (Bologna-Roma, 1958.) **2**: 361–368.

Jennings, H. S. (1906). **Behavior of the Lower Organisms.** New York: Columbia University Press.

Kalmus, H. (1964). "Comparative physiology: navigation by animals." *Ann. Rev. Physiol.* **26**: 109–130.

Karlson, P. (1960). "Pheromones." *Ergeb. Biol.* **22**: 212–225.

Keeton, W. T. (1969). "Orientation by pigeons: Is the sun necessary?" *Science* **165**: 922–928.

Kramer, G. (1949). "Uber Richtungstendenzen bei der nachtlichen Zugunruhe gekafigter Vögel." In: **Ornithologie als biologische Wissenschaft** (E. Mayr and E. Schulze, eds.), pp. 269–283. Heidelberg: Winter Verlag.

Kramer, G. (1952). "Experiments on bird orientation." *Ibis* **94**: 265–285.

Lamar, D. L. and P. M. Merifield (1967). "Cambrian fossils and origin of Earth-Moon system." *Geol. Soc. Am. Bull.* **78**: 1359–1368.

Lenhoff, H. M. (1961). "Activation of the feeding reflex in *Hydra littoralis*. I. Role played by reduced glutathione and quantitative assay of the feeding reflex." *J. Gen. Physiol.* **45**: 331–344.

Lenhoff, H. M. (1965). "Some physicochemical aspects of the macro- and microenvironments surrounding *Hydra* during activation of their feeding behavior." *Am. Zool.* **5**: 515–524.

Lenhoff, H. M. (1968). "Behavior, hormones, and hydra." *Science* **161**: 434–442.

Lenhoff, H. M. and H. A. Schneiderman (1959). "The chemical control of feeding in the Portuguese man-of-war, *Physalia physalia* L., and its bearing on the evolution of the Cnidaria." *Biol. Bull.* **116**: 452–460.

Lenhoff, H. M. and J. R. Zwisler (1963). "Zinc activation of a coordinated response in *Hydra*." *Science* **142**: 1666–1668.

Lettvin, J. Y. and R. C. Gesteland (1965).

"Speculations on smell." *Cold Spring Harbor Symp. Quant. Biol.* **30**: 217–226.

Lindauer, M. (1961). **Communication among Social Bees.** Cambridge, Mass.: Harvard University Press.

Lindauer, M. (1963). "Kompassorientierung." *Ergeb. Biol.* **26**: 158–181.

Loomis, W. F. (1955). "Glutathione control of the specific feeding reactions of Hydra." *Ann. N.Y. Acad. Sci.* **62**: 209–228.

Loomis, W. F. (1964). "Microenvironmental control of sexual differentiation in Hydra." *J. Exp. Biol.* **156**: 289–306.

Loomis, W. F. and H. M. Lenhoff (1956). "Growth and sexual differentiation of Hydra in mass culture." *J. Exp. Zool.* **132**: 555–573.

Lüscher, M. (1960). "Hormonal control of caste differentiation in termites." *Ann. N.Y. Acad. Sci.* **89**: 549–563.

Lüttges, M., T. Johnson, C. Buck, J. Holland, and J. McGaugh (1966). "An examination of 'transfer of learning' by nucleic acid." *Science* **151**: 834–837.

McConnell, J. V. (1966). "Comparative Physiology: Learning in invertebrates." *Ann. Rev. Physiol.* **28**: 107–136.

McGill, T. E. (1965). **Readings in Animal Behavior.** New York: Holt, Rinehart & Winston, Inc.

Matolsky, A. G. and P. F. Parakkal (1965). "Membrane-coating granules of keratinizing epithelia." *J. Cell Biol.* **24**: 297–307.

Matthews, G. V. T. (1955). **Bird Navigation.** New York: Cambridge University Press.

Matthews, G. V. T. (1968). **Bird Navigation.** 2nd ed. New York: Cambridge University Press. 197 pp.

Menaker, M. and A. Eskin (1966). "Entrainment of circadian rhythms by sound in *Passer domesticus.*" *Science* **154**: 1579–1581.

Merrill, D. (1965). "The stimulus for case-building activity in caddis-worms (Trichoptera)." *J. Exp. Zool.* **158**: 123–132.

Michener, M. C. and C. Walcott (1966). "Navigation of single homing pigeons: airplane observations by radio tracking." *Science* **154**: 410–413.

Mills, J. N. (1966). "Human circadian rhythms." *Physiol. Rev.* **46**: 128–171.

Milne, L. J. and M. Milne (1962). **The Senses of Animals and Men.** New York: Atheneum Publishers. 305 pp.

Moncrieff, R. W. (1951). **The Chemical Senses.** London: Leonard Hill. 2nd ed. 538 pp.

Moulton, D. G. (1963). "Electrical activity in the olfactory system of rabbits with indwelling electrodes." In: **Olfaction and Taste** (Y. Zotterman, ed.), pp. 71–84. New York: Pergamon Press, Inc.

Naylor, A. F. (1959). "An experimental analysis of dispersal in the flour beetle, *Tribolium confusum.*" *Ecology* **40**: 453–465.

Neuhaus, W. (1956). "Die Unterscheidungsfähigkeit des Hundes für Duftgemische." *Z. Vergl. Physiol.* **39**: 25–43.

Pannella, G. and C. MacClintock (1967). "Biological and environmental rhythms reflected in molluscan shell growths." *J. Paleontol.* **42**: 64–80.

Pardi, L. and F. Papi (1952). "Die Sonne als Kompass bei *Talitrus saltator* (Montagu) (Amphipoda Talitridae)." *Naturwissenschaften* **39**: 262–263.

Pittendrigh, C. S. and V. G. Bruce (1957). "An oscillator model for biological clocks." In: **Rhythmic and Synthetic Processes in Growth.** (D. Rudnick, ed.), pp. 75–109. Princeton, N. J.: Princeton University Press.

Rainey, R. C. (1960). "Applications of theoretical models to study of flight-behavior in locusts and birds." In: **Models and Analogues in Biology.** (J. W. L. Beament, ed.), *Symp. Soc. Exp. Biol.* **14**: 122–139.

Renner, M. (1957). "Neue Versuche über den Zeitsinn der Honigbiene." *Z. vergl. Physiol.* **40**: 85–118.

Renner, M. (1960). "Das Duftorgan der Honigbiene und die physiologische Bedeutung ihres Lockstoffes." *Z. vergl. Physiol.* **43**: 411–468.

Richter, C. P. (1965). **Biological Clocks in Medicine and Psychiatry.** Springfield, Ill.: Charles C. Thomas, Publisher. 109 pp.

Runcorn, S. K. (1964). "Changes in the Earth's moment of inertia." *Nature* **204**: 823–824.

Rushforth, N. B., A. L. Burnett, and R. Maynard (1963). "Behavior in *Hydra*: contraction responses of *Hydra pirardi* to mechanical and light stimuli." *Science* **139**: 760–761.

Sauer, E. G. F. (1957). "Die Sternenorientierung nächtlich ziehender Grasmücken (*Sylvia atricapilla, borin*, und *curruca*)." *Z. Tierpsychol.* **14**: 29–70.

Sauer, E. G. F. and E. M. Sauer, (1960). "Star navigation of nocturnal migrating birds." *Cold Spring Harbor Symp. Quant. Biol.* **25**: 463–473.

Schmidt-Koenig, K. (1964). "Über die Orientierung der Vögel: Experimente und Probleme." *Naturwissenschaften* **18**: 423–431.

Schneider, D. (1962). "Electrophysiological investigation on the olfactory specificity of sexual attracting substances in different species of moths." *J. Insect Physiol.* **8**: 15–30.

Schneider, D. (1966). "Chemical sense communication in spiders." *Symp. Soc. Exp. Biol.* **20**: 273–298.

Schneider, D. (1969). "Insect olfaction: deciphering system for chemical messages." *Science* **163**: 1031–1037.

Schweiger, E., H. G. Wallraff, and H. G. Schweiger (1964). "Endogenous circadian rhythm in cytoplasm of *Acetabularia*: Influence of the nucleus." *Science* **146**: 658–659.

Scrutton, C. T. (1964). "Periodicity in devonian coral growth." *Paleontology* **7**: 552–558.

Sebeok, T. A. (1965). "Animal communication." *Science* **147**: 1006–1014.

Shibuya, T. (1964). "Dissociation of olfactory neural response and mucosal potential." *Science* **143**: 495.

Snyder, S. H. and J. Axelrod (1965). "Circadian rhythm in pineal serotonin: effect of monoamine oxidase inhibition and reserpine." *Science* **149**: 542–544.

Sollberger, A. (1965). **Biological Rhythm Research.** New York: American Elsevier Publishing Company. 461 pp.

Thurm, U. (1964). "Mechanoreceptors in the cuticle of the honey bee: fine structure and stimulus mechanism." *Science* **145**: 1063–1065.

Tucker, D. (1963). "Physical variables in the olfactory stimulation process." *J. Gen. Physiol.* **48**: 559.

Walker, B. W. (1952). "A guide to the grunion." *Calif. Fish and Game Comm.* **38**: 409–420.

Wells, M. J. (1961). "What the Octopus makes of it: our world from another point of view." *Am. Sci.* **49**: 215–227.

Wells, M. J. (1966). "Learning in the Octopus." *Symp. Soc. Exp. Biol.* **20**: 477–508.

Wenner, A. M. (1962). "Sound production during the waggle dance of the honey bee." *Anim. Behav.* **10**: 79–95.

Wenner, A. M. (1964). "Sound communication in honeybees." *Sci. Am.* **210**: 116–124.

Wilson, E. O. (1965). "Chemical communication in the social insects." *Science* **149**: 1064–1071.

Wilson, E. O. and W. H. Bossert (1963). "Chemical communication among animals." *Recent Prog. Hormone Res.* **19**: 673–716.

Witt, P. N. and C. F. Reed (1965). "Spider-web building." *Science* **149**: 1190–1197.

Wolbarsht, L. and F. E. Hanson (1965). "Electrical activity in the chemoreceptors of the blowfly. III. Dendritic action potentials." *J. Gen. Physiol.* **48**: 673–683.

Wyman, R. (1965). "Notes on the behavior of the hydroid, *Corymorpha palma.*" *Am. Zool.* **5**: 491–497.

Author Index

Subject Index

B

E

J

K

L

Q

R

T